Reprinted from PHYSIOLOGY AND BIOPHYSICS

19th Edition of Howell–Fulton Textbook of Physiology

Edited by
Theodore C. Ruch, Ph.D. and Harry D. Patton, Ph.D., M.D.

SECOND EDITION

Neurophysiology

THEODORE C. RUCH, Ph.D.

Professor of Physiology and Biophysics
University of Washington School of Medicine

HARRY D. PATTON, Ph.D., M.D.

Professor of Physiology and Biophysics,
University of Washington School of Medicine

J. WALTER WOODBURY, Ph.D.

Professor of Physiology and Biophysics,
University of Washington School of Medicine

ARNOLD L. TOWE, Ph.D.

Professor of Physiology and Biophysics,
University of Washington School of Medicine

W. B. SAUNDERS COMPANY, Philadelphia and London, 1965

Neurophysiology

CONTRIBUTORS

JOHN T. CONRAD, Ph.D.

Assistant Professor, Department of Physiology and Biophysics, University of Washington School of Medicine

MITCHELL GLICKSTEIN, Ph.D.

Associate Professor of Physiology and Biophysics and of Psychology, University of Washington, and Regional Primate Research Center, Seattle, Washington

ALBERT M. GORDON, Ph.D.

Assistant Professor of Physiology and Biophysics, University of Washington School of Medicine

HARRY D. PATTON, Ph.D., M.D.

Professor of Physiology and Biophysics, University of Washington School of Medicine

THEODORE C. RUCH, Ph.D.

Professor of Physiology and Biophysics, University of Washington School of Medicine; and Director, Regional Primate Research Center, Seattle, Washington

ORVILLE A. SMITH, JR., Ph.D.

Associate Professor of Physiology and Biophysics, University of Washington School of Medicine; Assistant Director, Regional Primate Research Center, Seattle, Washington

ARNOLD L. TOWE, Ph.D.

Professor of Physiology and Biophysics, University of Washington School of Medicine

FRANK W. WEYMOUTH, Ph.D.*

Professor of Physiology, Emeritus, Stanford University; Professor of Physiological Optics, Los Angeles College of Optometry

J. WALTER WOODBURY, Ph.D.

Professor of Physiology and Biophysics, University of Washington School of Medicine

* Deceased.

PREFACE

THIS VOLUME comprises the neurophysiologic chapters of *Physiology and Biophysics*, which, in turn, is the nineteenth edition of Howell's classic textbook, dating back to 1896. The printing of this portion simultaneously with the publication of the parent work is made in response to the requests of those whose interest does not extend over the whole field of physiology.

We are happy to have *Neurophysiology* appear as a separate volume because in these sections we have come closest to our goal in the parent volume, to present physiology "in depth." The chapters by Dr. Woodbury illustrate one way in which depth is attained, namely by bringing the university disciplines of physics, mathematics and physical chemistry to bear simply and directly upon the subject. Inevitably this makes the approach quantitative. Few will quarrel with this objective. It is not so well accepted that the inclusion of pathophysiology adds depth to a subject. Nevertheless, neurophysiology is treated here as a continuum stretching from the physics of the neuron to the physiologic interpretation of signs and symptoms of neurologic disease. This philosophy is well illustrated in Chapters 6 and 7, which bridge between membrane phenomena at the synapse and the clinical significance of reflexes.

In dealing with the higher levels of the nervous system we have continued to stress functional anatomy as elucidated by physiologic means. This approach, it is hoped, will provide a framework into which can be fitted the electrophysiologic studies of neural components that have flourished so greatly since the sixteenth edition. It is further hoped that the emphasis on functional anatomy will make this reprint useful for courses in neuroanatomy, whether taught separately or conjointly with neurophysiology. Some have found the previous edition useful for courses in physiologic psychology.

Many who sympathize with an attempt to bring physiology closer to physics and physical chemistry bridle at the thought of bringing physiology closer to psychology. In recent years there has been a rapprochement between these two disciplines which has yet to be fully reflected in textbooks of physiology. We have included a new chapter on the neurophysiology of motivation (O. A. Smith, J.) and one on learning and memory (Glickstein) and have devoted separate chapters to "emotion" and the "association areas." Several of the chapters on the sensory systems have a psychological orientation. It is hoped that this volume will serve as a text or as collateral reading in advanced courses of physiological psychology.

Other new or entirely rewritten chapters are those on the nerve impulse (Woodbury), muscle (Woodbury, Gordon and Conrad) and the receptor (Patton). Others have been extensively revised.

It is hoped that the references in the text to other chapters of *Physiology and Biophysics* will remind the reader that the nervous system does not exist in isolation and, in fact, permeates all other systems of the body. Although omitted in this reprinting, the discussions in the parent volume of the neural control of the heart, circulation, respiration, micturition, and food and water intake utilize the principles presented here.

We would again like to thank Walter Eva and Helen N. Halsey for the splendid editorial and art work, respectively, and to add our thanks to Mr. John Dusseau of the W. B. Saunders Company for making this reprint possible.

T. C. RUCH
H. D. PATTON

Seattle, Washington

CONTENTS

Chapter 8

Chapter 9

Chapter 10

Chapter 11

Chapter 12

Chapter 13

SECTION IV.   SENSORY FUNCTIONS OF THE NERVOUS SYSTEM

SECTION V. CEREBRAL CORTEX IN GENERAL: NEUROPHYSIOLOGY OF BEHAVIOR

Chapter 26

NEUROPHYSIOLOGY OF EMOTION 508
By Theodore C. Ruch

SECTION I

BIOPHYSICS OF THE CELL MEMBRANE

CHAPTER 1

The Cell Membrane: Ionic and Potential Gradients and Active Transport

By J. WALTER WOODBURY

1

ANY animal tissue such as muscle or brain is composed of closely packed cells and the solution surrounding and bathing them, the *interstitial* fluid. The cell plasm or *intracellular* fluid and the interstitial fluid are similar; both consist largely of water and both fluids have roughly equal numbers of particles per unit volume dissolved in them. The functional boundary between the intracellular and interstitial fluids is a thin (75 Ångstroms, 7.5 nanometers), highly organized, bimolecular lipoprotein layer which severely restricts the interchange of materials. The differences between the intracellular and interstitial fluids are more striking than their similarities. This chapter deals with two of these differences. (i) The concentrations of ions are markedly different. The concentrations of sodium (Na^+) and chloride (Cl^-) are much higher in the interstitial fluid than in the intracellular fluid. The situation is just reversed for potassium (K^+); its concentration is much higher in intracellular than in interstitial fluid (see Table 1). (ii) There is an electric potential difference between the intracellular and interstitial fluids. In skeletal muscle cells, the cell plasm is about 90 mV. (.09 V.) negative to the interstitial fluid. It must be kept in mind that the cell interior is highly organized, containing the nucleus, nucleolus, mitochondria, endoplasmic reticulum, etc. Nevertheless, it is convenient and meaningful to regard the cell fluid as a single aqueous phase when discussing ion exchange across cell membranes.

Since these large differences in concentration and potential appear across the thin functional membrane of the cell, it is reasonable to suppose that this membrane plays an important role in the maintenance of these differences. Two aspects of the cell membrane are largely responsible for the observed concentration and potential differences. (i) Ions diffuse through the membrane at a minute fraction of the rate at which they diffuse through water. This barrier to diffusion is a result of the nonpolar nature of the lipid portion of the membrane. In most cell membranes, the rate of diffusion of Na^+ is much slower than is the diffusion rate of K^+ and Cl^-. (ii) Energy derived from metabolism is used by cells to transport Na^+ out of the cell and K^+ into the cell. These ionic movements just balance, on the average, the diffusion of Na^+ into and K^+ out of the cell. This *active transport* of Na^+ and K^+ maintains the intracellular Na^+ concentration at low values and the intracellular K^+ at

high values. The voltage arises because potassium permeates the membrane much more readily than does sodium.

More generally, the role of the membrane in cellular function is to regulate the interchange of materials between a cell and its environment. The nature of the membrane is such that nutrients enter and waste products leave the cell relatively easily, while those substances necessary to cellular function, whether inside or outside the cell, cross only with difficulty. Because of the crucial functions of the cell membrane in regulating interchange of ions and other substances, a description of its properties is a useful starting point for a study of physiology. The transfer of nonionized* substances is not treated here. The permeation and active transport of ions through the membrane and the consequences of these ion movements are the subject matter of this chapter. These concepts are necessary for an understanding of a wide range of physiologic phenomena: (i) the electrical activity of nerve and muscle cells and the processes of synaptic transmission (Chaps. 2, 3, 5 and 6); (ii) the distribution of ions and water between the various body fluid compartments (Chap. 45) and the regulation of interstitial and intracellular pH (Chap. 46); (iii) the role of active ion transport in the secretive and absorptive processes of the gastrointestinal tract and in the formation of urine by the kidney (Chap. 44).

In this chapter the main ideas concerning the origins of transmembrane concentration and potential differences will first be sketched. Then the step-by-step development of present concepts of the origins of these potential and concentration differences will be described, and, where necessary, the underlying physical and chemical principles will be briefly reviewed in the text or in more detail in the appendix to Chapter 2. Lastly, the problems of regulation of cell volume and of intracellular pH are discussed briefly. Most of the concepts presented in this and the next chapter were developed during the past 20 years, largely through the efforts of A. L. Hodgkin, A. F. Huxley and their co-workers at Cambridge.[8,9,10] Hodgkin and Huxley received the 1963 Nobel Prize in physiology for their pioneering efforts in this field. There are numerous reviews[1,3,6,23,24,29] and symposia[5,22,25,26,27] on various aspects of this subject.

* Substances lacking an electric charge are more appropriately termed "un-ionized"—a word which becomes ambiguous in the unhyphenated form.

ELECTRIC POTENTIALS AND ION CONCENTRATIONS IN MUSCLE

As stated above, there are two striking characteristics of cells to be considered in this chapter: the large difference in ion concentrations and the large difference in electric potential between the inside of the cell and the interstitial fluid.

Although these facts have been known for several decades, refinements in old techniques and introduction of new techniques were required to establish them with sufficient accuracy to make possible crucial tests of the various possible interpretations. The advent of radioactive isotopes made it possible to show, contrary to previous belief, that sodium can penetrate the membrane; the development of intracellular potential recording techniques made possible accurate estimates of transmembrane voltages. In order to give a concrete picture of the existence and size of a transmembrane potential difference in muscle cells one method for making such measurements is described here. Radioactive tracer methods are described later.

Intracellular Recording. Figure 1 is a schematic diagram showing how the difference in electric potential between the inside and the outside of a cell can be measured directly and accurately. The technique for this was perfected by Ling and Gerard.[20] An ultramicroelectrode* is made by drawing a piece of glass tubing down to a small tip and then filling the tubing with a concentrated solution of KCl. If the electrode tip is no larger than about 1 μ, it can be inserted transversely through the cell membrane of a muscle fiber without detectable damage to the membrane. Any electrode larger than this at the tip appreciably damages the membrane and lowers the measured potential. The potential of the microelectrode tip when it is in the solution bathing the muscle is taken as zero. When the microelectrode is advanced toward the surface of the muscle, the potential of the electrode does not change until the tip penetrates a cell membrane. At this time (*arrow* in Fig. 1), the potential drops abruptly to -90 mV. (inside negative) and remains at this value as long as the electrode is in the cell. This transmembrane potential is commonly called the *resting potential*

* This designation is in conformity with the histologists' conventions—the tip size being just below visibility by light microscopy.

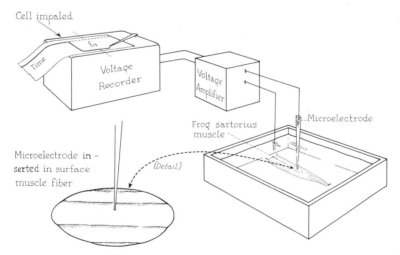

Fig. 1. Intracellular recording. Schematic diagram of experimental arrangement for measuring transmembrane electric potential differences. A frog sartorius muscle is dissected free and pinned to a wax-bottomed chamber (right) filled with a physiologic (Ringer's) solution. A capillary ultramicroelectrode is held in position over the muscle with a micromanipulator (not shown). Electrical connection is made to microelectrode and chamber by means of spirals of chlorided silver wires. Potential difference between tip of microelectrode and bathing medium is amplified and displayed as a function of time by recorder. When electrode penetrates the cell membrane (arrow on record at left), pen is suddenly deflected, thus indicating the existence of a steady transmembrane potential ($\mathcal{E}_s$). Drawing at lower left is enlarged view of electrode inserted through membrane of a single cell to show that tip of electrode (0.5 μ) is much smaller than diameter of muscle fiber (100 μ).

TABLE 1. *Approximate Steady State Ion Concentrations and Potentials in Mammalian Muscle Cells and Interstitial Fluid**

INTERSTITIAL FLUID		INTRACELLULAR FLUID		$\dfrac{[Ion]_o}{[Ion]_i}$	$\mathcal{E}ion = \dfrac{61}{Z} \log \dfrac{[Ion]_o}{[Ion]_i} (mV.)$
[Ion] μM. per cm.^{3}		[Ion] μM. per cm.^{3}			
Cations		Cations			
Na$^+$	145	Na$^+$	12	12.1	66
K$^+$	4	K$^+$	155	1/39	−97
H$^+$	3.8×10^{-5}	H$^+$	13×10^{-5}	1/3.4	−32
pH	7.43	pH	6.9		
others	5				
Anions		Anions			
Cl$^-$	120	Cl$^-$	.4†	30	−90
HCO$_3^-$	27	HCO$_3^-$	8	3.4	−32
others	7	A$^-$	155		
Potential	0	−90 mV.		1/30†	−90

*Vertical double line represents membrane
†Calculated from membrane potential using the Nernst equation for a univalent anion, i.e.,
     Z = −1

but also will be referred to here as the *steady** potential ($\mathcal{E}_s$), the $\mathcal{E}$ being derived from electromotive force. Measured transmembrane steady potentials in different tissues vary from about −20 mV. to −100 mV., but their generation by active Na$^+$ transport is probably the same in all tissues.

Ion Concentrations in Muscle. The term "extracellular fluid" refers to all fluids not inside cells. Blood, lymph, cerebrospinal fluid, etc., are in this category. "Interstitial fluid" is the fluid in direct contact with the tissue cells, and, therefore, knowledge of the concentrations of ions in this fluid is necessary in the study of membrane phenomena. The concentrations of ions in the interstitial fluid are slightly different from those in blood plasma, because plasma contains an appreciable concentration of ionized protein, i.e., there is a Gibbs-Donnan equilibrium (Chap. 45) between plasma and interstitial fluid, maintained across the capillary wall. However, ion concentrations in interstitial fluid can be calculated from measured concentrations in the blood if the concentrations of plasma proteins and their charges are known.

The left hand columns in Table 1 give the

*The term *steady* emphasizes that this unvarying voltage is one aspect of a steady-state of cellular function maintained by metabolism. On the other hand, *resting* contrasts with *active* in describing impulse conduction in excitable tissues.

approximate concentrations of the more important ions in the interstitial fluid of mammals. Intracellular concentrations are estimated from chemical analysis of a known weight of tissue and a measurement of the fraction of the tissue water which is in the interstitial space. The total amount of any ion in the interstitial fluid is then obtained by the product of the interstitial concentration and the fractional volume. This amount is subtracted from the total amount of ion in the tissue sample to give the amount of ion in the intracellular water. Intracellular concentration is the ratio of the amount of ion to the amount of water in the cells. The middle columns in Table 1 show the concentrations of the more important ions in the intracellular water of mammalian skeletal muscle. Although intracellular concentrations vary considerably from tissue to tissue, the electrolyte pattern of muscle is fairly representative. To summarize Table 1, interstitial fluid has high concentrations of Na$^+$ and Cl$^-$; the intracellular fluid has high concentrations of K$^+$ and the largely unknown organic anions (A$^-$). The right hand columns are explained later.

Factors Affecting Ion Diffusion Through Membranes. *Passive factors.* Because of their random thermal motion, the individual molecules of a dissolved substance are continually intermixing (diffusing). If the concentration of the dissolved substance is higher in one region than in an adjacent one, molecules will move both ways, but more will move from the region of higher to the region of lower concentration. Thus Na^+ and Cl^- tend to diffuse into cells and K^+ and A^- tend to diffuse out of cells. The rate of diffusion of these substances through the membrane depends not only on the concentration difference but also on the ease with which they pass through the membrane. In fact, the cell membrane so severely limits the rate at which substances diffuse through it that the rate of movement is determined solely by the membrane. That is, diffusion of ions through water is so much faster than through the membrane that the ion concentrations near the membrane differ negligibly from those in the surrounding bulk medium.

If the substance is ionized, the transmembrane potential also affects the rate of diffusion of the substance through the membrane. This effect is exerted because a transmembrane potential difference means that electric charges are separated by the cell membrane. This follows from the definition of potential difference between two points as the work done against electrical forces in carrying a unit positive charge from one point to the other. No electrical work is done in carrying a charge through the membrane unless charges are separated by the membrane. These separated charges (inside negative) exert a force on any ions in the membrane. This force tends to drive cations (+) into the cell and anions (−) out of the cell; i.e., any cations which enter the membrane are attracted by the negative charges on the inside and are repelled by the plus charges on the outside of the membrane.

K^+ tends to diffuse out of the cell because of its high internal concentration, but it tends to diffuse into the cell because of the electric charges separated by the membrane. These two tendencies nearly, but not quite, cancel each other, so that there is a slight tendency for K^+ to diffuse out of the cell. A similar argument holds for Cl^-, but in this instance the tendency for Cl^- to diffuse into the cell because of its high interstitial concentration is exactly balanced by the tendency of the electric forces to keep the negatively charged Cl^- from entering the cell. Since there is no net tendency for Cl^- to diffuse through the membrane, the inside and outside concentrations of Cl^- are in electrochemical equilibrium.

Active transport. The situation is quite different for Na^+ and A^-; both the concentration and potential difference act in the same di-rection. There is a strong tendency for A^- to diffuse out of the cell and for Na^+ to diffuse into it. However, the membrane is believed to be impermeable to A^- and is much less permeable to Na^+ than to K^+. Nevertheless, there is an appreciable steady leakage of Na^+ into cells. Despite this leakage, the internal concentration of Na^+ remains at low values in living cells. Therefore, some mechanism present in the cell must carry Na^+ out of the cell as fast as it enters, on the average. Since work must be done to carry Na^+ from a region of lower to a region of higher concentration and from a lower to a higher electric potential, it must be concluded that energy derived from cellular metabolism is used to carry Na^+ out of the cell.

Little is known of how metabolic energy is used to extrude Na^+ from the cell. It is known that the extrusion of a Na^+ is usually accompanied by the uptake of a K^+. This process is often referred to as active Na^+ transport, as the *Na^+–K^+ pump,* or more simply as the *Na^+ pump.* The word "pump" denotes that metabolic energy is required by the process. *Active transport* is a generic term referring to the process whereby metabolic energy is continuously expended to maintain transport of a substance in a direction opposite to that in which it tends to diffuse because of differences in concentration, potential, pressure, etc. The linkage of K^+ uptake to Na^+ extrusion accounts for the slight unbalance in the distribution of K^+; the net outward diffusion of K^+ is balanced by the inward pumping of K^+. The transmembrane potential arises because the membrane is much more permeable to K^+ than it is to Na^+ and because the Na^+–K^+ pump maintains the internal Na^+ concentration at a low value. K^+ would diffuse out of the cell faster than Na^+ would diffuse into it if there were no membrane potential; K^+ diffusing out must leave the nonpermeating A^- behind and thus the membrane is charged.

Summary. The factors that determine the rates at which ions move through the membrane can be expressed quantitatively, either as forces per mol or as potential energy per mol of ions. Thus it is easy to see that the charges separated by the membrane exert a force on charged particles within the membrane. The size of this force is expressed as the electric field intensity (force per unit charge) or, since the thickness of the membrane is constant, as the transmembrane potential (work done to carry a unit positive charge across the membrane against the electric field). Similarly, but not nearly so obviously, an ion concentration difference existing between the two solutions which bathe the membrane can be thought of as exerting a force on these ions, tending to make them move from regions of higher to regions of lower concentration.

Four factors which together determine the rate of flow of ions through the membrane have been mentioned: (i) transmembrane concentration differences, (ii) transmembrane potential differences, (iii) active Na^+–K^+ transport, and (iv) the mechanical barrier to ion movement imposed by the structure of the cell membrane, which can be thought of as a frictional force. The remainder of this chapter describes these forces, their interrelationships, and their role in the functioning of the cell.

PASSIVE FACTORS AFFECTING ION MOVEMENTS

Concentration Gradient. *Diffusion.* All the molecules in a solution, both solute and solvent, move in random directions between collisions with other molecules. The average kinetic energy of the molecules attributable to random motion is directly proportional to the absolute temperature. The random motion of the molecules is such that the rate at which molecules diffuse out of a small volume is proportional to the concentration [mols (M.) per liter or millimols (mM.) per cm.^{3}] of the substance in the small volume. Even in a solution in which the concentration of a substance is everywhere constant, a molecule found in one region at one time may be found in any region at a later time. This process of intermixing of solute (and solvent) particles is called *diffusion*.

Gradient and flux. In a solution where the concentration of a substance varies from one region to another, there will be a net movement of solute particles from regions of higher to regions of lower concentration, because more molecules per second leave than enter the region of higher concentration. This net diffusion is most conveniently expressed quantitatively in terms of the *flux* (**M**), defined as the number of mols per second passing through an area of 1 cm.^{2} oriented perpendicularly to the direction of flow of the substance (mols per cm.^{2}-sec.). The net diffusion of a substance from regions of higher to lower concentrations is analogous to the flow of water in a river. The rate of flow is proportional to the steepness of the stream bed:

the steeper the grade, the faster the flow. Water flows directly downhill, i.e., in the direction of steepest slope; a substance diffuses "downhill" in the direction of "steepest slope." The magnitude of the steepest slope or rate of change of concentration and the direction of this steepest slope constitute a vector. This vector is called the *concentration gradient*, abbreviated "grad [S]." Square brackets are used to denote concentration of the substance included in them; thus, [S] denotes the concentration of the substance S (usually given as μM. per cm.^{3}). Similarly flux (**M**) is a vector whose direction is opposite to that of the concentration gradient.

Any quantity that varies with distance has a gradient which can be calculated at any point. If concentration increases with increasing distance, then **grad** [S] is positive. However, net flux is in the opposite direction, so the net flux of S (**M**$_S$) is proportional to $-$**grad** [S] (Fig. 2*a*). For a given concentration gradient, **M**$_S$ depends on the ease with which the molecules of S move through the solvent; the greater the ease of movement (the less the frictional resistance to flow), the greater the flux. The measure of the ease of motion is called the *diffusion constant* (D). Therefore, $\mathbf{M_S} = -\mathbf{D_S}\ \mathbf{grad}\ [S]$ (for nonionized substances or for ions in regions *with no* electric field). In words, the net flux of S (M. per cm.^{2}-sec.) is given by the product of the diffusion constant of that substance (D$_S$; in cm.^{2} per sec.) and the concentration gradients of S (in M. per cm.^{3}-cm. or M. per cm.^{4}).

The presence of a cell membrane in a system greatly simplifies the description of the diffusion of a substance because most dissolved substances diffuse through the membrane so much more slowly than they diffuse through water that the diffusion time in water usually can be neglected (Fig. 2*b*). More precisely, the rate of diffusion of a substance through the membrane is so slow that a negligibly small concentration gradient in the aqueous media suffices to bring the substance up to the membrane as rapidly as it diffuses through the membrane. Thus, appreciable changes in concentration occur only in and near the membrane. Therefore, the rate of penetration of a substance depends on the properties of the membrane and on the concentration gradient of the substance in the membrane. Since the membrane is a thin, fixed structure and the concentration gradient in the solution is negligible, the average concentration gradient through the membrane is obtained, to a good approximation, by dividing the difference in concentration between the interstitial and intracellular fluids by the thickness of the membrane (δ). Thus, in the membrane, **grad** $[S]_m = ([S]_o - [S]_i)/\delta$. (Distance increases in the direction from inside to outside.) The subscript "m" is used to denote the value of a quantity in the *membrane*; the subscript "o" (for *outside* the cell), the value in the interstitial fluid; and the subscript "i" (for *inside* the cell), the value in the intracellular fluid. Thus, $[S]_o$ means the concentration of S in the interstitial fluid.

Cell Membrane. The concentration gradient of a substance can be thought of as a force tending to move the substance. However, the rate of movement of S is determined not only by **grad** [S] but also by the frictional resistance to flow. Resistance is one of the forces listed above as affecting the movement of a substance. In a tissue, most resistance to flow of materials is in the cell membrane and its immediate vicinity. Therefore, the membrane structure and the various mechanisms whereby a substance may cross the membrane are important for understanding transport of materials into and out of cells. Also the high frictional resistance of the membrane ensures that the directions of the concentration and voltage gradients are perpendicular to the membrane.

Permeability. The net efflux ($\mathbf{M_S}$) of a non-ionized substance through the membrane is simply calculated from the following equation (see Fig. 2*b*):

$$\mathbf{M_S} = -\mathbf{D_S}\,\mathbf{grad}\,[S]_m = -(D_S/\delta)([S]_o - [S]_i)$$
$$= P_S([S]_i - [S]_o) \qquad (1)$$

The ratio D_S/δ is called the *permeability* of the membrane to the substance S (P_S). D_S is the diffusion constant of S in the membrane. P_S depends only on the properties of the membrane and of the substance. Permeability is thus a measure of the ease with which a substance can penetrate the membrane; i.e., the greater the permeability, the less the frictional drag force exerted by the membrane on the substance. In words, equation 1 states that the net flux of a substance (number of mols leaving the cell each second through 1 cm.² of membrane minus the number of mols per cm.²-sec. entering the cell) is equal to the permeability constant times the difference between the internal and external concentrations of the substance. In amphibian skeletal muscle the permeability of the cell membrane to K^+ (P_K) is about 10^{-6} cm. per second, whereas P_{Na} is about 10^{-8} cm. per second. The permeability to K^+ of a layer of water of the same thickness as the membrane (75 Ångstroms) is about 10 cm. per second, or ten million times greater than the P_K of the cell membrane. This

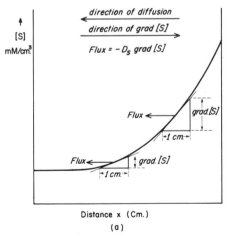

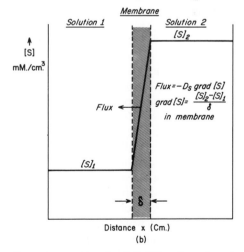

Fig. 2. Concentration gradient and flux in one dimension. *a*, Graph of concentration of a substance ([S]) against distance in a one compartment aqueous system. [S] increases from left to right; consequently, net diffusion of S is from right to left. Rate of diffusion is proportional to concentration gradient, **grad** [S], i.e., flux = $-D_S$ **grad** [S], where D_S is the diffusion constant. **Grad** [S] is defined, in one dimension, as the slope of the [S]-x curve as shown. *b*, A thin membrane divides the system into two compartments. S is assumed to diffuse much more slowly through the membrane than through the aqueous media on both sides. Therefore, **grad** [S] in the water is nearly zero, and **grad** [S] across the membrane is large. The average gradient of S in the membrane is difference in [S] across the membrane ($[S]_2 - [S]_1$), divided by the membrane thickness, δ. **Grad** [S] is large if δ is thin, but flux is small because D_S is so small in the membrane.

ratio indicates the extreme effectiveness of the cell membrane in limiting the flow of ions.

One way fluxes. It is natural to regard the net flux of a substance through a membrane as consisting of the difference between outward and inward one way fluxes: net flux = efflux − influx. Thus, efflux is the number of mols of a substance which diffuses from the internal medium to the external medium in one second through one cm.² of membrane and similarly for influx. On this basis, efflux can be calculated from equation (1) by setting the external concentration to zero so that net efflux consists solely of one way efflux: $M_S = P_S [S]_i$. However, this calculation is based on the assumption that each particle moves through the membrane independently of any other particle (the independence principle), a situation that does not always exist in the membrane, as will be seen below.

Experimentally it is usually not feasible to reduce the concentration of a particular substance to zero in one or the other of the solutions bathing the membrane since this change at the very least would likely alter the permeability characteristics of the membrane. However, the same effect can be obtained without producing appreciable changes in the media by adding a small amount of a radioactive isotope of the substance under study to the bathing medium. The concentration of radioactive material is zero inside the cell initially; the total concentration of the substance is normal. Measurements of the uptake rate of the isotope is a measure of the influx. Similarly, reducing the external isotope concentration to zero and measuring the rate of loss of isotope from the "loaded" tissue gives a measure of efflux. The measurement of one way fluxes under various conditions gives important information concerning the means by which substances penetrate the membrane, even—or especially—in those cases in which the independence principle does not hold, e.g., carrier mediated transport (see next section).

Membrane structure.[4, 5, 10, 23, 24] The cell membrane probably consists of outer and inner monomolecular layers of protein separated by a bimolecular lipid layer. In the lipid layer, the long, thin lipid molecules are closely packed, with their long axes parallel and oriented perpendicular to the membrane. The nonpolar ends of the lipid molecules are opposed. The protein layers are bonded to the lipids at their polar ends. Lipids are hydrophobic, and it seems unlikely that water and water-soluble substances can penetrate the membrane in a region where the lipid layer is closely packed.

In view of this probable membrane structure, the problem becomes not one of accounting for the low permeability of the membrane to water-soluble substances but of explaining the occurrence of any penetration at all. Lipid-soluble substances presumably penetrate by dissolving in the membrane substance. The available data suggest that ions and some other substances tra-

verse the membrane by one or both of the following means:

(i) The membrane is perforate, containing small-diameter (about 7 Ångstroms), water-filled pores.[24,26] Ions could diffuse through these pores rapidly. The limitation of fluxes is attributed to the comparatively small number of pores per unit area of membrane and to restrictive effects of the pores. The membrane is normally about 100 times more permeable to K^+ than it is to Na^+. This difference is apparently due to the greater hydrated radius of the Na^+ ion; the smaller positively charged Na atom attracts and holds more dipolar water molecules than does K. Na^+ ions are about 5 Ångstroms and K^+ ions are about 4 Ångstroms in diameter[26] and it is reasonable to suppose that the movements of Na^+ through a 7 Ångstrom pore are appreciably hindered with respect to those of K^+. Most ions appear to move through the membrane independently of each other but the "in file" behavior of K^+ in *Sepia* giant axon membranes[14] is an exception.

(ii) There is a special lipid-soluble *carrier* molecule (possibly a phosphatide), limited to the membrane, which combines highly preferentially with particular ions. An ion from the interstitial fluid could combine with this carrier molecule at the outer surface of the membrane; the ion-carrier complex might then diffuse through the membrane to the inner surface. The ion might there dissociate from the carrier and enter the intracellular fluid. It has become increasingly necessary to postulate carriers to explain some aspects of both passive (diffusion) and active transport of ions and other substances. The exact manner in which ions cross the membrane is not known, but for passive movements it does not matter. When transport is passive, the net flux is approximately proportional to the concentration gradient of the ion across the cell membrane; the concept of permeability still applies.

Membrane Charge and Voltage Gradient. *Ion diffusion and charge separation.* Electric forces also affect the rate at which ions move through a membrane or solution. For an uncharged (nonionized) substance in a nonflowing solution, the only passive force tending to cause a net movement of the solute is the concentration gradient. However, if particles in solution are electrically charged, their movements may also be influenced by electric forces; and, conversely, their diffusion may generate a voltage. More precisely, voltage gradients as well as concentration gradients exert forces on charged particles in solution. The mechanism whereby voltage gradients can affect the diffusion of ions is most easily understood in terms of the forces acting on an ion moving through a membrane permeable only to small diameter ions.

Figure 3 is a diagram of a portion of a simplified membrane bathed by interstitial and intracellular fluid. This hypothetical membrane has been drawn with holes or pores piercing it at intervals. The diagram should be used only as an aid to thinking, not as a portrayal of a real membrane, for the scheme is far too simple. Nevertheless, it is useful in describing the generation of voltage gradients by the diffusion of ions.

The pores in the membrane are assumed to be just large enough to permit easy passage of K^+ and Cl^- but small enough that the slightly larger Na^+ can penetrate only with difficulty, i.e., P_K and P_{Cl} are much greater than P_{Na}. (Although Na has a lower atomic weight than K, Na^+ are larger than K^+ and Cl^- in solution because Na^+ bind more water molecules; i.e., they are more hydrated.) The large A^- are presumed too large to penetrate; i.e., $P_A = 0$. The concentration of each ionic species in the interstitial and intracellular fluid is shown qualitatively in

Figure 3 by the size of its symbol at the left and right edges. Even if it is supposed that there is no potential difference (no charges are separated) across the membrane at some instant, a voltage will be generated immediately thereafter by the diffusion of K^+ and Cl^- along their concentration gradients. This potential arises because K^+, which permeate the membrane easily, diffuse out of the cell through the pores and Cl^- diffuse inward. Hereafter, the behavior of K^+ only will be described, but it must be kept in mind that Cl^- give rise to the same effects. Wherever the outward diffusion of K^+ is mentioned, the inward diffusion of Cl^- would produce the same electrical effects.

Consider the sequence of events as each K^+ diffuses out of the cell. Although K^+ are charged particles, their outward movement cannot be accompanied by a corresponding movement of A^-, nor can an equal number of Na^+ move inward in exchange for outflowing K^+. Thus, K^+ ions reach the outside of the membrane alone and are not replaced within the cell by Na^+. Consequently, the outside acquires a net positive charge and the inside a net negative charge. Since electric charges of opposite sign attract each other, the excess K^+ ions on the outside are

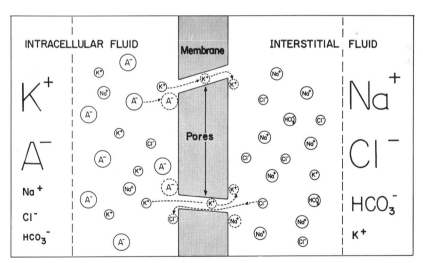

Fig. 3. Development of transmembrane voltage by an ion concentration gradient. Diagram of an intracellular fluid–membrane–interstitial fluid system. Membrane shown has some, but not all, properties of a real cell membrane. Hypothetical membrane is pierced by pores of such size that K^+ and Cl^- can move through them easily, Na^+ with difficulty, and A^- not at all. Sizes of symbols in left- and right-hand columns indicate relative concentrations of ions in fluids bathing the membrane. Dashed arrows and circles show paths taken by K^+, A^-, Na^+ and Cl^- as a K^+ or Cl^- travels through a pore. Penetration of the pore by a K^+ or Cl^- follows a collision between the K^+ or Cl^- and water molecules (not shown), giving the K^+ or Cl^- the necessary kinetic energy and proper direction. An A^- or Na^+ unable to cross the membrane is left behind when a K^+ or Cl^-, respectively, diffuses through a pore. Because K^+ is more concentrated on left than on right, more K^+ diffuses from left to right than from right to left, and conversely for Cl^-. Therefore, right-hand border of membrane becomes positively charged (K^+, Na^+) and left-hand negatively charged (Cl^-, A^-). Fluids away from the membrane are electrically neutral because of attraction between + and − charges. Charges separated by membrane stay near it because of their attraction.

attracted to the excess A^- left inside the cell. Therefore, the excess charges stay in the immediate vicinity of the membrane, as shown in Figure 3. Note that, despite the electrical attraction between the K^+ and A^-, movement of the K^+ back toward the inside of the cell is counteracted by the concentration gradient of K^+, which exerts an outward force on them. The outward diffusion of K^+ due to the concentration gradient separates positive and negative charges and thus generates a *voltage gradient* or an *electric field. Electric field intensity,* E, at a point is a vector defined as the force that would be exerted on a unit positive exploring charge placed at that point. This electric field retards further outward diffusion of K^+ (or any cation) and speeds their inward diffusion. Any positively charged ion in the membrane (Fig. 3) is acted upon by the charges the membrane separates. The positive charges on its outer surface exert an *inward* repulsive force on a positive ion in the membrane; the negative charges on the inner surface exert an additive inward attractive force.

Since the diffusion of a single ionic species through the membrane generates its own retarding force, the electric field, the process is self-limiting, and eventually a state will be reached (equilibrium) in which the efflux equals influx (net flux is zero). At equilibrium, the tendency for K^+ to diffuse out, resulting from the high value of $[K^+]_i$, is exactly balanced by the tendency for them to diffuse inward that results from the electric field in the membrane. Because K^+ inside the cell are more concentrated, they will enter pores in the membrane as a result of their random motion much more frequently than will the K^+ outside. However, a cation entering a pore from the inside must have much kinetic energy to move through the membrane against the retarding electric field. Conversely, because of the low $[K^+]_o$ few K^+ enter the pores from the outside, but nearly all those that do will continue on through the membrane, aided by the electric field. Since much of present knowledge of cell membrane function has come from measurements of the electrical characteristics of the membrane, knowledge of some principles of electricity is necessary for an understanding of membrane function. For this reason, a brief review of the pertinent principles of electricity is included as an appendix at the end of Chapter 2 for use by readers whose physics may be "rusty." Some problems related to the material presented in this and in Chapters 2 and 3 may be found at the end of the appendix.

Cell membrane capacity and charge. An animal cell and its surrounding fluids form a capacitor: two conductors, the interstitial and intracellular fluids, are separated by an insulator, the cell membrane. Since ions can penetrate the membrane to a limited extent, the cell is not a perfect capacitor. Charges separated by the membrane will eventually leak through unless there are some means of restoring the charge as fast as it leaks through. Membrane capacity is relatively high because the membrane is extremely thin. The cell may be regarded as a parallel plate capacitor, because the distance between the conductors is small compared to the diameter of a cell. It is convenient to give membrane capacities in terms of capacity per unit area, because the capacity of a parallel plate capacitor is proportional to its surface area and cells vary considerably in size. The nerve fibers of the squid, which have been studied extensively because they are large, have membrane capacities of about 1 μf. per cm.^{2}. The capacities of frog skeletal muscle fibers are nearly 10 μf. per cm.^{2}. The amount of charge (q) separated by 1 cm.^{2} of muscle cell membrane is the product of the steady potential difference ($\mathcal{E}_s$) across the cell membrane and the capacity (C_m) $q = C_m \mathcal{E}_s$ (see appendix, Chap. 2). $\mathcal{E}_s$ for a frog muscle fiber is -90 mV., so $q = 10 \times 10^{-6}$ f. per cm.$^2 \times 0.09$ V. $= 9 \times 10^{-7}$ coulombs per cm.^{2}.

Since the charges separated by the membrane are ions, the amount of charge can be given more meaning by expressing it in mols per cm.^{2} rather than in coulombs per cm.^{2}. There are 6.023×10^{23} molecules in 1 M. of any substance, and a monovalent ion has a charge of ± 1 electronic charge; therefore, since one electron has a charge of 1.6×10^{-19} coulombs, the charge of 1 M. of monovalent ions is (6.023×10^{23} monovalent ions per M.) $\times$ (1.6×10^{-19} coulombs per monovalent ion) $= 96,500$ coulombs per M. of monovalent ions. It follows that a charge of 9×10^{-7} coulombs per cm.^{2} on a muscle fiber membrane means that there are only 9.5×10^{-12} M. of ions separated by 1 cm.^{2} of cell membrane. By comparison, 1 cm.^{3} of interstitial or intracellular fluid contains 155×10^{-6} M. of cations (or anions). In other words, a layer of interstitial fluid only 6×10^{-8} cm. (6 Ångstroms) thick is sufficient to supply the ions necessary to charge the cell membrane capacity to 90 mV.

Charge neutrality. The charging of the membrane by the outward movement of K^+ produces a readily measurable voltage across the membrane. However, the change in $[K^+]_i$ necessary to charge the membrane is not detectable by chemical measurements. Despite the extremely small changes in ion concentration required to charge the membrane capacity, it is worth emphasizing that the law of macroscopic electroneutrality does not apply to macroscopic parts of the intracellular fluid–membrane–interstitial fluid system. The whole system is electrically neutral, but the intracellular fluid contains a slight excess of anions and the interstitial fluid an equal excess of cations. These excess charges are, of course, attracted to each other, and thus distribute themselves with uniform density over the surfaces of the membrane.

Charging membrane capacity. The process whereby the diffusion of an ionic species down its concentration gradient can generate a counteracting voltage gradient, briefly discussed above, can now be summarized in terms of the charging of the membrane capacitor and the consequent generation of an electric field in it (Fig. 3). When a K^+ traverses a pore (dashed lines, Fig. 3) and leaves the cell, this cation leaves behind a nonpermeating A^-. The outside fluid thus acquires a positive charge and the inside a negative charge. In other words, the membrane capacity is slightly charged, and a voltage difference is built up between the conductors. More simply, the separation of charge means that there is an electric field in the membrane and that work must be done on a unit $+$ charge to carry it out of the cell. The electric field in the membrane is uniform because the separated charges must distribute themselves uniformly over its surfaces in order to make the electric field zero everywhere in the inside and outside conducting fluids (see appendix, Chap. 2). This is true even in the case of penetration of the membrane by a single ion; the excess cation on one side and the excess anion on the other move the charges in the conducting media. This movement has the effect of distributing the single charge over the cell membrane surface. The electric field in the membrane is approximately constant, so the voltage across the membrane is simply the product of the electric field ($\mathbf{E}$) and the membrane thickness (δ), $\mathcal{E}_s = -\mathbf{E}(-\delta) = \mathbf{E}\delta$.

IONIC EQUILIBRIUM

As pointed out above, if a membrane's permeability to one ion is greater than to another and if ion concentration differences exist across the membrane, then a transmembrane voltage will develop. For example, if a membrane is permeable only to K^+, the diffusion of K^+ through the membrane down its concentration gradient is self-limiting. The first K^+ to penetrate the membrane generate an electric field which retards the diffusion of other K^+ ions. As long as there is a net efflux of K^+, $+$ and $-$ charges are being separated and the electric field is increasing, so that eventually $\mathbf{E}$ must attain a strength to permit influx to equal efflux. Outflowing K^+ are driven by the high $[K^+]_i$ and retarded by $\mathbf{E}$; inflowing ions are accelerated by $\mathbf{E}$, but the low $[K^+]_o$ means that K^+ enter the membrane at a slower rate. *If no work is needed to carry a small amount of a substance across the membrane, that substance is said to be distributed at equilibrium.* An alternative statement of the equilibrium condition is that influx and efflux are equal. This statement is true because there can be no net flux of the substance unless there is a force acting on it, and the existence of a force acting on ions means that a potential energy difference must also exist.

The equilibrium condition for uncharged molecules is simply that the internal and external concentrations are equal, for this is the condition at zero net flux (equation 1). The equilibrium condition for ions is more complicated: both the concentration and the voltage difference across the membrane must be known in order to calculate the potential energy difference between the inside and outside and thus the equilibrium condition. Any inside concentration of an ionic species may be brought into equilibrium with any outside concentration by applying the appropriate transmembrane voltage. Experimentally, this situation may be achieved by separating the two ionic solutions with a membrane permeable only to the ionic species for which the equilibrium is desired. The charging process illustrated in Figure 3 then generates a potential difference which equalizes influx and efflux. *The transmembrane potential which equalizes fluxes for a particular ion is called the equilibrium potential for that ion.* Its value depends on the ratio of the internal and external concentrations of the ion.

Electrochemical Potential. The relationship between the external and internal concentrations of an ion and the transmembrane potential at equilibrium is obtained by setting to zero the expression for the total transmembrane potential energy difference for that ion. This total potential energy difference per mol of ion is called the *electrochemical potential difference* $(\Delta\mu)$ and is the sum of the electrical and concentration energy differences across the membrane for that ion. An expression for the electrochemical difference for K^+ will be developed here, but the same considerations hold for any ion present in a tissue.

The *electric potential energy difference* of 1 mol of K^+ is the work that must be done solely against electric forces to carry 1 mol of K^+ across the membrane, from outside to inside, with the transmembrane potential held at its original value. This work (W_E) is simply the product of $\mathcal{E}_m$, the transmembrane voltage (joules per coulomb), F, the Faraday (number of coulombs per mole of charge) and Z_K, the valence of the K^+ ion: $W_E = Z_K F \mathcal{E}_m$. The *concentration potential energy difference* W_C is the work required to carry 1 mol of K^+ from outside to inside solely against the concentration gradient, with the external and internal K^+ concentrations held at their original values. W_C is not easily calculable, but it can be shown that W_C is proportional to the difference between the logarithms of the internal and external concentrations* rather than directly proportional to their difference. Thus $W_C = RT(\log_e[K^+]_i - \log_e[K^+]_o)$, where R is the universal gas constant, T is the absolute temperature, and e is 2.718 (the base of natural logarithms); RT has the unit of energy per mol. The electrochemical potential difference for K^+ is, then, $\Delta\mu_K = W_E + W_C$, so

$$\Delta\mu_K = Z_K F \mathcal{E}_m + RT \log_e \frac{[K^+]_i}{[K^+]_o} \qquad (2)$$

If $\mathcal{E}_m$, $[K^+]_o$ and $[K^+]_i$ are such that $\Delta\mu_K = 0$, then K^+ are equilibrated across the membrane. If $\Delta\mu_K$ is not zero, it is a measure of the net tendency of K^+ to diffuse through the membrane. The larger $\Delta\mu_K$, the greater the net efflux of K^+.

Nernst Equation. The condition for ionic equilibrium is that the electrochemical potential of an ion is zero. Setting $\Delta\mu_K = 0$ in equation 2, replacing $\mathcal{E}_m$ by $\mathcal{E}_K$, and solving for $\mathcal{E}_K$ gives

$$\mathcal{E}_K = \frac{RT}{FZ_K} \log_e \frac{[K^+]_o}{[K^+]_i} \qquad (3)$$

---

* Strictly speaking, activities rather than concentrations should be used. However, the activities appear only as ratios and these ratios are close to the equivalent concentration ratios in value. Thus, the error is not large and does not affect the conclusions reached here.

This is the Nernst equation. The term $\mathcal{E}_K$ indicates that this equation determines the value that $\mathcal{E}_m$ must have if K^+ are to be in equilibrium. $\mathcal{E}_K$ is called the *potassium equilibrium potential*. By substituting the values R = 8.31 joules per mol-degree abs., T = 310 degrees abs. (37° C.), F = 96,500 coulombs per mol, and Z_K = +1, converting to logarithms to the base 10 and expressing $\mathcal{E}_K$ in millivolts, a useful form of the Nernst equation is obtained:

$$\mathcal{E}_K = 61 \log_{10} \frac{[K^+]_o}{[K^+]_i} \text{ mV}. \qquad (4)$$

Note that if $\mathcal{E}_K = 0$, the equilibrium condition for ions reduces to that for neutral substances, i.e., $[K^+]_o = [K^+]_i$. The Nernst equation can be written for every ion present in the system.

An ion whose equilibrium potential is equal to the steady membrane potential, that is, equilibrated, is said to be distributed *passively*. This term means that there are no active forces on the ion. With the equilibrium conditions for ion concentrations quantitatively stated by the Nernst equation, it is possible to determine which ions in a cell's environment are distributed passively. The requisite numbers for the most important ions in mammalian skeletal muscle are given in Table 1. The external and internal concentrations, their ratio, and the equilibrium potentials are ·given in the main body of the table. The steady transmembrane potential $\mathcal{E}_s$, as measured with an intracellular microelectrode, is given at the bottom of the table to facilitate comparison with calculated ionic equilibrium potentials. $\mathcal{E}_s$ is defined as the potential of the inside solution minus the potential of the outside solution. Since the cell interior is negatively charged, $\mathcal{E}_s$ is a negative number. K^+, Cl^- and Na^+ will be discussed here and H^+ and HCO_3^- in Chapter 46.

Potassium ions. From Table 1, $[K^+]_o$ = 4 μM. per cm.^{3} and $[K^+]_i$ = 155 μM. per cm.^{3}; therefore, $\mathcal{E}_K$ = 61 $\log_{10}$ (4/155) = −97 mV. This value is close to the measured $\mathcal{E}_s$, −90 mV. This calculation accords with qualitative arguments given above that the concentration gradient for K^+ is largely counteracted by the membrane voltage gradient; i.e., little energy is needed to carry 1 mol of K^+ across the membrane. Experimental errors make it uncertain whether or not $\mathcal{E}_K$ and $\mathcal{E}_s$ are different in this case, but there is good evidence, nevertheless, that K^+ are not quite at equilibrium in tissues.

Chloride ions. The extracellular concentration of chloride is high, and its intracellular concentration is low. Because of the negative valence of Cl⁻, the electrical and concentration forces affecting Cl⁻ act in opposite directions. However, the value of $\mathcal{E}_{Cl}$ is uncertain because $[Cl^-]_i$ is difficult to estimate from analyses of the chloride content of the tissues, since these determinations include both extracellular and intracellular fluids, and most of the tissue Cl⁻ is in the interstitial fluid. Hence, less direct means must be used to determine cell chloride concentration in tissues. There is good indirect evidence that chloride is equilibrated in frog skeletal muscle. Hodgkin and Horowicz[12] found that sudden changes in $[Cl^-]_o$ can produce large but always transient changes in transmembrane potential. This means that P_{Cl} is comparable to P_K and that the net fluxes of Cl⁻ resulting from sudden changes in its concentration affect the potential until such times as Cl⁻ redistribution is completed and net flux of Cl⁻ returns to zero. Also, there is little doubt that Cl⁻ is equilibrated in red blood cells. However, Cl⁻ is not passively distributed in all tissues. Keynes[16] has direct evidence that the giant axon of the squid (see Chapter 2) actively accumulates Cl⁻. Nevertheless Cl⁻ distribution in tissues is assumed to be passive hereafter unless a specific statement is made to the contrary. The value of $[Cl^-]_i = 4 \mu M$. per cm.³ given in Table 1 was calculated on this assumption, i.e., $\mathcal{E}_{Cl}$ is set equal to the $\mathcal{E}_s = -90$ mV. and Nernst's equation solved for $[Cl^-]_i$.

Sodium ions. To a first approximation, K⁺ and Cl⁻ are distributed across the membrane in equilibrium with the membrane voltage ($\mathcal{E}_{Cl} = \mathcal{E}_s \simeq \mathcal{E}_K$). Two interpretations of this finding are possible: (i) the membrane voltage is generated by the existing concentration gradients of K⁺ and Cl⁻ ions in the manner described above, the mechanism whereby these concentration gradients are maintained not being specified, or (ii) the membrane voltage is maintained by unspecified means and the K⁺ and Cl⁻ distribute themselves in equilibrium with the voltage. Even though the evidence presented thus far does not permit differentiation between these two possibilities, they highlight the question of how the resting potential and the concentration gradients are generated and maintained by the cell. The key to this question lies in the behavior of Na⁺. Sodium is distributed far out of equilibrium with the membrane voltage; both the concentration gradient and the voltage gradient act

to drive Na⁺ into the cell. The Na⁺ equilibrium potential, $\mathcal{E}_{Na}$, is given by Nernst's equation: $\mathcal{E}_{Na} = (61/1) \log (145/12) = +66$ mV. This means that the membrane potential would have to be $+66$ mV. (inside positive) in order to counteract the inward concentration force on Na⁺, whereas $\mathcal{E}_s$ is actually -90 mV. (inside negative) in the steady state.

Membrane Ionic Flux, Current and Conductance. As mentioned in connection with equation 2, the transmembrane electrochemical potential difference of an ion species is a measure of the tendency for that ion to move through the membrane. The rate at which an ion moves through the membrane depends not only on the electrochemical potential but also on the ease with which the ion can penetrate the membrane, i.e., its permeability. Thus it is reasonable to write transmembrane flux of an ion as the product of a potential energy difference term and a permeability term. Such a relationship is actually a generalization of Ohm's law (see appendix, Chap. 2) relating current flow (I) and potential difference ($\mathcal{E}$): $I = (1/R)\mathcal{E} = g\mathcal{E}$, where R is resistance and $g = 1/R$ is called the conductance (unit: mho, ohm spelled backwards). Thus, by making use of Nernst's equation for the equilibrium potential (equation 3), and by using K⁺ as an example, the description of the electrochemical potential (equation 2) can be greatly simplified by expressing it as an electric potential difference:

$$\Delta\mu_K = Z_K F \left(\mathcal{E}_m - \frac{RT}{ZF} \log_e \frac{[K^+]_o}{[K^+]_i} \right)$$
$$= Z_K F (\mathcal{E}_m - \mathcal{E}_K) \qquad (5)$$

where $\mathcal{E}_K$ is the K⁺ equilibrium potential.

Ohm's law for ion fluxes. Current is defined as the number of coulombs passing a point in a second (units: coulombs/sec. = amperes). Current density is directly related to flux; current density is defined as coulombs per second and per cm.² of area perpendicular to direction of flow and flux is mols per sec.-cm.². The proportionality factor is the Faraday (F, units: coulombs per mol of monovalent ions) times the valence (Z): $I = ZFM$. The direction of current of flow and flux is mols per sec.-cm.². The propositive charge; hence current and flux are in the same direction for positive ions and in opposite directions for negative ions as indicated by the valence, Z. The current density of K⁺ (I_K)

through the membrane is proportional to the electrochemical potential difference:

$$I_K = M_K Z_K F = g_K(\mathcal{E}_m - \mathcal{E}_K) \qquad (6)$$

where the proportionality factor, g_K, is called the specific membrane conductance to potassium or simply potassium conductance (units: mho per cm.^{2}). I_K is actually current density but is usually referred to simply as potassium current.

Equation 6 expresses the rate of movement of an ion species through the membrane in terms of its ease of penetration and the divergence of the actual membrane potential from the equilibrium potential for that ion. Ion current is zero when $\mathcal{E}_m = \mathcal{E}_K$, which is, of course, the equilibrium condition. Similarly, the greater the difference between the two potentials, the greater the ion movement through the membrane.

Membrane ionic conductance. Membrane ionic conductance is a measure of the ease with which an ion penetrates the membrane; i.e., the measurement is made when the ions are driven by an electrical force. On the other hand, permeability is a measure of the ease with which a substance penetrates the membrane when driven by a concentration force. Thus ion conductance and ion permeability must be closely related quantities. However, the relationship between them is not simple, depending, among other things, on the transmembrane voltage itself. For example, in frog skeletal muscle, it has been found experimentally that g_{Cl} varies considerably with voltage but in the manner expected if P_{Cl} is constant. Despite the complicated nature of conductance, the Ohm's law approach is most frequently used in describing ion fluxes through membranes because conductances are usually easier to measure experimentally than permeabilities, because the relationship is easy to visualize and simple to use and because the relationship between flux, permeability and concentration and potential differences is complicated and difficult to use. Hence, Ohm's law for ion fluxes (equation 6) is used throughout the remainder of this chapter and in Chapters 2, 4 and 5 where appropriate. Thus it is extremely important at this juncture to understand the concepts of the ion equilibrium potential as defined by Nernst's equation (3) and Ohm's law (appendix, Chap. 2); e.g., Figure 6 (page 20), based on these concepts, shows the important factors in maintenance of steady transmembrane concentration and potential differences by active Na^+–K^+ transport.

ACTIVE SODIUM TRANSPORT

Sodium Influx. Na^+ is distributed so far from equilibrium—i.e., $\Delta\mu_{Na}$ is so high—as to pose forcefully the question of how this disequilibrium is maintained in living cells. There are at least two possibilities. If Na^+ ions are unable to penetrate the membrane, the disequilibrium would persist indefinitely. If Na^+ can penetrate the membrane, some other energy term must be included in the calculation of the expected Na^+ distribution. The first possibility is simple and, therefore, attractive. However, it must be rejected, since studies with radioactive Na^+ have shown that these ions penetrate the membrane, although not so readily as K^+ and Cl^-. Therefore, the second possibility must be explored.

Sodium tracer experiments.[11, 13] The penetration of Na^+ through the membrane is demonstrated experimentally by placing a small muscle or a single large nerve cell into a solution with an ionic composition the same as that of the interstitial fluid, a radioactive isotope of Na^+ constituting part of the Na^+. If Na^+ can penetrate the membrane, part of the nonradioactive Na^+ in the intracellular fluid will, in time, exchange positions with radioactive Na^+ in the bathing medium. The amount of radiosodium taken up by the muscle after a period of soaking is measured by counting the number of disintegrations per minute occurring in the tissue. The total Na^+ entry during soaking can be ascertained by comparing the number of counts per minute from the muscle with the number of counts per minute from a known volume of the radioactive bathing medium and its known Na^+ concentration. The result must, of course, be corrected for the amount of radiosodium in the interstitial fluid in the muscle and for the interstitial concentration of sodium. If the total surface area of all fibers in the muscle is known, the influx of Na^+ (mols per cm.^{2}-sec.) can be calculated.

Measured Na^+ influx in frog sartorius muscle is of the order of 5×10^{-12} M. per cm.^{2}-second.[11] If this influx were not matched by an equal efflux,* the internal Na^+ concentration in a muscle fiber 100 μ in diameter would increase at the rate of about 14 μM. per cm.^{3}-hour. Since $[Na^+]$ is about 12 μM. per cm.^{3}, $[Na^+]_i$ would about double in the first hour.

Sodium Efflux. To return to the second possibility mentioned above, namely, that another term is needed to balance influx and efflux of Na^+, there are three apparently contradictory facts about the behavior of Na^+ in tissues which must be considered. (i) The distribution of Na^+ in tissues is far from equilibrium. (ii)

---

* The expected passive efflux is negligible, less than 0.1 per cent of influx.

Na$^+$ can penetrate the cell membrane. (iii) This disequilibrium is maintained by living cells; [Na$^+$]$_i$ remains low and $\Delta\mu_{Na}$ remains high despite an appreciable influx of Na$^+$. Therefore, for some reason, Na$^+$ efflux must equal Na$^+$ influx; i.e., it is necessary to postulate that some force other than voltage and concentration gradients is expelling Na$^+$ from the cell at an average rate equal to the rate of passive entry.

Since Na$^+$ enters cells spontaneously, work must be done to carry Na$^+$ out of the cell. Further, Na$^+$ is entering all the time, so work must be continuously expended to eject the entering Na$^+$ and maintain a low [Na$^+$]$_i$. The power (time rate of supplying energy or of doing work) to eject Na$^+$ continually comes ultimately from the oxidation of glucose or other metabolites by the cell. *The process whereby the cell continuously uses metabolic energy to maintain an efflux of Na$^+$ is called active Na$^+$ transport* or, colloquially, *the Na$^+$ pump.*

The term "active transport" implies that the transport process requires a continuous supply of energy. By contrast, the diffusion of a substance down its electrochemical gradient is called "passive transport." The detailed mechanism involved in active Na$^+$ transport is not known. Nevertheless, in addition to the reasons given above for supposing there must be an active Na$^+$ transport, there is considerable direct experimental evidence that such a mechanism exists in many types of cells, e.g., giant nerve fibers of the squid,[13] human red blood cells[6, 7, 27] and frog skin (from outside to inside).[19, 22, 28, 29] In addition, active Na$^+$ transport almost certainly occurs in all nervous tissue and all skeletal,[1, 11, 17, 18] cardiac and smooth muscle. Active Na$^+$ reabsorption is probably the major energy-consuming process in the kidney. Na$^+$ pumping is also importantly involved in the formation of saliva and other ion-containing gastrointestinal secretions. Many substances besides Na$^+$ are actively transported by cells. The kidney is specialized for the active secretion or reabsorption of many inorganic and organic substances.

Energy requirements for active sodium transport. The postulate that the disequilibrium of Na$^+$ between cells and bathing medium is maintained through the expenditure of metabolic energy is subject to a stringent yet simple experimental test. The minimum power required to transport Na$^+$ out of a cell at the observed rate must be less than the rate of energy production of the cell. The rate of energy production can be calculated from the oxygen con-

sumption of the cell. The minimum transport power is the product of the transport work per mol of Na$^+$ and the number of mols of Na$^+$ transported per second, i.e., the product of the negative of the electrochemical potential of Na$^+$ and the Na$^+$ active efflux ($\mathbf{M}_{Na}^{out}$). Thus, the Na$^+$ transport power ($\dot{W}_{Na}$)* is $\dot{W}_{Na} = -\Delta\mu_{Na}\mathbf{M}_{Na}^{out}$. The negative sign is used in front of $\Delta\mu_{Na}$ because it is defined as the electrical and concentration work to carry 1 M. of Na$^+$ into the cell through the membrane; this work is, of course, the negative of the work to carry the Na$^+$ out. $\Delta\mu_{Na}$ is of the same form as $\Delta\mu_K$, given in equation 2, so

$$\dot{W}_{Na} = -\left(Z_{Na}F\mathcal{E}_m + RT\log_e\frac{[Na^+]_i}{[Na^+]_o}\right)\mathbf{M}_{Na}^{out}(7)$$

Keynes and Maisel[17] have made the necessary measurements on frog skeletal muscle to test whether the Na$^+$ transport power requirement is less than the energy production rate of a cell. In one experiment, they obtained the following data:

$\mathcal{E}_s = -88$ mV., $[Na^+]_o = 115$ μM. per cm.^{3}, $[Na^+]_i = 20$ μM. per cm.^{3}, $\mathbf{M}_{Na}^{out} = 8.7$ μM.

per hour and per gram of muscle.† Energy production, calculated from oxygen consumption, was 0.17 calorie per hour and per gram of muscle. Substituting these values in equation 5 gives the value $\dot{W}_{Na} = 0.027$ calorie per hour and per gram of muscle as the power requirement for Na$^+$ transport, assuming 100 per cent efficiency for the process. In other words, a minimum of 15 per cent of the oxygen consumption of a non-contracting muscle is used to pump Na$^+$. Keynes and Maisel obtained values of about 10 per cent in most of their experiments. It should be borne in mind that the pumping efficiency is unlikely to be greater than about 50 per cent, so that at least 20 per cent of resting oxygen consumption, probably more, goes for Na$^+$ transportation. In any event, the energy demands of the Na$^+$ pump are not excessive, and the postulate of active Na$^+$ transport is possible energetically. More recently, Keynes and Swan[18] have shown

---

*A dot over a symbol for a quantity means the time rate of change of the quantity; orally, such a symbol is referred to as "W-dot." Thus W_{Na} is work done on or energy of 1 M. of Na$^+$; $\dot{W}_{Na}$ is the time rate of doing work, or power.

†Strictly speaking this is not efflux, but it is the desired figure, since oxygen consumption is given in cubic millimeters per hour and per gram of tissue.

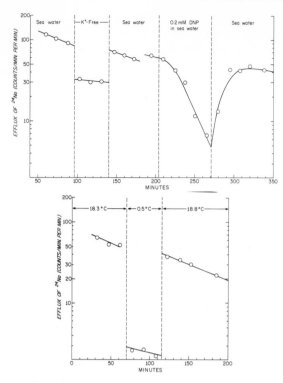

Fig. 4. Na+ efflux in giant axon of *Sepia* (cuttlefish). Ordinates are efflux of radioactive Na+ from cell; total (radioactive + normal) Na+ of efflux is proportional to radioactive efflux except for gradual dilution of radioactive Na+ by normal Na+ as these ions exchange (the gradual fall shown under sea water).

Upper, Effects of various bathing media. Second column from left shows that reducing $[K+]_o$ from 10 μM. per cm.³ to zero immediately reduces Na+ efflux to about one-third that in artificial sea water; this effect is immediately reversed when the axon is returned to artificial sea water (middle column). Next, adding the metabolic inhibitor DNP reduces Na+ efflux to values near zero within one to two hours; this effect is slowly reversible (right column).

Lower, The effects of temperature on another axon. Reduction of temperature from 18° to 0.5° C. immediately reduces Na+ efflux to near zero; raising the temperature immediately restores efflux. (From Hodgkin and Keynes. *J. Physiol.*, 1955, *128:*28–60.)

that about one-half of Na+ efflux is a one-for-one forced exchange for external Na+; i.e., Na+ efflux is reduced to one-half when $[Na+]_o$ is reduced to zero. This *exchange diffusion*, first postulated by Ussing,[28] does not require the expenditure of energy. Thus the calculated minimum power requirement for Na+ pumping in resting muscle is about twice too large.

Active Sodium–Potassium Exchange. Although the detailed mechanism for utilization of metabolic energy to carry Na+ out of the cell

is not yet known, the process has been intensively studied in many tissues and some of the broad characteristics of Na+ pumping have been defined. These characteristics seem to be much the same in all the tissues studied. Hodgkin and Keynes[13] carefully investigated Na+ and K+ movements in giant axons (150 to 300 μ in diameter) of *Sepia* (cuttlefish). These findings form a compact summary of the present state of knowledge. (i) Na+ efflux is a direct function of $[Na+]_i$. (ii) Na+ efflux is decreased to values near zero by the addition, at appropriate concentrations, of a metabolic inhibitor to the bathing medium (Fig. 4). Metabolic inhibitors are substances which block the metabolic cycle at some point. Such an inhibitor would be expected to stop Na+ extrusion by depriving the pump of its source of energy. (iii) K+ influx is greatly reduced by metabolic inhibitors. These inhibitors produce about equal decreases in K+ efflux and Na+ influx. (iv) Na+ influx and K+ efflux are not greatly affected by metabolic inhibitors. (v) Na+ efflux is greatly reduced, but not abolished, by removal of K+ from the external bathing medium (Fig. 4) and increases when $[K+]_o$ is increased. (vi) Na+ efflux (Fig. 4) and K+ influx are highly temperature-dependent; a reduction in temperature markedly decreases the fluxes (Q_{10} of 3 to 4, i.e., a temperature reduction of 10° C. reduces these fluxes to ⅓ to ¼ of their original values). On the other hand, Na+ influx and K+ efflux are relatively insensitive to temperature changes (Q_{10} from 1.1 to 1.4).

Figure 4 shows the effects of a K+-free solution, of the metabolic inhibitor 2,4 dinitrophenol (DNP), and of low temperature on the Na+ efflux of a *Sepia* axon. The ordinate, which indicates the number of disintegrations of radiosodium atoms per minute that occur among radiosodium ions that have left the cell in one minute, is nearly proportional to Na+ efflux.* It can be seen that removal of K+ from the bathing medium immediately reduces the Na+ efflux to

---

*The number of radioactive sodium ions in a sample is proportional to the number of counts per minute. After correction is made for the gradual dilution of the radioactive ions by inactive ones, the total number of Na+ present is proportional to the number of radioactive Na+ present. Counts per minute appearing in the external medium in one minute are thus of the form of mols per minute. Dividing by the surface area of the axon involved gives the flux in mols per cm.²-minute.

about 0.3 of its previous value. In contrast, the addition of DNP (0.2 μM. per cm.[3]) leads to a slow decline in efflux requiring one to two hours for completion. The slow onset of the effect of DNP is attributed to the time required for the axon to consume the energy stores on hand when metabolism is inhibited.

These findings are strong evidence for the existence of an active Na$^+$ transport process in cells. Further, the findings suggest that there is also an active uptake of K$^+$ and that this uptake is coupled with Na$^+$ extrusion. A reduction in the amount of available energy, either by metabolic inhibitors or by temperature reduction, has parallel effects in reducing Na$^+$ efflux and K$^+$ influx. A coupled Na$^+$–K$^+$ exchange mechanism is also suggested by the reduction in Na$^+$ efflux when all the K$^+$ is removed from the bathing medium and the increase in Na$^+$ exit when [K$^+$]$_o$ is increased. However, since Na$^+$ efflux is 30 per cent of normal when [K$^+$]$_o$ = 0, the linkage between Na$^+$ and K$^+$ is not rigid. The dependence of Na$^+$ extrusion on [K$^+$]$_o$ has been observed in a number of other tissues and the existence of such a relationship is presumptive evidence of a one-for-one Na$^+$–K$^+$ exchange. It will be assumed hereafter that Na$^+$ pumping is coupled with an equal uptake of K$^+$. This assumption, although not strictly true, simplifies, without invalidating, deductions on the consequences of active Na$^+$ for K$^+$ transport. The effects of active inward K$^+$ transport on the distribution of K$^+$ will be discussed later.

Since the existence of active Na$^+$–K$^+$ transport is well established, it is reasonable to ask how the cell does use metabolic energy to extrude Na$^+$ and take up K$^+$. Although no detailed answer can be given to this question, it is worthwhile, for the sake of concreteness, to describe a specific model of Na$^+$–K$^+$ transport (Fig. 5) and to describe a recently established correlation between Na$^+$ efflux and an adenosine triphosphatase activity which is found in red blood cell membranes and which is activated by Na$^+$ and K$^+$.

Model of active sodium–potassium exchange.[6] The hypothetical scheme of active cation transport illustrated in Figure 5 accounts for all the known phenomena but there are numerous other possible mechanisms. There are insufficient experimental data at present to distinguish between the various possibilities. The most probable method of pumping Na$^+$ is to "disguise" or "smuggle" it, i.e., to let Na$^+$ diffuse through the membrane down a concentration gradient of an organo-Na$^+$ compound that is continuously produced inside the cell and destroyed outside the cell. Another way of saying this is that the "force other than the concentration and potential gradients" that was invoked earlier to explain the efflux of Na$^+$ is simply a concentration gradient, maintained by metabolism, of an organo-Na$^+$ compound.

Figure 5 is a scheme of a hypothetical Na$^+$–K$^+$ exchange mechanism that accounts for many of the known facts. Na$^+$ is carried out of the cell combined with a substance (Y) which has a high affinity for Na$^+$; that is, the reaction Na$^+$ + Y = Na$^+$Y is far to the right. Y may or may not have a negative charge. Once outside the cell, or at the outer surface of the cell membrane, some of the Na$^+$Y dissociates into Na$^+$ + Y. Y is immediately converted into a K$^+$-specific carrier substance (X), the rate of the spontaneous reaction being increased by an enzyme on the outer surface of the cell membrane. X combines with K$^+$ and the K$^+$X diffuses into the cell under its own concentration gradient.

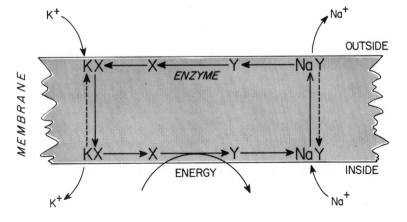

Fig. 5. Hypothetical scheme of a Na$^+$–K$^+$ exchange pump. The substances X and Y are assumed to be confined to the membrane. X has a high affinity for K$^+$; Y has a high affinity for Na$^+$. X and Y move through the membrane only when in combination with an ion. (Modified from Shaw by Glynn. *Progr. Biophys.*, 1957, *8*:241–307.)

The X formed when K+X dissociates inside the cell is converted to Y by an energy-requiring reaction, thus completing the transport cycle.

This scheme does not require a rigid Na+–K+ coupling. Thus, the maintenance of some Na+ efflux when external [K+] is zero can be explained by assuming either that Na+ has some affinity for the K+ carrier, X, or that Na+Y is shuttling back and forth across the membrane and that the Na+ bound to Y may exchange with Na+ in the interstitial fluid as well as in the intracellular fluid. This latter process does not require an energy supply and thus is a model of exchange diffusion.[18]

Sodium–potassium transport and membrane ATP-ase activity.[27]   Recent discoveries have given an inkling of the molecular basis of Na+–K+ transport: (i) Adenosine triphosphate (ATP) is an energy source sufficient to maintain pumping in squid nerve and in human red cell ghosts. (ii) There is present in human red cell membranes, in crab nerves and brain microsomes ("membrane" fraction of centrifuged cell fragments) an adenosine triphosphatase activity which requires Mg^{++} and whose activity, i.e., rate of ATP hydrolysis, is increased by the presence of Na+ and K+ in the medium. (iii) This ATP-ase activity is inhibited by cardiac glycosides (digitalis-like substances). These glycosides are also potent inhibitors of Na+–K+ active transport; indeed glycoside inhibition of a measured flux is presumptive evidence of active transport. (iv) Tosteson's[27] experiments have established a striking correlation between the amount of Na+–K+ activated ATP-ase present in red cell membranes and an index of intact red cell pumping activity. He did this by taking advantage of marked differences in the Na+ and K+ contents of red blood cells from genetically different sheep. The red cells of most sheep have high Na+ and low K+ concentrations, while the red cells of a few of the sheep in the same herd have low Na+ and high K+ concentrations. The low [K+]$_i$ condition is a simple dominant. Tosteson found that the ratio of the pumped K+ influxes between red cells having high [K+]$_i$ and those having low [K+]$_i$ was 4.1. Similarly, the ratio of Na+–K+ stimulated ATP-ase activities between the high and low [K+]$_i$ red cells had the identical value, 4.1. This is strong evidence that some membrane ATP-ase activity is closely related to the active Na+–K+ transport process and that the pumping mechanism is located in the membrane.

GENERATION AND MAINTENANCE OF ION AND POTENTIAL DIFFERENCES

If all the important factors affecting the movements of ions have been analyzed in the previous section, then it should be possible to explain the observed transmembrane concentration and voltage differences of cells solely in terms of these factors. In this section it will be shown (i) that the Na+–K+ exchange pump is sufficient to maintain voltages and concentrations at their observed values (steady state) and (ii) how, starting with interstitial fluid on both sides of the membrane, a neutral Na+–K+ pump can establish the observed voltage and intracellular ion concentrations (transient state). Although the picture presented here accounts in a satisfactory way for a large amount of our knowledge of these matters, it should be remembered that it is simplified and thus inaccurate; all membrane phenomena are not taken into account.

Maintenance of Ionic Distributions by a Sodium–Potassium Pump.   *Steady state.*   In this discussion of a cell system, the term *steady state* indicates that the concentrations and voltages are unvarying in time but that the system is not in equilibrium. Energy must be continuously expended to maintain the steady state. There is a steady flow of oxygen and glucose into the cell and a steady flow of carbon dioxide and H_2O out of the cell. Substance Y is constantly made from X and flows out of the cell; X is made from Y and flows into the cell (Fig. 5). "Unchanging ionic concentrations" means that the net flux of each ion is zero. Thus the steady state condition occurs when the influx and efflux of a substance are equal if the substance is neither manufactured nor destroyed in the cell; otherwise net efflux is equal to the rate of production of the substance in the cell, or the net influx equals the rate of destruction in the cell. If a chemical species is distributed at equilibrium, its influx and efflux are equal and passive; in the steady state the influx equals the efflux, although the fluxes may have both active and passive components if the species is neither produced nor destroyed.

Potassium ion distribution.   The one-way flux of an ion equals the sum of the passive and active fluxes. The influx of K+ consists of a passive component, K+ driven inward by the voltage gradient, and an active component, the inward leg of the Na+–K+ exchange pump. K+ efflux is passive. If the steady state membrane potential ($\mathcal{E}_s$) were just equal to the K+ equilibrium potential ($\mathcal{E}_K$), the passive fluxes would be equal; the active influx would thus be unbalanced, and $[K^+]_i$ would be increasing at a rate determined by the pumping rate and cell volume. Therefore, in the steady state, $\mathcal{E}_s$ cannot be as large a number as $\mathcal{E}_K$. In other words, $[K^+]_i$ must be larger than predicted from the Nernst equation in order to make the passive efflux equal to the summed passive and active influxes. The steady state values given in Table 1 show that $\mathcal{E}_K$ (-95 mV.) has a slightly larger negative value than $\mathcal{E}_s$ (-90 mV.). The difference need be no greater than this in the steady state, because of the relatively high permeability of the membrane to K^+. A small increase in $[K^+]_i$ suffices to increase K^+ efflux enough to match the active influx. In view of the possible errors in the measurement of $[K^+]_i$ and $\mathcal{E}_s$, the difference between $\mathcal{E}_K$ and $\mathcal{E}_s$ is not significant. However, significant differences have been consistently found in other tissues; e.g., in frog muscle the difference is about 20 mV., which means that $[K^+]_i$ in these cells is about twice what it would be if $\mathcal{E}_K = \mathcal{E}_s$ (however, see Mullins and Noda[21]). In human red blood cells $\mathcal{E}_K$ is about -90 mV., whereas $\mathcal{E}_s$ is about -10 mV.

Sodium ion distribution. Qualitatively, Na^+ distribution across the membrane is a mirror image of K^+ distribution: Na^+ low inside, K^+ low outside; Na^+ pumped out, K^+ pumped in; Na^+ high outside, K^+ high inside. The arguments concerning K^+ fluxes given in the preceding paragraph apply equally well to Na^+ fluxes simply by interchanging the words "influx" and "efflux" wherever they occur. Here, however, the symmetry ends. The membrane is more than 50 times more permeable to K^+ than to Na^+. $[K^+]_i$ need be only slightly higher than at equilibrium for net passive efflux to balance the active influx. However, because P_{Na} is low, $[Na^+]_i$* will fall to values much lower than the equilibrium value before the net inward driving force is large enough to make the passive influx equal active efflux. These arguments indicate that the steady state transmembrane potential is near $\mathcal{E}_K$, because P_K is much greater than P_{Na}, but they do not reveal what processes lead to the separation of charge across the membrane that generates $\mathcal{E}_s$.

Figure 6 is a schematic diagram which com-

*The arguments given here are based on the assumption that the composition of the extracellular fluid is constant in the face of changes in intracellular concentrations. This is a good approximation in view of the effectiveness of the regulatory mechanisms (see Section IX).

pactly summarizes the fluxes of Na^+ and K^+ in the steady state. Although the diagram is explained in detail in the legend, it should be emphasized that the ordinate is the difference between the transmembrane potential and the equilibrium potential for either Na^+ or K^+, i.e., an indication of the driving force on the ion. Cl^- and A^- are not discussed here nor included in the diagram, because Cl^- are probably distributed in equilibrium with $\mathcal{E}_s$ and because the membrane is assumed to be impermeable to A^-.

Generation of Transmembrane Potential by a Sodium–Potassium Pump. *Transient state.* If a system is not in a steady state—if some quantities are changing in time—then the system is in a *transient* or *changing state*. The transient state in a cell with respect to changes in ionic concentrations and membrane potential can be classified according to the rate at which these quantities change. For example, if in a steady state system, $[K^+]_o$ is suddenly increased and $[Na^+]_o$ is decreased the same amount by changing the bathing medium, the transient state preceding the establishment of a new steady state is characterized by two distinct transients: (i) a fast transient lasting a few milliseconds during which there is a net penetration of charge; i.e., some of the added K^+ cross the membrane and reduce the potential. This net charge influx continues until $\mathcal{E}_m$ is reduced to the value where increasing K^+ efflux and Cl^- influx just balance the increased K^+ influx; i.e., net membrane charge flow is zero. (ii) However, this is not a steady state; the cell is gaining K^+ and Cl^- and losing Na^+. This slow transient lasts minutes or hours. During this time, the internal concentrations are changing toward their new steady state values. Some aspects of the slow transient are described here. Other aspects of it and the fast transient are discussed in Chapter 2.

Slow transient in cells. The existence of a steady potential difference across a membrane always means that electric charges are separated by the membrane. If the extrusion of a Na^+ is always accompanied by the uptake of a K^+, how does this electrically neutral pump give rise to the transmembrane potential? This question can be conveniently answered by considering the sequence of changes that occurs when a Na^+–K^+ pump is started up in a hypothetical cell whose membrane potential is zero and whose intracellular fluid has nearly the same composition as the interstitial fluid. In this way, the processes which lead to the separation of

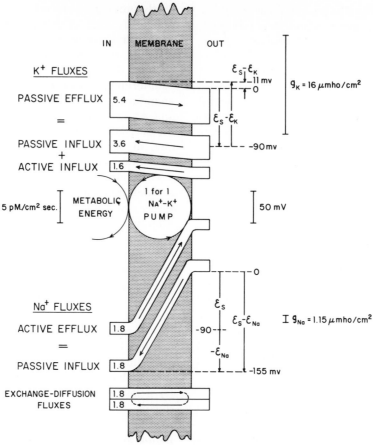

Fig. 6. Active and passive Na^+ and K^+ fluxes of a frog skeletal muscle fiber in the steady state. Intracellular fluid is represented at left, membrane in middle and interstitial fluid at right. Circle represents a 1 for 1 Na^+–K^+ pump driven by metabolic energy. Each band represents a one-way flux whose magnitude is proportional to the width of the band and whose direction is given by the arrow. Numbers within the bands just to left of membrane give the one-way flux in picamols per $cm.^2$-sec. (1 picamol [pM.] = 10^{-12} mols). Driving force on ion is given by slope of band within the membrane and also by total height difference as shown to the right and is equal to the difference between the steady membrane voltage, $\mathcal{E}_s$, and the ion equilibrium potential, $\mathcal{E}_{Na}$ or $\mathcal{E}_K$. Net passive flux of an ion is proportional to product of driving force and ionic conductance, g_{Na}, or, g_K (equation 6). In steady state, net fluxes are zero. For Na^+, passive efflux is negligible, so passive influx = active efflux = 1.8 pM. per $cm.^2$- sec. This flux results from a large driving force (−155 mV.) and a small conductance (0.07 g_K) as shown by the steepness of the band and the small bar representing g_{Na}. Active efflux of Na^+ must be accomplished against this electrochemical gradient. For K^+, net passive efflux = passive efflux − passive influx = 5.4 − 3.6 = 1.8 pM. per $cm.^2$-sec. In contrast to Na^+, the passive flux is the product of a small driving force (11 mV.) and a large conductance. Since active fluxes of Na^+ and K^+ are equal and opposite, net passive efflux of K^+ must also equal net passive influx of Na^+ = 1.8 pM. per $cm.^2$-sec. The equal and opposite exchange diffusion fluxes of Na^+ are shown at the bottom. (After Eccles. The Physiology of Nerve Cells. Baltimore, Johns Hopkins Press, 1957. Flux data are from Hodgkin and Horowicz, *J. Physiol.*, 1959, *145*:405–432, and Keynes and Swan, *J. Physiol.*, 1959, *147*: 591–625.)

charges across the membrane and to the establishment of ionic concentration differences will become evident.

It is not possible to build up the observed steady state from an intracellular fluid having a composition identical to the interstitial fluid, because the cell finally has a high concentration of anions (A^-), absent from the bathing medium,

which are unable to penetrate the membrane. This difficulty can be avoided by supposing that the hypothetical cell has an initial volume large compared to its final volume and that the cell fluid consists of interstitial fluid containing K^+A^- at a low concentration. The membrane is assumed to be perfectly elastic, to contain a Na^+–K^+ pump, and to have the same ion permeabilities as a real cell membrane. As will be shown below, operation of the pump gradually reduces cell volume until in the steady state the A⁻ ions have been concentrated to their observed high value (Table 1).

Figure 7 illustrates the changes that occur initially when the Na⁺–K⁺ pump is suddenly started at a fixed rate at some instant, $t = 0$. Suppose that in a jiffy* 400,000 Na⁺ are extruded and that simultaneously 400,000 K⁺ are

* A "jiffy" is a short length of time—in this case about 20 thousandths of a second.

taken into the cell. This exchange slightly reduces [Na⁺]$_i$ and increases [K⁺]$_i$. As mentioned above, extracellular volume is assumed to be infinite, so the external concentrations are not altered by the exchange. Although the concentration gradients set up by this exchange are small, some of the pumped Na⁺ will diffuse back into the cell and some of the K⁺ will diffuse out of it. P_K is about 50 times as large as P_{Na}, so that, since the concentration gradients of Na⁺ and K⁺ are equal, the net flux of K⁺ initially is 50 times as great as the net flux of Na⁺. Thus 4

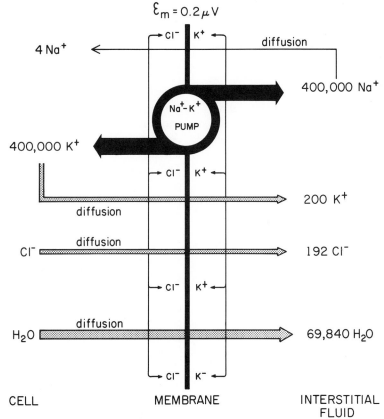

Fig. 7. Simplified scheme of ion and water movements during the first jiffy of operation of a Na⁺-K⁺ pump in a hypothetical cell. Cell membrane is assumed to contain a one-for-one Na⁺–K⁺ exchange pump and to be 50 times more permeable to K⁺ and Cl⁻ than to Na⁺. Cell is assumed to have a large initial volume, and ionic compositions of interstitial and intracellular fluid are assumed to be the same except that the latter also contains K⁺A⁻ at a low concentration. Width of arrow indicates size of flux. As shown, exchange of 400,000 Na⁺ for 400,000 K⁺ by the pump in a jiffy results in net movement of 399,800 K⁺ into the cell and 399,996 Na⁺ and 192 Cl⁻ out of the cell. The net efflux of $200 + 192 - 4$ $= 388$ ions requires a net efflux of 69,840 H₂O molecules to maintain osmotic balance. Four K⁺ and Cl⁻ have separated, charging the membrane capacity (fine line branches from K⁺ and Cl⁻ efflux lines and generated a transmembrane potential of 0.2 microvolts which maintains the Cl⁻ concentration difference, a 192 Cl⁻ deficit inside the cell. Operation of pump gradually reduces cell volume and increases $\mathcal{E}_m$; [Cl⁻]$_i$ decreases and [A⁻]$_i$ increases. In steady state, all net fluxes are zero and cell volume has decreased until [A⁻]$_i$ is approximately equal to [Cl⁻]$_o$. Na⁺–K⁺ pumping rate and membrane permeabilities in real cells are such that hours would be required to achieve steady state condition. Final cell diameter $= 10~\mu$; $P_K = P_{Cl} = 4.5 \times 10^{-6}$ cm. per second; $P_{Na}/P_K = 1/50$ active flux $= 10$ pMol per cm.²-sec.; 1 jiffy $= 20$ milliseconds; $C = 10^{-6}$ F. per cm.². Fluxes calculated on basis of steady state membrane area.

Na^+ will diffuse into and 200 K^+ out of the cell in a jiffy (Fig. 7). This net efflux of $+$ ions attracts Cl^- so that the net charge efflux is only 4 cations in the first jiffy. The resultant membrane voltage (0.2 μV.) is just sufficient to maintain the Cl^- concentration difference resulting from the net exit of 192 Cl^-.

In other words, the Cl^- will not completely neutralize the excess K^+, because the only force acting to move Cl^- out of the cell is the voltage gradient; therefore, the outside must be slightly positive to maintain the now slightly lower $[Cl^-]_i$. The concentration gradients of K^+ and Cl^- both act to maintain a transmembrane potential which is inside negative.

Since the pump is neutral, the transmembrane voltage results from the fact that K^+ penetrates the membrane more readily than does Na^+, so that the back diffusion of K^+ (out of the cell) generates an outside positive potential difference.

In addition to the ion movements, water will also move out of the cell during the first jiffy. The cell has lost a net of $200 - 4 = 196$ cations and 192 Cl^-. Thus 388 particles dissolved in water have left the cell. This exit increases the concentration of water in the cell, so that a slight gradient develops across the membrane. Since the membrane is highly permeable to water, this gradient forces water out of the cell. Each liter (55.5 M.) of water in extracellular fluid contains 0.31 M. of particles. For every particle that leaves the cell, $55.5/0.31 = 180$ molecules of water must also leave. Therefore, $180 \times 388 = 69,840$ water molecules leave the cell in the first jiffy. One jiffy's operation of the Na^+–K^+ pump results, then, in a net loss of Na^+, Cl^- and water and a net gain of K^+ by the cell and an increase in $[A^-]_i$ due to water loss.

In the second and each succeeding jiffy following the start of the Na^+–K^+ pump, 400,000 more Na^+ and 400,000 more K^+ are pumped across the membrane. There is now a small potential difference across the membrane which hinders the back diffusion of K^+ and helps the back diffusion of Na^+. Nevertheless, $[K^+]_i$ increases and $[Na^+]_i$ decreases. The resulting concentration gradients are larger and so, therefore, is back diffusion. The voltage increases slightly during each jiffy, causing more Cl^- to move out, and water accompanies the Na^+ and Cl^-. The changes in concentration, voltage and volume are smaller in each succeeding jiffy. The net extrusion of Na^+, Cl^- and water reduces the cell volume and, therefore, increases $[A^-]_i$. In other words, as $[Cl^-]_i$ decreases, $[A^-]_i$ increases equally. Eventually, a steady state is reached in which the net fluxes of Na^+, K^+, Cl^- and water are zero, the membrane potential is constant, and $[A^-]_i$ is about equal to $[Cl^-]_o$, as illustrated in Figure 6 for Na^+ and K^+.

The steady state value of the transmembrane potential depends on the ratio of P_{Na} to P_K and the Na^+ pumping rate. For example, an increase in P_{Na} would increase the net influx of Na^+ and thus reduce the charge separation and $\mathcal{E}_s$. Similarly, $\mathcal{E}_s$ is near zero if there is no Na^+ pumping; the steady-state condition is that illustrated in Figure 7 for $t = 0$, i.e., before the pump is started.

Factors determining cell volume. The volume of a cell depends directly on the number of particles dissolved in the cell water. Since the membrane is highly permeable to water, there can be no appreciable concentration gradient of water across the membrane in the steady state. As a result, the concentration of water in the cell equals the concentration in the bathing fluid. The greater the number of dissolved particles per unit volume of solution, the lower the concentration of water; so an equivalent statement of the equality of water concentrations is that total solute concentrations are equal.

A large fraction of the substances dissolved in interstitial and intracellular water is ionized. In the cell, A^- constitute about half of the dissolved particles. Because A^- cannot penetrate the membrane, and because they do not exist in appreciable quantities outside the cell, cell volume would be very large in the absence of Na^+ pumping. Operation of the Na^+ pump reduces $[Na^+]_i$, and the consequent development of a membrane potential reduces $[Cl^-]_i$. A net exit of NaCl reduces the cell volume correspondingly. Since the total amount of A^- in a cell is relatively fixed, cell volume changes reflect changes in $[Cl^-]_i$, which in turn depends on $\mathcal{E}_s$. However, if $\mathcal{E}_s$ is 60 mV. or greater, $[Cl^-]_i \leq 0.1\ [Cl^-]_o$. A rather large reduction in $\mathcal{E}_s$ is therefore required to increase cell volume appreciably; e.g., at $\mathcal{E}_s = 18$ mV. cell volume would be increased about 50 per cent. On the basis of the simple picture of ion transport developed here, it is seen that the Na^+–K^+ pump not only maintains the transmembrane differences in ion concentration and potential, but also prevents swelling and bursting of the cells. Cell volume also depends on intracellular H^+ concentration since the A^- are weak acids and also exist in the form HA (Chap. 46).

Control of sodium pumping rate. As pointed out above, an adequate rate of active sodium extrusion is necessary for cellular integrity. Excitable cells, in particular, must maintain a low internal [Na+] because the upstroke of the action potential is generated by the net inflow of sodium resulting from a transient increase in P_{Na} (Chap. 2). Thus it would be expected that an increase in internal Na+ concentration would act through some (unknown) regulatory mechanism to increase the rate of active Na+ extrusion. In frog muscle the relationship between extrusion rate and $[Na^+]_i$ is S-shaped. Keynes and Swan[18] found that Na+ efflux varies roughly with the third power of $[Na^+]_i$ over the range of concentrations normally found. The curve is less steep at both higher and lower than normal internal sodium concentrations. Clearly the curve must level off when the $[Na^+]_i$ is high because the maximum extrusion rate is limited by the cell's ability to supply energy to the pump. The flattening of the curve at low Na+ concentrations is probably due to lack of saturation of the reaction $Na^+ + Y = Na^+Y$; i.e., there is an appreciable amount of Y in the uncombined form. Further, the third power relationship suggests that the reaction with Y is of the form $3 Na^+ + Y = Na_3^+ Y$ and that Y can penetrate the membrane only in the form $Na_3^+ Y$. A calculation of steady state potential made on the assumption that pumping rate is proportional to $[Na^+]_i$ is given in the appendix, Chapter 2. The effects of increasing Na+ influx by increasing the rate of stimulation of frog skeletal muscle on the steady-state voltage and internal Na+ and K+ concentrations for first, second and third power relationships between Na+ pumping rate and $[Na^+]_i$ have been calculated by Woodbury.[30] The results show that a third power relationship is necessary to prevent inordinately large changes in these quantities even at quite modest stimulus rates.

Human red blood cells.[6, 7, 27] Human red cells have an interesting pattern of intracellular electrolyte concentrations: $[Na^+]_i = 20 \mu M.$ per cm.³ $[K^+]_i = 140 \mu M.$ per cm.³ and $[Cl^-]_i = 80 \mu M.$ per ml. The intracellular concentrations of Na+ and K+ are about the same as those in muscle, but $[Cl^-]_i$ is much higher than it is in muscle. Also, the red cell membrane is several thousand times more permeable to Cl− and HCO_3^- than it is to K+ or Na+. The high anion permeability is important for the carrying of carbon dioxide by the blood (Chap. 40). The ionic distribution of red cells is easily explained by supposing that the cell membrane has a Na+-K+ exchange pump and that the membrane is nearly as permeable to Na+ as to K+. If it is assumed that Cl− and HCO_3^- are passively distributed, then the transmembrane potential is: $\mathcal{E}_s = \mathcal{E}_{Cl} = -61 \log_{10} 120/80 = -10$ mV. As pointed out above, $\mathcal{E}_s$ depends on the ratio of P_{Na} to P_K; the higher P_{Na}/P_K, the lower $\mathcal{E}_s$.

There is considerable evidence for the existence of a Na+-K+ exchange pump in red cells.[27] Indeed, some of the earliest evidence of this type of pumping process was found in red cells.[7] Flux measurements indicate that ion movements are more complex than expected from this simple explanation, but there seems little doubt that it is generally correct. Because of the high $[Cl^-]_i$ and high P_{Cl}, the cell is quite liable to rather large, rapid changes in volume. However, these cells can swell considerably without bursting, owing to their shape, biconcave discs.

Cellular Hydrogen and Bicarbonate Ion Concentrations.[2, 3] The concentrations of hydrogen (H+) and bicarbonate (HCO_3^-) ions in the interior of the cell are not those that would be expected from the external concentrations and the membrane potential; i.e., these ions are not at equilibrium with $\mathcal{E}_s$. With glass electrodes, Caldwell[2] measured directly the intracellular *p*H in crab muscle fibers. The intracellular *p*H (*p*H$_i$) is normally about 7.0, as compared with the *p*H$_o$ = 7.4 of the blood plasma. (By definition, *p*H = $-\log_{10}[H^+]$, so $[H^+]_i = 10^{-7}$ M. per liter or mM. per cm.³) This value agrees well with indirect measurements in other tissues. If H+ were distributed in accordance with membrane voltage, $[H^+]_i$ would be about 30 times $[H^+]_o$, or *p*H$_i$ would be $-\log (30 H_o) =$ *p*H$_o - \log 30 = 5.9$ and, since $[H^+] \cdot [HCO_3^-] = K[H_2CO_3]$ (Chap. 46), $[HCO_3^-]_i$ would be $[HCO_3^-]_o/30$.

If, as seems likely, either or both H+ and HCO_3^- can penetrate the membrane, then the existence of a disequilibrium between the external and internal concentrations of H+ and HCO_3^- forces the conclusion that one or both ions must be actively transported—H+ out of the cell or HCO_3^- into the cell. Nothing is known of the mechanism of this active transport process but it does seem more probable that H+ is extruded than that HCO_3^- is taken up Further, it is natural to hypothesize that H+ has some affinity for the Na+ carrier substance Y (Fig. 5): $H^+ + Y = H^+Y$. This hypothesis has been given some experimental basis by the findings of Keynes[15] that raising $[H^+]_i$ by means of increasing pCO₂ from 0 to about 40 mm. Hg at constant $[H^+]_o$ changes the relationship between Na+ extrusion rate and $[Na^+]_i$ from a direct dependence on the cube of $[Na^+]_i$ to a direct dependence on the square of $[Na^+]_i$. This suggests that H+ can be one of the three ions which must be attached to the Y carrier before it can penetrate the membrane, the other two being Na^+. Regulation of $[H^+]_o$ and $[H^+]_i$ will be discussed in Chapter 46.

SUMMARY

A brief review of the physics and physical chemistry pertinent to the material in this chapter is given in the appendix of Chapter 2.

Cell Membrane. The interchange of materials between a cell and its environment is greatly limited by the cell membrane; substances dissolved in the interstitial and intercellular fluids penetrate the membrane at rates only a small fraction of the rates at which they penetrate through an equal thickness of water. The structure which limits diffusion, the membrane, consists of outer monomolecular layers of protein facing the aqueous solutions and an inner bimolecular layer of closely packed lipid molecules. It is the closely packed hydrophobic lipid layer which acts as a barrier to movements of dissolved particles and water. Ionized substances probably cross the membrane via water-filled pores or in combination with carrier molecules which are limited to the membrane (Figs. 3 and 5).

Transmembrane Concentration and Potential Differences. The interstitial fluid contains high concentrations of Na^+ and Cl^- and low concentrations of K^+. In contrast, intracellular fluid contains K^+ in high and Cl^- and Na^+ in low concentrations. In addition, there is a potential difference across the cell membrane which is about -90 mV. (inside negative) in mammalian skeletal muscle (Table 1). The existence of a potential difference means that there are charges separated by the membrane in an amount proportional to the voltage. The cell is a capacitor; the interstitial and intracellular fluids are electrolyte solutions and hence ionic conductors and the membrane separating them is an insulator. Ions can penetrate the membrane to a limited extent so the maintenance of charge separation and a potential difference implies that there are nonelectrical, nonmechanical forces present which act to keep charges separated.

Ion Penetration Through Membrane. The passive rate of penetration of the membrane by an ionized substance (net flux, mol per cm.^{2}-sec.) is determined by three quantities: (i) The concentration gradient of the substance across the membrane is a measure of the force which tends to drive a substance from a region of higher to a region of lower concentration (diffu-

sion). The average concentration gradient is (outside concentration–inside concentration)/membrane thickness. (ii) The voltage gradient across the membrane (from outside to inside) tends to drive cations into the cell and anions out of the cell. (iii) The permeability of the membrane, i.e., the ease with which a substance penetrates the membrane, determines how many particles per second cross the membrane for a given driving force (the sum of the concentration and voltage gradient driving forces). If ions penetrate the membrane through water-filled pores, then permeability is proportional to the number of pores per square centimeter of membrane. Diffusion through the membrane is so much slower than through the surrounding aqueous solutions that the concentration gradients in the solutions necessary to supply substances which are diffusing through the membrane are negligibly small, i.e., concentrations near the membrane are equal to those in the bulk medium in most circumstances.

Ionic Equilibrium. A nonionized substance is distributed at equilibrium across the membrane when the concentrations on the two sides are equal. Ionic equilibrium concentrations depend on the transmembrane potential difference. Alternatively, if concentrations are specified, then these can be brought into equilibrium by setting the transmembrane potential difference to a value given by the Nernst equation; e.g., for K^+, $\mathcal{E}_K = (RT/Z_K F) \log_e [K^+]_o / [K^+]_i$. The equilibrium potential of a substance can also be thought of as the potential that would be developed across a membrane permeable only to that substance. Thus, a membrane permeable only to potassium ions would become positively charged on the side of lowest concentration because of diffusion down the concentration gradient of the positive ions. The Nernst equation furnishes a simple test to determine if an ionized substance is distributed at equilibrium across an actual membrane; if the equilibrium potential of the substance is equal to the actual transmembrane potential then the substance is equilibrated. Nonequilibrium indicates either that the substance cannot penetrate the membrane or that other forces than those exerted by concentration and voltage gradients are acting on the substance.

Ion Distribution in Muscle. Comparison of the various ion equilibrium potentials with the actual transmembrane potential shows that Cl^- is distributed at equilibrium, i.e., $\mathcal{E}_{Cl} = \mathcal{E}_s$, that $[K^+]_i$ is about twice as great as expected, i.e.,

$\mathcal{E}_K$ is more negative than $\mathcal{E}_s$, and that the Na+ equilibrium potential is opposite in sign from the actual potential (Table 1). In other words, both the concentration gradient (outside high, inside low) and voltage gradient (inside negative) tend to force Na+ into the cell. Radioactive tracer studies show that all these ions can penetrate the membrane. K+ and Cl− penetrate with about equal ease and about 50 times more easily than Na+. The organic anion, A−, is assumed to be nonpermeating.

Active Na+–K+ Transport. Since internal Na+ concentration remains at its low levels in the living animal, it follows that some force besides concentration and voltage gradients is acting to carry Na+ out of the cells. Further since Na+ flows spontaneously from outside to inside, work must be done continuously by the cell to expel Na+. This expenditure of the cell's metabolic energy is termed active transport. Available experimental evidence indicates that the transport process is mediated by carriers limited to the membrane and that the extrusion of Na+ is accompanied by a coupled uptake of K+ (Fig. 5).

Origin of Transmembrane Potential. A coupled one-for-one Na+-for-K+ exchange pump is capable of maintaining observed ion concentrations and the membrane potential (Fig. 6). A neutral pump extruding Na+ and taking up K+ generates concentration gradients of these ions across the membrane but in itself does not separate charges. Charges are separated, however, by the back diffusion of these ions; K+ can penetrate 50 times more easily than Na+ so, for the equal concentration gradients which are generated by the neutral pump, 50 times as many K+ will diffuse out of the cell as Na+ will diffuse in if the transmembrane potential is zero. This imbalance in back diffusion does separate charge; the excess K+ diffusing outward charges the outside of the membrane positively and thus generates the transmembrane voltage. This voltage in turn draws Cl− out of the cell, almost but not quite neutralizing the membrane charge, since some potential is required to hold out the Cl−. The net result is an outward movement of Na+, Cl− and water and an accumulation of K+ (Fig. 7). Thus the movements of Na+ and K+ down their gradients is balanced by the exchange pump. The size of the steady-state membrane voltage depends on the pumping rate and the ratio, P_{Na}/P_K. [Cl−]$_i$ and cell volume thus depend on the potential.

Cell Volume. The cell membrane is perme-able to water and has little mechanical strength; hence the volume of the cell depends on the number of solute particles within it. The internal anions are nonpermeating and thus the minimum volume is determined by the number of these anions and their counter ions. In addition, there is a small amount of internal Na+, determined by the sodium pumping rate and a small amount of Cl−, determined by the transmembrane potential. Hence any reduction in pumping rate or increase in P_{Na} increases the number of internal particles and hence the volume of the cell. Cell volume also depends on internal H+ concentration because A− can exist in the undissociated form HA in appreciable amounts.

REFERENCES

1. ADRIAN, R. H. *Circulation,* 1962, *26:*1214–1223.
2. CALDWELL, P. C. *J. Physiol.,* 1954, *126:*169–180.
3. CALDWELL, P. C. *Int. Rev. Cytol.,* 1956, *5:*229–277.
4. FINEAN, J. B. *Exp. Cell Res.,* 1958, Suppl. *5:*18–32.
5. FISHMAN, A. P., ed. *Symposium on the plasma membrane.* New York, New York Heart Association, Inc., 1962.
6. GLYNN, I. M. *Progr. Biophys.,* 1957, *8:*241–307.
7. HARRIS, E. J. and MAIZELS, M. *J. Physiol.,* 1951, *113:*506–524.
8. HODGKIN, A. L. *Biol. Rev.,* 1951, *26:*339–409.
9. HODGKIN, A. L. *Proc. roy. Soc.,* 1957, *B148:*1–37, pl. 1.
10. HODGKIN, A. L. *The conduction of the nervous impulse,* Springfield, Ill., Charles C Thomas, 1964.
11. HODGKIN, A. L. and HOROWICZ, P. *J. Physiol.,* 1959, *145:*405–432.
12. HODGKIN, A. L. and HOROWICZ, P. *J. Physiol.,* 1959, *148:*127–160.
13. HODGKIN, A. L. and KEYNES, R. D. *J. Physiol.,* 1955, *128:*28–60.
14. HODGKIN, A. L. and KEYNES, R. D. *J. Physiol.,* 1955, *128:*61–88.
15. KEYNES, R. D. *J. Physiol.,* 1963, *166:*16P–17P.
16. KEYNES, R. D. *J. Physiol.,* 1963, *169:*690–705.
17. KEYNES, R. D. and MAISEL, G. W. *Proc. roy. Soc.,* 1954, *B142:*383–392.
18. KEYNES, R. D. and SWAN, R. C. *J. Physiol.,* 1959, *147:*591–625.
19. KOEFOED-JOHNSEN, V. and USSING, H. H. *Acta physiol. scand.,* 1958, *42:*298–308.
20. LING, G. and GERARD, R. W. *J. cell. comp. Physiol.,* 1949, *34:*383–396.
21. MULLINS, L. J. and NODA, K. *J. gen. Physiol.,* 1963, *47:*117–132.
22. MURPHY, Q. R., ed. *Metabolic aspects of transport across cell membranes.* Madison, University of Wisconsin Press, 1957.
23. ROBERTSON, J. D. *Progr. Biophys.,* 1960, *10:*343–418.
24. SHANES, A. M. *Pharmacol. Rev.,* 1958, *10:*59–164.
25. SHANES, A. M., ed. *Biophysics of physiological and pharmacological actions.* Washington, D.C., American Association for the Advancement of Science, 1961.
26. SOLOMON, A. K. *J. gen. Physiol.,* 1960, *43:*1–15.
27. TOSTESON, D. C. *Fed. Proc.,* 1963, *22:*19–26.
28. USSING, H. H. *J. gen. Physiol.,* 1960, *43:*135–147.
29. USSING, H. H., KRUHØFFER, P., HESS THASEN, J. and THORN, N. A. *The alkali metal ions in biology.* Berlin, Springer-Verlag, 1960.
30. WOODBURY, J. W. *Fed. Proc.,* 1963, *22:*31–35.

SECTION II

NERVE AND MUSCLE

CHAPTER 2

Action Potential: Properties of Excitable Membranes

By J. WALTER WOODBURY

26

THE initiation and propagation of the nerve impulse is a subject which has been greatly illuminated in recent years by the invention of ingenious experimental techniques and by the application of physical and mathematical principles. These advances have resulted largely from studies begun twenty years ago at Cambridge University by Hodgkin and Huxley, who were awarded the 1963 Nobel Prize in Physiology. The main advances resulted from the development of the technique of "voltage clamping" by K. S. Cole in the late 1940's. The explanations of impulse conduction worked out by Hodgkin and Huxley make considerable use of the principles of physics and physical chemistry and hence are not easily comprehended by those not well trained in these fields and in biology. For this reason, the material in this chapter is mostly descriptive of the process of impulse generation and conduction; qualitative explanations are given for the various basic factors: stimulating and recording techniques; effects of current flow on long, thin cells (cable properties); threshold, all-or-nothing behavior; and propagation by local circuit currents. This is followed by a somewhat more quantitative explanation of the voltage clamping experiments which furnished the information for the mechanism of impulse conduction given in the earlier sections. Necessary physical concepts, notably Ohm's law, are described briefly in the text and more quantitatively in the appendix at the end of the chapter. Ohm's law and cable properties are described in some detail and illustrative problems are included.

The reader desiring more detailed and comprehensive presentation of this material is referred to Hodgkin's lucid writings, particularly his recent book,[9] his reviews,[5, 7, 8] the original Hodgkin and Huxley papers,[10,11,12,13,14,15] and Huxley's summary.[19] Another review[26] may also be consulted.

In Chapter 1 was shown how a cell develops and maintains a steady transmembrane potential. In addition, the membranes of some cells possess the highly distinctive property of being *excitable*. In excitable cells, an environmental change (called a *stimulus*) brings about a transient depolarization usually by increasing the permeability of the membrane to Na^+ or to Na^+ and K^+. Influx of Na^+ depolarizes the membrane, thereby in turn increasing Na^+ permeability, which leads to further depolarization, and so on in a regenerative manner.

Depolarization is followed shortly by a spontaneous recovery or repolarization process which restores the original state. This sequence of changes is called an impulse and the accompanying voltage change is called an *action potential*. The definitive property of an excitable membrane is a regenerative interaction between depolarization and permeability to Na^+.

Most excitable cells are long and thin, e.g., nerve and muscle cells. In elongated cells, an impulse once initiated by a stimulus is propagated rapidly from the stimulus site to adjacent regions of the membrane and thus spreads as a wave over the membrane of the entire cell. This property is known as *conductivity* or *self-propagation*. The properties of excitability and conductivity adapt nerve cells for the function of transmitting information from one part of the body to another. The ability of nerve cells to generate and conduct impulses and of synapses to modify the impulse discharge patterns are the basis of an animal's adaptive behavior to environmental changes or stimuli.

A simple, concrete example may serve to illustrate how the nervous system detects changes in the environment and transmits messages to the muscles which, by contraction, make the appropriate response. If the hand touches a hot object, the muscles of the arm contract so that the hand is withdrawn and tissue damage is either avoided or limited. Although this protective response occupies only a fraction of a second, it can be shown that the following sequence of events, illustrated diagrammatically in Figure 1, takes place. The stimulus (heat and tissue damage) initiates impulses in nerve endings in the skin (*A*). Once initiated, these impulses are propagated over the *afferent nerve fibers* (*B*) which traverse the dorsal root to reach the spinal cord, where they make connections (*C*) with a second nerve cell, an *interneuron*. The impulses in the intraspinal afferent endings constitute stimuli to the interneurons; the resulting impulses in turn initiate impulses in the *motor* or *efferent* neurons. The latter impulses are propagated over the ventral root to the muscle, where they constitute stimuli (*D*) giving rise to muscle impulses which then spread rapidly over the membranes of the muscle cells. The spread of impulses over the muscle membranes activates the contractile elements within the cells (*E*) and movement occurs. The entire system including the afferent neurons, the interneurons, the motor neurons and the muscle is a

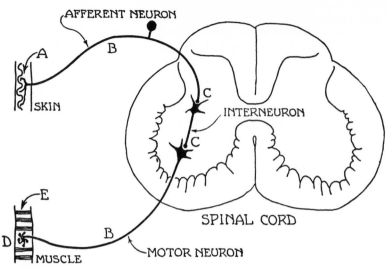

Fig. 1. Diagram of simple reflex arc. Excitation of afferent neurons occurs at point *A*. Conduction of impulses takes place in nerve fibers, *B*. Impulses are conducted toward central nervous system in the afferent fibers and away from central nervous system in motoneurons. Synaptic transmission between neurons occurs at *C*. Neuromuscular transmission occurs at *D*. Contraction occurs in muscle fiber, *E*.

simple *reflex arc*. In more complex reflex systems more interneurons may be interposed. The afferent neuron may arise in tissues other than skin, e.g., viscera, special sense organs, muscle itself. The final effector organ need not be skeletal muscle (*somatic reflex arc*), but may be smooth muscle, heart muscle or gland tissue (autonomic reflex arc).

The somatic reflex arc is the physiologic mechanism by which the organism reacts to its external environment. Autonomic reflex arcs are responsible for automatic regulation or adjustment of the functional level of visceral structures (e.g., the heart and blood vessels)—adjustments which adapt the organism not only to external environmental changes (e.g., temperature) but also to internal environmental changes occasioned by somatic behavior (e.g., exercise). *The principle of the reflex arc is that regulation of an organ's function is based in large part on sensory information from the organ being regulated. This is the most important single concept in physiology.* The description of reflex regulation of function culminates description of function. Analysis of reflexes thus permeates all phases of physiology and is, therefore, treated in some detail in the initial chapters of this book.

For this purpose it is convenient to break the reflex arc up into its component parts. In this and the next two chapters the nature of the message—i.e., the impulse and the way in which it is initiated—is considered. In Chapter 5 the transfer of the message from nerve to muscle, the muscle membrane, and the contractile mechanism of muscle are described (*D* and *E* in Fig. 1). Chapter 6 deals with the mechanism of excitation of nerve cell by nerve cell (*C* in Fig. 1) and Chapters 7, 10 and 11 describe synthetically the functional organization of somatic and autonomic reflex regulatory systems.

Moreover, the description of a system's function is usually followed by a description of its regulation. Frequently, a system's level of functioning is under both endocrine and nervous control.

PROPERTIES OF ELONGATED, EXCITABLE CELLS[5, 7, 8, 9, 19, 24]

It has been recognized for more than a century that the nerve impulse is an electrical phenomenon. A clear picture of the mechanism of the action potential was not developed, however, until critical experiments were made possible by intracellular recording techniques, which were introduced independently in 1939–1940 by Cole and Curtis in the United States and by Hodgkin and Huxley in England.

Direct measurement of transmembrane potentials was delayed until this late date because most mammalian nerve and muscle fibers are exceedingly small (usually less than 100 μ in diameter) and hence difficult to penetrate with a recording electrode. In 1936, J. Z. Young discovered in the squid and cuttlefish giant nerve fibers or axons as large as 1 mm. in diameter. With such large nerve fibers it is relatively easy to introduce an internal electrode longitudinally down the axon and measure its potential with respect to an externally located electrode. Also, sufficient quantities of axoplasm can be extruded from the giant axon to permit chemical analysis. The first studies of transmembrane potentials of resting and excited nerve fibers were made on such giant fibers. Subsequently, with the development of ultramicroelectrodes (see Chap. 1), it became possible to confirm in mammalian nerve and muscle fibers many of the observations made on giant axons.

The Resting or Steady Potential. ·Like other cells, nerve and muscle fibers maintain a steady potential (inside negative) across their membranes. This steady potential is usually referred to as the *resting potential* to distinguish it from the action potential. In Chapter 1 it was shown that the size of the resting potential generated by the sodium–potassium pump depends largely on the relative permeability of the membrane to sodium and potassium ions; the greater the ratio of the permeability to potassium to the permeability to sodium, the greater the potential. In nerve and muscle this ratio is quite high, more than 50 to 1, and the resting potential is -70 to -90 mV. In the steady state, chloride anions are equilibrated with the resting potential in most excitable tissues, with the notable exception of the squid giant axon (see reference 16, Chap. 1). Internal sodium concentration is much lower and the internal potassium concentration higher than expected from the membrane potential. The resting potential creates the conditions necessary for regenerative interaction between depolarization and Na+ permeability increase.

The Action Potential. When a sufficiently strong, brief electric current* is passed outward through the membrane of an axon or a muscle cell, the membrane potential undergoes a unique stereotyped sequence of changes which is peculiar to excitable cells. This sequence constitutes the *action potential*.

---

*Excitable tissues may also be stimulated by mechanical or chemical means; but in experimental work electrical stimuli are used almost exclusively, because the intensity and duration can be easily and quantitatively varied and because mild electrical stimuli, even when repeated many times, do not damage the tissue.

Overshoot, duration and propagation. Figure 2*A* shows diagrammatically the experimental arrangement for eliciting and recording an action potential in a nerve fiber and introduces the symbols for a stimulator with its electrodes and the recording device with its leads. The fiber is supplied with two pairs of stimulating electrodes (S_1 and S_2) placed at different distances from the recording site (R). When the microelectrode penetrates the axon, the steady or resting potential is registered. When a sufficiently large, brief electric shock (signaled by the shock artifact, a deflection in the recorded signal at the time of and due to the stimulus) is applied to the nerve through S_1, the membrane potential decreases rapidly toward zero but *overshoots, so that for a brief period the membrane potential is reversed*, i.e., the inside becomes positive to the outside. Thereafter the potential reverts somewhat more slowly to the resting level. The action potential of a cat dorsal root fiber is shown in Figure 2*C*. For such large myelinated fibers the duration of the action potential is 0.5 to 0.6 millisecond, and the total amplitude is 120 mV., the overshoot accounting for 30 mV. When the shock is applied at the more distant electrode S_2 rather than at S_1, the sequence of events is exactly the same, except that the *latency* (time interval between shock artifact and the beginning of the action potential) is longer. Systematic investigation reveals that this latency is directly proportional to the distance between the stimulating and recording electrodes. The action potential is thus revealed as a brief potential reversal of the membrane, beginning at the stimulating electrodes and sweeping at a constant speed as a wave along the axon. Large mammalian myelinated nerve fibers conduct at speeds of up to 120 meters per second.

Threshold, all-or-nothing properties. The action potential of a single fiber has two other unique characteristics: (i) There is a minimal strength of stimulus, the *threshold*, required to evoke a propagating action potential; an insufficient (subthreshold) stimulus has no effect at a distant recording electrode, while a sufficient (suprathreshold) stimulus, no matter how strong, evokes a stereotyped response like that of Figure 2*C*. (ii) This response is fixed in size, shape, duration and conduction speed no matter where recorded from a fiber. This is termed *all-or-none* or *all-or-nothing* behavior. Threshold and all-or-nothing behavior are different

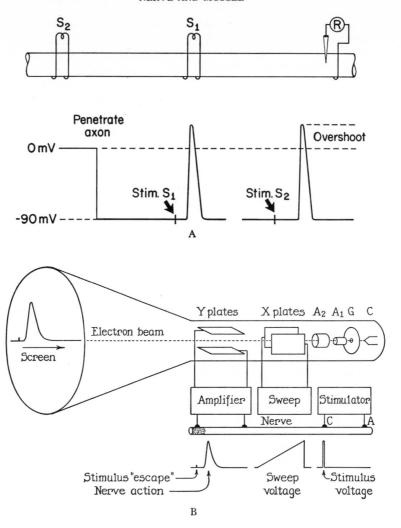

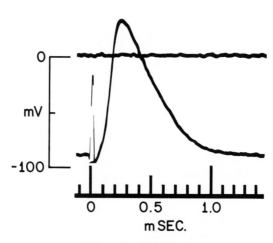

CAT DORSAL ROOT NERVE
FIBER

C

Figure 2. (See opposite page for legend.)

aspects of the same regenerative mechanism, as will be shown. Threshold (all-or-nothing) behavior is obscured when a whole nerve is studied with external electrodes as explained in Chapter 3.

SUBTHRESHOLD CURRENTS IN ELONGATED CELLS; CABLE PROPERTIES

A weak current flowing through a nerve fiber may not initiate an action potential; nevertheless, there are always local changes in transmembrane potential. These subthreshold changes will be described first, since an explanation of them is necessary for understanding impulse generation and propagation. The effects of electric currents are particularly prominent in nerve and muscle fibers because these fibers are approximately cylindrical and have lengths many thousands of times their diameters. With this geometry, the cell plasm is highly resistant to current flow, and different potentials exist at different distances from the current source during current flow. The combination of cell plasm resistance and membrane resistance and capacitance found in nerve fibers acts in a typical manner to attenuate in distance and slow in time the effects of current flow on membrane potentials. This behavior of a nerve cell is denoted by the term "cable properties." This term is used because an undersea telephone cable may have very similar electrical characteristics.* The general nature of cable properties can be usefully introduced by describing how a current applied to a nerve by means of two external electrodes can excite the

*The words "electrotonus," "electrotonic potential" and "polarization potential" have frequently been used in the physiologic literature to denote the cable properties of nerve. For reasons given by Hodgkin and Rushton[17] these terms are misleading and hence undesirable.

Fig. 2. *A, upper,* A method for studying electrical activity of nerve fibers. Two pairs of stimulating electrodes, S_1 and S_2, are applied to a dissected nerve trunk at different distances from recording microelectrode (far right). Microelectrode may be inserted into any fiber in trunk. *Lower,* Sequence of potential changes recorded by microelectrode inserted into a fiber when nerve trunk is stimulated by short shocks applied first at S_1 and then at S_2. *Abscissa,* time, a few milliseconds; *ordinate,* transmembrane potential in millivolts. When microelectrode is inserted into a nerve fiber, recorded potential changes abruptly from 0 to about -70 to -90 mV. Following stimulation at S_1 (indicated in recording by stimulus "escape" or "artifact"), an action potential (AP) is recorded after a short but definite delay. An AP rises rapidly to a peak (depolarization) and then recovers somewhat more slowly to the steady value (repolarization). At peak of AP, transmembrane potential has reversed in sign, the inside being positive to the outside. Depolarization and repolarization processes occupy about 0.5 millisecond. After a pause, indicated by break in line, nerve is stimulated at S_2. An identical AP is recorded but delay following stimulus is longer.

B, Apparatus for stimulating nervous tissue and for obtaining records of its response. Recording instrument is a cathode ray oscilloscope. Records are obtained by photographing screen while spot formed by electron beam striking fluorescent material of screen traces electrical changes impressed upon X and Y deflecting plates. Within tube itself, hot cathode (C) serves as source of electrons, grid (G) controls intensity of electron beam and so brightness of spot, first anode (A_1) compresses flow of electrons into narrow beam (in effect "focuses" the beam) and second anode (A_2) or "gun," being highly positive, accelerates beam of electrons. Stimulator applies a brief (or any chosen) voltage pulse to nerve via stimulating electrodes, one of which is cathode (C), the other anode (A). Potential changes in nerve, nerve action potential, are led to amplifier by means of recording electrodes and thence to Y plates of cathode ray oscillograph to cause vertical displacement of spot. The left recording lead is placed on a crushed region of the nerve. The crushing destroys the membranes and thus the lead is analogous to a connection to the insides of the fibers. The right lead is placed on an intact region and is thus the external electrode (see Chap. 3). At instant of stimulation a stimulus "escape" causes deflection in amplifier. Time between this and beginning of action potential is the latency, which in this example would be due to conduction time. Sweep generates a "saw-tooth" sweep voltage that moves beam from left to right at a constant speed. Sweep is repeated many times each second. Stimulus is given at a fixed time after beginning of each sweep so that nerve activity is repeatedly traced as a function of time, as indicated on screen in diagram. (After Erlanger and Gasser, *Electrical signs of nervous activity.* Philadelphia, University of Pennsylvania Press, 1937.)

C, Tracing of action potential recorded from cat dorsal root fiber. Conduction distance about 1 cm. Photograph is a double exposure, consisting of one sweep when microelectrode was in fiber and one sweep immediately after electrode was withdrawn from fiber.

nerve. This account, in turn, necessitates a brief description of the factors determining current flow in conductors (Ohm's Law).

Stimulation. Experimentally, a stimulus is usually electrical and applied by means of two platinum or silver wire electrodes placed in direct contact with the nerve or muscle to be stimulated. Excitation, the initiation of an impulse, occurs in membrane regions which have been depolarized to threshold.* A current flowing between two electrodes in contact with a nerve (Fig. 2B) has two effects, hyperpolarization of membranes in the region of the stimulating anode (positive terminal) and depolarization in the region of the cathode. Current is defined as the number of charges passing through a cross-section of the conductor in a unit time (see appendix) and its direction is that of the movement of positive charges. Thus, some of the positive charges leaving the anode tend to pile up on the outside of the membrane, forcing positive charges inside the cell away from this region and toward the cathode. At the cathode, positive charges tend to pile up inside the membrane and free positive charges outside the membrane to move to the cathode, thus completing the circuit. The same arguments apply to negative charges flowing in the opposite direction; no distinction can be made in this case since the current flow in an electrolytic solution is carried by both positive and negative ions. The result of current flow then is that regions of membrane near the anode have increased amounts of charge on them, i.e., are hyperpolarized, and regions near the cathode are depolarized. A current which depolarizes to threshold the region of membrane under the cathode will initiate an impulse.

Current Flow in Conductors; Ohm's Law. The physical factors determining current flow in a conductor will be briefly reviewed here; a more extensive development and discussion of Ohm's law is given in the appendix. Three concepts or definitions are involved: (i) There are

devices capable of maintaining a constant potential difference between two conducting terminals, e.g., a battery; these devices supply power by doing electrical work on charges continuously. (ii) Current consists of a flow of electric charges. (iii) Charges flowing in a conductor give up energy to its molecules by colliding with them and increasing their random kinetic energy.

A battery is a device that transforms chemical potential energy into electrical potential energy, i.e., does work on charges. The most obvious example here is the transmembrane potential of living cells. Even without active ion transport, the potential across the membrane is maintained relatively constant for long periods because of the large amount of chemical potential energy stored in the potassium concentration differences even though there is a constant current drain in the form of the inward leakage of sodium. Flashlight batteries function because the zinc ions in metallic zinc tend to go into solution more readily than do the carbon atoms in the graphite anode; when the zinc goes into solution, two electrons are left behind.

A conductor is defined as a material in which a substantial number of charges are free to move. An electric field is generated in a conductor when it is connected to the terminals of a battery. This field exerts a force on *every* charge in the material; those free to move are accelerated simultaneously by the electric field. However, each charge travels only a short distance before colliding with some molecule of the conductor and giving up some kinetic energy to it. Thus the random kinetic energy of all the molecules (temperature) is increased and the potential energy of each free charge is decreased. The potential energy given to charges by the battery is changed into kinetic energy of accelerating charges and this in turn is converted into heat in the conductor. On the average, a fixed amount of energy is given up per collision. If the conductor is uniform, the loss of energy per charge (and hence the voltage fall) per unit distance is constant. The acceleration–collision process goes on continuously for all free charges (ions in electrolytic solutions) and the net result is that the charges move through the medium at an unvarying, rather slow average speed. It must be emphasized that although the average speed of charge movement is slow, all free charges start to move simultaneously upon application of an electric

---

*The process of charge separation is often called *polarization*. A cell is said to be *polarized* when the transmembrane charge and voltage are at their steady-state values. Any increase in the amount of charge separated by the membrane and hence in the size of the transmembrane potential is called *hyperpolarization;* any decrease is called *depolarization*. Although *hypopolarization* is a more accurate term than depolarization, it is difficult to distinguish between *hyper*polarization and *hypo*polarization both when written and when spoken.

field and that therefore current flow begins immediately because charges immediately move through every cross-section in the circuit. One battery terminal supplies charges of that sign to the conductor; the other accepts them from the conductor. The battery, at the expense of chemical energy, does work on the charges and supplies them to the first terminal. Thus current flow involves the circulation of charges in a closed path.

Ohm's law describes current flow in a conductor if the average speed of charge movement is directly proportional to the electric field and hence to the applied voltage, i.e., friction is proportional to speed. The situation is somewhat akin to a steel ball falling through molasses; the ball is accelerated by gravity but this kinetic energy is converted to heat due to friction and the ball falls with constant speed; if its speed of fall is proportional to the applied force, the fall is "ohmic." Ohm's law states that the current flowing through a conductor is proportional to the applied voltage. This relationship follows because the force on the charges is proportional to voltage, the speed of the ions is proportional to the force on them, and the current is proportional to their speed; the faster the charges move, the greater the number of charges passing a given cross-section per second.

Ohm's law can be written in the form $I = \mathcal{E}/R = G\mathcal{E}$ where G is called the conductance and is equal to the reciprocal of the resistance, R. The resistance of a particular block of material depends on its physical properties and dimensions. For a fixed applied force, the average speed of charge movement depends on the properties of the material, such as the frictional resistance to charge movement and the number of free charges per unit volume. In a solution of univalent strong electrolyte (e.g., NaCl) the number of free charges per unit volume is proportional to the sum of the individual ion concentrations. A large frictional resistance to charge movement means there is a large electrical resistance; large ion concentrations mean low electrical resistance. Dimensionally, resistance is proportional to length and inversely proportional to cross-sectional area: The resistance of a block of material 2 cm. long is twice that of a 1 cm. block because for the same applied voltage, the force exerted on a charge is only one-half as great in the 2 cm. sample. Similarly, for a fixed length, doubling the cross-sectional area of a block halves its resistance

because the force on each charge is the same but the number of free charges affected by the applied field has been doubled; for the same applied voltage, the current is twice as great and hence the resistance is halved.

Measurement of Cable Properties. In Figure 3A and B is shown an experimental arrangement for measuring the effects of current flow on the transmembrane potentials of a giant axon or a skeletal muscle fiber. Two microelectrodes are inserted into a cell (Fig. 3B); an abruptly applied current (Fig. 3A) is passed out through one electrode, and the other is used to record the resulting changes in the transmembrane potential ($\Delta\mathcal{E}_m$).* Current flows out of the electrode into the axoplasm and then out through the membrane by the lowest resistance path available. $\Delta\mathcal{E}_m$ as a function of time is recorded at one position of the recording electrode. This electrode is then removed from the cell and reinserted at another distance from the current-applying electrode (Fig. 3B). In this way, $\Delta\mathcal{E}_m$'s at several distances are recorded. The results of such an experiment, conducted on frog sartorius muscle fibers, are shown in Figure 3C. These results are typical of those obtained for all long, thin cells—myelinated and unmyelinated nerve and skeletal, cardiac and smooth muscle cells. In response to an abruptly applied constant current (internal electrode positive), $\Delta\mathcal{E}_m$, recorded near the current electrode, increases rapidly at first and then gradually levels off to a fixed value (Fig. 3C, x = 0). $\Delta\mathcal{E}_m$ rises progressively more slowly and reaches a smaller final value as the recording electrode is moved farther from the current electrode in either direction (Fig. 3B, x = 2.5 or x = 5.0 mm.).

Figure 3C (t = ∞) shows the way the final, maximum voltage change across the membrane varies with distance from the current-applying electrode. The curve for t = 8 milliseconds shows that the voltage changes are much more closely confined to the region of the current electrode shortly after the current is turned on than at longer times.

Explanation of Cable Properties. Cable properties are inherent in the structure of long

---

*A capital delta (Δ) is placed before a symbol to indicate a change in the value of the quantity represented by the symbol. Here $\Delta\mathcal{E}_m$ refers to a change in $\mathcal{E}_m$ from its steady value; $\Delta\mathcal{E}_m = \mathcal{E}_m - \mathcal{E}_s$. $\mathcal{E}_m$ symbolizes the transmembrane voltage at any time and place.

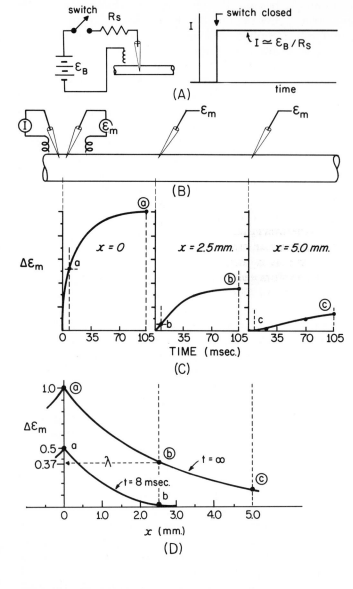

(A)

(B)

(C)

(D)

Fig. 3. Experimental measurement of cable properties in a skeletal muscle fiber. *A, Left,* Generation of a constant current and its application to a fiber via an intracellular electrode. A battery whose voltage ($\mathcal{E}_B$) is hundreds of times larger than transmembrane potential is connected to fiber through the high resistance (R_S), microelectrode resistance (R_e) and return electrode in bathing medium of negligible resistance. Current flows when switch is closed and is $I = \mathcal{E}_B/(R_S + R_e + R_f)$ where R_f is the resistance of fiber. R_S is made much larger than R_e and R_f so $I = \mathcal{E}_B/R_S$ approximately and is independent of R_e and R_S. *Right,* Applied current as a function of time, zero with switch open and constant with switch closed.

B, Constant current is suddenly applied to fiber at extreme left ($x = 0$) via the intracellular electrode labeled with circled I. Changes in transmembrane potential, $\Delta\mathcal{E}_m$, at several points along the fiber are measured with another intracellular electrode system, $\mathcal{E}_m$.

C, Transmembrane potential changes as a function of time after switch closure are recorded at the distances indicated by the dashed upward extensions of ordinate lines. Note that as distance increases, potential rises progressively more slowly and reaches lower final value.

D, Replot of data shown in C. Voltage change is plotted as function of distance along fiber on same scale as in *B* and for two different times, t = 8 milliseconds (lower curve) and t greater than 150 milliseconds (labeled t = ∞, upper curve). Lettered points in *D* correspond to the same lettered points in *C*. Note that spatial spread at early times is much less than at later times.

thin cells: (i) Although a relatively good conductor, the cell plasm is so long with respect to its diameter that its resistance plays an important role in determining the pattern of current flow. (ii) The cell plasm is separated from the interstitial fluid by the thin insulating membrane, forming the membrane capacitor. (iii) Ions can penetrate the membrane; hence it is an imperfect insulator and has a high electrical resistance. The slowing of the time rate of change in transmembrane potential at a distance from the current electrode (Fig. 3*C*) is a consequence of membrane capacitance; it takes time for an applied current to change the amount of charge on the membrane. The dim-

inution of the final $\Delta\mathcal{E}_m$ with distance (Fig. 3*D*) is a consequence of both protoplasmic and membrane resistance.

Precise understanding of cable properties requires an analysis of the complicated network of resistors and capacitors which is equivalent to a fiber (appendix). However, the general nature of cable properties can be comprehended from a study of Figure 4. The two ways that current can go through the membrane are shown in part *A*. The arrow indicating a K+ penetrating the membrane via a pore represents an ionic current flow, an actual physical transfer of the same charge from the inside to the outside. Similarly a Cl⁻ moving into the

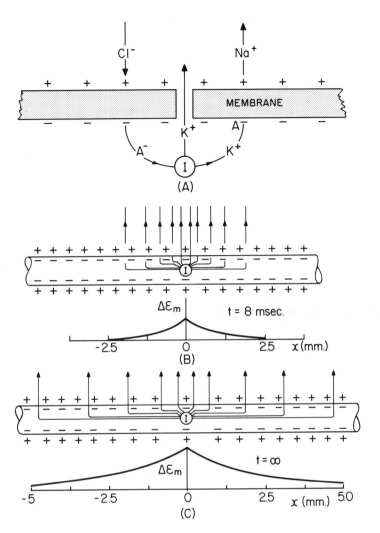

Fig. 4. Current flow patterns in elongated cells. *A*, Diagram showing the two types of membrane current flow, ohmic and capacitive. Circled I represents tip of current-supplying intracellular micro-electrode. Arrows indicate some of the paths of charge movement (current flow). Arrow showing passage of K^+ through pore represents ionic current flow through membrane resistance (ohmic flow). Current can also be carried out by inflow of Cl^- (not shown). Arrows originating and terminating on membrane at left and right represent ion flow neutralizing membrane charge. Arrow at right shows a K^+ migrating from plasm to inside of cell membrane and neutralizing A^- and releasing a plus charge (Na^+) from outside of membrane which moves into the bathing medium. Thus, current can, in effect, flow through the membrane without actual penetration of charge (capacitive current).

B, Diagram illustrating current distribution in fiber 8 milliseconds after beginning of current (upper) and transmembrane potential as a function of distance (lower). Distance scale applies to both parts. Compare with Fogure 3*D*. Upper, applied current flows out of cell in all directions perpendicular to axon axis but only the current flowing upward is represented. Most current lines are interrupted at membrane to indicate that current is mostly capacitive at this early time and confined to the region immediately around the electrode. The greater the spacing between + signs the greater the reduction in ε_m. Diameter of the fiber is greatly exaggerated (about ten times) with respect to length to show current pattern more clearly.

C, Current distribution for longer periods; otherwise same as *B*. All current flow through membrane is resistive. Current has spread much farther along axon. See text for further explanation.

cell through a pore constitutes an outward ionic current. Such ion flows are calculable from Ohm's law; the change in transmembrane voltage is equal to applied current times membrane resistance, $\Delta \mathcal{E}_m = IR_m$.

CAPACITATIVE CURRENT.   Current can, in effect, also flow through the membrane capacitor without actual ion penetration of the membrane. This is shown in Figure 4A; right and left hand arrows show ions, forced by the electric field, moving up to the membrane and neutralizing charges stored thereon; e.g., a K^+ moves up to the inside of the membrane and neutralizes one of the negative charges separated by the membrane, shown on the right as an A^-. The neutralized internal minus charge now has no attraction for the corresponding external plus charge, and this plus charge is now free to migrate in the outside fluid under the influence of the electric field. In this case also, there are charges moving through the internal and external media (i.e., current), but the charges which carry the current change at the membrane; there is no actual penetration of the membrane by charges. It does not matter which particular ion carries the current; the chemical identities of charges are indistinguishable electrically. Capacitative current is defined as the rate of accumulation of charge on the conductors of a capacitor; this is a slightly different physical meaning for current flow than previously given but the units are the same and there is actual current flow in the conductors, carrying charges to and from a capacitor. A current flowing into a capacitor changes the amount of charge on the conductors and thus changes the voltage, which is proportional to charge. A constant current supplies charge at a fixed rate, so the voltage increases linearly with time. When a current is first applied to a fiber, all of it must go to charging or discharging the membrane capacitor, since no ionic current can flow through the membrane until the transmembrane voltage is altered from its steady-state value and a net driving force is built up across the membrane.

EARLY CURRENT DISTRIBUTION PATTERN.   The path followed by the charges flowing through a conductor is determined at any point by the direction of the electric field at that point. In the complicated geometry of a nerve or muscle fiber, the direction of flow is not easily calculated. However, a general idea can be obtained by application of the rule that the pattern of

current flow adjusts itself so that the total resistance of the circuit is a minimum; i.e., for a given applied voltage the current flow is maximum, the charges taking the paths of least resistance. Many charges follow the most direct electrical paths; fewer follow more circuitous paths.

Figure 4B represents the pattern of current flow shortly (8 milliseconds) after the current is turned on. Most of the arrows which represent paths of current flow are interrupted at the membrane to indicate that the flow is capacitative. The electric field generated by the current supplying battery (Fig. 3A) acts simultaneously on all ions and they start migrating. Some leave the electrode (circled I) and enter the plasm; those in the plasm move through the plasm; some leave the plasm and neutralize charges on the membrane. On the outside, some charges stored on the membrane are freed to move into the interstitial fluid and on toward the external electrode (not shown in Fig. 4). At first the path of least resistance for charge flow is straight from the electrode and out through the immediately adjacent membrane (x = 0). The charge neutralizing process does not impede flow, for the current does not go through the membrane. At the somewhat later time represented in Figure 4B, the current flow has appreciably altered the transmembrane charge (and voltage) in the immediate vicinity of the electrode. This means that some of the current is now traversing the membrane via pores and thus encountering resistance as shown by the two lines drawn through the membrane (Fig. 4B). In this situation, the path of least resistance is for the current to spread through the plasm to adjacent regions of membrane where the current flow is capacitative. However, this spreading process is limited by the resistance of the cell plasm; the farther the current spreads, the greater the plasm resistance and the less the current taking this particular path. This is shown in the figure by the decreasing number of current flow lines with increasing distances from the current electrode (Fig. 4B, C).

The slower changes in voltage at greater distances from the current electrode are explained by the foregoing argument; the changes near the electrode are rapid from the start because initially all of the current is used to charge the small area of membrane in the immediate vicinity. Later the same amount of current has to charge larger areas of membrane at greater distances, so the rate of charging and hence rate of voltage change is less. Furthermore, current does not even start to flow at the more distant regions until the closer regions have been partially charged (or, in this case, discharged). The farther the recording electrode is from the current electrode, the longer it is before any appreciable current is diverted to that region by the progression of charging at nearer regions. This accounts qualitatively for curves of voltage versus time of the type shown in Figure 3C.

TRANSITION TO THE STEADY-STATE. As the current flow proceeds, charging the membrane capacity and altering the membrane voltage, progressively more of the current is carried through the membrane by ion flow; as the voltage departs from its normal steady-state value, an increasingly large electrochemical gradient acts to drive ions through the membrane. Thus for an outward current, the membrane is discharged and depolarized and the concentration gradient of K^+ acts increasingly to drive K^+ out of the cell as the counteracting voltage gradient diminishes. Similarly, the concentration gradient of Cl^- is greater than the opposing voltage gradient and a net influx (outward current) of Cl^- results. Eventually, the depolarization *must* reach a value where all of the current supplied by the intracellular electrode is carried out of the cell by ions, and none goes to charge the membrane, i.e., the voltage stops changing. As long as any of the current charges the membrane, the voltage is changing and the driving forces on ions are increasing; the voltage cannot continue to change indefinitely.

Time constant. The time required for the attainment of the steady state depends on both the membrane capacitance and resistance: a longer time is required to charge a larger capacity up to the final value. For a larger membrane resistance, the membrane voltage must be altered more to make ionic current equal applied current; hence a longer time is required to reach the steady-state. Thus, the time scale depends on the product of membrane resistance and capacitance. This product is called the *time constant* of the membrane, $\tau_m = R_m C_m$. In the examples of Figure 3 the time constant is 35 milliseconds. This is a typical value for skeletal muscle fibers. The time constant of a squid giant axon is about 1 millisecond.

STEADY-STATE CURRENT DISTRIBUTION. After the applied current has flowed for a sufficiently

long time (about 150 milliseconds in the example of Fig. 3) all the membrane has charged to its final value (Fig. 4C), and the voltage is unchanging in time. In the steady-state, the current spreads far down the plasm in both directions so as to pass out through a large membrane area; the larger the area of high resistance membrane perpendicular to the direction of current flow, the lower the total resistance offered by the membrane. However, the current will not spread indefinitely in the plasm, seeking a greater membrane area to exit through because such longitudinal current flow also encounters the plasm resistance. Some balance must be struck between the spreading out to achieve low membrane resistance and a lack of spread to achieve low plasm resistance.

Space constant. Quantitatively, the measure of the extent of current spread in the steady-state is the *space constant*, λ, defined as the distance at which the change in transmembrane voltage has fallen to 0.37 ($= 1/e$, e $= 2.718$ is the base of natural logarithms) of the maximum value as shown in Figure 3D. The relative values of plasm resistance and surface membrane resistance determine how far a current will spread; the space constant is the fiber length where the resistance of the membrane covering that fiber segment is equal to the longitudinal plasm resistance of the segment. Clearly such a distance exists because, as the segment's length increases, the plasm resistance increases in proportion while the transverse resistance of the membrane decreases because the membrane area increases. In large fibers, the space constant is of the order of a few millimeters; in the example illustrated in Figures 3 and 4, λ is 2.5 mm. The space constant is proportional to the square root of fiber diameter if the electrical properties of the plasm and membrane are held constant.

Summary. When a constant current is suddenly applied to an axon at x $=$ 0 (Figs. 3, 4), at first all the current flows directly through the membrane because $\mathcal{E}_m$ cannot change until the charge on the membrane at that point is changed. Since I $=$ $\mathcal{E}/R$, no current will flow laterally through the plasm or directly through the membrane until $\mathcal{E}_m$ is altered. Immediately after the current is applied, it is confined to the immediate region of application. As time passes $\Delta \mathcal{E}_m$ gradually changes and some current is diverted to adjacent regions of membrane. As the charge and $\mathcal{E}_m$ rise in immediately adjacent regions, the current spreads to still greater distances. Finally, after a long time, the membrane is fully charged and all the current is carried through the membrane by ions.

The transition between initial and final states is shown in the curves giving potential as a function of time at different distances (Fig. 3C). Hodgkin and Rushton[17] have analyzed mathematically the passive cable properties of an unmyelinated nerve and have developed methods for measuring membrane resistance and capacitance and plasm resistance.

A different, possibly helpful way to think of resistors and capacitors representing a fiber is as reservoirs and partially clogged or small-bore pipes, respectively. Voltage is analogous to pressure (height of water in a reservoir), charge to amount of water and current to flow of water. The applied current is analogous to the constant flow from a high pressure source through a very small pipe. At first all the flow goes to filling the reservoir at the point of entry. Later some of the water flows slowly through the clogged or small pipes and starts to fill adjacent reservoirs or to drain out through leaks in the reservoirs (membrane resistance).

THRESHOLD PHENOMENA IN ELONGATED CELLS

Events Near Threshold Voltage. The cable properties of a fiber are such that a signal in the form of membrane hyperpolarization or depolarization at one point is undetectable more than a few millimeters (a few space constants) away. Since signals are transmitted for distances of up to two meters in man, some method of boosting the signal at least every few millimeters is needed. The energy for boosting the signal is supplied by the sodium concentration difference across the membrane. The signal is kept to a fixed height by means of the threshold, all-or-nothing regenerative mechanism. The boost occurs at all points in unmyelinated nerve fibers and in muscles and at nodes of Ranvier in myelinated nerve fibers.

Experimentally, an action potential may be initiated in a nerve or muscle fiber by sufficiently depolarizing the membrane with an outward current applied through an intracellular microelectrode. Another microelectrode, for measuring membrane potential, may be inserted near the stimulating electrode (Fig. 5A). The changes in $\mathcal{E}_m$ associated with the initiation

of an impulse are shown diagrammatically in Figure 5B. Hyperpolarizing currents (curve 1) of any size and small depolarizing currents (curve 2) change $\mathcal{E}_m$ in the manner expected from the cable properties of the fiber (compare with x = 0, Fig. 3C). When the depolarizing current applied to skeletal muscle fibers is just strong enough to reduce $\mathcal{E}_m$ from resting values (−90 mV.) to threshold voltage (about −55 mV.) (curve 3, Fig. 5B), there are two possible responses. The response to about half of the stimuli is a propagating action potential (curve 3b). If an action potential is not initiated, there is a *local response* (curve 3a); i.e., the voltage falls back toward the resting level, but initially more

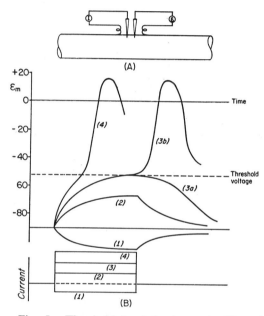

Fig. 5. Threshold in skeletal muscle fiber. *A*, Schematic diagram of experimental arrangement showing intracellular stimulating (*I*) and recording (*E*) electrodes. *B*, Changes in $\mathcal{E}_m$ (*upper records*) produced by suddenly applied and terminated constant currents (*lower records*). Curve *1* in current records produced voltage changes shown by Curve *1* in $\mathcal{E}$ records, and so forth for Curves *2* to *4*. Hyperpolarizing and subthreshold depolarizing currents of any strength produce the $\mathcal{E}_m$ changes expected from cable properties (Curves *1* and *2*). Current of just threshold strength will produce one of two responses: Either membrane potential returns to steady value after a delay (*3a*), or an action potential is generated with its typical rapid rise and fall (*3b*). Any stronger stimulus (*4*) also generates an action potential, but progressively shorter times are required to depolarize membrane to threshold. Duration of action potentials is greatly exaggerated to show time course of action potential more clearly. Every action potential has the same time course.

slowly than expected from the cable properties. As the name implies, a local response is non-propagated, i.e., local membrane activity. If the recording electrode impales the fiber farther from the stimulating electrode, a potential quite similar to curve *3b* is recorded but delayed in time when an action potential is initiated; otherwise, only the cable response is seen which is negligible a few space constants away. The value of $\mathcal{E}_m$ at which an action potential is just initiated by a depolarizing current is called the *threshold voltage*. A lesser depolarization does not produce a propagated response, but a greater depolarization does. A current that barely depolarizes the membrane to threshold is called a *threshold stimulus*.

Threshold and the All-or-Nothing Law. Once the membrane has been depolarized to threshold, the action potential develops explosively and is thereafter independent of the stimulus. *The energy for the action potential is contained in the axon; the stimulus, by lowering the membrane potential, serves merely to trigger the axon into activity.* Thus, once the stimulus reaches threshold intensity, any additional increase in stimulus intensity has no effect on the amplitude of the action potential. For a given stimulus the axon either responds with a full-sized action potential or it does not; its behavior is thus "all-or-nothing." It should not be inferred that the action potentials of an axon always have the same amplitude; many factors can alter the energy stores of the axon and hence alter the amplitude of the action potential. For any given state, however, the axon always responds maximally to a threshold stimulus.

General Features of Threshold and Recovery. Threshold, all-or-nothing properties are not unique to excitable cells or to living systems; many objects encountered in everyday life have these properties. Possibly the simplest example is that of a brick standing on its end. A small sideways push on the top edge of the brick may tip it slightly; releasing the brick allows it to fall back to its original stable equilibrium position, perhaps with a little rocking back and forth. Such a push is a subthreshold stimulus. A stronger push may tip the brick so that it balances on its edge, a position of unstable equilibrium. A slight further displacement tips the brick over and it falls rapidly to the flat position, an even more stable (lower potential energy) equilibrium position. This is

clearly threshold, all-or-nothing behavior; when displaced to or past threshold, the brick always goes to the same final position regardless of the strength of the stimulus.

Many useful devices have thresholds, e.g., light switches, thermostats, mouse traps, matches. However, excitable tissues differ from these devices in having an additional property: spontaneous recovery to the original low threshold state. This means that the cell must be supplied further energy to restore the original state, i.e., to recover excitability. In contrast, a brick has to be stood on end again to restore its low threshold to tipping. The most common device having a threshold and spontaneous recovery is the flushing mechanism of a water closet. A slight rotation of the handle is the required threshold stimulus; this lifts the float valve in the bottom of the tank sufficiently that it floats upward, releasing a torrent of water. The flow continues until the tank is empty, the float valve reseats and the tank begins to refill from a water source at higher pressure through another valve whose orifice depends on the level of another float such that, as the water rises, the inflow rate is reduced. The cycle is completed and the system is back to its original low threshold state when the tank is filled to that level which shuts off the inflow valve. The system will not respond to a rotation of the handle when the tank is emptying and for a short part of the refilling period. In the language of neurophysiology and speaking of a nerve, this would be called the *absolutely refractory period*. At some time during the refilling cycle a small flush can be initiated by a larger rotation of the handle. As the tank fills, the needed initiating stimulus becomes smaller and the response grows; this period of subnormal responsiveness corresponds to the *relatively refractory period* in nerves. These phenomena in nerves, then, are examples of the behavior of threshold systems having spontaneous recovery.

Strength–Duration Relation. The strength of an abruptly applied and terminated current (square wave) required to initiate an impulse in an axon or muscle fiber depends on the length of the time during which the current flows. For an impulse to be initiated, the membrane must be depolarized to threshold over a small region. If a current applied at a point on an axon flows for a long time, the membrane capacitors will become fully charged, and the change in membrane potential will be maximal

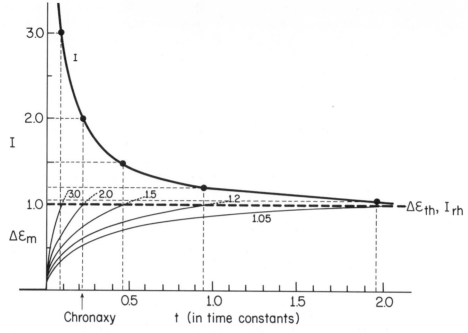

Fig. 6. Strength–duration relation (solid, heavy curve) of an excitable cell or tissue. Both the cause, square pulses of current (dashed, fine lines) applied to a fiber or tissue, and the effect, the result-ing changes in transmembrane potential at the stimulus site (solid, fine lines), are plotted as functions of time. Horizontal, dashed, heavy line at 1.0 represents both threshold current strength at long times (I_{rh}) and difference ($\Delta\mathcal{E}_{th}$) between threshold membrane voltage ($\mathcal{E}_{th}$) and resting voltage ($\mathcal{E}_{s}$). Ordi-nates, strength of applied current, (I) turned on at t = 0, measured in units of I_{rh}, the strength a long lasting current pulse must have to depolarize the membrane to threshold; and the change in trans-membrane potential measured in units of $\Delta\mathcal{E}_{th}$. Abscissa, time since start of current pulse measured in units of the membrane time constant (τ), i.e., if the time constant is 30 milliseconds, t = 1 time con-stant means t = 30 milliseconds. I_{rh} (as defined above) is termed the *rheobasic current* or *rheobase*. Indi-vidual points on the strength–duration curve are obtained in the following way: A current of strength I = 1.05 (actually, I = 1.05 I_{rh}) causes the voltage changes at the site of the stimulating electrode shown by the lowermost light, solid line (labeled 1.05). This curve is identical in shape to that in Figure *3C* (x = 0). The transmembrane voltage crosses threshold ($\Delta\mathcal{E}_{th}$) at t = 1.96 time constants. An action potential (not shown) would be initiated at this time and hence the current could be turned off as shown without affecting action potential generation; leaving the current on would also have no effect. This exactly threshold stimulus is represented by the pulse jumping from zero to 1.05 at t = 0, continuing at this value until t = 1.96 and then dropping back to zero; the heavy dot at the pulse's termination is a point on the strength–duration curve. Other points are obtained in the same way by selecting a stimulus current value, letting it flow until the membrane potential crosses threshold and then terminating the current. The stronger the stimulating current, the shorter the time it must flow to carry the membrane potential to threshold; doubling the current doubles the change in voltage at any particular time (dashed curve labeled 2.0). The time required for a stimulus of twice rheobasic strength to carry the membrane potential to threshold is called the *chronaxy*. In this example the chronaxy is 0.21 time constants. The number by each voltage curve refers to the current strength which produces that voltage change. Current strength is read directly off the ordinate scale.

for that current. Therefore, the threshold cur-rent strength for a prolonged stimulus is less than that for a shorter stimulus. A curve relat-ing the strength of a threshold stimulus to its duration is called a *strength–duration* curve. Clearly, the shape of such a curve is directly re-lated to the cable properties of the fiber. The relation is derived graphically in Figure 6. The

shape of the strength–duration curve is very nearly the same for all tissues, although the time and current scales vary. One way of calcu-lating its shape is derived in the appendix to this chapter. *Chronaxy* is one point on the strength–duration curve, i.e., the length of time a current twice rheobase strength must flow in order to excite a cell. Chronaxy is directly proportional to the membrane time constant and hence is greater in muscle than in nerve. With external electrodes chronaxy can be measured easily in a whole nerve or muscle; hence an estimate of membrane time constant can be made without recourse to technically difficult intracellular stimulating and recording techniques.

Effect of Subthreshold Currents on Excitability. *Excitability* is defined as the reciprocal of threshold. If an applied current is slightly subthreshold, the depolarization persists for some time after the termination of the current; the size of a threshold stimulus is reduced during this period, and the excitability is increased. To measure the change in excitability produced by a subthreshold shock it is necessary to probe or test the excitability at varying time intervals by using a second shock of an intensity which can be varied. The time course of an excitability change caused by the first shock can be determined. This procedure, known as the *conditioning–testing technique,* is widely used in neurophysiology; the shock used to induce the change is called the "conditioning" shock, and that used to measure or test the change is called the "test" shock.

The heightened excitability persisting after a subthreshold conditioning shock is a consequence of the cable properties of the cells. The slowly waning voltage change induced by the conditioning shock persists after the shock and can sum with the voltage changes induced by the test shock. Moreover, as expected from cable properties, the heightened excitability is not spatially confined to the stimulus site but extends on either side; the threshold increases more and more gradually with distance, finally reaching the resting threshold level.

The same procedure can be used to test the effect of prolonged rather than brief subthreshold conditioning shocks. In this instance excitability increases at the stimulating cathode with the onset of current flow, but, even though current flow continues at a constant level, excitability then drops to a steady intermediate value. This decline from peak excitability during constant current flow is called *accommodation*. Following cessation of current flow, excitability at the cathode declines below the resting level and recovers only slowly. This is known as *postcathodal depression.* The mechanisms of accommodation and postcathodal depression will be discussed later.

Refractory Period; Recovery Following Excitation. The conditioning–testing procedure can be used to study the changes in excitability which follow the generation of an action potential. In this instance the conditioning shock is suprathreshold, and the intensity of test shock required to elicit a second action potential at varying conditioning–testing intervals is determined. For a brief period following the action potential it is impossible to elicit a second action potential, no matter how intense the test shock. As mentioned above, this interval is known as the *absolutely refractory period.* Thereafter a second action potential (usually of less than normal amplitude) can be elicited, but only if the test shock is considerably above the resting threshold value. Excitability then returns to the resting threshold along an approximately exponential time course. The interval between absolute refractoriness and complete recovery to resting excitability is known as the *relatively refractory period.* Refractoriness limits the frequency of impulse discharge in nerve fibers; for example, an axon with an absolutely refractory period of 0.5 millisecond can be driven continuously at rates not exceeding 1000 impulses per second—and then only if the stimulus is considerably more intense than that required to initiate a single action potential in the axon at rest. With continous high frequency stimulation, the minimum interval between spikes is about double the absolutely refractory period.

IMPULSE GENERATION AND PROPAGATION[9]

Active Na^+–K^+ transport and cable properties are attributes of all animal cell membranes. The membrane of an excitable cell has certain unique properties in addition. These properties were precisely described by Hodgkin and Huxley in their classic studies on the behavior of the squid giant axon when its membrane potential was held constant by artificial means (voltage clamping). The defining property of excitable cells is that rapid depolarization (reduction of transmembrane voltage) increases the membrane permeability to Na^+ (P_{Na}). Within limits, the greater the depolarization, the greater the increase in P_{Na}. An ancillary property is that the increase in P_{Na} induced by depolarization is transient; even if the membrane voltage is maintained near $\mathcal{E}_{Na}$ by other means (e.g., external current), P_{Na} falls to its resting value in a matter of a few milliseconds. The properties of the excitable membrane are described in terms of changes in membrane permeability or conductance, because no information is yet available regarding the molecular mechanisms which give rise to the large and specific changes in membrane ionic permeability.

There are three principal methods of studying the changes in ionic permeability during activity: (i) observing the effects of changes in external ion concentrations on the action potential, (ii) studying by means of radioisotopes the net and one-way ionic fluxes during activity, and (iii) voltage-clamping, measuring membrane current as a function of time while $\mathcal{E}_m$ is fixed. The first two methods yield only a rough estimate of peak or mean ion permeabilities during activity. Voltage clamping,[15] however, made possible a detailed quantitative analysis of the time and voltage dependencies of Na^+ and K^+ conductances.

Sequence of Events during the Action Potential. In 1902, Bernstein formulated the membrane theory in a form which has endured to this day in its essential aspects. He proposed that the surface membrane is permeable only to potassium in the resting state, giving rise to the resting potential. He attributed the action potential to a transient loss of the membrane's selectivity for potassium, the membrane becoming permeable to all ions and the potential falling to near zero. This hypothesis was sufficient until the introduction of intracellular recording techniques in about 1940 showed that there is an overshoot of the action potential, the inside becoming positive with respect to the outside. This finding necessitated modification of Bernstein's hypothesis. Reference to Table 1 in Chapter 1 reveals that the only biologically occurring ion which has a positive equilibrium potential and can penetrate the membrane is sodium. In 1949, Hodgkin and Katz[16] proposed and tested the hypothesis that the upstroke or depolarization phase of the action potential is brought about by a brief and highly specific increase in the membrane's permeability to Na^+. This increase would permit Na^+ to enter the cell at a greatly increased rate, driven both by the concentration and voltage gradients and thus charge the membrane toward the sodium equilibrium potential. Repolarization to the resting state would

occur as the increased Na^+ permeability died out and the efflux of K^+ exceeded influx of Na^+. A simplified version of this hypothesis is that the action potential can be represented as a sudden switch from the resting state with the membrane potential near the potassium equilibrium potential, a "potassium membrane," to the active state with the potential changing rapidly toward the sodium equilibrium potential, a "sodium membrane," followed by a somewhat slower reversion to the potassium membrane condition. Of course, the membrane is not permeable solely to K^+ in the resting state nor to Na^+ in the active state. Hodgkin and Katz supported their hypothesis by showing that the overshoot and the rate of rise of the action potential vary with changes in external Na^+ concentration in approximately the manner expected from the Nernst equation. Before presenting this evidence it is pertinent to answer briefly two questions raised by this hypothesis: (i) How does a threshold depolarization act to produce the dramatic increase in Na^+ permeability? (ii) What processes bring about the rapid repolarization to the original resting condition?

(i) The large (500-fold) increase in permeability to sodium is brought about by depolarization; sodium permeability varies rapidly with voltage in the region of threshold. This change is an intrinsic property of the excitable membrane; the molecular basis is unknown. Thus there is a regenerative or vicious circle relationship between depolarization and sodium permeability; depolarization increases sodium permeability, increasing Na^+ entry and further depolarizing the membrane. This regenerative, circular sequence of events was compactly summarized by Hodgkin[5] in the following diagram, which might, therefore, be aptly termed the "Hodgkin cycle":

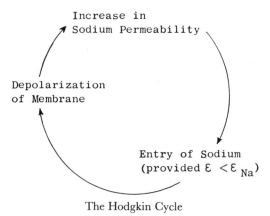

The Hodgkin Cycle

(ii) The recovery from the rapid depolarization produced by the Hodgkin cycle is due to two factors: (a) The increased permeability to Na$^+$ during activity is transient; the permeability falls to near resting values in a millisecond or so. This spontaneous fall in Na$^+$ permeability is called *inactivation*. (b) When the membrane is depolarized, the permeability to K$^+$ commences to increase comparatively slowly (after a delay of about a millisecond). This property is also intrinsic to the membrane. Both the increase in permeability to K$^+$ and the decrease in permeability to Na$^+$ make the potential fall rapidly toward the resting level. Following the return of the membrane potential to the resting level, permeability to K$^+$ falls slowly to its normal value. Both these events limit the duration of the action potential and lead to repolarization.

Effects of External Sodium and Potassium Concentration on Membrane Potentials. The flux of an ion depends on the membrane permeability to that ion, on the transmembrane voltage and on the external and internal concentrations of the ion. Thus, a change in concentration should alter membrane voltage to an extent which depends on the membrane's relative permeability to the ion. If the membrane is solely permeable to the ion (S) being studied, the change in voltage with external or internal concentration is given by the Nernst equation $\mathcal{E}_m = \mathcal{E}_s = 61 \log [S]_o/[S]_i$. A lesser change is expected if other ions permeate the membrane. In most experiments, only external ion concentrations can be varied. However, it has been recently discovered that, in some circumstances, the axoplasm can be squeezed out of squid giant fibers without destroying the membrane and the inside can be perfused with an artificial solution.[9] The excitability of an axon bathed in sea-water is restored by perfusing the interior with a solution having a high potassium concentration, regardless of the accompanying anion. External potassium concentration is ordinarily increased by replacing some of the sodium with potassium, leaving chloride unchanged. Sodium can be reduced either by replacing Na$^+$ with some presumably inert cation such as choline$^+$ or by replacing NaCl with an inert, nonionized substance such as dextrose or sucrose.

RESTING POTENTIAL AND CHANGES IN EXTERNAL POTASSIUM CONCENTRATION. Since the resting membrane is relatively highly permeable to potassium, an increase in external potassium concentration should have substantial effects on the resting potential. Such an increase momentarily increases the K$^+$ influx until membrane charge and voltage are reduced to such a level that the efflux is increased to equal the increased influx. If the only permeable ion were potassium, the change in potential would be predictable by the Nernst equation; the extent to which this is found experimentally to be not true gives an estimate of the contributions of other ions under the particular circumstances. The effects of external potassium concentration on the resting potential of excised frog skeletal muscle are shown in Figure 7. Since $\mathcal{E}_K = 58 \log_{10} [K^+]_o/[K^+]_i$ at room temperature, a plot of the resting potential against the logarithm of the external potassium concentration will give a straight line with a slope of 58 mV. per tenfold change in external potassium concentration if the transmembrane potential is a potassium equilibrium potential.

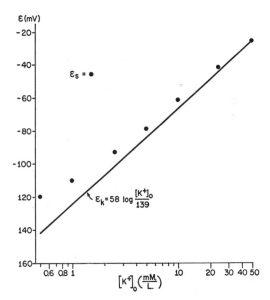

Fig. 7. Immediate changes in steady transmembrane potential ($\mathcal{E}_S$) of frog sartorius muscle fibers produced by alterations in external potassium concentration, $[K^+]_o$. *Abscissa,* $[K^+]_o$ on a logarithmic scale; *ordinate,* $\mathcal{E}_S$ potential of intracellular fluid minus potential of extracellular fluid. Points are experimental results. Straight line is plot of equilibrium potential for potassium, $\mathcal{E}_K$ at room temperature. Note that at high values of $[K^+]_o$, $\mathcal{E}_S$ changes with $\mathcal{E}_K$ and that at K$^+$ concentrations in normal range, $\mathcal{E}_S$ changes much less rapidly than $\mathcal{E}_K$. (After Adrian, *J. Physiol.,* 1956, *133:* 631–658.)

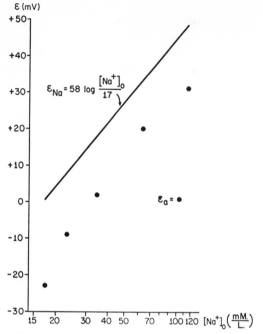

Fig. 8. Changes in the height of the action potential of frog sartorius muscle fibers produced by changes in external Na+ concentration. NaCl in bathing solution was replaced by choline chloride. *Abscissa,* [Na+]o on logarithmic scale; *ordinate,* potential of intracellular fluid minus potential of extracellular fluid at peak of action potential. Points are experimental results; straight line is plot of equilibrium potential for Na+ ($\mathcal{E}_{Na}$). Note that peak of action potential is considerably lower than $\mathcal{E}_{Na}$, but that both change at about same rate with changes in [Na+]o. (After Nastuk and Hodgkin, *J. cell. comp. Physiol.,* 1950, *35:*39–74.)

The solid points show the measured membrane potential for different values of [K+]o, the latter being plotted on a logarithmic scale; the solid line shows the relation between $\mathcal{E}_K$ and [K+]o calculated from the Nernst equation. The membrane potential changes toward zero as [K+]o increases, and when [K+]o = [K+]i the membrane potential is zero. Through a considerable range, the membrane potential varies linearly with log [K+]o, as would be expected from the Nernst equation. However, at low values of [K+]o (near the normal values for extracellular fluid) the curve deviates markedly from linearity, and increments of [K+]o cause less than the expected change in the potential. This deviation of observed from calculated values reflects the action of the Na+–K+ pump. With normal and near normal values of [K+]o, a significant part of the K+ influx is propelled by the pump. At higher values of [K+]o the passive K+ influx increases, so the *proportion* of

the total K+ influx due to the steady action of the pump is diminished, and the membrane potential approaches $\mathcal{E}_K$, as predicted from the Nernst equation. It should be kept in mind that the potential reached immediately after the change in [K+]o is not steady; internal concentrations are slowly changing; e.g., [K+]i and [Cl−]i increase. However, these concentrations change so slowly (order of hours) that they can be considered constant during an experiment.

EFFECTS OF EXTERNAL SODIUM CONCENTRATION ON THE ACTION POTENTIAL. Hodgkin and Katz[16] supported their explanation of overshoot by studying the effects of changes in [Na+]o on the amplitude of the action potential in the squid giant axon. They found that replacing some of the NaCl in the bathing medium with dextrose reduced the amplitude of the action potential by about the amount that would be expected from the Nernst equation for Na+: $\mathcal{E}_{Na} = 58 \log_{10} [Na+]_o/[Na+]_i$. For example, there should be no overshoot unless the concentration of Na+ is greater outside than inside the fiber. If the two concentrations are equal, the equilibrium potential is zero.

A dependence of the action potential on [Na+]o is found in nearly all types of excitable tissues and is strong evidence of the validity of the Na+ hypothesis. Figure 8 shows the changes in amplitude of the action potential of excised frog skeletal muscle as [Na+]o is varied. For comparison, the value of the sodium equilibrium potential as calculated from the Nernst equation for [Na+]i = 17 μM. per cm.[3] is also shown. It can be seen that the membrane reversal during activity is rather less than the Na+ equilibrium potential but varies with [Na+]o about as rapidly as does this potential. Hodgkin and Katz interpreted the failure of the action potential to reach the Na+ equilibrium potential as evidence that the contributions of other ions are not negligible, i.e., that the permeability to K+ and Cl− ions is an appreciable but not large fraction (about one-tenth) of the permeability to Na+ at the peak of the action potential.

Role of acetylcholine. Nachmansohn[23] has forcefully advanced the hypothesis that the liberation and destruction of acetylcholine (ACh) are essential steps in the generation of the action potential in nerve as well as at the neuromuscular junction (Chap. 5). The postulated role of ACh in nerve conduction is as follows: (i) Depolarization liberates ACh from a bound, inactive form already present in the membrane. (ii)

The ACh acts to increase membrane permeability to Na^+ by combining with a "receptor" protein. (iii) The ACh is in equilibrium with the receptor protein, so that some of the ACh is unbound and thus susceptible to rapid hydrolysis (inactivation) by the high concentration of AChE present in the membrane. (iv) Destruction of the acetylcholine reduces Na^+ permeability and repolarization occurs. The wide distribution and high concentration of AChE in nervous tissue leave little doubt that ACh has an important role in nervous function. However, the evidence that this hypothesis describes ACh's function is no more than suggestive. Furthermore, it is difficult to acount for some experimental findings with this hypothesis; e.g., if ACh causes the specific increase in permeability to Na^+ during activity, inhibition of the AChE would allow ACh to accumulate in the membrane and repolarization and recovery of excitability should be greatly prolonged or prevented. Anticholinesterase drugs in high concentrations do block conduction, but the slight elongation of the action potential that occurs just before block is far less than expected on the basis of this hypothesis and about the same as occurs when conduction is blocked by local anesthetics. Thus, Nachmansohn's hypothesis is attractive but not convincing.

PROPAGATION

Measurement of Conduction Speed. The propagation of an action potential along an excitable fiber can be measured with the technique used for measuring cable properties (Fig. 3). If a threshold, depolarizing current is applied to a fiber at x = 0 (Fig. 3B), an action potential will be generated at that point after the length of time necessary for the membrane potential to reach threshold (curve 0, Fig. 9A). The action potential propagates in each direction at constant speed and amplitude. Thus, if the experiment is repeated with the recording electrode implanted 1 millimeter away, the potential changes due to cable properties are much smaller and slower; the action potential appears with full amplitude but is delayed by about 0.05 millisecond (curve 1, Fig. 9A). Repetition of the experiment at recording distances of 2, 5 and 10 millimeters gives the corresponding curves in Figure 9A. At distances greater than about 2 millimeters, the cable effects are negligibly small and the shape of the action potential becomes constant and concave upward at subthreshold values. Except for the cable effects near the stimulating electrode, the action potential is fixed in shape but occurs in-

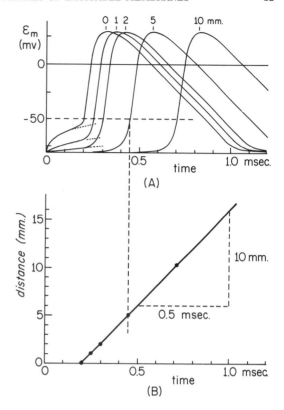

Fig. 9. Measurement of conduction speed. *A*, Action potentials initiated and recorded by the technique illustrated in Figure 3A and B. Ordinate, transmembrane potential (ε_m); abscissa, time since beginning of stimulating current pulse. Number attached to each action potential is the distance in millimeters of the intracellular recording electrode from the stimulating electrode. Note that records at 0, 1 and 2 mm. show, at subthreshold levels, the decrementing potential changes characteristic of cables (compare with Fig. 3C).

B, Distance–latency relation of action potentials shown in *A*. Ordinate, distance between stimulating and recording electrodes in millimeters; abscissa, latency of the action potential measured from time of start of stimulating current to the time the action potential reached the fixed level of − 50 millivolts. Scale is same as in *A*. Dashed horizontal line in *A* is at this level; its intersection with the action potential recorded at 5 millimeters is shown by the vertical line which extends down to the 5 mm. distance on the ordinate in *B*. Other points, obtained in the same way, fall on a straight line whose slope, 10 mm. per 0.5 milliseconds = 20 meters per second, is the conduction speed of the impulse. This is typical for a $10\,\mu$ diameter frog myelinated nerve fiber. The intercept of the line on the abscissa is the time for the stimulus to bring the fiber to threshold and for the spontaneous depolarization process to carry the voltage to − 50 mV. and thus has no great significance.

creasingly later at increasingly greater record-ing distances from the stimulus site. If the time from the beginning of the stimulus to the time some particular voltage is reached (− 50 mV. in Fig. 9*A*) by the action potential is plotted against the distance of the recording electrode from the stimulating electrode, a curve like that in Figure 9*B* is obtained. It is seen that the time delay or latency increases linearly with dis-tance; i.e., the action potential is propagated with a constant speed along the fiber. The speed is given by the slope of the distance–time curve and is 10 millimeters per 0.5 millisecond = 20 meters per second. This is about the conduction speed of squid giant axons and of a 10 μ frog myelinated nerve fiber. A mammalian myeli-nated nerve fiber of the same diameter would have a conduction speed of about 60 meters per second.

IMPULSE AS A WAVE. In the physical sense, a wave is any disturbance that moves with con-stant velocity and unchanging shape. Thus, the nerve impulse is a wave. Common examples of true waves are ocean waves, radio and light waves and sound waves. The most characteristic property of a wave is that its shape is the same as a function of time and as a function of dis-tance, e.g., a disturbance of fixed shape moving at constant speed. A person standing in the ocean can see a wave approaching; he sees the shape of the wave in space. As the wave passes him, he can feel the water level rise and recede around him as the wave passes; he can feel it in time. The nerve impulse cannot be seen but the time course can be measured at many different points, and hence the space distribution can be found at any particular time. In both cases, the space course is the same as the time course; the conversion factor from time to distance is simply the conduction speed. The spatial extent (L) of an impulse can be calculated from the duration of the action potential (t_{AP}) and the conduction speed (v): L = vt_{AP}. In the ex-ample of Figure 9, the duration is about 0.8 millisecond and the conduction speed is 20 millimeters per millisecond; the spatial extent is thus 0.8 millisecond × 20 millimeters per millisecond = 16 millimeters (Fig. 10*A*). In the fastest mammalian nerve fibers, the wave length is about 60 millimeters or 4 inches, a dis-tance of 3,000 times the diameter of the fiber (20 μ).

Local Circuit Propagation.[4, 9] Once an action potential has been initiated, the Na+ per-meability is high in a local region and the membrane potential is near the Na+ equilib-rium potential. The potential of the adjacent inactive membrane is near the K+ equilibrium potential. There is a potential difference be-tween these regions; consequently, current flows from the active region through the intra-cellular fluid to the inactive region (arrows di-rected to left in Fig. 10*B, C*), and discharges the membrane capacitor. The return current flows through the interstitial fluid back to the active region (arrows directed to right in Fig. 10*B, C*) and through the membrane as inward Na+ current, driven by $\mathcal{E}_{Na}$. This *local circuit* current

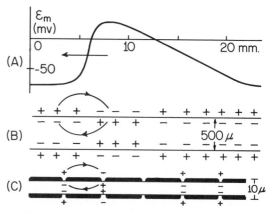

Fig. 10. Propagation by local circuit stimulation. *A*, Spatial variation of an action potential at a fixed time. Ordinate, transmembrane potential, $\mathcal{E}_m$; ab-scissa, distance along fibers shown in *B* and *C*. Action potential is the same as shown in Figure 9 and is propagated at a speed of 20 meters per second to the left, as shown by the arrow crossing its upstroke. Note that the upstroke is much steeper than the downstroke.

B, Unmyelinated nerve fiber. Plus and minus signs represent approximately the transmembrane voltage given accurately in *A*. Distance scale of *A* applies. Di-ameter of cell is grossly exaggerated with respect to length as shown. Arrows represent current flow in a local circuit or loop due to the differences in trans-membrane potential caused by the different properties of the membrane: highly permeable to K+ on left and right, even more highly permeable to Na+ in central regions. Local circuit flow acts to reduce charge in inactive regions but has much less effect on charge in active regions because of high Na+ permeability. Propagation is achieved by depolarizing action of local current flow.

C, Same as *B* except myelinated. For clarity, dis-tance between nodes is shown as 4 mm. or twice actual distance. Because of low capacity of sheath, charge is shown only at nodes (amount of charge in whole internodal region is about one half that at the node). Local circuit flow is thus largely from node to node as shown by arrows.

flow acts to reduce membrane charge and voltage in the inactive region. When threshold is reached, permeability to Na^+ increases rapidly, the inactive region becomes active and the membrane potential approaches the Na^+ equilibrium potential here also. Thus, by local circuit current flow an active region stimulates the adjacent inactive regions to threshold and an impulse is conducted away from a stimulating cathode in both directions at a constant speed. The stimulation of an inactive region by an active region is analogous to the sudden connection of a battery, of voltage ε_{Na}, through a comparatively low axoplasmic resistance (because the distance is short) to a capacitor, charged to ε_K. The high permeability to Na^+ of the active membrane means that the battery can supply a large current and thus quickly discharge the inactive region to threshold and makes it active. Figure 10 illustrates the principle of local circuit stimulation. Local current loops flow around the point of fastest voltage change. There are many such loops, but for clarity only one is shown in Figure 10*B* and *C*.

As mentioned above, recovery to the resting state is brought about by a spontaneous fall in Na^+ permeability and a delayed rise in K^+ permeability. In a matter of a few tenths of a millisecond, outward movement of K^+ exceeds inward movement of Na^+ and repolarization begins. This process follows depolarization automatically, so that the propagated wave has the typical humplike shape shown in Figures 2, 9 and 10. There is also local circuit flow behind the impulse as a consequence of the repolarization process (not shown in Fig. 10).

Myelinated Nerves: Saltatory Conduction.[18, 20, 24] The myelinated or medullated nerve fiber is one of the functional developments which make large size possible among the cold-blooded vertebrates and the elevated body position among mammals. Myelination greatly increases nerve fiber conduction speed without greatly increasing diameter and thus decreases reaction time. Invertebrates have achieved high conduction speed by developing giant axons. The sheer physical size of these axons prevents an animal from having large numbers of them.

The myelin sheath of medullated nerve fibers is formed by Schwann cells. A Schwann cell covers about 2 millimeters of axon in the largest diameter fibers (20μ). The Schwann cell surrounds the fiber and then wraps itself around the fiber many times to form the sheath. In the wrapping process, all the Schwann cell plasm is squeezed out, leaving the membranes closely opposed and forming a layer 170 Ångstroms thick. Since the myelin sheath is 2μ thick in large fibers, there are at least 100 wrappings. There is a gap of approximately 1μ between adjacent Schwann cell wrappings where the axon membrane is in free communication with the interstitial fluid. This interruption in the myelin sheath is called a *node of Ranvier* and the sheathed portion is called the *internode*.

Since the myelin sheath is composed of many layers of closely packed membranes, it is a good insulator. If there are 100 double membrane layers in the sheath, then the resistance of a 1 cm.^{2} patch of sheath will be 200 times the resistance of 1 cm.^{2} of membrane, since current flow is perpendicular to the membrane surface. Similarly, the capacity of 1 cm.^{2} of sheath is 200 times smaller than that of 1 layer of membrane and thus, *the amount of charge stored across the sheath for a given potential difference is also 200 times less.* Because of the thick sheath, the amount of charge stored on the whole internodal region (2 mm.) is only about one-half of the charge on the nodal region (1 μ). This is the reason that membrane charges are shown only at the nodes in Figure 10. There are, of course, some charges separated by the myelin sheath.

Resting and action potentials are generated only at the nodes in myelinated nerves. The voltages generated at the node by ion diffusion down concentration gradients charge up the internodal capacity. When a fiber is depolarized only the nodes become active. If one node is active and an adjacent node is inactive (Fig. 10*C*), there is a local circuit flow between the nodes, depolarizing the inactive node. The length of time taken for an active region to depolarize an adjacent inactive one to threshold is determined by the amount of charge that must be removed and the resistance of the axoplasm between the regions. Since the membrane charge is greatly reduced by the myelin sheath, the conduction speed of a myelinated nerve fiber is many times greater than that of an unmyelinated fiber of the same diameter and membrane properties. Impulse propagation in myelinated nerve fibers can be summarized as the hopping of excitation from node to node; internodal regions have a low charge, are well insulated and unexcitable. Propagation by this means is called *saltatory conduction* (from the Latin *saltare*, to dance).

Determinants of Conduction Speed. Two classes of factors determine the speed of impulse conduction in excitable fibers: physical properties of the cell and geometry of the cell.

PHYSICAL FACTORS. (i) The most important physical property of an excitable cell is the extent of the depolarization-induced increase in sodium permeability. The greater the peak permeability, the greater the sodium current and hence the greater the rate of rise of the action potential. In turn, a faster rising action potential means a larger spatial voltage gradient along the fiber and hence greater local circuit currents, faster excitation of adjacent regions and greater conduction speed. (ii) A reduction in the amount of depolarization to reach threshold would increase conduction speed, other things being equal, because the local current would not have to flow for as long to excite an inactive region. (iii) The size of the membrane capacitor per unit area determines the amount of charge stored on the membrane per unit area for a given voltage and hence the length of time a current must flow to depolarize to threshold. A larger capacity means a smaller speed. (iv) Similarly, the size of local current flow is determined by the resistivity of the cell plasm. Other things being equal, the greater the concentration of highly mobile ions, the greater the current flow for a given voltage. (v) Temperature has large effects on the rate of increase of sodium conductance;[15] conduction speed increases with temperature.

FIBER GEOMETRY AND CONDUCTION SPEED.[6, 9] The foregoing arguments indicate that conduction speed depends on membrane capacity and plasm resistance and thus on fiber diameter. In myelinated fibers speed also depends on the thickness of the myelin sheath relative to axon diameter and on the distance between nodes. Sheath thickness and internodal distance have values which maximize conduction speed. The resistance of the axoplasm is inversely proportional to the cross-sectional area and hence to the square of the diameter; conduction speed therefore increases rapidly with fiber diameter. On the other hand, the capacity of the fiber membrane per unit length is directly proportional to diameter, tending to decrease speed. The net result is that speed increases with fiber diameter. In unmyelinated fibers, the speed is proportional to the square root of the diameter,[6] whereas in myelinated fibers it is directly proportional to diameter (Chap. 3). Thus it is not possible to generalize about how much myelination increases conduction speed. A squid giant axon has a conduction speed of about 20 meters per second and a diameter of about 500 μ. On the basis of the square root rule, a squid axon 20 μ in diameter would have a speed of about 4 meters per second. A frog myelinated fiber this size has a speed of 40 meters per second, 10 times greater than that of the unmyelinated fiber. Perhaps a better comparison is that a 10 μ frog fiber has the same conduction speed as a 500 μ squid axon and that nearly 2500 10 μ fibers can be packed into the same volume as the giant axon. It is this characteristic—fast conduction in small axons—that makes possible the fast, precise control of muscle contraction necessary in warm-blooded vertebrates for maintaining an elevated posture. A mammalian muscle nerve typically contains about 1000 large fibers (10 to 20 μ in diameter) and is about 1 millimeter in diameter. If a similar nerve were composed of unmyelinated nerve fibers having the same conduction speeds, it would be about an inch and a half in diameter.

INTRINSIC PROPERTIES OF EXCITABLE MEMBRANES

Voltage Clamping.[1-3, 10-13, 15] It is difficult to learn the detailed kinetics of an explosive process by studying the explosions as such. A better way to study them is by controlling a variable so that threshold, all-or-nothing characteristics are eliminated. In the example of the brick given previously, the threshold behavior can be eliminated by applying sufficient external force (e.g., by holding it) so that the brick's position is determined by the experimenter rather than by the force of gravity. The kinetics of the threshold process can then be obtained in detail simply by measuring the force required to hold the brick in a particular position as a function of that position. For slight displacements of the brick, the force exerted by the brick is small and opposed to the applied force. At the threshold, unstable equilibrium point the applied force has decreased to zero and for larger displacements it becomes negative, i.e., a pull rather than a push must be exerted on the brick. The curve of force against displacement is smooth and shows no threshold behavior in this kind of experiment.

In nerve, the equivalent of the position of the brick is voltage and the equivalent of the applied force is applied current. Thus threshold behavior can be eliminated by "clamping" the voltage at values set by the experimenter. The relation between membrane voltage and membrane ionic current is measured by supplying to the nerve, from an external source, whatever current is required to maintain the membrane voltage constant—i.e., connecting it to a battery—for different values of the voltage. For small depolarizations, an outward current must be applied to carry K^+ outward. The supplied current must be decreased to zero at threshold voltage and directed inward to carry sodium ions at larger depolarizations where increasing sodium permeability makes sodium current exceed potassium current. In other words, the dependence of Na^+ current, and hence sodium permeability (P_{Na}), on $\mathcal{E}_m$ and on time can be measured directly by the voltage clamp technique. Regenerative interactions between $\mathcal{E}_m$ and P_{Na} are prevented by artificially maintaining $\mathcal{E}_m$ constant. This procedure is equivalent to connecting a battery between the inside and the outside of the cell so that $\mathcal{E}_m$ must equal the battery voltage. If $\mathcal{E}_m$ is not changing in time, all the membrane current must be carried by ions, since none would go to charge the membrane capacity. If voltage is clamped at only one point on a nerve fiber, part of the current supplied by the external source will spread away from that point because of the fiber's cable properties. Therefore, voltage clamping requires that $\mathcal{E}_m$ must be held constant over the length of the fiber. If $\mathcal{E}_m$ does not change with distance, no current will flow from one region to another, and all applied current must flow with uniform density through the membrane. Figure 11A is a highly simplified schematic diagram of a voltage clamp experiment on squid giant axon. Figures 11B and C show the results obtained.

When the potential of the battery is set equal to $\mathcal{E}_s$, no current will flow through the membrane (switch is in position 1, Fig. 11A) because $\mathcal{E}_s$ is the voltage at which the net flow of charge is zero. When the switch is moved to position 2, current will flow through the external circuit and bring $\mathcal{E}_m$ to the new voltage ($\mathcal{E}$) if the resistance between the long internal and external electrodes is mostly in the membrane, i.e., if the resist-

ance of the axoplasm and the external bathing fluid and the resistance between the electrodes and the solution are negligible compared to the membrane resistance. In practice, the resistance between the internal electrode and the axoplasm is an important factor, and rather elaborate measures are necessary to circumvent this and other difficulties.[15, 22]

When the switch is thrown to position 2, the membrane potential is abruptly changed to a new value. In order to change $\mathcal{E}_m$ it is necessary to change the charge on the membrane capacity. This process, however, is brief, because the low radial resistance of the axoplasm allows a high current flow from the battery to the membrane capacitance. The membrane conductance does not change immediately after a sudden change in $\mathcal{E}_m$; therefore, there is an immediate membrane current proportional to $\Delta\mathcal{E}_m$; i.e., K^+ flows outward and Cl^- inward. This change is reflected in a sudden small initial jump in outward current (visible in middle record, Fig. 11C). Shortly after a sudden depolarization and the consequent outward current, the total membrane ionic current (I_i) begins to decrease, passes through zero, reaches a negative peak in about 1 millisecond, and then slowly changes back to a large maintained positive value. The contributions of Na^+ and K^+ to the total current at various times can be deduced from varying the amount of depolarization and the external Na^+ concentration. Cl^- current is nearly negligible and is neglected here.

Sodium Ion Current. The curves of membrane current versus time for different depolarizations differ in detail, but the sequence of events in each curve is nearly the same until $\Delta\mathcal{E}_m$ exceeds about 100 mV. (curves 4 and 5, Fig. 11B). The early inward current disappears at a particular $\Delta\mathcal{E}_m$ (about 95 mV.), and an early outward current hump appears at larger depolarizations (curve 5). From measurements of $[Na^+]_i$ and $[Na^+]_o$, $\mathcal{E}_{Na}$ can be calculated. Such analysis demonstrates that the early current hump changes sign when $\mathcal{E}_m = \mathcal{E}_{Na}$, or $\Delta\mathcal{E}_m = \mathcal{E}_{Na} - \mathcal{E}_s$. This finding, together with the finding that changes in the early current reversal voltage vary exactly with changes in $\mathcal{E}_{Na}$ (varied by altering $[Na^+]_o$), leads to the conclusion that early membrane current is carried by Na^+. *The crucial evidence is that this current reverses sign at exactly the $\mathcal{E}_m$ at which the driving force on Na^+ changes sign.*

Potassium Ion Current. The late, maintained outward current appears to be largely an outflow of K^+. Direct evidence for this conclusion has been obtained only recently because $[K^+]_i$ could not be changed rapidly until the development of a technique for internal perfusion. The membrane must be depolarized to

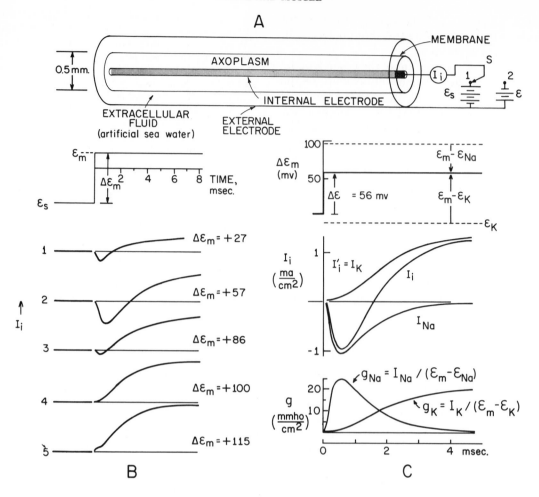

Fig. 11. Voltage clamping in squid giant axon. *A,* Transmembrane voltage ($\mathcal{E}_m$) is held constant over a considerable length of membrane by connecting internal and external media to battery through long electrodes. $\mathcal{E}_m$ can be changed suddenly from $\mathcal{E}_S$ ($I_i = 0$) to any other value by flipping switch, S, to position 2. Total current (I_i) through membrane is measured as function of time by ammeter (cathode ray oscilloscope).

B, Transmembrane current flow as function of time after a sudden change in $\mathcal{E}_m$. Uppermost curve is $\mathcal{E}_m$ as function of time. Curves 1 to 5 show membrane current which flows after membrane is depolarized, increasing amounts (in millivolts) shown at right. In curve 4, depolarization was near $\mathcal{E}_{Na}$ and, in curve 5, $\mathcal{E}_m$ was greater than $\mathcal{E}_{Na}$. Thus, for all but largest depolarizations, early component of current flows in direction opposite to that expected from change in $\mathcal{E}_m$ and late current flows in the same direction. Time scale at top applies to all records in *B.*

C, Components of total membrane current and conductance. Top curve, $\mathcal{E}_m$ as function of time; $\mathcal{E}_{Na}$ and $\mathcal{E}_K$ are indicated by dashed lines. Middle curve, total membrane ionic current (I_i) broken up into its two components, I_{Na} and I_K. (I_{Cl} is constant, small and neglected here.) Separation was made by reducing $[Na^+]_o$ to a value at which a depolarization of 56 mV. equaled $\mathcal{E}_{Na}$. Since $I_{Na} = 0$ under these conditions, total ion current (I_i') is equal to I_K as labeled. Bottom curve, g_{Na} and g_K as functions of time for the step change in $\mathcal{E}_m$ shown in top curve. Conductances are same shape as current curves because they are calculated, as shown, by dividing ionic current by effective voltage driving ion (indicated in top curves). Time scale at bottom applies to all records in *C.* The g_{Na} versus $\mathcal{E}_m$ curve of Figure 12 was obtained by measuring peak height of g_{Na} for different depolarizations. (Part *B* after Hodgkin and Huxley, *J. Physiol.,* 1952, *116:*449–472; part *C* after Hodgkin, *Proc. roy. Soc.,* 1958, *B148:*1–37.)

produce the delayed, prolonged outward current, and such depolarization tends to drive K+ out of the cell. Tracer studies with radioactive K+ have shown that membrane depolarization increases K+ efflux sufficiently so that it could carry the late outward current.[14] As mentioned above, a high [K+]$_i$ with almost any anion restores excitability in perfused axons; the repolarization phase of the action potential is, however, somewhat slower than in normal axons.[9]

Sodium and Potassium Ion Conductances.[10, 11] The total membrane current can be separated into Na+ and K+ currents by analyzing the manner in which changes in [Na+]$_o$ affect the shapes of curves relating current to time. It has been found that changes in [Na+]$_o$ change I$_{Na}$ but not I$_K$. Thus, the change in I$_i$ due to a change in [Na+]$_o$ is carried by Na+. Figure 11C shows the partition of I$_i$ into Na+ and K+ currents for a depolarization of 56 mV. I$_{Na}$ rises rapidly along an S-curve, reaches a peak in about 0.5 millisecond and then declines to near zero in another 2 milliseconds. I$_K$ also rises along an S-curve, but much more slowly, and then levels off at a high maintained value in about 4 milliseconds. If Na+ and K+ components are correctly identified, the conductance of Na+ (g$_{Na}$) and that of K+ (g$_K$) as functions of time can be determined by dividing the ionic current by the driving force on that ion. The term g$_K$ was explained and defined in Chapter 1 [see equation (6)]. Thus, g$_K$ = I$_K$/(ε_m − ε_K) and g$_{Na}$ = I$_{Na}$/(ε_m − ε_{Na}). In voltage clamp, ε_m is held constant, so g$_{Na}$ and g$_K$ have the same shape as I$_{Na}$ and I$_K$, respectively (Fig. 11C).

Since the voltage clamp technique has made possible precise measurements of the changes in membrane conductance that accompany changes in membrane potential, the properties of the membrane which give rise to the action potential can be defined more clearly. The time course of the action potential, the recovery of excitability, the conduction speed, and the ion exchanges and resistance changes during activity of a squid giant axon can be accurately predicted. However, there is still no definite knowledge of the physiochemical and structural bases for the active changes in membrane conductance.

Voltage Dependence of Sodium and Potassium Ion Conductances. The upstroke of the action potential results from a depolarization-induced increase in P$_{Na}$. The dependence of g$_{Na}$ (equivalent to P$_{Na}$) on voltage can be measured quantitatively from voltage clamp experiments by making a series of measurements of g$_{Na}$ as a function of time for different clamping voltages and plotting the peak g$_{Na}$ against these voltages. Figure 12 shows peak g$_{Na}$ as a function of clamping voltage; e.g., the peak g$_{Na}$ in Figure 11C is 25 mmho. per cm.^{2} for a depolarization of 56 mV. The curve is S-shaped. Small depolarizations have little effect on g$_{Na}$, moderate depolarizations cause large increases in g$_{Na}$, and large depolarizations have little further effect. The final value of g$_K$ depends on ε_m in much the manner that peak g$_{Na}$ does.

Activation and Inactivation of Sodium Ion Conductance. A suddenly applied, fixed depolarization produces a large increase in Na+ conductance. However, despite the continuance of the depolarization, the conductance falls rapidly. This drop is called *inactivation* of Na+ conductance. Inactivation begins as soon as the membrane is depolarized; the greater

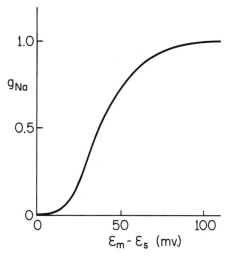

Fig. 12. Effects of sudden changes in membrane voltage on peak membrane sodium conductance (g$_{Na}$). Ordinate, ratio of peak g$_{Na}$ for a given depolarization to the peak g$_{Na}$ for a large (120 mV.) depolarization. Maximum value of curve is thus 1.0. The g$_{Na}$ vs. time curve in Figure 11C has a peak value of 25 mmho. per cm.^{2} for a depolarization of 56 mV., corresponding to a value of 0.8 on this curve. Resting g$_{Na}$ is about 0.04 mmho. per cm.^{2}, not discernible on the scale used here. Abscissa, displacement, ε_m − ε_s, of membrane potential from its resting value. Threshold depolarization is at about 12 mV.—about the voltage where the curve is first noticeably different from zero. (After Hodgkin and Huxley, *J. Physiol.*, 1952, *116*:449–472).

the depolarization, the faster the rate of inactivation. Fast depolarization of the membrane has two effects which relate to Na$^+$ conductance: g_{Na} increases rapidly, and the *rate* at which inactivation of g_{Na} proceeds also increases immediately. Repolarization of the membrane has the reverse effects; any Na$^+$ conductance not already inactivated will decrease rapidly. Simultaneously the rate of inactivation decreases and the rate of activation increases. There is an important difference between the decrease in Na$^+$ conductance due to inactivation and that due to polarization of the membrane. Time is required to reactivate inactivated g_{Na}, whereas a decrease in g_{Na} brought about by polarization is immediately available; i.e., a depolarization following shortly after a repolarization will cause an increase in g_{Na}. Inactivation is the main cause of the refractory period (see below).

HYPOTHETICAL MODEL OF ACTIVATION–INACTIVATION OF SODIUM CONDUCTANCE. The activation–inactivation process is undoubtedly the most difficult and also the most crucial concept in understanding action potential generation and the refractory period. Hodgkin and Huxley[13] developed a hypothetical model which accurately describes the variations of g_{Na} with time and voltage in terms of two separate but interacting rate processes. They supposed that a membrane channel or pathway through which Na$^+$ can pass relatively easily is formed when three M molecules and one H molecule are situated at specific sites in the membrane (Fig. 13). Sodium conductance is assumed to be proportional to the number of these channels per cm.^{2} of membrane. The probability that an M or H molecule is at the proper site for channel formation depends on the transmembrane voltage. Such variation in probability can be explained by supposing that M and H molecules are charged or dipolar, so that the molecules' position or orientation is affected by membrane voltage.

At the resting potential, the kinetics of the M substance are such that most of these molecules are not at the proper site for channel formation. If M designates molecules at effective sites and M′ those at ineffective sites, then the reaction between the two, M = M′, is equilibrated far to the right. However, a large depolarization greatly increases the rate of movement of M′ molecules to the M position and greatly decreases the opposite reaction, the equilibrium

of the M = M′ now being far to the left. The time required for equilibration is well under 1 millisecond but depends on the final voltage. Three M molecules must be in place to form a channel; only one need be absent to close the channel. Thus on sudden depolarization, the number of channels having three M molecules in place increases slowly at first and then more rapidly (third order kinetics); the rise in g_{Na} is S-shaped (Fig. 11C, rising phase of g_{Na} curve). Repolarization closes the channels rapidly because only one M need move out of place.

The kinetics of the H substance are the same as those of the M substance except that the variation of the forward and backward rate constants with voltage is reversed; the reaction H = H′ is equilibrated far to the left at the resting potential; most of the H are in position. The equilibration rate of the H reaction is about 10 times slower than for M, several milliseconds being required (Fig. 11C, falling phase of g_{Na} curve). The fraction of H molecules at effective sites is called the *activation* of g_{Na}. Under the circumstances of the voltage clamp experiments, the resting potential was somewhat depressed and the resting activation was about 0.6. Maintained hyperpolarization increases activation to 1.0 (all H form) and it is decreased to zero (all H′ form) by maintained depolarization.

A sudden depolarization thus has two effects on sodium conductance: M molecules move rapidly into effective sites and establish Na$^+$ channels at sites where H molecules are in position; hence g_{Na} rises rapidly. Even as M molecules are moving into position, H molecules are moving out but at a much slower rate. Thus g_{Na} rises to a peak as M molecules align with H molecules to form channels and then falls over a period of several milliseconds as the H molecules move away from the effective sites (Fig. 11C, g_{Na} curve). If the membrane is repolarized after inactivation is completed, there would be little change in the already low g_{Na} but M molecules would move out of place rapidly and H molecules would move into place slowly. Thereafter, another depolarization would produce an increase in g_{Na} proportional to the fraction of H molecules that had moved into place during the polarized state. This consideration suggests the experimental method actually used by Hodgkin and Huxley[12] to measure the kinetics of the activation–inactivation process—a two-step or pulse experiment

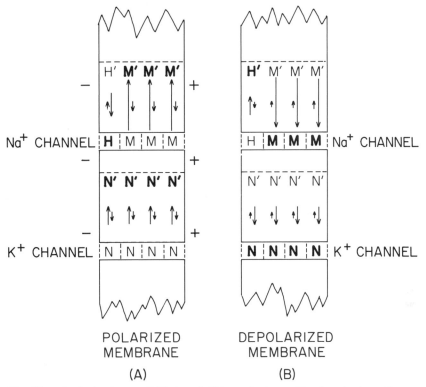

POLARIZED
MEMBRANE

(A)

DEPOLARIZED
MEMBRANE

(B)

Fig. 13. Hypothetical scheme of Na$^+$ and K$^+$ conductance kinetics. A channel or pathway through which sodium ions can pass easily is formed if and only if 3 M molecules and 1 H molecule are in proper positions or sites (Na$^+$ channel). Similarly, a K$^+$ channel is formed when 4 N molecules are in position. For all these substances, there is an equilibrium distribution of molecules between effective and ineffective sites or positions. Ineffective sites (primed letters) are shown diagrammatically vertically above effective sites. The arrows between effective and ineffective sites represent the rates of the two one-way reactions; heavy letters represent equilibrium positions of most molecules.

A, Polarized membrane. Transmembrane potential near resting value. Kinetics of M are such that, in reaction M = M′, equilibrium is far to right (above in figure, heavy letters) and, in H = H′ reaction, equilibrium is far to left (below, heavy H); Na$^+$ channels are closed because most M's are out of position. Shorter arrows indicate that H reactions are about ten times slower than M reactions. M reactions are completed in a few tenths of a millisecond; H reactions require several milliseconds. At rest, K$^+$ channels are closed because equilibrium of N = N′ is far right (above, heavy letters). Reaction rates are about the same as for H but equilibrium is far in opposite direction.

B, Depolarized membrane. Depolarization greatly changes the rate constants of all the reactions; all equilibria are shifted to the opposite side as shown by arrows. The result is that immediately after a depolarization, M molecules move rapidly to M positions and open Na$^+$ channels until H molecules have moved out of position (inactivation). At about the same time, N's move into position and open K$^+$ channels which remain open for duration of depolarization.

analogous to the conditioning–testing stimulus technique previously described.

Kinetics of Potassium Conductance Changes. The kinetics of g_K are much the same as those for M, only about ten times slower. A potassium channel is formed when four N molecules are at four effective sites simultaneously (Fig. 13). At rest the reaction M = M′ is equilibrated far right (top in Fig. 13*A*); depolarization shifts the equilibrium point far to the left (bottom). Thus depolariza-

tion produces an S-shaped increase in g_K Fig. 11*C*) but much slower than that of g_{Na}. Repolarization produces an uninflected, rapid fall to low levels.

PREDICTION OF EVENTS OF ACTION POTENTIAL FROM VOLTAGE CLAMP DATA[2, 3, 13, 19]

Hodgkin and Huxley[13] expressed their volt-

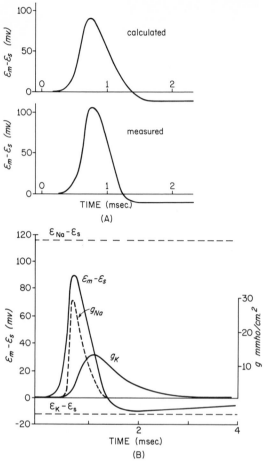

Fig. 14. *A, top,* Action potential calculated from measurements on voltage clamped axon. Calculated conduction speed, 18.8 meters per second. *Bottom,* Propagated action potential in an axon. Measured conduction speed 21.2 meters per second. Calculated and measured action potentials differ somewhat, but both show same general features. (After Hodgkin and Huxley, *J. Physiol.,* 1952, *117*:500–544.) *B,* Calculated time courses of membrane voltage ($\mathcal{E}_m - \mathcal{E}_s$), sodium conductance ($g_{Na}$) and potassium conductance (g_K) in squid giant axon. Note time relationships between upstroke of action potential and g_{Na} and between g_K and downstroke and after hyperpolarization. (After Hodgkin, *Proc. roy. Soc.,* 1958, *B148*:1–37.)

age clamp data from squid giant axons in mathematical form. The model described above was used in formulating their equations. The solutions of these equations were found to predict accurately the size and shape of the action potential, the refractory period, the existence and size of threshold, conduction speed and other properties of the nerve impulse. The analysis permitted calculation of the time course of the changes in Na+ and K+ conductances during the action potential and the

degree of inactivation of g_{Na}, factors which are not directly measurable but are the "essence" of the impulse. These calculations are also the basis of the statements made above concerning the sequence of events during the action potential. Recently, Frankenhaeuser and Huxley[3] have shown that the same type of analysis accurately predicts the excitable properties of frog myelinated nerve fibers. This finding greatly extends the generality of the Hodgkin–Huxley analysis.

Depolarization.   Calculated conductance and voltage changes during the impulse are shown in Figure 14. The experimentally measured action potential (Fig. 14*A,* bottom) is noticeably but not significantly different from the calculated one (top). The differences are mainly in the falling phase. The regenerative sequence of changes in Na+ conductance and membrane voltage which generate the rising phase of the action potential has already been adequately described (Hodgkin cycle) and will not be further considered. Note, however, that g_{Na} does not start to rise rapidly until the membrane has been considerably depolarized. This initial depolarization is due to local current flow to the approaching impulse; g_{Na} rises rapidly at threshold depolarization. It can be seen from Figure 14*B* that g_{Na} reaches its peak slightly before the voltage does. Also note that g_{Na} has fallen to about one-sixth of its peak value at a time when repolarization is only half completed. This indicates, and direct calculation confirms, that the major factor acting to decrease Na+ conductance at this time is inactivation not repolarization.

The calculated conduction speed of the top action potential in Figure 14*A* is 18.8 meters per second; the measured value of a representative axon is 21.2 meters per second. This is remarkably good agreement considering the uncertainties in the measurements and calculations. This accurate prediction of a propagating response is strong evidence for the general validity of the Hodgkin–Huxley analysis.

Repolarization.   The regenerative nature of the depolarization process insures that it proceeds at the fastest possible rate; i.e., the greater the depolarization, the faster the rate of depolarization until the saturation point is reached. Repolarization, on the other hand, is a *de*generative process; the greater the degree of repolarization, the more slowly it proceeds. The delayed increase in K+ conductance (Fig. 14*B*) is the membrane change responsible for rapid repolarization. If g_K did not increase during activity, nearly complete repolarization would still occur because of the inactivation of Na^+ conductance. However, in such a case the rate of depolarization would be much slower, little faster than the changes in a passive membrane due to its cable properties.

The sequence of events in repolarization is as follows. At the peak of depolarization g_{Na} is falling because of inactivation, and g_K is beginning to increase (Fig. 14*B*). The resulting increase in K^+ and decrease in Na^+ influx bring about repolarization. This voltage change in turn hastens the decrease in g_{Na} and, after a delay, g_K. As a consequence, g_K is still above normal when repolarization is complete, and the membrane hyperpolarizes, i.e., the potential goes nearer to $\mathcal{E}_K$ than the resting potential is. Thereafter, g_K and $\mathcal{E}_m$ fall slowly back to their resting values.

The conductance changes which occur during propagation can be compactly summarized on the basis of the hypothetical scheme described above (Table 1). This scheme also aids in understanding the basis of the refractory period.

Threshold. Threshold is one of three values of $\mathcal{E}_m$ at which the inward Na^+ current just equals the outward K^+ and Cl^- currents (Cl^- influx). The other two values of $\mathcal{E}_m$ are the resting potential and the peak of the action potential. Thus, as the membrane is depolarized by current outflow, P_{Na} (or g_{Na}) increases (Fig. 12) and the inflow of Na^+ ions increases. This increase more than compensates for the slightly decreased electrochemical gradient of Na^+. The net K^+ and Cl^- fluxes increase because the reduction of $\mathcal{E}_m$ has increased the electrochemical gradients driving these ions. If the net movement of ionic charges through the membrane is zero (i.e., if net Na^+ influx equals net K^+ efflux plus net Cl^- influx), the membrane voltage is steady. The potential will stay constant only until inactivation of P_{Na} reduces Na^+ influx. The potential will then begin to fall, and the fall in potential will in turn further reduce P_{Na}. The potential in this case follows a path similar to curve 3*a*, Figure 5*B*. On the other hand, if the applied depolarizing current is made slightly larger or the threshold of the fiber has fallen slightly owing to random fluctuations, the net Na^+ influx through the membrane slightly exceeds the sum of the net K^+ efflux and the net Cl^- influx, so that there is a net movement of positive ions into the fiber and the action potential upstroke ensues via the Hodgkin cycle: A decrease in membrane voltage acts to increase P_{Na}; this increase, in turn, causes additional depolarization.

Refractory Period. Since inactivation of g_{Na} is almost complete at the end of the action potential, a depolarizing current applied at this time will not cause much increase in g_{Na}. Therefore, the fiber is refractory (inexcitable); a stimulating current, no matter how strong, cannot initiate a regenerative response. A little later, after some activation has occurred, a depolarizing current will cause a larger increase in g_{Na}, and an action potential smaller than normal may be generated. The threshold current will be above normal because the available g_{Na} is low and also because g_K is still above normal. Inactivated Na^+ conductance means that excitability is low (threshold high), because greater depolarization is needed to increase g_{Na} enough to make net Na^+ inflow exceed net K^+ outflow. A raised g_K means that more current is required to produce a given depolarization; hence this factor decreases excitability also. Taken together, these two effects, which disappear in a few milliseconds, account for both the absolute and the relatively refractory periods.

TABLE 1. *Sodium and Potassium Conductance Channel Patterns During the Action Potential*

RESTING MEMBRANE		RISING PHASE		REPOLARIZATION		AFTER HYPERPOLARIZATION	
Na^+ Channels	K^+ Channels	Na^+ Channels	K^+ Channels	Na^+ Channels	K^+ Channels	Na^+ Channels	K^+ Channels
—	—	M	—	M	N	—	N
—	—	M	—	M	N	—	N
—	—	M	—	M	N	—	N
H	—	H	—	—	N	—	N

Ion channels are open if a column is filled with letters. See legend to Figure 13 for meanings of terms.

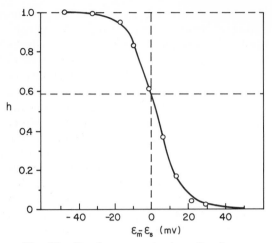

Fig. 15. Steady-state activation of sodium conductance as a function of transmembrane potential. Ordinate, fraction (h) of H molecules at effective sites (see Fig. 13); abscissa, difference between transmembrane potential ($\mathcal{E}_m$) and the resting potential ($\mathcal{E}_s$). A sudden depolarization causes a transient increase in g_{Na} but h steadily declines to a lower steady-state value. Similarly, hyperpolarization increases steady-state value of h. Note that small changes in $\mathcal{E}_s$ would have a large effect on h: A hyperpolarization of 20 millivolts increases h to nearly 1.0 (the reaction rates of H = H' are changed so that equilibrium is far to the left). Similarly, a depolarization of 20 millivolts reduces h to nearly 0 and the reaction H = H' equilibrates far to the right. Actual g_{Na} at any time is determined by both the H and M systems; the fraction of H's in position determines the size of the increase in g_{Na} following a sudden depolarization.

Accommodation and Block.

A brief subthreshold stimulus applied to a nerve fiber increases excitability (lowers threshold) in the region of application which can be detected by the response to a second stimulus delivered to the same or a nearby point. In contrast, a prolonged subthreshold stimulus may either increase or decrease excitability. The change in excitability depends on the relative effect of the depolarizing current on $\mathcal{E}_m$, and on the effect of the changes in $\mathcal{E}_m$ on the steady state inactivation of g_{Na}. The curve relating activation to $\mathcal{E}_m$ is a very steep S-shaped curve as shown in Figure 15; a depolarization reduces the g_{Na} available. If, as in the squid giant axon, the resting potential is such that an appreciable amount of g_{Na} is always inactivated (dashed lines, Fig. 15), the depolarization produced by a prolonged subthreshold stimulus may reduce g_{Na} to such low levels that the stimulus required to initiate an impulse must be

stronger than normal; i.e., the reduction in g_{Na} has increased the threshold voltage (toward zero) more than the current has reduced actual membrane voltage. This is quite possible in view of the steepness of the curve in Figure 15. An additional factor may be the depolarization-induced increase in g_K, which makes an applied current less effective in changing $\mathcal{E}_m$. If a prolonged subthreshold depolarization reduces the excitability of a nerve, or increases it less than expected, the nerve is said to have *accommodated* to the stimulus. The process of *accommodation* is evidently closely related to the g_{Na} activation–inactivation process.[2]

Conduction can be blocked at a point on a nerve fiber by a strong, slowly rising, depolarizing current. If the depolarizing current increases slowly enough, inactivation occurs concomitantly. As a result, g_{Na} will not increase sufficiently to reverse the membrane current. Similarly, a suddenly applied suprathreshold current may block conduction after first initiating one or more impulses; the block occurs when inactivation has proceeded far enough. The blockage of impulse generation by depolarizing current occurs only in the region of the stimulating cathode. Impulses will propagate on either side of the blocked region, but not through it. This method of blocking impulse conduction is often called *cathodal block*. Better terms are *depolarization block* or *inactivation block*.

Depolarization block can be produced in many ways other than by applying current. Since a sufficient increase in $[K^+]_o$, anoxia and injury all depolarize the membrane, they all block impulse conduction. An expected characteristic of depolarization block is that stimuli not strong enough to cause block increase the excitability. Anoxia probably blocks indirectly by reducing the activity of the Na^+–K^+ pump, so that K^+ ions lost from cells accumulate in the extracellular fluid. An injury such as crushing blocks by destroying the structure of the membrane; its selective permeability properties are lost and depolarization occurs. At the moment of the crush, a number of impulses are discharged before inactivation is completed in adjacent undamaged, depolarized regions. Local anesthetics block conduction in nerve by increasing inactivation without altering membrane voltage.[25] Depolarization block, no matter how induced, is relieved by a hyperpolarizing current simply because it increases the absolute value of $\mathcal{E}_m$ and activates g_{Na}.

A sufficient hyperpolarization of the membrane can also block conduction in a nerve. Block occurs if $\mathcal{E}_m$ is made so large that local circuit flow from the hyperpolarized region into an approaching active region is insufficient to depolarize the hyperpolarized region to threshold. This phenomenon is called *anodal* or, better, *hyperpolarization block*.

Ion Exchange During Activity.[13, 21] It has been stressed that the rising phase of the action potential is brought about by a sudden, large influx of Na^+ ions and repolarization by an efflux of K^+ ions. It might be supposed that these "large" fluxes involve the movement of enough ions to change greatly the internal concentrations of Na^+ and K^+. Actually, the concentration changes are very small, the reason being that, although the fluxes are high, they flow only for a short time, and, chemically speaking, the amount of ions necessary to charge the membrane is small. The minimum net influx of Na^+ required during activity is simply the amount of charge necessary to change the voltage across the membrane capacitor roughly from $\mathcal{E}_K$ to $\mathcal{E}_{Na}$. A similar net efflux of K^+ suffices to recharge the membrane.

The amount of charge on a capacitor is the product of its capacity and the voltage across it. Such a calculation for squid giant axon shows that the minimum Na^+ entry (or K^+ exit) during one impulse is 1.6 picamols per cm.^{2} (pM. $= 10^{-12}$ M.) of membrane. A crucial test of the Na^+–K^+ theory of the action potential is to measure net fluxes of Na^+ and K^+ during an impulse by means of radioactive Na^+ and K^+. These measured net fluxes must be greater than the minimum required because, as can be seen from Figure 14*B*, there must be considerable simultaneous inflow of Na^+ and outflow of K^+ during the action potential; such an ion exchange does not affect the charge on the membrane. The measured net Na^+ influx in the squid giant axon is about 4.0 pM. and the net K^+ efflux about 3.0 pM per cm.^{2}-impulse.[21] These values are greater than the minimum and about what is predicted by the equations.[13]

The change in internal concentrations during an impulse depends not only on the net entry or loss of the ion but also on the volume of axoplasm in which the extra ions distribute themselves. The bigger the fiber, the smaller the concentration change per impulse. For example, in a squid axon 500 μ in diameter, a net Na^+ entry of 3 pM. per cm.^{2}-impulse raises the internal concentration by only 1.5 $\times$ 10^{-10} M. per cm.^{3} The internal concentration of Na^+ in the squid is about 50 μM. per cm.^{3}, some 300,000 times greater. However, under the same conditions, the increase in internal Na^+ concentration for a 50 μ fiber would be ten times as great. Nevertheless, the conduction of 30,000 impulses in such a fiber would only double internal Na^+ concentration, even if the Na^+ pump were inoperative. Thus in ordinary sized axons, the increase in $[Na^+]_i$ and decrease in $[K^+]_i$ during one impulse is very small. Some mammalian unmedullated axons are only 0.1 μ in diameter and rough calculation shows that one impulse will increase internal Na^+ concentration by 10 per cent. Hence, the Na^+ pumping rate must be quickly responsive to activity. The large post-spike hyperpolarization in these fibers is probably associated with increased active Na^+ extrusion (see Chap. 3).

Nerve fibers conduct impulses up to 100 times per second in normal bodily function. At rest, the amount of Na^+ extruded by the Na^+ pump in one second is about the same as the net entry of Na^+ during one impulse. Therefore, during impulse conduction at 100 per second Na^+ entry is 100 times greater than the resting entry. Since, in order to maintain excitability, $[Na^+]_i$ must be kept at a low and $[K^+]_i$ at a high value, the rate of Na^+ pumping must increase as much as 100 times during maintained activity. The function of nerve fibers is to conduct impulses, so the main energy production of nerve likely is used to transport sodium.

REFERENCES

1. COLE, K. S. and MOORE, J. W. *Biophys. J.*, 1960, *1*:1–14.
2. FRANKENHAEUSER, B. and VALLBO, A. B. *Acta physiol. scand.* 1965, *63*:1–20.
3. FRANKENHAEUSER, B. and HUXLEY, A. F. *J. Physiol.*, 1964, *171*:302–315.
4. HODGKIN, A. L. *J. Physiol.*, 1937, *90*:183–210.
5. HODGKIN, A. L. *Biol. Rev.*, 1951, *26*:339–409.
6. HODGKIN, A. L. *J. Physiol.*, 1954, *125*:221–224.
7. HODGKIN, A. L. *Proc. roy. Soc.*, 1958, *B148*:1–37.
8. HODGKIN, A. L. *Science*, 1964, *145*:1148–1154.
9. HODGKIN, A. L. *The conduction of the nervous impulse.* Springfield, Ill., Charles C Thomas, 1964.
10. HODGKIN, A. L. and HUXLEY, A. F. *J. Physiol.*, 1952, *116*: 449–472.
11. HODGKIN, A. L. and HUXLEY, A. F. *J. Physiol.*, 1952, *116*: 473–496.
12. HODGKIN, A. L. and HUXLEY, A. F. *J. Physiol.*, 1952, *116*: 497–506.

13. Hodgkin, A. L. and Huxley, A. F. *J. Physiol.*, 1952, *117:* 500–544.
14. Hodgkin, A. L. and Huxley, A. F. *J. Physiol.*, 1953, *121:* 403–414.
15. Hodgkin, A. L., Huxley, A. F. and Katz, B. *J. Physiol.*, 1952, *116:*424–448.
16. Hodgkin, A. L. and Katz, B. *J. Physiol.*, 1949, *108:*37–77.
17. Hodgkin, A. L. and Rushton, W. A. H. *Proc. roy. Soc.*, 1946, *B133:*444–479.
18. Hodler, J., Stampfli, R. and Tasaki, I. *Amer. J. Physiol.*, 1952, *170:*375–389.
19. Huxley, A. F. *Science,* 1964, *145:*1154–1159.
20. Huxley, A. F. and Stampfli, R. J. *Arch. Sci. Physiol.*, 1949, *3:*435–448.
21. Keynes, R. D. *J. Physiol.*, 1951, *114:*119–150.
22. Moore, J. W. and Cole, K. S. In: *Physical techniques in biological research,* Volume 6: *Electrophysiological methods,* part B, W. L. Nastuk, ed. New York, Academic Press, 1964.
23. Nachmansohn, D. *Chemical and molecular basis of nerve activity.* New York, Academic Press, 1959.
24. Tasaki, I. Chap. 3 in *Handbook of physiology. Section 1: Neurophysiology,* vol. 1, J. Field, ed. Washington, D.C., American Physiological Society, 1959.
25. Taylor, R. E. *Amer. J. Physiol.*, 1959, *196:*1071–1078.
26. Woodbury, J. W. Chap. 11 in *Handbook of physiology. Section 2: Circulation,* vol. 1, W. F. Hamilton and P. Dow, eds. Washington, D.C., American Physiological Society, 1962.

CHAPTER 2 APPENDIX

By ALBERT M. GORDON and J. WALTER WOODBURY

ELECTROSTATICS

Charge. Electric charge, like mass, is a fundamental property of matter. There are two kinds of charge, arbitrarily designated as positive (+) (protons) and negative (−) (electrons). Like electric charges repel and unlike charges attract each other. Since each atom contains one or more electrons and an equal number of protons, the total number of charges in a macroscopic object is extremely large, but there is little or no net charge. The strong mutual attraction of unlike charges is sufficient to insure electroneutrality in any object unless other forces (e.g., mechanical or chemical) act to separate the charges and keep them separated. The common unit of electric charge is the *coulomb*. A coulomb is the charge of 6.25×10^{18}

electrons. The charge on an electron is thus 1.6×10^{-19} coulombs. The force between charges is most easily considered in a system in which all the charges are held in a fixed position in vacuum (electrostatics). Nonelectrical forces are required to keep the charges separated and static.

Electric Field Intensity. The magnitude of the force (F) of attraction or repulsion between two point charges (q_1 and q_2) in a vacuum is given by Coulomb's law:

$$F = K(q_1 q_2 / r^2)$$

where K is a constant determined by the units chosen and r is the distance between the two point charges. If q is in coulombs, r is in meters, and F in newtons (1 kg.-m. per second^2), $K = 9 \times 10^9$ joule-meter per coulomb^2. The force is a vector* and is in the direction of the line joining the two charges. Repulsion is defined as a positive force, attraction as a negative force.

The *electric field intensity* (E) at a point is defined as the electric force that would be exerted on a unit positive charge placed at that point (Fig. 16). In other words, the electric field is the electric force per unit charge (E = F/q). E, like F, is a vector. The existence of an unchanging electric field at any point in space means that electric charges of opposite sign have been separated. These separated charges attract each other and also either attract or repel any other charge brought into the neighborhood. The electric field at any point is a convenient way of specifying the electric forces acting in a region. A more convenient way to describe the field is to calculate the electric potential, a scalar quantity.

Electric Potential, Voltage.   Because of the force of attraction between + and − charges, work must be done to separate them. Work is done when a force acts through a distance and is defined as the product of force and distance in the direction of the force. Since the work done depends only on the size of the force and the distance moved, work is a scalar.

The *potential* or *voltage difference* between two points is defined as the amount of work, done against electrical forces, required to carry a unit positive charge (1 coulomb) between the two points. Since in electrostatics the charge is fixed and the exploring charge is halted at the two end points, A and B, the potential difference is the difference in potential energy per unit charge between the two points. The electrical *potential* or *voltage* ($\mathcal{E}_p$) at a point (P) is defined as the work done in bringing a unit positive charge to that point from a large distance away, i.e., the potential difference between that point and one at a large distance.

The work done in moving an exploring charge (q_e) a distance, ds, (path P_2, Fig. 16) in the electric field is dW = − Eq_e (cos θds). To obtain the potential difference between two points ($\mathcal{E}_{AB}$, Fig. 16), the work, dW, must be summed for all ds distances along any path between A and B with q = +1. It is important to note that since the electric field is directed out radially from the charge +q and work is done only when a charge is moved in the direction of the field, work is done only when motion is in a radial direction; i.e., cos θds = dr. Since any small motion (see path P_1) can be broken up into a radial component (cos θ = −1 or 1, depending on whether ds is toward or away from +q) and a circumferential component (cos θ = 0), along the arc of a circle centered at +q,

the total work along any path is the work in moving the unit + charge radially from r_B to r_A. Thus, the work done in moving along path P_1 is the same as that along path P_2 or P_3. Therefore, because work done on a charge is independent of path, the concept of potential is useful. If r_A (Fig. 16) is less than r_B, work must be done to move a positive charge from B to A; the potential difference is positive. If work is done by the charge (this would happen if +q were replaced by a negative charge), the potential difference is negative.

In the example of Figure 16, the potential between A and B ($\mathcal{E}_{AB}$) is most easily calculated along BA'A. The force (E) on a unit + charge at any distance (r) from q is E = K(q/r^2). The work done (d$\mathcal{E}$) to move the unit + charge a radial distance (−dr) is d$\mathcal{E}$ = −Edr. The negative sign is used because r is measured outward from q and because potential is defined as increasing when a + charge is moved toward another + charge. The electric field is directed radially in this case. The total work done on the charge as it moves from B to A is shown in the following equation:

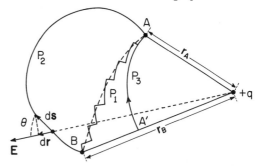

Fig. 16.   Voltage and voltage difference in the neighborhood of a fixed charge of +q coulombs. E is the force, due to charge +q, on a charge of +1 coulomb at any point. E is directed radially outward, and E = K(q/r^2); distance from +q to any point is r; dr is a small movement in a radial direction away from +q. Distance traveled by exploratory +1 charge along any path between B and A (P_1, P_2, P_3) is s; ds is a small movement along any path. Arrows on path P_2 illustrate the relationship between force, displacement and work. Work done in displacing a charge, q, a distance, ds, in the electric field, E, is by definition dW = −qE cos θ ds, where qE is the size of the force on the charge and θ is the angle between the direction of **ds** and **E**. Cos θ ds gives the projection of ds along the direction of E. Since cos θ ds = dr, all the work is done in moving in a radial direction. Voltage at point B ($\mathcal{E}_B$) is work required to bring +1 charge from a large distance up to point B; $\mathcal{E}_B$ = Kq/r_B. Voltage difference ($\mathcal{E}_{AB}$) between A and B is work required to carry +1 charge from B to A; $\mathcal{E}_{AB}$ = $\mathcal{E}_A$ − $\mathcal{E}_B$. Since work is done only when the +1 moves in a radial direction, the work to go from B to A is the same no matter what path (P_1, P_2, P_3, etc.) is taken. Along path P_2 (BA'A) all the work is done along BA' (radial); no work is done along A'A. So $\mathcal{E}_{AB}$ depends only on r_A and r_B; $\mathcal{E}_{AB}$ = Kq(1/r_A − 1/r_B).

---

* A vector has both magnitude and direction, e.g., force, velocity and displacement (distance and direction). A scalar has magnitude only (i.e., charge, concentration, volume, time, speed). Bold-faced type will be used to represent vectors. Regular type will be used to represent scalars and magnitudes of vectors. The magnitude of a force is designated F, vector force **F**. The velocity of an object is represented by **v**, its speed (magnitude of the velocity) by v.

$$\mathcal{E}_{AB} = \int_{r_B}^{r_A} - E dr = \int_{r_B}^{r_A} - K\frac{q}{r^2}dr = Kq\left(\frac{1}{r_A} - \frac{1}{r_B}\right)$$

The potential at point A is obtained by taking $r_B = \infty$. Since $1/\infty = 0$, $\mathcal{E}_A = Kq/r_A$. Similarly, $\mathcal{E}_B = Kq/r_B$;

thus, $\mathcal{E}_{AB} = Kq\left(\dfrac{1}{r_A} - \dfrac{1}{r_B}\right) = \mathcal{E}_A - \mathcal{E}_B$, the same as

that computed above from the work done in moving a unit + charge from A to B along path P_3. This additive property of the potential, a scalar quantity, is the source of its usefulness; if $\mathcal{E}_A$ and $\mathcal{E}_B$ are known, $\mathcal{E}_{AB}$ may be computed directly without having to integrate as has been done above. For example, $K = 9 \times 10^9$ joule-meter per coulomb², and if $q = 10^{-12}$ coulombs (1 picacoulomb), $r_A = 0.1$ m., and $r_B = 1$ m., then $\mathcal{E}_A = (9 \times 10^9 \times 10^{-12})/0.1 = 0.09$ joules per coulomb $= 0.09$ V. and $\mathcal{E}_{AB} = 9 \times 10^9 \times 10^{-12} [(1/0.1) - (1/1)] = 9 \times 10^{-3} (10 - 1) = 0.081$ V. In words, 0.09 joules of work must be done on a +1 coulomb charge to carry it from a large distance to 0.1 m. away from a charge of 10^{-12} coulombs.

Voltage gradient. The electric field is often referred to as the (negative) voltage gradient (**grad** $\mathcal{E}$)—the rate at which voltage changes with distance in the direction in which the voltage is changing most rapidly. This reverse definition of electric field in terms of voltage follows from the definition of voltage as the potential energy per unit charge and the definition of a gradient. This potential energy is derived from the work done on the charge in order to move it against the electric field. Thus, the rate of change of work (energy) with distance is the force, and the rate of change of voltage with distance is the electric field.

By definition $d\mathcal{E} = -E \cos\theta ds$ where, as before, θ is the angle between the direction of **ds** and **E**. If the electric field is due to a point charge as in Figure 16, $d\mathcal{E} = -Edr$; therefore, $E = -(d\mathcal{E}/dr) = -\textbf{grad}\ \mathcal{E}$, the components in other directions being zero. In general, $E = -\textbf{grad}\ \mathcal{E}$, where **grad** has the direction of the maximum rate of voltage change.

Because of this relation, the electric field is referred to as the negative of the voltage gradient and is the electric force on a unit positive charge, just as **grad** [S] is the diffusional force per unit volume.

Capacitors. *Conductors.* A *conductor* is a substance in which charges are free to move. Metals are good conductors because their outer shell electrons are loosely bound to the nuclei. Salt solutions are also good conductors because their solute particles are charged (ionized) and can move freely in the solvent. Because charges can move freely in a conductor, no electric field can exist inside it when charges are not moving. If the conductor contained a field, it would exert forces on the free charges, and some of them would move into positions on the surface of the conductor such that the field would be reduced to zero. Since the field must be zero in a conductor, all points in and on it must be at the same potential, for no electric work is required to move a charge through a region where **E** is zero.

The potential of an isolated conductor is not necessarily zero. For example, if some excess charges, all positive or all negative, are put on an isolated conductor, they will exert a force on any charge outside the conductor, and work will be required to bring a +1 charge from infinity. The excess charges must be on the surface of the conductor in order to cancel **E** everywhere in the interior. More simply, the excess charges repel each other and so distribute themselves as widely as possible on the surface.

Insulators. An *insulator* is any region in which there are no free charges, e.g., a vacuum. In an insulating material called a *dielectric,* all electrons are tightly bound to their nuclei and cannot migrate under the influence of an external electric field. The charges in a dielectric are not rigidly fixed, so they separate slightly in an external field. This charge separation in the dielectric is usually proportional to **E** and is such as to reduce **E**. However, the force on an exploring charge in a dielectric varies in the same way as the force on a charge *in vacuo,* but the forces in a dielectric are reduced by a factor $1/\kappa$. The denominator κ is the *dielectric constant.* Its value depends on the nature of the material; for example, κ is 5 to 10 for most oils. The cell membrane is a dielectric. Its dielectric constant is unknown, but since the membrane contains a high proportion of lipids κ is likely 5 to 10. This figure is also obtained from electrical measurements of membrane capacity and electron-microscopic estimates of membrane thickness (see problem 5 below).

Capacity. In a static situation, the existence of a potential difference between two points (A and B) means that + and − charges have been separated. This condition follows from the definition of $\mathcal{E}_{AB}$ as the work done against *electric* forces in carrying a +1 charge from B to A and because there are no electric forces in a region unless charges are separated there. The greater the amount of charge separated, the greater the electric field and the greater is $\mathcal{E}_{AB}$. In particular, if + charges are put on an insulated fixed conductor (A) and an equal number of − charges are put on a second fixed conductor (B), the potential difference between the two conductors is directly proportional to the amount of charge on either conductor. Any arrangement of two conductors, A and B, separated by an insulator is called a *capacitor* or *condenser.* The proportionality constant relating charge to voltage is called the *capacity* or *capacitance* (C) of a capacitor and is given by the equation $C = q/\mathcal{E}_{AB}$, where q is the total amount of charge on either conductor.

The capacity of a capacitor depends on the geometry of the conductors (i.e., on their spatial extent and separation) and on the dielectric constant of the insulating material. These dependencies arise because the force between two charged conductors is determined by the distance separating them and because the relative distribution of the charges on the surface of an insulated conductor is the same no matter how much charge there is on the conductor. The less the work per unit charge required to place a fixed amount of charge on a capacitor, the higher its capacity. Hence, the closer two conductors are together, the higher the capacity between them, for less work is required to move a unit charge through the shorter distance. In addition, the higher the dielectric constant of the insulating material, the larger the capacity. This is reasonable since both the electric field in the insulator and therefore the work done in moving a charge between the conductors decrease with increasing dielectric constant. It follows, then, that the capacity between two closely spaced parallel sheets or plates of metal separated by an insulator is high. Since the electric field in the region between the plates depends only on the number of charges per unit area (charge density), increasing the area of the plates permits the addition of charges to the plates without an increase in the electric field between them. Therefore, the greater the surface area of the plates, the greater the capacity between them. The opposite charges on the plates of a capacitor attract each other, and so they must be on the inner surfaces of the conductors. The charges are prevented from recombining by the insulator separating the conductors. However, if the insulation is not perfect—if some charge can move through the insulator—charges placed on the conductors will slowly leak off.

The unit of capacity is the farad (f.). A capacitor has a capacity of 1 f. if 1 coulomb of charge taken from one plate and placed on the other produces a potential difference of 1 V. between the plates. In terms of physical size, a 1 f. capacitor is large;* the capacitors commonly encountered have capacities of about 1 microfarad (1 μf. = 10^{-6} f.).

Problems. The following problems deal with the electrical membrane of the squid giant axon. Assume that the membrane thickness is 75 Å. = 7.5×10^{-9} meters, capacity is 1 μf. per cm.^{2} = 10^{-2} f. per meter^2 and transmembrane potential difference is 75 mV. = 7.5×10^{-2} V. (inside negative).

1. Assuming that the electric field is uniform and constant inside the membrane, what is the magnitude and direction of the field in the membrane?

Ans. $\mathbf{E} = -\mathbf{grad}\ \mathcal{E}$. Since the membrane is very thin, it is equivalent to a parallel plate condenser with the plates separated by 7.5×10^{-9} meters. In the space between the plates, $\mathbf{E}$ is constant and perpendicular to them. The potential varies linearly with distance between the plates; thus $-\mathbf{grad}\ \mathcal{E} = -d\mathcal{E}/dx = \mathcal{E}/\delta$, where δ = membrane thickness. Thus, $\mathbf{E} = 7.5 \times 10^{-2}$ V./7.5×10^{-9} meters = 10^7 V. per meter (10 million V. per meter). The direction of $\mathbf{E}$ is inward through the membrane, perpendicular to the two boundaries.

2. What is the force on a sodium ion in the membrane due to the electric field computed above? e = 1.6×10^{-19} coulombs (electronic charge).

Ans. 1.6×10^{-12} newtons.

3. How much charge per unit area separated by the membrane is due to the resting potential? Calcu-

late answer in coulombs per meter^2 and mols of univalent ion per cm.^{2}

Ans. 7.5×10^{-4} coulombs per meter^2, 7.8×10^{-13} mols per cm.^{2}

4. An axon is 100 μ in diameter and 10 cm. long. Sodium ions are actively transported out of this axon at the rate of 3×10^{-11} mols per cm.^{2} per second. How much work must be done per hour by the active transport mechanism against the electrical forces only tending to hold the sodium ions in the cell? (The resting potential is 75 mV.)

Ans. 2.45×10^{-4} joules per hour.

5. The formula for the capacity of a parallel plate capacitor is C = $\kappa \mathcal{E}_0 A/\delta$ where κ is the dielectric constant of the insulating material, ε_0 = 8.85×10^{-12} coulomb^2 per joule-meter (K = $1/4\pi\varepsilon_0$), A is the area of the plates, and δ is the separation of the plates. What is the dielectric constant of the membrane material, if the membrane, considered to be the insulator in a parallel plate capacitor, is 75 Å. = 7.5×10^{-9} meters thick and has a capacity of 1 μf. per cm.^{2}?

Ans. 8.5.

ELECTRIC CURRENT, OHM'S LAW

Current, Current Density. As mentioned above, when an electric field is applied to a conductor, whether metallic or an ionic solution, charges flow in a manner which tends to neutralize the field applied. Unless energy is supplied to keep + and − charges separated, the field in the conductor rapidly decreases to zero. In order to keep charges separated, positive charges must be taken continuously from the negative region, given energy and supplied to the positive region by an appropriate energy source, e.g., a battery or generator. Thus, charges move continuously; i.e., a current flows in a conductor under the influence of an electric field.

Electric current is a vector; it has direction and magnitude. The current strength or magnitude is defined as the amount of charge passing per unit time through a cross section of the conductor perpendicular to the direction of flow of charge or, more simply, as the time rate of flow of charge, I = dq/dt. Direction of flow traditionally is defined as that of positive charges. The unit of current (I) is the ampere (1 coulomb per second). The net passage of 6.25×10^{18} unitary charges (electrons, sodium ions) per second is an ampere. For convenience, charge flow frequently is expressed as current per unit area (current density, J, amperes per cm.^{2}), rather than as current. Current density is directly proportional to ionic flux (M); flux is mols per cm.^{2}-sec.; current density is coulombs per cm.^{2}-sec. The relationship is thus M = FZJ, where F is the Faraday.

Ohm's Law. It is found that for many conductors $\mathbf{J} = \sigma\mathbf{E}$, where σ is called the *conductivity* of the conductor. This form of Ohm's law states that the current density is proportional to the electric field and in the same direction. This is equivalent to the statement

---

*To attain a capacity of 1 farad, two parallel metal plates separated by an air gap of 0.1 mm. would each have to have an area of about 4 square miles!

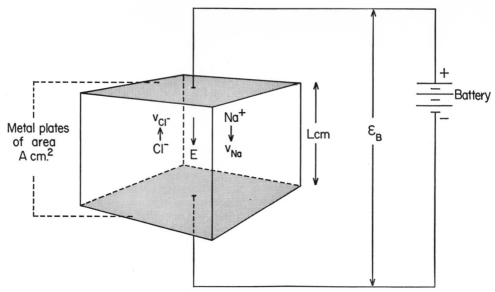

Fig. 17. Illustration of Ohm's law. A box L cm. long with a cross-sectional area of A is filled with solution of NaCl in water. A battery of voltage $\mathcal{E}_B$ is connected to metal plates at each end of box. E is electric field set up in medium by applied voltage; v_{Na} and v_{Cl} are average drift velocities of Na+ and Cl− ions, respectively, and are proportional to E.

that the average velocity of the charges in the conductor is proportional to the electric field (see below). This relationship between current density and field is known as Ohm's law; its more usual form is that current is proportional to voltage.

A more detailed description and derivation of Ohm's law is as follows. Figure 17 is a diagrammatic representation of an electrolytic conductor and some of the factors governing the flow of the ions in the solution. The metal plates at the opposite ends of the box are charged by the battery to $\mathcal{E}_B$, and these charges exert a downward force ($E = \mathcal{E}_B/L$) on a + charge anywhere in the box, where L is the length of the box. The Na+ ions in the solution are acted upon by a downward electric force (Ee) and the Cl− ions by an upward force (−Ee), e being the charge of a cation in coulombs. Gravitational forces are negligible. The direction of the force is determined by the valence (Z), so force equals EeZ.

In the absence of opposing forces, the ions would accelerate in the electric field. However, an ion moving through a solution encounters frictional resistance to flow. The ion frequently collides with H_2O molecules; between collisions the ion accelerates under the influence of the applied force, but some kinetic energy is lost in each collision. The ion soon reaches a velocity at which, on the average, the energy lost in each collision just equals the kinetic energy gained from acceleration between collisions; i.e., there is a net movement of the ion at a constant velocity in the direction of the applied force superimposed on its random motion. The greater the applied force, the greater the average velocity ($\bar{v}$)* of the ions; under most circumstances, v is proportional to E; $\bar{v} = \eta EeZ$,

$\bar{v}_{Na} = \eta_{Na}Ee$, $\bar{v}_{Cl} = -\eta_{Cl}Ee$. The constant η is a measure of the *mobility* of the ion, the ease with which it can move through the solution. The mobility constant and the diffusion constant are closely related properties of an ion in solution.

The current I (in amperes) flowing through the box in Figure 17 is defined as the total amount of charge (in coulombs) flowing through any cross section in 1 second. By definition, current flows in the direction in which the positive charges move, which is the direction of E. In an electrolyte, the total current is the sum of the currents carried by each ionic species; anions flowing upward and cations flowing downward both constitute a downward current. The current flowing through the box can be calculated from the average velocity of the ions. For example, suppose that the Na+ are moving downward with an average velocity of 0.3 cm. per second, that the concentration of Na+ is 10 μM. per cm.³, and that the cross sectional area (A) is 10 cm.²; then the Na+ current passing through 1 cm.² (current density) is 10 μM. per cm.³ × 0.3 cm. per second = 3 μM. per cm.²-second, and the total Na+ current (I_{Na}) is 30 μM. per second. To convert this current to amperes, multiply by F = 0.0965 coulombs per μM.; I_{Na} = 2.9 coulombs per second = 2.9 amperes. In algebraic form,

$$I_{Na} = Z_{Na}\bar{v}_{Na}[Na^+]FA, \text{ and } I_{Cl} = Z_{Cl}\bar{v}_{Cl}[Cl^-]FA$$

For Cl− both Z and $\bar{v}_{Cl}$ are negative, so the current is positive.

* A line above a symbol is a common convention for indicating an average or mean quantity.

In words, current density is proportional to the velocity and the concentration of the ions. Ion velocity is proportional to the electric field, and the field is proportional to the applied voltage. Thus current flow is proportional to the applied voltage. This is *Ohm's law*.

The proportionality between I and $\mathcal{E}$ can be obtained by combining the equations relating $\mathcal{E}_B$ and E, v and E, and I and v. The relationship obtained is:

$$I = \frac{AFe}{L}(Z^2_{Na}[Na^+]\eta_{Na} + Z^2_{Cl}[Cl^-]\eta_{Cl})\mathcal{E}_B = \frac{A}{L\rho}\mathcal{E}_B$$

$$R = \frac{L\rho}{A},$$

where R is the resistance of the box. All terms in the middle portion except T, L and $\mathcal{E}_B$ have been combined into the constant ρ, called the *specific resistivity* of the substance. From the equation it can be seen that resistivity depends inversely on ionic concentrations and mobility. Concentrated solutions containing ions of high mobility and valence have a low resistance. The numerical value of ρ (in ohm-cm.) is the resistance between the faces of a 1 cm. cube. In mammalian extracellular fluid ρ approximately equals ($\simeq$) 60 ohm-cm.

The resistance of a block of conductor depends on the properties of the material (e.g., number of free charges, energy loss per collision) and on the dimensions of the block. Consider the box containing a solution of NaCl illustrated in Figure 17. The greater the cross-sectional area of the box (perpendicular to the direction of current flow), the lower the resistance, because more ions are available to carry current; the greater the length of the block (parallel to flow), the higher the resistance. In longer blocks, ions move at a slower velocity because the force on each ion is reduced. Thus, the resistance of a block of conducting material (a resistor) depends on the properties of the material (*specific resistivity*), is directly proportional to the length of the block, and is inversely proportional to its cross-sectional area.

Current Flow in Capacitors. In principle any amount of charge can be put on a capacitor, but the greater the charge, the greater the work per unit charge (voltage) that must be done to add charge to the capacitor. In a capacitor, current is the time rate of flow of charge onto the capacitor's conductors or the time rate of accumulation of charge on them. Since, for a capacitor, $q = C\mathcal{E}$, capacitive current is proportional to the rate of change of voltage across the capacitor: $I = dq/dt = C\, d\mathcal{E}/dt$. A constant current flowing through a resistor produces an unchanging voltage across it: $\mathcal{E} = IR$. A constant current (charge flow) to a capacitor produces a constant voltage change rate. In practice, a constant or unidirectional current cannot flow into a capacitor indefinitely because this would require a battery of infinite voltage.

Time constant. The simplest case of transient capacitative current flow occurs in the circuit (Fig. 18*D*, left) in which a battery is suddenly connected to a resistor (r) and a capacitor (c) in series. The voltage

on the capacitor ($\mathcal{E}_c$), initially zero, must increase eventually to the battery voltage ($\mathcal{E}_S$) but this takes time since the charge must be delivered through the resistor, which limits current flow to a maximum value of $\mathcal{E}_S/R$ (when $\mathcal{E}_c = 0$). However, after a long time the current declines to zero because the capacitor is fully charged; $\mathcal{E}_c = \mathcal{E}_S$ and, hence, the potential difference across the resistor is zero. Since current flow in the circuit is everywhere the same, the current through the resistor, $(\mathcal{E}_S - \mathcal{E}_c)/r$, is equal to the current through the capacitor, $I = dq/dt = cd\mathcal{E}_c/dt$. This relationship can be solved to get an equation describing the time course of the voltage across c and of the current through r; e.g., $\mathcal{E}_c = \mathcal{E}_S(1 - e^{-t/re})$. The graph of this function has the same shape as the curve in Figure 19*A*, right. The product (rc), having the units of time, is called the time constant (τ) of the circuit: $rc = (\mathcal{E}/I)(q/\mathcal{E}) = q/I = q/(q/t) = t$ where the symbols refer to the units of these quantities rather than to the quantities themselves. The time constant is a measure of how long it takes the capacitor to charge to a fixed fraction (0.63) of its final value.

The membrane has resistance and capacitance in parallel and hence can show the transient behavior just described. However, in this case, the time constant of the membrane is measured by applying a constant current to the membrane with an intracellular electrode; part of the current flows through the resistor and part through the capacitor (Fig. 19*A*, left). In this case, the voltage ($\Delta\mathcal{E}_m$) across the membrane rises slowly in response to the abruptly applied current (Fig. 19*A*, right). The reason is that time is required for the flow of charges (current) to alter the amount of charge on the capacitor and thus the voltage across it. At the instant the switch is closed all the charge supplied by the current source goes to charging the capacitor; there is no current through the resistor because the potential across it and the capacitor is zero. As time passes, the charge on the capacitor increases; $\Delta\mathcal{E}_m$ increases, and some current is diverted to the resistor, the rate of charging the capacitor being correspondingly decreased. This process continues—more and more current flowing through the resistor and less and less through the capacitor—until, finally, all current is flowing through the resistor.

The time course of these potential changes is shown in Figure 19*A*, right. Also shown is $\Delta\mathcal{E}_m$ as a function of time after the switch is opened. In this case, the charge on c_m leaks off through r_m, rapidly at first and then progressively more slowly. The time constant (τ) of this circuit is defined as the product of the resistance (r_m) and the capacitance (c_m): $\tau = r_m c_m$. If r_m is in ohms and c_m is in farads, τ is in seconds. A means of measuring the time constant is also shown in Figure 19*A*, right. The shape and time course of $\Delta\mathcal{E}_m$ are the same no matter what values r_m and c_m have individually, as long as their product is a constant.

Equivalent Circuit of an Axon. The membrane has capacity because of its insulating, charge-separating properties and has high resistance because ions are able to penetrate it at a limited rate. The axo-

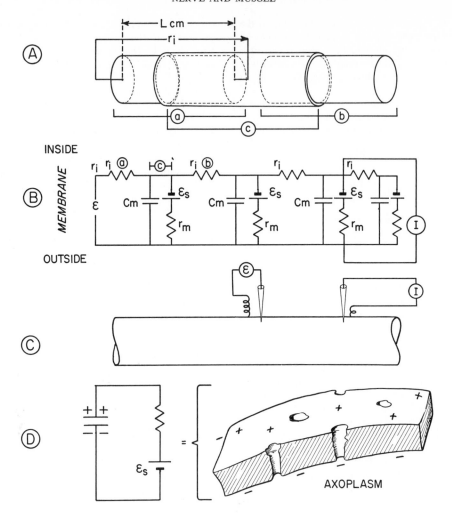

Fig. 18. Derivation of approximate equivalent electrical circuit of a long, thin, cylindrical axon. In an electrical circuit diagram, a straight line (————) represents an ideal conductor (zero resistance), a zigzag line (⌇⌇⌇⌇⌇) represents an ideal resistance (no capacitance between its terminals), and ——┤├—— represents an ideal capacitor (infinite resistance between its terminals). In *A*, the axoplasm and membrane are each marked off into halfway overlapping segments L cm. long (accurate representation of the nerve requires that L be no more than about 0.05 cm.). Any segment of axoplasm has a resistance (r_i) which is in series with the adjoining segments. Thus the upper line in *B* consists of a series of resistors, each of which is the electrical equivalent of the correspondingly labeled segment of axoplasm in *A*. Extracellular fluid is large and is assumed to have no resistance; this is represented by lower horizontal line in *B*. Equivalent circuit of a segment of membrane (*c*) must be connected between intracellular and extracellular fluid equivalents at the junction of two r_i's. For example, segment *c* is connected between the axoplasmic segments *a* and *b*.

C, Experimental arrangement for measuring cable properties. Compare with *B*, where a current source is shown applied across the membrane at one point; the "transmembrane potential" of the equivalent circuit can be measured at any other point. If *B* is an accurate electrical representation of the nerve fiber, then curves of the type shown in Figure 15 should be obtained in the equivalent experiment.

D, Derivation of equivalent circuit of a membrane segment. Equivalent consists of a capacitor (c_m) representing the insulating, ion-impermeable regions of membrane in parallel with a resistor (r_m) representing the ion-permeable regions of membrane. (For convenience, ion-permeable region is indicated by pores penetrating the membrane.) A battery of potential ε_s is connected in series with r_m to signify the existence of a steady transmembrane potential.

plasm and interstitial fluids, being solutions of ions, are resistors. If an axon is marked off into short segments, an approximately equivalent circuit consisting of resistors and capacitors can be drawn for each segment. When connected, the circuit equivalents of adjacent segments will constitute an equivalent circuit for the whole axon. This equivalent circuit has the same response to an applied current as has the nerve fiber it represents.

Figure 18 illustrates how the equivalent circuit is obtained. The electrical equivalent of a segment of axoplasm is simply a resistor (r_i) whose resistance is that of the segment (segments a and b in Figure 18A and the correspondingly marked resistors in Figure 18B).

Since the axoplasm is a rather dilute (0.3 M. per liter) solution of ionized substances, it has a comparatively high specific resistivity ($\rho \simeq 200$ ohm-cm.). The

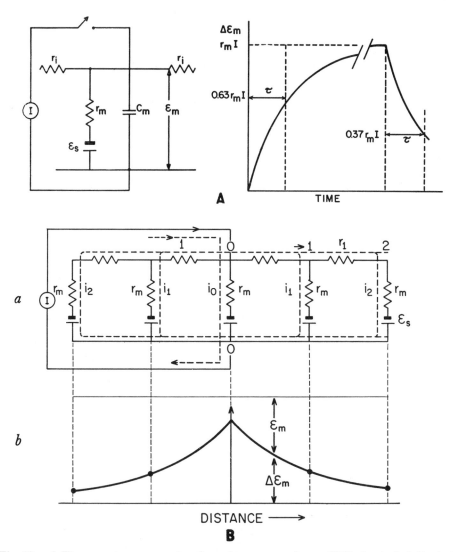

Fig. 19. *A,* Time constant; properties of a resistance–capacitance (RC) circuit. *Left,* Equivalent circuit of a segment of membrane and means for switching on or off an external current source (I). *Right,* Time course of voltage changes ($\Delta \mathcal{E}_m = \mathcal{E}_m - \mathcal{E}_s$) across the capacity when the switch is closed and then, after a long time, opened. A method for measuring the time constant ($\tau = r_m c_m$) of the membrane is shown.

B, Space constant. *a,* Approximate equivalent circuit of an axon with the membrane capacity removed. Current flow in a circuit with capacitors is the same, after a long time, as the current flow in this circuit at any time. Arrows show various paths of flow of applied current, I. The longer the current flow path, the greater the resistance and hence the smaller the proportion of current flowing in that branch. *b,* Graph of membrane voltage as a function of distance from point of current application.

resistance to axial current flow in the axoplasm of a nerve fiber is high because of the high specific resistivity and the small cross-sectional area. For instance, in a myelinated nerve fiber 14 μ in diameter, the axoplasm is only 10 μ in diameter, and the *longitudinal resistance* (r_i) of a segment 1 cm. long is 260 million ohms ($r_i = \rho_i L/A = 200$ ohm-cm. $\cdot$ 1 cm./$\pi \cdot (5 \times 10^{-4}$ cm.$)^2 = 2.6 \times 10^8$ ohm). The larger the diameter, the less r_i is; in a muscle fiber 100 μ in diameter, $r_i = 2.6$ million ohms per cm. Current inside the cell must flow within the volume surrounded by the cell membrane. The interstitial medium, on the other hand, is large; hence current can spread widely as it flows. Therefore, although the specific resistivity of the extracellular fluid is half as large as for intercellular fluid, the total resistance (r_o) of the interstitial fluid is negligible in comparison with r_i. Thus, r_o is not included in the equivalent circuit of Figure 18B. If r_o were appreciable, it would be put in the bottom horizontal line opposite the r_i's (Fig. 18B).

The equivalent circuit of a segment of membrane is more complicated, consisting of three components derived as shown in Figure 18D: (i) a capacity (c_m) representing the insulating charge-storing aspect of the membrane, (ii) a resistance (r_m) representing the limited ability of ions to penetrate the membrane, and (iii) a battery of voltage $\mathcal{E}_S$, the steady potential. The battery and the resistance are drawn in series because the membrane capacity is charged by ions (principally K^+ and Cl^-) driven through the membrane resistance by concentration gradients. In Figure 18A, the segment of membrane (c) is placed halfway between the two segments of axoplasm (a and b) to illustrate how the circuits representing the axoplasmic and membrane segments must be connected: the r_i's in series and the membrane portions connected between the junction of two r_i's and the line (representing a zero resistance conductor) that is equivalent to r_o, the extracellular resistance (Fig. 18B). An axon has cable properties because it has the particular electrical circuit properties shown in Figure 18B. In turn, these circuit properties are a consequence of the axon's structure.

Figure 18C is a duplicate of Figure 3B, which illustrates how cable properties are observed experimentally. Current is applied through an intracellularly placed electrode (I electrode), and the changes in membrane potential some distance away are recorded with the other ($\mathcal{E}$) electrode. The same type of experiment on the equivalent circuit is shown in Figure 18B, right; current is applied across a segment of membrane and the potential is recorded across a membrane segment one r_i away.

The advantage of drawing an equivalent circuit for an axon is that the behavior of this type of circuit is amenable to mathematical analysis. Such an analysis shows that the circuit always behaves in the manner described above and that the cable properties are completely characterized by two numbers: (i) the *time constant* (τ), which is a measure of the slowness of voltage changes in time, and (ii) the *space constant* (λ), a measure of the rate at which the voltage falls off with distance.

Membrane Time Constant. Since a segment of membrane can be represented electrically by a resistor and a capacitor in parallel (the battery does not affect the properties under discussion), the segment has a time constant associated with it. The time constant of the membrane segment shown in Figure 19A is $\tau_m = r_m c_m$. The time constant of any other segment of membrane of the same properties but different area is exactly the same although the resistance and capacitance are each different. Thus, this time constant characterizes the time behavior of the voltage changes across the membrane. It should be borne in mind, however, that the membrane voltage changes in a whole fiber are much more complex than those in a single resistance-capacitance circuit, although both are determined by τ. The differences arise because current applied at one point is not restricted to one segment of membrane but spreads out through the axoplasm to other segments of membrane. The result is that the voltage rises more quickly at the point of current application than in a simple RC circuit and more slowly at distant points. The equality of the time constants of any two segments of different length can be seen by calculating τ for segments 1 and 2 mm. long. Membrane resistance of the 2 mm. segment is half that of the 1 mm. segment, because, with respect to current flow from the interior to the exterior of the cell, two adjacent 1 mm. segments are in parallel. Alternatively, doubling the membrane area doubles the number of ions in a position to penetrate the membrane under a particular driving force. Thus the membrane conductance is doubled and the resistance halved. The double segment has twice the capacity because capacity is proportional to membrane area. The time constant of the double segment is 2 $c_m \times r_m/2 = r_m c_m$. Since the same arguments apply to segments of any length, the number $\tau = r_m c_m$ depends only on the properties of the membrane. In *Carcinus* (crab) axons specific membrane resistance is about 7500 ohms-cm.^{2}, and specific capacity is about 1 μf. per cm.^{2}; hence $\tau = 7.5$ milliseconds. τ is about 1 millisecond in squid giant axons and about 35 milliseconds in frog sartorius muscle fibers. This large value results from the high membrane capacity of muscle, about 10 μf. per cm.^{2}

Membrane Space Constant. The other factor necessary to specify completely the cable properties of a nerve fiber is the space constant, a measure of the spatial decay of $\Delta\mathcal{E}_m$. The diminution of membrane voltage changes with increasing distance from the current-applying electrode results from the series-parallel relationship between the resistance of a segment of membrane (r_m) and the longitudinal resistance of a segment of axoplasm (r_i). Each successive segment reduces the voltage.

Figure 19B shows the equivalent circuit of a nerve fiber with the membrane capacitors removed so that the spatial features of cable properties are emphasized. The current flow in the resistors is the same as would occur in a nerve fiber a long time after the application of the current when all the capacitors are fully charged. If a constant current is applied to the resistor network (Fig. 19B, top) at O, some of the current spreads into adjoining regions. Most of the current will flow directly through branch O. Because the axoplasm has a high resistance, successively lesser amounts will flow through other branches of the circuit (1, 2, 3, etc.). The longer the current flow path, the greater is its resistance and hence the less the current, because the voltage drop around any current flow path must be the same as that across branch O; $\Delta\mathcal{E}_o = r_m i_o$.

Experimentally, the quantity measured is the transmembrane potential at any point. Internal longitudinal current flow causes a voltage drop in the axoplasm, but changes in $\mathcal{E}_m$ result *only* from current flow through the membrane. However, to reach the point where it penetrates the membrane, this current must flow in the axoplasm as well and is thus attenuated. If the internal resistance were zero, the axoplasm would be isopotential, and all membrane elements would be in parallel. The cable properties would then consist merely of simple resistance–capacitance charge and discharge curves; i.e., there would be no spatial component. This situation obtains, approximately, in nearly spherical cells such as the nerve cell body. In such a case, the applied current produces nearly equal $\Delta\mathcal{E}_m$'s at every point.

The decay of potential with distance has the same shape as the decay of potential with time in a resistance–capacitance circuit, i.e., exponential. Figure 19B, bottom, shows a plot of $\Delta\mathcal{E}_m$ as a function of distance from the point of application of the current. The size of the space constant (λ) depends directly on membrane resistance and inversely on axoplasmic resistance. More precisely $\lambda = \sqrt{r_m/r_i}$, where r_m is the membrane resistance and r_i is the axoplasmic resistance of a 1 cm. length of fiber. Since both r_m and r_i depend on fiber diameter as well as on fiber properties, λ also depends on diameter: the larger the diameter, the larger the space constant. In frog skeletal muscle fibers 100 μ in diameter, λ is about 2.5 mm. Similar or smaller values are found in nerve fibers. Thus if a fiber were depolarized to zero at one end by a current, changes in membrane potential would be undetectable 1 cm. away. This fact shows how rapidly a fiber attenuates an applied "signal." It also shows that some method is needed to boost the signal at suitable intervals if information is to be transmitted over the distances found in the body.

Strength–Duration Relation. The equivalent circuit for an axon which was derived above can be used to derive an equation for the strength–duration curve shown in Figure 6. Assume that the area of membrane affected by the stimulating current is small enough to be represented by a single resistance–capacitance circuit (Fig. 19) and that the requirement for a threshold stimulus is that $\mathcal{E}_m$ be depolarized a fixed amount. The change in $\mathcal{E}_m$ ($\Delta\mathcal{E}_m = \mathcal{E}_m - \mathcal{E}_t$) is described by the equation

$$\Delta\mathcal{E}_m = I_s r_m (1 - e^{-t/\tau})$$

where I_s is the portion of the stimulating current flowing through the membrane resistance (r_m) at the site of the stimulating electrode, and $\tau = r_m c_m$ (the membrane time constant). The fiber will fire if $\Delta\mathcal{E}_m$ reaches

some critical value ($\Delta\mathcal{E}_{th}$). Setting $\Delta\mathcal{E}_m = \mathcal{E}_{th}$ in the above equation and solving for I_s as a function of t gives

$$I_s = \frac{\Delta\mathcal{E}_{th}}{r_m(1 - e^{-t/\tau})}$$

This is a relation between the length of time (t) that a stimulating current flows and the strength of the current. If t is large, the strength of the stimulating current (I_m) is minimum; $I_m = \Delta\mathcal{E}_{th}/r_m$. If t is small, larger currents are required. If $I_m = \Delta\mathcal{E}_{th}/r_m$ is substituted into this equation, it becomes, for a time, much less than τ; $I_s = I_m \tau_m/t$, or $I_s t = I_m \tau_m$. In other words, for short shocks, a constant amount of charge ($I_m \tau_m$) will stimulate the fiber; i.e., all the applied current enters the membrane capacity. Chronaxy, defined in Figure 6, is directly proportional to the membrane time constant. Chronaxy $= \tau_m \log_e 2$. Actually, the time course of the voltage change at the stimulating electrode is faster than given above. A somewhat more accurate version of the strength duration curve is obtained if this difference is taken into account, as has been done in plotting the curve in Figure 6.

Problems

1. The resistance of 1 cm.^{2} of squid axon membrane is 1000 ohm-cm.^{2}. If the membrane is uniform and 75 Å thick, what is the specific resistivity of the membrane?

Ans.

$R = \rho\delta/A$ ρ = specific resistivity
$\qquad\qquad\quad \delta$ = thickness
$\qquad\qquad\quad$ A = area ($= 1$ cm.^{2} in this problem)
$\qquad\qquad\quad$ R = resistance

Therefore, $\rho = (RA)/\delta$. In this problem RA $= 1000$ ohm-cm.$^2 = 10^{-1}$ ohm-cm.^{2} $\rho = 10^{-1}/7.5 \times 10^{-9}$ $= 1.33 \times 10^7$ ohm-meter.

2. Suppose the resistance of the squid axon membrane of problem 1 is due to the presence of cylindrical holes or pores 0.7×10^{-9} meters in diameter and 75 Å long (membrane thickness), in a perfect insulating membrane material and filled with fluid of specific resistivity 0.15 ohm-meter (sea water). If Ohm's law holds for the fluid in the pores, how many pores must exist in 1 cm.^{2} of membrane to account for an R_m of 1000 ohms-cm.^{2}? How far apart are these pores if they are arranged in a square pattern?

Ans. 2.9×10^6 pores per cm.^{2}, 5.9×10^{-4} cm. (5.9 μ) between pores.

3. Calculate the specific resistivity in ohm-meters of a 0.15 M. NaCl solution when the mobility of (η_{Na}) of Na ions is 3.2×10^{11} (meters per sec.-newton) and of Cl ions is 4.9×10^{11} (meters per sec.-newton.).

Ans. 0.53 ohm-meter.

4. The resistance of the membrane covering a unit length of a long, thin cell is 1.25×10^5 ohm-cm. and the capacity per unit length is 0.008 μf. per cm. The resistance per unit length of the cytoplasm is 4.1×10^7 ohm per cm. Calculate the space constant and time constant of this cell.

Ans. $\lambda = 5.5 \times 10^{-2}$ cm. $= 0.5$ mm.; $\tau = 1 \times 10^{-3}$ seconds $= 1$ millisecond.

5. A long, thin cylindrical cell 100 μ in diameter is covered by a membrane with a specific resistance of 100 ohms-cm.^{2} and with a time constant of 10^{-3} seconds. If the cytoplasm of this cell has a specific resistivity of 1 ohm-meter, what is the space constant and membrane capacity per square meter of this cell?

Ans. $\lambda = 1.6 \times 10^{-3}$ meters, $c_m = 10^{-2}$ f. per meter.^{2}

6. The rheobase of a muscle to external stimulating electrodes is 2 milliamperes and the average membrane time constant is 30 milliseconds. Calculate and plot several points on the strength–duration curve. Measure the chronaxy from the plotted curve and compare with the calculated value of chronaxy $= \tau_m \log_e 2$. Note that $\log_e 2 = 0.69$ and $e^{-x} = 1/e^x = 1/10^{x/2.3}$.

PHYSICAL CHEMISTRY

Electrochemical Potential. The electrochemical potential is a useful concept in discussing the physical chemistry of the system composed of two solutions separated by a membrane which are at or near equilibrium. Electrochemical potential is defined as the rate of change of free (or available) energy of a system with respect to the number of mols of the particular substance considered (units: joules per mol), the number of mols of other substances, the temperature and pressure being held constant. The formula for the electrochemical potential used in Chapter 1 can be derived rather simply, but not rigorously, in the following way. The electrochemical potential, μ_s, of species of substance, S, is $\mu_s = Z_s F \mathcal{E} + RT \log_e [S]$. The contribution of the electrical potential to the energy of 1 mol of S is simply $Z_s F \mathcal{E}$, the work done per mol in bringing the substance to a region where the potential is $\mathcal{E}$; $Z_s F$ converts from joules per coulomb to joules per mol. The calculation of concentration potential energy is more difficult. The RT $\log_e [S]$ term is obtained by using the approximation that the species, S, acts like a perfect gas in the solution, i.e., there is no interaction between the S molecules. For a perfect gas $PV = nRT$ where P is the pressure, V the volume, n the number of mols, R the universal gas constant, and T the absolute temperature. Work is done on a gas by compressing it; hence $dW = -Fds = -PAds = -PdV$ where A = cross-sectional area. The concentration potential energy is thus the work to compress a mol of S from infinite volume to its actual concentration in the solution. By definition, $[S] = n_s/V$, so $V = n_s/[S]$ and $dV = -n_s \, d[S]/[S]^2$. Writing the gas law in the form $P = RTn_s/V = RT[S]$, substituting into $dW = -PdV$ and dividing through by n_s gives $\dfrac{dW}{n_s} = RT \dfrac{d[S]}{[S]}$, the work per mol of S done in changing the concentration of S by $d[S]$. Integrating gives the work done in changing the concentration from $[S]_o$ to $[S]_i$.

$$\frac{W}{n_s} = \int_{[S]=[S]_o}^{[S]=[S]_i} \frac{dW}{n_s} = RT \int_{[S]=[S]_o}^{[S]=[S]_i} \frac{d[S]}{[S]} = RT \, (\log_e[S]_i - \log_e[S]_o)$$

$$= RT \log_e \frac{[S]_i}{[S]_o} \quad (1)$$

If all electrochemical potentials are referred to the value for $[S] = [S]_o$ (only electrochemical potential differences are considered), then

$$\mu_s = Z_s F \mathcal{E} + RT \log_e[S] \quad (2)$$

Activity coefficient. There are, however, interactions between ions and so [S] must be multiplied by a factor γ to describe the observed behavior, $\gamma[S]$ being called the activity. The factor, γ, depends on concentration, approaching one for very dilute solutions, e.g., for a 0.15M NaCl solution it is 0.75. Tables and approximate formulae for γ are available if more exact values of the electrochemical potential are needed. The frequently made assumption that $\gamma = 1$ is not as inaccurate as a γ of 0.75 indicates since nearly all calculations involve concentration (or activity) ratios in which γ is usually canceled; i.e., the concentration ratio is an accurate approximation to the activity ratio in most circumstances.

Ionic Fluxes. *The flux equation.* Most animal systems are in osmotic equilibrium, because osmotic pressures are very large for relatively small concentration differences (see below). As pointed out in Chapter 1, biologic membranes separate solutions in which the concentrations of various species differ, although the total number of particles is nearly the same. Since most membranes are somewhat permeable to many of the ions, it is important to derive an expression for the flow of these ions through membranes as an aid in interpreting experimental data. Several assumptions are made to simplify this derivation: (i) The only force acting on the ions are concentration and voltage gradients. (ii) The individual ions move through the membrane independently of each other. (iii) The system is in osmotic equilibrium. (iv) Concentration gradients and electric fields exist only in and very near the membrane; concentrations are the same everywhere in each solution (but may differ between solutions), and the electric field is zero everywhere in each solution.

The passive forces acting on ions are concentration gradients and electric fields. The ionic flux of the species, S, due to the concentration gradient ($\mathbf{M}_s^D$) is $\mathbf{M}_s^D = -D_s \, \mathbf{grad} \, [S]$ (see Chap. 1) where D_s is the diffusion coefficient for S in the membrane and [S] is its concentration at any point in the membrane. $D_s = 0$ if the membrane is impermeable to S.

The ionic flux of S through the membrane due to an electric field ($\mathbf{M}_s^E$) can be computed from the formula for ionic current in the section above on Ohm's law. Thus, $\mathbf{M}_s^E = J_s/Z_s F = I_s/AFZ_s = \dfrac{\mathcal{E}_m}{L} Z_s e[S] \eta_s$. $\mathcal{E}_m/L$ is a simple form of the potential gradient in the membrane, **grad** $\mathcal{E}$. The mobility, η_s, of S in the membrane, the average velocity per unit force on the ion, and D_s are related since both represent the ease with which an ion moves through the membrane. Einstein first showed that $\eta_s = \dfrac{FD_s}{eRT}$. The total flux is the sum of the concentration and voltage gradient fluxes:

$$-\mathbf{M}_s = -(\mathbf{M}_s^D + \mathbf{M}_s^E) = D_s \textbf{ grad } [S] + Z_s \frac{FD_s}{RT}[S] \textbf{ grad } \mathcal{E} \qquad (3)$$

This equation specifies the flux of an ion but the difficulty arises that both [S] and $\mathcal{E}$ must be specified at each point in the membrane; if one is known the other may be calculated. The calculation of both [S] and $\mathcal{E}$ from first principles is difficult and requires a specific membrane model. However, the equilibrium potential can be calculated without further assumptions.

Equation 3 can be put in a simpler form by multiplying both sides by $e^{FZ_s\mathcal{E}/RT}$ to obtain

$$-\mathbf{M}_s e^{FZ_s\mathcal{E}/RT} = D_s e^{FZ_s\mathcal{E}/RT} \textbf{ grad } [S] +$$

$$\frac{D_s Z_s F}{RT}[S]e^{FZ_s\mathcal{E}/RT} \textbf{ grad } \mathcal{E} = D_s \textbf{ grad } ([S]e^{FZ_s\mathcal{E}/RT}) \ (4)$$

since **grad** $AB = A$ **grad** $B + B$ **grad** A. This is the ordinary diffusion equation with [S] replaced by $[S]e^{FZ_s\mathcal{E}/RT}$. Thus, with respect to transmembrane fluxes, voltage affects concentrations exponentially.

Equilibrium potential. The equilibrium potential ($\mathcal{E}_s$) of an ion is the $\mathcal{E}_m$ at which $\mathbf{M}_s = 0$. It is the potential across a membrane that is permeable only to this ion species.

$$-\mathbf{M}_s = D_s \textbf{ grad } ([S]e^{FZ_s\mathcal{E}/RT}) = 0 \qquad (5)$$

If the membrane is considered as a plane of thickness δ oriented perpendicular to the x direction, the boundary conditions are $[S] = [S]_o$ and $\mathcal{E} = 0$ on the outside of the membrane and $[S] = [S]_i$ and $\mathcal{E} = \mathcal{E}_s$ on the inside. Equation (5) can be integrated directly to give: $[S]_o e^o - [S]e^{FZ_s\mathcal{E}/RT} = 0$.

$$\mathcal{E}_s = \frac{RT}{FZ_s}\log_e \frac{[S]_o}{[S]_i} \qquad (6)$$

the Nernst equation for the equilibrium potential of an ion. This is the electric potential necessary to balance out diffusional forces on the ion species, S. In Chapter 1 the Nernst equation was derived from the electrochemical potential difference $\Delta\mu_s$, across the membrane. $\Delta\mu_s = FZ_s\mathcal{E}_m + RT\log_e [S]_i/[S]_o$. If $\Delta\mu_s = 0$, $\mathcal{E}_m = \mathcal{E}_s$ and $\mathcal{E}_s = \dfrac{RT}{FZ_s}\log_e [S]_o/[S]_i$. Hence the equilibrium potential can be calculated from equating electrical and diffusional forces or potential energies.

Membrane Potential. *Non-steady state: Goldman equation.* In cells, most ions are not equilibrated and the net passive fluxes of permeating ion species are not zero. This is true in the steady state maintained by active transport and generally in transient states produced by changes in the external solution, in membrane potential (e.g., voltage clamping), or in membrane permeability (e.g., action potential). The relationship between ion fluxes and transmembrane potential is complicated and depends on the specific membrane model used. However, in conditions in which the voltage is changing so slowly that capacitative current is negligible (seconds or greater), the assumption made by Goldman (see reference 16) that the electric field inside the membrane is everywhere constant yields an accurate relationship. For a constant field, the potential at any distance (x) through the membrane is $\mathcal{E} = \mathcal{E}_m x/\delta$. Inserting this into equation 4 and integrating, when I_S is in a steady state (charges would pile up in the membrane if I_S varied with x) gives

$$I_S = P_s \frac{F^2 Z_s^2 \mathcal{E}_m}{RT}\left[\frac{[S]_i e^{FZ_s\mathcal{E}_m/RT} - [S]_o}{1 - e^{FZ_s\mathcal{E}_m/RT}}\right] \qquad (7)$$

where $P_s = D_s/\delta$. I_S is positive if the net current due to S is outward.

If $\mathcal{E}_m$ is changing slowly, capacitative current is zero and the total ionic flow through the membrane must be zero. In most animal cells, the only ions carrying appreciable currents through the membrane are Na^+, K^+ and Cl^-. Hence $I_{Na} + I_K + I_{Cl} = 0$ or $M_{Na} + M_K - M_{Cl} = 0$. Writing separate equations like 7 for each of these ions, adding the equations and setting the sum to zero give a relationship which can be solved for $\mathcal{E}_m$:

$$\mathcal{E}_m = \frac{RT}{F}\log_e \left[\frac{P_K[K]_o + P_{Na}[Na]_o + P_{Cl}[Cl]_i}{P_K[K]_i + P_{Na}[Na]_i + P_{Cl}[Cl]_o}\right] \qquad (8)$$

Curves of $\mathcal{E}_m$ versus $[K^+]_o$ like the one in Figure 7 are accurately predicted by this equation with a proper choice of the ratios P_{Na}/P_K and P_{Cl}/P_K.

Steady state in cells. The preceding discussions deal only with passive fluxes through membranes, no account being taken of active transport. However, active transport is required to maintain a nonequilibrium steady state in which concentrations and voltage are not changing in time and net ion fluxes (passive plus active) are zero.

It is of importance to know whether a one-for-one sodium–potassium exchange pump can develop and maintain a steady state resembling the one actually found in cells. Since the pump is neutral and chloride is equilibrated ($I_{Cl} = 0$), the transmembrane potential is given by equation 8 with the chloride terms omitted:

$$\mathcal{E}_s = \frac{RT}{F}\log_e \left[\frac{[K]_o + \dfrac{P_{Na}}{P_K}[Na]_o}{[K]_i + \dfrac{P_{Na}}{P_K}[Na]_i}\right] \qquad (9)$$

$\mathcal{E}_s$ instead of $\mathcal{E}_m$ is used to denote steady state. This expression shows that the membrane potential is closest to the equilibrium potential of the most readily permeating ion; $\mathcal{E}_s$ is close to $\mathcal{E}_K$ if the ratio P_{Na}/P_K is much less than one ([Na] terms small compared to [K] terms).

Equation 9 is adequate for calculating steady state membrane potentials if the internal concentrations are known. However, these depend on the active transport rate, so an adequate test of whether a one-for-one pump can produce a steady state comparable to the actual one is to calculate $\mathcal{E}_s$ as a function of external concentrations, passive permeabilities and active transport rates only.

The dependence of $\mathcal{E}_s$ and cell volume (V_c) on P_{Na}/P_K and the Na^+ pumping rate can be calculated approximately by making certain assumptions: (i) Total cellular A^- content is known. (ii) P_{Na} and P_K are known. (iii) All Na^+ extrusion is by means of a one-to-one Na^+–K^+ exchange. (iv) The rate of active Na^+ extrusion (M_{Na}^{out}) is directly proportional to $[Na^+]_i$; $M_{Na}^{out} = j_{Na}[Na^+]_i$, where j_{Na} is the specific active transport rate of Na^+ and has the units of permeability. Active Na^+ extrusion is probably proportional to $[Na^+]_i^3$ in this range (Chap. 1). However, this assumption simplifies the mathematics without changing the final result for high pumping rates. (v) The cell is in osmotic equilibrium. (vi) Only Na^+, K^+, Cl^- and A^- ions are considered. (vii) The constant field flux equation describes passive fluxes. Equations based on these assumptions give $\mathcal{E}_s$ and V_c in terms of external ion concentrations, the total amount of intracellular A^- and its valence (Z_A), and the ratios j_{Na}/P_{Na} and P_{Na}/P_K. However, in most cells (but not in red cells) Z_A is about 1 and j_{Na}/P_{Na} is so large that $\mathcal{E}_s$ and V_c do not depend on the exact value of j_{Na}/P_{Na}. The large value of j_{Na}/P_{Na} reduces $[Na]_i$ to a very low value. In this case, the steady state transmembrane potential and the cell volume are given by the following equations:

$$\mathcal{E}_s = -\frac{RT}{F} \log_e \frac{[Na^+]_o + [K^+]_o}{[K^+]_o + [Na^+]_o \dfrac{P_{Na}}{P_K}} \quad (10)$$

$$V_c = \frac{A^-}{[Na^+]_o \left(1 - \dfrac{P_{Na}}{P_K}\right)} \quad (11)$$

These equations are somewhat more complicated if Z_A is not equal to 1, or if j_{Na}/P_{Na} is less than about 100. The term $(P_{Na}/P_K)[Na^+]_o$ can be considered an effective external Na^+ concentration. From the values in Table 1, $P_{Na}/P_K = 1/650$ for mammalian skeletal muscle. The equation for cell volume shows that V_c is constant for values of P_{Na}/P_K much less than 1. If $P_{Na}/P_K = 1$, cell volume is infinite, as expected. These equations are only approximately correct, but they clearly indicate the important factors in the determination of $\mathcal{E}_s$ and V_c; both are sensitively dependent on P_{Na}/P_K.

Osmotic Pressure and Balance. If two aqueous solutions are separated by a membrane which is permeable only to water, water tends to flow through the membrane equalizing its concentration and thus the total dissolved particles per unit volume in both solu-

tions. A hydrostatic pressure must be applied to the more concentrated solution to prevent this movement. The hydrostatic pressure difference necessary to maintain the unequal concentration of total dissolved particles in the two solutions is equal and opposite to the *osmotic* pressure. Water (only aqueous solutions will be dealt with here) tends to flow down its concentration gradient and hence from the solution with the lower concentration of dissolved particles to that with the higher concentration.

The pressure needed to stop the net flow of water is approximated by the formula, $\pi = RT(\Delta C)$, where R is the universal gas constant (8.21×10^{-2} liter-atmospheres/deg. K mol), T is the absolute temperature (degrees Kelvin), ΔC is the difference in concentration of the dissolved particles between the two solutions (mol per liter) and π is the osmotic pressure in atmospheres. The concentration of dissolved particles in a solution is usually expressed in osmols per liter. An *osmol* is 6.023×10^{23} particles (Avogadro's number—the number of particles in a gram molecular weight of a substance) without regard to the species of the particle (as long as it is not water). In calculating the number of particles, it should be noted that ionized substances contribute one particle for every ion formed in the dissociation of a molecule (i.e., $NaCl$ gives 2 particles per molecule, Na_2SO_4 gives 3, etc.). The osmotic strength of a solution can be found by summing the molar concentrations of all the ions and undissociated molecules.

The term "tonicity" is used to describe the osmolarity of one solution in comparison to another. A solution is said to be *hypertonic, isotonic* or *hypotonic* with respect to another solution, depending upon whether it contains more, the same number of, or fewer dissolved particles per liter. Although these terms are relative, they are frequently used in an absolute sense. When used in this manner, the reference solution is the interstitial fluid or plasma. Mammalian serum contains approximately 310 milliosmols per liter. Thus a 155 millimolar solution of $NaCl$ is isotonic to mammalian serum.

In living systems the effective osmotic pressure of a solution is less than the total osmotic pressure because cell membranes are permeable to many substances besides water. The osmotic pressures of intracellular and interstitial fluids are equal. However, the blood plasma contains about one millimol of protein molecules which are too large to penetrate the capillary wall and which are not as concentrated in interstitial fluid. Smaller molecules penetrate the capillary, so the osmotic pressure difference between the two fluids is due only to the plasma protein. Since one osmol has an osmotic pressure of about 25 atmospheres at body temperature (22.4 at 0° C.), one milliosmol has a pressure of $0.025 \times 760 = 19$ mm. Hg. A capillary hydrostatic pressure of more than 19 mm. Hg is necessary to overcome the osmotic pressure of the plasma protein alone. Additional pressure will be needed because of a second condition in the ionic distributions, the Gibbs–Donnan equilibrium.

Gibbs–Donnan Equilibrium and Osmotic Pressure. It was shown above that the net osmotic pressure across a membrane is $[S]RT$, where $[S]$ represents the total concentration of all nonpermeating substances. However, if one of the nonpermeating substances is ionized, the net osmotic pressure is modified and a transmembrane potential is developed. Consider the case of a membrane permeable to Na^+, Cl^- and water, and impermeable to A^- separating two solutions. On side 1 are $[Na^+]_1$, $[Cl^-]_1$ and $[A^{Z-}]_1$, with valence size Z, and on side 2, $[Na^+]_2$ and $[Cl^-]_2$ as shown by the table:

1	2
$[Na^+]_1$	$[Na^+]_2$
$[Cl^-]_1$	$[Cl^-]_2$
$Z[A^{Z-}]_1$	

If the osmotic pressure is balanced by an external pressure, $[Na^+]$ and $[Cl^-]$ will equilibrate across the membrane (active transport is assumed to be absent).

The Gibbs–Donnan equilibrium condition can be determined from the $[Na^+]$ and $[Cl^-]$ concentrations on the two sides by equating their electrochemical potentials:

$$RT \log_e [Na^+]_1 + RT \log_e [Cl^-]_1 = \\ RT \log_e [Na^+]_2 + RT \log_e [Cl^-]_2$$

$$[Na^+]_1[Cl^-]_1 = [Na^+]_2[Cl^-]_2 \qquad (12)$$

The nonpermeating anions do not contribute to the electrochemical potential difference across the membrane, and the voltage terms cancel. However, there is a transmembrane potential; since $[Na^+]_1/[Na^+]_2$ does not equal unity, a voltage is necessary to balance the concentration gradient so that net flux of this permeating ion is zero. Charge neutrality requires that $[Na^+]_1 = [Cl^-]_1 + Z[A^{Z-}]_1$ and $[Na^+]_2 = [Cl^-]_2$, where Z is the size of the valence of the nonpermeating anion, A^-. Substitution in the Gibbs–Donnan relation (equation 12) gives

$$([Cl^-]_1 + Z[A^{Z-}]_1)[Cl^-]_1 = ([Cl^-]_2)^2 \quad (13)$$

Dividing through by $[Cl^-]_2$ and $([Cl^-]_1 + Z[A^{Z-}]_1)$ gives a more understandable form:

$$\frac{[Cl^-]_1}{[Cl^-]_2} = \frac{[Cl^-]_2}{[Cl^-]_1 + Z[A^{Z-}]_1} = \frac{[Na^+]_2}{[Na^+]_1} \quad (14)$$

It can be seen from this relationship that $[Cl^-]_2$ is greater than $[Cl^-]_1$ and less than $([Cl^-]_1 + Z[A^-]_1)$. Since $[Cl^-]_2 > [Cl^-]_1$, the contributions of the diffusible ions to the osmotic pressure must be investigated. This will be done in the example below. The concentration ratio (ρ) for any diffusible univalent ion is the same as that for Na^+ and Cl^- in this equation. The potential is given by the Nernst equation, $RT/ZF \log_e \rho$.

The chloride concentration ratio between blood plasma and interstitial fluid is about 0.95. This ratio arises from the plasma protein, which has a concentration of about 1 millimol per liter and a valence of about −18. Also, $[Na^+]_2 = [Cl^-]_2 = 155$ millimols

per liter in interstitial fluid. Substituting in equation 13 gives

$$([Cl^-]_1 + 18 \times 1)[Cl^-]_1 = 155^2$$

Solving the quadratic equation gives $[Cl^-]_1 = 146.25$ millimols per liter for the plasma chloride concentration. Charge neutrality requires $[Na^+]_1 = [Cl^-]_1 + Z[A^-]_1 = 146.25 + 18 = 164.25$ millimols per liter. The Donnan concentration ratio for Na^+ is thus $155/164.25 = 0.944$ and the voltage across the capillary wall is $61 \log_{10} 0.944 = -1.5$ millivolts (plasma negative to interstitial fluid).

The total osmotic pressure is proportional to the difference between the total particle concentrations on the two sides of the membrane. On the plasma side this is $[Na^+]_1 + [Cl^-]_1 + [A^-]_1 = 164.25 + 146.25 + 1 = 311.5$ millimols per liter and on the interstitial side the sum of sodium and chloride concentrations is simply $2 \times 155 = 310$ millimols per liter. The difference is 1.5 millimols per liter, 50 per cent more than that due to the nondiffusible anion. The remainder is composed of diffusible ions held by the nondiffusible anions. The osmotic pressure is thus 50 per cent greater than the value of 19 mm. Hg due to 1 millimol of plasma protein. The total osmotic pressure, which is balanced by the hydrostatic pressure of the blood in the capillaries is thus about 29 mm. Hg, a value in agreement with measured capillary hydrostatic pressures (Chap. 32).

Problems

1. (a) If the membrane of the unicellular plant *Chara* has a permeability coefficient to glycerol of 2×10^6 cm. per second, what is the net movement of glycerol in mols per second across an area of 10^{-2} cm.^{2} if a concentration difference of 10^{-1} mols per liter exists across the membrane?

(b) Calculate the net movement of glycerol through a "membrane" made of water of the same area (10^{-2} cm.^{2}) and thickness (assumed to be 7.5×10^{-9} meters) as the *Chara* membrane for the same concentration gradient if the diffusion constant of glycerol (D_G) in water is 7.2×10^{-6} cm.^{2} per second.

Ans. (a) 2×10^{-12} mols per second. (b) 9.6×10^{-6} mols per second.

2. Calculate the hydrogen ion equilibrium potential across a muscle cell membrane if the *p*H of the intracellular fluid is 7.0 and the *p*H of the extracellular fluid is 7.4. If the transmembrane potential is −90 mV. (inside negative), is the hydrogen ion equilibrated? RT/F has the value 26.7 mV.

Ans. 24 mV. (inside negative). Not in equilibrium.

3. In a voltage clamping experiment, the peak sodium conductance (g_{Na}) following a sudden change in membrane potential from the resting level to a value of −20 mV. (inside negative) is found to be 5×10^{-2} mhos per cm.^{2} What is the peak sodium current density at this membrane potential if the sodium equilibrium potential is +35 mV.? What is the direction of the current?

Ans. 2.8×10^{-3} amps. per cm.^{2}; inward.

4. Using equation 7 for ion current as a function of $\mathcal{E}_m$ and P_K, compute the net potassium flux. Assume that $[K]_i = 155$ mM per liter, $[K]_o = 4$ mM. per liter, $\mathcal{E}_m = -90$ V. (inside negative), $P_K = 10^{-6}$ cm. per second.

Ans. With the constant field approximation the equation for passive current and net passive flux is

$$M_K = \frac{I_K}{F} = P_K \frac{F\mathcal{E}_m}{RT} \left[\frac{[K]_i e^{\,F\mathcal{E}_m/RT} - [K]_o}{1 - e^{\,F\mathcal{E}_m/RT}} \right]$$

Inserting the given values for F/RT, P_K, $\mathcal{E}_m$, and $[K]$ and converting the concentrations to mols per meter^3 gives

$$M_K = 10^{-8} \times 37.5 \,(-9 \times 10^{-2}) \left[\frac{155\, e^{-(37.5)(0.09)} - 4}{1 - e^{-(37.5)(0.09)}} \right]$$

$$= 10^{-8} \times 3.4 \times \frac{1.18}{.966}$$

$$= 4.2 \times 10^{-8} \text{ mol per meter}^2\text{-sec. outward flux.}$$

5. Using equation 9, compute the membrane potential for a muscle cell in which $[K]_i = 155$ mM. per liter, $[Na^+] = 12$ mM. per liter, $[K^+]_o = 4$ mM. per liter, $[Na^+]_o = 145$ mM. per liter, and $P_K/P_{Na} = 100$.

Ans. -89 mV.

CHAPTER 3

Special Properties of Nerve Trunks and Tracts

By HARRY D. PATTON

METHODS OF COMPARING SPECIAL PROPERTIES

IN the preceding chapters attention was focused on the general electrical properties common to the membranes of all excitable elements. For that purpose it was desirable to concentrate on data obtained from single nerve and muscle cells with the aid of intracellularly placed ultramicroelectrodes because such methods provide the most direct measure of membrane properties. Also, in initial consideration of the general properties of excitable membranes, quantitative variances arising from differences in cell species could profitably be overlooked.

Even though all axons are qualitatively alike, close scrutiny reveals that individual specimens display considerable quantitative variance in such parameters as, for example, conduction speed and threshold to externally applied electrical currents. It is the purpose of this chapter, then, to describe these special properties of the individual constituents of nerve trunks and tracts and to relate these properties to structural differences such as fiber diameters.

Data for comparison of the special properties of individual nerve fibers may be obtained in two ways. First, intracellular recordings from a great many individual fibers may be made in an attempt to sample the entire population of a trunk. This method has been employed on a limited basis,[17] but is tedious and time consuming. In addition, it suffers from the defect that sampling is distributed in time, so that the conditions may alter from sample to sample or from preparation to preparation. Also, intracellular sampling is biased, because small fibers are less tolerant of penetration than are larger axons. A more satisfactory method is to record the activity of a bundle of nerve fibers excited in concert. Such activity in a nerve trunk is called the *compound action potential,* a term which implies that the recorded potential is compounded from the individual action potentials of the constituent axons.

To record compound potentials the recording electrodes must, of course, be placed extracellularly, for an intracellular electrode is little influenced by activity in fibers adjacent to the one penetrated. Usually, one electrode is placed on the nerve trunk; the other is placed either on some other part of the same trunk or on some inactive structure such as bone or skin. With this arrangement, a difference of potential is re-

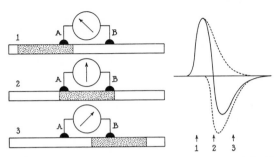

Fig. 1. Diphasic recording of action potential of nerve.

Left, Stippled area represents action potential progressing from left to right in 1, 2, and 3. In 1, electrode *A* is negative to electrode *B;* on 2, *A* and *B* are equipotential; in 3, *B* is negative with respect to *A*.

Right, Solid line trace is recorded diphasic action potential; numbered arrows below indicate instantaneous potential differences corresponding to three stages of conduction shown at left. Broken lines indicate true electrical changes at each electrode; recorded potential is their algebraic sum.

corded between the "active" electrode as it is passed by conducted action potentials and the "reference" electrode on some structure which is inactive at that time.

An important feature of extracellular recording is that the potential sources, i.e., the nerve fibers, are invariably surrounded by an aqueous conducting medium, either the interstitial fluid or some artificially constructed electrolytic medium applied to the trunk to prevent desiccation. Such a system, in which the potential source is immersed in a conducting medium is called a *volume conductor,* and interpretation of differences of potential between two points in the conducting medium requires special knowledge of the properties of volume conductors.

The influence of the external conducting medium is appreciable only when its volume is very large with respect to the volume of the structure generating the potential. Such is the case when potentials are recorded through electrodes placed on the surface of the brain or the spinal cord, or when the electrical activity of the contracting heart is recorded through electrodes placed on the surface of the body (electrocardiogram). In these instances, the entire body acts as a uniform conducting medium surrounding the relatively small structures generating the potentials. Happily, the volume of the external conducting medium surrounding peripheral nerve trunks can be limited simply by lifting the nerve onto electrodes in air or, better still, by suspending the nerve in an insulating medium

such as mineral oil so that only a thin film of external conductor surrounds the fibers and the trunk. The relatively simple compound action potential of peripheral nerve trunks will therefore be considered first, the discussion of potential configurations recorded in volume being postponed.

Diphasic and Monophasic Recording. Figure 1 shows diagrammatically an electrode arrangement suitable for recording the compound action potential of a nerve trunk. The nerve is equipped with a pair of recording electrodes, *A* and *B;* to minimize contact with the surrounding tissues, it is either lifted into the air or immersed in a pool of mineral oil. In the resting state the fibers under both recording leads are externally electropositive, and no difference of potential between them is recorded. When a volley of impulses* (stippled area) approaching *A* from the left reaches the position indicated in *1,* a difference of potential is recorded between *A* and *B,* because the active fibers at *A* are externally electronegative to the as yet quiescent portion of the same fibers at *B.* This difference in potential is registered as an upward deflection of the recording beam, as shown in the accompanying trace (heavy line).† In diagram *2,* the conducted volley has progressed so that both electrodes are in contact with equally depolarized fibers; consequently, the recording beam has returned to the zero potential. In diagram *3,* the wave of depolarization has progressed beyond *A* (i.e., the fibers under *A* have repolarized), so that *B* is now relatively negative to *A* and the recording beam is accordingly deflected downward. As the depolarization passes beyond *B,* the beam returns to zero. The potential configuration recorded in this way, shown diagrammatically by the heavy line tracing in Figure 1, is known as a *diphasic compound action potential.*

Diphasic recording is useful if one wishes to determine whether an electrical change is propagated, but for other purposes the method has certain undesirable features. First, if, as in Fig-

*A *volley of impulses* means a discharge set up in a multifibered nerve trunk or tract by a single brief stimulus, so that, although many constituent fibers are excited, none discharges more than once. The term should not be confused with a *train* or *burst of impulses,* terms which imply repetitive discharge of the constituent fibers, as, for example, when the trunk is *tetanically* or repetitively stimulated.

†The direction of the deflection is, of course, arbitrary and can be reversed by reversing the connections to the recording system.

ure 1, the distance between the recording electrodes is less than the wave length of the action potential (i.e., the length of fiber occupied by an action potential at any time), both the time course and the amplitude of the electrical events at each electrode are distorted, because activity reaches the distal electrode before repolarization occurs at the proximal electrode. The extent of this distortion may be seen in Figure 1 by comparing the traces depicted by the dotted lines (which are extrapolations of the electrical changes at each electrode) with the actually recorded algebraic summation of these changes (heavy line). This kind of cancellation is difficult to avoid, since the wave length of an action potential in a large nerve fiber is as much as 6 cm.

An even more serious defect arises from the fact, shortly to be developed, that the speed of conduction differs in different fibers in the trunk. Consequently, activity in rapidly conducting nerve fibers can reach the distal electrode at a time when the action potentials in more slowly conducting fibers have proceeded only as far as the proximal electrode. Hence, the contributions of rapidly and slowly conducting fibers may tend to cancel one another, for the recording arrangement detects only differences of potential.

Fortunately, the defects inherent in diphasic recording are easily circumvented by changing the experimental conditions to those shown in Figure 2. To block conduction, the fibers underlying electrode B are permanently depolarized by crushing, burning, cutting, or topically applying potassium salts. As a result, a steady difference of potential, the *injury* or *demarcation potential*,* develops between electrodes A and B. Now, when a volley of impulses approaches and passes A, the full course of the activity at A is recorded as a negative-going variation of the steady demarcation potential, as illustrated in Figure 2. Activity recorded in this manner is called a *monophasic compound action potential.* For the reasons mentioned above, monophasic recording is used almost exclusively in studies of the compound action potential of nerve trunks.

In physiology the convention is to arrange the recording leads so that external negativity (i.e., activity under the "active" electrode) yields an upward deflection. This deviation from the convention in physics of displaying potentials "positive-up, negative-down" originally resulted from esthetic considerations. The first bioelectric transient observed was the negative-going monophasic action potential, or negative variation, and since rising deflections are generally more pleasing psychologically and esthetically than descending ones, the arbitrary convention of "negative-up, positive-down" was adopted. On a sheer priority basis, therefore, physiologists who record positive-going deflections (e.g., cortical surface potentials) have the choice of heretical nonconformism or submission to the fate of purveying depressing descending deflections.

Components of the Compound Action Potential of Peripheral Nerves. The compound action potential recorded monophasically from

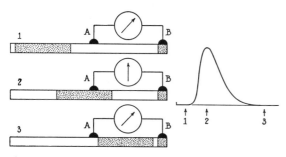

Fig. 2. Monophasic recording of nerve action potential.

Left, Small stippled area under B indicates nerve has been injured at this point. Consequently a steady injury potential is recorded in 1, B being negative to A. As action potential (long stippled area) progresses to A in 2, A and B become equipotential. In 3, action potential progresses beyond A and B is once more negative to A.

Right, Recorded monophasic action potential; numbered arrows indicate instantaneous potentials recorded at three stages of conduction shown at left.

*The demarcation potential might be expected to approximate the membrane potential of the injured fiber, since electrode B is connected to a region in which the steady membrane potential has been reduced to zero by destruction of the membrane. However, current will flow in the external medium from adjacent uninjured regions into the injured region and return through the axoplasm in each fiber. Consequently, the potential drop between the electrodes depends on the relative external and internal resistances of each fiber. Since internal resistance in fibers of the size considered here is quite high, the demarcation potential is only about one-fourth to one-third of the steady transmembrane potential. The shunting can be minimized by increasing the resistance of the external medium, e.g., by bathing the nerve at one recording site with isotonic sucrose. In such instances the demarcation potential approaches closely the true membrane potential. This method has proved useful in measuring action and membrane potentials of fibers too small to tolerate direct measurements with intracellular electrodes.

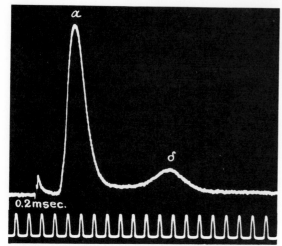

Fig. 3. Compound action potential of cat's saphenous nerve recorded 3.4 cm. from locus of stimulation. Temperature 37.5° C. (Courtesy of Dr. H. S. Gasser.)

a nerve trunk excited by a maximal* shock is usually irregular in contour, displaying two or more elevations displaced in time. Figure 3 shows a representative tracing, on a fast time base, of the first portion of the compound action potential in the cat saphenous nerve, recorded 3.4 cm. from the locus of stimulation; the successive components are labeled with Greek letters. Two hypotheses may be formulated to explain the polymodal contour of the compound potential: (i) some fibers may discharge repetitively to the stimulus, or (ii) the constituent fibers may conduct impulses at different speeds so that arrival time at the recording electrode is different for impulses in different fibers.

The second hypothesis can be put to a simple experimental test; if different fibers conduct impulses at different speeds, the temporal separation of the elevations should increase as the conduction distance increases. Figure 4 shows an experiment in which the first two components (labeled α and β) of the compound action potential in a frog sciatic nerve were tested for compliance with this requirement. Monophasic recording leads were attached to the nerve at four sites to sample the configuration of the compound action potential at four distances from

*Generally, a maximal stimulus or shock is one which produces a maximal response of the stimulated structure; i.e., stronger stimuli do not produce greater responses. For a nerve trunk a maximal stimulus is one which is adequate to excite all of the constituent fibers of the trunk and therefore produces a maximal compound action potential.

the stimulating electrode (S). At the farthest recording site (distance: 143 mm.), the α and β components were clearly separated. At the successively shorter conduction distances, the two elevations merged progressively until, at the most proximal electrode site (distance: 21 mm.), the overlap was so nearly complete that the individual components were scarcely distinguishable. Diagonal lines were then drawn between zero distance and the respective beginnings of α and β in the lowermost record, where the two components are clearly separated. The line so constructed for α intercepts with satisfactory precision the beginning of the α deflection in all

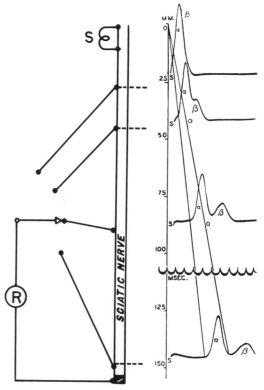

Fig. 4. Compound action potential of frog sciatic nerve recorded at different distances from site of stimulation.

Left, Diagram of recording apparatus: *S,* stimulus; *R,* recorder.

Right, Only the first two elevations, α and β, are shown. As conduction increases, α and β become clearly separated in time (temporal dispersion) because they reflect activity of fibers' conduction at different rates. Diagonal straight lines are drawn through onsets of α and β deflections; slopes of these lines give conduction rates of most rapidly conducting α and β fibers. (After Erlanger and Gasser, *Electrical signs of nervous activity.* Philadelphia, University of Pennsylvania Press, 1937.)

traces. Similarly, the line for the β deflection falls close to the computed onset of the β component indicated by small circles in the two intermediate traces. These results are best explained if it is assumed that impulses beginning together at S become temporally dispersed as the conduction distance increases because they traverse fibers with different uniform conduction speeds.

Closer scrutiny of the traces in which the components are clearly separated reveals that at increasing distances each deflection becomes broader in base and lower in amplitude. Nevertheless, planimetric measurements indicate that the area lying under each deflection remains constant, irrespective of the conduction distance. This finding suggests that within a group, as well as from group to group, there is a continuous spectrum of conduction speeds. This conclusion is borne out by determinations of conduction velocity in single axons. Among mammalian myelinated somatic fibers, representatives can be found for all speeds between about 5 m. per second and 120 m. per second. It will be pointed out later that the separation of peaks in the compound action potential results not from absolute discontinuities in the velocity spectrum but rather from unequal numerical distribution of fibers representing restricted bands of the spectrum.

Another readily demonstrable difference between fibers contributing to the various components (α, β, γ, etc.) of the compound action potential lies in the *thresholds to externally applied electrical stimuli*. As the shock to a nerve trunk is increased progressively from its threshold to maximal intensities, the successive components appear in the recording in the order α, β, γ, etc. In other words, conduction velocity and electrical threshold are inversely related, the rapidly conducting axons being more easily excited than the slower ones. It can be justifiably argued that axon thresholds to externally applied electrical stimuli have little intrinsic physiologic significance, but the relationship just described provides a valuable experimental maneuver, for it permits selective excitation of rapidly conducting fibers to the exclusion of slowly conducting fibers.

This maneuver is used repeatedly in neurophysiologic experimentation. An example pertinent to the present discussion is shown in Figure 5, which illustrates an experiment demonstrating conclusively that the α and β components of frog nerve arise independently from activity in different nerve fibers. The compound action potential was recorded from a site on the nerve trunk at a distance from the stimulating electrodes sufficient to separate clearly the α and β deflections. Two shocks of different intensities

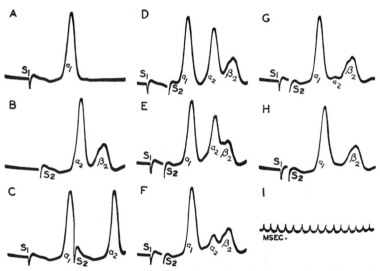

Fig. 5. Demonstration of independent conduction of α and β elevations of frog sciatic nerve. *A*, Stimulation by single shock (S_1) at strength just sufficient to produce maximal alpha elevation (α_1). *B*, Stimulation by stronger shock (S_2) produces an alpha elevation (α_2) and a beta (β_2) elevation. In records *C-H*, S_2 follows S_1 at progressively shorter intervals, so that deflection α_2 falls increasingly into refractory period of deflection α_1 until, in *H*, α_2 is completely obliterated. β_2 deflection is unaltered by refractory obliteration of α_2. *I*, Time scale. (From Erlanger and Gasser, *Electrical signs of nervous activity*. Philadelphia, University of Pennsylvania Press, 1937.)

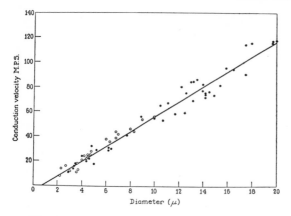

Fig. 6. Linear relation between conduction rate and diameter of mammalian myelinated nerve fibers. Slope of line is approximately 6 m. per second per μ of diameter. (After Hursh, from Gasser, *Ohio J. Sci.,* 1941, *41:*145–159.)

were used. The first stimulus was relatively weak and elicited only an α deflection, seen in *A.* The second shock was more intense and produced both α and β deflections (labeled α_2 and β_2 in *B).* In traces *C-H,* both shocks were applied to the nerve at gradually decreasing intershock intervals. At short intervals (traces *E-H*) α_2, coming in the refractory period of α, was progressively delayed and attenuated until, in trace *H,* α_2 was completely obliterated. At all intervals β_2 remained constant in amplitude and latency. The failure of α activity to induce refractoriness in elements responsible for β activity is an elegant and compelling proof that α and β components of the compound action potential are independently conducted by different fibers. Similar observations on later components indicate that these, too, are mediated by separate groups of axons.

RELATION BETWEEN CONDUCTION SPEED AND FIBER DIAMETER. The finding that nerve trunks are composed of elements having different properties (conduction speed and electrical threshold) leads naturally to the question: Can these differences in properties be correlated with morphologic differences between axons? There are numerous structural differences between axons, such as diameter and the presence or absence of a myelin sheath. At present, attention is focused on variations in diameter. For this purpose it is instructive to examine the myelinated somatic axons, or A fibers, as they are called, because they constitute a set in which diameter is the only prominent morphologic variable. It is the A fibers that are responsible

for the elevations labeled α and δ in Figure 3. When cross sections of various somatic nerve trunks treated with the myelin stain osmic acid are examined, the largest stained fibers are about 22 μ in diameter, the smallest about 1 μ. Between these two extremes there is a continuous spectrum of diameters, but the number of fibers in each portion of the diameter spectrum varies; indeed, in some nerve trunks certain bands of the spectrum may lack representation altogether.

The A fibers taken as a whole constitute a similar spectrum with respect to conduction rates. On purely theoretical grounds one would expect the largest fibers to conduct most rapidly, since their internal longitudinal resistance (the local circuit through which, according to theory, current must flow to excite adjacent nodes) is relatively low. In fact, it can be shown that the conduction rate and the fiber diameter of A fibers are linearly related. Hursh[11] plotted maximal conduction rates of various nerve trunks against the sizes of the largest myelinated fibers he found when he examined the trunks histologically, the trunks having been selected so that they provided a wide range of maximal fiber diameters. As shown in Figure 6, his results indicate that a straight line with a slope of 6 m. per second per μ of over-all diameter fits the observed points with reasonable accuracy.

Gasser and Grundfest[9] found an even closer approximation to exact linearity when they measured the diameter of the axon within the myelin sheath, rather than the over-all diameter; in their study, the ratio between conduction rate (in meters per second) and axon diameter (in microns) was 8.7. The relationship between conduction speed and fiber diameter is exceedingly useful because it permits reasonably accurate computation of one variable if the other is known. It must be emphasized, however, that the specific quantitative relationships just described apply only to the A fibers and not to other fiber types.

Once the relationship between fiber diameter and conduction velocity is recognized, it is easy to understand why large, rapidly conducting axons have lower thresholds to externally applied electrical shocks than do smaller, slowly conducting axons. When a shock is delivered through two electrodes placed in external contact with a nerve trunk, current flows between the two electrodes. Much of this current flows through the low-resistance interstitial fluid be-

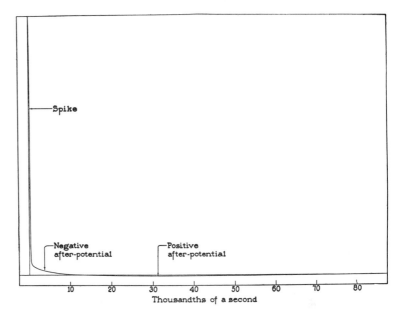

Fig. 7. Scale diagram of complete action potential of large myelinated nerve fibers in the cat, drawn so that spike potential and afterpotentials appear in their correct relative sizes and time relations. (From Gasser, *J. appli. Physiol.*, 1938, *9*:88–96.)

tween the fibers and is ineffective in excitation. If the shock is sufficiently strong, however, some current flows in through the membrane at the anode, longitudinally through the axoplasm and out through the membrane at the cathode. Outward transmembrane current flow depolarizes the membrane underlying the cathode and, if of threshold magnitude, triggers the Hodgkin cycle as described in Chapter 2. This condition is easy to obtain with large axons because the longitudinal resistance is relatively low; with small axons the longitudinal resistance is higher and larger currents must be passed before adequate amounts traverse the effective path in through the membrane, longitudinally through the axoplasm and out through the membrane at the cathode. Thus the relationships of conduction velocity and of threshold to fiber diameter are both relatively simple and predictable consequences of the relationship between internal longitudinal resistance to fiber diameter.

Afterpotentials. The compound action potential recorded at short conduction distances to minimize dispersion of components does not always terminate with the negative variation or spike potential. Often, a negative deflection, the *negative afterpotential,* is grafted onto the tail of the declining spike. Following the decline of the negative afterpotential to the baseline, a prolonged positive deflection, the *positive afterpotential,* occurs.

Negative and positive afterpotentials have certain features in common. (i) Both are consequences of, and hence dependent upon, ante-cedent spike activity. (ii) Both are of very low amplitude and (iii) of long duration relative to the spike (see Fig. 7). (iv) Both are highly labile and heavily dependent upon the metabolic state and previous history of the fiber.

Since the afterpotentials reflect post-spike changes in the degree of polarization of the fibers, it is not surprising that they are accompanied by changes of excitability. During the negative afterpotential, the axons are slightly

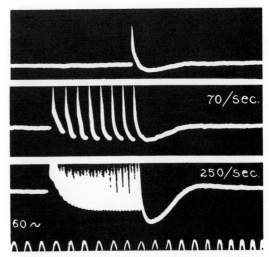

Fig. 8. Afterpotentials of phrenic nerve following single (*upper* trace) and repetitive (*middle* and *lower* traces) stimulation. Amplification is so high that spike crest is far off this page. Records shown begin with negative afterpotential and continue below baseline into positive afterpotential. Time scale, 16.7 milliseconds. (From Gasser, *J. appl. Physiol.*, 1938, *9*:88–96.)

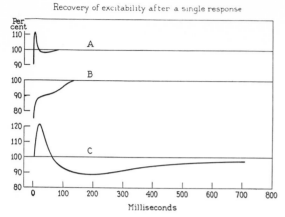

Recovery of excitability after a single response

Milliseconds

Fig. 9. Recovery cycles of A, B and C fibers. *Ordinates,* Excitability in terms of resting threshold set at 100. *Abscissae,* Time interval between conditioning and test shocks. (From Gasser, *Ohio J. Sci.,* 1941, *41:*145–159.)

depolarized and their excitability is elevated; during the positive afterpotential the fibers are slightly hyperpolarized and their excitability is depressed (Fig. 9). These post-spike alterations of excitability are called the *supernormal* and *subnormal periods,* respectively.

The origin of the afterpotentials is not entirely clear. Their timing suggests that they reflect metabolic processes associated with recovery. It is significant that 95 to 98 per cent of the increase in heat production of tetanized nerve occurs during the recovery period and runs a time course roughly corresponding to that of the afterpotentials. It is also significant that afterpotentials (especially the positive afterpotential)

are markedly accentuated in magnitude and duration by repetitive activity, which imposes a recovery "debt" on the fibers. Moreover, afterpotentials are most prominent in small fibers; for example, the positive afterpotential of C fibers may be as much as 10 to 30 per cent of the amplitude of the spike. Other things being equal, the influx of Na^+ during the passage of a spike along a segment of axon depends on the surface area of membrane, which is proportional to the radius. The change in intracellular concentration of Na^+, however, is inversely related to the volume of the segment, which varies with the *square of the radius.* It might therefore be expected that spike activity would produce a greater change in axoplasmic composition in a small fiber than in a larger fiber.

It has been suggested that the negative afterpotential results from extracellular accumulation of K^+ following the spike.[10] Calculations of the ion exchange during the spike indicate that this explanation is valid only if there is some barrier outside the axon which prevents ready diffusion of extruded K^+ throughout the extracellular space and thereby keeps the K^+ concentration high in the space immediately surrounding the axon membrane. As described in more detail below, C fibers lie in invaginations of Schwann cells (Fig. 10) so that the immediate extracellular space is peculiarly restricted in such a way that extracellular accumulation of K^+ during activity may well produce appreciable increases in external concentration of this ion.

Two mechanisms appear to be responsible for

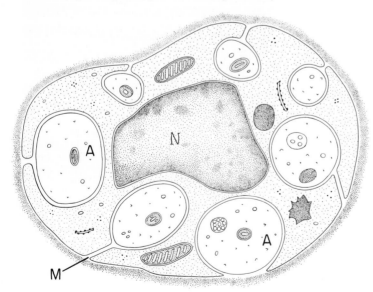

Fig. 10. Diagram of relation of C fibers to Schwann cells. Drawing represents cross section through single Schwann cell surrounding seven C fibers. *N,* Nucleus of Schwann cell; *A,* axon; *M,* mesaxon. Note that Schwann cell membrane is everywhere intact but is invaginated by nerve fibers. (After Elfvin, *J. Ultrastructure Res.,* 1958, *1:*428–454.)

TABLE 1. *Properties of Mammalian Nerve Fibers*

	A	B	s.C	d.r.C
Fiber diameter, μ	1–22	≤ 3	0.3–1.3	0.4–1.2
Conduction speed, m. per sec.	5–120	3–15	0.7–2.3	0.6–2.0
Spike duration, msec.	0.4–0.5	1.2	2.0	2.0
Absolutely refractory period, msec.	0.4–1.0	1.2	2.0	2.0
Negative afterpotential amplitude,				
per cent of spike	3–5	none	3–5	none
Duration, msec.	12–20	. . . .	50–80	. . . .
Positive afterpotential amplitude,				
per cent of spike	0.2	1.5–4.0	1.5	*
Duration, msec.	40–60	100–300	300–1000	*
Order of susceptibility to asphyxia	2	1	3	3
Velocity/diameter ratio	6	?	?	1.73 average

*A post-spike positivity 10 to 30 per cent of spike amplitude and decaying to half size in 50 msec. is recorded from d.r.C fibers. This afterpositivity differs from the positive afterpotential of other fibers (see text).

positive afterpotentials. (i) It has already been pointed out that the downstroke of the spike is due to a waning of Na^+ permeability and a rather prolonged increase in K^+ permeability. Since in the resting state K^+ is actively pumped into the axon, the resting membrane potential is slightly less than the K^+ equilibrium potential. During the post-spike period of elevated K^+ permeability, the membrane seeks a potential level closer to the K^+ equilibrium potential, i.e., becomes hyperpolarized. In accord with this theory, the positive afterpotential of C fibers is diminished by artificially increasing the external K^+ concentration.[10] (ii) The rate of the Na^+–K^+ pump increases with increased internal Na^+ concentration. Increased active extrusion of Na^+ drives the membrane potential farther from the Na^+ equilibrium potential, i.e., in a hyperpolarizing direction. Acceleration of the Na^+–K^+ pump appears to be principally responsible for the large positive afterpotentials following repetitive activity (Fig. 8), for replacing extracellular Na^+ with lithium or blocking the Na^+–K^+ pump with metabolic poisons abolishes post-tetanic positive afterpotentials.[15]

Types of Nerve Fibers.[6, 7] Systematic examination of the compound action potentials of various nerves of different composition reveals that axons can be classified into four distinctive types known as A, B, s.C and d.r.C fibers. The A fibers have already been described as myelinated, somatic, afferent and efferent fibers. The B fibers are myelinated, efferent, preganglionic axons found in autonomic nerves. The C fibers are unmyelinated, the s.C group being the efferent postganglionic sympathetic axons, and the d.r.C group the small unmyelinated afferent axons found in peripheral nerves and dorsal roots. The distinctive properties of these fiber types are summarized in Table 1 and Figure 9.

It should be noted that the A fibers, although comprising a wide range of fiber diameters, constitute a homogeneous group except in respect to conduction speed, which varies predictably with diameter in the manner already described.

The B fibers are histologically indistinguishable from small A fibers and, as can be seen in Table 1, have conduction rates within the range exhibited by the A group, the smallest of which conduct impulses at speeds as low as 5 m. per second. B fibers are principally distinguished from A fibers by the absence of a negative afterpotential. Correspondingly, the recovery cycle of B fibers lacks a supernormal period, the relatively refractory period merging directly with the subnormal period (Fig. 9B). B fibers also differ from A fibers in spike duration, which for B is more than twice as great as for A fibers. Although a sizable range of conduction rates is represented, the compound action potential of B fibers, even at long conduction distances, is relatively smooth and does not break up into discrete elevations. This configuration is seen because all parts of the velocity spectrum have relatively equal numerical representation.

Unlike both A and B fibers, C fibers lack a

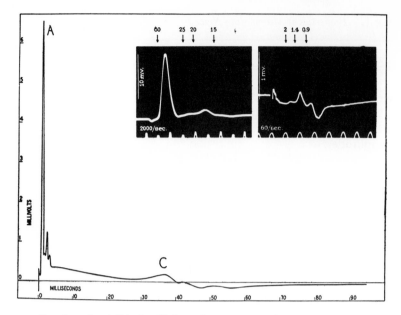

Fig. 11. Scale drawing of complete compound action potential of mammalian saphenous nerve. *Left inset,* Recording of A fiber components. *Right inset,* Recording of C fiber components. Numbers above arrows give maximal conduction rates (m. per sec.) of each component. (Combined from Gasser, *J. appl. physiol.,* 1938, *9*:88–96 and *Ohio J. Sci.,* 1941, *41*:145–159.)

myelin sheath visible by light microscopy and exhibit a unique relation between the Schwann sheath and the axon.[5, 8] A single Schwann cell forms the sheath of several C fibers, which lie in grooves formed by the invagination of the outer surface of the Schwann cells (Fig. 10). When the fibers are deeply embedded, the edges of the invaginated Schwann membrane lie in close approximation, forming narrow channels (*mesaxons*) to the outside. The space between the Schwann membrane and the axon membrane and that between the bounding membranes of the mesaxon appears to be of the order of 100 Ångstroms. It is this narrow communication with the outside which presumably forms the external diffusion barrier mentioned above.

Functionally, C fibers are distinguished from A fibers by slow conduction rates, long spike durations, high electrical thresholds and relatively great resistance to asphyxia. The various parts of the velocity and diameter spectra are unequally represented in the nerve trunks, and the conducted compound action potential displays a number of discrete elevations of surpassing complexity.

C fibers are divided into two groups, s.C and d.r.C, largely on the basis of differences in their afterpotentials.[7] The s.C group, postganglionic sympathetic axons, has pronounced negative and positive afterpotentials. The d.r.C group, comprised of the unmyelinated afferent fibers of peripheral nerves and dorsal roots, has no negative afterpotential but typically displays a large afterpositivity, which differs from the conven-

tional positive afterpotential in that it is converted by repetitive activity into a negative deflection.

Composition of Peripheral Nerves. A typical peripheral nerve such as the sciatic nerve contains both afferent and efferent A fibers, afferent d.r.C fibers and s.C fibers supplying smooth muscle and glandular structures. Because the discrepancy in conduction rate and amplitude between the A and C groups is so great, it is not feasible to record the entire compound action potential of a mixed peripheral nerve on a single sweep of the oscilloscope, but the picture may be resynthesized graphically from several records taken with appropriate amplifications and time bases. Figure 11 shows such a resynthesized action potential, drawn to scale, for the saphenous nerve (a purely afferent cutaneous nerve), along with the recordings which provided the requisite data.

To prepare for discussions in subsequent chapters it is important to know the respective diameter spectra of the afferent and efferent A fibers in the various nerves. For cutaneous nerves, in which all the A fibers are afferent, the spectrum is determined simply by inspection of sections of the whole nerve stained with osmic acid. To ascertain the spectra for mixed nerves, it is necessary to cut the contributory ventral or dorsal roots (distal to the ganglion) and allow the efferent or afferent fibers, respectively, to degenerate. The remaining fibers may then be counted. Figure 12 shows the diameter distributions of the afferent fibers in a cutaneous nerve

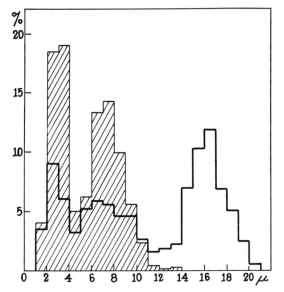

Fig. 12. Comparison of afferent fiber diameter distribution in a muscle nerve (heavy line) and a cutaneous nerve (hatched area). *Ordinates,* Number of fibers expressed as percentage of total. *Abscissae,* Fiber diameter in μ.

the two prominent clusters, from 12 to 20 μ and from 2 to 8 μ, being separated by a definite nadir in the range from 8 to 12 μ. Corresponding to the two distinctly separated clusters in the histogram are two distinct elevations in the conducted compound action potential (see Fig. 17, Chap. 7). As will be discussed in a subsequent chapter, these two groups of motor fibers differ functionally.

Deafferented nerve trunks (but not ventral roots) contain, in addition to the A fibers, unmedullated postganglionic autonomic axons (s.C) which supply smooth muscle and glandular structures.

The diameter distribution shown in Figure 13 is, in general, typical of all ventral roots, but there are minor individual differences. The most marked difference is between those roots (thoracic and upper lumbar) which contribute white rami to the sympathetic chain and those which do not. In the former, but not in the latter, there is a sizable peak below 3 μ in the range of distribution; this peak is composed of B fibers.

(thin line, crosshatched area) and in a "demotored," deep or muscle nerve (heavy line). The cutaneous afferent fibers have a bimodal distribution, one peak lying between 1 μ and 5 μ and the other between about 6 μ and 12 μ. The histogram for the muscle nerve, however, shows three peaks, two of which are approximately coextensive with the two peaks in the cutaneous nerve distribution. The third peak is comprised of large fibers, 12 to 21 μ in diameter, which are almost completely lacking in the cutaneous nerve. Systematic examination of the afferent fiber composition of different nerves shows that the relationships indicated in Figure 12 can be generalized: *the large (12 to 21 μ) afferent fibers are confined to muscle nerves, whereas the other two groups (1 to 5 μ and 6 to 12 μ), although varying somewhat in proportions, are represented in all somatic nerve trunks.*

It should be remembered that both cutaneous and "demotored" muscle nerves contain a great many unmedullated d.r.C fibers as well as the medullated A fibers. In fact, in some cutaneous nerve trunks unmedullated fibers may be three or four times as prevalent as A fibers.

The diameter spectra of efferent fibers is illustrated in Figure 13, which shows the diameter distributions in a ventral root and in a typical muscle nerve deafferented by degenerative dorsal root section. In both the root and the nerve the distribution is distinctly bimodal,

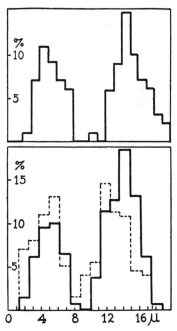

Fig. 13. Diameter distributions of efferent fibers. Coordinates as in Figure 12. *Upper,* Data from ventral root. *Lower,* Data from gastrocnemius nerve, from which afferent fibers were removed by degenerative section of dorsal roots. *Solid line,* Data from sample taken 50 mm. from muscle. *Broken line,* Data from sample 8 mm. from muscle. Since daughter fibers are of lesser diameter than parent fibers, spectrum shifts slightly to left at the closer distance. (After Eccles and Sherrington, *Proc. roy. Soc.,* 1930, *B106:*326–357.)

Terminology. It has already been mentioned that the Greek letters α, β, γ, δ (and sometimes ε) are often used to designate the successive elevations of the compound action potential of the A fibers in a nerve trunk. Since these elevations result from activity in fibers conducting at different velocities, proportional to fiber diameter, the Greek-letter designation may also be used as a categorization of fiber diameters. A difficulty arises, however, because an elevation in the compound action potential reflects not only the diameter but also the number of fibers involved. In nerves with similar function and origins, e.g., cutaneous sensory nerves, the diameter spectra are surprisingly constant. However, when nerves with different origins and functions are compared, striking discrepancies are evident; for example, the first major deflection of the compound action potential of a "demotored" muscle nerve occupies fibers of a diameter range which is sparsely represented in cutaneous nerves. For the afferent fibers of deep nerve trunks, it is current practice to use Lloyd's[12] Roman-numeral designations, which are based on fiber diameter rather than on electrogram elevations. According to this classification, the A fibers of muscle nerves are divided into three groups: I, 12 to 21 μ; II, 6 to 12 μ; and III, 1 to 6 μ. The C fibers (both the d.r. and the s. subgroups) are sometimes referred to as Group IV.

For cutaneous afferent fibers the Greek-letter designations are preferable: *alpha* (6 to 17 μ) and *delta* (1 to 6 μ). Cutaneous unmyelinated afferent fibers are called simply C fibers.

Unfortunately, Greek-letter and Roman-numeral designations are often used interchangeably. The following relations approximately equate the two designations: (i) A-alpha corresponds to Groups I and II. (ii) A-delta corresponds to Group III. (iii) The C group corresponds to Group IV. In cat nerve the deflections originally labeled beta and gamma are apparently largely or wholly artifacts and have no equivalents in the Roman-numerical classification.

Conduction in Regenerating Axons.

When an axon is severed, the portion disconnected from the cell body undergoes a sequence of morphologic changes known as *Wallerian* or *secondary degeneration.** These changes consist of

---

*Changes occurring in the cell body after its axon has been amputated are called *retrograde degeneration.* These changes include disappearance of Nissl granules (chromatolysis), swelling of the perikaryon, and displacement of the nucleus from its typical central position to the periphery. In some neurons (e.g., spinal motoneurons) retrograde degeneration is reversible, and the cell body eventually regains its normal morphologic features and functional properties. In others (e.g., thalamic neurons) retrograde degeneration is irreversible, and the dead perikaryon is removed by phagocytes. Rarely, morphologic changes similar to those of irreversible retrograde degeneration occur in a cell body

chemical alteration of the myelin, leading ultimately to its complete dissolution, along with fragmentation and eventual dissolution of the axis cylinder. The degeneration products of both the myelin and the axis cylinder are removed by macrophages.

This process would leave a hollow tube of Schwann sheath if an exuberant proliferation of the Schwann cells did not fill the lumen with a solid column of Schwann cells. At the level of transection, the Schwann cells also grow out of the end of the stumps and, if the gap is not excessive, bridge the space between them, reestablishing continuity. From the end of the axon in the proximal stump, a multitude of sprouts develop and grow between the Schwann cells of the bridge into the column beyond. Although many such sprouts cross the bridge, usually only one survives and continues to advance distally at a rate which may be as great as 3.5 to 4.5 mm. per day. The advancing tip of the regenerating fiber is unmyelinated, and its diameter is small compared to that of the Schwann column in which it grows. Maturation of the fiber, i.e., increase in diameter and acquisition of a myelin sheath, eventually restores the morphological picture typical of mature nerves. Maturation is much slower than longitudinal advance. There is evidence that maturation is progressive along a regenerating stretch of nerve; i.e., at any time the proximal segments are more mature than are the distal segments.

The conduction speed in a regenerating nerve increases as regeneration progresses and constitutes a reliable measure of the time course of maturation. It may be that normal conduction rates are never regained after nerves are cut and resutured. For example, Berry *et al.*[1] found that the maximum conduction rate in a sciatic nerve more than a year (450 days) after section and suture was about 85 m. per second, whereas a normal sciatic nerve contains fibers conducting at rates up to 120 m. per second. Histologic examination revealed that the largest fiber in the regenerated nerve measured 16 μ, compared with 20 μ in the normal nerve. Failure to mature completely appears to be re-

---

after section of the axons making synaptic connections with it; this phenomenon is known as *transneuronal degeneration.* An example is degeneration of neurons in the lateral geniculate body following section of the optic nerve.

lated to extensive branching (which results in daughter fibers smaller than the parent axon) at the suture line. When the nerve is crushed rather than sectioned, complete maturation occurs, apparently because the continuity of the sheaths is not broken, and the axons grow into their own sheaths without branching.

In the clinical treatment of injuries to peripheral nerves, the major consideration is to establish continuity of the stumps, for, if the gap is large, the probability of sprouts successfully traversing the bridge and reaching the distal stump is reduced. Sprouts meeting an obstruction may form a painful tumor called a *neuroma*. When the nerve has merely been crushed, the prognosis is good. If the trunk is interrupted, the ends of the stumps are approximated by suturing through the epineurium or by gluing the ends together with fibrinogen. When the gap is too large to permit approximation of the severed ends, *cable grafts* are sometimes employed; i.e., segments of expendable nerves (for example, cutaneous nerves) are removed and sutured between the stumps to provide the framework for a bridge.

POTENTIALS IN A VOLUME CONDUCTOR* [14]

A nerve fiber is surrounded by interstitial fluid and by other fibers. Although the other fibers, especially if they are myelinated, are good insulators,† the interstitial fluid is a volume conductor which extends throughout the body. Unless current is flowing in a volume conductor, it is isopotential. In the body, current flows in the interstitial fluid only during impulse conduction in excitable cells; no current flows in quiescent cells. The existence of a current flow in a volume conductor means that there must be a voltage source present. This

*This section written by J. W. Woodbury.

†In tissues other than myelinated nerve, membrane resistance is much lower and capacitance much higher than in nerve, and an appreciable part of the local current may flow through adjacent inactive cells. Part of this current flows through the membrane resistor and, during rapid changes in potential in the interstitial fluid, part flows through the membrane capacitor. Thus, to a limited extent, inactive cells are a portion of the volume conductor surrounding an active cell.

source, in an impulse, is the voltage difference between the active region and the inactive region.

In comparison with the potentials recorded from an isolated nerve trunk, the potential at a point in a volume conductor (recorded with respect to an electrode so distant that its potential is negligible) is difficult to interpret. (i) It is difficult to determine the location of the active fibers because their currents spread throughout the body. (ii) The size and time course of the volley are uncertain because, as the distance between the recording electrode and the active tissue is increased, the recorded potential becomes smaller and slower. (iii) The relationship between the changes in transmembrane potential and the resulting current flow in the volume conductor is quite complicated.

However, the estimation of potentials occurring in a volume conductor as a result of nerve activity is made fairly simple if the action potential is approximated by a square wave, i.e., if depolarization and repolarization are treated as if they were instantaneous (see Fig. 19*b*). The potential set up at a point in a volume conductor by a square action potential is proportional to the product of the height of the transmembrane action potential and the solid angle of the wave boundaries as measured at the recording electrode. The solid angle is a measure of the apparent size of an object as viewed from a particular point. The square wave approximation to the action potential is quantitatively inaccurate, but this approximation does give an accurate estimate of the sequence of potential changes. The use of this approximation is justified by the great conceptual and computational simplification that results.

Since the variation of recorded potential with distance from the active tissue depends solely on the solid angle of the wave boundaries, and since the concept of a solid angle is unfamiliar to most students, the first parts of this section present a definition of the solid angle. It is then shown that the potential due to a dipole layer is proportional to the solid angle subtended by the potential at the recording electrode. The section concludes with a description of how this principle is applied to the interpretation of the potentials set up in a volume conductor by nerve activity.

Solid Angle. A solid angle is measured in a manner analogous to measurement of a plane angle, and therefore, the manner of measur-

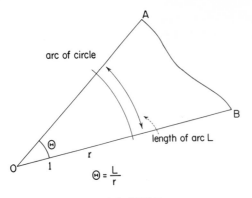

$$\Theta = \frac{L}{r}$$

a. PLANE ANGLE

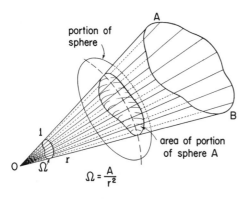

$$\Omega = \frac{A}{r^2}$$

b. SOLID ANGLE

Fig. 14. Calculation of plane and solid angles. *a,* Measurement of plane angle Θ, subtended by a curving line AB from point O. Arc of a circle of radius r with center at O is inscribed. Length of arc, L, between lines OA and OB is measured. Θ is defined as equal to L/r. *b,* Measurement of solid angle, Ω, subtended by surface AB from O. Radii are drawn from O to all points on periphery of AB. This irregular cone is a solid angle. Ω is measured by inscribing a sphere of radius r with center at O and measuring the area, A, on the surface of sphere cut out by the irregular cone. Ω is defined as A/r^2.

ing a plane angle will be reviewed here. The angle Θ, subtended at O by a curved line AB (Fig. 14a), may be measured in degrees; but a more general and natural way to measure the angle is as follows. A circle of any radius (r) with a center at O is drawn. The angle Θ, in radians, is defined as the ratio of the length of an arc (L) between lines OA and OB to the radius; $\Theta = L/r$. This definition conforms with experience; when the angle is fixed, L increases proportionately with r, so L/r remains constant. An angle of 1 radian is such that the arc length is equal to the radius. The circumference of a circle is $2\pi r$, so a full circle is an

angle of $2\pi r/r = 2\pi$ radians. Therefore, 1 radian $= 360°/2\pi = 57.4°$. Angular measure in radians is dimensionless.

A solid angle is the three-dimensional equivalent of a plane angle. The solid angle subtended at a point by any object is proportional to the apparent size of the object when the object is viewed from the point. For this reason, the potential at a point in a volume conductor is often referred to as being "seen" by the electrode. An object looms larger as it is brought nearer to the eye, even though the dimensions of the object do not change. The solid angle subtended at point O (Fig. 14b) by the object AB may be outlined by drawing lines from O to every point on the perimeter of AB. The size of a solid angle Ω (omega) is calculated by drawing a sphere of radius r about O as the center; the area (A) cut out by the solid angle on the surface of the sphere is then measured, just as the length of the arc was measured to determine the size of a plane angle. Since the surface area of a sphere is $4\pi r^2$, A depends on the square of the radius. Therefore, just as $\Theta = L/r$, $\Omega = A/r^2$. The dimensionless unit of solid angle measure is the *steradian*. One steradian is the solid angle subtended by an area of 1 cm.^{2} (of any shape) on the surface of a sphere with a radius of 1 cm. The solid angle of an object that completely surrounds O is $4\pi r^2/r^2 = 4\pi$ steradians.

Potential Due to Dipole Layer. Two equal and opposite charges (q) held a short distance (δ) apart constitute a *dipole* of moment (m); $m = q\delta$ (Fig. 15a). The electric field of a dipole

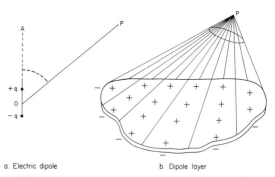

a. Electric dipole   b. Dipole layer

Fig. 15. Dipole and dipole layer. *a,* In dipole charges +q and −q are the distance δ apart. Potential at P is calculated in terms of angle Θ, between lines OA and OP, and r, the length of OP. *b,* Potential at P is proportional to Ω, the solid angle subtended at P by the dipole layer. q_A is surface charge per unit area and δ is thickness of dipole layer.

falls off rapidly with distance, because the + and − charges exert nearly equal and opposite forces on an exploring charge. At distances large compared with δ, the electric field is inversely proportional to the cube of the distance r; and the potential is inversely proportional to r^2 rather than to r, as it is with a single charge. A *dipole layer* or surface is formed by separating + and − charges across a layer of thickness δ (Fig. 15*b*). Each region of the layer contains equal numbers of + and − charges; i.e., the + and − charges have been separated from each other. However, the number of + or − charges per unit area of the surface may vary from one region to the next. The dipole moment per unit area (m_A) of a dipole layer is the product of the charge per unit area (q_A) and the thickness of the layer; $m_A = q_A\delta$. A charged cell membrane is a closed dipole layer since + and − charges are separated across the membrane. In a quiescent cell m_A is a constant. During activity m_A at a fixed point varies rapidly in time, or, at a fixed time, m_A varies rapidly with distance.

Since the membrane is a capacitor, the amount of charge per unit area is directly proportional to the transmembrane potential at any point. The calculation of the potential arising from cell membrane charge is the same as the computation of the potential of a dipole layer. The potential ($\mathcal{E}$) of a point in a volume conductor is defined as the difference in potential between that point and a point a large distance from the dipole layer. The potential due to a dipole layer is inversely proportional to the square of the distance to it, and so the potential at a sufficiently distant second or indifferent recording electrode can be made arbitrarily small. *At any point, the potential due to a dipole layer of constant moment is proportional to the solid angle subtended by the surface at the point;* $\mathcal{E} = (\mathcal{E}_m/4\pi)\Omega$, where $\mathcal{E}_m$ is the transmembrane potential (Fig. 15*b*). The sign of the potential is the same as the sign of the charge on the face of the dipole layer nearest to P. This rule reduces the problem of computing the potentials in a volume conductor to a problem in solid geometry.

Derivation of potential due to dipole layer. Figure 16*a* shows the geometry involved in computing the potential at P due to the dipole AB. Since the membrane is only about 100 Ångstroms thick, any recording elec-

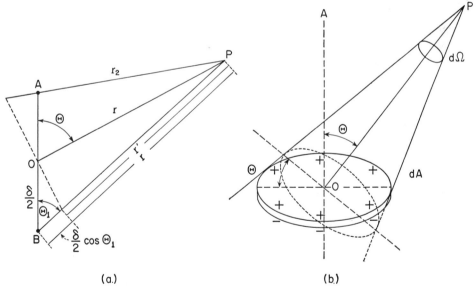

Fig. 16. *a,* Diagram used to calculate potential at P due to a dipole when r is much greater than δ (r is disproportionately short in this drawing). When r is much greater than δ, lines AP, OP, and BP are considered to be parallel and $\Theta_1 = \Theta_2$.

b, Solid angle, dΩ, subtended at point P by a small circular segment, of area dA, of dipole layer. (Both δ and dA are actually much smaller than r, but dA is shown disproportionately large here for clarity.) Sphere of radius r is drawn around P. Area cut out on surface of sphere by dA is dA cos Θ, where Θ is the angle between OA and OP. OA is drawn from center of dA, perpendicular to dA and toward its positively charged surface. If Θ is greater than π/2 (90°), dΩ is negative. Therefore, dΩ = dA cos Θ/r^2.

trode is a large distance away from the membrane compared to its thickness. Although, for the sake of clarity, Figure 16a is drawn with δ nearly as large as r, in the real situation r is much larger than δ; so lines AP, OP and BP are nearly parallel, and $\Theta = \Theta_1$. The potential at P is the sum of the potentials due to the charge $+q$ at A and $-q$ at B:

$$\mathcal{E} = K\left(\frac{q}{r_2} - \frac{q}{r_1}\right) \tag{1}$$

To a good approximation, r_1 and r_2 are given by

$$r_1 = r + \frac{\delta}{2}\cos\Theta$$

$$r_2 = r - \frac{\delta}{2}\cos\Theta$$

Substitution of these into Equation 1 gives

$$\mathcal{E} = Kq\left(\frac{1}{r - \dfrac{\delta}{2}\cos\Theta} - \frac{1}{r + \dfrac{\delta}{2}\cos\Theta}\right) = \frac{Kq\delta\cos\Theta}{r^2 - \dfrac{\delta^2}{4}\cos^2\Theta}$$

or

$$\mathcal{E} = K\frac{m\cos\Theta}{r^2} \tag{2}$$

The last step follows from the definition of m and the approximation that $\delta^2/4$ is negligible compared with r^2. Equation 2 shows that the potential at a point depends inversely on r^2, as stated above, and also on the angle between the dipole and the point. This dependence is expected because the potential along a line through O and perpendicular to AB must be zero, since the component of the electric field along this line is always zero.

Exactly the same arguments apply to any small area (dA) of a dipole layer (Fig. 16b), since each element of area has charges, $+q_A dA$ and $-q_A dA$, at points separated by the distance δ. Therefore, the contribution of dA to the potential at P is

$$d\mathcal{E} = K\frac{q_A dA\delta\cos\Theta}{r^2} = K\frac{m_A dA\cos\Theta}{r^2} \tag{3}$$

Part of Equation 3, dA/r^2, is in the form of an element of solid angle, $d\Omega$. This fact suggests that the solid angle of dA at P should be calculated (Fig. 16b). To calculate $d\Omega$, a sphere of radius r and center P is drawn through dA; dA is then projected onto the surface of this sphere. The area of this projection is dA $\cos\Theta$, so the solid angle is, by definition:

$$d\Omega = \frac{dA\cos\Theta}{r^2} \tag{4}$$

Substitution of Equation 4 in Equation 3 gives

$$d\mathcal{E} = Km_A\frac{dA\cos\Theta}{r^2} = Km_A d\Omega \tag{5}$$

Integration of Equation 5 over the whole of the dipole surface (S) gives

$$\mathcal{E} = K\int_S m_A d\Omega \tag{6}$$

If m_A is constant, Equation 5 is a perfect differential and Equation 6 becomes simply

$$\mathcal{E} = Km_A\Omega \tag{7}$$

where Ω is the solid angle of the surface as seen from P. The simplicity of Equation 7 compared to Equation 6 is the reason for approximating the action potential by a square wave. The integration indicated by Equation 6 is accurate* but is difficult and tedious for the action potential. Equation 7 is comparatively easy to evaluate. The quantity Km_A can be evaluated in terms of $\mathcal{E}_m$, the transmembrane potential. As will be shown below, the potential outside a quiescent cell is everywhere zero because the effective solid angle of the cell is zero. Moving the recording electrode inside the cell changes the potential from zero to $\mathcal{E}_m$ and the effective solid angle from 0 to 4π. Therefore, inside the cell Equation 7 becomes

$$\mathcal{E}_m = Km_A \cdot 4\pi \text{ or } Km_A = \frac{\mathcal{E}_m}{4\pi} \tag{8}$$

The relation then becomes

$$\mathcal{E} = \frac{\mathcal{E}_m}{4\pi}\Omega \tag{9}$$

POTENTIAL OF QUIESCENT CELL. The proportionality between potential and the solid angle of the dipole layer means that the potential depends only on the apparent size of the layer and is independent of its detailed shape. Figure 17 shows that the transmembrane potential of a quiescent cell does not influence the potential at an external point, because any point outside the cell is faced by two equally but oppositely charged surfaces of the same solid angle. Since the transmembrane potential is everywhere constant in a quiescent cell, the potential due to the part of the surface of the cell facing P (Fig. 17b) is $+(\mathcal{E}_m/4\pi)\Omega$, and that due to the portion facing away from P (Fig. 17c) is $-(\mathcal{E}_m/4\pi)\Omega$ because the negatively charged surface faces P. The total potential at P is the sum of the potentials due to all portions of the dipole layer, so

$$\mathcal{E} = +(\mathcal{E}_m/4\pi)\Omega - (\mathcal{E}_m/4\pi)\Omega = 0.$$

* Equation 6 is correct for a nerve fiber only if the specific resistivity of the intracellular fluid is equal to that of the interstitial fluid. The specific resistivity of the axoplasm is about twice that of the interstitial fluid.

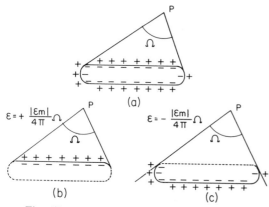

Fig. 17. Axial section of a closed cylindrical cell, drawn to illustrate that the potential outside a quiescent cell is zero. *a*, From point P, the electrode "sees" two equally and oppositely polarized cell membranes subtending the solid angle Ω. *b*, Calculation of potential at P due to the near membrane; potential is $+(|\mathcal{E}_m|/4\pi)\Omega$ because positive side of membrane faces P. *c*, Potential of the far membrane is $-(|\mathcal{E}_m|/4\pi)\Omega$ because negative side of membrane faces P. Total potential is sum of the individual potentials: $\mathcal{E} = (|\mathcal{E}_m|/4\pi)\Omega - (|\mathcal{E}_m|/4\pi)\Omega = 0$, where $|\mathcal{E}_m|$ indicates absolute value of E_m.

This rather formal method of calculation conforms with earlier statements that the external potential due to a quiescent cell is zero because there is no external current flow. It should be emphasized that potential changes in a volume conductor arise from current flow. The current flow due to a dipole layer is such that the potential is proportional to the solid angle.

POTENTIAL OF ACTIVE CELL. As mentioned above, the calculation of the potential generated in a volume conductor by an active cell is simplified by approximating the smoothly rising and falling action potential wave with an abruptly rising and falling square wave. A nerve fiber carrying an impulse can be divided into two regions, quiescent and active. In the square wave approximation it is assumed that the quiescent region has a constant potential ($\mathcal{E}_s$), that the active region has a constant potential equal to the overshoot of the action potential ($\mathcal{E}_a$), and that the transition between the two regions occurs at a point.* Figure 18 shows

* The action potential of a large myelinated nerve fiber rises in about 0.1 millisecond and has a velocity of 100 m. per second. Therefore, the wavefront occupies 100 mm. per millisecond $\times$ 0.1 millisecond = 10 mm. This is 500 times the fiber diameter. Because of this slow rise, potentials recorded in volume from an active nerve are longer and lower than those expected from square-wave solid-angle analysis.

how the potential due to a wavefront of depolarization can be calculated. Figure 18*a* is a diagram of an axial section of an excitable cell with a wave of depolarization near the center. The solid angles Ω_1 and Ω_3 contribute no potential to P, because the proximal and distal portions of the membrane contribute equal and opposite potentials. However, in Ω_2 the proximal membrane is active and contributes a negative potential to P; the distal membrane is inactive and also contributes a negative potential to P. The potential at P is $-(\mathcal{E}_a/4\pi)\Omega_2$, where $\mathcal{E}_a$ is about 130 mV. As Ω_2 is the solid angle of the wavefront, it is seen that the potential at an external point depends only on the solid angle subtended by the boundaries between the ac-

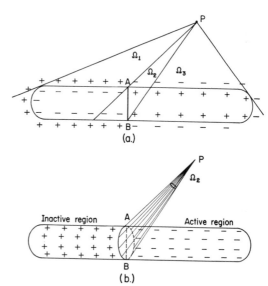

Fig. 18. Potential at an external point P due to the rising phase of action potential in a cell at some instant. Line AB indicates where the transmembrane potential reverses; for simplicity the reversal is assumed to occur abruptly.

a, Axial section through a cylindrical cell showing cell membrane; diameter has been exaggerated. Total solid angle of cell is divided into three portions, Ω_1, Ω_2 and Ω_3 by lines PA and PB. Potential at P due to solid angles Ω_1 and Ω_3 is zero, since the nearer and farther membranes contribute equal but opposite potentials (see Fig. 17). However, in Ω_2 the nearer membrane is active (outside negative) and contributes a potential at P of the same sign as the more distant, inactive membrane.

b, Diagram to show that under conditions in *a*, the potential at P is the same as would be obtained if the membrane charges were placed on the cross section AB. The size of the potential at P at any instant is proportional to the apparent size of the cross section of the nerve at the wavefront.

tive and inactive regions. Figure 18*b* is a perspective sketch of the solid angle of a wave boundary in a nerve fiber.

A nerve impulse is a wave traveling at constant speed, so Figure 18 represents the situation at one instant in time. As this wavefront moves from right to left, the solid angle first increases and then gradually decreases to zero. Figure 19 shows the method of estimating the sequence of potential changes as a single wave-

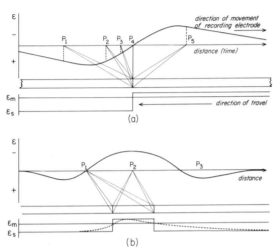

(a)

(b)

Fig. 19. Potential generated by propagating wavefronts.

a, Diphasic potential due to a wavefront traveling from right to left at constant velocity. Time sequence of potential changes at a fixed point is shown along line parallel to nerve fiber. Sequence is constructed by supposing that wavefront is stationary and that a recording electrode is moved from left to right along a line parallel to nerve. When the recording electrode is at points P_1, P_2, P_3, it "sees" positive side of wavefront. Dashed line at P_1 has a height proportional to the solid angle of the wavefront from P_1 and thus proportional to the voltage recorded at P_1. As the recording electrode moves toward the right, solid angle of wavefront at first increases slowly owing to closer approach and then decreases rapidly as the electrode sees the wavefront more and more on edge. At P_4 the potential is zero and immediately thereafter becomes negative. The plot is both of ε as a function of distance at a fixed time and of ε as a function of time at a fixed point.

b, Triphasic potential due to an idealized impulse. Solid angles of waves of both depolarization and repolarization must be added to obtain ε. Construction method same as in *a*. P_1 is point of zero potential; note that it is to left of wavefront. Triphasic $(+,-,+)$ potential is typical of a propagated nerve impulse. Note that the maximum external potential is much smaller than the internal potential. An internal electrode at P_2 would see positive changes over 4π; while outside, even on the surface of the fiber, the solid angle is of the order of $4\pi/100$.

front (*a*) or a nerve impulse (*b*) travels from right to left at a constant velocity. A recording electrode put anywhere on the line P_1P_5 (Fig. 19*a*) would record the positive-negative sequence of potential changes as the wavefront approaches, passes and leaves the point nearest the electrode. The curve may be constructed by supposing that the wave is fixed and that the recording electrode is moving in the opposite direction (left to right) at the same constant velocity. The solid angle at each point P_1, P_2, etc. is measured and an ordinate proportional to the solid angle is drawn at that point. In this way the diphasic positive-negative potential sequence is constructed. The graph can be a plot of potential as a function of distance at a fixed time, or as a function of time with the recording electrode fixed. This diphasic volume-conductor potential is frequently seen in recordings from heart tissue during depolarization, because about 0.5 second elapses between depolarization and repolarization in a heart cell.

Figure 19*b* shows the sequence of potential changes expected from a nerve impulse. The triphasic wave $(+, -, +)$ arises because the waves of depolarization and repolarization are sufficiently close together that both contribute significantly to the potential. To the left of P_1 the wavefront dominates and the potential is positive. At P_1 the two solid angles are equal and opposite in sign, and ε is zero; at P_2 both boundaries contribute a negative potential; and at P_3 the departing wave of repolarization dominates, and the potential is again positive. Triphasic waves are recorded from active nerve fibers in volume, but the last positive phase is much smaller and longer than the first, because repolarization is slower than depolarization (Fig. 20*b*).

Consider the situation in which an impulse originates at a distance from a recording electrode and travels away from it. Such a situation is encountered when an electrode is inserted in the vicinity of a cell body: an impulse initiated in the cell body by synaptic activity travels along the axon away from the cell body. When the cell body becomes active, the electrode sees negativity. ε remains negative but gradually diminishes as the wave of depolarization recedes. Repolarization in the cell body rapidly changes the potential to a large positive value, which falls off as the repolarization recedes.

Figure 20*a* shows the potential recorded from a bullfrog sciatic nerve at a region near its entry

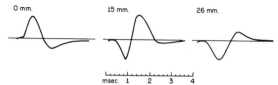

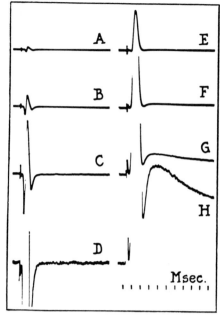

Fig. 20. Nerve action potentials in a volume conductor. An excised bullfrog nerve is arranged so that it enters a volume conductor at x = 0 and exits from it at x = 26 mm. *Ordinate,* Potential of a close electrode with respect to a distant one (negative upward). *Abscissa,* Time.

a, Potential set up by a nerve volley when recording electrode is at level of nerve entry (x = 0) and distant electrode is 3 mm. away from nerve (y = 3). *b,* Potential recorded at x = 15 mm., y = 3 mm. *c,* Potential at x = 26 mm., y = 3 mm. (After Lorente de Nó, *Stud. Rockefeller Inst. Med. Res.,* 1947, *132*(2): 384–482.)

into a volume conductor.[14] The geometry is the same as that just described for a cell body and an axon. The negative-positive diphasic sequence is as expected. The same type of argument shows that an impulse that approaches but does not reach a recording electrode sets up a positive-negative diphasic sequence of potential changes (Fig. 20c). A recording situation of this sort is found where a fiber terminates before reaching the recording electrode or, more commonly, where the recording electrode has penetrated, injured and blocked the active fibers so that activity cannot reach the electrode.

PROPERTIES OF SPINAL TRACTS

Activity in spinal structures must of necessity be recorded in volume, for it is usually impossible to reduce the extracellular conducting medium to negligible proportions. As already mentioned, this circumstance creates some special problems. The first relates to identification of the structures that originate potentials recorded from the spinal cord. This problem arises because potentials in a volume conductor may be recorded at points distant from the site of activity. One method of localizing activity is to thrust an electrode into the suspected tract. The injury thus inflicted blocks activity in the conducting fibers, and the recorded response then consists of a monophasically positive deflection typical of approaching activity ("killed end" recording).* Conversion of a triphasic (positive-

Fig. 21. Responses of frog sciatic nerve recorded in volume (*left*) and in an insulating medium (*right*). Each pair of traces (*A–E, B–F,* etc.) recorded at same gain, but between each pair from above downward gain was progressively increased approximately five-fold. Note in volume recorded responses relatively small amplitudes and absence of any sign of negative afterpotential, which is clearly seen in *G* and *H*. (From Lloyd in *Biology of mental health and disease.* New York, Hoeber, 1952.)

negative-positive) response to a monophasic positive response by penetration indicates that the electrode has damaged active fibers. When the potential sequence remains triphasic, inactive tracts have been penetrated.

A related problem is the computation of conduction times from volume recordings. In insulated nerve trunks conduction times are estimated by measuring the time interval between the shock artifact and the onset of the action potential. In volume, however, positive potentials are recorded before the activity reaches the electrode. The arrival of the conducted wave of depolarization at the level of the recording electrode is approximately signaled by the reversal from positivity to negativity.†

A final peculiarity of volume recording is that the recording electrode records a potential only when the conducting structures are un-

* The response is +, − diphasic, but the negative part is usually negligibly small.

† A somewhat better measure is to a point midway between the first reversal and peak negativity. For synchronous volleys when the negative component rises rapidly, little error is incurred by using the reversal point.

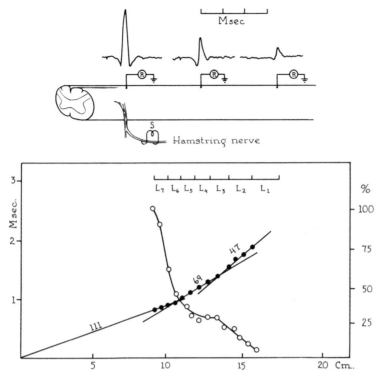

Fig. 22. Conduction in intramedullary projections of Group I afferent fibers. *Upper diagram,* Recordings from surface of dorsal column following a Group I afferent volley originating in hamstring nerve. *Graph* shows conduction time (filled circles, ordinate on left) and relative amplitude (open circle, ordinate on right) of response as a function of conduction distance. Conduction speed indicated by numbers above lines. Scale above locates spinal segments. (After Lloyd and McIntyre, *J. Neurophysiol.,* 1950, *13*:39–54.)

equally or oppositely polarized. When a cell is completely polarized or completely depolarized, no potential is recorded, because every solid angle is matched by an equal and electrically opposite solid angle. It follows that prolonged changes in polarization with decay constants which are long in relation to conduction time do not appear in volume recordings. The afterpotentials have these characteristics and are not observed in volume recordings (Fig. 21).

Fiber Constitution of Spinal Tracts. The white matter of the spinal cord consists chiefly of fibers extending longitudinally for varying distances. All sizes of myelinated and unmyelinated fibers are represented. As yet, histologic and oscillographic studies have yielded only scattered information on the fiber constitution and conduction properties of spinal tracts, but several important generalizations can be made.

PROPRIOSPINAL FIBERS. The spinal cord contains vast numbers of fibers that arise and terminate wholly within the spinal cord. These are known by several names, the most usual being "propriospinal" fibers or "intrinsic" spinal fibers. Tower *et al.*[16] studied the propriospinal fibers after all other fibers (the "extrinsic" fibers) were removed by section of the cord above and below a selected region and division

of all the dorsal roots to that region. When sufficient time elapses for degeneration of the extrinsic fibers after such an operation, only propriospinal fibers remain. Upon examination of histologic preparations after this procedure, there are still so many fibers in the cord that it is difficult to appreciate the loss of fibers. The propriospinal fibers exist everywhere throughout the white matter, although they are not evenly distributed. In the dorsal columns most of the propriospinal fibers are small (about 1 μ), but there is a scattering of larger fibers. In contrast, the ventrolateral columns contain fibers of all sizes, many being as large as any found in the normal spinal cord. These large propriospinal fibers are the only ones that have been studied oscillographically; they are known to conduct impulses at rates up to 120 m. per second.

EXTRINSIC FIBERS. The *ascending fibers* in the spinal cord arise from neurons within the cord itself or, in the case of the dorsal columns, from neurons in the dorsal root ganglia. In the dorsal columns the largest fibers are ascending branches of Group I afferent fibers arising from muscle nerves.[13] After a Group I afferent volley, a surface electrode on the ipsilateral dorsal column at the level of the activated dorsal roots records a large triphasic deflection, which has a latency compatible with a maximal conduction rate of 110 to 120 m. per second (Fig. 22). As the electrode is moved rostrally along the dorsal column, two changes occur in the recorded response: (i) its amplitude diminishes and eventually reaches zero, and (ii) its conduction rate progressively decreases.

For example, a Group I afferent volley initiated in the quadriceps nerve is traveling at a rate of 117 m. per second at the time of entry at L_5, has decelerated to a rate of 24 m. per second when L_1 is reached, and cannot be traced much beyond the T_{12} segment. The explanation is that the conducting fibers branch along their ascending course, giving off collaterals to the cells of Clarke's column. With each branching the parent fiber becomes smaller and hence conducts more slowly. Eventually all the activity of the Group I fibers is relayed into Clarke's column and thence upward in the dorsal spinocerebellar tract. The Group I fibers are thus temporary occupants of the dorsal columns. The most rapidly conducting permanent occupants of these columns (i.e., the fibers which remain in the dorsal columns throughout the length of the cord) have conduction rates which usually do not exceed 70 m. per second. This tract also contains many smaller fibers (Fig. 23).

The dorsal spinocerebellar tract, which originates from cells in Clarke's columns, occupies the dorsolateral white matter. This tract is characterized by a significant number of large fibers (Fig. 23), some of which conduct at velocities exceeding 120 m. per second. Mixed in with these fibers are others originating in unidentified cell groups in the lumbar gray matter. These are destined to pass, via a relay in the cervical cord, to the contralateral olive and are called spino-olivary fibers. They conduct impulses at rates up to about 60 m. per second.[4]

The fibers comprising the spinothalamic tract in the anterolateral white matter are small (Fig. 23), and their conduction rates are not known. Some of the larger fibers (greater than 5 μ) in the anterolateral white matter of the lumbar segments are said to constitute the ventral spinocerebellar tract and have conduction rates ranging from 30 to 80 m. per second.[3]

The *descending tracts* include the pyramidal or corticospinal tract, the vestibulospinal tract and the reticulospinal tract. The latter two tracts are of fairly uniform size and conduct at rates comparable to those of the large A fibers. The pyramidal tract contains fibers ranging through a wide band of fiber sizes, the largest conducting at rates of about 65 m. per second. The compound action potential of the bulbar and upper cervical portions of this tract includes two elevations, one conducting at 35 to 40 m. per second and the other at 12 to 16 m. per second.[2] This finding is surprising because the fiber spectrum of the tract at the bulbar level is not bimodal.

Despite the lack of systematic observations such as we have on peripheral fibers, it may be said in general conclusion that nerve fibers in the central nervous system have the same properties of conduction as do peripheral nerve fibers. Scattered data on the refractory period, the diameter-velocity relation, the velocity-threshold relation and the velocity-spike relation of fibers in the central nervous system indicate that their properties do not vary greatly from those of peripheral fibers.

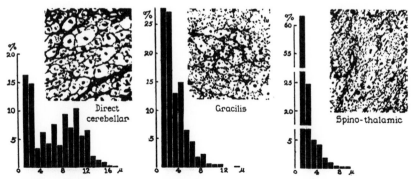

Fig. 23. Fiber distribution plots and typical sections of areas of white matter containing dorsal spinocerebellar tract, fasciculus gracilis and spinothalamic tract. Selected areas contain, in addition to tracts named, numerous propriospinal fibers. Note striking representation of large-diameter fibers in spinocerebellar tract as contrasted with small fibers which make up spinothalamic tract. Fasciculus gracilis is intermediate in fiber constitution. (After Häggqvist, *Z. micr.-anat. Forsch.*, 1936, *39*:1–34.)

REFERENCES

1. BERRY, C. M., GRUNDFEST, H. and HINSEY, J. C. *J. Neurophysiol.*, 1944, *7*:103–115.
2. BISHOP, P. O., JEREMY, D. and LANCE, J. W. *J. Neurophysiol.*, 1953, *16*:537–550.
3. CARREA, R. M. E. and GRUNDFEST, H. *J. Neurophysiol.*, 1954, *17*:203–238.
4. DIBIAGIO, F. and GRUNDFEST, H. *J. Neurophysiol.*, 1955, *18*:299–304.
5. ELFVIN, L. G. *J. Ultrastructure Res.*, 1958, *1*:428–454.
6. GASSER, H. S. *Ohio J. Sci.*, 1941, *41*:145–159.
7. GASSER, H. S. *J. gen. Physiol.*, 1950, *33*:651–690.
8. GASSER, H. S. *Exp. Cell Res.*, 1958, Suppl. *5*:3–17.
9. GASSER, H. S. and GRUNDFEST, H. *Amer. J. Physiol.*, 1939, *127*:393–414.
10. GREENGARD, P. and STRAUB, R. W. *J. Physiol.*, 1958, *144*:442–462.
11. HURSH, J. B. *Amer. J. Physiol.*, 1939, *127*:131–139.
12. LLOYD, D. P. C. *J. Neurophysiol.*, 1943, *6*:293–315.
13. LLOYD, D. P. C. and MCINTYRE, A. K. *J. Neurophysiol.*, 1950, *13*:39–54.
14. LORENTE DE NÓ, R. *Stud. Rockefeller Inst. med. Res.*, 1947, *132*(2):384–482.
15. RITCHIE, J. M. and STRAUB, R. W. *J. Physiol.*, 1957, *136*:80–97.
16. TOWER, S., BODIAN, D. and HOWE, H. *J. Neurophysiol.*, 1941, *4*:388–397.
17. WOODBURY, J. W. *J. cell. comp. Physiol.*, 1952, *39*:323–339.

CHAPTER 4

Receptor Mechanism

By HARRY D. PATTON

In Chapter 2 it was emphasized that the distinctive and unique property of axon and muscle fiber membranes is the ability to undergo transient permeability changes when the *transmembrane voltage is decreased*. Specifically, depolarization increases sodium permeability of excitable membranes. Depolarization to a critical threshold value so increases sodium permeability that the resulting Na^+ influx in itself causes further transmembrane voltage drop which, in turn, by further increasing Na^+ permeability, leads to greater Na^+ influx and to greater depolarization. These explosive self-perpetuating events, known as the Hodgkin cycle (see p. 42), underlie the rapid reversal of membrane potential which constitutes the upstroke of the action potential. A region of membrane thus reversed in electrical polarity provides a sink for outward current flow through adjacent regions of membrane which are, in turn, depolarized to threshold and driven toward the Na^+ equilibrium potential. Depolarization begets depolarization and so the action potential progresses from point to point or, more precisely, from node to node.

Thus the critical initial event in impulse initiation is membrane depolarization. Experimentally, depolarization is simply but artificially accomplished by passing outward through the membrane a current from a battery or other suitable device. In nature, however, apart from chance accidents to amateur electricians, nerve impulses are rarely so initiated; indeed, the physical stimuli which normally initiate neural action include a variety of energy forms, none of which is electrical—light, heat, mechanical distortion of nerve endings, chemicals, etc. Such nonelectrical stimuli are effective because, applied to appropriate specialized afferent fiber terminals, they produce depolarization of the ending. The magnitude of the resultant depolarization is directly related to the intensity of the physical stimulus; if the latter is sufficiently intense, depolarization may reach threshold value and initiate impulse discharge by the mechanisms already described. The terminal afferent endings which undergo depolarization in response to specific kinds of physical stimuli are called *receptors*, and the membrane potential decrease thus produced in the terminals is called the *generator* or *receptor potential*.[6]

It is important to recognize clearly the difference between the generator potential and the action potential. The stationary, nonpropagated generator potential is confined to the terminals and diminishes rapidly with distance along the fiber. In contrast, the action potential is a self-propagating process and is conducted without decrement along the fiber. The generator potential is graded; i.e., through a large range, amplitude is a direct function of stimulus intensity. The action potential is "all or nothing"; provided the stimulus exceeds threshold, response amplitude is fixed and independent of stimulus intensity. The generator potential is *graded* and *stationary;* the action potential, *all-or-nothing* and *conducted.*

RECEPTORS AS TRANSDUCERS

The receptor performs as a transducer, i.e., as a structure which transforms one kind of energy into another. Irrespective of the kind of physical stimulus which excites it, the immediate response of any receptor is an electrical change—a depolarization which is an approximate analog of the physical stimulus in time and magnitude. Depolarization, in turn, leads to repetitive discharge of all-or-nothing conducted action potentials, the frequency of discharge being directly related to the amplitude of the depolarizing generator potential. In a single receptor, then, the spike discharge frequency is the coded indicator of stimulus intensity. The sequence may be summarized as follows: Physical stimulus of intensity I → Generator potential of amplitude $A = f(I)$ → Spike discharge of frequency $F = f(A)$. Stated in engineering terminology, the receptor transduces one form of energy (e.g., pressure or heat) to an electrical change, the intensity being coded by amplitude modulation; in the transformation from local, graded to conducted, all-or-nothing signals, intensity is coded by frequency modulation.

Although the principles described above apply generally to all receptors, the transducer process sometimes includes other intermediate events. This is particularly true of the organs of special sense. For example, the initiation of visual signals involves an intermediate chemical event, photic breakdown of a visual pigment being an essential step in the development of the generator potential. In some receptive systems, e.g., the ear, the initial graded response probably arises in accessory elements closely related to the nerve terminals rather than in the neural membrane itself.*

In the present chapter, attention is confined to some simple representative receptors chosen to illustrate general receptor properties and their range of variation. Detailed descriptions of more complex receptors are found in subsequent chapters.

DIFFERENTIAL SENSITIVITY OF RECEPTORS

A basic postulate concerning receptor function is that each receptor is adapted for detecting a particular kind of energy. Thus, we speak of photoreceptors, thermoreceptors, chemoreceptors and mechanoreceptors. Among the mechanoreceptors are numerous types which preferentially respond to various kinds of mechanical stimuli, e.g., stretch of muscles or tendons, rotation of joints, light deformation of the skin, bending of hairs, distension of hollow structures such as blood vessels or abdominal viscera. Selective sensitivity of receptors and the range of their sensitivities determine what kinds of external energy are signaled to the central nervous system. Some forms of energy (e.g., very long or very short electromagnetic wave lengths, very high and very low frequency vibrations of air) neither arouse sensations nor evoke reflex response because man lacks receptors capable of detecting and signaling such environmental stimuli. Receptors behave as "pass filters" admitting to the central nervous system some kinds of information about the external world and rejecting other kinds.

The concept of differential or selective sensitivity is subject to certain qualifications. Even the most specialized receptors may be excited by more than one kind of stimulus provided that the stimulus intensity is sufficiently high. Receptor selectivity is thus relative and takes

---

* Davis[2] has proposed that the term "generator potential" be reserved for graded depolarizations arising in neural membranes and directly triggering the conducted spikes and that the term "receptor potential" be used to describe electrical responses of specialized accessory receptor cells which are incapable of conducting all-or-nothing responses. Unfortunately, for most receptors detailed knowledge of basic mechanisms is inadequate to permit clear distinction and most authors use the two terms interchangeably.

the form of a relatively low threshold to one kind of energy without excluding responsiveness to intense stimuli of other kinds. The energy form to which the receptor responds most readily is called the *adequate stimulus* of that receptor. Thus, as Sherrington put it, the receptor serves to lower the threshold of excitability of reflex arcs to the adequate stimulus and to heighten it to others.

Some receptors respond only to stimuli which are sufficiently intense to cause tissue damage, and the energy form (crushing, strong pressure, cutting, burning) employed to produce damage is unimportant. In other words, the adequate stimulus for these receptors is not a particular kind of energy but rather the immediate consequence of strong stimulation, viz., tissue damage. Such high-threshold receptors are called *nociceptors;* their excitation gives rise to sensations of pain and elicits stereotyped protective reflex patterns which are described in Chapter 7.

An exception to the principle of differential sensitivity is found in one kind of cutaneous receptor which responds both to light mechanical distortion of the skin and to thermal changes.[14, 18, 19, 34] At temperatures above 42° C. or below 22° C., discharge of these receptors ceases and even mechanical deformation of the skin fails to excite them. Such receptors thus appear to have dual roles as mechanoreceptors and thermoreceptors. Other cutaneous receptors are selectively responsive to thermal changes and insensitive to mechanical distortion, while still others respond readily to mechanical stimuli but not to thermal changes even through the broad range of 12 to 43° C.[14, 34]

Differential Sensitivity and Morphological Differentiation. Although the peripheral terminations of most afferent nerve fibers consist fundamentally of thin unmyelinated prolongations of the parent axon, the morphological configuration and shape of the terminals and their relations with non-neural structures are highly variable. Some fibers branch repeatedly to form a fine but extensive terminal arborization; in others the terminal branches may anastamose to form a network. Still other fibers terminate in complicated whorls or helices or in flattened plates, knobs or beaded terminals. Many endings are surrounded by elaborate connective tissue capsules; others terminate in baskets around specialized non-neural cells.

The organs of special sense show an even greater range of morphological specialization.

Morphological differentiation of receptor types suggests a correlated functional differentiation and consequently much effort has been directed toward assigning to the various morphological species of receptors specific functional properties. To some extent these efforts have been successful; for example, there is little doubt that the fine nerve endings surrounding the base of the hair follicle are selectively sensitive to mechanical distortion occasioned by displacement of the hair. Similarly, the elaborately encapsulated pacinian corpuscle found in the cat's mesentery, in subcutaneous tissue and in the interosseus membrane is selectively sensitive to distortion produced by rapid compression of the laminated capsule.[8, 9, 27] However, correlation between gross morphological structure and functional specificity of receptors is not always possible. For example, hairy skin is sensitive to mechanical distortion (touch), to thermal stimuli (warmth and cold) and to noxious stimuli (pain) but contains only two morphologically identifiable receptors: hair follicle endings and free unencapsulated nerve endings.[12] The cornea contains only free nerve endings but is sensitive to each of the modalities listed above.[25] It is therefore obvious that receptor function is not necessarily morphologically labeled. Differential sensitivity of receptors probably depends on more subtle structural differences than are revealed by light microscopy, viz., molecular structure of the receptor membrane.

Lack of correlation between gross morphological and functional properties is not in itself a contradiction of the principle of differential sensitivity of receptors. Discovery that the multisentient cornea contains only one structurally identifiable species of ending does not mean that each of the structurally similar endings is promiscuously sensitive to all energy forms but rather that the "tuning" of a receptor to specific kinds of energy cannot be determined by simple histological inspection. Differential sensitivity can be tested only by functional studies in which the responsiveness of single receptors to various kinds of stimuli is tested. Such studies have, with the exceptions mentioned in the preceding section, confirmed the principle of differential sensitivity.[9]

MEASUREMENT OF GENERATOR POTENTIALS

The receptor terminal's initial response to an

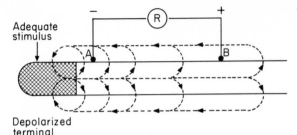

Fig. 1.   Diagram illustrating method of recording with externally placed electrodes the generator potential of a receptor. Hatched area at left represents terminal depolarized by adequate stimulus. Direction of current indicated by dotted lines and arrows. Dense outward current flow at A drops transmembrane potential to a level below that at B. Recorder R registers voltage (IR) drop due to external current flow from B to A.

applied adequate stimulus is a graded nonpropagated depolarization—the generator potential. To measure this local response in isolation and uncomplicated by propagated spikes it is necessary either to employ only stimuli so weak that the resultant generator potential does not exceed threshold or to block selectively the spike-generating mechanism by drugs such as procaine or tetrodotoxin, a toxin obtained from the puffer fish, which in low concentrations appear to have no influence on the generator mechanism. The latter procedure, while carrying with it the hazard that the drug may not be entirely selective in its action and may thus cause some unsuspected aberration of the generator process, has the advantage that it permits quantitative investigation of stimulus–response relations through a large range of stimulus strengths.

Since the stimulus-induced depolarization is normally restricted to the unmyelinated terminal, the ideal recording would measure with an intracellular electrode the transmembrane potential of the terminal. Unfortunately, this ideal arrangement is not possible because the fineness of the terminals precludes successful impalement and also because, in many instances, the terminals are surrounded by tough, impenetrable connective tissue elements. Therefore indirect methods employing external electrodes are usually employed to detect generator potentials. In Chapter 2 it was pointed out that a stationary depolarization confined to a segment of membrane causes in adjacent segments outward current flow which diminishes exponentially with distance from the site of the

stationary depolarization as in Figure 1. Since outward current flow is greater at A than at B, the membrane is depolarized more at A than at B and current flows in the external circuit from B to A. An external recording circuit thus registers a voltage drop due to the current flowing between B and A through the resistance of the external medium. Since the current is small, it is desirable to make the external resistance between A and B as high as possible to increase the voltage (or IR) drop. This is accomplished by immersing the segment between A and B in a high-resistance medium such as mineral oil, isotonic sucrose or air. It should be emphasized that such indirect measurements do not provide absolute values of the generator potential but, instead, smaller voltages which are proportional to the depolarization of the terminal.*

In some receptors it is possible to record the transmembrane potential near, but not within, the region of the generator terminal. In such instances, the recorded potentials again only approximate the magnitude of the generator potential because transmembrane potential changes due to a stationary depolarization attenuate rapidly with distance along the fiber.

PROPERTIES OF GENERATOR POTENTIALS IN DIFFERENT RECEPTORS

Generator potentials have been clearly demonstrated in several receptors which have been studied intensively because their structures favor detection of such potentials. One such receptor is the pacinian corpuscle, an encapsulated ending found in the mesentery of the cat (Fig. 2A). The organ consists of a single myelinated nerve fiber which penetrates the central core of a macroscopic (about 1.2 mm. by 0.8 mm.) multilaminated connective tissue capsule. Within the capsule, the fiber loses its myelin coat and runs as a nearly straight, naked fiber to end blindly near the distal end of the core. The receptor is exquisitely and selectively sensitive to mechanical compression of the capsule; a displacement of 0.2 to 0.5 μ causes a detectable generator potential.[8, 27] Figure 3 shows generator potentials recorded from a pacinian

---

* Because of the cable properties of the nerve fiber, this method of recording also produces some distortion of the time course of generator potentials, especially if the rates of potential change are rapid.

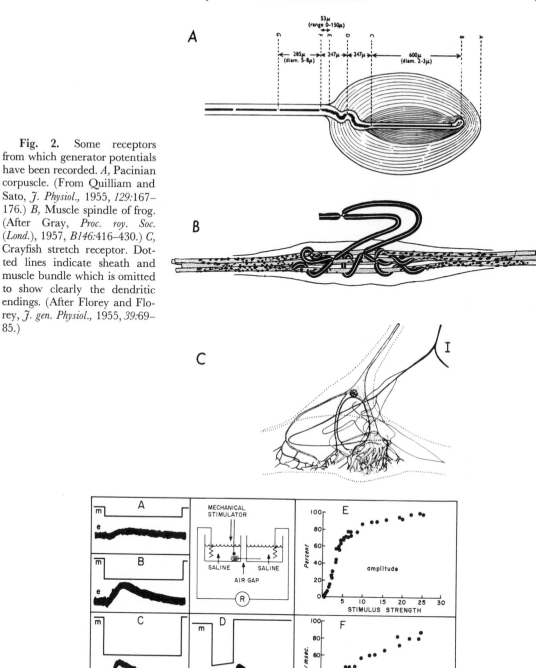

Fig. 2. Some receptors from which generator potentials have been recorded. *A,* Pacinian corpuscle. (From Quilliam and Sato, *J. Physiol.,* 1955, *129:*167–176.) *B,* Muscle spindle of frog. (After Gray, *Proc. roy. Soc. (Lond.),* 1957, *B146:*416–430.) *C,* Crayfish stretch receptor. Dotted lines indicate sheath and muscle bundle which is omitted to show clearly the dendritic endings. (After Florey and Florey, *J. gen. Physiol.,* 1955, *39:*69–85.)

Fig. 3. Generator potentials of pacinian corpuscle. Insert shows stimulating and recording arrangement. *A, B* and *C,* Generator potentials (e) elicited by mechanical compressions of different magnitudes shown by m. Upward deflections of e indicate relative negativity of terminal. *D,* Short mechanical pulse elicits both "on" and "off" responses which sum. *E,* Relation between amplitude of generator potential and stimulus strength; ordinate, amplitude of generator potential expressed as percentage of maximum; abscissa, stimulus strength in arbitrary units. *F,* Relation between rate of rise of generator potential and stimulus strength. Ordinate, percentage of maximum amplitude attained in 1 msec.; abscissa, stimulus strength in arbitrary units. (After Gray and Sato, *J. Physiol.,* 1953, *122:*610–636.)

corpuscle treated with a weak solution of procaine to block spike generation. The recording arrangement is shown in the inset. The stimulus was a minute mechanical compression of the capsule with a fine glass rod moved by a piezoelectric crystal; in each frame the displacement is indicated by the upper trace (m) and the receptor response is shown in the lower trace (e), an upward deflection signaling negativity of the receptor ending. In A, B and C rectangular mechanical pulses of increasing magnitudes were applied to the corpuscle for about 9 milliseconds. Several important characteristics of the recorded generator potentials are evident. First, both the peak amplitude and the rate of rise of the generator potential increase as stimulus intensity increases. The graphs in Figure 3E and F show the relationships between those variables plotted over a wide range of stimulus intensities. As stimulus intensity increases, generator potential amplitude increases approximately exponentially to a steady value beyond which further increments of stimulus intensity cause little further increase. In the intermediate range of stimulus strengths, potential amplitude signals stimulus intensity although not in simple linear proportionality. The rate of rise of the potential (Fig. 3F), on the other hand, continues to increase with increasing stimulus intensity even through the range at which potential amplitude has become relatively stable; within the latter range the relationship between stimulus intensity and rate of change of potential is approximately linear.

In addition, it should be mentioned that the pacinian corpuscle is rate-sensitive. If the magnitude of the mechanical stimulus is held constant, the amplitude of the generator potential varies with velocity of displacement.

Another peculiarity of the generator potential of the pacinian corpuscle is illustrated in Figure 3A, B and C: when a long mechanical pulse is applied to the corpuscle, the generator potential rises to peak value and then declines to zero although the mechanical stimulus persists. Figure 3D further shows that when the mechanical compression is released, a second generator potential (the "off-response") is generated. The receptor thus behaves in an "on-off" fashion signaling the onset and cessation of the stimulus. When, as in Figure 3D, the stimulus is discontinued before the "on" response is dissipated, "on" and "off" responses sum. This peculiarity is discussed in more detail later; for the present it should be noted that, because of this property, the generator potential of the pacinian corpuscle is an imperfect analog of the mechanical stimulus.

A second receptor in which generator potentials can be readily recorded is the stretch receptor of frog muscle.[7] This structure, similar to the somewhat more complex stretch receptor of mammalian muscle (see Chap. 7), consists of three to twelve slender specialized muscle fibers (called intrafusal fibers) which are segregated from the surrounding muscle fibers (extrafusal fibers) by a spindle-shaped connective tissue capsule (Fig. 2B). At several points the capsule is penetrated by the branches (usually two) of individual afferent axons which, after traversing the lymph-filled capsular space, intertwine around the intrafusal fibers, eventually losing their myelin sheaths and terminating in fine naked varicosities. The adequate stimulus for the spindle is stretch that mechanically distorts the endings. Figure 4 shows the generator potential recorded from a procaine-treated spindle during a 1.3 mm. stretch. During the stretch

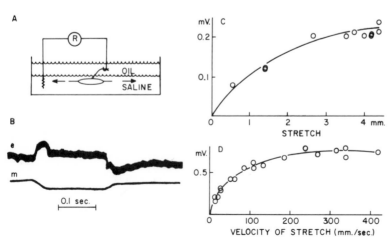

Fig. 4. Generator potential of frog muscle spindle. A, Diagram of recording arrangement. B, Generator potential (e) elicited by 1.3 mm stretch of muscle indicated by m. Upward deflection in e signifies relative negativity of terminal. C, Relation between amplitude of the static component (ordinate) and magnitude of stretch (abscissa). D, Relation between amplitude of the dynamic component (ordinate) and velocity of stretch (abscissa). (After Katz, J. Physiol., 1950, 111:261–282.)

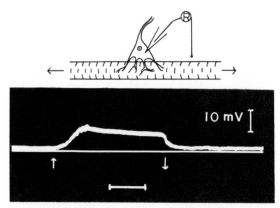

Fig. 5. Generator potential of crayfish stretch receptor. Diagram shows recording arrangement. Muscle bundle stretched at first arrow and released at second arrow. Upward deflection signifies reduction of transmembrane potential. Horizontal bar below, 1 sec. (From Eyzaguirre and Kuffler, *J. gen. Physiol.*, 1955, *39*:87–119.)

the ending becomes depolarized to a maximal value, which declines, when the lengthening is complete, to a lower steady value that persists throughout the stretch. Finally, when the stretch is discontinued, the generator potential transiently reverses ("off-effect") and then slowly climbs to the baseline value. The generator potential of the stretch receptor is thus divisible into three components: (i) a dynamic phase, which coincides with the period of active lengthening of the muscle, (ii) a static phase during sustained but invariant stretch, and (iii) the off-response at the termination of stretch. The amplitude of the dynamic phase is related to the velocity of stretch of the muscle as in Figure 4*D*, which shows the amplitude of the dynamic component when the muscle was stretched by a constant amount but at variant rates. The static component, on the other hand, varies with the magnitude of the stretch, as shown in Figure 4*C*, and is little influenced by velocity of stretch. The off-response is highly variable but when present is, unlike the depolarizing off-response of the pacinian corpuscle, always in the hyperpolarizing direction.

A third receptor in which generator potentials are readily measured is the muscle stretch receptor of the crayfish (Fig. 2*C*). It consists of a large (100 µ diameter), peripherally located neuron with a complex system of dendrites that terminate among the muscle fibers bridging the abdominal segments. As shown in Figure 2*C*, the dendrites also receive an innervation via an efferent axon I, the function of which will be

discussed later. The receptor cell has a single axon directed toward the central nervous system. Stretch of the muscle fibers mechanically distorts and depolarizes the dendrites. The large receptor cell body can be easily impaled with a microelectrode to measure the transmembrane potential shifts induced by depolarization in the dendrites. Figure 5 shows the intracellular recorded potential induced by brief stretch of the muscle bundle of such a receptor. The potential declines slightly during the stretch and decays to the baseline at the termination of the stimulus. In some instances a hyperpolarizing off-response, similar to that seen in the frog muscle spindle, may occur.

ADAPTATION

In neither the pacinian corpuscle nor in the two stretch receptors described is the generator potential a perfect analog of the applied stimulus, for if the stimulus is prolonged, the amplitude of the potential declines. This decrease of the magnitude of the generator potential during sustained stimulation is called *adaptation.** In the case of the pacinian corpuscle the departure from analog is extreme, for the depolarization declines to zero during a sustained stimulus; in the stretch receptor the generator potential during a prolonged stretch drops only from the high value of the dynamic phase to the steady lower value of the static phase. Receptors like the pacinian corpuscle in which adaptation reduces the membrane potential below the firing level are sometimes called rapidly adapting receptors, whereas those (e.g., the stretch receptor) in which the generator potential shows only a limited decrease with time are called slowly adapting receptors. Since the important distinction is between magnitudes rather than between rates of adaptation, the two types are more appropriately called *phasic*

* More commonly the term "adaptation" is used to describe the decrease in spike frequency during a sustained stimulus. Since frequency of firing is largely determined by the amplitude of the generator potential, there is usually no confusion in using the same term to describe both phenomena. However, it should be remembered that adaptation of spike discharge may be influenced by properties (e.g., inactivation of sodium conductance) which are peculiar to the all-or-nothing spike mechanism and which are not necessarily applicable to the adaptation of the generator potential.

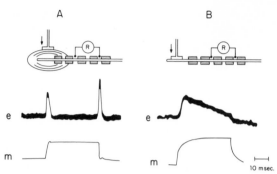

Fig. 6. Generator potential in pacinian corpuscle before (A) and after (B) removal of connective tissue capsule; e, generator potential; m, mechanical stimulus. (After Mendelson and Lowenstein, *Science*, 1964, *144*:554–555.)

and *tonic* receptors. Examples of phasic receptors, other than the pacinian corpuscle, are the mechanoreceptors ending around hair follicles; tonic receptors include, among others, the mammalian muscle stretch receptor and the tendon stretch receptor, the pressoreceptors in the carotid sinus and certain cutaneous touch and thermal receptors. Phasic receptors signal only the onset and cessation of stimulation, whereas tonic receptors continuously signal a persistent stimulus.

The mechanism of adaptation is not known and may be different for different receptors. One might suspect that the physical properties of the structures surrounding mechanoreceptor terminals might account in part or wholly for adaptation, because mechanical stimuli must be transmitted through these structures to reach the nerve endings. Hubbard,[16] using an ingenious technique of flash microphotography, measured the displacement of capsular lamellae in the pacinian corpuscle during compression. During a prolonged pulse the deeper lamellae nearest the nerve terminal moved inward transiently and then gradually resumed their location with a time course comparable to the decay of the generator potential. Since displacements of the inner laminae are those which are directly transmitted to the sensitive neural membrane, he suggested that adaptation results wholly, or in large part, from the viscoelastic properties of the capsule. Displacements during release of compression were not studied.

Recently Mendelson and Lowenstein[31] have investigated directly the role of the lamellated capsule in adaptation. By careful microdissection the capsule can be removed almost completely, and the response of such denuded receptors to mechanical stimuli can be compared with that of intact receptors. Figure 6A shows the generator potentials recorded from an intact receptor subjected to a prolonged mechanical pulse. Depolarization occurs at the onset of compression but decays to the baseline in about 6 milliseconds. At the end of the stimulus an "off-response" of similar duration occurs. Figure 6B shows the response of a "stripped" receptor to a long mechanical pulse. Depolarization, although declining slowly from the initial peak value, persists throughout the period of mechanical compression. The slow decay of the generator potential in the denuded receptor must be ascribed to some property of the receptor membrane perhaps akin to accommodation. The rapid and complete adaptation of the intact corpuscle signifies the contribution of the lamellated capsule. Evidently the capsule is a poor transmitter of elastic force; only velocity-dependent viscous force is significantly transmitted to the center of the capsule, where the receptor ending is located. A puzzling and as yet unexplained finding is the absence of a depolarizing off-response in the denuded preparation.

To what extent non-neural structures contribute to adaptation in other receptors is not certain. Matthews[29] suggested that the dynamic phase of the stretch receptor might result from the viscous properties of the intrafusal fibers so that sudden extending forces cause momentarily high tensions which diminish as the intrafusal fibers belatedly adjust to a new length. Katz[22] suggested that the dynamic component and the off-effect result from changes of capacitance of the endings. If stretching a polarized membrane decreases the thickness of the barrier between the charges and increases its surface area, the capacitance would be expected to increase and the voltage to diminish momentarily, returning along a time course determined by the newly established time constant. But these are merely speculations and the precise mechanism of adaptation is obscure.

IONIC MECHANISM OF THE GENERATOR POTENTIAL

In all three receptors described, the adequate stimulus decreases the transmembrane potential of the terminals. This transducer action is most highly developed in the unmyelinated terminals. For example, the terminal 700 μ of the pacinian receptor stripped of its capsule responds to minute local compressions of only 0.4 to 0.8 μ, whereas at the adjacent first node of Ranvier compressions sufficient to reduce axon diameter by 60 to 80 per cent (displacements up to 10 μ) are ineffective (Fig. 7).

Although highly developed in some receptor terminals, mechanotransduction is not a unique property of axon terminals. Sufficient (10 to 15 μ) mechanical distortions applied to regions of axons far removed from the terminals cause depolarization and may induce discharge.[21] It may be that the high mechanical sensitivity of terminals as compared to that of other regions of the axon is a simple consequence of size difference; a given displacement should increase surface area relatively more (and thus stretch the membrane more) in small than in large fibers.

Because transducer action occurs in the minute terminals, investigation of the intimate details of the process is difficult. Nevertheless, several indirect lines of evidence suggest that the stimulus produces depolarization of the terminal by *nonselectively increasing membrane permeability to ions.*

In Chapters 1 and 2 it was pointed out that the value of the axon transmembrane potential depends immediately upon the transmembrane concentration gradients of charged ions and upon the *permeability of the membrane* to these ions. In the resting axon Cl$^-$ is at equilibrium and is distributed in the extra- and intracellular compartments in accordance with the Nernst equation. Both K$^+$ and Na$^+$, however, are actively pumped across the membrane against their concentration gradients. In the resting cell, Na$^+$ and K$^+$ are in a steady state (i.e., influx equals efflux) but not in true equilibrium as defined by the Nernst equation. For such actively transported ions the discrepancy between the true equilibrium potential and the steady-state transmembrane potential is a function of the membrane permeability to the ion. The resting membrane is about 50 times more permeable to K$^+$ than to Na$^+$; accordingly, the steady-state membrane potential deviates from the K$^+$ equilibrium potential by only a few millivolts but is some 155 mV. removed from the equilibrium potential for Na$^+$ (cf. Table 1, Chap. 1). It follows that an increase of membrane permeability to an actively transported ion will establish a new steady-state potential value closer to the equilibrium potential of that ion. Thus, it has already been emphasized that the upstroke of the action potential results from transient selective increase of P_{Na^+}, a change which drives the transmembrane potential in the direction of the Na$^+$ equilibrium potential.

A nonselective increase of membrane permeability to Na$^+$, K$^+$ and Cl$^-$ might be expected to drive the membrane potential toward a value near zero. A simple way to visualize the process is to think of a polarized membrane in which holes have been punched permitting ions to flow freely along their concentration gradients and thus to dissipate the transmembrane charge. If the number of such leaks is large, the membrane potential will in time reach zero; fewer leaks would cause the membrane potential to reach a value intermediate between the resting level and zero. In other words, the degree of depolarization might be expected to vary with the number of shunting holes in the membrane. Conversely, the amount of depolarization occasioned by perforating the membrane with a given number of shunting holes should vary as a direct function of the initial transmembrane potential.

It follows from the foregoing considerations that the steady state potential toward which the transducer process drives the membrane of the crayfish stretch receptor can be determined by measuring the amplitudes of generator potentials produced by standard equal stretches when the resting membrane potential is artificially adjusted to different levels. Such meas-

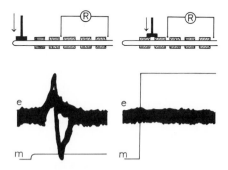

Fig. 7. Localization of mechanosensitive portion of pacinian corpuscle. Decapsulated preparation. On left, small mechanical stimulus (m) to denuded terminal produced generator potential and sometimes a diphasic spike. Record e contains many superimposed traces. On right, much larger mechanical compression to first node of Ranvier consistently failed to excite. (After Lowenstein, *J. Neurophysiol.,* 1961, *24*:150–158.)

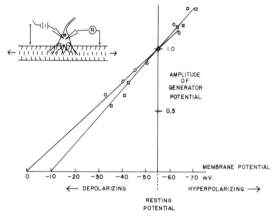

Fig. 8. Estimation of equilibrium level of generator potential in crayfish stretch receptor. Inset shows receptor impaled with two microelectrodes. Circuit on left was used to pass current through the membrane and thus to adjust the membrane potential to any desired level. Standard stretch of muscle bundle produced generator potential the amplitude of which is plotted on the ordinate against the membrane potential on the abscissa. Data from two experiments showing by extrapolation that generator potential amplitude is zero when initial membrane potential is near zero. (After Terzuolo and Washizu, *J. Neurophysiol.,* 1962, *25*:56–66.)

urements require impaling the receptor with two microelectrodes (Fig. 8). One electrode is connected with a battery which can be used to drive current through the membrane and thus to adjust the membrane potential to any desired level. The other electrode records the generator potential produced by a standard stretch of the muscle bundle.

Figure 8 shows the results of such an experiment and indicates that, as predicted, the amplitude of the generator potential diminishes linearly as the resting membrane potential is decreased. Extrapolation indicates that the amplitude of the generator potential would be zero when the resting potential is about zero and that zero is therefore the steady state potential toward which the generator mechanism drives the membrane potential. These data are thus consistent with the hypothesis that stretch depolarizes the dendritic endings by inducing in them a nonselective increase in ionic permeability. An ancillary bit of information is that membrane resistance can be reduced to about one half by stretching the muscle bundle,[33] a finding consistent with the hypothesis of altered ionic permeability.

Such measurements are not possible on the minute terminals of pacinian corpuscles, but

less direct clues suggest that in this receptor also the generator potential results from nonselective increase in membrane permeability. Permeability increase to Na^+ would be expected to contribute most to depolarization for, as has been mentioned, Na^+ is the ion most removed from equilibrium. It might therefore be expected that reducing the external Na^+ concentration would markedly reduce, but not abolish, the generator potential. Simply immersing the corpuscle in a Na^+-free bathing solution abolishes the spike but does not alter the generator potential. This disappointing negative result is, on reflection, not surprising, for the critical extracellular space of the receptor terminal is segregated from the Na^+-deficient medium by the thick impervious capsule, which is an efficient barrier to diffusion.* To change periterminal extracellular ion concentrations it is necessary to perfuse solutions through the tiny capillary which penetrates the capsule along with the axons.[3] When Na^+-deficient solutions are thus perfused, the generator potential undergoes the anticipated diminution, the reduction varying directly with Na^+ reduction. However, perfusion with Na^+-free solutions (made isotonic with choline chloride or sucrose) does not abolish the generator potential but only reduces it to about 10 per cent of the control value. This residue probably represents the contribution to the membrane current by ions other than Na^+ (K^+ and/or Cl^-). It thus seems likely that the generator potential of the pacinian corpuscle derives from increased permeability to Na^+ and probably to other ions as well.

The proposed model for the transducer process explains the changes in the generator potential with increasing intensities of stimulus.[8] Imagine that mechanical distortion opens pores in the membrane through which ions can pass readily. The membrane potential then shifts toward the steady state value of zero. If the number of holes is progessively increased (by increased compression) the potential will approach and eventually reach zero, after which further perforation will produce no additional depolarization (Fig. 3E). The rate of rise of the potential suffers no such limitation, however, for this variable depends on the rate of discharge of the membrane capacity, which continues to increase with further reduction of membrane resistance (Fig. 3F).

* Probably for a similar reason, the generator potential of the frog muscle spindle bathed in Na^+-free solutions also persists unaltered.[22]

DISCHARGE OF TONIC RECEPTORS

In the procaine-treated receptor impulse generation is blocked and stimulation elicits only the steady depolarization of the generator region. In the unblocked preparation this depolarization in turn triggers repetitive discharge of all-or-nothing spikes, which are then propagated along the fiber by the local circuit mechanism described in Chapter 2. The spike discharges are the ultimate product of the generator process and compose the message that reaches the central nervous system.

If spikes are recorded close to the terminal by the methods described, they ride superimposed on the generator potential; conventional recordings from the fiber more than a few millimeters central to the terminal register conducted spikes but give no evidence of the generator potential, which, being stationary, attenuates rapidly with distance. Only in selected re-

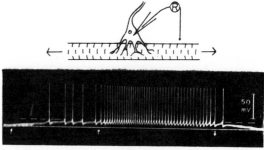

Fig. 9. Generator potential and spike discharge in crayfish stretch receptor. Slight stretch applied at first arrow. At second arrow stretch increased. Stretch released at third arrow. Dotted line indicates firing level. (From Eyzaguirre and Kuffler, *J. gen. Physiol.*, 1955, *39:* 87–119.)

ceptors are recordings close to the terminal possible, but recordings of axon spikes have been made on a wide variety of receptors.

Figure 9 shows an intracellular recording

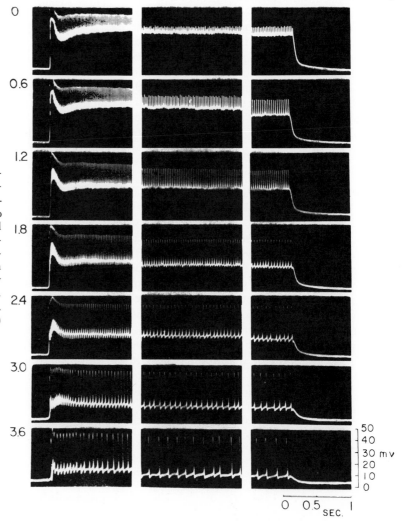

Fig. 10. Generator potential and spike discharge recorded intracellularly from photoreceptor of horse-shoe crab eye. Responses to 20-second light stimuli. Gaps between records are 8.4 seconds each. Figures at left indicate attenuation of light intensity (i.e., intensity diminishes from top to bottom). (From Fuortes and Poggio, *J. gen. Physiol.*, 1963, *46:*435–452.)

from a crayfish stretch receptor. Slight stretch of the muscle initiated at the first arrow elicited a slowly developing depolarization which, upon reaching a threshold value of about 12 mV., generated a spike. After the spike the depolarization again built up slowly to discharge at the same threshold value a second, third, fourth and fifth spike. At the second arrow the stretch was increased and held constant until the third arrow, when the stretch was discontinued. The increased stretch was accompanied by an accelerated discharge rate. The threshold firing level (marked by the dotted line) remained the same as before* but the rate of depolarization following each spike was much greater than during the period of mild stretch. Finally, it is clear that during the stretch the frequency declined from an initial high value to a stable lower value (adaptation). When at the third arrow the stretch was relaxed, the receptor discharged one impulse and the potential declined slowly to the resting level.

The discharge properties illustrated in Figure 9 have been duplicated in a wide variety of tonic receptors, including the frog stretch receptor, mammalian stretch receptors, carotid sinus pressoreceptors, photoreceptors (Fig. 10) and many others. Particular attention is directed to adaptation and the relationship between intensity of stimulus and frequency of discharge.

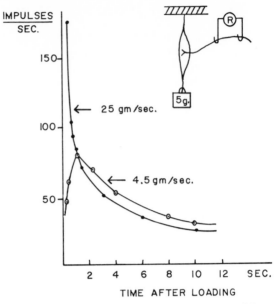

Fig. 11. Adaptation of spike discharge of frog muscle spindle subjected to different rates of stretch. With higher velocity loading initial discharge rate is greater but steady state discharge rate is little affected by rate of loading. (After Matthews, *J. Physiol.*, 1931, *71*:64–110.)

ADAPTATION OF SPIKE DISCHARGE AND OFF-EFFECTS

Adaptation of spike discharge is as mysterious as adaptation of the generator potential. It has already been mentioned that the amplitude of the dynamic, but not of the static, component of the stretch receptor potential is directly related to the *velocity* of muscle stretch. The same relations hold for discharge rates; if the displacement amplitude is held constant but the velocity is varied, the final adapted discharge rate is invariant but the discharge frequency during and immediately following stretch is directly related to velocity (Fig. 11).

The hyperpolarizing off-effect of the stretch

---

* At higher intensities, the firing level increases, for with increasing discharge rate, the interspike interval is so reduced that each spike falls within the relatively refractory period created by its predecessor.

receptor potential also has its correlate in discharge properties. If in an adapted stretch receptor an imposed stretch is suddenly reduced to a lower value, discharge rate decelerates or ceases briefly only to build up once again to a value appropriate to the newly established milder stretch.[29]

INTENSITY-FREQUENCY RELATIONSHIPS AND INFORMATION CODING

All tonic receptors studied display graded increases of discharge rates when the stimulus intensity is increased. In many, the relationship is such that the steady adapted discharge frequency is a linear function of the log of the stimulus intensity. Much has been made of the logarithmic relationship, principally because of its presumed relationship to Fechner's famous generalization that sensation is proportional to the log of stimulus intensity, a "law" which is currently disputed. For receptors the logarithmic intensity–frequency relationship is a fair approximation provided that the range of stimulus intensities is appropriately chosen and provided that the appropriate parameter of the stimulus is measured as "intensity." For example, in the crayfish stretch receptor, discharge frequency is, over a considerable range, directly related to the log of the load or force producing the stretch, but is directly proportional to the length of the muscle.[33] Lacking intimate details of the mechanical distortion sustained by the dendrites when the muscle bundle in which they are imbedded is stretched and put under tension, we have no way to decide which parameter they signal.

However, apart from these semiphilosophical considerations, the fact remains that, within limits, the frequency–log load relationship is descriptively accurate and it is of interest to enquire at which stage of the transducer process the logarithmic function enters. For the crayfish receptor[33] and photoreceptors of the horseshoe crab eye,[5] the answer is: at the transducer stage. In these receptors amplitude of the generator potential (static component) is directly related to the log of stimulus intensity, whereas firing rate is linearly related to amplitude of generator potential. These transformations are diagrammatically illustrated in Figure 12. Similar relationships may be deduced for the frog stretch receptor, since frequency of firing is directly related to amplitude of the generator potential[22] and to the log of the load.[29]

Because of the rate–intensity relationship, the individual tonic receptor is able to provide continuously graded, frequency-coded information concerning stimulus intensity within the range between threshold and the intensity at which the generator potential is maximal. At higher intensity levels the transducer mechanism is saturated, limiting further information transmission. In a population of receptors, however, intensity of stimulation is signaled not only by the firing rate of individual receptors but also by the number of receptors active. In such a population, thresholds are distributed in accordance with a normal frequency curve so that, with increasing intensity of stimulation, more and more receptors of progressively higher thresholds are recruited, each firing at a rate determined by its threshold and the instantaneous magnitude of the intensity. The phenomenon of progressive recruitment of receptors expands the range of stimulus intensities that can be signaled to the central nervous system beyond that which can be signaled by any one receptor.

Variance of receptor thresholds is probably determined more by geometry and location than by variance of transmembrane voltage thresholds for discharge. In a population of muscle stretch receptors, for example, location within the muscle makes some bear more of the brunt of the stretch than others.

MECHANISM OF REPETITIVE FIRING IN TONIC RECEPTORS

Repetitive firing of sense organs was ingen-

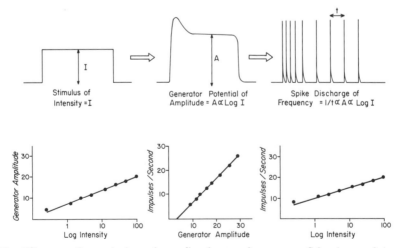

Fig. 12. Diagram of steps in intensity coding in a tonic receptor. Stimulus produces generator potential shown here as it might be recorded in a procainized receptor. The amplitude of the static phase is directly proportional to the logarithm of stimulus intensity. Generator potential elicits repetitive discharge of spikes. In the adapted state frequency of discharge is directly proportional to generator potential amplitude and thus proportional to the log of stimulus intensity. Graphs below show data obtained from photoreceptor of crab eye. (After Fuortes, *Amer. J. Ophthalmol.,* 1958, *46:*210–223.)

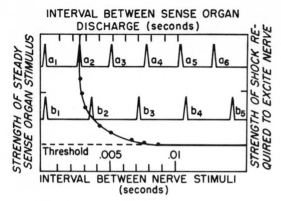

Fig. 13. Diagram illustrating refractory period hypothesis of sense organ rhythmicity. Curve is conventional recovery curve (absolutely and relatively refractory periods) for frog nerve and represents actual experimental data. Schematized action potential records (a, b) are hypothetical. They show how a strong, continuous sensory stimulus might excite earlier in the refractory period and fire the sensory axon at a higher rate. (Redrawn from Adrian, *The basis of sensation,* London, Christophers, 1928.)

iously explained by Adrian,[1] who proposed that the frequency–intensity relationship was determined by the recovery cycle of the fiber. In Chapter 2 it was pointed out that after a nerve fiber has generated a spike, the threshold to a second stimulus is increased. For a short period of time (the absolutely refractory period) the threshold is infinite and a second stimulus, no matter how strong, is ineffective. Thereafter, for a period (relatively refractory period) a second shock will excite, but only if it is of greater than resting threshold intensity. Figure 13 shows graphically the time course of the threshold changes in a frog nerve after it has conducted an impluse. Adrian suggested that the physical stimulus induces in a receptor a steady, maintained change to which the neural element can respond only periodically because of its characteristic recovery cycle. (Adrian's steady change would, in modern parlance, be the generator potential, then undiscovered.) An intense steady stimulus would fire the fiber in Figure 13 at a_1 and again after the threshold has dropped to the level of the steady stimulus, at a_2. Recovery from the a_2 spike would lead to a_3, etc. A weaker steady stimulus (b) would yield a longer interspike interval because after each spike a longer recovery time is required for the threshold to fall to the level of the weaker steady stimulus.

A difficulty with this explanation is that receptors, except under abnormal conditions, do not fire as rapidly as measured refractory periods would predict, the upper limit being 100 to 200 impulses per second rather than 800 to 1000, as calculated from refractory periods. Also, weakly excited receptors fire rhythmically and regularly at frequencies far below those anticipated from mere refractoriness. The discrepancy may mean, as Adrian suggested, only that the fine unmyelinated receptor terminal has a slower recovery cycle than its parent axon.

Another factor determining discharge frequency is the rate of depolarization following each spike in the train.[15] Figure 14 shows superimposed traces of spikes in a crayfish stretch receptor adapted to three magnitudes of stretch, the oscilloscope sweep being triggered in each instance by the first spike on the left. The straight horizontal line marks the firing level (spike threshold) for the conditions in A. The firing level is unchanged in B, but in C the spikes do not arise until the depolarization has proceeded about 7 mV. farther because the interspike interval encroaches on the relatively refractory period. Refractoriness thus appears to limit discharge rate significantly only at higher frequencies. The striking difference between records A and B is in the rate of depolarization during the interspike interval. Following each spike the membrane repolarizes beyond the threshold level and then depolarizes slowly in A, more rapidly in B, and still more rapidly in C. The traces in D show the time course of depolarization over an even greater range of frequencies. Although the complex mechanisms governing transmembrane potential during the interspike interval are not known, it may be postulated that Na^+ inactivation and elevated K^+ conductance act to promote repolarization, while the steadily maintained nonselective conductance increase associated with the transducer process tends to drive the membrane in a depolarizing direction. It has already been mentioned that the rate of rise of the generator potential in a blocked receptor is directly related to stimulus intensity (see Fig. 3F). The graded slopes of depolarization in Figure 14 are a manifestation of the same phenomenon superimposed upon post-spike repolarization.

In summary, the intensity–frequency relationship of receptors through the range of slight to moderate intensities appears to depend almost exclusively on the rate of depolarization.

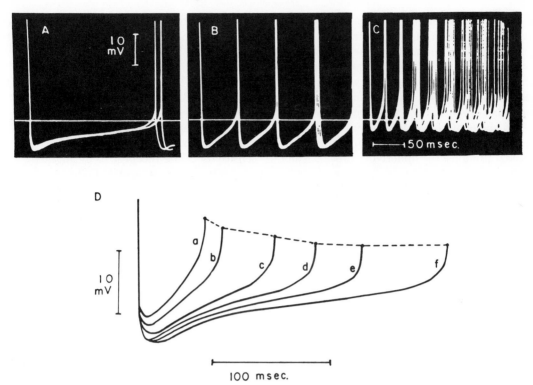

Fig. 14. Interspike events in repetitively discharging crayfish stretch receptor. Traces A, B and C are superimposed traces, each sweep being triggered by the first spike of the left. Gain very high so that peak of spike is off record. Horizontal line marks firing level for near-threshold stretch in A. Note firing level is same in B for greater stretch, but is about 7 mV. higher in C where stretch was still greater. D shows interspike events at six levels of stretch; dotted line shows firing levels. (From Eyzaguirre and Kuffler, *J. gen. Physiol.*, 1955, *39*:87–119.)

At higher intensities interspike interval encroaches on relative refractoriness, and elevated threshold becomes a controlling factor.

DISCHARGE OF PHASIC RECEPTORS

In phasic receptors the intensity–frequency relationship does not hold because prompt adaptation limits the discharge. Even with displacements up to 30 times threshold, a pacinian corpuscle rarely responds to a square wave compression with more than one spike.[10] Subjected to vibratory stimuli, however, these receptors respond repetitively,[17, 31] discharging one spike per cycle (Fig. 15). Maximum sensitivity is to frequencies of about 300 cycles per second; on either side of this frequency thresholds become higher. Intensity of stimulus thus determines the range of frequencies to which the corpuscle responds. At high intensities oscillation between 40 and 1000 cycles per second are faithfully signaled. With weaker stimuli the effective frequency range shrinks.

SITE OF IMPULSE ORIGIN IN RECEPTORS

In this chapter the fundamental difference between the *graded* generator potential and the

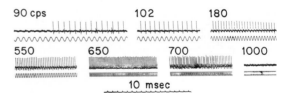

Fig. 15. Responses of pacinian corpuscle to sinusoidal vibratory stimuli. Upper trace shows spikes recorded from axon; lower trace shows sinusoidal stimulus. Numbers above traces give stimulus frequencies. Time trace 10 milliseconds. (From Hunt, *J. Physiol.*, 1961, *155*:175–186.)

all-or-nothing spike has been emphasized repeatedly. The all-or-nothing behavior of the action potential is a consequence of the voltage sensitivity of sodium permeability. Depolarization increases sodium permeability, which in turn leads to sodium entry and further depolarization; the response, once triggered, is self-sustaining and explosively independent of the stimulus. In the graded receptor response to a physical stimulus, the underlying process is not voltage-sensitive and hence not regenerative; within wide limits each increment of stimulus produces an increment of depolarization. Impressed by these fundamental differences, some neurophysiologists have argued that the two processes cannot be supported by the same membrane.[11] Thus, it has been widely believed that the unmyelinated terminal is incapable of all-or-nothing behavior and responds to mechanical distortion with only a graded depolarization; impulse generation was postulated to result from outward current flow through the voltage-sensitive membrane of the first node of Ranvier.[8, 9, 26, 28]

Although some neural membranes may be capable of only graded, nonpropagated responses to stimulation, there is no outrageous inconsistency in the simple hypothesis that a macroscopic area of membrane may display both graded and all-or-nothing processes. Indeed, in the denuded pacinian corpuscle it has been shown conclusively that the unmyelinated portion which undergoes graded depolarization

in response to mechanical deformation can conduct all-or-nothing spikes throughout its full extent.[20]

INHIBITION IN RECEPTORS

Some receptors are impinged upon by efferent axons. Excitation of these axons reduces the sensitivity of the receptor to its adequate stimulus. The process by which discharge of a nerve fiber depresses the excitability of the structure it supplies is called *inhibition*. Excitation is a mechanism for "turning on" a cell, inhibition for "turning off." In receptors receiving an inhibitory innervation, sensitivity to adequate stimulation is continuously biased by impulse traffic in the inhibitory fibers, and discharge behavior is determined by the balance between the influences of inhibitory action and of excitatory depolarization.

A simple example of a receptor supplied with inhibitory fibers is the crayfish stretch receptor.[24] The inhibitory axon derives from a centrally located cell body and terminates in the muscle bundle in close apposition to the stretch-sensitive dendrite of the receptor (Fig. 2C). Figure 16A shows the effect of low-frequency stimulation of the inhibitory axon supplying a receptor discharging repetitively in response to constant stretch. During the inhibitory action firing ceases. At higher gain (Fig. 16B) it can be seen that each inhibitory impulse drives the

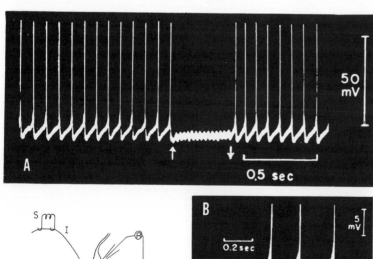
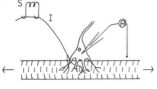
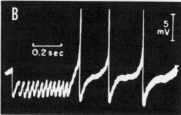

Fig. 16. Inhibition of crayfish stretch receptor. *A*, Discharge in receptor subjected to stretch is inhibited by stimulating inhibitory axon during period between arrows. *B*, Amplifier gain much higher to show that each inhibitory volley (first part of record) causes hyperpolarization of cell. (After Kuffler and Eyzaguirre, *J. gen. Physiol.*, 1955, *39*:155–184.)

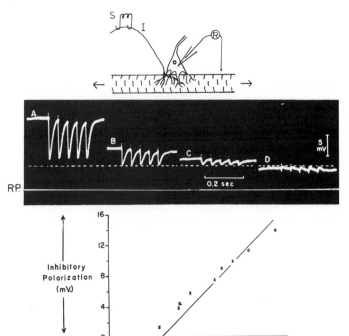

Fig. 17. Equilibrium potential of inhibitory process in crayfish stretch receptor. Cell depolarized to varying degrees by stretch was subjected to five inhibitory volleys. Solid line RP marks resting potential; dotted line marks potential at which sign of inhibitory potential reverses. Figure below shows graphically that inhibitory potential reverses when the cell is depolarized by about 6.5 mV. (After Kuffler and Eyzaguirre, *J. gen. Physiol.*, 1955, *39:*155–184.)

membrane in the direction of repolarization, thus preventing the stretch-induced depolarization from reaching threshold.

Some idea of the mechanism of inhibition can be obtained by determining the steady state potential toward which inhibitory impulses drive the membrane.[13, 24] The analysis is similar to that employed to study the intimate mechanism of the generator potential. Figure 17*A* shows the consequences of stimulating repetitively the inhibitory nerve fiber of a stretch receptor depolarized about 16.5 mV. by stretch. Each inhibitory impulse caused a peak repolarization of 9.7 mV. In *B* and *C*, when the receptor was held under less stretch and was therefore less depolarized, the inhibitory repolarization became progressively smaller. In *D* still further relaxation decreased the depolarization to only 6 mV. (dotted line) beyond the resting level, and each inhibitory impulse then produced a small *depolarization*. The reversal level for the inhibitory potential thus lies between the potential levels of *C* and *D*. The lower part of Figure 17 shows graphically results from another experiment in which the straight line connecting the points intersects the abscissa at a membrane potential 7 mV. less than the resting level. Studies in which

membrane potentials were shifted by passing currents through the membrane rather than by stretching the receptor also indicate that the inhibitory process invariably seeks a stable value within a few millivolts of the resting level.[13]

The implication of such results is that the inhibitory process results from selectively increased permeability of the membrane to one or more ions which are close to true electrochemical equilibrium in the resting cell. This consideration eliminates Na^+, which is far removed from equilibrium. K^+ and Cl^- are equally likely candidates, for both are near equilibrium in the resting cell. Experiments in which inhibitory potentials were recorded in cells bathed in solutions deficient in these ions suggest that both are involved. In K^+-deficient solutions resting membrane potentials of receptors increase and the inhibitory potential becomes more strongly hyperpolarizing.[4] Depletion of extracellular Cl^-, on the other hand, shifts the reversal level of the inhibitory potential toward zero; i.e., in the same direction as the anticipated change of Cl^- equilibrium potential.[13] Inhibitory impulses thus appear to exercise their influence on the stretch receptor membrane by increasing selectively the permeability to K^+ and Cl^- ions. This change tends to stabilize the membrane at a voltage near the resting level, and as long as this condition persists it is more difficult to depolarize the membrane toward the threshold level, which is, of course, a necessary condition for discharge. The cell is inhibited and discharge ceases.

A final question relates to the mechanism by which nerve impulses in the inhibitory axon alter dendritic membrane permeability. The answer is that nerve impulses liberate from the inhibitory axon terminals a chemical agent which diffuses across the minute gap between axon and dendrite and selectively alters the ionic permeability of the dendritic membrane. There is much, although not conclusive, evidence that in crayfish inhibitory fibers the transmitter is *gamma aminobutyric acid*. This substance can be extracted from neural tissue and, when topically applied to the isolated receptor, mimics in many ways the permeability and excitability changes induced by stimulating the inhibitory axon.[13, 23, 30]

REFERENCES

1. ADRIAN, E. D. *The basis of sensation.* London, Christophers, 1928.
2. DAVIS, H. *Physiol Rev.,* 1961, *41:*391–416.
3. DIAMOND, J., GRAY, J. A. B. and IMMAN, D. R. *J. Physiol.,* 1958, *142:*383–394.
4. EDWARDS, C. and HAGIWARA, S. *J. gen. Physiol.,* 1959, *43:* 315–321.
5. FUORTES, M. G. F. *Amer. J. Ophthal.,* 1958, *46:*210–223.
6. GRANIT, R. *Receptors and sensory perception.* New Haven, Yale University Press, 1955.
7. GRAY, E. G. *Proc. roy. Soc.,* 1957, *B146:*416–430.
8. GRAY, J. A. B. *Prog. Biophys. biophys. Chem.,* 1959, *9:*286–324.
9. GRAY, J. A. B. Chap. 4 in *Handbook of Physiology, Section 1: Neurophysiology,* vol. 1, J. Field, ed. Washington, D. C., American Physiological Society, 1959.
10. GRAY, J. A. B. and MALCOLM, J. L. *Proc. roy. Soc.,* 1950, *B137:*96–114.
11. GRUNDFEST, H. Chap. 5 in *Handbook of physiology, Section 1: Neurophysiology,* vol. 1, J. Field, ed. Washington, D. C., American Physiological Society, 1959.
12. HAGEN, E., KNOCHE, H., SINCLAIR, D. C. and WEDDELL, G. *Proc. roy. Soc.,* 1953, *B141:*279–286.
13. HAGIWARA, S., KUSANO, K. and SAITO, S. *J. Neurophysiol.,* 1960, *23:*505–515.
14. HENSEL, H. and BOMAN, K. K. A. *J. Neurophysiol.,* 1960, *23:*564–578.
15. HODGKIN, A. L. *J. Physiol.,* 1948, *107:*165–181.
16. HUBBARD, S. J. *J. Physiol.,* 1958, *141:*198–218.
17. HUNT, C. C. *J. Physiol.,* 1961, *155:*175–186.
18. HUNT, C. C. and McINTYRE, A. K. *J. Physiol.,* 1960, *153:* 99–112.
19. HUNT, C. C. and McINTYRE, A. K. *J. Physiol.,* 1960, *153:* 88–98.
20. HUNT, C. C. and TAKEUCHI, A. *J. Physiol.,* 1962, *160:*1–21.
21. JULIAN, F. J. and GOLDMAN, D. E. *J. gen. Physiol.,* 1962, *46:*297–313.
22. KATZ, B. *J. Physiol.,* 1950, *111:*261–282.
23. KUFFLER, S. W. and EDWARDS, C. *J. Neurophysiol.,* 1958, *21:*589–610.
24. KUFFLER, S. W. and EYZAGUIRRE, C. *J. gen. Physiol.,* 1955, *39:*155–184.
25. LILE, P. P. and WEDDELL, G. *Brain,* 1956, *79:*119–154.
26. LOWENSTEIN, W. R. *Ann. N.Y. Acad. Sci.,* 1959, *81:*367–387.
27. LOWENSTEIN, W. R. *J. Neurophysiol.,* 1961, *24:*150–158.
28. LOWENSTEIN, W. R. and RATHKAMP, R. *J. gen. Physiol.,* 1958, *41:*1245–1265.
29. MATTHEWS, B. H. C. *J. Physiol.,* 1931, *71:*64–110.
30. McLENNAN, H. *Synaptic transmission.* Philadelphia, W. B. Saunders Co., 1963.
31. MENDELSON, M. and LOWENSTEIN, W. R. *Science,* 1964, *144:*554–555.
32. SATO, M. *J. Physiol.,* 1961, *159:*391–409.
33. TERZUOLO, C. A. and WASHIZU, Y. *J. Neurophysiol.,* 1962, *25:*56–66.
34. WITT, I. and HENSEL, H. *Pflüg. Arch. ges. Physiol.,* 1959, *268:*582–596.

CHAPTER 5

Muscle

By J. WALTER WOODBURY, ALBERT M. GORDON,
and JOHN T. CONRAD

THE function of a muscle is to contract. Skeletal muscles are attached to bones by tendons and act to move these bones with respect to each other. Cardiac muscle and visceral smooth muscle occur in the walls of hollow viscera and act by exerting pressure on the fluid visceral contents. The contraction of skeletal muscle is wholly and directly controlled by reflex and voluntary activity of the central nervous system. Cardiac and smooth muscle contractions, although regulated by nervous activity, are intrinsically rhythmic; these muscles, notably the heart, contract at regular intervals even when denervated. This automaticity of cardiac and smooth muscle is in accord with their functions in maintaining the internal environment of the body, the pumping of blood and the movements of the digestive tract. However, motor nerves do regulate the contractile activity of arteriolar smooth muscle and thus control the blood flow through the arterioles. Muscular contraction is the most impressive example of "living machinery."

Skeletal muscle has been more intensively studied and is better understood than cardiac or smooth muscle. Hence, in this chapter the current concepts of skeletal muscle contractile activity and its control are presented first to give a more comprehensive framework for understanding the physiology of muscle. This is followed by shorter sections in which the properties of cardiac muscle and the various types of smooth muscle are compared and contrasted with those of skeletal muscle. Finally diseases of the motor unit are presented, showing how pathologic conditions can be illuminated and organized from physiologic study.

SKELETAL MUSCLE

Skeletal muscle is the means by which an organism reacts to its external environment. "All the endless diversity of the external manifestations of the activity of the brain can be finally regarded as one phenomenon—that of muscular movement" (Sechenov, 1863). The preoccupation of the brain with skeletal muscle was also stressed by Sherrington, who pointed out that any path traced in the brain leads directly or indirectly to muscle. The performance of a smooth, efficient and coordinated bodily movement is the outward sign of complex and extensive activity in the central nervous system.

A bodily movement involves three more or less distinct types of activity: (i) central nervous system activity, reflex and voluntary; (ii) events intervening between the impulse in a motor nerve and the beginning of contraction; and (iii) the contractile process itself. Reflex control of movement is discussed in Chapter 7; this section covers the remaining types of activity. The following brief description may help to keep the details of the processes in their proper perspective.

Events Leading to Contraction. A number of distinct events intervene between the synaptic initiation of an impulse in a spinal motoneuron and the contractions of the muscle fibers it innervates. (i) The impulse is conducted along the motoneuron axon to its termination on the muscle's motor end-plate. (ii) The impulse causes the liberation of a chemical transmitter substance, acetylcholine, from the axon terminals. (iii) By inducing a greater than threshold depolarization of the muscle fiber membrane, acetylcholine initiates a self-propagating impulse in it. (iv) The depolarization of the muscle membrane by the conducted impulse is followed by a brief phasic contraction of the muscle fiber—a *twitch*. The phrase *neuromuscular transmission* refers to the events between the arrival of the nerve impulse at the nerve endings and the initiation of an impulse in the muscle; the events between the muscle fiber impulse and contraction are referred to as *excitation–contraction coupling* to distinguish them from the contraction process itself.

These events are more conveniently studied with experiments of the type illustrated in Figure 1. A single supramaximal shock applied to the motor nerve initiates a volley of impulses in the nerve, which in turn initiates a volley in all of the muscle's fibers, these latter impulses arising at the motor end-plate. In Figure 1B is shown the diphasic action potential generated by the passage of the volley across the recording electrodes, R. After a delay of a few milliseconds, the muscle action potentials initiate a twitch—a synchronous, phasic contraction of all fibers. The contractile tension rises to a peak in about 50 milliseconds and then declines more slowly to the initial or resting tension. The contractile response of a single muscle fiber to a conducted action potential is the

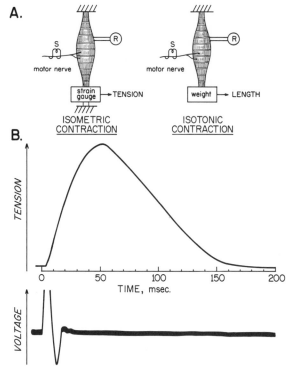

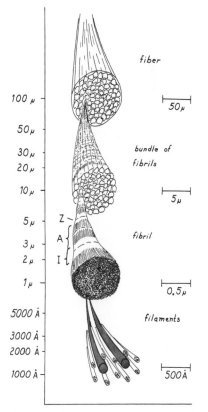

A.

motor nerve

S

R

strain gauge → TENSION

ISOMETRIC CONTRACTION

motor nerve

S

R

weight → LENGTH

ISOTONIC CONTRACTION

B.

TENSION

VOLTAGE

0 50 100 150 200
TIME, msec.

Fig. 1. Twitch contraction of whole muscle. *A,* Arrangement for recording contractile responses of whole muscle. Left, isometric recording arrangement; length is held constant, and developed force (tension) is measured with a strain gauge and recorded as a function of time. Contraction is initiated by a supramaximal stimulus delivered to motor nerve via a pair of electrodes, S. Muscle action potential recorded by surface electrodes, R. Right, isotonic recording arrangement; tension is held constant by hanging a weight on muscle and changes in length are measured as a function of time. Stimulating and recording as at left. *B,* Action potential (below) and isometric tension (above) recorded in tibialis muscle of cat. Abscissae represent time; upper ordinate, tension in arbitrary units; and lower ordinate, voltage in arbitrary units (upward deflection incomplete). Note that electrical activity starts several milliseconds before contraction but contraction far outlasts electrical activity. Action potential is diphasic because both electrodes are on active tissue. (After Creed *et al., Reflex activity of the spinal cord.* Oxford, Clarendon Press, 1932.)

same as for the whole muscle; the whole muscle's twitch is the summated tensions of the twitches of its individual fibers.

GRADATION OF CONTRACTION. The number of motor axons innervating a muscle is a small fraction of the number of fibers in the muscle. Counts have shown that a motor axon innervates from 3 to 150 muscle fibers, the number depending on the function of the muscle. The

motoneuron and the muscle fibers it innervates are termed a *motor unit.* The contractile response to one impulse in one motoneuron is a twitch contraction in all the fibers it innervates. Thus the smallest unit of muscular activity that occurs normally is the contraction of a single motor unit. The twitch response typical of a motor unit contrasts sharply with the smooth maintained contraction of muscle during normal movements. This observation raises a further question: How is the contraction of a muscle smoothly *graded* in strength?

Functional Structure of Muscle: the Sliding Filament Theory. RESTING MUSCLE. Understanding of muscular contraction requires a detailed knowledge of muscle's fine structure. Although the structure of cross-striated skeletal muscle is described here, many of the same features are found in cardiac muscle. The main features of muscle structure are shown in Figure 2. A muscle is composed of many fibers, each bounded by a cell membrane. Each fiber (top, Fig. 2) consists of many bundles of closely packed fibrils. (A fibril is the smallest natural

Fig. 2. Logarithmic extension diagram of skeletal muscle and filament structure. (After Buchthal and Kaiser, *Dan. Biol. Medd.,* 1951, *21*:1–318.)

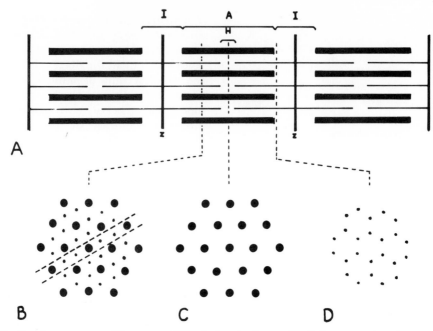

Fig. 3. Arrangement of filaments within the bands of a myofibril. Sarcomere length corresponds to slightly extended length in the body. Transverse distances grossly exaggerated. *A*, Longitudinal view showing overlap of thick and thin filaments and their relationship to striation bands. *B*, Cross section of region of overlap showing double hexagonal array. Dotted lines indicate direction and width of electron micrograph sections shown in Figure 4. *C*, Cross section through H band showing hexagonal array of thick filaments only. *D*, Cross section through I band showing thin filaments only. (After H. E. Huxley, Chap. 7 in *The cell,* vol. IV, Brachet and Mirsky, eds. New York, Academic Press, Inc., 1962.)

muscle unit from which a contraction has been obtained.) Fibrils in turn are made up of two types of myofilaments—thick and thin—which so interact that they slide past each other during shortening. These filaments are closely packed in a parallel array with both ends of like filaments in register (Figs. 3 and 4). This organization gives the characteristic cross-striated or banded appearance of whole muscle, as seen with the light microscope, and of fibrils, as seen with the electron microscope.

Striation bands. These bands were named by light microscopists but can be seen much more clearly with the electron microscope (Fig. 4, top). The darker regions indicating greater absorption of electrons (electron-dense) are called the A bands; these are the more highly refractive, *a*nisotropic regions seen with the light microscope. The lighter bands bisected by the dark lines are I bands or *i*sotropic regions. The lighter region in the center of the A band is called the H band and is less refractive than its surroundings. The region between two adjacent Z lines traditionally is termed the sarcomere,

which is the basic repetitive unit of muscle structure. However, the functional sarcomere is centered on, rather than between, Z lines. In resting vertebrate skeletal muscle the sarcomere is about 2.5 μ long and decreases in length as the muscle shortens.

Filaments.[46, 57] The A band, as shown by Figure 4 (middle), is composed of thick parallel filaments (100 to 120 Å in diameter and 1.6 μ long), which give rise to the band's anisotropy and high electron density. The I band consists of thinner filaments (60 to 70 Å in diameter) and thus is less electron-dense. The I band filaments are attached at their center point to Z line structures and extend about 1 μ on each side. The two sets of filaments overlap in the A band. The A band's central region, which has no filament overlap, is the H band. These characteristics are summarized in Figure 3. A transverse section through the H band shows that the thick filaments are spaced about 450 Å apart in a hexagonal pattern. Where the thick and thin filaments overlap, the thick filament hexagonal pattern remains intact while

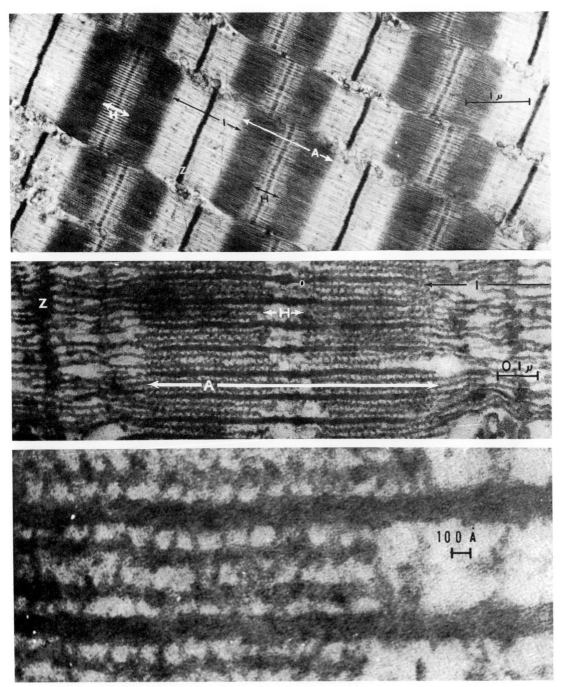

Fig. 4. Electron micrographs of longitudinal sections of rabbit psoas muscle. *Top,* Low-power view of several sarcomeres, showing A, H, and I bands and Z line. *Middle,* One sarcomere. Direction and width of section shown in Figure 3*B.* Thick filaments run from one end of the A band to the other. Pairs of thin filaments are attached at the Z line, interdigitate with the thick filaments, and terminate at the edge of the H band. *Bottom,* High magnification of A band showing bridges between thick and thin filaments. Direction and width of section shown in Figure 3*B.* (From H. E. Huxley, Chap. 7 in *The cell,* vol. IV, Brachet and Mirsky, eds. New York, Academic Press, Inc., 1962.)

each thin filament is surrounded by three thick filaments. In the I band, only thin filaments are seen.

The thick and thin filaments apparently are connected by "bridges" (Fig. 4, bottom). Bridges to each neighboring thin filament occur approximately every 400 Å; these project out from the thick filament along its entire length, except in the central 0.15 μ section.[46]

CONTRACTING MUSCLE. When a muscle is stimulated, it contracts and exerts a force on its tendons. If the force is sufficient, shortening occurs and the two sets of interdigitating filaments slide past each other. Light microscope observations in isolated muscle fibers and fibrils have shown that, during active shortening, I and H bands narrow equally while the A band, if such shortening is not too great, is unchanged.[42] "Contraction bands" form at sarcomere lengths of less than 2 μ in active shortening. Electron micrographs of muscles in various stages of contraction show that over wide ranges the lengths of the thick and thin filaments are nearly constant. Hence, all changes in sarcomere length are due to a relative motion of the two sets of filaments.[42, 44] This and other evidence[45] have firmly established that the sliding filament model provides an accurate description of the contractile process.

The relative motion implies that, during contraction, the interaction of the two filaments generates a force, tending to pull the thin filament toward the center of the A band. The interaction may take place at many sites along the filaments, possibly at the bridges. As the filaments slide past one another, connections are made and broken in such a way that a net shortening force is developed even if the muscle does not change length.[41] Furthermore, shortening usually occurs without any change of length in the filaments; e.g., a collapsible telescope can be shortened without changing the length of its tubular elements.

SARCOPLASMIC RETICULUM. An extensive membranous cytoplasmic component, the *sarcoplasmic reticulum*, plays an important role in the excitation–contraction coupling process. This structure is a continuous, membrane-limited system of tubules which form a close network around each fibril (Fig. 5, top). The sarcoplasmic reticulum differs from the endoplasmic reticulum of most other cells in that it lacks ribosomes and thus is agranular and in that certain characteristic features reoccur at fixed positions in every sarcomere. Longitudinal sections show a characteristic triad structure consisting of a central or transverse tubule with terminal cisternae on both sides (Fig. 5, bottom). The dilated, circumferential terminal cisternae are formed by anastomoses of the longitudinally oriented, finger-like tubules which surround the fibril. The central tubules run transversely through most of the fiber, weaving among the fibrils. These tubules appear to be separate from, but in close contact with, the longitudinal tubular system. The transverse tubules extend toward and may coalesce with the surface membrane so that they open to the extracellular space. Such openings have been observed in the muscles of some species[29] but not as yet in mammalian skeletal muscle. However, large (110 Å in diameter), electron-dense, nonpermeating ferritin molecules do enter the transverse tubules from the extracellular space but not the terminal cisternae.[47] The reticular triad is always fixed in position with respect to striation pattern, but the position varies according to species. In most mammals the triad is centered near the A-I junction; in frogs, it coincides with the Z line (Fig. 5, bottom).

Molecular Basis of Contraction.* CONTRACTILE PROTEINS. There are three major sarcoplasmic proteins—actin, myosin and tropomyosin—which probably play a role in contraction. Neither the localization of tropomyosin nor its role in muscular contraction has been established. However, the localization of actin and myosin with respect to the striation pattern has been determined from selective extraction[45] and labeling with fluorescent antibodies.[68] With appropriate solvents, myosin can be extracted quantitatively from the A bands of glycerol-extracted muscle preparations (see p. 120). The I band and Z line are little affected. However, the I band can then be dissolved with solutions known to extract actin. This, along with other evidence,[45] indicates that the thin I band filaments are composed almost exclusively of actin and the thick A band filaments largely of myosin and possibly of other protein components.

*Since this chapter was written, a discussion on the subject "The Physical and Chemical Basis of Muscular Contraction" has appeared in *Proc. roy. Soc.*, 1964, *B460:*433–542. In that discussion, organized by A. F. Huxley and H. E. Huxley, much of the material presented in this section is reviewed in greater detail.

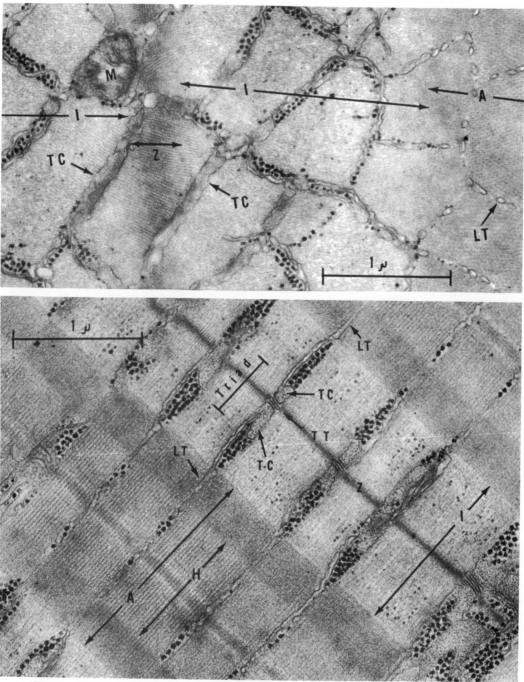

Fig. 5. Electron micrographs of frog sartorius muscle showing the sarcoplasmic reticulum and its relationship to the contractile structures. Sections were cut in different orientations. *Top,* Slightly oblique transverse section through a fiber. The Z line, A and I bands are indicated. Note that the reticulum completely surrounds most of the fibrils. Larger spaces in the I band near the Z line are terminal cisternae (TC). M is a mitochondrion. Dark spots are clusters of glycogen granules. *Bottom,* Longitudinal section of a fiber. Note A band, I band, Z line, components of the triad structure of the sarcoplasmic reticulum [transverse tubule (TT) and terminal cisternae (TC)] and the longitudinal tubules (LT). In this muscle, the triad is centered on the Z line. (*Top,* courtesy of Dr. Lee D. Peachey. *Bottom,* from Peachey, *J. cell. Biol.,* in press.)

Actin molecules (M.W. about 70,000) can unite to form long filaments which probably have the same structure as the thin filaments of the I band. In dried preparations, these filaments consist of two chains wound in a double helix. Myosin (M.W. about 428,000) can be fragmented by trypsin into two components, one consisting of two molecules of light meromyosin (M.W. 96,000) and the other of one molecule of heavy meromyosin (M.W. 236,000).[45] In solution, the myosin molecule is in the form of a rod with a ball at one end.[46] When solutions of actin and myosin are mixed, they combine to form *actomyosin*, a compound normally having a high association constant.

Myosin, but not actin, is an enzyme (an ATP-ase) which catalyzes the hydrolysis of adenosine triphosphate (ATP) to adenosine diphosphate (ADP) and phosphate. Actomyosin, also an ATP-ase, has somewhat different properties. For example, myosin ATP-ase is activated by Ca^{++} and inhibited by Mg^{++}, whereas actomyosin ATP-ase is activated by both Ca^{++} and Mg^{++}. The ATP-ase activities of myosin and actomyosin reside in the heavy meromyosin fraction. Through this enzymatic action, part of the free energy of the ATP terminal phosphate bond can be made available to actomyosin for contractile activity.

ROLES OF ATP AND CALCIUM IN CONTRACTILE ACTIVITY. *Contraction and relaxation in model systems.* Much has been learned about the contractile mechanism of muscle by studying the contractile-like properties of a "model system" derived from muscle subjected to various analytic procedures. Such procedures primarily are designed to remove the large diffusion barrier presented by the surface membrane so that the effects of various substances—e.g., Ca^{++} and ATP—on the contractile mechanism can be studied directly. Investigation of these model systems has revealed that ATP plays a dual role in the contraction–relaxation process, that ATP is the energy source for contraction and that Ca^{++} is mainly concerned with the control of contraction. Two model systems are discussed here—the glycerol-extracted preparation[64] and the actomyosin solution. Of course, the relevance to the intact system of any conclusions drawn from either model system must be determined.

GLYCEROL-EXTRACTED MUSCLE.[45, 72] Storage of a muscle in a strong glycerol solution at low temperature for several days destroys the membranes and extracts most of the soluble proteins and crystalloids. The contraction machinery seems intact. This glycerol-extracted muscle cannot be made to contract by electrical stimulation, of course, but chemical stimulation can produce contraction–relaxation cycles in which the tension and degree of shortening are quantitatively comparable to responses of whole muscle to electrical stimulation. If extracted muscle is suspended in a medium resembling the intracellular medium—e.g., isotonic KCl—the extracted muscle is quite stiff or unextensible, a condition resembling the rigor of poisoned or dead muscle. Raising the ATP concentration to about 3 mM. causes shortening and tension. Since the actomyosin hydrolyzes ATP, the stiff state slowly returns and the extracted muscle "sets" at its new length. If an extracted muscle is undergoing an ATP-induced contraction, addition of actomyosin ATP-ase inhibitors causes relaxation; the preparation remains in an extensible or *plasticized* state as long as the ATP is present. Substances such as inorganic pyrophosphate and ADP also plasticize muscle but, unlike ATP, do not cause tension. Thus, ATP has two actions: It causes tension, accompanied by hydrolysis of ATP, and it also plasticizes the muscle.

ACTOMYOSIN SOLUTION.[45, 55] Actin and myosin bind strongly together in isotonic KCl to form soluble actomyosin. Adding Ca^{++}, Mg^{++} and ATP initiates a dramatic "superprecipitation" of actomyosin, accompanied by hydrolysis of ATP. But the reaction is not controlled by Ca^{++} (see below) if the solution is formed from pure actin and myosin. Solutions obtained by less precise methods apparently contain impurities required for Ca^{++} control—possibly tropomyosin. The superprecipitation reaction, since it is produced by similar conditions, is believed analogous to contraction in whole muscle. It is partly reversed by chelating Ca^{++}. Measuring viscosity, sedimentation and light-scattering in appropriate solution shows that ATP separates actin and myosin. This effect, unaccompanied by ATP hydrolysis, is also produced by ADP and inorganic pyrophosphate. This dissociation reaction is believed analogous to relaxation in extracted muscle.

Role of calcium.[27] Calcium and magnesium are intimately involved in the mechanism which gives rise to the dual role of ATP: Ca^{++} stimulates the ATP-ase of both actomyosin and myosin, but Mg++ stimulates the ATP-ase of actomyosin only. Of the two ions, calcium seems to play the more important physiologic role. Injection of Ca++ into an intact muscle fiber causes local contraction,[33] as does the more quantitative procedure of dropping Ca++ solutions onto fibers whose membranes have been partially dissolved away or stripped off.[59] Reducing the Ca++ concentration to below 10^{-6} mols. per liter in actomyosin solutions brings about the relaxation-like effects of ATP; higher concentrations are required for the contraction-like effects of ATP.[71] These findings suggest that contractile activity is controlled by variations in sarcoplasmic calcium concentration. If this is so, the excitation–contraction coupling mechanism must release calcium to induce contraction and some mechanism must take up or sequester* it to induce relaxation of the muscle. There is considerable evidence for the existence of the latter mechanism, less for the former. This relaxing factor has been discussed in a recent symposium.[27]

A muscle fraction consisting mainly of sarcoplasmic reticulum has been found capable, if ATP is present in physiologic concentrations, of picking up enough Ca++ that its concentration in the medium surrounding the muscle is lowered to about 10^{-7} mols. per liter. This sequestering of Ca++ requires energy obtained from ATP hydrolysis. Thus, muscle apparently has a mechanism whereby its Ca++ concentration can be reduced to the value required for relaxation.[71] Whether this is the primary sequestering mechanism in the intact system is not known.

Although the exact site is unknown, experiments on frog muscle indicate that Ca++ is released near the transverse tubule of the sarcoplasmic reticulum. This observation also coincides with the present knowledge of the excitation–contraction coupling mechanism (see discussion of excitation–contraction coupling, p. 124). Further, the turnover rate of Ca++ in muscle is directly dependent on the muscle's contractile activity.[5]

Thus, the experiments on model systems clearly indicate that ATP plays a dual role in the contraction–relaxation process. When the actomyosin ATP-ase is active, addition of ATP causes a contraction-like event; when the ATP-

*Sequestering of Ca++ refers to its removal from the contractile elements and the medium surrounding them and its storage in a separate compartment.

ase is inhibited, addition of ATP causes a relaxation-like event.

ENERGY SOURCES FOR CONTRACTION.[12, 55] Experiments on model systems have established that the energy source for their contraction-like events is the hydrolysis of the ATP terminal phosphate group. However, work on the disappearance of ATP failed for many years to establish ATP as the energy source for contraction in intact muscle. All sources of ATP synthesis must be blocked, of course, if a decrease in ATP concentration is to be a measure of ATP consumption. Addition of iodoacetic acid (IAA) to and removal of O_2 from the bathing medium has long been known to block the major ATP synthesizing pathways. The ATP concentration in anoxic, IAA-treated contracting muscles does not decrease as long as the contractile activity is normal. However, if the muscle "fatigues" or goes into "rigor" (a stiff, relatively inextensible state, akin to or duplicating dead muscle) ATP concentration does decrease.[12, 55] On the other hand, contraction in anoxic, IAA-treated muscles is accompanied by a decrease in creatine phosphate (CP) concentration[13] (CP is a high energy phosphate compound). Indeed, CP decreases proportionately to both the work done by the muscle and to the total heat produced during a twitch.[13] Total heat and work are also proportional to each other for each normal muscle twitch. Nevertheless, CP is not considered the immediate energy source for contraction. Rather, it is believed that ATP concentration is maintained at the expense of CP by means of the Lohmann reaction, CP + ADP = ATP + C. This idea has long been held but only recently has it been given experimental support. Davies found that, when the Lohmann reaction is inhibited with fluorodinitrobenzene and when other ATP-synthesizing pathways are sufficiently slowed, ATP decreases concomitantly with contraction.[48] Muscles poisoned with fluorodinitrobenzene give normal contractile responses until the ATP supplies are depleted.

MOLECULAR INTEPRETATION OF THE SLIDING FILAMENT THEORY. Electron microscopic and physiologic evidence for the sliding filament theory in intact muscle and the chemical data obtained from model systems and other studies form two somewhat separate bodies of information concerning muscle function. The objective is, of course, to fit all the facts together into a coherent, reasonable picture of the kinetics of

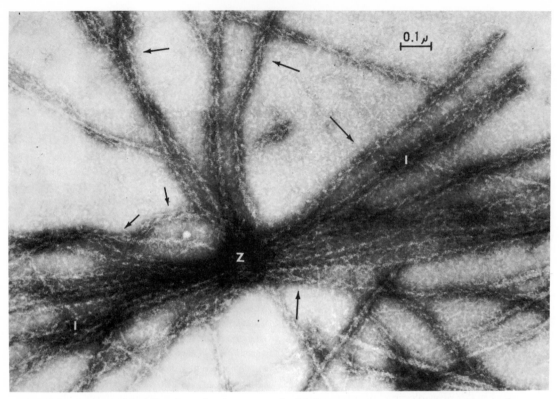

Fig. 6. An isolated I segment has been treated with heavy meromyosin, which attaches to the thin filaments, producing arrowhead-like structures (note places indicated by arrows). These are polarized and point outward from either side of the Z line. Segment prepared by blending glycerol extracted muscle in a medium which separates thick and thin filaments. (From H. E. Huxley, *J. molec. Biol.*, 1963, 7:281–308.)

the contraction process. Although a satisfactory picture is not presently available, certain speculations can be made which are helpful in understanding the types of processes occurring during contraction. This picture has emerged rapidly during the past half-dozen years.

Asymmetry of filament interactions. The mechanism using the energy in the ATP bond to produce contractile tension must be asymmetrical in the sense that the bonding between ATP, actin and myosin must form in a preferential direction to generate a net translational force. If the bonds at two successive sites exert their forces in opposite directions, no net force is developed. More specifically, the interaction of the two filaments is probably via ATP and must tend to pull the thin filaments toward the center of the A band. In other words, the thick filaments on each side of a Z line are pulled toward that Z line. H. E. Huxley[46] has direct electron micrographic evidence which gives a structural basis for this functional asymmetry. By reacting heavy meromyosin with thin fila-

ments, he formed filaments which, as shown in electron micrographs (Fig. 6), consisted of arrowhead-like structures (heavy meromyosin) with the heads always pointing away from the center. Note that the filaments join at their central points, presumably in a Z line-like combination.

Sliding filaments and dual action of ATP. The ideas of Davies,[17] A. F. Huxley[41] and H. E. Huxley[45] form the basis of a reasonable, but speculative, picture of how muscle might work. This picture, which serves mainly to integrate the known facts, should not be taken too literally. The data from muscle models indicate that ATP is directly involved in the formation of bridges between the thick and thin filaments. Thus, it might be supposed that in the relaxed state ATP is normally attached at only one side of a bridge site—i.e., on the heavy meromyosin —near the ATP-ase, preventing combination of actin and myosin and thus permitting the filaments to slide freely past each other. Tension could develop with the release of divalent calcium ions if they connected the two filaments by combining with ATP on one side and with special sites on the thin filament on the other. Shortening could result if the Ca++ were to bond to a flexible portion of a bridge projecting from the thick filament and extending by mutual repulsion between the quadrivalent ATP anions and some fixed negative charges on the thick filament. The Ca++ would neutralize some of the net negative charge on ATP, causing the extended bridge to shorten.[17] Shortening of the bridges would exert a force parallel to the filaments if the bridges were formed and broken at acute angles with respect to the filaments. This shortening of the bridge could in turn bring the ATP into the immediate vicinity of the ATP-ase and thus cause hydrolysis of ATP and breakage of the bond. In this way Ca++ may activate the ATP-ase. Creatine phosphate could then regenerate ATP and, if the muscle had shortened, another bond would form with the next site on the thin filament. This process would be happening more or less simultaneously at many sites along the filaments so that the contraction would be smooth and sustained. Thus, in normal shortening, many ATP molecules could be hydrolyzed by a single thick filament site interacting with a number of thin filament sites as they moved by. If there were no shortening, the force would be produced by the repetitive interaction and consequent turnover of ATP at fixed sites. In this case no external work is done but energy is consumed in maintaining tension. Relaxation would occur as the calcium was removed by the sequestering mechanism, thereby resulting in removal of the bridging link and inactivation of ATP-ase activity. Quite possibly, removal and inactivation are closely related, both being an intimate part of the contractile process. Although the foregoing is speculative, it can be seen how the data from muscle models can form a basis for a coherent picture of muscular contraction.

Rigor. The stiff, unextensible state of muscle, called rigor, results from conditions which reduce organic pyrophosphate activity—i.e., death and stimulation of IAA-poisoned muscle. Thus, it seems reasonable to suppose that rigor is caused by an *in vivo* formation of actomyosin —i.e., tight cross-bridges between thin and thick filaments—which is normally blocked by various pyrophosphates. The stiffness would arise from the cross-binding of the filaments

and their consequent inability to slide past each other.

Membrane Properties of Skeletal Muscle. The electrical properties of skeletal muscle are similar to those of the squid giant axon. The differences in most cases are clearly related to the role of the muscle membrane in conducting impulses and initiating contraction.

CONDUCTION OF THE IMPULSE. The action potentials of skeletal muscle normally have an overshoot of about 20 mV. which can be varied by changing the external sodium concentration. Thus, the upstroke of the action potential is much like that of the squid giant axon. The action potential lasts a few milliseconds, excluding the long-lasting negative afterpotential (see Figs. 20, 21A). In mammalian muscle, the action potential spreads from its point of initiation, normally at the neuromuscular junction, by means of the local circuit mechanism at a speed of about 5 meters per second. An impulse initiated at the center of a fiber 10 cm. long would require 10 milliseconds to reach the ends, an appreciable fraction of the contraction time of about 30 milliseconds.

MEMBRANE CAPACITY. Another indication that the transverse tubular system of the sarcoplasmic reticulum may be electrically connected to the surface membrane is the finding that the electrical capacity per unit area of fiber surface is about 10 times as large in skeletal muscle as it is in squid axon.[26] Since, for constant membrane thickness, capacity is directly proportional to the total surface area of membrane, this finding suggests that membrane area is much greater than surface area and thus that the reticulum is electrically continuous with the surface membrane. A more detailed analysis[23] has shown that the capacity can be divided into two components, one about the same value as for squid axon and another much larger one which is in series with a small resistance that possibly represents the transverse tubular resistance.

POTASSIUM PERMEABILITY. The upstroke of the action potential results from a regenerative interaction between membrane permeability to Na+ and transmembrane voltage. Although this interaction is much like that found in squid axons, the recovery process is quite different: (i) Following depolarization, the increase in potassium permeability is delayed, as in squid axons. Unlike squid, however, the increase is not appreciable for depolarizations of less than about 20 mV. Therefore, the rapid repolarization phase of the action potential terminates while the fiber is incompletely polarized. Thereafter, the potential returns to the resting level over a period determined by the resting time constant of the membrane (about 30 milliseconds) (see Fig. 21A). (ii) In squid axons, a maintained depolarization maintains an increased potassium permeability, whereas, in muscle, a depolarization greater than 20 mV. produces only a transient rise in P_K. This indicates that potassium permeability is inactivated by a process similar to, but slower than, that for sodium permeability.

In the resting state, potassium permeability exhibits "anomalous" behavior in that it is much higher when the K^+ electrochemical gradient is inward than when it is outward.[38] This is just the reverse of the behavior which occurs on depolarization, i.e., the delayed increase in potassium permeability. This anomalous behavior appears to be associated with a special region of the muscle which also accumulates potassium during activity.[30, 38] The special region seems to consist of the sarcoplasmic reticular membranes and contents or, at least, the transverse tubular portions of them. In this interpretation, the surface membrane seems to have more normal properties with respect to its potassium permeability; the significance of the peculiar permeability properties of the reticular membrane is not known.

Excitation–Contraction Coupling. Skeletal muscle contraction begins when the membrane is depolarized at least 40 mV. from the resting value. This is normally accomplished by an action potential. Membrane depolarization itself, rather than accompanying longitudinal currents, brings about contraction. This implies that depolarization of the surface membrane can initiate contraction in the interior of the cell within a few milliseconds in the faster muscles (Fig. 1). Since Ca^{++} is directly involved in the activation of the contractile mechanism, the question arises: If Ca^{++} is released at the surface by depolarization, can it diffuse into the interior fast enough to cause contraction in the experimentally observed time? A. V. Hill[35] has calculated that diffusion is too slow to account for the contraction times of larger or faster fibers. This discrepancy can be eliminated by supposing that a portion of the sarcoplasmic reticulum is directly connected to the surface

membrane and hence is depolarized with it and by further supposing that calcium is released from the reticulum, where the diffusion distance to the contractile material is much shorter.

A. F. Huxley and Taylor[43] found that there are specific sites on the muscle fiber's surface where it can be stimulated to contract by local depolarization, whereas most regions are insensitive to the local depolarization (see Fig. 7). In those muscle fibers where the center of the triad of the sarcoplasmic reticular system is at the Z line, local depolarization at a Z line often produces local contraction. The shortening is symmetrical in the two halves of the I band on either side of the Z line below the electrode. On the other hand, local depolarization between neighboring Z lines produces no contractions at the same current strengths. When the triad is centered near the junction of the A and I bands, local stimulation near the A–I junction often produces local contraction of the neighboring half of the I band. No contraction is produced at the same current strengths if the electrode tip is between neighboring triads. Thus, depolarization of the surface membrane probably also depolarizes the transverse tubules of the sarcoplasmic reticulum by direct electrotonic spread. These tubules are large enough (about 400 Å in diameter)[47] to permit this spread with little delay. This transverse activation greatly decreases the diffusion path from depolarizable membrane to contractile material—e.g., in a 100 μ fiber, the diffusion distance is reduced from 50 μ to 1 μ. Various mechanical, thermal and optical changes, collectively termed activation, precede the actual mechanical response of a pull on the tendon.

The events leading to contraction include the following: (i) Depolarization of the surface membrane by the action potential causes passive depolarization of the transverse tubules and possibly of the remainder of the sarcoplasmic reticulum. (ii) This depolarization causes some part of the reticulum to release Ca^{++}, which diffuses to the region of thick and thin filament overlap. (iii) The Ca^{++} completes the conditions necessary for tension-generating reactions between thick and thin filaments; thus, these reactions continue as long as Ca^{++} is present. (iv) Relaxation seems to result from the sequestering of Ca^{++} into special regions, possibly into the remainder of the reticular system. On this basis calcium is released on depolarization of the reticulum and sequestered on repolarization.

Mechanical Properties of Muscle. CLASSES OF CONTRACTION.

The term "contraction" as used here refers to the muscle's internal events which are manifested externally by either shortening or tension development or both. Indeed, the tension a muscle can develop between its points of attachment is the fundamental functional property of muscle.* This tension is utilized mechanically in several ways. The contracting muscles may shorten and produce movement. Since a force acts through a distance during this movement, whether it is walking, running or lifting, work is performed by the muscle. This type of contraction—shortening under constant load—has been called *isotonic* (equal tension) since Fick introduced the term in the last century. He applied the term *isometric* (equal length) to contractions in which the whole system does not change length. Such contractions produce tension rather than short-

---

* The force exerted by a muscle on its attachment is surprisingly high. At a very moderate rate of walking, the triceps surae exerts a tension almost four times the person's weight, and during running the gastrocnemius may exert a tension some six times the runner's weight. According to Fick's estimate, the human gluteus may exert a force of 1450 pounds. If all our muscles, containing an estimated 2.7×10^8 individual fibers, exerted their tensions in the same direction, they could develop a force of at least 25 tons.

ening and work. The tension or force developed in contracting muscles that do not shorten is utilized to oppose other forces (usually gravity), in holding an object and in posture. In this type of contraction no external work is done; the tension developed is used to prevent motion. This classification of contractions is useful but not realistic; although isometric contraction is common in postural muscles, isotonic contraction seldom occurs in normal bodily movements because the load ordinarily varies considerably during shortening. Nevertheless, the gross contractile properties of muscle can be understood from study of the two types of contraction.

If the opposing force or load is greater than the maximum isometric contraction tension, the muscle is stretched or lengthened while actively contracting. Such lengthening occurs, for example, when the extensor muscles of the hip check the velocity of the leg as it approaches the forward limit of its swing during walking or running. Thus physical work is done on the muscle by its antagonist in stretching it. The extensor muscle cannot store all this energy while actively contracting and some appears as heat. However, less energy is degraded to heat in the extensor muscle than that resulting from the sum of the work done on the extensor and the energy necessary to maintain the extensor in the contracted state.[37] After checking the forward velocity, the stretched muscle will

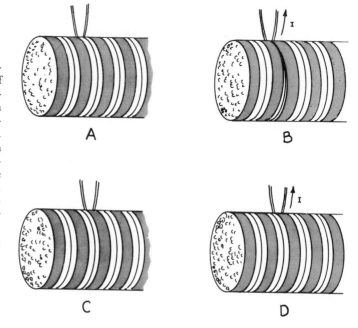

Fig. 7. Diagrammatic representation of local stimulation experiments of A. F. Huxley and Taylor.[43] The sarcoplasmic reticular triads are centered on the Z lines. *A,* Electrode applied to muscle surface at sensitive spot near Z line. *B,* Current passed while electrode is in same position as in *A.* Adjacent half sarcomeres contract locally. *C,* Electrode applied to surface over an A band. *D,* Current flow produces no local contraction. (After Fawcett, in *The myocardium, its biochemistry and biophysics,* Fishman, ed. New York, New York Heart Association, 1961.)

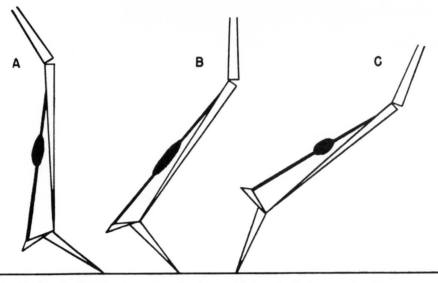

Fig. 8. Length changes of a contracting leg muscle bundle during running. Tension developed during contraction which has begun in position *A* is not sufficient to check forward movement of body, thus causing contracting muscle bundle to be stretched to length shown in position *B*. After this phase in running cycle, muscle is in position to shorten, propelling leg forward to position *C*. (Prepared and kindly furnished by Dr. H. Elftman.)

shorten as it accelerates the limb in the opposite direction. We thus have an example of both lengthening and shortening in a contracting muscle, as is schematically illustrated in Figure 8. This type of contraction normally occurs in muscles operating in antagonistic pairs. Note that in isometric, shortening and lengthening contractions the muscles perform no work or positive external work or negative external work. This classification, shown in Table 1, was proposed by Fenn.[28]

RECORDING MUSCLE CONTRACTION. Methods for recording isometric and isotonic contractions are illustrated in Figure 1. In isotonic recording, one end (usually the bony origin) of the muscle is held fixed, and the tendon on the other end is attached to a freely movable weight or weighted lever (to set tension). Shortening of the muscle is measured by recording the position of the weight or weighted lever mechanically, optically or electronically. If the recording system responds rapidly enough, the time course of muscle shortening can be accurately measured. For isometric recording, one end (usually the bony origin) is held fixed and the tendon of the other end is attached to a rigidly mounted tension-measuring device (strain gauge) that is moved only negligibly by the contraction of the muscle but develops a signal proportional to the tension which the muscle exerts on it. The signal from the strain gauge (or mechano-electric transducer, a device for transforming a mechanical signal into a more easily amplified and recorded electrical signal) is amplified and recorded on film or paper as a function of time.

TWITCH. The brief contractile response of skeletal muscle to a single maximal volley of

TABLE 1. *Classes of Muscular Contraction*

TYPE OF CONTRACTION	FUNCTION	EXTERNAL FORCE ON MUSCLE	EXTERNAL WORK BY MUSCLE
Shortening	Acceleration	Less	Positive
Isometric	Fixation	Same	None
Lengthening	Deceleration	More	Negative

impulses in the motor neurons supplying it is called a *twitch*.* The mechanical response in Figure 1 is a record showing the isometric twitch of the cat tibialis anterior muscle elicited by a single maximal stimulus to its motor nerve. The interval between the beginning of the electrical response and the peak of the tension record is the *contraction time*. By definition, the whole system (i.e., the muscles, the tendon and the isometric lever) does not shorten during isometric contraction. There is, however, *internal* shortening. The activation induced by stimulation results not only in sudden development of internal tension but also in a capacity to shorten. Under isometric conditions, the contractile elements shorten and pull on the tendon and on the series-elastic components within the fiber, thereby transmitting the tension to the recording lever or, in the body, to the bony lever. The twitch curve, recorded isotonically and isometrically, is the external manifestation of the activated contractile machine. The actual curves differ markedly in shape from those expected from the contractile machine. In an isometric twitch elastic components of the fibers and tendon in series with the contractile parts must be stretched before the muscle pulls on its tendons. Thus, tendon tension rises much more slowly than does contractile element tension. The rise is slowed so much that the contractile elements are starting to relax before tendon tension reaches its maximum.

The twitch response to a single stimulus is as

---

*Not all striated muscle fibers respond with a twitch to an impulse in their motor nerve fibers. A *slow* or *tonus* fiber differs from an ordinary twitch fiber in that it (i) has a great many motor end-plates instead of one or two; (ii) is usually incapable of propagating an action potential; and (iii) has a small diameter (15 to 20 μ) and a poorly developed sarcoplasmic reticulum. Tonus fibers are found widely in nonmammalian vertebrates but have been identified recently in the extraocular muscles of the cat.[34] As explained below, the effect of a motor nerve impulse on a muscle end-plate is a local depolarization of the muscle membrane. Since local depolarization causes local contraction, a maintained contraction can be produced in these fibers by a continuous barrage of impulses to the multiple end-plates. The rate of contraction of these muscles is much slower than twitch fibers (about one second). Thus, they are adapted for maintaining a steady tension. Only twitch fibers will be considered further in this chapter; reference to "slow" fibers means slowly contracting twitch fibers.

typical of a single isolated muscle fiber as it is of a whole muscle. As can be seen from Figure 1 the action potential is over before the contraction begins. In terms of the hypothesis of the contractile mechanisms given above, this delay would be made up of the time necessary for the transverse tubules to depolarize, plus the time needed for the release and diffusion of Ca^{++} to the sites on the filaments plus the time needed for Ca^{++} to react with these sites and activate the contractile process. Since a fixed amount of Ca^{++} is released, relaxation occurs when the Ca^{++} sequestering system reduces the Ca^{++} concentration below the critical value.

The form of the twitch contraction curve, when recorded under the same conditions, is similar for all striated twitch muscles, but the contraction time and the total twitch duration vary a great deal in different types of muscle and in different animals. There are "fast" and "slow" twitch muscles. The most rapidly contracting mammalian muscle studied is the internal rectus of the eye, which has a contraction time of 7.5 milliseconds. The limb muscles of the cat fall into two ranges. Physiologic flexors (e.g., tibialis anterior) and superficial extensor muscles bridging two joints (e.g., gastrocnemius) tend to be fast muscles, having contraction times between 25 and 40 milliseconds. Usually a deep extensor muscle acting at a single joint (e.g., soleus) is a slow muscle with a contraction time in the range of 94 to 120 milliseconds.[14] In the cat, slow muscles are red (owing to greater concentration of myoglobin) and fast muscles are pale or "white"; however, it is better to speak of "slow" and "fast" muscles, since not all fibers in the soleus are red but all are slow. Furthermore, in many vertebrate muscles red and pale fibers are completely intermixed. In the cat, fast muscles are those called upon for rapid phasic movement; slow muscles are concerned with posture. Thus, relative to the maximal tension each muscle can produce, the myotatic stretch reflex (Chap. 7) is larger in the soleus than in the gastrocnemius.

SUMMATION AND TETANUS. When a single maximal stimulus is delivered to a motor nerve or directly to a muscle, all the fibers of the muscle are activated and the maximum twitch tension is developed. Even if the electrical stimulus to the motor nerve is increased to a supramaximal intensity, the response will not be greater than that to a maximal stimulus. If, however, two maximal stimuli are delivered rapidly

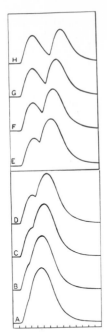

Fig. 9. Summation of muscular contraction by double stimulation. Isometric records of median head of gastrocnemius responding to two supramaximal stimuli to the motor nerve in succession. Ordinate, tension, arbitrary units; abscissa, time, 20 millisecond time marks below A. Intervals in milliseconds between stimuli in different records are: *A,* 24; *B,* 32; *C,* 40; *D,* 48; *E,* 57; *F,* 69; *G,* 77; *H,* 88. (After Cooper and Eccles, *J. Physiol.,* 1930, *69*:377–385.)

enough in succession that the second stimulus arrives before the contraction cycle is over, the response will be greater than that elicited by a single maximal stimulus. This is true for a single fiber or the whole muscle. The extent of increase in isometric tension or total shortening depends upon the interval between the two stimuli (Fig. 9). The stimulus interval, however, must be greater than the refractory period of the muscle to allow for two propagated responses. It must be emphasized that, in contrast to the action potential, the activation of the contractile material is not all-or-none. Since the state of activation depends on Ca^{++} concentration, there is a continuum of states of activation between fully activated and relaxed. In a twitch, because of the series elastic elements, the contractile elements have partially relaxed before the external tension reaches a peak. This indicates that a larger external response can be obtained by reactivating the contractile elements during the twitch. This is possible because the mechanical response far outlasts the electrical response (Fig. 1). A second action potential causes the release of more Ca^{++} while the first mechanical response is still present, thus reactivating the partially relaxed contractile elements and giving a larger external response. There is thus a mechanical fusion or summation of contractions. The degree of fusion is greater when the stimulus interval is shortest, and the tension of such a summated contraction may be more than twice the tension of a single twitch. The degree of summation decreases as the interval between the stimuli approaches the duration of a single twitch response (Fig. 9).

If a series of several stimuli is delivered at a rapid rate, the third summates with the first two, each subsequent volley adding a diminishing increment of tension until further volleys add no more tension but do maintain the contraction. This response is called a *tetanus.*[*] It occurs when all contractile elements are maximally activated and elastic elements have attained a fixed length. The tension developed in a tetanus is usually about four times that of a single twitch. With rates of repetitive stimulation too slow to cause complete mechanical fusion, an undulatory jerky response termed an incomplete tetanus is obtained. As the rate of stimulation is increased, the responses to individual volleys become less distinct, and the mechanical fusion becomes progressively greater until complete tetanus occurs (Fig. 10). Similarly, the tension produced increases progressively as the tetanus becomes more fused. Any

---

[*] The physiologic term "tetanus" has been used in naming two neuromuscular disorders: (i) tetany, caused by hypocalcemia, and (ii) tetanus, caused by the toxin of a bacillus. Tetanic contractions of muscles occur in both diseases.

Fig. 10. Isometric tension of single muscle fiber (ordinate) as a function of time (abscissa) during continuously increasing and decreasing stimulation frequency (2 to 50 per sec.). Time intervals at top of record, 0.2 second. (From Buchthal, *Dan. Biol. Medd.,* 1942, *17*(2):1–140.)

Fig. 11. Recordings of electrical (e) and mechanical (m) activities of the cat extensor digitorum longus, showing the development of tetanus. Ordinates, tension (m) or voltage (e), arbitrary units; abscissa, time, 15 milliseconds between successive action potentials in (e). Rate of stimulation, 67 per second; onset and termination of stimulation shown by electrical record. Note that action potentials are discrete whereas contractions are fused. (From Creed *et al., Reflex activity of the spinal cord.* Oxford, Clarendon Press, 1932.)

additional increase in frequency of stimulation beyond this critical rate increases tension only slightly.

This rate is, as might be expected, higher for fast muscles with their relatively brief contraction times and lower for slow muscles with their longer contraction times. A rate of 350 stimuli per second, for example, is necessary to produce a complete tetanus in the internal rectus of the eye, whereas a rate of 30 per second is adequate for the slower soleus (i.e., the "slowlyest") muscle. About 100 stimuli per second are required for complete tetanus in a fast limb muscle. In contrast to the mechanical fusion of responses to repetitive stimuli, the spike potentials accompanying such contractions always remain discrete and discontinuous (Fig. 11). This finding emphasizes the fundamental difference between membrane and contractile mechanisms.

LENGTH–TENSION RELATION. Skeletal, cardiac and smooth muscles are elastically extensible. Unstimulated skeletal muscle in the body is normally under slight tension, since it shortens (about 20 per cent) if the tendons are cut. The muscle length at which maximal contractile tension is developed is called the *resting length* because this is also near the length the muscle normally has in the body. The elastic tension of unstimulated muscle is negligible for lengths somewhat shorter than the resting length, but increases exponentially for greater lengths (Fig. 12). Stretch is reversible up to 1.5 times resting length. Cardiac muscle has this same general type of passive length–tension relation.

Since muscles change length during contraction, it is essential to know how such changes influence the contractile tension developed. The maximum force developed by a contracting muscle when all its fibers are stimulated at

optimal frequencies is specifically related to the initial length at the time of stimulation. Figure 12 shows the relation between tension developed during maximal voluntary effort and the change in length of the triceps muscle in man. The net or active, voluntary tension curve is obtained by first determining the passive tension produced by stretching the muscle fibers and connective tissue to any given length and then subtracting the value obtained from the total tension exerted by the contracting muscle at the same length. As can be seen the net ac-

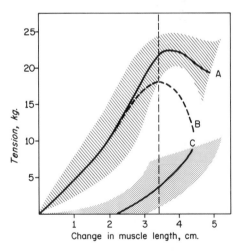

Fig. 12. Isometric length–tension curve for human triceps muscle. Muscle length changes taken from length at which total muscle tension is zero. The curves are a summary of many results. A, Most probable total-tension curve. Shaded area around this curve indicates range of results. C, Most probable passive tension curve with range indicated. B, Net voluntary tension curve obtained by subtracting C from A. (After University of California, *Fundamental studies of human locomotion and other information relating to design of artificial limbs,* vol. 2, 1947.)

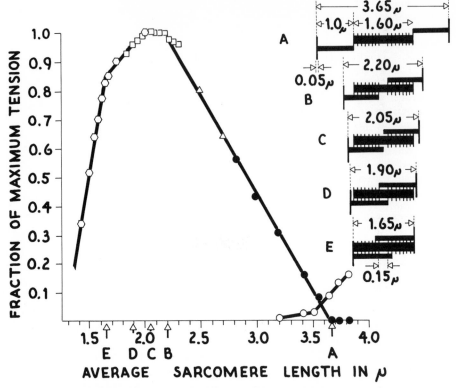

Fig. 13. "Sarcomere" isometric length–tension curve from single frog semitendinosus muscle fibers which were so controlled that length of a short central section is held constant (see text for details of technique). Ordinate, maximum active isometric tetanic tension and passive tension in fractions of maximum tension. The curve is the result of experiments on many single fibers. The accuracy of the curve requires that, in each region of sarcomere length, different fibers be used for obtaining the data. When stimulation is continued and tension is high, nonuniformities in sarcomere length may develop in the fiber's central region. The data from a few fibers (different types of points) are plotted on the curve to show agreement between data from individual fibers and data from all fibers used. The open circles indicate passive tension in the fiber giving the closed circle points. On the right are shown filament positions for the five sarcomere lengths. A, No overlap. B, Maximum overlap of thin filaments with bridges on one-half of thick filaments. C, Thin filaments meet in center of A band. D, Double overlap of thin filaments. E, Thick filaments meet Z lines. The figures are drawn with the following dimensions: thick filaments, 1.60 μ, thin filaments (including Z line), 2.05 μ,[57] Z line, 0.05 μ, region in center of thick filaments without bridges, 0.15 μ.[46] (Data from Gordon, A. F. Huxley, and Julian, *J. Physiol.*, 1964, *171*:28P–30P.)

tive tension increases more or less linearly with increasing initial length until a maximum is reached. If the initial length is greater than this maximum, less tension is developed. The optimal initial length corresponds roughly to the "natural" or resting length of the muscle in the body. This same general shape of the length–tension relationship for contracting muscle has been observed in many types of striated whole muscle and single fibers for both maximum tetanic tension and maximum twitch tension. The contractile tension developed by cardiac muscle depends on ventricular volume in much the same way. Thus the length–tension rela-

tionship is a fundamental property of contracting muscle and reflects the nature of contractility.

Length–tension relation of sarcomere.[31] The most crucial requirement for any theory of muscular contraction is that it explain the length–active tension curve. The sliding filament hypothesis can easily explain the general features of the curve, but whether it can explain the curve in greater detail depends on knowledge of the length–tension relation for a single sarcomere. The length–tension curve for a single sarcomere would be the same as that for a whole muscle or muscle fiber if all sarcomeres in the muscle were equal in length for all total muscle lengths during contraction. If this were the case, the length of each sarcomere would be directly proportional to the total muscle length. However, the lengths of individual sarcomeres along a fiber vary considerably during contraction. They are much shorter near the ends of the fiber than in the middle, where the lengths are reasonably constant. A. F. Huxley[31] has gotten a good estimate of sarcomere length–tension relation by holding constant the length of a short segment in the central region of a single fiber and measuring the tension developed during tetanic stimulation; this "length clamping" technique is similar in principle to "voltage clamping" (Chap. 2). This "sarcomere" length–tension diagram consists of a series of straight lines of different slopes, the transition between linear regions being sharply curved (Fig. 13). The striking correlation between relative overlap of thick and thin filaments at various sarcomere lengths and the length–tension diagram can be seen by comparing the lettered points on the abscissa with the corresponding inset drawings. As is shown by the negative slope on the right, the tension falls off linearly as the overlap of thick and thin filaments decreases (sarcomere length changing from 2.2 μ to 3.65 μ). At 3.65 μ there is no overlap and little active tension. The horizontal plateau from 2.2 μ to 2.0 μ occurs when filament overlap is increasing but in a region with no bridges on the thick filament. This is strong evidence that maximum isometric tetanic tension is directly proportional to the number of such bridges and further that the bridges are the sites of interaction and force generation between the two sets of filaments. The break in the curve at about 2.0 μ occurs where the thin filaments meet in the center of the A band (2.05 μ) or where they start to interact with the oppositely-directed bridge sites past the midline gap of the thick filaments (1.9 μ). Thus, tension drops off rapidly with length in this region because of the collision of opposing thin filaments with each other or the interaction of the thin filaments with the bridges on the opposite side of the thick filaments, or both. The break in the curve at 1.65 μ occurs where the thick filaments come into contact with the Z lines. The "corners" on the length–tension curve occur precisely at points predicted by the sliding filament hypothesis, thus giving it strong support.

The total amount of tension that a muscle can exert under optimal conditions is a function of the total number of fibers and the number of myofilaments per fiber. This tension, when expressed as kilograms per square centimeter of area perpendicular to the fiber direction, represents the absolute muscle force. This force is about 4 kg. per sq. cm. in man. To do external work a muscle must shorten; thus, the realizable work depends upon the fiber's length as well as on its cross section. In man this length varies from 5 mm. for the shortest bundles of the multifidus to more than 400 mm. for the sartorius muscle. Parallel-fibered muscles in the human body can shorten during contraction to about 60 per cent of their maximal extended lengths. In pennate muscles the excursions are less.

Load–speed of shortening relation. Both the rate and the degree of muscle shortening during contraction depend upon the load. With a greater load, the muscle shortens less and more slowly. It is a common experience that lighter objects can be lifted more rapidly than heavier ones. The relation between speed of shortening and load in the human pectoralis is given by the load–speed curve in Figure 14. To measure this relation, the muscle is kept slightly stretched and then is stimulated to contract maximally. The muscle lifts a load (weight or weighted lever) which has been supported by a block, and the muscle's length is then recorded as a function of time. The rate or speed of shortening starts at a high value and slowly decreases to zero as shortening approaches the maximum. The initial high speed is defined as the shortening velocity or speed. The rate of shortening must be measured at a fixed length for each load lifted since the maximum isometric tension varies with length. When the short-

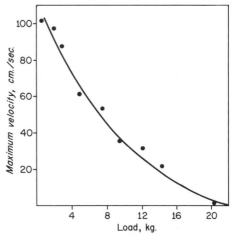

Fig. 14. Load–maximum shortening velocity (magnitude of velocity or speed) curve for human right pectoralis major muscle. Muscle initially was stretched by a load of 0.32 kg. to a length slightly beyond resting. Greater loads were supported by a block at this same length before excitation. (Based on data of Ralston, Inman, Strait, and Shaffrath, *Amer. J. Physiol.*, 1928, *86*:312–319.)

ening is maximal, the speed is zero and isometric tension develops for that length. At this point, the length is the shortest at which the muscle can lift the load. The general form of the load–shortening velocity curve follows directly from the sliding filament hypothesis (although it is not unique in this respect): When a muscle shortens rapidly, the filaments slide past one another rapidly, leaving little time for interaction of thick and thin filaments and consequent generation of tension. Thus there are fewer interacting sites and less tension development than if the muscle shortens slowly. In any case, the muscle never exerts as much force while shortening as it does when contracting isometrically. In the body, muscle speed is also limited by the mechanical inertia of the moving parts. Since the absolute amount of shortening depends on the length of the muscle, the intrinsic speed of the muscle is given by its maximum velocity divided by its length. The intrinsic speed, as mentioned in the discussion of the twitch, varies a good deal among muscles of the same animal and between different animals.

For further analysis of the relation between mechanical power, developed efficiency, total power used and speed of shortening, the student may refer to the paper of A. V. Hill.[36] A. F. Huxley[41] and H. E. Huxley[45] discuss more completely the mechanical properties of whole muscle. For an analysis of the dynamics of motion, the effective utilization of forces of muscle contraction, and the interrelationship of the geometric arrangement of the bony levers and the dynamics of muscle contraction, refer to Elftman[22] and to the University of California studies.[69]

The Motor Unit and Gradation of Muscular Activity.

MOTOR UNIT.   The functional unit of the motor system is neither the entire muscle nor the individual muscle fiber but the *motor unit*. Just before and just after entering the muscle, the axon from each ventral horn cell (motoneuron) branches many times and innervates a number of muscle fibers. Therefore, *the motor unit consists of a single motoneuron, its axon and the group of muscle fibers innervated by this single axon*. The motor unit, not the single muscle fiber, represents the unitary, minimum or quantum basis of normal muscular activity; normal skeletal muscle responses are quantitatively graded in terms of motor units and, in Sherrington's words, "a muscle with its motor nerve may be thought of as an additive assemblage of motor units."

The average size of the motor unit—the number of muscle fibers in a motor unit—is learned from the innervation ratio. The innervation ratio is determined by dividing the number of fibers in a muscle by the number of motor axons in the nerve serving the muscle. For example, innervation ratios in cat muscles vary from 1:3 in extrinsic eye muscles to 1:150 in some leg muscles; the ratio depends on the function of the muscle. Fine gradation of eye muscle contraction is necessary for object fixation, but only coarse gradation is needed for postural muscles; smaller ratios (fewer muscle fibers per nerve fiber) permit greater delicacy in gradation of movement.

Average motor unit tension. The tension yielded by a whole muscle under maximal stimulation of its nerve divided by the number of motor fibers in the nerve gives the average tension of the individual motor units. Following this reasoning, Eccles and Sherrington[21] determined the total tension developed by representative muscles during motor twitches and tetani after the dorsal root ganglia had been removed and the afferent fibers in the muscle nerves allowed to degenerate. Subsequently, the motor fibers passing to the tested muscle were enumerated and the average motor unit tension was calculated. In cat leg muscles, these values ranged from 8 to 25 grams for tetanic stimulation and from 2 to 6 grams for twitches. The number of motor units ranged from 250 to 550. It has since been learned that many of the nerve fibers which would be counted in such preparations are γ efferents innervating intrafusal fibers of the muscle spindles. These fibers, which constitute about 30 per cent of the motor fibers, do not add to the tension of muscle contraction. Eccles and Sherrington's values for motor unit tension should therefore be increased by 40 per cent (100/0.7 − 100). If, as Hunt and Kuffler claim,[40] a single muscle fiber may be innervated by more than one nerve fiber, the average tension value of a unit would be still greater.

MECHANISMS OF GRADATION.   Since motor units are the smallest functional units of muscle, the weakest possible *natural* movement due to twitch fibers is the twitch of a single motor unit. As more force is required, three things happen in an overlapping sequence: (i) more motor units are activated (recruitment); (ii) the active motor units discharge more frequently but not rapidly enough for muscular summation (i.e., the response is subtetanic); and (iii) with further increase of frequency, the motor unit twitches summate to form a tetanus. In both stage ii and stage iii, the more rapid the frequency the greater the tension becomes, although the reasons for this are somewhat different in the two stages. It should be kept in mind that the total tension exerted on a tendon at any instant is simply the sum of the tensions being generated by each motor unit at that instant. Some units are contracting, some relaxing and some resting.

To visualize these relations it is necessary to know the rate at which single motoneurons discharge. This rate was measured by Adrian and Bronk, who recorded activity of single motor units through concentric needle electrodes thrust into a muscle. During voluntary contraction the discharge rates of single motoneurons varied between 5 and 50 impulses per second as the contraction increased from light to maximal effort. During postural reflex contraction, Denny-Brown found discharge rates of 5 to 25 impulses per second. It is clear that no significant degree of muscle summation occurs at the lower rates; each unit is producing a series of twitches. Nevertheless, tension grades with frequency. A necessary condition for occurrence of this gradation is that the units contract asynchronously, which they will do because they are recruited at different times and are activated at different rates. Figure 15 shows how four motor units twitching asynchronously at very low rates sum to produce a relatively smooth, maintained tension on the tendon. Not only will the asynchronized trains of impulses in many motoneurons result in a smooth contraction of the whole muscle, but this contraction will vary according to the average frequency of the twitches in the individual units. Think of the twitch as a quantum of contraction. With more rapid rates of motoneuron discharge the number of units twitching at any one time increases, and their individual forces combine to pull on the tendon.

For the stronger grades of muscular tension the third mechanism comes into play as the frequencies of motoneuron discharge enter the tetanic range. As was seen earlier, as twitches fuse to form a tetanus the tension produced is proportional to the frequency of stimulation up to the fusion frequency. Higher frequencies yield little additional tension. In rapid muscles fusion occurs at about 40 to 50 stimuli per second, which agrees well with the top range of motoneuron discharge during voluntary activity.

NEUROMUSCULAR TRANSMISSION

Events in Neuromuscular Transmission. How a nerve impulse initiates an impulse in a muscle fiber membrane poses a problem not encountered in impulse propagation in either structure. This problem arises from the rapidly changing geometry at the junction of nerve and muscle. If the local circuit current flow of the nerve impulse directly stimulates the muscle fiber membrane, then the nerve fiber must supply a large current in order to depolarize the muscle membrane to threshold. This necessity can be seen from Figures 16 and 17, which show the main structural features of the neuromuscular junction (end-plate region of the muscle). The diameter of the naked axon near its termination is 1 to 2 μ, the diameter of the muscle fiber is about 100 μ. If there were a low-resistance connection between the axoplasm and the sarcoplasm, activity at the nerve terminal would cause local current flow from the inactive muscle membrane. However, the area of muscle membrane that must be depolarized is at least 1000 times larger than the area of the nerve terminal. It is unlikely that the nerve can supply the required current; it is

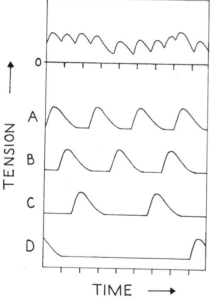

Fig. 15. Summation (top) of tensions developed by four motor units contracting (twitching) asynchronously at different frequencies. Result is a relatively smooth tendon tension. Ordinates, top, tendon tension; A, B, C, D tensions developed by each of four motor units. Abscissa, time (100 millisecond markers). The motor units are stimulated at rates of 4.3, 3.5, 2.4 and 1.1 per second; each produces the same maximum tension. Note that the summed tension is much smoother than that developed by each motor unit.

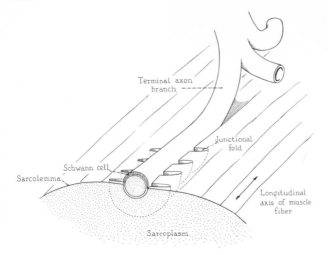

Terminal axon
branch

Junctional
fold

Schwann cell

Sarcolemma

Longitudinal
axis of muscle
fiber

Sarcoplasm

Fig. 16. End-plate region of the frog. The trough in which the terminal axon branch lies runs parallel to the axis of the muscle fiber. Myelin sheath has ended before terminal branching, leaving only the Schwann cell over the axon. (After Birks, H. E. Huxley and Katz, *J. Physiol.*, 1960, *150*:134–144.)

even more unlikely that there is protoplasmic continuity between nerve and muscle in view of recent electron micrographic studies of the nerve muscle junction (Fig. 17).[6] These considerations, together with earlier physiologic evidence and the highly specialized structure of the nerve terminal and the end-plate membrane, overwhelmingly indicate that neuromuscular transmission is accomplished by means other than local circuit flow, e.g., chemically.

There is an enormous amount of evidence that neuromuscular transmission is mediated by a chemical—acetylcholine (ACh), a methylated quaternary ammonium salt. The sequence of events is as follows: (i) The depolarization of the naked nerve terminal during activity causes the release of a small amount of ACh. (ii) The ACh diffuses across the small gap between the nerve ending and the end-plate and reacts with a *receptor* in the end-plate. (iii) The ACh–receptor complex acts to increase the permeability of the end-plate membrane to cations, specifically to Na^+ and K^+, and is quickly destroyed by the enzyme acetylcholinesterase (AChE), which is localized in high concentrations in the end-plate regions of the membrane. (iv) The membrane potential of the end-plate changes toward zero, no matter

what the original potential. (v) If the transmitter action is strong enough, and if the muscle membrane is excitable, the end-plate membrane is depolarized to threshold, and an impulse is propagated away from the end-plate in both directions.

ACETYLCHOLINE LIBERATION.[25, 51] The depolarization due to the arrival of an impulse at the nerve terminals liberates a minute amount of ACh (about 10^{-17} M.). From studies of the electrical potentials at the end-plate it appears that the ACh is liberated from a large number (200 to 300) of sites in the form of small packets or quanta containing a constant number of ACh molecules. The exact number is unknown but is 1000 to 10,000 molecules per packet, possibly more. This physiologic evidence conforms with biochemical evidence that ACh exists in bound form and with the findings by electron microscopy that the nerve terminals contain many vesicles a few hundred Ångstroms in diameter (Fig. 17). Individual packets are liberated spontaneously at random intervals in the absence of propagated activity in the nerve. During an impulse not all of the ACh liberation sites actually do release a packet of ACh. The number of sites that do release ACh during activity increases directly with the

---

Fig. 17. Electron micrographs of transverse and longitudinal sections through the end-plate region of frog muscle fiber, showing relationship between terminal axon and muscle cell. Compare with Figure 16. Axon terminal (AT), Schwann cell (SC), mitochondrion (M), neurolemma (NL), sarcolemma (SL), sarcoplasm (SP), junctional fold (JF), myofilaments (MF), vesicles (V). *Top*, Transverse section through terminal axon branch, muscle fiber and junctional fold. Thus, sarcolemma is seen near neurolemma for only a short distance at left. *Bottom*, Longitudinal section showing relationships between structures involved. Note junctional folds penetrating into the muscle fiber and the existence of a gap between neurolemma and sarcolemma. (From Birks, Huxley, and Katz, *J. Physiol.*, 1960, *150*:134–144.)

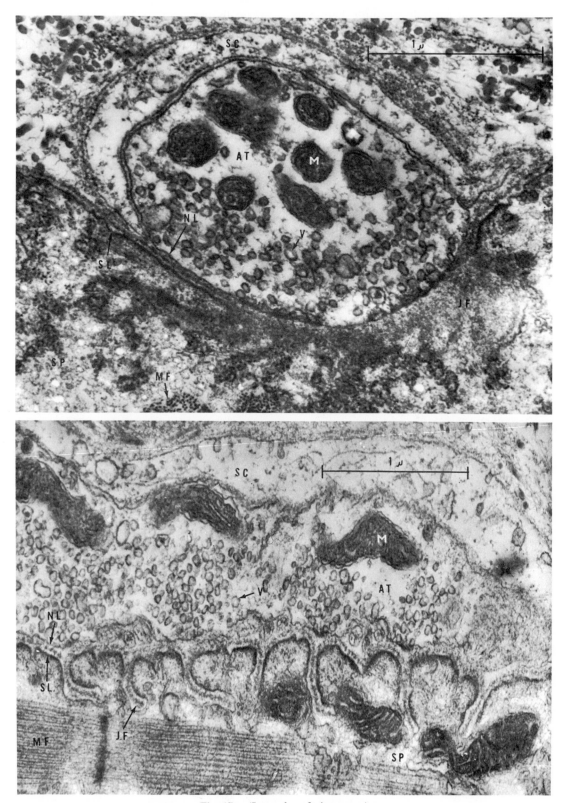

Fig. 17.   (Legend on facing page.)

calcium and inversely with the magnesium concentration in the bathing medium. However, the amount of ACh in each packet remains constant over a range of calcium concentrations that changes the total amount of ACh released from near zero to well above normal—indicating that calcium is directly involved in the secretion of the packets of ACh.

END-PLATE RECEPTORS.[25, 51] The muscle end-plates contain two kinds of ACh receptors. One, the receptor proper, combines with ACh to form the complex which leads to end-plate depolarization. The other "receptor" is the enzyme AChE, which inactivates ACh by speeding its hydrolysis to choline and acetate, which are inactive. It is quite possible that these two receptors are part of the same protein molecule, but differential drug effects leave little doubt that there are two sites having different properties. It is probable that the initial receptor–ACh complex is inactive but quickly changes into an active depolarizing form. Simultaneously, ACh is being destroyed by the AChE. The concentration of AChE in the end-plate region is sufficiently high to account for the destruction of the ACh in a few milliseconds, in accord with the calculated duration of transmitter action at the end-plate. It is supposed that both ACh–receptor complexes are in equilibrium with ACh. Therefore, as ACh is hydrolyzed by AChE, more ACh will dissociate from the receptor and, in turn, be hydrolyzed by the AChE. In this way, ACh can exert its transmitter action in the presence of high concentrations of AChE, but only briefly as required to prevent repetitive firing of the muscle fiber. This sequence of events can be diagrammed as shown at the bottom of this page.

During ACh release, part presumably combines with receptor (R) and part with acetylcholinesterase. After release, the ACh combined with receptor (R) dissociates as AChE becomes available after destroying its ACh and, hence, reaction goes from upper right, where all steps are reversible, to lower right where the right hand reaction is irreversible.

Acetylcholine Action at the End-Plate.[51] In their classic analysis of neuromuscular transmission, Fatt and Katz concluded that the action

of ACh on the end-plate membrane is to increase its permeability to all free ions in the intracellular and interstitial fluids. However, later evidence indicates that the permeability changes are limited to increases in P_{Na} and P_K to quite large values. Such a change in the properties of the end-plate membrane might result from the creation of a pore through the membrane large enough for these ions to penetrate it rather easily. If Na^+ and K^+ could penetrate this pore with equal ease, then the transmembrane potential near it would go to about zero. Since enough ACh is released by a nerve impulse to produce a large number of such pores, the whole end-plate membrane potential discharges toward zero. However, the duration of the transmitter action is so short that the depolarization process does not reach a steady value. The fall in the potential at the end-plate sets up local circuit flow from adjacent regions, so that the depolarization spreads passively along the muscle membrane. If the depolarization at the end-plate region reaches threshold, an impulse is generated which propagates away from the end-plate in both directions. The end-plate potential (frequently abbreviated e.p.p.) is defined as the potential changes in the neighborhood of the end-plate induced by activation of the ACh receptors which cause the increase in end-plate permeability to Na^+ and K^+. This activation may be induced by means of the ACh released spontaneously from or by activity of the nerve terminals, or by ACh or ACh-like substances applied from an external source.

ANALYSIS OF THE END-PLATE POTENTIAL.[26] Analysis of the e.p.p. is facilitated by adding the blocking agent, curare, to the bathing medium. Curare blocks neuromuscular transmission by reducing the e.p.p. below the threshold of the muscle membrane. This reduction comes about because curare competes with ACh for receptors and forms an inactive complex with them. In consequence, only part of the ACh released by a nerve impulse can combine with receptors to depolarize the end-plate. If the concentration of curare is properly controlled, some ACh–receptor complexes will form, so that the e.p.p. is not abolished and can be studied without inter-

$$\text{ACh release} \rightarrow \text{ACh} \quad \begin{array}{l} + \text{ R} \rightleftharpoons \text{AChR} \rightleftharpoons \text{AChR}' \text{ (increase in } P_{Na}, P_K). \\ \\ + \text{AChE} \rightleftharpoons \text{ACh·AChE} \rightarrow \text{Acetate}^- + \text{Choline}^+ + \text{AChE}. \end{array}$$

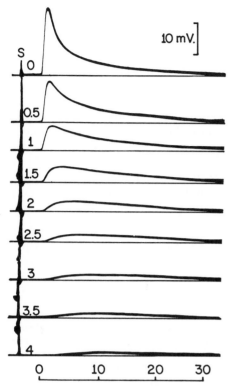

Fig. 18. Transmembrane potential changes produced in a curarized muscle fiber by stimulation of motor nerve to the muscle. *Abscissa,* Time in milliseconds. *Ordinate,* Change in transmembrane potential in millivolts. *S,* Stimulus artefact, signaling time of stimulus to motor nerve. Number by each curve is distance (in mm.) of intracellular recording microelectrode from muscle end-plate. As distance increases, the recorded potential becomes smaller and slower. (From Fatt and Katz, *J. Physiol.,* 1951, *115:*320–370.)

ference by propagated action potentials in the muscle.

If a microelectrode is inserted at the end-plate region in a curarized muscle fiber, a typical monophasic potential change, the e.p.p., is recorded after stimulation of the motor nerve. The size of the e.p.p. depends inversely on curare concentration; the shape of the potential is not affected. That the e.p.p. originates at and is confined to the end-plate region is demonstrated by the recordings in Figure 18. The potentials shown were recorded at successive 0.5 mm. intervals away from the end-plate. It can be seen that the peak height and rise time of the e.p.p. diminish rapidly as the distance increases. Analysis of these records shows that the change in the size and shape of these potentials is accurately in accord with the cable properties of the fiber. These findings lead to

the conclusion that the transmitter action at the end-plate discharges the membrane at that point and that this induced potential change spreads passively in both directions along the muscle fiber membrane.

Anticholinesterases. Many compounds, e.g. prostigmine and di-isopropylfluorophosphate (DFP), inhibit the ability of AChE to hydrolyze ACh. Inhibition of AChE activity at the end-plate by one of these drugs leads, as expected, to a large increase in the size and duration of the e.p.p. A dramatic example of the effect of prostigmine is seen when neuromuscular transmission is blocked by replacing 80 per cent of the sodium chloride in the bathing solution with an equivalent amount of sucrose. The resulting e.p.p. is somewhat slower than the e.p.p. during curarization. Addition of neostigmine to the bath enormously prolongs the e.p.p., as can be seen in Figure 19. The relatively enormous amount of charge displaced from the muscle membrane could not be supplied by current flow from the active nerve terminals, but is a necessary consequence of the ACh theory.

The different ways curare and neostigmine affect the e.p.p. constitute strong evidence that there are two distinct sites of ACh-binding on the end-plate membrane; curare competes with ACh for the receptor and reduces the e.p.p., whereas neostigmine competes with ACh for AChE and increases the e.p.p.[51] The receptor sites for ACh lie on the outside of the membrane; application of ACh, carbaminylcholine

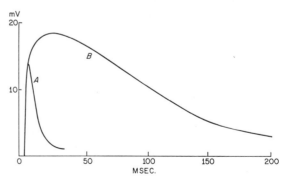

Fig. 19. Effects of an anticholinesterase drug on end-plate potential of single muscle fiber. *Abscissae,* Time in milliseconds. *Ordinates,* Change in transmembrane potential (millivolts) produced by stimulation of motor nerve. *A,* e.p.p. when neuromuscular transmission is blocked after reduction of sodium concentration in bathing medium. *B,* e.p.p. from same fiber after addition of neostigmine to the sodium-deficient bathing medium. (From Fatt and Katz, *J. Physiol.,* 1951, *115:*320–370.)

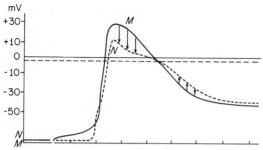

Fig. 20. Action potentials of a single muscle fiber recorded with intracellular electrode in end-plate region. *Abscissa,* Time in milliseconds. *Ordinate,* Transmembrane potential in millivolts. *M,* Action potential recorded at end-plate when muscle is stimulated by electrodes applied directly to it. *N,* Action potential recorded when muscle is stimulated via its motor nerve. Dashed line shows approximate "equilibrium potential" of end-plate membrane in presence of neuromuscular transmitter agent. Arrows indicate how the transmitter action modifies action potential shape. Note reversal in direction of arrows on opposite sides of the dashed "equilibrium potential" line. (From Fatt and Katz, *J. Physiol.,* 1951, *115*:320–370.)

(an ACh-like compound that is hydrolyzed much more slowly), or curare to the inside of the end-plate region has none of the effects on the end-plate that close external application produces.[51]

NEUROMUSCULAR TRANSMISSION.[26] In an uncurarized muscle the e.p.p. is usually greater than threshold strength, and an action potential arises out of the e.p.p. as it crosses threshold. The threshold potential at the end-plate is the same whether determined by indirect or direct stimulation. However, the shape of the action potential recorded at the end-plate in response to indirect (motor nerve) stimulation differs from the shape of the potential recorded following direct stimulation of the muscle. Figure 20 shows that, in comparison to the directly evoked action potential, the one indirectly evoked is small and rather bizarrely shaped. Close inspection reveals that the changes in the shape of the indirect action potential are always toward a fixed potential slightly below the zero line (arrows). This altered shape is confined to the end-plate region; an action potential recorded a few millimeters away has a normal shape, no matter what the mode of stimulation.

Fatt and Katz interpreted this finding as indicating that the final steady value of the e.p.p. is slightly less than zero and that the membrane resistance of the end-plate is greatly reduced during transmitter activity, which persists with diminishing intensity throughout most of the action potential. Note that time is much more spread out in Figure 20 than it is in Figure 18, and thus that the peak of the e.p.p. occurs about 3 milliseconds after it starts, a time comparable to the duration of the action potential. This persisting resistance change explains the divergence of the indirect end-plate spike toward zero. The reduction in membrane resistance during the rising phase of the action potential is quite large (Chap. 2). The transmitter action must produce a roughly equal additional reduction in resistance at the end-plate because the peak height of the end-plate action potential is considerably reduced.

Other evidence supports the idea that the final steady level of the e.p.p. is near zero. Changes in the end-plate membrane potential produced by applied currents produce proportionate changes in the e.p.p. Additionally, indirect stimuli delivered at various times during the passage of a directly evoked action potential through the end-plate region always produce changes in the potential toward zero. Under normal conditions, sodium ions must carry most of the depolarizing current during transmitter activity, since this is the only ion appreciably out of equilibrium with the steady membrane potential. However, the e.p.p. steady value near zero is below the sodium-ion equilibrium potential, and it must be supposed that potassium ions reduce the amount of depolarization as the membrane potential moves away from the potassium equilibrium potential. Further evidence that potassium permeability is increased during end-plate activity is the finding that the membrane resistance changes when ACh is applied to the end-plate of a muscle depolarized by bathing it in isotonic potassium sulfate.

CARDIAC AND SMOOTH MUSCLE

Classification of Muscle. There are two general classes of smooth muscle. *Visceral smooth muscle* is found in the walls of the gastrointestinal tract and the genitourinary tract. *Multi-unit* or *motor unit smooth muscle* is found in structures such as the precapillary sphincters, the intrinsic muscles of the eye and the pilo-erector muscles, where direct nervous control is required. Smooth muscle is differentiated from striated muscle histologically by the absence of cross-striations and physiologically by a relative slowness of contraction. Bozler[7] drew a close analogy between the properties of striated and smooth muscle and suggested the following functional classification of muscle:

$$\text{Striated Muscle} \begin{cases} \text{Skeletal} \begin{cases} \text{Many Units} \\ \text{Motor Nerves} \end{cases} \text{Multi-Unit} \\ \\ \text{Cardiac} \begin{cases} \text{Automatic} \\ \text{Syncytial} \end{cases} \text{Visceral} \end{cases} \Bigg\} \text{Smooth Muscle}$$

The properties of multi-unit smooth muscle with motor nerves are quite similar to those of skeletal muscle; and the properties of cardiac and visceral smooth muscle are quite similar.

Cardiac Muscle. SYNCYTIAL CONDUCTION.[75] One of the most striking features of the heart is that large parts of it contract almost simultaneously. Certainly, the synchronous contraction of the ventricle is necessary for the efficient expulsion of blood. Synchronous contraction or systole could be produced in skeletal muscle by simultaneous activation of all the motor units. However, the heart beats synchronously and spontaneously when completely denervated. Cardiac muscle is thus different from skeletal muscle in being both automatic and a functional syncytium. The term "automatic" refers to the intrinsic ability of a tissue to generate impulses spontaneously and rhythmically, and "functional syncytium" means that the whole tissue acts electrically like a single large cell.

Visceral smooth muscle also has these properties.

As in skeletal muscle, the normal stimulus for contraction of cardiac and smooth muscle is membrane depolarization. In the heart this depolarization is brought about by conducted action potentials; therefore, the synchronous contraction of cardiac muscle arises from its electrical activity. If a microelectrode is inserted into a ventricular cell and the membrane potential is recorded throughout one cycle, the pattern of the recording is the same, save for slight time differences, no matter from which ventricular cell the recording is obtained (Fig. 21*B*). The action potential propagates rapidly throughout the ventricle by local circuit activation; activity in one cardiac cell soon brings adjacent cells into activity. A suprathreshold stimulus applied anywhere in the ventricle initiates activity which spreads throughout the ventricle.

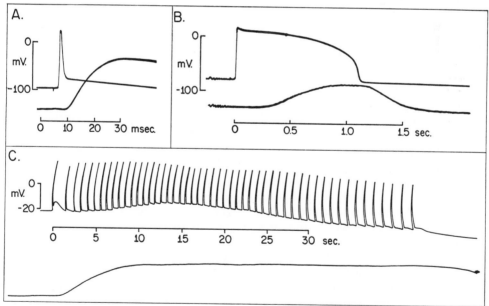

Fig. 21. Simultaneously recorded transmembrane potentials and contraction in three types of muscle. *A,* Isolated frog skeletal muscle fiber. *B,* Whole frog ventricle; action potential recorded from one "cell." *C,* strip of pregnant rat uterus (smooth muscle); action potential recorded from one "cell, spontaneous activity." *Abscissae,* Time in milliseconds (*A*) or seconds (*B* and *C*). *Ordinates,* Upper trace, millivolts; lower trace, arbitrary units of contractile tension. (Part *A* after Hodgkin and Horowicz, *J. Physiol.,* 1957, *136*:17P–18P.)

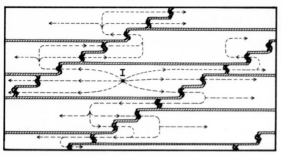

Fig. 22. Simplified and formalized structure of a portion of rat atrial trabecula. Thin straight lines represent regular, excitable cell membranes having high electrical resistance; thickened heavy lines represent intercalated disc membranes or nearby "tight" junctions having low resistance. Each cell is completely surrounded by membrane. Large dot (I) in center indicates location of an intracellular current electrode. Dashed lines with arrowheads indicate major pathways of current flow from the electrode. Current flow through regular membranes into the extracellular fluid is small and is not shown. Intracellular current flow at right angles to the fiber direction follows the zigzag path of least resistance shown largely through the intercalated discs or adjacent low resistance sites. This structure accounts for the spatially nonuniform spread of current. Contractile material is not shown for simplicity. (From Woodbury, *Handbook of physiology, Section 2: Circulation,* vol. I, Hamilton and Dow, eds. Washington, D.C., American Physiological Society, 1962.)

The spread of activity by local circuit flow in a nerve fiber (Chap. 2) was described in terms of a continuous axoplasm with a specific resistivity several orders of magnitude smaller than that of the membrane. In the heart, however, electron micrographs show rather clearly that each cell is surrounded by a distinct membrane, so there is no anatomic continuity of the myoplasm between cells. Yet, equally clearly, activity spreads through cardiac muscle from cell to cell. This is the reason for using the term "functional syncytium." There are specialized regions of "contact" between adjacent cardiac muscle cells, the *intercalated discs*. At the discs, the membranes are close together—about 100 Ångstroms apart—and are greatly folded and interdigitated so that their surface areas are increased. This close approximation and the large area of contact between the surfaces of adjacent cells are both factors which tend to increase the flow of the local currents of an active cell through adjacent inactive cells. Two types of evidence support the idea that flow through low-resistance disks or other low-resistance regions is likely to be the basis of the functional

syncytium: (i) Propagation through cardiac muscle requires the flow of local circuit currents; interruption of this flow by insertion of a high resistance in the circuit blocks conduction.[3] (ii) Current applied via an intracellular electrode in one cell produces in adjacent cells voltage changes of sufficient magnitude to insure depolarization to threshold by an action potential.[76] Additionally, it was found that current spreads as far in the direction of the fibers as it does in the direction perpendicular to the fibers, a further indication that the low resistance regions are in or near the intercalated discs. A possible interpretation of these findings is given by Figure 22.

Two dimensional and three dimensional spread.[76] Activity initiated in one region of the heart spreads in all directions at a velocity depending on the cable and excitable properties of the cells (see Chap. 2). This spread behavior is distinctly different from that of nerve or skeletal muscle fibers. In a nerve fiber the activity travels in one direction, that of the fiber; spread of activity is one dimensional. In syncytial tissues, spread is two or three dimensional. Spread in thin-walled tissues, such as the atrium or the gut wall, is two dimensional; an action potential originating at a point spreads over the surface as a wave.

Such a wave is somewhat analogous to the ripple produced in the surface of a pond by a falling pebble. However, the water wave gradually diminishes in amplitude as it spreads, whereas the electrical wave in tissue is kept constant in amplitude by the excitation of the membrane at each point. In this respect, the electrical wave is more nearly analogous to the wave of "excitation" produced when a lighted match is touched to the center of a sheet of gunpowder spread evenly over a surface. The process of spread is identical in principle. The gunpowder is set afire by the conduction of heat in advance of the burning region; unexcited membrane is "set afire" by the spread of currents in front of the excited area of membrane. The analogy ends there—the membrane presently recovers its excitability. The ventricle, especially the left ventricle, is a thick-walled organ and the spread of excitation is three dimensional. In fact, knowledge of the pathway of the spread of excitation through the ventricle is essential to the understanding of its contributions to the electrocardiogram (Chap. 30). Another way of stating the differences between nerve, atrium and ventricle is that, in nerve, the wave front is a point; in atrium, a line; and in ventricle, a surface.

MEMBRANE POTENTIAL AND CONTRACTION.[75] The action potential of cardiac muscle is usually several hundred milliseconds long. In most circumstances, the contraction time is approximately equal to the duration of the action potential (Fig. 21*B*). This is expected since the available evidence indicates that cardiac muscle contraction, like that of skeletal muscle, is initiated and maintained by calcium release consequent on depolarization and terminated by the sequestering of calcium following repolarization. It is convenient to think of the upstroke of the action potential as "turning on" the contraction and the fast repolarization as turning it off. The long duration of the action potential insures that each contraction is sufficiently prolonged to be maximal; i.e., the tension corresponds to a tetanus in skeletal muscle.

Since the membrane is refractory until repolarization is well advanced, there can be no summation in cardiac muscle. This behavior is consonant with the function of the heart. A strong synchronous contraction is necessary for the efficient ejection of blood from the heart; the contractile properties of cardiac muscle are otherwise much the same as tetanic contractions of skeletal muscle. The length–tension relationships are qualitatively indistinguishable. The mechanical properties of cardiac muscle are described in Chapter 29.

One interesting aspect of cardiac muscle is that the duration of the action potential depends on the heart rate: the faster the rate, the shorter the duration. Over the usual physiologic range, the action potential duration is roughly one-half of the interval between beats. This insures that an increase in heart rate will bring about a maximal increase in cardiac output, because both diastolic filling time and systolic ejection time are reduced. A reduction in the filling time alone would occur if the action potential duration were invariant.

Cardiac action potential. The action potential of cardiac muscle differs from that of nerve or skeletal muscle in its greater duration and in the great variability of duration with rate. The dependence of the rate of rise and the overshoot of the action potential on the external concentration of sodium indicates that the upstroke of the action potential is brought about by a large increase in membrane permeability to sodium.[8, 74] However, the nature of the permeability changes underlying the greatly prolonged period of depolarization—the *plateau phase*—is not known.

Weidmann[73] has shown that total membrane slope resistance is increased during the plateau. This indicates that permeability to sodium is increased and permeability to potassium is reduced during the plateau. A simple explanation[8] of the long duration of the action potential and the dependence of its duration on rate is to suppose that two types of sodium conductance are available (see Chap. 2). The first type of conductance, responsible for the upstroke of the action potential, is initially large, but it is rapidly inactivated (order of milliseconds) following depolarization and just as rapidly activated following repolarization, i.e., like that of squid nerve. The second type, responsible for the plateau, is comparatively small but slowly inactivated (order of seconds) and just as slowly activated following repolarization. After the upstroke of the action potential and the inactivation of the fast sodium conductance, the slowly inactivated sodium conductance, although small, persists. It maintains the membrane potential near zero because the conductance of potassium has fallen, it being assumed that depolarization decreases K^+ conductance rather than increasing it as in squid nerve. As the slowly inactivated sodium conductance decreases, the potential falls slowly until a potential is reached where one or more other conductances begin to change rapidly with membrane voltage. Sodium conductance is "turned off" and potassium conductance is "turned on," so repolarization proceeds with increasing rapidity. Following repolarization, excitability returns with activation of the fast sodium conductance, but an action potential initiated at this time will be short because the slow sodium conductance is only slowly activated. The plateau will occur at a lower voltage, so the potential at which rapid repolarization occurs will be reached more quickly. Trautwein and associates[18] have recently succeeded in making voltage clamp measurements on short segments of Purkinje fibers. Their results are, generally, in agreement with the above hypothesis except that the behavior of potassium ion conductance is dependent on both time and voltage.

AUTOMATICITY OF HEART. Many regions of a syncytial tissue can originate propagating action potentials. However, in the heart there is a region specialized for origination of impulses, the *pacemaker* region in the sino-atrial (S-A) node. The S-A nodal region determines the rate of the heart beat, because its intrinsic rate is faster than those of the atrium and A-V node. An action potential from the S-A node reaches these regions before they have time to develop an intrinsic beat. Pacemaker activity results from special properties of the membrane; action potentials of a pacemaker region are distinctive. The characteristics of a pacemaker cell membrane are such that the membrane potential has no stable value. During diastole, the membrane potential falls slowly toward zero instead of remaining steady as it does in nonpacemaker regions. This slow diastolic depolarization is called the *pacemaker potential* or *prepotential* (see Chap. 10, Fig. 5A).

When the pacemaker potential reaches the threshold voltage, an impulse is generated and propagated away from the pacemaker region in all available directions in the sheet of muscle (Chap. 30). The repolarization process involves a decrease in permeability to sodium and an increase in permeability to potassium, and the membrane voltage approaches the equilibrium potential for potassium. The membrane permeability to sodium during diastole is rather higher in pacemaker tissue than in other tissues; and, as the permeability changes that cause repolarization die out, the potential begins to fall from near the potassium equilibrium potential to a rather low steady value (because of high permeability to sodium).[67] However, this steady value is so low that the potential crosses threshold first and another impulse is initiated. The rate of initiation of impulses depends primarily on the slope of the prepotential. This slope is extremely dependent on the temperature, the ion concentrations and the presence or absence of small concentrations of acetylcholine and epinephrine.

Smooth Muscle. STRUCTURE OF SMOOTH MUSCLE.[62]   The precise alignment of contractile filaments which gives rise to the characteristic cross-striated appearance of skeletal and cardiac muscle is absent in smooth muscle. Nevertheless, the contractile material and mechanism of smooth muscle is much the same as in striated muscle. The typical smooth muscle cell is shaped like a rod, tapering at both ends. Individual cells are typically 4 to 8 μ in diameter in the center and 50 to 200 μ long. Cells are closely packed into long, thin, cylindrical bundles; the thickest part of one fiber lies alongside the tapering parts of its neighbors. There is little extracellular space within these bundles, but between them are large spaces. The bundles are 50 to 100 μ in diameter and branch and coalesce with other bundles every few millimeters. This network of bundles forms into sheets or larger bundles, depending on the function of the tissue.

The cell plasma membrane of smooth muscle differs from that of skeletal muscle; in particular, there are dense thickenings which alternate with thinner regions. The thick regions often coincide with similar regions in adjacent cells. In some smooth muscles, certain membrane regions are greatly convoluted.

The contractile proteins of skeletal muscle—actin, myosin and tropomyosin—have been identified in various types of smooth muscle.[56] However, in comparison with skeletal muscle, the concentrations of the contractile proteins are lower in smooth muscle and the ATP-ase activity is lower and varies differently with pH and with calcium and magnesium ion concentrations.

Myofilaments.[58, 65]   Although thick and thin myofilaments have been observed in some kinds of smooth muscle, they are difficult to demonstrate directly in all; however, other evidence indicates their presence. In relaxed intestinal muscle, the filaments are oriented parallel to one another and with the longitudinal axis of the cell. It is not clear whether these myofilaments originate or terminate at the plasma membrane. The attractive possibility that they may attach to the dense areas of the plasma membrane is weakened by the finding that these dense areas are not found in all smooth muscle cells. Electron microscope studies on molluscan smooth muscle have revealed a more ordered structure of myofilaments:[53] (i) The contractile apparatus contains only two kinds of filaments, thick and thin. (ii) The thin filaments appear to be actin and the thicker filaments are thought to contain myosin and tropomyosin. (iii) These filaments are cross-linked in the same way as in striated muscle. Although there is no conclusive evidence, contraction probably occurs in smooth muscle, as in skeletal, by a relative sliding of two sets of filaments. The muscles are unstriated because the lateral alignment of the filaments is far less regular than in striated muscle.

Syncytium.   Most, if not all, smooth muscle structures can function as an electrical syncytium. There are two kinds of cell-to-cell contact which may provide low resistance intercellular pathways for transmission of excitation. The first is in the relatively large area where the end of one cell makes contact with the midportion of another. Secondly, small "intercellular bridges" (0.1 to 0.5 μ long, 0.2 to 0.7 μ in diameter) between cells have been observed in electron micrographs of some smooth muscle cells.[4] If intercellular protoplasmic contact exists at these "bridges," they would function as effective pathways for the conduction of impulses despite their small size.

Innervation.[11] Smooth muscle is innervated by small diameter (0.1 to 1.7 μ) autonomic postganglionic fibers which are predominantly unmyelinated. These fibers branch extensively in the muscle, forming a fine plexus which is embedded in a Schwann cell syncytium. Small branches of the plexus (2 to 8 fibers) enclosed in one Schwann cell run between muscle cells; the Schwann cells are frequently interrupted where a naked axon comes into close proximity with a muscle cell. In these regions, the axon is loaded with vesicles which are characteristic of presynaptic terminations. There is no evidence of postsynaptic specialization like the end-plate of skeletal muscle. The degree of innervation of smooth muscle appears to depend on its function; the nictitating membrane, iris and arteriolar smooth muscle are heavily innervated, whereas the gut and uterus are lightly innervated. It seems likely that all gradations of innervation occur and that the terms "multiunit" and "visceral" smooth muscle represent the extremes of considerable and little nervous control.

ELECTRICAL ACTIVITY OF VISCERAL MUSCLE.[10] The nature of visceral muscle electrical activity varies from time to time in any one tissue and from tissue to tissue in accordance with the function being performed. Small, slow variations and larger, slow-pacemaker variations with superposed, spikelike or cardiac muscle-like action potentials have all been recorded separately and in various combinations. Usually, no "resting" potential exists since the membrane potential is never relatively constant for any period. However, potentials are low, ranging from 30 to 70 mV. and averaging about 50 mV. The small, slow variations in membrane potential are nearly sinusoidal with no regenerative action potentials superposed. The period of oscillation is about 0.5 second. Larger variations of this type become more peaked on the depolarization phase and, if these variations are large enough, threshold is reached (about -30 mV.) and regenerative action potentials are initiated at regular intervals. In some tissues, action potentials are spikes, 0.1 second or less in duration, which may or may not overshoot (Fig. 21*C*), e.g.,

uterus, small intestine. In other tissues—e.g., ureter—action potentials resemble those of cardiac muscle (Fig. 21*B*) but may last many seconds. Presumably the type of action potential depends on the function of the muscle: spike-like in muscles where tension is widely graded and plateau-like where a maximal or tetanic type of contraction is needed. In some circumstances, plateau responses change into spike trains and vice versa, depending on unknown conditions. Action potentials may be initiated by pacemaker activity, by conduction, and by neural, chemical or mechanical stimuli.

Effects of stretch. Stretch depolarizes smooth muscle membrane, and thus may initiate firing or may increase the rate. The response depends strongly upon the rate of application of the stretch; a fast stretch produces a response with a short latency, whereas with a slow stretch the latency is longer and the contractile response more prolonged. Of course, the stretch must depolarize the membrane potential beyond threshold. There is a range of depolarizations, the "firing zone," which produces contractile tension as a result of the generated spike activity. Polarizations on either side of the "firing zone" result in a cessation of firing and a fall in tension.

Syncytial conduction. In cardiac muscle, an impulse originating in any part propagates over that entire part except in abnormal circumstances; the syncytial connections are always effective. In visceral muscle, on the other hand, the syncytial connections are much less efficient; whether or not an impulse spreads from one cell to another depends sensitively on local conditions, particularly on the muscle's tension or length or both and on the concentrations of such substances as acetylcholine, epinephrine and ions in the extracellular medium. Another indication of the low safety factor of syncytial transmission is the finding that individual cells in smooth muscle recover their excitability in 50 to 100 milliseconds following an effective stimulus, while 1 to 5 seconds are required for intercellular impulse conduction to recover. A general pattern of visceral muscle activity is that a number of pacemaker regions generate impulses which spread radially for a short distance and then are blocked. As mentioned above, stretch depolarizes the membrane and, depending on the original conditions, could activate a region as a pacemaker, increase its frequency, or cause depolarization block which could confine activity to a small region. The variations in the efficiency of syncytial conduction with local conditions probably play an important role in coordinating the contractions of visceral muscle so that it performs its different functions. This may account in part for the intrinsic self-regulatory capabilities of this tissue.

Automaticity. Like cardiac muscle, one of the characteristic properties of visceral muscle is intrinsic, rhythmic impulse generation. Unlike normal heart, pacemaker activity is not restricted to a specialized region; rather, the pacemaker focus often shifts from one place to another. Particularly in intestine, various pacemaker regions occur, each with a surrounding area into which its impulses reach. These domains are isolated from each other by regions which temporarily do not conduct. Both the pacemaker regions and the blocked regions shift from time to time. Another difference is that visceral muscle pacemaker activity is much more sensitive to stretch than is cardiac muscle. Indeed, stretch appears to be one of the main determinants of pacemaker activity.

ELECTRICAL ACTIVITY OF MULTI-UNIT MUSCLE.[11] The vas deferens is a multi-unit smooth muscle, heavily innervated by the hypogastric nerve. A single maximal stimulus to the hypogastric nerve produces in every cell of this muscle subthreshold transient depolarization which has many of the characteristics of the end-plate potential (e.p.p.) found in skeletal muscle. These potentials summate and reach threshold at stimulus frequencies of about one per second. These e.p.p.'s have about the same amplitude in each cell but their latencies vary from 20 to 70 milliseconds. This suggests that the bare regions where nerve fibers approximate to muscles are sites of transmitter liberation and that all cells are effectively innervated. The variable latencies are attributed mostly to variations in the diffusion distance between bare nerve and muscle fiber.

The vas deferens is normally quiescent but can be brought into spontaneous, co-ordinated, activity by small doses of norepinephrine; slow pacemaker potentials and propagating spikes are recorded from the muscle cells. Thus, multi-unit muscle can resemble visceral muscle in that both have syncytial interconnections and can be spontaneously active.

EXCITATION–CONTRACTION COUPLING.[10, 16] As in skeletal and cardiac muscle, contractile activity in smooth muscle is initiated by depolari-zation of the cell membrane and mediated by Ca^{++}. The tension developed when the membrane is completely depolarized by bathing it in a Ringer's solution in which NaCl has been replaced by K_2SO_4 and sucrose is eliminated if the calcium is removed from the bathing solution. Thus, it appears that the calcium ion acts to couple the depolarization of the cell membrane to contraction. The sarcoplasmic reticulum is not well developed but, because of the smallness of cells and the slowness of the mechanical response, calcium ions released at the surface of the cell by depolarization have sufficient time to diffuse into the center of the cell and activate the contractile elements in the interval between the electrical and the mechanical responses.

Contraction is generally initiated by action potentials and not by slow potential changes. In spike-generating muscles a "tetanus" is brought about by a train of spontaneously generated action potentials (Fig. 21C); in such a muscle contractile tension increases with spike frequency. Most long-term active changes in length or tension, called "tone," appear to be due to spike production. However, some types of tone are due mainly to passive properties of the muscle.[50]

MECHANICAL PROPERTIES OF SMOOTH MUSCLE. *Noncontracting muscle.* Visceral musculature in performing its functions undergoes enormous changes in length with comparatively small changes in tension. Bozler[7] found that if a constant load is placed on a strip of smooth muscle, the muscle will, after a rapid initial elongation, continue to elongate at a slower rate until it is increased 50 per cent in length. Furthermore, if a strip of uterine smooth muscle is stretched to a fixed length, the tension, after an initial rise, falls with time to slightly above its initial value. These examples indicate that resistance to stretch in smooth muscle is mainly that of a viscous body with a small elastic component; however, visco-elastic properties vary considerably from tissue to tissue. It is unknown how much of these visco-elastic properties are attributable to the contractile material and how much to the supporting elements. The functional capabilities of a tissue likely depend as much on its passive as on its contractile properties.

Contractile activity.[15, 50] Compared with skeletal muscle, smooth muscle contracts slowly. The duration of the "twitch" of a smooth muscle is 15 to a few hundred times longer than the twitch of a skeletal muscle from the same animal. All phases of contraction are slow. Comparison of Figure 21*A* with 21*C* shows that the contraction time (time to peak tension) is about 30 milliseconds in a frog skeletal muscle twitch compared with several seconds in a tetanus of rat uterus. The active length–tension relationship of smooth muscle is quite similar to that of striated muscle; maximal tension is developed at an optimal length. Developed tension is less for lengths shorter or longer than the optimal length. Characteristically, smooth muscle is capable of developing tensions for long periods of time and with a relatively low rate of energy expenditure. This behavior is probably the result of the low ATP-ase activity; a slow rate of making and breaking the bridges between thick and thin filaments would maintain tension at a low cost in energy consumption, but rate of contraction would be correspondingly reduced.

NEURAL AND HUMORAL CONTROL.[10, 11, 60] Multi-unit muscles are activated both electrically and mechanically by a few stimuli to the motor nerve; visceral smooth muscle is spontaneously active but its level of activity depends on the amount and kind of motor input. Multi-unit muscles ordinarily are not spontaneously active and do not respond to stretch; visceral types are spontaneously active and are stimulated by stretch. Thus, the lack of pre-emptory nervous control over a smooth muscle structure is accompanied to a certain degree by autorhythmicity and self-regulation.

As in skeletal muscle, neuromuscular transmission in smooth muscle is mediated by chemical transmitter substances, two of which are acetylcholine and epinephrine (or norepinephrine). There may be other chemical transmitters or hormones which also act on smooth muscle. Acetylcholine and epinephrine come from cholinergic and adrenergic fibers, respectively. Generally, stimulation of these two types of nerves produces antagonistic effects on smooth muscle. For example, in the rabbit colon stimulation of cholinergic fibers increases the activity whereas stimulation of adrenergic fibers decreases it. This antagonism can be seen more dramatically by observing the effects of the neurotransmitters, acetylcholine and epinephrine (or norepinephrine), on various types of visceral smooth muscle. However, there are exceptions; e.g., in the nictitating membrane of

the cat, stimulation of either cholinergic or adrenergic fibers increases activity. A two-component response is obtained, a "fast" one due to acetylcholine (reduced by acetylcholine-blocking drugs) and a "slow" component due to epinephrine or norepinephrine (reduced by anti-epinephrine drugs).

The mode of action of acetylcholine on smooth muscle is much the same as on skeletal muscle; acetylcholine depolarizes by increasing the permeability of the muscle membrane to sodium, potassium and, possibly, other ions. The amount of depolarization produced by acetylcholine depends upon the initial membrane potential. Acetylcholine can depolarize the membrane only to a value of -15 to -25 mV., so, as the resting potential becomes lower, the depolarizing action of acetylcholine becomes smaller. The mode of action of epinephrine is not known. There are two opposing actions: (i) In those smooth muscle structures activated by epinephrine it depolarizes the membrane by increasing membrane permeability, at least to sodium ions. (ii) There is a delayed hyperpolarization which stops spike generation in part, by increasing the membrane potential. The hyperpolarization is probably secondary to an acceleration of active sodium extrusion.

In addition to the neuronal control of smooth muscle activity, there are humoral or hormonal factors as well. The relative contributions of these various means of control—stretch, neural and hormonal—are not known. Smooth muscle cells are sensitive to the various neural transmitters over their entire surface; skeletal muscle cells are sensitive only at the end-plate. In addition, these transmitters, particularly epinephrine and norepinephrine, are not destroyed rapidly in smooth muscle. Thus, smooth muscle activity may be influenced by circulating transmitter substances, particularly epinephrine and norepinephrine; cholinesterase is a widely occurring enzyme, so the concentration of ACh in blood is usually negligible. Thus, neural transmitters also act as hormones and in this role exert a widespread influence on smooth muscle activity.

The effects of female sex hormones on the activity of uterine smooth muscle are a unique example of hormonal control. Not only does estrogen cause hypertrophy of uterine cells, but it produces an increase in membrane potential. Estrogen increases spontaneous activity and the uterus grows into a structure capable of forceful contractions. In contrast, contractions do not occur in the immature uterus. On the other hand, progesterone decreases activity and blocks contraction. The interplay of these two hormonal actions is important in timing the birth process. Estrogen is necessary to prepare the uterus for activity and progesterone holds it in a quiescent state until the fetus has developed and is ready for delivery.

CLINICAL CORRELATIONS: SKELETAL MUSCLE

Motor Unit Disease. The skeletal muscle motor unit provides a systematic, rational basis for classification of peripheral motor diseases based on the place of attack and the physiologic mechanism disturbed. Diseases attacking each of five points in the motor unit (Fig. 23) would produce different effects. These points are the motoneuron cell body (I), the axon of the motoneuron (II), the neuromuscular junction (III), the muscle membrane (IV), and the contractile machinery of the muscle itself (V).

DESTRUCTION OF CELL BODY OR AXON (I, II). Sudden (acute anterior poliomyelitis) or slow (progressive muscular atrophy) destruction of the motoneuron cell body or sudden destruction of the axon (peripheral nerve injury) produce certain classic signs and other less obvious changes in muscle:

1. Flaccid paralysis: weakness of voluntary movements combined with flaccidity or deficient muscle tone.
2. Absent or hypoactive tendon reflexes.
3. Atrophy and degeneration of muscle.
4. Fibrillation and fasciculation.
5. Altered sensitivity to drugs, especially

acetylcholine, and increased threshold to brief electrical stimuli.

6. Biochemical and histologic changes.

The first of these signs is obviously consequent to a reduction in the number of functioning motor units available for voluntary and reflex response.

Atrophy[1, 2] *and degeneration.* A change in the volume of a tissue may be due to changes in cell volume, number of cells or both. A decrease in muscle cell volume is called *atrophy;* an increase is *hypertrophy.* An increase in number of cells is *hyperplasia.*

Atrophy in the human results from denervation, disease, old age, cachexia and some myopathies. In all of these situations fiber size is reduced to about 75 per cent of normal. Cross-striations remain until the cells become quite small. In denervation atrophy the changes are more profound and this type of atrophy is distinguished as *degeneration.* A few months or a year after denervation, granularity develops in the sarcoplasm with a loss of myofibrils; finally, only groups of sarcoplasmic nuclei remain in the muscle fiber. Later even these disappear. The changes in disuse atrophy are seldom this severe. Fibrillation is common in some stages of degeneration but is rare in other atrophies. In certain myopathies (progressive muscular dystrophy and polymyositis or dermatomyositis) both atrophy and hypertrophy may be present. The pattern of these changes is haphazard and does not follow the motor unit distribution.

Electromyography (EMG).[52] The proper diagnosis of a disease depends, to a great degree, on the clinical acumen of the physician. However, the small differences between the clinical mani-

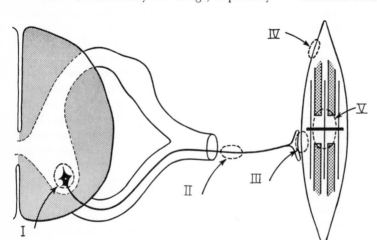

Fig. 23. Diagram representing sites of injury (Roman numerals) in diseases of motor unit.

festations of the various motoneuron diseases sometimes require the aid of various instruments and techniques in the differential diagnosis. The techniques most frequently used involve the following: electromyography, histochemistry, electronic instruments for stimulation and recording of bioelectric and physiologic events, drugs, and the electron microscope to study pathologic changes in ultrastructure. Electromyography will be briefly described here, since it has greatly aided the classification of motoneuron diseases. An electromyogram (EMG) is a recording of electrical activity from a portion of the muscle. This activity can arise from voluntary movement or from direct electrical stimulation or can occur spontaneously in the muscle or nerve. In the clinic, electromyograms are obtained by inserting an electrode about the size of a 24-gauge hypodermic needle into the muscle to be studied. The electrode consists of a wire insulated everywhere but at the tip. The potential of this electrode is the sum of the volume conductor action potentials of surrounding muscle fibers. Thus, most of the electrical activity is from active fibers near the electrode. The other electrode is a large metal plate applied to the skin over an inactive region. In normal muscle, a brief burst of activity (rapid deflections of the pen) is recorded when the electrode is inserted. This is due to action potentials set up in fibers injured by the electrode before depolarization block occurs. There is little or no activity during rest; potentials recorded during contraction are the resultant of the asynchronous discharges of motor units in the electrode's vicinity. Changes in the patterns of activity in disease are helpful in diagnosis (see Fig. 24).

Finer detail may be observed with staggered multilead electrodes[24] or, under certain conditions, intracellular electrodes.[49] With the multilead electrode technique, it is possible to stimulate and record from individual muscle fibers or small groups of fibers and thus to measure absolute refractory periods, absolute irresponsive periods, recovery of excitability and conduction speeds. Intracellular recordings may be informative but are technically difficult.

Fibrillation and fasciculation.[20] In certain motor unit diseases, muscles exhibit small, local, "spontaneous" contractions. Investigations with the EMG have led to the conclusion that one of the common classic neurologic signs—fibrillation—was misnamed. This name sug-

gests that the motor unit discharging spontaneously is the muscle fiber, whereas analysis shows that what was called fibrillation is actually a discharge of a whole motor unit.

Fibrillation, as redefined by Denny-Brown and Pennybacker[20] from electrophysiologic studies, is characterized by 10 to 200 μV. potentials with a duration of 1 to 2 milliseconds. They are irregular and asynchronous, produce no detectable shortening of the muscle, and cannot be observed through the skin. By contrast, the potentials recorded during normal motor unit discharges have an amplitude of 2 to 6 mV. and a duration of 5 to 8 milliseconds. It follows that the unit potential in denervated muscle is the "spontaneous" activation of *single muscle cells* or muscle fibers, and hence properly called fibrillation. The activity reaches a peak

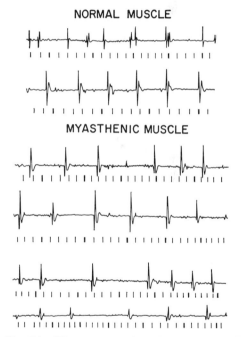

NORMAL MUSCLE

MYASTHENIC MUSCLE

Fig. 24. Electromyographic recordings of motor unit discharge during muscular action in normal and myasthenic persons. Ordinate, voltage, arbitrary units; abscissa, time, 23 milliseconds between marks. Normal muscle: upper trace, two motor units discharging at different frequencies; lower trace, discharges of a single motor unit. Note the uniform amplitude and rate of the single motor unit. Myasthenic muscle: discharges of a single motor unit during continuous muscular action. Upper trace recorded at the start of activity; lower three traces after 40, 80 and 170 seconds of activity respectively. Note sharp decrease in amplitude of the single motor unit during continuous muscular effort without appreciable change in rate. (After Lindsley, *Brain*, 1935, *58:*470–482.)

about eight days after denervation and ceases when reinnervation occurs through nerve regeneration, or, if this fails, ceases when the muscle fibers have degenerated sufficiently. Fibrillation is lessened by curare and increased by prostigmine. That muscle fibers fire in the absence of nerve stimulation is an expression of the denervation sensitivity to acetylcholine, and the stimulus is presumably circulating acetylcholine. This increased sensitivity is explained in part by the finding that a denervated fiber's membrane becomes everywhere sensitive to acetylcholine instead of only at the end-plate.

According to Denny-Brown and Pennybacker's analysis, what was called fibrillation is properly termed *fasciculation*. It is visible through the skin or mucosa and represents a "spontaneous" discharge of motor units. The potential developed by the discharge of a squad of muscle fibers innervated by a single motoneuron would be expected to be greater than a single fiber discharge, since many fibers are involved. It would also be longer, owing to the somewhat asynchronous firing of the fibers. A motor unit discharge could lead to a local response in the muscle only if the fibers composing the squad were adjacent within a fasciculus and not dispersed widely throughout the muscle. This expectation has in fact been realized by histologic investigation. The triggering of the motor unit discharge would appear to lie with the motoneuron cell body. Fasciculation is indicative of lower motor neuron disease attacking the gray column of the spinal cord—amyotrophic lateral sclerosis, progressive muscular atrophy.

In some cases, the origin must be peripheral because procaine block of the motor nerves does not stop fasciculation. Therefore, it may originate at the endplate of a fiber, be conducted antidromically to the branching point of the motor axon, and, by an "axon reflex," reach all the fibers of a motor unit.

Related to fasciculation is the electromyographic phenomenon of *synchronization*. Potentials 10 to 15 times that developed by a single motor unit are observed in muscles of poliomyelitis patients. The best explanation appears to be that several motor units contract synchronously through some "locking" of the discharge of anterior horn cells. Another possible cause lies in the development of giant motor units when nondegenerated motoneurons sprout and capture (innervate) muscle fibers whose innervation has been destroyed. This kind of synchronization of motor units is to be distinguished from that seen in clonus or tremor and the less definite synchronization in spasticity and rigidity.[39]

Chemical and electrical excitability. The profound effects of denervation suggest that motor innervation exerts a "trophic" influence on muscle which is necessary for the maintenance of the muscle's chemical composition, electrical excitability, chemical sensitivity and metabolic reactions.[66] In addition to atrophy, one of the most striking effects of denervation is the muscle's eventual development of "supersensitivity" to acetylcholine and related substances, becoming 1000 to 100,000 times more sensitive to close intra-arterial injections of acetylcholine. Supersensitivity is apparently due to the enlargement of the ACh sensitive region from the end-plate in normal muscle to the whole fiber surface in the denervated muscle (Chap. 10).

The increased threshold of a denervated muscle to short (ca. 100 microseconds) electrical stimuli results from the fact that they excite intramuscular nerve fibers at lower strengths than they do muscle fibers. This is largely because nerve membrane has much smaller capacity per unit area than muscle membrane. However, this effect is partially counteracted by the larger diameter of the muscle fiber.

MYASTHENIA GRAVIS (III).[2, 70] As one proceeds peripherally in the motor unit, the next critical point is the neuromuscular junction. *Myasthenia gravis* is characterized by muscular weakness and extreme "fatigability" confined to the skeletal muscles but with a predilection for those of the face. Double vision (diplopia), drooping eyelids (ptosis), a toneless voice and difficulty in chewing and swallowing are often present at the initial examination. A repeated movement may initially be strong but becomes progressively weaker. Muscle strength is greatest in the morning and least in the evening.

Figure 24 is an electromyographic record from a normal muscle. The regular rhythm and equal amplitudes indicate that the electrical activity of a single motor unit is being recorded. Sample records taken throughout the course of a continued effort by a patient with myasthenia gravis are shown. Note that the rhythm does not alter, but the spike amplitude soon varies and, eventually, some spikes drop out completely. It follows from the previous discussion of gradation of contraction that the only way a motor unit can be fractionated is by some process occurring in the individual muscle fibers making up the squad. Further evidence that the disorder underlying myasthenia gravis lies in the neuromuscular junction is that the muscle fibers show no histopathologic alteration, respond normally to direct stimulation of the muscle, and are sensitive to drugs. Curare-like drugs aggravate myasthenia; anticholinesterase drugs reduce it and are in fact an effective therapeutic agent.

Physiologically there are four possible mechanisms or "sites" of derangement: (i) a deficient production or liberation of acetylcholine, (ii) an overactive cholinesterase system, (iii) a diminished sensitivity of the muscle end-plate to acetylcholine, and (iv) the circulation of a curare-like substance.

Another possibility is the recent suggestion by Simpson[63] that myasthenia gravis may be an "auto-immune" phenomenon in which the reticulo-endothelial system produces an antibody to end-plate protein. Combination of this antibody with the receptor protein would then reduce the response to endogenous acetylcholine and prevent normal function. This possibility is consistent with the well-known finding that a hyperplastic thymus is found in roughly half of all patients suffering from myasthenia gravis and with recent evidence that suggests an immunologic function for the thymus in the fetus and newborn. Perhaps myasthenia results from a pathologic change in thymus function.[32]

MYOTONIA (IV).[2] Myotonia is a failure of the muscles to relax normally. In dramatic contrast to myasthenia, myotonic muscles can be contracted promptly and forcefully but cannot be relaxed at will. Further, myotonia is most pronounced after a period of rest and decreases with repeated attempts; the patient's condition is better in the evening than in the morning. A tap anywhere on a myotonic muscle produces a local knot of prolonged contraction.

Because a strain of goats exhibits myotonia,[9] it has been possible to study this sign by electrical methods and isometric myography after stimulation of a sectioned nerve, as in a student laboratory experiment. The delayed relaxation is shown clearly in the myographic record in Figure 25, top. The repetitive electrical discharge is clearly the cause of the prolonged contraction. However, the repetitive discharge cannot be a persistent central discharge because the motor nerve has been sectioned. The response to acetylcholine is prolonged. The delay in relaxation occurs when the muscle is stimulated locally, even after degeneration of the motor nerve. These observations, together with the fact that mechanical or electrical stimulation anywhere on the muscle results in a prolonged electrical discharge and contraction,

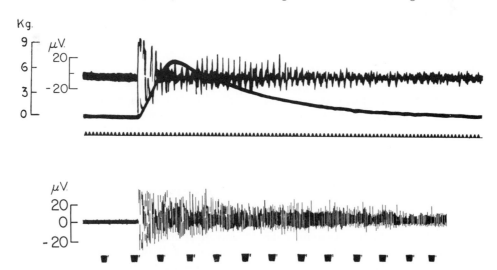

Fig. 25. Upper record: Electrical and contractile activity from a muscle of a myotonic goat in response to a single maximal volley to the motor nerve. Ordinate, voltage (μV.) or tension (kg.); abscissa, time, 10 milliseconds. Note prolonged electrical activity. Lower record: Electromyogram of denervated and curarized leg muscle of myotonic goat. Muscle was stimulated mechanically by a tap. Ordinate, voltage (μV.); abscissa, time, 0.2 second between marks. (After Brown and Harvey, *Brain,* 1939, *62:*341–363.)

even in the denervated, curarized muscle (Fig. 25, bottom), indicate a fault lying in the membrane of the muscle fibers.

DISEASES OF THE CONTRACTILE MECHANISM (v).[2] The fifth site of muscular pathologic disturbance is in the contractile mechanism of the muscle fiber. Progressive muscular dystrophy serves as an example. Nerves and motor nerve endings which appear normal histologically can occur when the muscle fibers are severely degenerated. (For reasons not pertinent to the physiology of muscular contraction, the muscles are greatly enlarged.) The muscle membrane is no doubt also abnormal, sharing in the striking destruction of the core of the muscle fiber; however, the functional status of the membrane is not known. Functionally, the disease is manifested as simple weakness unaccompanied by fibrillation, fasciculation or other evidences of abnormal excitability.

CONTRACTURE. "Contracture" is used clinically to designate a condition of fixed high resistance to passive stretch of a muscle. Contracture may result simply from a fibrosis of the tissue supporting the muscles or, more frequently, the joints. Such a condition may be caused by immobilization of a joint, for example. The term covers a number of unrelated phenomena and should be used in a generic sense, preceded by an appropriate adjective. That some contractures actually result from disorders of the muscle fiber, as opposed to connective tissue elements, is suggested by "myostatic contracture," first described by Moll (see Ref. 61). If the attachments of a muscle are approximated and immobilized or, simply, if the tendon is cut, *innervated* muscle becomes fixed at a shorter length. Muscles maintained at shorter lengths by neural activity—as in spasm induced by tetanus toxin or in spasticity caused by lesions of the descending motor systems—show a similar contracture. After experimental tenotomy, the isometric contraction tension is severely reduced.

"Physiologic contracture" refers to a reversible but prolonged state which lacks some of the features of muscular contraction. The principal difference is that contracture may be local and not accompanied by a propagated action potential. Although myotonia is a prolonged contraction, it is not a contracture. Physiologic contracture may be induced by a number of agents—thermal, electric, mechanical and chemical. It seems probable that some, if not all, of these agents achieve their effects by acting directly upon the contractile mechanism without intermediation of the membrane. However, the mechanisms of both myostatic and physiologic types of contracture cannot be stated with certainty.

Hypertrophy. EXERCISE. It is common knowledge that voluntary muscle increases in size as a result of exercise. This enlargement is an hypertrophy, an increase in the volumes of the individual fibers. Normally, striated muscle fibers do not proliferate by cell division; there is evidence that their number does not increase in the human embryo after 4 to 5 months.

An increase in cross-sectional diameter of a fiber may be due to an increase in sarcoplasm, indicating an increase in metabolic reserves or an increase of the contractile apparatus (myofibrils) or both.

From experiments on running dogs, Marpurgo[54] concluded that exercise hypertrophy results from an increase in the sarcoplasm of the smaller fibers, so that the range of fiber sizes is less. All fibers tend to be large but not larger than the largest fibers in the normal muscle. The size and number of myofibrils did not increase. Denny-Brown *et al.*[19] repeated these experiments with cats, but removed the tendon of the gastrocnemius and related aponeurosis of the plantaris and biceps femoris, leaving only the soleus intact. This treatment results in an almost pure form of isometric exercise for the soleus. After three months, the soleus on the operated side had hypertrophied as a result of a significant increase in the absolute number of myofibrils as well as an increase in sarcoplasm of the smaller fibers. In certain athletic endeavors, the development of maximum cross-sectional diameter of muscle is desired. However, nonisometric exercise increases sarcoplasm but not myofibrils. Since myofibrils are the actual tension-producing machinery of the muscle, a greater degree of force production would occur following their hypertrophy. The sufficient condition for myofibrillar hypertrophy is a contraction of at least two-thirds maximum tetanic tension, a feat of difficulty in animal experimentation and extreme determination in humans.[19] However, even a single daily isometric exercise (2 to 5 seconds) can lead to the same degree of myofibrillar hypertrophy as more prolonged conventional tonic exercises of longer duration repeated several times a day. Increase in muscle size is not the only goal in training;

there appears to be a limitation to size of individual fibers, beyond which the muscles become sensitive to "cramping." In prolonged, heavy exercise the limiting factor is the circulation.

PATHOLOGY. Enlargement of the muscle fiber as a result of disease is found most frequently in myotonia congenita and athetosis (dystonia). The mechanism is not completely understood,[1] but it could be an exercise hypertrophy. In athetosis the healthy portions probably hypertrophy to compensate for the diseased, atrophic portions. In myotonia, the repetitive responses of the muscle membrane to single stimuli could result in exercise hypertrophy.

REFERENCES

1. ADAMS, R. D. *Res. Publ. Ass. nerv. ment. Dis.*, 1960, *38*:318–354.
2. ADAMS, R. D., DENNY-BROWN, D. and PEARSON, C. M. *Diseases of muscle; a study in pathology.* New York, Paul B. Hoeber, 1953.
3. BARR, L. and BERGER, W. *Pflüg. Arch. ges. Physiol.,* 1964, *279*:192–194.
4. BERGMAN, R. A. *Bull. Johns Hopk. Hosp.,* 1958, *102*:195–202.
5. BIANCHI, C. P. and SHANES, A. M. *J. gen. Physiol.*, 1959, *42*:803–815; idem, 1123–1137.
6. BIRKS, R., HUXLEY, H. E. and KATZ, B. *J. Physiol.,* 1960, *150*:134–144.
7. BOZLER, E. *Cold Spr. Harb. Symp.,* 1936, *4*:260–266.
8. BRADY, A. J. and WOODBURY, J. W. *J. Physiol.,* 1960, *154*:385–407.
9. BROWN, G. L. and HARVEY, A. M. *Brain,* 1939, *62*:341–363.
10. BULBRING, E. *Physiol. Rev.,* 1962, *42*:160–174.
11. BURNSTOCK, G. and HOLMAN, M. E., *Ann. Rev. Physiol.,* 1963, *25*:61–90.
12. CARLSON, F. D., *Progr. Biophys.,* 1963, *13*:261–314.
13. CARLSON, F. D., HARDY, D. J. and WILKIE, D. R., *J. gen. Physiol.,* 1963, *46*:851–882.
14. COOPER, S. and ECCLES, J. C. *J. Physiol.*, 1930, *69*:377–385.
15. CSAPO, A. I. *Physiol. Rev.,* 1962, *42*:7–33.
16. DANIEL, E. E., SEHDEV, H. and ROBINSON, K. *Physiol. Rev.,* 1962, *42*:228–260.
17. DAVIES, R. E. *Nature (Lond.),* 1963, *199*:1068–1074.
18. DECK, K. A. and TRAUTWEIN, W. *Pflüg. Arch. ges. Physiol.,* 1964, *280*:63–80.
19. DENNY-BROWN, D. *Res. Publ. Ass. nerv. ment. Dis.,* 1960, *38*:147–196.
20. DENNY-BROWN, D. and PENNYBACKER, J. B. *Brain,* 1938, *61*:311–334.
21. ECCLES, J. C. and SHERRINGTON, C. S. *Proc. roy. Soc.,* 1930, *B106*:326–357.
22. ELFTMAN, H. *Biol. Symp.,* 1941, *3*:191–209.
23. FALK, G. and FATT, P. *Proc. roy. Soc.,* 1964, *B160*:69–123.
24. FARMER, T. W., BUCHTHAL, F. and ROSENFALCK, P. *Res. Publ. Ass. nerv. ment. Dis.,* 1960, *38*:714–720.
25. FATT, P. *Physiol. Rev.,* 1954, *34*:674–710.
26. FATT, P. and KATZ, B. *J. Physiol.,* 1951, *115*:320–370.
27. *Fed. Proc.,* 1964, *23*:885–939.
28. FENN, W. O. In: *Physical chemistry of cells and tissues,* R. Höber, ed. Philadelphia, Blakiston, 1945.
29. FRANZINI-ARMSTRONG, C. and PORTER, K. R. *Nature (Lond.),* 1964, *202*:355–357.
30. FREYGANG, W. H., JR., GOLDSTEIN, D. A. and HELLAM, D. C. *J. gen. Physiol.,* 1964, *47*:929–952.
31. GORDON, A. M., HUXLEY, A. F. and JULIAN, F J. *J. Physiol.,* 1964, *171*:28P–30P.
32. HARVEY, A. M. and JOHNS, R. J. *Amer. J. Med.,* 1962, *32*:1–5.
33. HEILBRUNN, L. V. and WIERCINSKI, F. J. *J. cell. comp. Physiol.,* 1947, *29*:15–32.
34. HESS, A. and PILLAR, G. *J. Physiol.,* 1963, *169*:780–798.
35. HILL, A. V. *Proc. roy. Soc.,* 1949, *B136*:399–420.
36. HILL, A. V. *Lancet,* 1951, *261*:947–951.
37. HILL, A. V. *Science,* 1960, *131*:897–903.
38. HODGKIN, A. L. and HOROWICZ, P. *J. Physiol.,* 1960, *153*:370–385.
39. HOEFER, P. F. A. *Res. Publ. Ass. nerv. ment. Dis.,* 1941, *21*:502–528.
40. HUNT, C. C. and KUFFLER, G. W. *J. Physiol.,* 1954, *126*:293–303.
41. HUXLEY, A. F. *Progr. Biophys.,* 1957, *7*:255–318.
42. HUXLEY, A. F. and NIEDERGERKE, R. *J. Physiol.,* 1958, *144*:403–425.
43. HUXLEY, A. F. and TAYLOR, R. E. *J. Physiol.,* 1958, *144*:426–441.
44. HUXLEY, H. E. *J. biophys. biochem. Cytol.,* 1957, *3*:631–648.
45. HUXLEY, H. E. Chap. 7 in *The cell,* vol. IV, J. Brachet and A. E. Mirsky, eds. New York, Academic Press, Inc., 1960.
46. HUXLEY, H. E. *J. molec. Biol.,* 1963, *7*:281–308.
47. HUXLEY, H. E. *Nature (Lond.),* 1964, *202*:1067–1071.
48. INFANTE, A. A. and DAVIES, R. E. *Biochem. biophys. Res. Commun.,* 1962, *9*:410–415.
49. JOHNS, R. J. *Res. Publ. Ass. nerv. ment. Dis.,* 1960, *38*:704–713.
50. JOHNSON, W. H. *Physiol. Rev.,* 1962, *42*:113–143.
51. KATZ, B. *Proc. roy. Soc.,* 1962, *B155*:455–477.
52. LAMBERT, E. H. *Res. Publ. Ass. nerv. ment. Dis.,* 1960, *38*:247–273.
53. LOWY, J. and HANSON, J. *Physiol. Rev.,* 1962, *42*:34–42.
54. MARPURGO, B. *Virchows Arch. path. Anat.,* 1897, *150*:522–554.
55. NEEDHAM, D. M. Chap. 2 in *The structure and function of muscle,* vol. II, G. H. Bourne, ed. New York, Academic Press, Inc., 1960.
56. NEEDHAM, D. M. *Physiol. Rev.,* 1962, *42*:88–96.
57. PAGE, S. and HUXLEY, H. E. *J. cell Biol.,* 1963, *19*:369–390.
58. PEACHEY, L. D. and PORTER, K. R. *Science,* 1959, *129*:721–722.
59. PODOLSKY, R. J. *J. Physiol.,* 1964, *170*:110–123.
60. PROSSER, C. L. *Physiol. Rev.,* 1962, *42*:193–206.
61. RANSON, S. W. and DIXON, H. H. *Amer. J. Physiol.,* 1928, *86*:312–319.
62. RHODIN, J. A. G. *Physiol. Rev.,* 1962, *42*:48–81.
63. SIMPSON, J. A. *Scot. med. J.,* 1960, *5*:419–436.
64. SZENT-GYÖRGYI, A. *Biol. Bull.,* 1949, *96*:140–161.
65. THAEMERT, J. C. *J. biophys. biochem. Cytol.,* 1959, *6*:67–70.
66. THESLEFF, S. *Physiol. Rev.,* 1960, *40*:734–752.
67. TRAUTWEIN, W. and KASSEBAUM, D. G. *J. gen. Physiol.,* 1961, *45*:317–330.
68. TUNIK, B. and HOLTZER, H. *J. biophys. biochem. Cytol.,* 1961, *11*:67–74.
69. UNIVERSITY OF CALIFORNIA. *Fundamental studies of human*

locomotion and other information relating to design of artificial limbs. Berkeley, 1947, 2 vols.

70. VIETS, H. R. and GAMMON, G. D., eds. *Amer. J. Med.*, 1955, *19*:655–742.

71. WEBER, A., HERZ, R. and REISS, I. *J. gen. Physiol.*, 1963, *46*:679–702.

72. WEBER, H. H. and PORTZEHL, H. *Progr. Biophys.* 1954, *4*:60–111.

73. WEIDMANN, S. *J. Physiol.*, 1951, *115*:227–236.

74. WEIDMANN, S. *J. Physiol.*, 1955, *127*:213–224.

75. WOODBURY, J. W. Chap. 11 in *Handbook of physiology, Section 2, Circulation,* vol. I, W. F. Hamilton and P. Dow, eds. Washington, D. C., American Physiological Society, 1962.

76. WOODBURY, J. W. and CRILL, W. E. In: *Nervous inhibition,* E. Florey, ed. New York, Pergamon Press, Inc., 1961.

SECTION III

REFLEX CONTROL OF SKELETAL AND VISCERAL MUSCULATURE

CHAPTER 6

Spinal Reflexes and Synaptic Transmission

By HARRY D. PATTON

PROPERTIES OF THE SYNAPSE

IN the foregoing chapters attention was focused on the distinctive properties of axons and muscle cells, taken as samples of excitable tissues. Stripped of detail, these properties are *excitability* and *conductivity*. An axon, when excited, responds by generating an action potential, which is then conducted in both directions away from the site of stimulation. Individual excitable cells, no matter what type or how excited, always respond to excitation in this stereotyped fashion; no other response is known. The action potential is thus the only mode of expression available to the nervous system; it is the message carried from sense organ to brain, giving rise to sensation; it is the message relayed from brain and spinal cord to muscle, giving rise to movement. Indeed, all feeling and action are reducible to orderly, sequential, neuronal exchanges of minute quantities of potassium for minute quantities of sodium.

Variety of experience and action results from the channeling of action potentials within the central nervous system and from modulation of action potential discharge patterns. Discharge patterns are initially determined by the proper-

153

ties of sense organs. The messages arriving at the sensory and motor centers of the central nervous system, however, may be quite different from those initiated at the sense organ.

In vertebrates, even the simplest experience and behavior derive from the conduction of action potentials over *chains* of neurons, which are linked together by apposition of the efferent process (axon) of one cell to the cell body or dendrites of another. Such a junction between nerve cells is called a *synapse*. During the latter half of the last century, many histologists argued that the nervous system was a syncytium and that nerve cells were joined together at the synaptic region by protoplasmic extensions between them. We now know, largely from Ramón y Cajal's studies, that neurons are individual units and that the synapse is a region of protoplasmic "contiguity, not continuity." This point is most important because it means that conduction through chains of neurons is discontinuous and, consequently, that the message may be fundamentally altered at each synaptic link. At the synapse, the presynaptic impulse initiates a distinctive process, which may tentatively be called the *transmitter process,* that serves to initiate new action in the post synaptic neuron. The present chapter is primarily concerned with the nature of this transmitter process and its influence on the messages of the central nervous system.

Some of the special properties of synapses may be briefly listed preliminary to a detailed consideration of synaptic function.

1. *Unidirectional conduction.* In contrast to action potentials in a nerve fiber, which are conducted in both directions, action potentials in a neuron chain are conducted in only one direction. For example, action potential messages set up in a dorsal root may be transferred, in the spinal cord, to nerve cells with which the root fibers make synaptic connection, thence to other nerve cells and then, over their axons, to the ventral root. On the other hand, impulses excited in a ventral root, although they traverse the axons and probably part of the perikarya and dendrites of the motoneurons, do not initiate action potentials in the nerve terminals which make synaptic connections with these motoneurons. The synapse is a "one way valve" which determines the direction of transmission.

2. *Repetitive discharge.* A nerve fiber usually responds only once to a single brief stimulus. A single synchronous volley of impulses delivered over a presynaptic path to a neuron often, but not always, evokes a burst or train of spikes in the postsynaptic neuron. The frequency of the postsynaptic discharge usually varies during the burst, but may approach 500 to 1000 impulses a second for short periods. Repetitive discharge is one way in which neural activity is amplified at the synapse.

3. *Failure to transmit faithfully frequencies of presynaptic volleys.* When a nerve fiber is stimulated repetitively, each stimulus elicits one action potential, unless the interval between stimuli is less than the refractory period. Refractoriness is thus the only limitation to faithful signaling of the stimulation frequency. In a chain of neurons, however, the postsynaptic neuron may not respond to each of a series of repetitive presynaptic volleys. For example, if the presynaptic path is stimulated 20 times a second, the postsynaptic neuron may respond only to the first volley reaching it. In general, the longer the chain (i.e., the greater the number of synapses), the less is its capacity to follow imposed frequencies faithfully. Obviously, at such rates of stimulation, frequency-following is not limited by the refractory period of the postsynaptic neuron; for repetitive discharge in response to a single presynaptic volley indicates that the cell is capable of generating impulses at rates up to one every millisecond. Some evidence suggests that high frequency blockage occurs in the fine presynaptic terminals. The special significance of this property of synapses is that temporal patterns of discharge initiated in the presynaptic pathway become significantly altered as they traverse successive synapses in a chain.

4. *Susceptibility to asphyxia, ischemia and depressant drugs.* The synapse is a region of low safety factor, and transmission is easily blocked. A nerve fiber will continue to conduct impulses many minutes after cardiac arrest, but synaptic transmission succumbs much earlier. In general, long chains with multiple synapses are more easily blocked than are shorter, simpler chains. The effectiveness of general anesthetic agents is largely due to the capacity to block synaptic transmission. Reflex movement, sensation and consciousness are abolished, whereas excitability of nerve trunks is little affected, as evidenced by lively muscle contraction when a motor nerve is stimulated directly.

5. *Synaptic delay.* Conduction over axons is continuous and uninterrupted, the rate of conduction being determined by axon diameter. The synaptic transmitter process consumes a finite interval of time. Conduction time over a chain of neurons is therefore greater than the sum of axonal conduction times, a discrepancy which increases with the number of synapses in the chain.

6. *Inhibition.* At some synapses, the consequence of presynaptic activity is not excitation but depression of activity in the postsynaptic neuron. This important property and its mechanism will be discussed in detail below.

ANALYSIS OF SYNAPTIC FUNCTION

The Monosynaptic Reflex.[25] To study the properties of the synapse it is obviously desirable to select a simple monosynaptic system, i.e., one having only a single synapse. The sympathetic ganglion fulfills this requirement, and for qualitative studies is a satisfactory synaptic model. Quantitatively, however, the peripheral synapses in ganglia are somewhat different from the central synapses in the brain and the spinal cord; for example, the delay at a sympathetic synapse is four to ten times as great as that at a central synapse. Also, one of the important synaptic processes, inhibition, is either poorly developed or lacking in ganglionic synapses. For these reasons, the synapses formed between dorsal root afferent fibers and motoneurons will be used as synaptic models in this discussion.

Figure 1 shows the intramedullary course of dorsal root fibers entering the spinal cord as revealed by silver stains. Some afferent fibers (*a*) plunge without interruption through the gray matter to terminate on motoneurons in the anterior horn (*B*). Such reflex arcs are *monosynaptic*. Other afferent fibers (*b, c*) terminate on neurons in the dorsal and intermediate regions of the gray matter. Although not shown, the axons of these neurons are in turn distributed to other intermediate neurons or to motoneurons to complete the circuit through the spinal cord. Such reflex arcs are *multisynaptic*, and impulses directed through them reach the motoneuron only after transfer through one or more *interneurons*, or *internuncial neurons*, the generic names for cells interposed between primary afferent neurons and the final motoneuron. The difference between monosynaptic and multisynaptic arcs is further clarified by the diagrammatic representation in Figure 2.

Happily, the monosynaptic and multisyn-

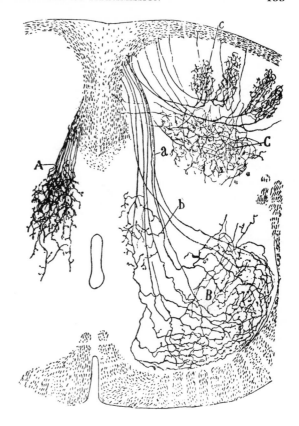

Fig. 1. Distribution of primary afferent collaterals in cross section of spinal cord. On right, collaterals *C* and *c* are distributed to dorsal horn and substantia gelatinosa Rolandi. *a*, Reflexomotor collaterals extending to ventral horn (*B*). *b*, Collaterals to intermediate nucleus of Cajal. On left, dense collaterals (*A*) to intermediate nucleus. (After Cajal, *Histologie du système nerveux*, Paris, Maloine, 1909.)

Fig. 2. Diagram of circumscribed reflex mechanism of Cajal (*left*) showing direct connection between afferent collaterals and motoneurons, and diffuse reflex mechanism of Cajal (*right*) in which an interneuron is intercalated between afferent fibers and motoneurons. (After Cajal, *Histologie du système nerveux*, Paris, Maloine, 1909.)

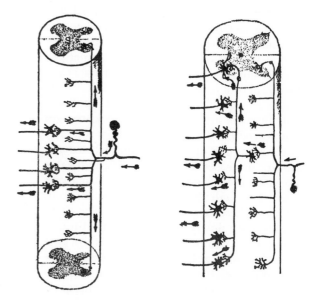

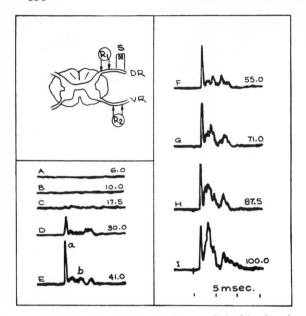

Fig. 3. Spinal reflex discharges elicited by dorsal root shocks of varying intensity. Single shocks were delivered to dorsal root (*DR*) through stimulating electrodes (*S*). Electrodes R_1 recorded dorsal root action potential; electrodes R_2 on ventral root (*VR*) recorded resultant reflex discharge. Traces *A–I* show reflex discharges at R_2 as shock strength was progressively increased. Numbers to right of traces, computed from R_1 recording, indicate number of afferent fibers excited expressed as a percentage of total fiber content of dorsal root. In *E: a*, monosynaptic discharge; *b*, multisynaptic discharges. (After Lloyd, *J. Neurophysiol.*, 1943, *6*:111–120.)

aptic arcs can be functionally distinguished. In experiments of the type illustrated in Figure 3, stimulating electrodes (*S*) are placed on a dorsal root near its entrance into the spinal cord, and recording electrodes (R_2) are attached to the proximal portion of the corresponding segmental ventral root to register the emergent reflex discharge. A minimally effective shock to the dorsal root (trace *C*) elicits a small ventral root discharge which begins about 3 milliseconds after the stimulus. As the shock strength is increased (*D–I*), the amplitude of the early synchronous part of the discharge (labeled *a* in trace *E*) increases rapidly to a maximal value (*E*) which is not increased by further increases in shock strength (*F–I*). The later asynchronous part of the discharge (labeled *b* in trace *E*) increases more slowly with increasing stimulus strength, but continues to increase in size after the early discharge has reached a stable amplitude. A reasonable hypothesis is that the early sharp spike reflects a motoneuron discharge re-

flexly elicited through monosynaptic spinal arcs, whereas the later asynchronous waves result from the firing of motoneurons through multisynaptic channels, with consequent repeated synaptic delays.

In point of fact, part of the discrepancy in the latency of the early and the late discharge is attributable to a difference in the sizes of the afferent fibers mediating these discharges, those responsible for the early discharge being larger and hence conducting impulses more rapidly. This difference is suggested by the observation that the early discharge grows most rapidly through a range of stimulus strengths adequate only for low threshold, rapidly conducting, dorsal root fibers; whereas the growth of the later discharges occurs at higher stimulus strengths. The differences in delay due to afferent conduction time are small when conduction distance is minimized by placing the stimulating electrodes close to the cord, and even when appropriate allowances for conduction differences are made, the central delay of the later discharge remains considerably longer than that of the early discharge. Thus, the original hypothesis that the later discharge is conducted over chains more complex than those mediating the early discharge remains plausible.

SYNAPTIC DELAY.[25]   To prove that the early discharge is monosynaptic, however, requires an independent measure of the duration of synaptic delay. An approximate value is provided by Renshaw's ingenious experiment shown in Figure 4. Electrodes (*R*) on the ventral root record the motoneuronal discharge elicited by stimulation through electrodes thrust into the intermediate gray matter of the cord in the region occupied only by elements presynaptic to the motoneurons. Weak shocks produce no response (trace *a*). Slightly stronger stimuli (traces *b* and *c*) evoke, after 1.0 millisecond, the response labeled *s*. Upon stronger stimulation, an additional and earlier (0.2 millisecond) discharge, *m*, appears (trace *d*); and, as *m* grows in size with increasing shock strength, the *s* discharge becomes correspondingly smaller (traces *e* and *f*).

The obvious interpretation of this experiment is that the weak shocks excite only the presynaptic elements near the electrodes, and that these elements then synaptically activate the motoneurons, giving rise to the *s* discharge. The latency of the earliest discharge thus elicited includes presynaptic conduction time, one synaptic delay and conduction time from moto-

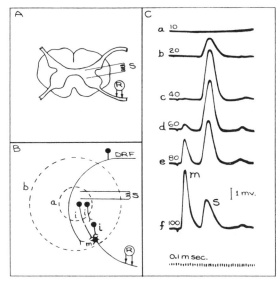

Fig. 4. Measurement of synaptic delay in spinal cord. *A,* Arrangement of stimulating (*S*) and recording (*R*) electrodes. *B,* Diagrammatic interpretation of traces in *C. C,* Responses as stimulus strength (indicated by numbers above traces) was increased. In *B,* only dorsal root fibers (*DRF*) and interneurons (*i*) within dotted circle *a* were excited by weak stimulus; shortest path to *R* therefore included one synapse, and delayed response, marked *s* in *C, b-f,* resulted. With strong stimulus, elements lying within dotted circle *b* were excited; these included some motoneurons (*m*) whose discharge gave rise to *m* in *C, d-f.* Difference in latency between *m* and *s* (about 0.8 millisecond) is approximate duration of synaptic delay. (After Renshaw, *J. Neurophysiol.,* 1940, *3*:373–387.)

neuron cell body to ventral root. With stronger shocks, however, sufficient current spreads to the ventral horn to excite some of the motoneurons directly, giving rise to the earlier *m* discharge (Fig. 4*B*). Because direct excitation renders the motoneurons refractory, the conducted interneuronal impulses find them inexcitable, and hence, as the *m* discharge increases with stronger shocks, the *s* discharge diminishes in amplitude. The latency of the *m* discharge is due to conduction time from motoneuron soma to ventral root recording site. It follows that the difference in latency between the *m* and the *s* discharge provides an estimate of synaptic delay. As measured in this experiment, the delay includes conduction time in the fine presynaptic terminals plus the true synaptic delay, i.e., the interval between the arrival at the motoneuron of a synchronous presynaptic discharge and the depolarization of the motoneuron to the firing level. Because the distances are short, presynaptic conduction time is prob-

ably negligibly small and *m–s* interval thus approximates synaptic delay.

In the experiment illustrated in Figure 4, the *m–s* interval is 0.8 millisecond. In a series of such experiments, the interval varied between 0.7 and 0.9 millisecond.[25] When the cord shock was delivered some 3 milliseconds after a dorsal root volley, the interval diminished to 0.5 to 0.7 millisecond. The central delay in transmission across a single spinal synapse is thus 0.5 to 0.9 millisecond. Comparable delays have been measured in monosynaptic transmission through the oculomotor nucleus, the lateral geniculate body and the cochlear nucleus.

With a measured value for synaptic delay, the hypothesis that the early reflex discharge is monosynaptic can be rigorously tested. Figure 5*b* shows the ventral root discharge evoked by a shock to the corresponding dorsal root; this discharge begins 1.05 milliseconds after the stimulus. The upper trace, labeled *a,* shows the response recorded at the dorsal root entry zone; the latency, 0.30 millisecond (measured to the point where the positive deflection returns to the baseline), gives the conduction time in the dorsal root. Trace *c* shows the ventral root discharge provoked by a shock applied through

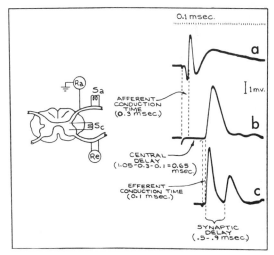

Fig. 5. Demonstration of monosynaptic reflex. Arrangement of stimulating and recording electrodes shown on left. *a,* Response recorded at *Ra* following stimulus at *Sa. b,* Reflex response at *Re* following stimulus at *Sa. c,* Response at *Re* following stimulus at *Sc,* as in Fig. 4. Subtracting afferent conduction time (derived from *a*) and efferent conduction time (from *c*) from latency of reflex in *b* gives central reflex delay of 0.65 millisecond, which falls within range of single synaptic delay derived from *m–s* interval in *c* and in Figure 4. (After Renshaw, *J. Neurophysiol.,* 1940, *3*:373–387.)

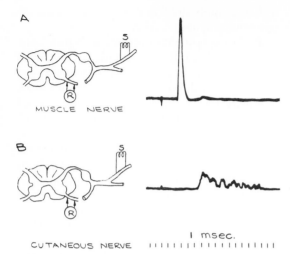

Fig. 6. Reflex responses to afferent volleys of different origin. *A,* Reflex discharge, almost exclusively monosynaptic, elicited by weak afferent volley in gastrocnemius nerve. *B,* Exclusively multisynaptic reflex response elicited by stimulating afferent fibers in sural nerve. (After Lloyd, *J. Neurophysiol.,* 1943, *6:*111–120.)

electrodes S_c with sufficient intensity to excite both intermediate presynaptic elements and some motoneurons as in Figure 4*f.* The latency of *m* in *c* (0.10 millisecond) gives the efferent conduction time in the axons. The central delay of the reflex discharge in this experiment is thus $1.05 - 0.30 - 0.10 = 0.65$ millisecond. In other experiments, similarly measured delays ranged from 0.65 to 0.90 millisecond in resting cord, and from 0.5 to 0.7 millisecond when the reflex was conditioned by an antecedent dorsal root volley. Since these delays are too short to permit more than one synaptic delay (0.5–0.9 msec.), it can be concluded that the early reflex discharge is monosynaptic, as initially postulated.

AFFERENT PATH OF THE MONOSYNAPTIC REFLEX. The monosynaptic reflex discharge evoked by stimulation of the dorsal root provides a satisfactory model system for a study of some synaptic properties. For certain experiments, however, the later multisynaptic discharge is an objectionable contaminant. As seen in Figure 3, some multisynaptic activity, in addition to monosynaptic discharge, is evident even with very weak dorsal root shocks, an occurrence suggesting considerable overlap in the sizes (and hence thresholds) of the dorsal root fibers mediating monosynaptic and multisynaptic reflexes. However, as the numbers to the right of the traces indicate, the rates of growth of the two types of reflexes with increasing dorsal root

volleys are quite different. The monosynaptic discharge is maximal when the dorsal root volley is only 41 per cent of maximal. The remaining 59 per cent of the dorsal root fibers, consisting of the smaller diameter group, contribute nothing to the growth of the monosynaptic discharge but contribute heavily to the multisynaptic arcs responsible for the late waves. This sequence suggests that the monosynaptic reflex is mediated exclusively by a restricted group of large afferent fibers, whereas the multisynaptic arcs are fed by smaller fibers.

It has already been mentioned (Chap. 3) that examination of the fiber constitution of "demotored" peripheral nerves, i.e., nerves in which motor axons have degenerated following ventral rhizotomy (root section), indicates that the myelinated afferent fibers of muscle nerves typically fall into three diameter clusters: Group I (12–20 μ), Group II (6–12 μ) and Group III (1–6 μ). The myelinated afferent fibers of cutaneous nerves, on the other hand, fall into two clusters: *alpha* (ca. 6–17 μ) and *delta* (1–6 μ). Both muscle nerves and cutaneous nerves contain, in addition, a large number of unmyelinated afferent fibers (C or Group IV fibers). The striking difference in the two distributions is the relative paucity of large fibers in cutaneous nerves (see Fig. 12, Chap. 3).

The difference in afferent fiber constitution of cutaneous and muscle nerves, coupled with the knowledge that only the largest afferent fibers make monosynaptic connections, suggests that monosynaptic reflexes originate in muscle nerves. Figure 6 shows that this is indeed the case. Both trace *A* and trace *B* were recorded from the first sacral ventral root. In *A,* the stimulus was a shock to the central end of the cut gastrocnemius nerve; in *B,* the afferent volley originated in a cutaneous nerve, the sural. The response to the gastrocnemius afferent volley is almost entirely monosynaptic and can be made completely so by adjusting the stimulus to strengths activating only Group I fibers. On the other hand, the discharge resulting from the sural afferent input is exclusively multisynaptic. Furthermore, systematic investigation using various nerves for afferent input indicates that this finding can be generalized, and that uncontaminated monosynaptic reflexes can be initiated by selectively stimulating Group I afferent fibers of any muscle nerve; when shock strength is increased to values exceeding the thresholds of Group II fibers, multisynaptic discharge also occurs and grows as increasing stimulus strength recruits Group III and IV fibers into the afferent volley. Weak or strong stimulation of cutaneous nerves elicits only multisynaptic reflex discharge.

DISTRIBUTION OF MONOSYNAPTIC DISCHARGE. Experiments of the kind described in the foregoing section establish clearly the afferent origin of monosynaptic reflexes, but do not indicate the peripheral distribution of the reflex discharge, because the recordings are made from the ventral root which supplies many muscles. To determine the "target" muscles of a monosynaptic discharge elicited by stimulating the Group I afferent fibers of a muscle nerve, it is necessary to leave the ventral root intact and place the recording electrode on various peripheral nerves supplying other muscles. When such an experiment is performed, the monosynaptic discharge so prominent in ventral root recordings cannot be detected in any of these peripheral nerves. This finding suggests that the monosynaptic discharge returns only to the muscle from which the afferent volley originates.

That a monosynaptic discharge does, in fact, occupy the efferent fibers of the muscle nerve in which the afferent discharge originates is indicated by the experiment illustrated in Figure 7. To obtain trace *A,* both the stimulating and the recording electrodes were placed on the tibial nerve with all central connections to the spinal cord intact. Stimulation at Group I strength, of course, elicited a compound action potential in the nerve. Because the conduction distance between the stimulating and recording electrodes was small, this compound action potential was fused with the shock artifact (*s*). Later, however, another deflection (*R*) occurred that was clearly of reflex origin, because it was abolished by dorsal rhizotomy (see trace *B*). When allowances for afferent and efferent conduction are made, the reduced central delay of the reflex discharge *R* identifies it as monosynaptic. *The monosynaptic discharge thus returns to— and, except under special conditions, only to—the stimulated muscle nerve.*

The peripheral distribution of a multisynaptic reflex discharge elicited by stimulating Group II, III or IV fibers of muscle nerves or alpha, delta or C fibers of cutaneous nerves is much more diffuse; such discharges can be detected in the motor fibers supplying many muscles in the limb. However, multisynaptic discharges do not indiscriminately activate all limb muscles. Systematic testing reveals that *in the ipsilateral extremity, multisynaptic discharges are distributed almost exclusively to flexor muscles;* extensor muscles receive at best only negligibly slight portions of the multisynaptic discharge. Further details of multisynaptic reflex distribution are given in the next chapter.

Minute Anatomy of the Synapse; Convergence and Divergence. At this juncture, closer scrutiny of the structural organization of spinal synapses is profitable. Figure 8 shows the appearance of fresh, unstained motoneurons isolated from human spinal cord. The cell body (sometimes called the *soma* or *perikaryon*) is usually about 70 μ across, has an irregular polygonal shape, and gives rise to a number of long processes. The initially thick (5 to 10 μ) processes which branch and taper are *dendrites.* Dendrites may extend as far as 1 mm. before breaking up into untraceably small branches. The *axon* originates from the conically shaped *axon hillock,* and in its *initial segment* shows a constriction. Beyond the initial segment, some 50 to 100 μ from the soma, the axon increases in diameter, acquires a myelin sheath, and proceeds from the spinal cord into the ventral root. The axon is distinguishable from the dendrites by its uniform diameter (except for the constriction of the initial segment) and by the scarcity of branches. Some axons give off branches within the spinal cord; they part from the parent fiber

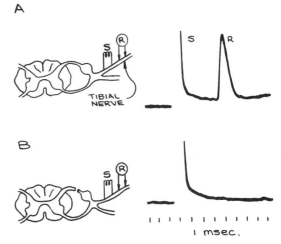

Fig. 7. Experiment proving that monosynaptic reflex discharge occupies efferent axons in nerve from which afferent volley originates. *A,* Responses recorded at *R* on left following weak shock, at *S* on left, to same nerve. *Right, S,* shock artifact and compound action potential of nerve; *R,* monosynaptic reflex discharge. *B,* After dorsal rhizotomy, *R* response is lacking; *R* is therefore reflex. (After Lloyd, *J. Neurophysiol.,* 1943, 6:293–315.)

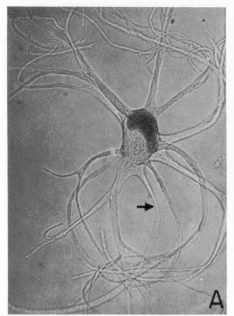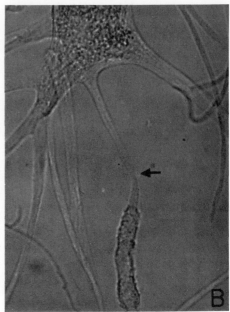

Fig. 8.   Isolated human motoneurons. *Arrows* indicate axons; other processes are dendrites. *On right,* initial segment of axon lacks myelin sheath, which begins just distal to axonal constriction marked by arrow. (From Chu, *J. comp. Neurol.,* 1954, *100*:381–414.)

at right angles, curve dorsally into the gray matter and terminate on interneurons. These branches are called *recurrent collaterals* of the axon.

When motoneurons are stained with basic dyes (toluidine blue, thionin, methylene blue), the cytoplasm surrounding the centrally placed, round nucleus is seen to be filled with granules known as *Nissl bodies* or *tigroid bodies*. These structures are said to be absent from the axon hillock and axon, but are seen in the dendrites, at least in the thicker proximal part of their stalks. Nissl bodies are nucleoproteins and undergo dissolution (*chromatalysis*) when the cells are injured as, for example, in amputation of the axon.

In silver-stained preparations of spinal cord, the terminations of presynaptic fibers on motoneurons can be seen (Fig. 9). The terminal branches of the presynaptic fibers are fine and tortuous; they end on both dendrites and soma in small (about 1 μ) round or oval expansions known variously as *synaptic knobs, boutons terminaux* or *end feet.* The soma is particularly richly encrusted with knobs; the dendrites are similarly covered, but the density of knobs diminishes as the dendrite divides into fine terminal branches. It has been estimated that up to 40 per cent of the soma-dendritic membrane is covered with knobs. The axon hillock and the unmyelinated initial segment of the axon are sparsely supplied with synaptic knobs.

Not all synapses in the central nervous system are characterized by knobs. Fibers terminating on the cells of Clarke's column do so by breaking up into a series of flat plates which are closely applied to soma and dendrites. The fibers of the medial lemniscus terminating in the relay nuclei of the thalamus break up into a rounded bush around the cells. In cerebral cortex presynaptic terminals often establish contact with minute pedunculated excrescences (the dendritic spines) which sprout from the lateral surface of the cylindrical dendritic stalk. The Purkinje cells of the cerebellar cortex receive "basket" endings which encase the soma. These cells also receive the climbing fibers, which run parallel to and in contact with the profusely branched dendritic tree, resembling a vine on a trellis. The climbing fibers and the olfactory glomeruli are examples of *axodendritic synapses* as opposed to *axosomatic* (basket endings) and *axodendrosomatic* synapses (motoneuron, cortical neuron, Clarke's column).

The fine structure of a synaptic knob is shown in the electron micrograph in Figure 10. The junction between the knob and the postsynaptic cell is marked by the arrow. Both the knob and the cell are surrounded by continuous membranes about 50 Å. thick. The knob appears to make a slight indentation in the cell. Between the two membranes there is a clear space about 200 Å. wide; this is the synaptic gap. In addition to nine lamellated mitochondria, the knob contains a profusion of small (about 200 to 600 Å.) round structures, which are called synaptic vesicles. It has been suggested that the vesicles contain chemical substances important in synaptic transmission.

It is well established that the many knobs on a single motoneuron derive from many different parent afferent fibers (Fig. 9). The motoneuron thus constitutes a *final common path* upon which many presynaptic fibers *converge*. There is reason to suppose that many knobs must be activated within a brief period to initiate an impulse in the motoneuron. Firing thus results from the nearly synchronous activity of many afferent fibers converging on the motoneuron; it is doubtful if activity in a single afferent fiber is sufficient to cause postsynaptic discharge.

Considered from the afferent side, the key feature of organization is *divergence*. Each dorsal root fiber breaks into many branches which establish synaptic contact with many postsynaptic cells (Fig. 9). Thus, although no single afferent fiber alone fires a motoneuron, each fiber contributes to the firing of many motoneurons. These basic principles of *convergence* and *divergence* should be kept clearly in mind while reading the following sections.

Facilitation and Occlusion. The amplitude of the monosynaptic reflex discharge elicited by an afferent volley in Group I fibers in a muscle nerve provides a convenient index of the *number of motoneurons* fired. This is true because the afferent volley is conducted to the motoneurons over a relatively homogeneous pathway with little temporal dispersion, so that the postsynaptic discharge is fairly synchronous. The action potentials of individual fibers in the ven-

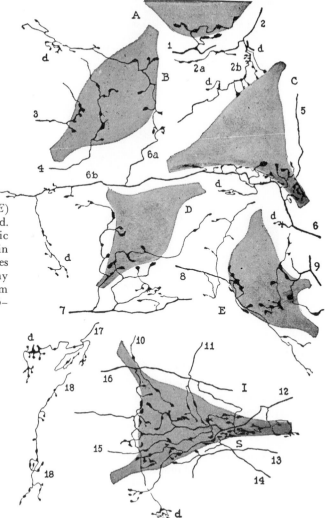

Fig. 9. Synapses on motoneurons (*A–E*) and on a large interneuron (*I*) of spinal cord. *1* to *18,* Presynaptic fibrils carrying synaptic knobs to the several cells; *d,* synaptic knobs in contact with dendrites. Note that fiber *6* supplies both cell *B* and cell *C, divergence,* and that many fibers supply each cell, *convergence.* (From Lorente de Nó, *J. Neurophysiol.,* 1938, *1:195–206.*)

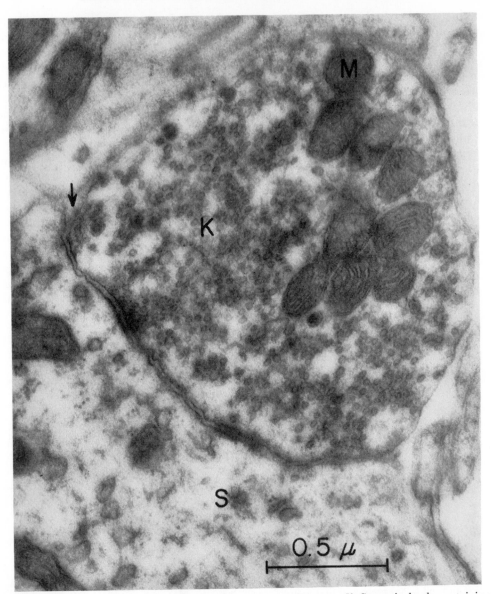

Fig. 10.   Electron micrograph of a synapse on a motoneuron. *K,* Synaptic knob containing mitochondria (*M*) and round profiles of many minute synaptic vesicles. *S,* Motoneuron soma. Arrow indicates synaptic gap. × 65,000. (From Palay, *Exp. Cell Res.,* 1958, *Suppl. 5:*275–293.)

tral root are thus approximately added at the recording electrode.* It follows that as stimulus parameters are varied, the excited fraction of the population of motoneurons available to the Group I fibers can be determined simply by measuring the amplitude of the monosynaptic discharge. It has already been shown in Figure

3 that, as the number of excited afferent fibers is increased, the size of the monosynaptic discharge increases, reaching a maximum when approximately one-half of the Group I fibers are recruited.

Reflex amplitude measures only the number of neurons actually *discharged* by the afferent volley. More subtle influences of the afferent volley on motoneurons can be detected by slightly altering the experimental conditions, as in the experiment illustrated in Figure 11*A.* Here, a dorsal root has been divided into two strands, each equipped with a stimulating electrode. A weak stimulus to strand *a* elicits the

---

* With multisynaptic reflexes, the area under the tracing rather than the amplitude represents the number of neurons fired; both wide ranges of afferent conduction times and multiple synaptic delays results in temporal dispersion, so that the discharge of impulses is asynchronous, and therefore individual impulses do not add at the electrode.

small ventral root discharge shown on the left, and a similar stimulus to strand *b* induces the small response shown in the middle trace. Simultaneous stimulation of *a* and *b* produces, on the right, a response which is far greater than the simple sum of the two individual responses. In other words, the number of motoneurons fired by simultaneous activation of strands *a* and *b* is greater than the total number fired by stimulating *a* and *b* separately. An extreme example of this phenomenon is seen when the shocks to *a* and *b* are reduced so that neither delivered alone can cause discharge of motoneurons, but both delivered simultaneously result in a measurable discharge.

The results of this experiment are most simply explained as follows. An afferent volley delivered to a population of motoneurons, a *motoneuron pool,* has varying effects on the individual motoneurons in the pool, these effects being quantitatively dependent upon the density of activated knobs. Some motoneurons receive many knobs from the activated afferent source and are liminally excited; these are said to be in the *discharge zone* of the afferent source. Other motoneurons receive too few knobs from the activated fibers to reduce the motoneuron membrane potential to the firing level. The excitability of these subliminally bombarded motoneurons, however, is increased, a phenomenon known as *facilitation.* These facilitated motoneurons are said to be in the *subliminal fringe* of the afferent source. As a result of the convergence, the subliminal fringes of two afferent sources may have common elements; i.e., some motoneurons may receive a subliminal number of activated knobs from each source. With simultaneous activation of both sources, the excitatory processes may summate, so that some cells in the common subliminal fringes are recruited into the discharge zone. These relationships are shown diagrammatically in Figure 11*B*.

It follows from the foregoing that merely monitoring the ventral root discharge, which indicates the size of the discharge zone only, gives an incomplete picture of the total effect of an afferent volley. The subtle excitability changes which occur in the many cells of the subliminal fringe are detectable only when two afferent volleys are delivered to the motoneurons, as in the experiment shown in Figure 11. The facilitation of the response, i.e., the difference between the response to the combined volleys and the sum of the responses to the two

volleys delivered separately, provides a quantitative measure of the size of the subliminal fringe.

Figure 12 shows diagrammatically the manner in which both discharge zone and subliminal fringe grow as the size of the afferent volley is increased. With weak afferent volleys, no motoneurons discharge, but the facilitation curve shows that considerable numbers of cells are subliminally excited. Indeed, Lloyd's[17] quantitative measurements on monosynaptic reflexes indicate that, when the afferent volley is 7 to 8 per cent of maximum, discharge is just beginning, but the subliminal fringe is already about 30 per cent of maximum. With further increase of afferent volley size, both the subliminal fringe and the discharge zone increase proportionately and reach maxima when the afferent volley is about 40 to 50 per cent of maximum. It should be noted further that no matter how strong the afferent volley, the discharge zone never becomes coextensive with the subliminal fringe. Any afferent volley fractionates its motoneuron pool, discharging only a

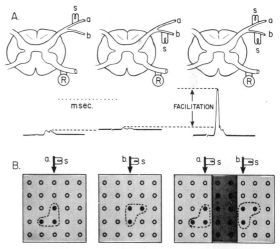

Fig. 11. *A,* Experiment demonstrating facilitation. Dorsal root was split into two strands, *a* and *b.* Weak stimulation of *a* and *b* separately produced reflex responses shown in left and middle traces respectively. Simultaneous weak stimulation of both elicited reflex discharge (trace on right) greater than sum of separate responses.

B, Diagram of mechanism of facilitation. Left and middle figures represent motoneuron pools served by afferent sources *a* and *b* respectively. Each source fires three motoneurons (filled circles enclosed by dotted contours); remaining neurons are subliminally excited. Subliminal fields of *a* and *b* are partially coextensive. When *a* and *b* are simultaneously excited (right), some neurons in common subliminal zones are liminally excited, and eleven rather than six neurons fire.

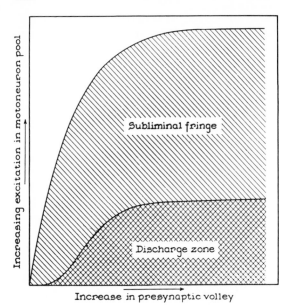

Fig. 12. Semidiagrammatic representation of relative sizes of discharge zone and subliminal fringe as a function of afferent volley strength. (From Lloyd, *J. Neurophysiol.,* 1943, 6:111–120.)

portion of the total number of motoneurons it serves. The reserve represented by the subliminal fringe is brought into active discharge only when other afferent pathways converging on the same motoneuron pool are activated, providing opportunity for overlap of fringes and summation of subliminal processes.

Because both the subliminal fringe and the discharge zone increase with increased afferent input, it might be expected that when both of two maximal afferent volleys are simultaneously delivered, the discharge zones as well as the subliminal fringes will include common elements, as in Figure 13*B*. If the overlap of the discharge zones is extensive, the response to both volleys delivered simultaneously might be less than the sum of the responses to both volleys delivered individually. That this reduction occurs is shown in Figure 13*A*. The left and middle traces shows the ventral root discharges resulting from maximal stimulation of each of two separated portions of a dorsal root. The trace on the right shows the response to simultaneous maximal stimulation of both branches; the resulting discharge is less than the sum of the separate responses. Such reduction in response, attributable to overlapping of the discharge zones, is called *occlusion.*

TIME COURSE OF FACILITATION.[18] The experiments just described indicate that, although the neurons of the subliminal zone are not fired by

an afferent volley, their excitability is increased. The processes leading to this increased excitability differ only quantitatively from those leading to excitation of cells in the discharge zone. Subliminally excited neurons thus provide a suitable medium for studying the processes that lead to synaptic excitation of neurons.

It is a great advantage if subliminally excited cells can be studied in isolation without the complication of actual firing of cells. One way this isolation can be accomplished is by using very weak afferent volleys (see Fig. 12). A more convenient way of studying subliminally excited motoneurons depends on a peculiarity of the central connections of Group I afferent fibers. As has already been emphasized, a Group I afferent volley can discharge only the *homonymous motoneurons,* i.e., the motoneurons supplying the muscle from which the afferent volley originates. *Heteronymous motoneurons* (those supplying muscles other than the one from

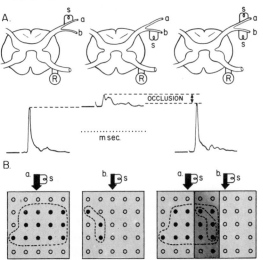

Fig. 13. *A,* Experiment demonstrating occlusion. Dorsal root split into two strands, *a* and *b*. Maximal stimulation of *a* and *b* separately elicited reflex responses shown in left and middle traces. Simultaneous maximal stimulation of strands elicited reflex discharge (right trace) smaller than the sum of separate responses.

B, Diagram of mechanism of occlusion. Left and middle figures represent motoneuron pools served by afferent sources *a* and *b*, respectively. Because the afferent volleys are larger, discharge zones (filled circles enclosed by dotted contours) constitute a greater fraction of total field than in experiment shown in Figure 11*B*. Discharge zones of *a* and *b* overlap. Simultaneous stimulation of *a* and *b* (right) fires only 14 motoneurons rather than expected sum, 16, fired by *a* and *b* separately. Note that one neuron in common subliminal fringe discharged.

which the afferent volley originates) are not fired (except in special circumstances), but conditioning-testing studies indicate that their excitability is altered in a direction which depends upon the relation of their target muscle to the muscle from which the afferent volley originates. For the moment, attention is confined to the motoneurons supplying muscles which are synergistic, i.e., muscles which act on the same joint and in the same way.

An experiment designed to test the influence of an afferent volley arising in a muscle nerve on the motoneurons supplying a synergist of that muscle is illustrated in Figure 14. Stimulating electrodes were situated on the central ends of the cut nerves supplying the two heads of biceps femoris which are, of course, synergistic. Recording electrodes were affixed to the S_1 ventral root. A volley in the larger branch induced the small reflex discharge shown in *A*. A weak Group I volley in the smaller nerve branch evoked no reflex discharge (*B*). (Even if a reflex discharge had occurred, it is known from previous experiments that such discharge occupies only the homonymous motoneurons.) When both nerves were stimulated so that the afferent volleys from the two pathways arrived at the spinal cord simultaneously (*C*), the reflex discharge was greatly increased. It can therefore be concluded that the Group I afferent volley traversing the smaller branch, although not sufficiently strong to fire any motoneurons, produced a subliminal fringe and that this subliminal fringe included the motoneurons supplying the muscle fraction innervated by the larger branch.

From systematic investigations of various muscle nerves, the finding illustrated in Figure 14 can be generalized; i.e., *for any Group I afferent volley, the subliminal fringe includes the heteronymous synergistic motoneurons.*[19] It should be emphasized that this generalization applies only to direct synergists—muscles acting on the same joint and in the same way as the muscle from which the Group I volley originates. Thus, a lateral gastrocnemius Group I volley facilitates the motoneurons supplying the medial gastrocnemius and those supplying the soleus, but has no detectable effect on the excitability of motoneurons innervating the hip or toe muscles.

Heteronymous synergistic motoneurons thus provide a pure pool of subliminally excited cells. By measuring the response of motoneurons to homonymous Group I volleys delivered at various intervals after these motoneurons have been subliminally excited by conditioning volleys in the heteronymous synergistic nerve, it is possible to determine accurately the time course of facilitation.

Figure 15 shows the results of such an experiment in which two branches of the nerve supplying the biceps femoris were used. The conditioning volley was insufficient to elicit a discharge; the test volley delivered to the other branch produced the response seen in traces *A* and *O*. Traces *B* through *N* show how the conditioning volley affects the test response at different conditioning-testing intervals. Facilitation is maximal when the conditioning and testing volleys arrive at the spinal cord at the same time (*B*), but the number of motoneurons responding to the test volley in such pairs of stimuli remains greater than the number responding to the test volley alone (*A* and *O*) for a considerable time after the conditioning volley has reached the spinal cord. The graph in Figure 15 shows the pooled results of seven such experiments. When absolute differences related to individual experiments are eliminated by expressing facilitation as a percentage of maximum facilitation in the particular ex-

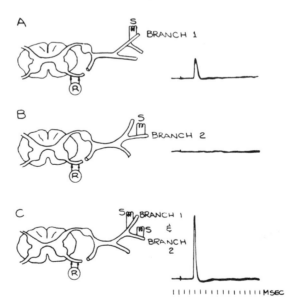

Fig. 14. Facilitation of heteronymous synergistic motoneurons by Group I afferent volley. Two branches of biceps nerve used as afferent paths. *A*, Response elicited by stimulating Branch *1*. *B*, Stimulating Branch *2* elicited no reflex response. *C*, Simultaneous stimulation of branches elicited response larger than control response in *A*. (After Lloyd, *J. Neurophysiol.*, 1946, *9*:421–438.)

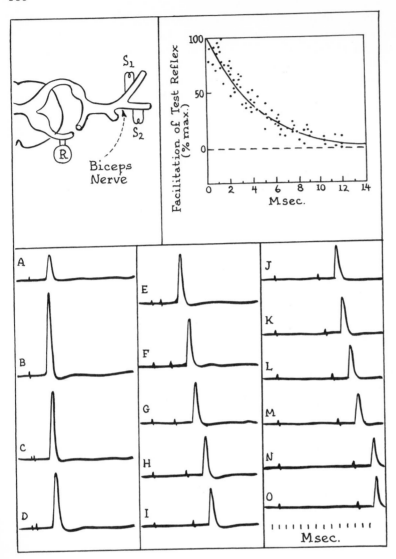

Fig. 15. Time course of facilitation. Group I fibers in two branches of biceps nerve used as afferent paths. Conditioning volley (S_1) applied to one branch elicited no reflex discharge. Test volley (S_2) applied to other branch elicited reflex discharge seen in *A* and *O*. Traces *B–N* show reflex discharges elicited by combined S_1 and S_2 separated by increasing intervals. Graph shows relation between test reflex increase (expressed as percentage of maximal) and conditioning-test interval; data from seven experiments. (After Lloyd, *J. Neurophysiol.*, 1946, *9*:421–438.)

periment, it is clear that the time course of facilitation is remarkably constant. Indeed, the curve shown in Figure 15 can be described mathematically as an exponentially decaying curve which declines to about one-third of its initial value in 4 milliseconds.

The duration of facilitation (or the "central excitatory state" as Sherrington termed it) is of special interest because it outlasts the presynaptic volley as recorded in the dorsal root. The discrepancy implies that between the arrival of the brief presynaptic spike at the knob and the initiation of the postsynaptic spike, some intermediate event of more gradual time course intervenes. Later, evidence will be presented that the presynaptic spike liberates from the knob a chemical transmitter, which diffuses across the narrow synaptic gap to exercise a depolarizing

action on the postsynaptic membrane. The duration of facilitation reflects the time course of action of the transmitter prolonged by the electrical time constant of the postsynaptic membrane. Because of this intermediate step, excitation outlasts the presynaptic spike and the cell stores information—or "remembers" what has happened—for several milliseconds after the spike has decayed.

Inhibition.[18] In the foregoing section it was seen how the use of paired stimuli to different afferent trunks (the "conditioning-testing" technique) can be used to detect subtle changes in neuronal excitability (facilitation) which are not revealed by single stimuli. Further, by varying the interval between conditioning and testing afferent volleys, it was possible to determine the time course of the changes in postsynaptic excitability leading to firing. In the present section, it will be seen that the conditioning-testing technique can also be used to reveal a new and entirely different influence of certain presynaptic fibers on motoneurons, *inhibition*. In inhibition, the afferent volley produces in the postsynaptic neuron a change which reduces its excitability. Inhibition can be detected by testing the responsiveness of neurons to excitatory volleys arriving at various intervals after the neurons have been subjected to an inhibitory volley.

It should be emphasized that mere unresponsiveness of motoneurons following an afferent volley is not adequate proof of inhibition as defined above. For example, when two pathways converge on the same pool of neurons, an *excitatory* volley in one pathway may render the neurons less responsive to a subsequent excitatory volley arriving in the other pathway because of refractoriness or postexcitatory subnormality. Such reduction of response is logically categorized as *occlusion*, although it is sometimes termed "indirect inhibition." True or direct inhibition implies a process that is the opposite of excitation and does not depend on previous discharge of any element in the arc displaying the depressed excitability. The distinction between inhibition and occlusion first became possible when a postconditioning deficit in the responses of monosynaptic arcs was demonstrated, for there, and only there, is it possible to be certain that the conditioning volley has not caused discharge of at least some postsynaptic elements (e.g., interneurons) in the chain.

Excitatory processes (facilitation and/or discharge) result when a pool of motoneurons receives Group I impulses from the muscle supplied by these neurons (homonymous) or from that muscle's synergists (heteronymous synergistic). Motoneurons are inhibited when they receive impulses via Group I afferent fibers originating in muscles antagonistic to the muscle supplied by the neurons (heteronymous antagonistic).[19] Figure 16 shows a typical experiment demonstrating inhibition. Recordings were made from the first sacral ventral root. Traces *A* and *M* show the monosynaptic discharge recorded following an afferent volley set up in Group I afferent fibers originating in the nerve supplying the gastrocnemius. Records *B–L* show the changes in this discharge when

Fig. 16. Time course of inhibition. Group I fibers of two nerves supplying antagonistic muscles used as afferent paths. Weak stimulus S_1 elicited no reflex discharge. Stimulus S_2 elicited monosynaptic reflex seen in traces *A* and *M*. Traces *B–L* show discharges elicited by combined S_1 and S_2 separated by increasing intervals. Graph shows relation between test reflex responses to S_2 at different S_1–S_2 intervals; data from four experiments. (After Lloyd, *J. Neurophysiol.*, 1946, *9*:421–438.)

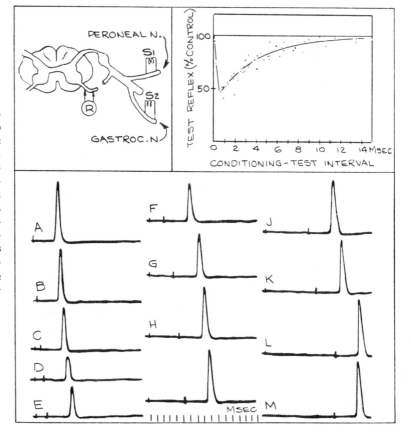

the test shock to the gastrocnemius nerve was preceded by a conditioning volley in Group I fibers in the deep peroneal nerve which supplies the dorsiflexors of the ankle, i.e., the muscles antagonistic in action to the gastrocnemius. Although no motoneuron discharge was elicited by the weak conditioning shock, it nevertheless greatly reduced the number of neurons discharging to the excitatory test volley.

The graph in Figure 16 shows the time course of inhibition occurring in four different motoneuron pools as a result of conditioning volleys delivered through their respective heteronymous antagonistic pathways. The ordinate shows the percentage decrease in the test reflex discharge when the conditioning inhibitory volley preceded the test excitatory volley by the intervals indicated on the abscissa. The curves indicate that, when conditioning and testing volleys arrive at the spinal cord at the same time (zero on the abscissa), there is little or no inhibitory effect. Inhibition does not reach its maximum until about 0.5 millisecond after the inhibitory volley reaches the spinal cord; thereafter, the process decays exponentially along a time course which is a mirror image of the facilitatory curve seen in Figure 15. Indeed, both the facilitatory and the inhibitory curve decay to 1/e in about the same time, 4 milliseconds.

The reason for the delayed (0.5 millisecond) maximum of the inhibitory curve is controversial. Lloyd and Wilson[22] find no evidence of an interneuron interposed in the inhibitory pathway. Eccles,[4] on the other hand, believes that the inhibitory pathway is disynaptic and that the intercalated interneuron accounts for the delay in maximal inhibition. For the present discussion, the question is largely academic and of secondary importance. The important and universally accepted point is: *different presynaptic fibers can exert one of two fundamentally opposite effects on postsynaptic neurons, either facilitation or inhibition.* A neuron receiving a sufficient number of facilitatory impulses within a sufficiently restricted period is excited and discharges an impulse. If a neuron receives a sufficient number of synchronized impulses from inhibitory afferent fibers, its excitability may be so reduced that the neuron no longer responds to excitatory impulses which otherwise are adequate to discharge it.

Facilitation and Inhibition in Multisynaptic Pathways. The two basic synaptic processes of facilitation and inhibition were de-duced from studies of monosynaptic arcs, for reasons already discussed. Similar processes may be presumed to occur at each synapse in more complex neuron chains. It is true that inhibition and occlusion cannot be distinguished clearly in multisynaptic chains, but there is every reason to believe that inhibition rather than occlusion underlies many response deficits in multisynaptic reflexes conditioned by volleys in appropriate afferent channels.

Synaptic processes in multisynaptic arcs differ from those in monosynaptic arcs in two respects: (i) the time course of facilitation and inhibition and (ii) the functional interrelations between the inhibitory and facilitatory pathways.

The time course of reflex facilitation (Fig. 17A) following a single conditioning volley via a multisynaptic path may be much longer than that for a monosynaptic discharge conditioned by a homonymous synergistic volley. Moreover, the development and decay of facilitation via multisynaptic paths is not the smooth and predictable function of time seen in the monosynaptic arc, but rather is typically a varying series of slowly waning maxima and minima. The same characteristics are also obvious in multisynaptic inhibition (Fig. 17B). These characteristics arise not because the fundamental synaptic processes differ in any way, but because the addition of interneurons to the chain increases the time span of motoneuron bombardment by presynaptic impulses. This increase in the duration of bombardment is due partly to the tendency of the interneurons to fire repetitively in response to a single afferent volley.[10, 15, 28] A second reason is that a motoneuron may receive impulses through several chains of various degrees of complexity. Lorente de Nó[23] has classified interneuron chains into two general types: the closed chain and the multiple chain (Fig. 18). In the closed chain (C), collateral branches permit recirculation or reverberation of impulses through the chain, so that bursts of impulses arrive at the motoneurons at intervals determined by the length and complexity of the chain. In the multiple chain (M), sequential activation of parallel chains of interneurons, through collateral branches, results in prolonged bombardment of the motoneurons, the delay in each chain varying with the number of synapses involved. In either instance, the motoneuron is subjected to a variable and asynchronous barrage which prolongs and compli-

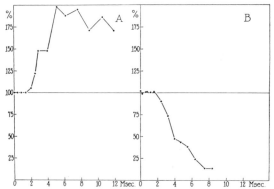

Fig. 17. Facilitation and inhibition through multisynaptic paths. In both experiments the conditioning volley originated in Group II afferent fibers. In *A*, the test reflex was a monosynaptic discharge from a flexor motoneuron pool; in *B*, a monosynaptic discharge from an extensor motoneuron pool. *Ordinates* give size of test reflex discharge, the control size being taken as 100. *Abscissae* show interval between conditioning (Group II) and test (Group I) volleys. (From Lloyd, *Res. Publ. Ass. nerv. ment. Dis.*, 1952, *30*:48–67.)

cates the time course of facilitation and inhibition.

The second difference between multisynaptic and monosynaptic arcs is in the origin and central distribution of their respective inhibitory and facilitatory pathways. Monosynaptic spinal reflexes originate from Group I afferent fibers, found only in muscle nerves. The efferent discharge is *discretely* delivered to the muscle from which the afferent input originated. The same input facilitates motoneurons supplying synergistic muscles and inhibits motoneurons supplying antagonistic muscles. In multisynaptic arcs, the afferent limb is composed of Group II, III, or IV fibers of muscles nerves, or of alpha, delta or C fibers of cutaneous nerves. Irrespective of origin—cutaneous, subcutaneous, muscular, synovial or periosteal—these afferent fibers have, generally speaking, similar *central connections excitatory to motoneurons supplying ipsilateral flexor muscles and inhibitory to motoneurons innervating ipsilateral extensor muscles.*

Multisynaptic discharges thus occupy efferent pathways that originate from several segments of the spinal cord and that are distributed diffusely to flexor muscles acting at all joints of the extremity. Similarly, the motoneurons supplying extensor muscles acting at all joints of the extremity are inhibited by multisynaptic paths initiated through cutaneous or through Group II, III or IV afferent fibers. The multisynaptic reflex may thus originate from widely dispersed afferent fibers and has *diffuse* central connections involving motoneurons supplying muscles acting at different joints. The monosynaptic reflex has a *discrete* origin in muscle nerves and has *discrete* central connections involving only motoneurons supplying muscles acting at a single joint.

It should not be inferred from the foregoing that multisynaptic discharges are stereotyped. The magnitude of the reflex discharge to the various flexor muscles (as well as the intensity of inhibition of motoneurons supplying the various extensor muscles) varies markedly when the site of afferent stimulation is varied. This property of *local sign*, i.e., variation of efferent discharge pattern with changing locale of afferent origin, is discussed in greater detail in the next chapter.

Reciprocal Innervation. A striking feature of reflex organization is the way in which facilitation and inhibition influence motoneurons reciprocally so that reflexly induced muscular contraction occurs without opposition. Such reciprocal central relations are not confined to the reflex arcs specifically described above, but are found in most reflex arcs, even those influencing smooth muscle, cardiac muscle and glands. The principle of reciprocal innervation may be stated formally as follows: *when the motoneurons supplying a given muscle are reflexly excited by an afferent volley, the motoneurons supplying antagonistic muscles are inhibited by that afferent volley.*

This dual action confers on the afferent volley an especially sensitive and powerful control over the limb reflexes, a control simultaneously initiating muscular contraction of one kind and inhibiting all opposing muscular contraction. These relations for the monosynaptic arc and

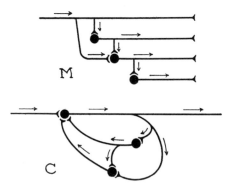

Fig. 18. Plans of the two fundamental types of neuron circuits. *M,* Multiple chain; *C,* closed chain. (After Lorente de Nó, *J. Neurophysiol.*, 1938, *1*:207–244.)

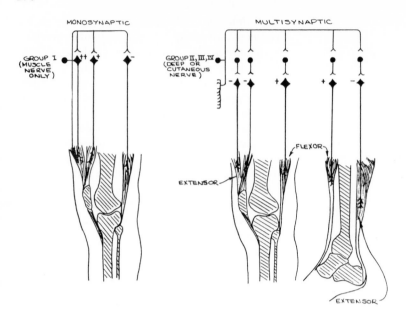

Fig. 19. Reciprocal relations of monosynaptic and multisynaptic reflex arcs. Note that Group I afferent fibers influence only motoneurons supplying muscles acting at a single joint, whereas Group II, III and IV afferent fibers diffusely influence motoneurons supplying muscles acting at several joints.

for the multisynaptic arc are illustrated diagrammatically in Figure 19. It should not be assumed, however, that reflex action lacks flexibility and variability. The diagrams in Figure 19 show the central influences of only a single afferent pathway. In actual fact, each motoneuron receives connections from a host of afferent pathways, and the excitability and behavior of the cell depends at all times upon the relative balance between the excitatory and inhibitory impulses which it receives from these pathways.

It should also be noted that the relationships shown in Figure 19 apply to the motoneurons ipsilateral to the afferent volley. Motoneurons on the contralateral side of the cord are also conditioned by an afferent volley, but generally the effects there are opposite to those found ipsilaterally. Thus, a cutaneous afferent volley excites ipsilateral flexor motoneurons and inhibits ipsilateral extensor motoneurons, but on the contralateral side, the flexor motoneurons are inhibited and the extensor motoneurons excited. This general arrangement of function is called *"double reciprocal innervation";* it is discussed further in the next chapter.

Intracellular Recording from Motoneurons.[3, 5, 6, 9, 28] Although the technique of recording ventral root discharges emerging from a spinal cord subjected to various afferent volleys serves to demonstrate the basic phenomena of facilitation and inhibition and to delineate their respective time courses, such studies of cell populations or pools are poorly suited to investigation of the intimate mechanisms of excita-

tion and inhibition. For study of such problems, it is desirable to measure directly what happens to the membrane of a motoneuron subjected to excitatory or inhibitory afferent volleys.

Happily, such measurements can be made with ultramicroelectrodes similar to those described in earlier chapters. With electrodes having tip diameters less than 0.5 μ, penetration of the soma membrane can be accomplished without killing the cell, its vitality being evidenced by stable, predictable responses to afferent volleys. Often a cell survives impalement for several hours. The advantage of the technique is that it enables the experimenter to measure the potential across the membrane of a single cell and to observe the voltage changes which result when that cell is subjected to synaptic bombardment over various afferent pathways.

Penetration of spinal cord elements must, of course, be carried out blindly by slowly advancing the electrode through the cord (Fig. 20). Penetration of a membrane is signaled by the abrupt registration of a stable DC potential —the resting membrane potential. It is then necessary to identify the element penetrated. If the element responds to an antidromic ventral root volley with a single spike of invariant latency, it may be presumed that the electrode has lodged in a motoneuron. The identity of the motoneuron is next established by testing its responsiveness to Group I afferent volleys originating in various muscle nerves, since Group I volleys usually fire only their homonymous

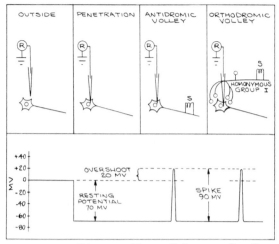

Fig. 20. Diagram of intracellular recording from motoneurons.

motoneurons.* Thus, for example, a penetrated element which responds to antidromic ventral root stimulation and to an orthodromic Group I afferent volley originating in the lateral gastrocnemius nerve may be presumed to be a motoneuron which supplies the lateral gastrocnemius muscle.

Such tests serve to identify the type of element penetrated but do not indicate the part of the cell penetrated—dendrite, soma or axon— because there are no absolute criteria for distinguishing penetration sites.

Action potentials recorded from ultramicroelectrodes in acellular regions (peripheral nerves, dorsal and ventral roots, dorsal columns) usually last about 0.6 millisecond. Intracellularly recorded spikes from spinal gray matter fall into two classes: those having durations of 0.6 millisecond and those with durations of about 1.5 milliseconds. The former probably represent axon spikes; the latter, either soma or dendrite spikes.

MEMBRANE RESTING POTENTIALS OF MOTONEURONS. When a motoneuron is penetrated with a microelectrode, a sustained difference of potential between the internal microelectrode and the external medium is recorded. Sometimes this DC potential increases gradually for the

* It is, of course, also possible to determine the peripheral connection of an impaled motoneuron by antidromically stimulating its axon in the muscle nerve, provided that the ventral root is left intact. Usually, for a variety of reasons, the ventral root is severed, and identification is established by the only slightly less certain method of orthodromic testing.

first few minutes; this phenomenon suggests a sealing of the ruptured membrane around the tip and a consequent decrease in the shunting currents which make the initial potential reading spuriously low. Stable membrane potentials of motoneurons range from 60 to 80 mV., with a mean value of about 70 mV.; they invariably indicate that the inside of the membrane is electronegative to the outside.† The polarity of the resting cell membrane is thus the same as that of the axon membrane, but the magnitude of the polarization usually appears to be somewhat less in the soma membrane. The lower value of the soma membrane potential may reflect continuous subliminal synaptic bombardment, so that the measured potential is not a true "resting" potential; or the lower value may result from injury to the dendritic tree inflicted by the electrode as it approaches the cell body.

Reasoning largely by analogy, one may assume that the mechanisms maintaining the membrane potential in cells and in axons are at least qualitatively the same (see Chap. 2). Unfortunately, with spinal neurons it is not feasible to test this assumption directly by changing the ionic composition of the external medium surrounding the penetrated structure, as has been done with axons. Changes in *intracellular* ion concentrations can be effected by electrophoretic injection of ions through the penetrating electrode;[3] but, unfortunately, the amount of K^+ ion which can be added to the cell sap in this fashion is small compared to the natural high internal K^+ concentration, and the injection has little effect on membrane potential. Attempts to reduce the intracellular concentration of K^+ ion by replacing it with

† The student is here reminded again that it is conventional to use the algebraic signs + or − to indicate the *direction* of membrane polarization. Thus, a membrane potential of − 70 mV. means that the inside of the membrane is 70 mV. negative to the outside. It must be clearly understood that the signs refer only to the direction of polarization, and are not to be taken in the algebraic sense when, for example, the membrane potential changes. Thus a change from − 70 to − 60 mV. is called a decrease, not an increase, in membrane potential, because the absolute voltage across the membrane is decreased, the direction of polarization remaining constant. Similarly, a change from −70 to − 80 mV. represents an increased membrane potential. Decreases of membrane potential are often referred to as depolarization, increases as hyperpolarization.

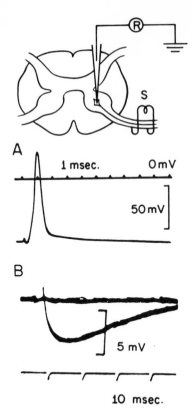

A

1 msec.   0 mV

50 mV

B

5 mV

10 msec.

Fig. 21. Intracellularly recorded antidromic action potentials of motoneurons. Diagram shows arrangement of recording (*R*) and stimulating (*S*) electrodes. *A*, Antidromic spike recorded on fast time base and at low amplification. *B*, Antidromic spike recorded on slow time base and at high amplification to show after-hyperpolarization; most of spike was off the screen. Note that during recovery the trace overshoots the resting potential, indicated by horizontal baseline. Figure made by superposing about 20 responses on one negative. (After Eccles, *The neurophysiological basis of mind*, London, Oxford University Press, 1953; and *The physiology of nerve cells*, Baltimore, Johns Hopkins Press, 1957.)

some other injected cation (Na+ or tetramethylammonium) are more effective and produce expected decreases of 10 to 30 mV. in the membrane potential. When Na+ is the replacing ion, the membrane voltage recovers its initial value in several minutes, presumably because the Na+–K+ pump rapidly restores the resting ionic state. Following tetramethylammonium replacement of K+, restitution of the full membrane potential is much slower, presumably because the membrane is only slightly permeable to the tetramethylammonium ion.

The estimated concentrations of Na+, K+ and Cl− ions in the internal and external media of

cat motoneurons are given in Table 1. Also shown are the equilibrium potentials for these ions, computed from the Nernst equation. It should be noted that at a resting membrane potential of − 70 mV., the K+ ion is not at equilibrium ($\mathcal{E}_{K^+}$ = −90 mV.). This inequality presumably occurs because K+ is actively pumped into the cell by some metabolic mechanism, so that the resting membrane never reaches the equilibrium potential of K+.

ACTION POTENTIALS OF MOTONEURONS. The intracellularly recorded action potential of a motoneuron antidromically fired (Fig. 21*A*) usually has an over-all amplitude of 80 to 100 mV. With a resting potential of − 70 mV., the "overshoot" is thus 10 to 30 mV.; in cell bodies, as in axons, the membrane potential is reversed during the action potential. This reversal during action is presumably triggered by an increased permeability to Na+ ions when the membrane potential is reduced to a critical value by the current flow in the axon. The flow of Na+ ions along their steep concentration gradient into the cell establishes a potential across the membrane which approaches that of the Na+ equilibrium potential (+ 60 mV.; see Table 1). The potential does not overshoot to this extent, because the increased Na+ permeability is short-lived and because there follows a period of increased permeability to K+ during which the membrane potential tends to return toward the K+ equilibrium potential of −90 mV. High K+ permeability is persistent. Consequently, after the spike, the membrane becomes hyperpolarized by about 5 mV. (i.e., the membrane potential reaches about − 75 mV.) and does not return to the resting level of − 70 mV. for some 100 milliseconds (Fig. 21*B*).

These concepts are supported by observations on the spike potentials of motoneurons in which the intracellular ionic concentrations have been altered by iontophoretic injection of ions through the intracellular electrode. When,

TABLE 1. *Ionic Concentrations and Computed Equilibrium Potentials of Cat Motoneurons**

ION	OUTSIDE (mM./l.)	INSIDE (mM./l.)	E(mV.)
Na+	150	ca. 15	ca. +60
K+	5.5	150	−90
Cl−	125	9	−70

* From Eccles.[3]

for example, a current is passed from a Na_2SO_4-filled intracellular electrode to the outside medium, current is largely carried from the electrode to the cell sap by Na^+ ions, whereas the flow outward across the membrane is largely carried by K^+ ions. Thus, intracellular K^+ is replaced by Na^+ ions. It has already been mentioned that such a procedure diminishes the resting potential as a result of depletion of K^+ and consequent increase in the ratio of K^+ outside to K^+ inside the cell. This procedure also causes a reduction in the amplitude and the rate of rise of the action potential, because the added intracellular Na^+ reduces the Na^+ concentration gradient. In addition, when intracellular K^+ is replaced by either Na^+ or tetramethylammonium ions, the after-hyperpolarization is abolished and the decline of the spike is slowed.

If, as suggested by ion injection experiments and by reasoning from analogy with axons, after-hyperpolarization represents a seeking of the K^+ equilibrium potential during the postspike period of high K^+ permeability, no after-hyperpolarization should be observed if the membrane potential is artificially adjusted to equal $\mathcal{E}_{K^+}$. Eccles[3] devised the ingenious technique of adjusting the membrane potential to any desired level by introducing a double-barreled microelectrode into the cell (see drawing in Fig. 22). One barrel of the electrode is used for recording the membrane potential in the conventional fashion. The other barrel is used to pass a brief DC current through the membrane and thus to vary the membrane potential artificially. When the current is passed from the microelectrode outward through the membrane, the membrane potential is decreased, whereas a current passed from the external medium through the membrane into the electrode hyperpolarizes the cell. If the polarizing currents are brief, the membrane potential can be adjusted to any desired level without significantly altering the ion concentrations. Figure 22 illustrates how such variations in membrane potential affect the hyperpolarization following an antidromic spike. As the membrane potential is reduced below the resting level, the afterpotential increases in amplitude, whereas artificial hyperpolarization decreases the afterpotential.

The relationship between the membrane potential and after-hyperpolarization is shown graphically in Figure 22. It usually is imprac-

tical to hyperpolarize the cell sufficiently to reduce the after-hyperpolarization to zero, because at such high membrane potentials the impulse may fail to invade the cell. However, it can be seen that the points fit reasonably well onto a straight line which, by extrapolation, intersects the abscissa at a membrane potential of about 90 mV. Intersection at this point means that K^+ exchange, which is presumably responsible for postspike hyperpolarization, is "satisfied," or in a steady state only when the membrane potential is -90 mV., or about 20 mV. greater than the resting level. Calculated from the Nernst equation with the assumption of an external K^+ concentration of 5.5 mM. per liter and $\mathcal{E}_{K^+} = -90$ mV., the internal K^+ concentration must be about 150 mM. per liter, or approximately twice that required to maintain the observed resting membrane potential of -70 mV. The internal K^+ concentration is unexpectedly high because K^+ is pumped into the cell against its concentration gradient by some active metabolic process. There is reason to believe that the mechanism pumping K^+ into the cell is linked to that pumping Na^+ out (see Chap. 1).

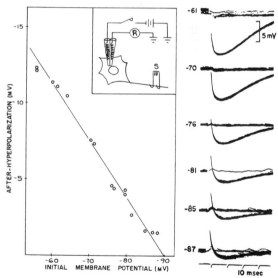

Fig. 22. Effect of membrane potential on amplitude of after-hyperpolarization. Traces show after-hyperpolarization recorded at different membrane potentials established by passing current through polarizing barrel of double-barreled microelectrode. Numbers to left of traces give membrane potential. Graph indicates that after-hyperpolarization is lacking at membrane potential of 90 mV. (After Eccles, *The physiology of nerve cells*, Baltimore, Johns Hopkins Press, 1957.)

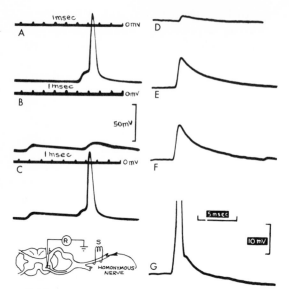

Fig. 23. Intracellularly recorded responses of motoneurons to homonymous Group I afferent volleys. *A,* Response to barely liminal volley. *B,* Response to two subliminal volleys. *C,* Same as *B* except that interval between volleys is reduced so that the second EPSP sums with first and discharges cell. *D–G,* Responses of another cell to afferent volleys of increasing intensity. In *G* the EPSP reaches threshold and the cell discharges. (After Eccles, *The neurophysiological basis of mind,* London, Oxford University Press, 1953.)

The origin of motoneuron spikes.[3, 12] The rising limb of the motoneuron spike typically displays a slight notch when the depolarization has proceeded to about 30 to 40 mV. This notch is a constant feature if the spike is generated by an antidromic volley, by a presynaptic volley, or by a depolarizing current passed directly through the membrane via one barrel of a double-barreled electrode.

Analysis indicates that the notch reflects the spread of depolarization from a low threshold portion of the cell to a high threshold portion. When the cell is depressed, e.g., during recovery from an antecedent discharge, the spike often does not reach its full size of 80 to 100 mV., but declines from a peak of about 30 to 40 mV. above the resting level. In other words, in the depressed cell the spike amplitude is about equal to, or slightly less than, that of the notch seen in full-sized spikes of the undepressed cell. In antidromically elicited spikes, it can be seen that the portion of the membrane giving rise to the small spike is triggered when the membrane is depolarized by about 10 mV. For various reasons, it is believed that the small, low threshold spike (called the A spike by Fuortes *et al.*[12]) originates in the region of the axon hillock or initial segment of the axon. The higher threshold B spike seems to originate in the soma and/or dendrites. Eccles[3] assumed that the low threshold small spike originates in the initial segment of the axon, and he called it the "IS spike." The high threshold spike he labeled

the "SD spike" because he believed that it originates in the soma and dendrites. In view of uncertainties regarding the exact origin of the two components, the noncommittal designations "A" and "B" are preferable. Fuortes *et al.*[12] have shown that an orthodromically elicited A spike is all that is necessary to generate a full-blown spike in the axon; hence, effective synaptic transmission need involve only a fraction of the total postsynaptic membrane.

SYNAPTIC EXCITATION; THE EPSP. Figure 23*A* shows an action potential recorded intracellularly from a motoneuron subjected to a liminal homonymous Group I afferent volley. Prior to the onset of the spike, a small depolarization appears; when this reaches about 10 mV., the spike is generated. A prepotential of this type is consistently observed in neurons subjected to excitatory presynaptic volleys, and is believed to reflect the pre-excitatory change induced in the membrane by the excitatory volley. For this reason, the prepotential is called the excitatory postsynaptic potential, or EPSP.[3]

To study the full time course of the EPSP, it is convenient to avoid firing the cell, because the spike obscures all but the rising phase of the EPSP. Firing can be prevented by reducing the size of the afferent volley until the induced EPSP is too small to initiate a spike, or, in other words, by recording from the cell when it is in the subliminal fringe rather than in the discharge zone.* Examples are shown in Figure 23*D, E* and *F.* The EPSP begins about 0.5 millisecond after the primary afferent volley enters the spinal cord, rises to a summit in 1.0 to 1.5 milliseconds after being initiated, and then declines slowly along an approximately exponential time course with a time constant of slightly more than 4 milliseconds. It is significant that the time course of the decay of the EPSP is of the same order as that of the facilitation curve determined by the conditioning-testing method applied to motoneuron populations.

Figure 23*D, E* and *F* shows another important characteristic of the EPSP—that it is a graded process capable of summation. In contradistinction to the size of the propagated spike, which is "all-or-nothing," the size of the

---

* A convenient method for studying EPSP without the complication of superimposed spikes is to deliver the Group I volley over the heteronymous synergistic pathway. Such volleys produce an EPSP which is qualitatively indistinguishable from, but smaller than, the EPSP produced by subliminal postsynaptic volley via the homonymous pathway.

EPSP is a direct function of volley size. Moreover, when two subliminal volleys are delivered within a time interval less than the EPSP decay time, as in Figure 23*B* and *C,* the second EPSP may sum with the "tail" of the first EPSP and cause sufficient depolarization (about 13 mV. in this instance) to discharge the neuron. The behavior of the EPSP thus parallels closely the process of facilitation and may be presumed to be the electrical manifestation of that process.

When the membrane potential is artificially altered by passing brief polarizing currents through an intracellular electrode, the EPSP induced by an excitatory volley displays a marked alteration in amplitude and configuration. As the membrane potential is decreased, both the amplitude and the rate of rise of the EPSP diminish until, when the membrane potential is artificially set at about 0 mV., the excitatory volley produces no change in membrane potential. When the polarizing current is such that it reverses the membrane potential (i.e., makes the outside of the cell negative to the inside), the EPSP is reversed in sign. Thus, the process underlying the EPSP seems to be one which is in equilibrium at about 0 mV.; when the membrane potential is above or below this value, an excitatory volley makes the membrane seek this equilibrium value. In the normal cell, of course, the effect is depolarization.

For a number of reasons, it seems likely that excitatory impulses cause a nonspecific increase in permeability to all ions. For example, injection of various ions into the cell has little or no effect on the amplitude and time courses of the EPSP. These data are best explained by assuming that the excitatory impulses initiate a transmitter process which "short-circuits"* the postsynaptic membrane beneath the synaptic knobs, permitting ions to flow along their concentration gradients and thus reduce the membrane potential. The extent of the depolarization depends on the number of "short circuits" produced, and this number in turn depends on the number of activated synaptic knobs. If the EPSP reduces the membrane po-

tential by about 10 mV. (i.e., to about -60 mV.), the threshold is reached, and the membrane becomes specifically highly permeable—first to Na^+ and then to K^+ ions—and a propagated spike is generated.

THE SYNAPTIC EXCITATORY TRANSMITTER.[24] It will be recognized that the EPSP is very similar to the end-plate potential recorded at motor end-plates when motor fibers are excited. The end-plate potential results from the liberation of a chemical transmitter agent, presumably acetylcholine. It is almost certain that excitatory synaptic knobs also liberate a chemical transmitter which renders the subjacent postsynaptic membrane highly permeable to all ions, just as the neuromuscular transmitter renders the end-plate permeable to cations. Unfortunately, the identity of the central excitatory transmitter is not known; it may be that more than one such substance exists. Although there is some reason to believe that acetylcholine is the excitatory transmitter at some spinal synapses, it seems unlikely that acetylcholine is the transmitter between dorsal root afferents and motoneurons, because analysis indicates that dorsal root fibers contain very little acetylcholine and choline-acetylase (an enzyme which, in the presence of ATP, acetylates choline). A full discussion of the efforts to identify transmitter agents at various synaptic junctions is given in monographs by Eccles[3, 6] and by McLennan.[24]

A commonly proposed hypothesis is that the numerous vesicles seen in electron micrographs of synaptic knobs comprise packets of preformed transmitter. Further, the action potential of the knob (or of the fine terminal fiber from which it derives) is supposed somehow to trigger rupture of vesicles through the membrane, thus releasing transmitter into the narrow synaptic cleft whence it reaches the postsynaptic membrane by diffusion. Intimate details of the electrosecretory coupling mechanism and of the synthesis, storage and release of transmitter are unfortunately lacking. However, there is evidence that the effectiveness of a presynaptic spike in liberating transmitter varies with (a) the amplitude of the presynaptic spike,[14, 26] and (b) the concentrations of Ca^{++} and Mg^{++} in extracellular fluid.[14, 26]

The relation between presynaptic spike size and transmitter release can be demonstrated directly in the giant synapse of the squid stellate ganglion, an axo-axonal synapse in which both

---

* The term "short-circuit" is used here in a relative sense. Computations indicate that, with maximal presynaptic action, the total membrane resistance drops from about 8×10^5 ohms to as low as 5×10^5 ohms. This latter resistance is composed of many higher resistances in parallel, the resistances of the patches of membrane under activated and nonactivated knobs.[3]

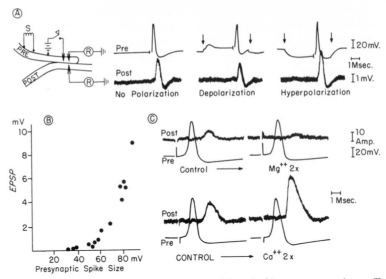

Fig. 24. Influence of presynaptic membrane potential and of ions on transmitter efficacy of presynaptic spike in squid giant synapse. *A,* Diagram at left shows location of stimulating, recording and polarizing electrodes. In middle and right traces the membrane potential was artificially altered by polarizing currents passed during the period between arrows. Depolarization (middle) diminished spike and EPSP, hyperpolarization (right) produced opposite effects. *B,* Graph of relation between presynaptic spike and EPSP amplitudes. *C,* Upper traces, increased Mg^{++} concentration reduced EPSP without altering presynaptic spike size. Lower traces, increased Ca^{++} concentration increased EPSP without altering spike size. (After Takeuchi and Takeuchi, *J. gen. Physiol.,* 1962, *45*:1181–1193.)

the pre- and postsynaptic fibers are sufficiently large to permit intracellular recording at the site of synaptic contact. In the experiment illustrated in Figure 24*A,* the presynaptic fiber was impaled with two electrodes, one being used to record the presynaptic spike initiated by a shock at *S,* the other, connected to a battery circuit, serving as a means of artificially adjusting the membrane potential. A single electrode inserted into the postsynaptic fiber recorded the EPSP, the amplitude of which, under the conditions of the experiment, measured the amount of transmitter released. When the presynaptic fiber was depolarized, the over-all amplitude of the presynaptic spike was correspondingly reduced and the EPSP was smaller. Conversely, hyperpolarization of the presynaptic ending resulted in increased amplitude of presynaptic spike and of EPSP. Figure 24*B* shows graphically the variation of EPSP (transmitter release) with variations of spike amplitude.

The relationship between presynaptic spike amplitude and transmitter release explains the phenomenon of *post-tetanic potentiation* of spinal reflexes in intact mammals.[7, 20, 27] The amplitude of monosynaptic reflex discharge to single-

shock stimulation of a dorsal root is enormously increased following a brief period of high frequency stimulation of the dorsal root. Post-tetanic reflex discharges may attain amplitudes five or six times the control size and some degree of potentiation may last for as long as five minutes. In Chapter 3 it was pointed out that high frequency repetitive stimulation of a nerve trunk results in a prolonged positive after-potential or hyperpolarization of the tetanized fibers (see Chap. 3, Fig. 9). It might, therefore, be expected that following a dorsal root tetanus, the presynaptic terminals within the spinal cord would become similarly hyperpolarized and that spikes generated in such hyperpolarized fibers would be correspondingly increased in amplitude. Even a small increase in the amount of transmitter released from the synaptic knobs of hyperpolarized fibers causes a large increase in the numbers of motoneurons discharged by recruiting into the discharge zone many cells from the subliminal fringe. Lloyd[20] showed that, following tetanization, the compound action potential recorded from the dorsal root undergoes a slight increase in size, the increase running a time course similar to that of post-tetanic potentiation of reflex discharge. Also, spike potentials recorded intracellularly from single presynaptic fibers within the spinal cord (presumably near their terminal ends) increase in amplitude following a conditioning tetanus.[7]

A pathway potentiated by tetanization recruits into the discharge zone neurons which are normally in the subliminal fringe. It has been stressed that a Group I afferent volley normally facilitates but does not fire its heteronymous synergistic motoneurons. After Group I afferent fibers have been tetanized, they may discharge not only homonymous motoneurons, as usual, but also some heteronymous synergistic motoneurons.[21] Such "cross-firing" substantiates the concept that the state of motoneurons in the subliminal fringe differs only quantitatively and not qualitatively from that of neurons in the discharge zone.

The roles of Ca++ and Mg++ in transmitter release are indicated by the experiment illustrated in Figure 24*C*. Increasing Ca++ concentration in the bathing medium greatly increased the postsynaptic response to a presynaptic spike, whereas increasing Mg++ concentration produced the opposite result. These effects were not due to alterations in presynaptic spike amplitude, for, with the concentrations employed, the presynaptic spike was unaltered. Because of its blocking action on transmitter release, Mg++ is an effective anesthetic agent; the block can be rapidly reversed by injecting Ca++.

CENTRAL SYNAPTIC INHIBITION; THE IPSP. When a resting motoneuron is subjected to an inhibitory volley of impulses delivered over its heteronymous antagonistic pathway, the membrane often undergoes a transient hyperpolarization, as shown in Figure 25. The change in membrane potential which follows a synaptic inhibitory volley is called the inhibitory postsynaptic potential, or IPSP.[3] The IPSP, like the EPSP, is a graded nonpropagated response of the postsynaptic cell to presynaptic activation. The IPSP usually begins 1.25 to 1.5 milliseconds after the primary afferent volley enters the spinal cord, reaches a summit in 1.5 to 2.0 milliseconds, and decays with a time constant of about 3 milliseconds. In cells with normal resting membrane potentials of about 70 mV., the amplitude of the IPSP rarely exceeds 5 mV. (In other words, the membrane potential may rise to as much as 75 mV. following an inhibitory afferent volley.) During the IPSP, the responsiveness of the cell to excitatory volleys is diminished. This decreased responsiveness is partly due to hyperpolarization of the membrane during the IPSP, but as will be seen below, postsynaptic hyperpolarization does not fully account for the effectiveness of an inhibitory volley.

Unlike the EPSP, which is little affected by ion injections, the IPSP is markedly altered by injections which alter the internal Cl⁻ or K+ concentration. Injection of Cl⁻ ions, for example, converts the hyperpolarizing IPSP into a depolarizing potential; indeed, following injection of Cl⁻ ions, a normally inhibitory volley may cause sufficient depolarization to fire the cell. Similarly, depleting intracellular K+ by replacement with Na+ or tetramethylammonium ions also converts the IPSP to a depolarizing response. These observations suggest that the inhibitory process exerts its effect by altering the permeability of the membrane to the small ions K+ and Cl⁻.

It will be recalled that the equilibrium potential for K+ is about −90 mV.; the Cl⁻ ion appears to be at equilibrium at a resting membrane potential of −70 mV. Consequently, it might be expected that, if the inhibitory process selectively increases membrane permeability to small ions (K+ and Cl⁻), the membrane potential would seek a value midway between the

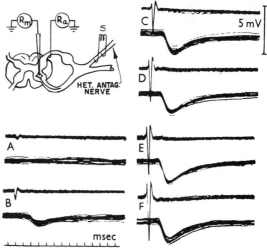

Fig. 25. Intracellularly recorded inhibitory postsynaptic potentials (IPSP). Responses recorded from biceps semitendinosus motoneuron following Group I afferent volley through quadriceps nerve (heteronymous antagonistic path). Traces *A–F* show afferent volley (upper trace) and intracellular response (lower trace) as stimulus strength was progressively increased. Each record formed by superimposing several traces. (After Eccles, *The physiology of nerve cells*, Baltimore, Johns Hopkins Press, 1957.)

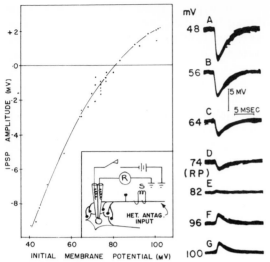

Fig. 26. Effect of membrane potential on IPSP. Traces show intracellularly recorded IPSP elicited by heteronymous antagonistic Group I afferent volley as membrane potential was artificially varied by polarizing electrode. Numbers to left of trace indicate membrane potential; *RP*, resting potential. Graph shows that IPSP is a hyperpolarizing response at membrane potentials less than 80 mV., but becomes a depolarizing response when membrane potential exceeds 80 mV. (After Eccles, *The physiology of nerve cells*, Baltimore, Johns Hopkins Press, 1957.)

respective equilibrium potentials of these two ions. As shown in Figure 26, when the membrane potential is artificially set at -80 mV., the inhibitory volley produces no detectable IPSP. When the membrane potential is less than 80 mV., the IPSP is a hyperpolarizing response; when the membrane potential is greater than 80 mV., the IPSP is a depolarizing response. These experimental findings are thus compatible with the hypothesis that inhibitory impulses increase K^+ and Cl^- permeability and tend to drive the membrane potential toward -80 mV. (i.e., the mean of the Cl^- and $K+$ equilibrium potentials).

In neurons with a normal resting potential and internal ionic composition, the IPSP is hyperpolarizing. However, an inhibitory volley depresses the motoneuron even when the IPSP is of the depolarizing type, e.g., when the IPSP is elicited in a cell artificially hyperpolarized by a polarizing current. It follows therefore that mere hyperpolarization is not the sole cause of inhibitory depression. Rather, it appears that the temporary stabilization of the membrane near the equilibrium potential for the IPSP (-80 mV.) makes it difficult to depolarize the membrane to the level (about -60 mV.) required to initiate an increase in Na^+ permeability.

THE INHIBITORY TRANSMITTER.[24]   It may be assumed that the difference between excitatory and inhibitory nerve fibers is in the chemical transmitters which they liberate. The excitatory transmitter causes a nonspecific increase in permeability to all ions, whereas the inhibitory transmitter causes a specific increased permeability to small ions, of which Cl^- and K^+ are the important naturally occurring species. On certain crustacean neurons gamma aminobutyric acid (GABA), which can be isolated from nerve tissue, mimics the action of an inhibitory volley.[16] The inhibitory transmitter agent at mammalian spinal synapses has not yet been identified.

The mechanisms underlying release of inhibitory transmitter are no better understood than those regulating release of excitatory transmitter. Inhibition, like excitation, displays post-tetanic potentiation;[20] it may, therefore, be concluded that, in both, transmitter release from knobs is quantitatively related to the amplitude of the triggering presynaptic spike. In some spinal reflex arcs strychnine[1] and tetanus toxin[2] diminish or even abolish the effectiveness of inhibitory volleys; the convulsive effect of these substances may be partly due to this property. It is not clear whether strychnine and tetanus toxin block release of transmitter from presynaptic terminals or whether they render the postsynaptic membrane insensitive to it.

PRESYNAPTIC INHIBITION.   Frank and Fuortes[8, 11] were the first to observe that some motoneurons subjected to inhibitory volleys showed no hyperpolarizing IPSP and no change in threshold to direct stimulation through a microelectrode. Nevertheless, such an inhibitory volley reduced by as much as 50 per cent the EPSP generated by an excitatory volley (Fig. 27). In such instances inhibition is *presynaptic;* i.e., the inhibitory volley in some manner either blocks presynaptic excitatory impulses or reduces their transmitter-releasing potency.

Eccles[5, 6] postulates that presynaptic inhibitory fibers terminate not on postsynaptic cells but on presynaptic excitatory knobs, which they depolarize. It has already been pointed out that lowering the membrane potential of a presynaptic fiber reduces the amplitude of its spike, making it less effective in liberating transmitter. According to this view then, the presynaptic inhibitory fibers act by limiting the amount of transmitter released from activated excitatory knobs. The following evidence is presented in support of the hypothesis: (i) Repetitive stimulation of presynaptic inhibitory pathways produces a prolonged depolarization of intramedullary presynaptic excitatory fibers measurable with intracellular electrodes. (ii) Potential changes of durations fitting the time course of presynaptic inhibition can be recorded from the dorsal roots, cord dorsum, and the gray matter following repetitive stimulation of presynaptic inhibitory pathways; the polarity and magnitude of these potentials recorded at different sites are consistent with the hypothesis that they derive from prolonged depolarization of presynaptic endings in the ventral horn gray. (iii) The electrical excitability of presynaptic terminals can be gauged by measuring the amplitude of the antidromic compound action potential of the dorsal root elicited by a shock delivered through an electrode thrust into the region of the presynaptic terminals in the ventral horn gray.[27] After conditioning tetani are delivered through presynaptic inhibitory pathways, the antidromic dorsal root spike to a standard test intramedullary shock increases, suggesting increased excitability of the presynaptic terminals, a finding consistent with the hypothesis that the tested terminals are depolarized.[5, 6] (iv) Electron micrographs of synaptic regions indicate that where knobs are densely clustered their borders often are in intimate contact and at some of these junction sites the closely apposed membranes show thickening and increased density, a presumed morphological sign of a transmission site.[13]

Summary of Synaptic Mechanisms.

It is now possible to reconstruct in some detail what changes occur in the spinal cord when a Group I afferent volley is directed into it (Fig. 28). At the homonymous synapses, the volley liberates a transmitter which increases permeability to all ions and permits the voltage across the membrane to run down. In some cells, many short circuits will occur because the cells receive many active synaptic knobs. In these cells, when the depolarization reaches about 10 mV. less than the resting membrane potential, there is a sudden large increase in Na+ permeability, so that the membrane potential shifts rapidly toward the Na+ equilibrium potential; hence, the potential across the membrane reverses. Following in the wake of high Na+ permeability, K+ permeability increases, driving the membrane potential back towards the K+ equilibrium potential of −90 mV. As the K+ permeability wanes, the membrane potential returns to the resting level of about −70 mV.

Other homonymous motoneurons and also the heteronymous synergistic motoneurons receive fewer active knobs and are consequently in the subliminal fringe of the excitatory volley.

In such motoneurons the short-circuiting action of the excitatory impulses is insufficient to reduce the membrane potential to the critical level required to activate the increase in permeability to Na+. Consequently, these cells do not discharge, but during the time course of the EPSP their excitability is increased.

Finally, the volley exerts an effect on the heteronymous antagonistic motoneuron pool. Here, the presynaptic impulses cause the release of an inhibitory transmitter which increases the permeability to K+ and Cl− ions. Consequently, the membrane potential is driven toward −80 mV. and the excitability of the cell is diminished. In addition, inhibitory volleys may block excitatory impulses in presynaptic fibers (presynaptic inhibition).

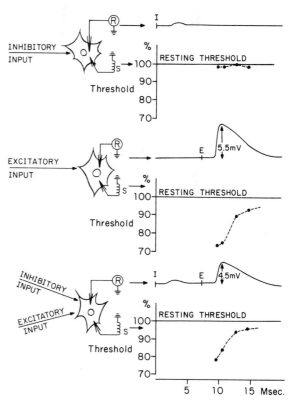

Fig. 27. Presynaptic inhibition in a spinal motoneuron. Sketches show intracellular recording electrode and intracellular stimulating electrode used to determine electrical threshold of motoneuron membrane. *Upper,* Inhibitory input alone caused no significant alteration of either membrane potential or threshold. *Middle,* Excitatory input alone depolarized motoneuron (EPSP) and decreased threshold. *Lower,* Inhibitory input preceded excitatory input; both amplitude of EPSP and its effectiveness in lowering threshold were diminished. (After Frank, *I.R.E. Trans. Med. Electron.*, 1959, *ME–6*:85–88.)

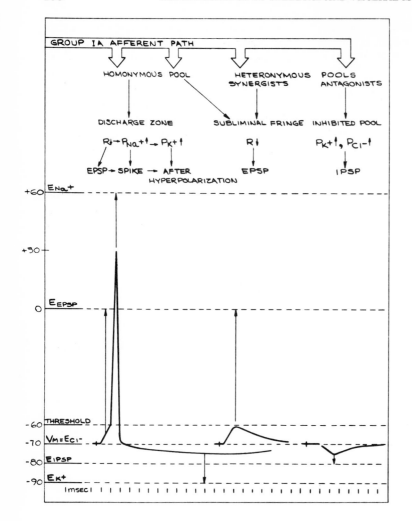

Fig. 28. Summary diagram of monosynaptic connections and events. *Upper,* Functional connections of Group I afferent fibers and permeability changes which they exert on various motoneuron pools; *R,* membrane resistance; *P,* permeability. *Lower,* Intracellularly recorded responses and equilibrium potentials (*E*) toward which each process tends to drive membrane potential; *Vm,* resting membrane potential.

REFERENCES

1. Bradley, K., Easton, D. M. and Eccles, J. C. *J. Physiol.,* 1953, *122:*474–488.
2. Brooks, V. B., Curtis, D. R. and Eccles, J. C. *J. Physiol.,* 1957, *135:*655–672.
3. Eccles, J. C. *The physiology of nerve cells.* Baltimore, Johns Hopkins Press, 1957.
4. Eccles, J. C. In: *Nervous inhibition.* E. Florey, ed. New York, Pergamon Press. 1961.
5. Eccles, J. C. *Ergebn. Physiol.,* 1961, *51:*299–430.
6. Eccles, J. C. *The physiology of synapses.* Berlin, Springer, 1964.
7. Eccles, J. C. and Krnjević, K. *J. Physiol.,* 1959, *149:*250–276.
8. Frank, K. *I.R.E. Trans. Med. Electron.,* 1959, *ME–6:*85–88.
9. Frank, K. and Fuortes, M. G. F. *J. Physiol.,* 1955, *130:*625–654.
10. Frank, K. and Fuortes, M. G. F. *J. Physiol.,* 1956, *131:*424–435.
11. Frank, K. and Fuortes, M. G. F. *Fed. Proc.,* 1957, *16:*39–40.
12. Fuortes, M. G. F., Frank, K. and Becker, M. C. *J. gen. Physiol.,* 1957, *40:*736–752.
13. Gray, E. G. *Nature (Lond.),* 1962, *193:*82–83.
14. Hagiwara, S. and Tasaki, I. *J. Physiol.,* 1958, *143:*114–137.
15. Hunt, C. C. and Kuno, M. *J. Physiol.,* 1959, *147:*346–363.
16. Kuffler, S. W. and Edwards, C. *J. Neurophysiol.,* 1958, *21:*589–610.
17. Lloyd, D. P. C. *Yale J. Biol. Med.,* 1945, *18:*117–121.
18. Lloyd, D. P. C. *J. Neurophysiol.,* 1946, *9:*421–438.
19. Lloyd, D. P. C. *J. Neurophysiol.,* 1946, *9:*439–444.
20. Lloyd, D. P. C. *J. gen. Physiol.,* 1949, *33:*147–170.
21. Lloyd, D. P. C., Hunt, C. C. and McIntyre, A. K. *J. gen. Physiol.,* 1955, *38:*307–317.
22. Lloyd, D. P. C. and Wilson, V. J. *J. gen. Physiol.,* 1959, 1219–1231.
23. Lorente de Nó, R. *J. Neurophysiol.,* 1938, *1:*207–244.
24. McLennan, H. *Synaptic transmission.* Philadelphia, W. B. Saunders Co., 1963.
25. Renshaw, B. *J. Neurophysiol.,* 1940, *3:*373–387.
26. Takeuchi, A. and Takeuchi, N. *J. gen. Physiol.,* 1962, *45:*1181–1193.
27. Wall, P. D. and Johnson, A. R. *J. Neurophysiol.,* 1958, *21:*148–158.
28. Woodbury, J. W. and Patton, H. D. *Cold Spr. Harb. Symp. Quant. Biol.,* 1952, *17:*185–188.

CHAPTER 7

Reflex Regulation of Movement and Posture

By HARRY D. PATTON

IN the previous chapter some simple reflex arcs were analyzed for the purpose of elucidating the principles of synaptic transmission. In the present chapter the *functional* role of spinal reflexes in the coordination of posture and phasic motor activity will be considered. It should be emphasized from the outset that, in assessing the function of reflex arcs in intact animals, certain experimental procedures allowable in analysis of synaptic mechanisms are excluded or, at best, must be used with reservation. For example, in the experiments described in Chapter 6, reflex discharges were commonly elicited by applying electric shocks to appropriate bundles of afferent fibers. Such stimulation excites many afferent fibers in synchrony, so that the spinal motoneurons receive a relatively brief-acting "packet" of impulses.

In studies of synapses synchronous bombardment of motoneurons is both advantageous and defensible because it allows accurate measurement of the time course of synaptic events. In nature, however, reflex action originates at the receptor organs, and the afferent inputs to the motoneurons are rarely synchronous because the receptors fire repetitively and out of phase with one another. An even more serious drawback to stimulation of a nerve trunk is that afferent fibers of different functional species may be excited in unnatural concert, since the correlation between fiber size (and hence threshold) and functional species is not absolute. For example, even the Group I afferent fibers of muscle nerves are not functionally homogeneous (see below). Therefore, in the present chapter, attention will be focused primarily on experiments in which reflexes are elicited by natural stimulation of the receptors.

Also, in evaluation of the functional significance of reflexes, emphasis is placed on observations made while reflex arcs are as nearly intact and uninfluenced by drugs as humane requirements to avoid causing pain permit. The study of reflexes in the truly "natural state" is impossible, for the uncertainty principle applies equally to physiologic and physical systems. However, many procedures (e.g., root sections, deep anesthesia) necessary for learning basic properties of reflex *components* can and must be avoided in studying the properties of the whole *system*. Stated in another way, the goal of this chapter is to present a *synthetic* rather than a purely *analytical* picture of reflex function by emphasizing the behavior of freely interacting components of the reflex arc rather than their behavior in controlled isolation.

181

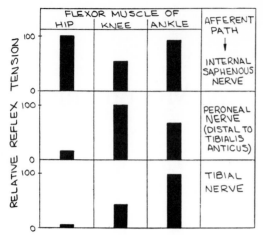

Fig. 1. Local sign in the flexion reflex. Bars indicate relative reflex tensions developed in three flexor muscles as a result of stimulation of each of three nerves (afferent paths) serving sensory endings in different portions of hindlimb. Each path activated all three muscles, but relative participation of the muscles in the reflex movement varied with afferent path. (After Creed and Sherrington, *Proc. roy. Soc.*, 1926, *B100*:258–267.)

The Flexion Reflex and Crossed Extension.[38] A convenient preparation for the study of spinal reflex patterns is an animal in which the spinal cord has been permanently transected above the lumbosacral enlargement—a "spinal animal."* Segments below the level of the transection are, of course, insensate, and hence the reflex patterns of these segments may be freely studied without the use of anesthetic drugs. In such a preparation, stimulation of the skin or deep structures of the hindlimbs, for example, elicits a variety of movements and postures which must be mediated solely by spinal reflex arcs, because the lower cord has been isolated from supraspinal structures by the transection. Two spinal reflex patterns are particularly prominent—the *flexion reflex* and the *tendon jerk.*

The flexion reflex is elicited by noxious stimulation (pinching, burning, strong electrical stimulation), particularly of the skin, although similar stimulation of deep structures after removal or denervation of the skin is also effective. The reflex response consists of contraction of the *ipsilateral* flexor muscles at the ankle, knee and hip so that the whole limb is with-

* In acute experiments the spinal cord is sometimes transected at C_1, and the animal is maintained by artificial respiration. Such an animal is referred to as a "high spinal" or "decapitate" preparation.

drawn from the noxious stimulus. Palpation of the muscles reveals that, as the flexor muscles contract, the extensor muscles relax, an event suggesting that the extensor motoneurons are inhibited. Thus, the afferent fibers subserving the flexion reflex make *reciprocal* connections (see Chap. 6) with the ipsilateral motoneurons, so that flexor withdrawal of the limb is not impeded by simultaneous contraction of the antagonistic extensor muscles. Because the adequate stimulus for eliciting the flexion reflex is one which is harmful to the tissues, Sherrington[38] called it a *nociceptive* reflex, and, because the reflex contraction results in removal of the extremity from the damaging stimulus, he looked upon the flexion reflex as protective.

Reflex withdrawal of the stimulated limb is associated with contraction of the extensor muscles and relaxation of the flexor muscles of the corresponding contralateral extremity. This contralateral component is known as the *crossed extension reflex.* The crossed extension reflex is not a separate reflex but is accessory to, or a part of, the nociceptive flexion reflex. The afferent fibers subserving the flexion reflex send to the opposite side of the spinal cord collateral branches which have reciprocal connections opposite those in the ipsilateral spinal cord. This arrangement is known as *double reciprocal innervation.* The crossed extension reflex supports the weight of the body when the ipsilateral limb flexes.

Often when the noxious stimulus is prolonged, the crossed extension reflex is not sustained, but gives way to a rhythmically alternating stepping movement. In Sherrington's words, "The irritated foot is withdrawn from harm and the other legs run away."

Prominent features of the flexion reflex are its broad receptive field and its wide sphere of action on muscles. Generally speaking, noxious stimulation anywhere on the distal portion of the limb causes reflex contraction of the flexor muscles at all joints in the limb. The pattern of contraction, however, is not stereotyped, for the relative strength of the contractions of various muscles varies with the site of stimulation. Figure 1 shows the relative participation of three flexor muscles in reflex limb movement elicited by electrical stimulation of three different afferent nerves supplying sensory fibers to different regions of the limb. It can be seen that each of the three afferent nerves drives the motoneurons of each muscle, but in quantitatively different combinations. Such data indicate that the nature of the limb movement and the final position of the limb vary, depending on the site of harmful stimulation. Such dependence of the reflex pattern on the origin of the afferent input is called *local sign*. Because of local sign, effective and appropriate withdrawal of the limb occurs irrespective of the site of injury.

Local sign is even more evident when the reflex is elicited by natural noxious stimulation of the skin rather than by electrical stimulation of nerve trunks. For example, pinching the skin on the proximal portion of the limb may elicit reflex patterns which depart from the standard ipsilateral flexion-crossed extension pattern, giving rise to bilateral flexion (dorsolateral surface of the thigh) or to bilateral extension (ventromedial surface of the thigh).[30] Effects of pinching the skin even on the distal portion of the limb are variable depending on the site of stimulation. For example, the motoneurons supplying an individual flexor muscle may be inhibited, rather than excited, if the skin overlying an antagonistic extensor muscle is pinched.[10]

AFFERENT PATH AND SYNAPTIC ORGANIZATION OF THE FLEXION REFLEX. Several features of the flexion reflex are strongly reminiscent of the multisynaptic discharges (see Chap. 6) elicited by electrical stimulation of cutaneous fibers and of deep afferent fibers less than 12 μ in diameter (Groups II, III, and IV) which form the afferent limb of polysynaptic reflexes. (i) The broad receptive field including deep structures as well as the cutaneous surface of the limb agrees with the ubiquitous distribution of afferent fibers which feed polysynaptic reflex arcs. (ii) The channeling of the reflex discharge exclusively into ipsilateral flexor muscles, with concomitant inhibition of ipsilateral extensor motoneurons, is also typical of multisynaptic arcs. The diffuse distribution of the efferent discharge, involving reciprocal action at all joints of the extremity, too, is peculiar to multisynaptic arcs and in striking contrast to the discrete distribution of monosynaptic discharges (cf., Fig. 19, Chap. 6). (iii) The flexion reflex typically displays *afterdischarge* (i.e., the contraction outlasts the stimulus), which is expected in multisynaptic systems where recirculation of impulses through interneuron circuits permits sustained motoneuron bombardment after the primary afferent volley has ceased. (iv) Finally, the

noxious or harmful nature of the adequate stimulus for the flexion reflex agrees with evidence indicating that many of the unmyelinated and small myelinated fibers supply the plexuses of free nerve endings which are sensitive to noxious or painful stimuli (see Chap. 14). There can be little doubt that the nociceptive reflex utilizes multisynaptic arcs having Group III (or delta) and IV fibers for their afferent limbs.

Cutaneous Alpha and Group II Reflexes. The functional significance of the Group II and of cutaneous alpha afferent fibers which mediate a multisynaptic reflex discharge to ipsilateral flexor muscles is not entirely clear, since there is no reason to suspect that the endings which these fibers supply are nociceptive. The Group II afferent fibers found in muscle nerves originate in the secondary or flower spray endings of the muscle spindles, which are sensitive to muscle stretch (see below). Alpha fibers of cutaneous nerves principally supply touch-sensitive or pressure-sensitive endings.[16]

Although excitation of alpha fibers elicits an ipsilateral flexion reflex, the crossed connections of these fibers differ from those of delta, Group III and Group IV fibers, which in addition mediate a crossed extension reflex. Electrical stimulation of alpha fibers facilitates contralateral flexor motoneurons and either does not affect or inhibits contralateral extensor motoneurons.[31] In other words, these fibers appear to mediate a bilateral flexion reflex of unknown functional significance. The crossed connections of Group II fibers are complex and vary with the muscle of origin.[32]

Other Polysynaptic Reflexes. In spinal preparations light pressure or stretch applied between the toe-pads elicits extension of the limb; this is called the *extensor thrust reflex*. The afferent fibers traverse the plantar nerves, but electrical stimulation of these nerves elicits only flexion and crossed extension, a finding that emphasizes the extent to which reflex patterns may be concealed when unnatural stimulation of whole nerve trunks is employed to trigger reflex action. The extensor thrust presumably plays a role in reflex standing or walking.

Rhythmically alternating, stepping movements of the hindlimbs can sometimes be initiated in the chronic spinal dog by tactile stimulation of the foot pad or, more consistently, by suspending the animal erect off the ground so that gravity imparts a stretch on the hip ex-

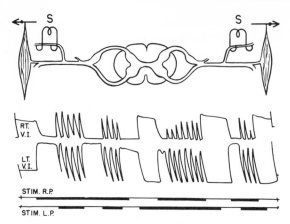

Fig. 2. Production of rhythmic reflexes (stepping by concurrent stimulation of right and left peroneal nerves. Diagram at top represents experimental arrangement. Upper two traces are myographic records of tension in right (*RT.*) and left (*LT.*) vastus intermedius muscles (knee extensors). Lower two traces signal repetitive stimulation of afferent fibers of right (*R.P.*) and left peroneal (*L.P.*) nerves. Note rhythmic alternation of muscle contraction during concurrent stimulation of the two nerves. (After Creed *et al., Reflex activity of the spinal cord,* Oxford, Clarendon Press, 1932.)

tensors. Since both the touch-pressure receptors of the feet and the stretch-sensitive spindle endings in the hip muscles are in a position to be alternately excited by normal stepping, it is tempting to assume that stepping is maintained by rhythmic variation of input from these receptors.

The mechanism of stepping, however, is complex. Sherrington found that denervation of the tactile receptors by section of all the cutaneous nerves of the leg impaired walking in the cat so little that an animal was able to walk accurately on a horizontal ladder. Moreover, rhythmically alternating stepping may be induced experimentally by simultaneous repetitive stimulation of afferent fibers originating in each of the hindlimbs. Figure 2 shows the results of an experiment in which the tensions in the right and left vastus intermedius muscles (knee extensors) were recorded during afferent stimulation of one or both peroneal nerves. When only one nerve was stimulated, the ipsilateral extensor muscle relaxed and its contralateral counterpart contracted. When both nerves were stimulated concurrently at equal intensities, rhythmically alternating contraction and relaxation of the two muscles occurred and persisted as long as the concurrent stimulation lasted. In this instance, the input to the two halves of the

cord is equal and nonperiodic. Further, such rhythmically alternating contractions of symmetrical muscles can be initiated after complete deafferentation of the limb. The mechanism for rhythmic alternation must therefore be a "built-in" feature of the spinal cord capable of operating in the absence of alternating afferent input such as that which stepping presumably initiates in the cutaneous and deep receptors.

The Tendon Jerk.   Another easily elicited spinal reflex, and one of great importance to the neurologist, is the tendon jerk. One can elicit this reflex in almost any muscle by sharply tapping either the muscle or the tendon, thus imparting a brief stretch to the muscle. The reflex response consists of a twitchlike contraction of the stretched muscle. The neurologist most commonly elicits these reflexes in the extensor muscles of the leg—e.g., quadriceps (knee jerk or patellar reflex) and triceps surae (ankle jerk or Achilles reflex)*—but flexor muscles show similar jerk responses to brief stretch (pluck reflexes). In the arm, the biceps, triceps and pectoral muscles are common test sites; in the face, tapping the lower jaw produces a "jaw jerk" of the masseter muscle.

Tendon jerks are characterized by short latency and absence of afterdischarge. Indeed, the quadriceps jerk has such a brief latency (19 to 24 milliseconds in man) that for many years its reflex nature was questioned; but Sherrington's[35] demonstration that the quadriceps jerk of experimental animals is subject to central inhibition and is abolished by dorsal or ventral

* Although deeply ingrained in medical jargon, the terms "knee" and "ankle" jerk should be dropped in favor of the more descriptive terms "quadriceps" and "triceps surae" jerk, respectively.

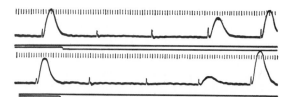

Fig. 3.   Inhibition of knee jerk in spinal cat. Myographic recording from quadriceps muscle; tendon taps delivered at three per sec. Sharp upward deflections record tendon taps; subsequent larger deflections represent jerk reflex contractions. Signal at bottom of each record indicates time of delivery of a single shock to an ipsilateral afferent nerve trunk. Time scale: 20 milliseconds. (From Ballif *et al., Proc. roy. Soc.,* 1925, *B98:*589–607.)

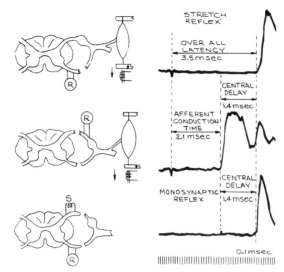

Fig. 4. Lloyd's experiment proving the monosynaptic nature of the stretch reflex. *Upper trace,* Reflex discharge recorded from ventral root following brief muscle stretch. *Middle trace,* Afferent discharge recorded from dorsal root following muscle stretch. *Lower trace,* Monosynaptic discharge recorded from ventral root following weak shock to dorsal root. The latency of the monosynaptic discharge is the same as the central delay of the stretch-induced discharge (over-all latency minus afferent conduction time). (After Lloyd, *J. Neurophysiol.,* 1943, *6:*317–326.)

rhizotomy clearly established the tendon jerk as a reflex. The short latency and the absence of afterdischarge suggest that tendon jerks are mediated by rapidly conducting monosynaptic pathways. Other similarities between the tendon jerk and the monosynaptic reflex discharge elicited by electrical stimulation of Group I afferent fibers are: (i) Both reflect into, and only into, the muscle or muscle fraction from which the afferent activity arises. (ii) Both reflexes, when initiated in extensor muscles, are inhibited by strong stimulation of cutaneous afferent trunks. The effect of a single inhibitory volley persists for periods as long as 1 second (Fig. 3). (iii) Both reflexes are inhibited by Group I afferent volleys initiated in nerves supplying antagonistic muscles, and in both the inhibitory input arises only from *direct* antagonists; afferent input from muscles acting at joints other than the one at which the test muscle works is ineffective. The jerk reflex of the quadriceps is also inhibited by stretching or kneading its antagonists, the hamstring muscles.[35]

The close similarity between tendon jerks and electrically evoked monosynaptic discharges is strong presumptive evidence that tendon

jerks are mediated by reflex arcs of two neurons responding to impulses originating in afferent fibers of Group I size. Lloyd's[25] experiments provide conclusive evidence that this is so. Brief stretches comparable to those imposed by tapping the tendon were applied to a muscle by a solenoid attached to its tendon. Stretch-induced afferent discharges, recorded from appropriate dorsal roots, had conduction velocities in the Group I range (about 116 m./sec.), indicating that muscle stretch excites receptors innervated by the largest and most rapidly conducting afferent fibers. Ventral root reflex discharges resulting from brief muscle stretch had the same central delay as monosynaptic discharges elicited by electrical stimulation of Group I afferent fibers (Fig. 4).

In man, Magladery *et al.*[26] have shown that it is possible to excite selectively the large-diameter afferent fibers by using weak shocks delivered through electrodes placed on the skin over mixed nerves. Recording electrodes inserted into the lumbar vertebral canal register two major deflections in response to such stimulation; the earlier appears to represent the afferent volley traversing the dorsal roots, whereas the later deflection represents the reflex discharge over the ventral roots (Fig. 5). The interval between the two deflections is thus a

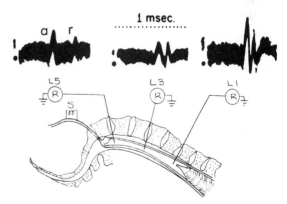

Fig. 5. Monosynaptic reflexes in man. Weak shocks to posterior tibial nerve excite large afferent fibers but not efferent fibers. Electrodes inserted into vertebral canal at levels shown recorded activity in the spinal roots as seen in the traces above (each record consists of several superimposed traces). Deflection *a* is afferent volley in dorsal roots; *r* is reflex efferent volley in ventral roots. Interval between deflections measures central delay plus variable root conduction time. At L_1 the interval was 1.5 milliseconds. Estimated root conduction time (dorsal plus ventral) was 0.6 millisecond, leaving a central delay of 0.9 millisecond. (After Magladery *et al.*, *Res. Publ. Ass. nerv. ment. Dis.,* 1952, *30:*118–151.)

measure of the time required for transmission through the roots central to the intrathecal electrode plus the delay in the spinal cord. With the recording electrode at L_1 (the termination of the cord in man), this delay was 1.5 milliseconds. If a reasonable allowance of 0.3 millisecond is made for conduction in each root, the cord delay is reduced to about 0.9 millisecond, which allows only a single synaptic delay. When the reflex muscular response to nerve stimulation is monitored electromyographically, the over-all latency is 19 to 24 milliseconds; this is also approximately the latency of the contraction elicited by tendon tap.[11] In both man and experimental animals, therefore, it is clearly established that the tendon jerk is mediated by a rapidly conducting monosynaptic arc.

The Stretch or Myotatic Reflex.[23, 24] The functional significance of the flexion reflex as a protective mechanism is obvious. In contrast, the significance of the tendon jerk is, at first thought, obscure. What can be the functional utility of a reflex that causes a muscle to twitch when its tendon is sharply rapped? The obscurity arises largely from the abnormal way in which the tendon jerk is elicited. It has already been suggested, and will be further proved below, that the adequate stimulus for the reflex mechanism mediating the tendon jerk is *stretch of the muscle*. Tapping the tendon or belly of the muscle to elicit the tendon jerk stretches the muscle between its points of origin and insertion only very briefly. The stretch-sensitive receptors in the muscle are excited synchronously, and, since the afferent pathway is relatively homogeneous in fiber diameter and conduction velocity, the afferent impulses arrive at the spinal cord as a rather synchronous volley. As a result, the motoneurons respond with little temporal dispersion, setting up in the motor nerve a synchronous discharge to which the muscle responds with a brief twitch much like the response of the muscle to a single electric shock to its motor nerve.

Normally, however, the stretches imposed on muscles are of a different nature. Indeed, except possibly for landing from a leap or jumping on a pogostick, it is unlikely that muscles are ever subjected to the sudden brief stretches that the neurologist commonly employs in eliciting a jerk reflex. Natural stretches are usually imposed on muscles by the action of gravity. Thus, during standing, the quadriceps muscle is subjected to stretch because the knee tends to bend

in accordance with gravitational pull. The resultant afferent discharge is highly asynchronous, because such a sustained stretch causes many stretch receptors to fire repetitively at frequencies which are determined by the thresholds of individual receptors and by the amount of stretch. Consequently, the motoneurons receive a prolonged asynchronous bombardment, and they discharge impulses with corresponding asynchrony. The result is a smooth, sustained contraction of the stretched muscle, so that the upright position is automatically maintained despite the action of gravity. When viewed in this light, the stretch reflex, of which the tendon jerk is a fractional and somewhat artificial manifestation, clearly is significant as a *mechanism for upright posture or standing*.

The role of the stretch reflex in posture was first appreciated by Sherrington[36] as a result of his observations on animals subjected to transection of the brain stem at the midcollicular level. In such *decerebrate* preparations the limbs assume a posture of rigid extension, the head and tail are held erect, and the jaw is tightly closed by tonic contraction of the masseter muscle. Although the animal executes no voluntary movements, it will, when placed upon its feet, stand in a rigid, immobile exaggeration of the normal upright posture. Sherrington[39] rightly surmised that such decerebrate rigidity resulted from overactivity of a spinal reflex mechanism that normally maintains upright posture. The overactivity results from interruption by the lesion of certain descending pathways (described in Chapter 9) which exert an inhibitory influence on the segmental spinal reflex.

Sherrington proved his hypothesis that decerebrate rigidity is a spinal reflex by demonstrating that division of the dorsal roots supplying a rigid limb abolishes its rigidity.[36] He next attempted to determine the origin of the requisite afferent inflow from the limb.[40] Section of cutaneous-nerves, or even skinning the legs and feet, did not alter the rigid state, findings indicating that the essential receptors are not cutaneous. Furthermore, when the joint was flexed after the tendons of its controlling muscles were cut, the freed muscles did not contract. This observation indicated that the receptors are not located in the joints. When, however, the tenotomized muscle was stretched by a sustained pull on the severed tendon, the muscle contracted and offered palpable resistance to stretch. By the process of exclusion,

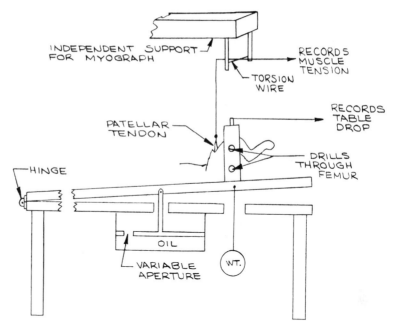

Fig. 6. Diagram of "fall table" similar to that used by Sherrington to demonstrate the stretch reflex.

Sherrington thus deduced that the receptors lie in the muscle itself and, further, that the adequate stimulus for the receptors is stretch of the muscle. Many sensory receptors, such as the retina, the ear and the tactile endings, are acted upon by agents of the external world. The stretch receptors of muscle, however, are excited by events occurring in the muscles themselves; the body itself acts as the stimulus to its own receptors. For this reason, Sherrington[40] termed the muscle stretch receptors *proprioceptors*.

To study the stretch reflex quantitatively, Sherrington constructed an ingenious device known as the "fall table,"[23, 24] the important feature of which was a top which could be lowered for measured distances at various rates (Fig. 6). The leg of an experimental animal was fixed rigidly to a stand on the table by means of drills passed through the bones of the leg. A muscle of the fixed leg was then dissected free and attached to a myograph mounted on a stand independent of the movable table top. Then, when the table top was lowered, the tension developing in the muscle in response to its elongation could be recorded. Figure 7 shows the results of such an experiment. The dotted line T indicates the extent of the table displacement; the heavy line M shows the tension developed in the muscle. Elongation of the muscle by only 8 mm. produced a sustained tension, initially amounting to 3.5 kg. and then decreasing to a stable plateau value of about 3.0 kg. Some of this tension was, of course, attributable

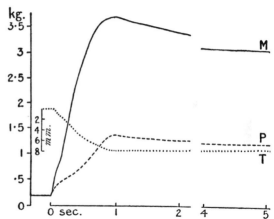

Fig. 7. Stretch or myotatic reflex of cat demonstrated with "fall table." *M,* Tension developed in innervated quadriceps muscle. *T,* Relative elevation of table, which was dropped 8 mm. *P,* Passive elastic tension developed by similar stretch after denervation of the muscle. Tension difference $(M - P)$ represents active reflex tension. (From Liddell and Sherrington, *Proc. roy. Soc.*, 1924, *B96*:212–242.)

to the elastic properties of the muscle, but this moiety could be quantitatively determined by repeating the stretch after denervation of the muscle (dashed line P). The difference between curves M and P (about 1.8 kg. at the plateau) represents the *reflex* contractile tension developed in the muscle by stretch.

The same experimental arrangement can also be used to show that the stretch reflex is subject to inhibition. Figure 8 illustrates inhibition of the stretch reflex in a knee extensor in-

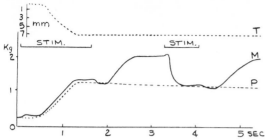

Fig. 8. Inhibition of stretch reflex in an extensor muscle by stimulation of an ipsilateral cutaneous nerve (afferent). *M, P* and *T* as in Fig. 7. During stimulation of cutaneous nerve, tension in innervated muscle was approximately the same as that in denervated muscle; in absence of inhibitory stimulation reflex tension of about 1 kg. (*M − P*) slowly developed. (After Liddell and Sherrington, *Proc. roy. Soc.,* 1924, *B96:*212–242.)

duced by repetitive stimulation of an ipsilateral cutaneous nerve trunk. This effect is comparable to inhibition of the knee jerk (Fig. 3) and of the monosynaptic discharge (Fig. 17, Chap. 6) induced by electrical stimulation of cutaneous afferent fibers. Figure 9 shows inhibition of a stretch reflex in an extensor muscle brought about by a physiologic stimulus—stretching of an antagonistic flexor muscle. The result is reminiscent of the inhibition of a monosynaptic discharge by stimuli traversing the heteronymous antagonistic Group I pathway (Fig. 16, Chap. 6).

Sherrington's experiments thus proved conclusively the existence of a reflex mechanism for posture and for skeletal muscle tone. By *tone* is meant the resistance of a muscle to passive elongation or stretch. When the stretch reflex arc is interrupted or when the descending central pathways facilitating the stretch reflex are severed, the muscle becomes flaccid or hypotonic, and offers little resistance to stretch. On the other hand, when central structures inhibitory to the stretch reflex are removed, as in the decerebrate preparation, the muscles are hypertonic and resist elongation so actively that passive flexion of the joint meets with marked resistance.

In man, such hypertonic stretch reflexes are commonly encountered following chronic lesions of the internal capsule, and the affected limb is said to be *spastic.* In both spasticity and decerebrate rigidity, the hypertonus is confined to the antigravity muscles, or physiologic extensors. In spastic man and monkey, passive flexion of a joint resulting in stretch of extensor

muscles at the ankle, knee or hip meets active resistance, but passive extension of these joints is accomplished without opposition. In the arm, resistance is most prominently displayed in the anatomic flexor muscles, for these are the muscles which counteract the forces of gravity. In the sloth, which habitually counteracts gravity with flexor muscles while hanging upside down from branches, decerebration produces a flexor rigidity. In quadrupeds that normally maintain upright posture (cat, dog), decerebrate rigidity principally affects the extensor muscles of both the front and the back legs. Indeed, in the decerebrate cat, a sustained stretch reflex from hindlimb flexor muscles cannot be elicited by the fall table technique. The flexor muscles respond readily to the synchronous volley elicited by a tap on the tendon (pluck reflex), but do not give sustained reflex contractions in response to the asynchronous afferent bombardment provided by the sustained stretches imposed by the fall table. It seems likely that the selective distribution of hypertonus to the antigravity muscles in the decerebrate and spastic states reflects the reciprocal connections of the descending pathways maintaining the hyperexcitable state, since the segmental mechanism for stretch reflexes appears to be as well developed in flexor as in extensor muscles.

Since the jerk reflex and the static stretch reflex utilize exactly the same pathways, it may seem strange that flexor muscles display the former but not the latter. The differentiation results from the nature of the stimulus, the opportunities for effective summation at the motoneuron pool being far greater with synchro-

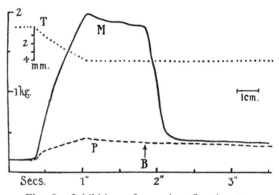

Fig. 9. Inhibition of stretch reflex in extensor muscle (quadriceps) by stretch of antagonistic flexor muscle (biceps femoris). *M, P* and *T* as in Fig. 7. At arrow (*B*) a 4 mm. stretch was applied to biceps femoris inhibiting quadriceps so that tension fell to that of paralyzed muscle. (From Liddell and Sherrington, *Proc. roy. Soc.,* 1925, *B97:*267–283.)

nous (tendon tap) than with asynchronous (slow stretch) inputs. In fact, synchronous inputs are so effective that a relatively severe reflex depression may not be obvious from tests of the tendon jerks alone. For example, after spinal transection in the cat, the lower extremities become flaccid and never again display a sustained stretch reflex;[27] but tendon jerks, although their nature is somewhat altered, are easily elicited. The tendon jerk taken alone is a gross and blunt diagnostic tool.

Receptors in Muscle and Tendon.[2,4]   Sherrington's studies of the stretch reflex implicated a stretch-sensitive receptor located in either the muscle or the tendon. Muscles and tendons are supplied with a variety of receptors—free nerve endings, encapsulated pacinian corpuscles, etc. —but with regard to postural reflexes, attention focuses principally on the *Golgi tendon organ* and the *muscle spindle*. The tendon organ is found in the tendons of all mammalian muscles, close to their muscular origins. The organ consists of a number of tendon fasciculi enclosed in a fusiform or cylindrical fibrous capsule which is penetrated by one or two myelinated nerve fibers (Fig. 10). After entering the capsule, the fibers break up into smaller and smaller branches, lose their myelin sheaths, and terminate in a rich arborization in the tendon bundle. Tension on the tendon distorts or displaces these endings and constitutes the adequate stimulus for receptor discharge. Because of its location in the tendon, the tendon organ is equally susceptible to, and does not distinguish between, mechanical stretch applied by a passive pull on the muscle and that applied by active muscular contraction, both being actions which exert tension on the tendon. The Golgi tendon organ is, as Fulton and Pi-Suñer[8] first emphasized, in "series" with the muscle (Fig. 11*B*).

The muscle spindle[2] is located within the muscle itself, and consists of a bundle of two to ten thin specialized muscle fibers (*intrafusal fibers*) surrounded by a connective tissue capsule which attaches (at its ends) to the endomysium of the regular or *extrafusal* muscle fibers, to the tendon, or to perimysial connective tissue (Fig. 12). The long, slender ends of the intrafusal fibers are striated and contractile, whereas the central or equatorial region, which is somewhat expanded and filled with nuclei, is unstriated and probably noncontractile. In this *nuclear bag* region of the spindle, and for a short distance on either side where nuclei are arranged in a central core (*myotube region*), the connective tissue capsule is separated from the intrafusal fibers by a lymph space traversed by delicate septa and nerve fibers. The latter are of three major types:[2] (i) Large (8 to 12 μ)* myelinated afferent fibers which, after entering the capsule, branch, lose their myelin and end in helical terminals that encircle the nuclear bag region of the intrafusal fibers. These endings are variously known as *annulospiral, primary* or *nuclear bag endings*. (ii) Smaller (6 to 9 μ) myelinated afferent fibers end in coils, rings or varicosities in the myotube regions on one or both sides of the nuclear bag endings. These are called *flower spray, secondary* or *myotube endings*. Some spindles lack myotube endings. Both the myotube and the nuclear bag endings degenerate after section of the dorsal roots. (iii) Small (3 to 7 μ) myelinated efferent fibers terminate in end-plates situated on the striated poles of the intrafusal fibers. These fibers are known to be motor, because they degenerate following ventral rhizotomy but not after dorsal root section. According to Barker,[2] both poles of the intrafusal fibers receive motor innervation. The functional significance of these *fusimotor fibers* or *gamma efferents* is discussed later in this chapter.

In addition to these three main types of fibers, muscle spindles receive a varying number of fine (0.5 μ) fibers, some of which appear

---

* The fiber diameters quoted here are measurements of the axons close to the spindle where they may well be smaller than the parent axons in the main nerve trunk.

Fig. 10. Golgi tendon organ. At left, muscle fibers (*m*) end in tendon bundles (*t*) that extend to right near the junction of muscle and tendon. Two nerve fibers (*n*) pass to tendon and branch profusely between and around the tendon bundles forming the end organ (*G*).

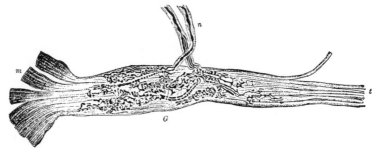

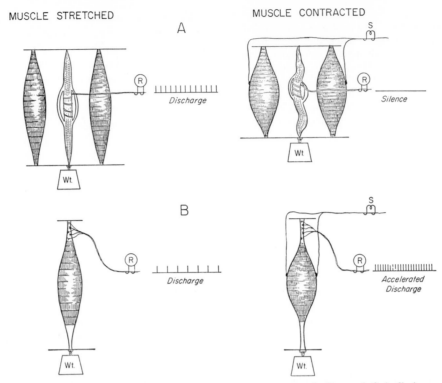

Fig. 11. Relation of muscle spindles and tendon organs to muscle fibers. *A,* Spindle is arranged "in parallel" with muscle fibers so that muscle contraction slackens tension on spindle. *B,* Tendon organ is arranged "in series" with muscle fibers so that both passive and active contraction of muscle cause receptor to discharge.

to be the sympathetic motor nerves for the vasculature of the spindles; others, which are afferent, ramify in the capsule as free nerve endings and probably mediate pain sensation.

From a study of teased stained spindles, Boyd[4] finds that intrafusal fibers are of two types distinguishable on the basis of structure, rate of atrophy following ventral root section, and type of innervation. *Nuclear bag fibers,* usually about two to a spindle, are relatively large (25 μ diameter) and long (7 to 8 mm.), stretching the full length of the spindle. In the equatorial region they have a prominent nuclear bag and, in the polar regions, a large number of myofibrils uniformly distributed in scant sarcoplasm. They degenerate slowly following ventral root section. *Nuclear chain fibers* are more numerous (usually 4 to 5 per spindle), smaller (12 μ diameter) and shorter (4 mm.); their ends attach to the surface of the nuclear bag fibers. In the equatorial region they display a single chain of nuclei, whence they derive their name. Myofibrils are less numerous and more variable in size and distribution than in nuclear bag fibers. They degenerate promptly following ventral rhizotomy.

Primary endings are distributed to both nuclear chain and nuclear bag fibers, but secondary endings are principally on nuclear chain fibers. Motor innervation of the two types of fiber also differs. Nuclear bag

fibers have 1 to 6 discrete end-plates at the extreme poles; these are supplied by the larger (2.5 to 4.5 μ) fusimotor terminals. Nuclear chain fibers are innervated by smaller (1 to 2 μ) fusimotor fibers which terminate all along the surfaces (except at the site of the primary ending) in a fine, complicated network lacking discrete end-plates.

To return to the afferent endings of the spindle, both the myotube and the nuclear bag endings are so arranged that they can easily be mechanically distorted by stretch of the muscle. However, unlike the Golgi tendon organ, the muscle spindle is arranged in "parallel" with the extrafusal fibers, so that contraction of the extrafusal fibers tends to remove spindle tension induced by external stretch (Fig. 11*A*). In the next section it will be pointed out that this feature permits experimental distinction between spindle endings and Golgi tendon endings merely by observation of the effect of muscle contraction on a stretch-evoked discharge recorded from their parent axons. It should also be noted, however, that if the intrafusal fibers are made to contract by action of the small motor nerve fibers supplying the two contractile poles, the noncontractile nuclear bag region is put under a tension which constitutes a mechanical stimulus to the nuclear bag and myotube endings equivalent to passive stretch of the whole muscle.

DISCHARGE PROPERTIES OF STRETCH RECEPTORS.[28]   The discharge properties of stretch receptors can be studied by recording from their parent axons during muscle stretch. If activity in a whole nerve trunk is recorded, the tracing shows only a chaotic flare of spike-like activity during muscle stretch, because the stimulus excites many end organs which fire out of phase with one another. Such records are usually too complex for analysis. Records satisfactory for analysis can be obtained by isolating one or, at most, a few axons supplying active receptors. Such "single unit" analysis of stretch receptors was first accomplished by Adrian and Zotterman[1] in 1926. They chose to study certain small muscles in the frog which have only a few stretch receptors. By successively paring off bits of the muscle, Adrian and Zotterman were able to whittle away all but one stretch receptor, the activity of which could be recorded in the nerve trunk supplying the muscle. In larger mammalian muscles, this technique for reducing the number of receptors is unsatisfactory, owing to the extensive injury incurred by the drastic carving of the muscle. Matthews[28] obtained the first successful recordings from stretch receptors in cats by subdividing the nerve trunk into small bundles until he isolated a strand containing only one axon which fired in response to muscle stretch. Successful isolation of a single stretch-sensitive unit is recognized by the occurrence during muscle stretch of rhythmically recurring, all-or-nothing spikes of constant amplitude and configuration. Stretch-sensitive units may also be isolated from the dorsal roots, where the rootlets are easily divided into strands. Another satisfactory method,[41] which eliminates the necessity for nerve teasing, is intracellular recording with an ultramicroelectrode in the nerve trunk, the dorsal root or the dorsal column, for an intracellular electrode is not appreciably affected by activity in adjacent fibers.

All stretch-sensitive units have properties in common. All respond to stretch with a regular rhythmic discharge of impulses. The rate of firing is somewhat higher during and immediately after the imposition of stretch, but the discharge rate rapidly reaches a relatively steady level,

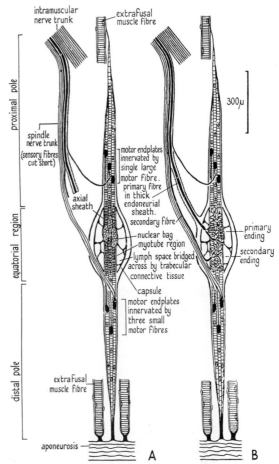

Fig. 12.   The muscle spindle and its nerves. *A* shows only the motor fibers (fusimotor fibers) innervating the intrafusal fibers; *B* shows in addition the afferent fibers and their termination in the equatorial or "nuclear bag" region. (From Barker, *Quart. J. micr. Sci.,* 1948, *89*:143–186.)

which is maintained for hours if the muscle stretch is held constant. When the tension on the muscle is increased, the number of impulses per unit time increases, but not in a linear fashion. The firing rate is approximately directly proportional to the log of the applied muscle tension.* *Discharge frequency is thus one way by which the receptor signals intensity of stimulus to the central nervous system* (see Chap. 4).

If the monitored strand of fibers contains several axons supplying stretch receptors, another correlate of intensity becomes evident. *As stimulus intensity is increased, the number of units re-*

* This relationship holds only within a limited range of applied tensions. At high tensions, the response falls short of the expected proportionality. Moreover, for different receptors, the slopes of the curves relating discharge rate to log tension are different.

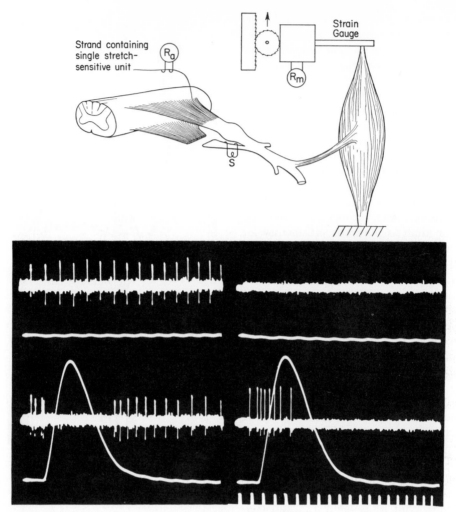

Fig. 13.   Behavior of spindle (A type) and tendon organ (B type) receptors during muscle stretch and muscle contraction. In the tracings the thick line is record from dorsal root strand (R_a in diagram); the thin line is record of muscle tension (R_m) in diagram. *Left,* A type discharge from spindle receptor. In upper record, moderate sustained stretch of muscle induced by moving tension recorder upward elicited regular rhythmic discharge of receptor. In lower record, discharge ceased during muscle twitch induced by single shock to ventral root at S in diagram. *Right,* B type discharge from tendon receptor. In upper trace, moderate muscle stretch failed to discharge high-threshold tendon organ. In lower trace, discharge occurred during muscle twitch. (Records provided by Dr. C. C. Hunt.)

sponding increases. The thresholds of stretch receptors are distributed in accordance with a normal frequency curve, so that an increase in the intensity of the stimulus, i.e., muscle stretch, recruits additional units.* Each of these receptors fires at a frequency which is determined by the extent to which the stimulus exceeds the

*Receptor variation in threshold is due partly to true variance in sensitivity to stretch and partly to variance in location in the muscle, some receptors bearing more of the brunt of muscle stretch than others.

threshold of the individual receptor. These two intensity-signaling variables—number of active units and frequency of unit discharge—account for the grading of reflex response to various degrees of stretch. It has already been pointed out in Chapter 4 that these properties are also found in other receptors.

Of more interest for the present discussion are the unique properties of different stretch receptors. Matthews[28] found that the stretch-sensitive receptors of muscle can be divided into two general types, designated A and B, which differ principally in their behavior during active muscle contraction. Units of the A type typically have a low threshold to muscle stretch, 1 to 2 grams of tension often being sufficient to evoke a sustained rhythmic discharge. If, during such a stretch-evoked sustained discharge, a twitch contraction of the stretched muscle is elicited by a single shock to the ventral root, the discharge *ceases* during the twitch (Fig. 13, *left*). The A receptor thus behaves as if it were in "parallel" with the contractile extrafusal fibers, so that contraction, by shortening* the muscle, removes the tension from the receptors (Fig. 11*A*). It will be recalled that the muscle spindle is anatomically arranged in parallel with the muscle fibers. In addition, the position of a unit under observation can be roughly localized by pressing on the muscle with a glass rod while the muscle is stretched, for such local mechanical distortion excites the receptors. Local warming, which accelerates the discharge of a firing unit, also serves to localize the unit. In these ways, Matthews[28] found that receptors of the A type lie in the belly of the muscle or near its top insertion, but never in the tendon. For these reasons, it seems almost certain that units of the A type are spindle endings.

In contrast to the A type or spindle ending, the units which Matthews labeled B consistently display *accelerated firing* during muscle contraction (Fig. 13, *right*). Another difference is that B receptors have relatively high thresholds to muscle stretch, usually requiring tensions of 100 to 200 grams or more for sustained firing. Consequently, when the tension on the muscle is slight but adequate to excite A endings, the B endings may not fire unless the muscle is caused to contract. Upon contraction of the muscle, a burst of spikes occurs during the twitch. The behavior of B units therefore is that of receptors arranged in "series" with the muscle, and anatomically the Golgi tendon organ fulfills this requirement. Further, Matthews found by local probing and warming that B units are located either in the tendon or in the musculotendinous junction where the Golgi tendon organ is found histologically.

The presence or absence of a silent period in unit discharge during muscle contraction can

* Discharges of A units cease during muscle contraction even when the twitch is isometric, presumably because the tendon is somewhat elastic so that even under isometric recording conditions some internal shortening occurs during a twitch.

thus be used experimentally to distinguish between spindle endings and tendon receptors. The strength of the contraction-producing stimulus to the ventral root is important, however. In A receptors, a single shock to the ventral root adequate to cause only a submaximal or, at most, a maximal isometric muscle twitch results in cessation of discharge during the twitch. If, however, the shocks are supramaximal (i.e., more intense than is required for development of maximal contractile tension), and particularly if they are delivered repetitively, the rate of discharge of the A unit may increase during contraction of the muscle. In other words, when the motor fibers are stimulated supramaximally, the A unit behaves as if it were in series with the muscle. As will be shown later, such stimulation activates the small, high threshold fusimotor fibers that are distributed exclusively to the intrafusal muscle fibers. The resulting contraction of intrafusal muscle fibers does not add detectably to the total muscle tension but markedly influences the spindle endings, because they are in series with the intrafusal fibers, so that contraction of the two poles of the intrafusal fibers takes up slack in the spindle caused by extrafusal contraction and puts the spindle endings under tension.†

AFFERENT FIBERS SUPPLYING STRETCH RECEPTORS. As just described, the differential behavior of receptors during muscle contraction permits recognition of spindle and tendon endings. Once a unit has been isolated and classified, its conduction velocity can be measured; in turn, the diameter of the axon supplying it can be estimated, for the axon diameter in microns is linearly related to the conduction rate in meters per second, the ratio being 6:1 (cf. Chap. 3). Hunt[14] isolated and classified several hundred stretch-sensitive units from cat soleus

† Hunt and Kuffler[15] point out that A units may occasionally discharge during contractions set up by motor volleys too weak to excite fusimotor fibers, especially if the contraction occurs under rigidly isometric conditions and when the initial tension on the muscle is high. Such deviant responses are thought to be due to some unusual distribution of tension within the muscle that increases the amount of stretch deformation on some spindle endings. By varying the conditions, the experimenter can always demonstrate the silent period of such elements, so that there is never serious difficulty in distinguishing them from B endings, which show accelerated discharge during contraction under all conditions.

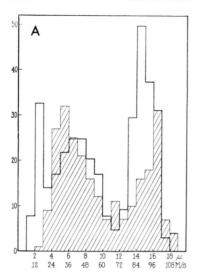

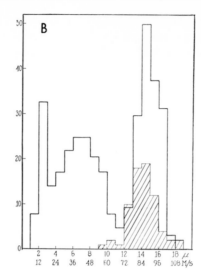

Fig. 14. Diameter distribution of afferent fibers supplying muscle spindles (*A*) and tendon organs (*B*). Heavy line in each graph plots diameter distribution of myelinated afferent fibers as determined histologically. Hatched area plots distribution of fibers supplying muscle spindles in *A* and tendon organs in *B* as determined by physiologic testing. *Ordinates,* Number of fibers in each 1 μ category. *Abscissae,* Diameter in μ and conduction rate in m. per sec. (After Hunt, *J. gen. Physiol.,* 1954, *38*:117–131.)

and gastrocnemius muscles by painstakingly dissecting and sampling the dorsal roots. The conduction rate in the axon was determined by electrically exciting the nerve trunk and measuring conduction time and distance to the dorsal root. The diameter was then computed by dividing the conduction rate by 6.

Figure 14*A* shows the distribution of computed axon diameters for spindle (A) endings of soleus muscle superposed on the afferent fiber distribution of the soleus nerve as determined histologically. Spindle endings fall into a bimodal distribution accounting for approximately half of the Group I fibers (12 to 20 μ) and for virtually all of the Group II fibers (4 to 12 μ) in the nerve. Because the fibers supplying the annulospiral or nuclear bag endings appear to be larger than those supplying the secondary or myotube endings, it is logical to conclude that Group I fibers supplying A receptors (hereafter called *Group IA fibers*) supply annulospiral endings, whereas the Group II fibers of the muscle nerve probably supply myotube or secondary endings. Recently ingenious techniques have been devised whereby the behavior of primary and secondary endings of the same muscle spindle can be simultaneously studied.[3] Apart from conduction rate, only small distinction can be made between annulospiral endings innervated by Group IA fibers and myotube endings innervated by Group II fibers. Both display silent periods during muscle contraction and both are accelerated by fusimotor stimulation. Myotube endings have slightly higher thresholds to stretch than do annulospiral endings, but the difference is slight (about 19:3 grams).

Figure 14*B* shows the diameter distribution of axons supplying endings of the B type (Golgi tendon organ). The distribution is unimodal and essentially confined to the Group I diameter range (>12 μ). *Group I fibers supplying B endings are called IB fibers.* Tendon endings supplied by Group IB fibers not only differ markedly from spindle endings in their response to muscle contraction (acceleration versus silent period), but also have significantly higher thresholds to stretch (100 to 200 grams). Furthermore, tendon endings are completely uninfluenced by stimulation of fusimotor fibers.

Together, the Group IA fibers supplying annulospiral spindle endings and the Group IB fibers supplying Golgi tendon organs account satisfactorily for the entire Group I population of the nerve. The entire Group II population appears to be devoted to spindle endings, presumably those of the myotube or secondary type.

Stretch Reflex Receptor. A question now arises: Which of the three nerve endings in muscle subserves the stretch reflex? The secondary endings of the spindle, innervated by Group II afferent fibers, may be eliminated. The reflex pattern elicited by exciting Group II fibers, whether of spindle or cutaneous origin, is that of the multisynaptic flexion reflex, whereas the stretch reflex is a monosynaptic arc served by Group I afferent fibers. Both the annulospiral spindle endings and the Golgi tendon organ, however, are innervated by Group I fibers, and hence are equally likely candidates.

It is generally believed (but admittedly largely on the basis of indirect evidence) that the annulospiral rather than the tendon endings are the receptors for the myotatic reflex. The low threshold to muscle stretch of the annulospiral endings, as opposed to the very high thresholds of tendon organs, is a suggestive datum, since the stretch reflex is elicited by exceedingly minute stretches. Secondly, selectively eliminating tendon organs by locally anesthetizing or resecting the tendon does not abolish the stretch reflex or tendon jerk. Finally, on the electrical record of a muscle engaged in a tendon jerk, the initial synchronous burst of activity which slightly precedes the onset of mechanical contraction is followed by a period of electrical silence which coincides with the reflex shortening of the muscle and which ends coincident with relaxation of the muscle. This *silent period* during the tendon jerk probably results partly from cessation of the excitatory afferent input from the receptors during muscle shortening, an interpretation which accords well with the properties of spindle endings but not with those of tendon organs.

Although this interpretation is probably partly correct, the genesis of the silent period is more complex. Denny-Brown[7] found that the silent period involved not only the muscle engaged in the jerk but also the tonic electrical activity of other muscles which are not participating in the jerk. He suggested that, during the silent period, there occurs not only withdrawal of excitatory input but also initiation of an active inhibitory input which affects both the motoneurons supplying the stretched muscle and those innervating adjacent muscles.*

There are at least two possible sources for this inhibition. One of these is the recurrent collaterals described by Cajal and by Renshaw. Before emerging in the ventral root, many motor axons give off recurrent collaterals which terminate on interneurons situated in the ventromedial region of the ventral horn.[34] These interneurons, sometimes called "Renshaw cells" after their discoverer, make inhibitory connections with the motoneurons.[33] A synchronous

reflex discharge, such as that elicited by tendon tap, is thus directed not only over the motor axons to the muscle but also, through the recurrent collaterals, to the Renshaw cells, which in turn deliver a high frequency burst of inhibitory impulses to the motoneurons.

The other, and probably more important, source of inhibition accounting for the silent period is the Group IB fibers supplying the tendon organs. Before this pathway is described, it may be pointed out that the implication of tendon organs and Group IB fibers in a proprioceptive arc inhibitory to the homonymous motoneurons is, by exclusion, a further and compelling reason for believing that the Group IA fibers supplying the annulospiral spindle endings constitute the afferent limb of the stretch reflex.

The Clasp Knife Reflex; Autogenic Inhibition. When one attempts to flex forcibly the rigid limb of a decerebrate preparation, resistance is encountered as soon as the muscle is stretched and increases throughout the initial part of the bending. This resistance is, of course, due to the hyperactive reflex contraction of the muscle in response to stretch. If flexion be forcibly carried farther, a point is reached at which all resistance to additional flexion seems to melt and the previously rigid limb collapses readily. Because the action is one which permits the stretched muscle to elongate freely, it is appropriately called a *lengthening reaction*. Also, because the resistance of the limb resembles that of a spring-loaded folding knife blade, this phenomenon is often called the "clasp knife" reaction. A similar phenomenon is regularly observed in human patients with spasticity, in whom the reaction is often best elicited by rapidly and forcibly flexing the spastic limb. Under these conditions, the clasp knife reaction is manifested by a "catch and give" in the resistance, i.e., the muscle first resists, then relaxes. In either instance, it appears that excessive (or rapid) stretch of the muscle brings into play some new influence which temporarily or permanently annuls the stretch reflex and allows the muscle to be lengthened with little or no tonic resistance.

Strong stretch of an extensor muscle also abolishes or diminishes the reflex contraction of that muscle brought about by means other than stretch. For example, when an extensor muscle is reflexly contracting in response to stimulation of a contralateral cutaneous nerve (crossed extension reflex) and the muscle is forcibly

---

* Electrical silence in direct synergists of the stretched muscle might be explained on the basis of withdrawal of excitation. The silent period, however, has a much wider distribution in limb muscles and may actually be observed in muscles which operate on joints different from that governed by the stretched muscle. Since there are no known excitatory monosynaptic connections between muscles acting at different joints, some process other than withdrawal of excitatory input must be postulated.

stretched, it may suddenly give and lengthen without resistance.

Sherrington[37] demonstrated that the clasp knife phenomenon is reflex in nature and dependent upon stretch of the muscle. When the clasp knife reaction is elicited, not only does the stretched extensor muscle relax but its antagonists (flexors) contract. Often there is a concomitant contraction of the extensor muscles of the contralateral limb (*Phillipson's reflex*) indicating doubly reciprocal connections of the responsible afferent pathways. The clasp knife reflex can be elicited in a muscle after all other muscles and structures of the limb have been denervated. When deafferented by appropriate dorsal rhizotomy, the stretched muscle, of course, becomes flaccid, and there is no tone against which to test for the clasp knife reflex. The deafferented muscle can, however, still be activated reflexly by stimulation of a contralateral cutaneous nerve (crossed extension reflex); strongly stretching the deafferented muscle does not abolish such a crossed reflex contraction as it does in the intact preparation.

These observations indicate that, in addition to the classic stretch reflex already described, there exists a proprioceptive stretch reflex arc of relatively high threshold which inhibits its homonymous motoneurons. Such inhibition, mediated by afferent fibers from a stretched muscle and acting on motoneurons supplying the stretched muscle, is known as *autogenic inhibition*. It follows that during muscle stretch the motoneurons supplying the stretched muscles are bombarded by impulses delivered over two competing pathways, one excitatory and the other inhibitory. The output of the motoneuron pool depends upon the balance between the two antagonistic inputs. With excessive stretch, the high threshold inhibitory pathway becomes an increasingly potent determinant and eventually dominates the motoneuron pool. Functionally the inhibitory pathway serves to *protect the muscle from overload* by preventing damaging contraction against strong stretching forces.

The influence of autogenic inhibition is detectable at degrees of stretch less than that required to annul the stretch reflex completely. For example, Sherrington[6] noted in fall table experiments that the reflex contraction elicited by small or moderate muscle stretch (2 per cent increase in length) was maintained at a steady level for half an hour or longer. When the stretch imposed on the same muscle was greater

(4 to 5 per cent increase in length), the reflex contraction often faded in 5 to 10 minutes.

THE GOLGI TENDON ORGAN AND AUTOGENIC INHIBITION. There are a number of indications that Group IB fibers innervating the Golgi tendon organ constitute the afferent limb of the clasp knife reflex. The tendon organs are, of course, sensitive to stretch, which is the adequate stimulus for the clasp knife reflex. The relatively high threshold of the tendon organ to stretch accords well with the observation that the clasp knife reflex dominates the motoneurons only when muscle stretch is extreme.

McCouch et al.[29] showed that the quadriceps jerk could be inhibited by local electrical stimulation of the tendon or the musculotendinous junction of the vastus intermedius muscle, but not by similar stimulation of the muscle belly. Further indication that the tendon organ feeds a reflex arc inhibitory to the homonymous motoneurons derives from the experiments by Hunt[13] and by Granit.[9] They found that tetanic contraction of a muscle induced by repetitive stimulation of the distal end of the cut ventral root inhibited a monosynaptic reflex discharge set up by stimulation of the Group I afferent fibers from the muscle. Since during muscle contraction the spindle discharge ceases and the tendon-organ discharge is accelerated, it seems reasonable to ascribe this inhibition to activation of the tendon organs.

In man Libet et al.[22] found that the electromyographic response of tibialis anticus during voluntary contraction was 50 per cent less when the muscle was in a stretched position (ankle ventroflexed) than when it was at short length (ankle dorsiflexed). The finding is consistent with the interpretation that extreme stretch of the muscle, by exciting tendon receptors, provides an inhibitory input to the homonymous motoneurons making them less accessible to the excitatory impulses in descending pathways underlying voluntary contraction. In accordance with this interpretation, it was found that electromyographic amplitude was independent of muscle length when the tendon was infiltrated with procaine.

CENTRAL CONNECTIONS OF GROUP IB FIBERS. The evidence discussed in the previous section strongly implicates the Golgi tendon organs, and the Group IB fibers which supply them as the afferent limb of the clasp knife reflex. To study the central connections of the clasp knife reflex it is desirable to depart from the method of natural stimulation and resort to the conditioning-testing technique, using Group IB fibers for the conditioning pathway. A difficulty is encountered here, however, because Group IB and IA fibers are of the same or only slightly different diameters and electrical thresholds,* so that selective stimulation of IB fibers apart from IA fibers is difficult.

Despite this technical handicap, Laporte and Lloyd[20] were able to distinguish between the effects on motoneurons occasioned by afferent volleys conducted in Group IA fibers and those resulting from activation of Group IB fibers. This distinction is possible because, as will be developed below, the Group IB fibers have interposed between their presynaptic endings and the motoneuron a single interneuron. In other words, the clasp knife reflex mediated by Group IB fibers is a *disynaptic reflex arc*, whereas the myotatic reflex mediated by Group IA fibers is, of course, monosynaptic. In the monosynaptic pathway the threshold for influence upon the motoneurons is that of the Group IA fibers exerting the influence. In the disynaptic pathway, the threshold for influence upon the final elements, the motoneurons, depends not only upon the threshold of the Group IB fibers but also upon the response threshold of the intermediary elements, the interneurons. For this reason, although Group IA and IB fibers have similar thresholds, the conditioning volleys required to exert detectable influence upon the motoneurons via the Group IB fibers are somewhat greater than those required to demonstrate excitatory conditioning through the simpler monosynaptic pathway fed by Group IA afferent fibers.

Figure 15 shows the effect of conditioning a monosynaptic test reflex of the plantaris muscle by volleys of varied intensity delivered over the nerve supplying the synergistic muscle flexor longus digitorum. With a feeble conditioning volley, the monosynaptic facilitation curve (*closed circles*) typical of Group IA fibers was obtained. When the intensity of the conditioning volley was increased (*open circles*), the

* The threshold of axons to electrical stimulation should not be confused with the threshold of the reflex to natural stimulation via the appropriate sense organs. Thus, Group IA and IB fibers are equally accessible to electrical stimulation of the nerve trunk, but the spindle endings supplied by Group IA fibers are far more sensitive to natural stimulation (stretch) than are the tendon organs innervated by Group IB fibers.

earliest part of the curve was unaltered, but, when the interval between the conditioning and the test volley was 0.5 to 0.6 millisecond, the smooth decay of the facilitation curve was interrupted by the sudden onset of an inhibitory process, and the test response was reduced far below the control level. The 0.5 to 0.6 millisecond delay in the onset of the inhibitory action was constant irrespective of the length of the afferent pathway, and therefore cannot be explained by assuming that the inhibitory impulses traverse a more slowly conducting system of fibers than that responsible for facilitation. Rather, the delay must be due to an intercalated interneuron.

The third curve of Figure 15 (*crosses*) was obtained when the conditioning volley was so increased that it activated Group II as well as Group I afferent fibers. A second phase of inhibition appeared at a conditioning-test interval of about 2 milliseconds, clearly reflecting the delays resulting from the multisynaptic organization of Group II-fed reflex arcs.

When the Group IB disynaptic linkages of

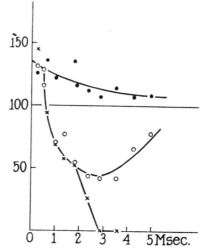

Fig. 15. Reflex conditioning of motoneurons by three intensities of afferent volley delivered over the heteronymous synergistic pathway. With weak Group I conditioning volleys the expected curve of facilitation was obtained (*filled circles*). When the intensity of the conditioning volley was slightly increased, the facilitation curve was interrupted at a conditioning-testing interval of 0.5 millisecond by a phase of inhibition (*open circles*). An additional increase in conditioning volley strength sufficient to activate Group II fibers (*crosses*) added a still later and more profound phase of inhibition beginning at a conditioning-testing interval of 2 milliseconds. (From Laporte and Lloyd, *Amer. J. Physiol.*, 1952, 169:609–621.)

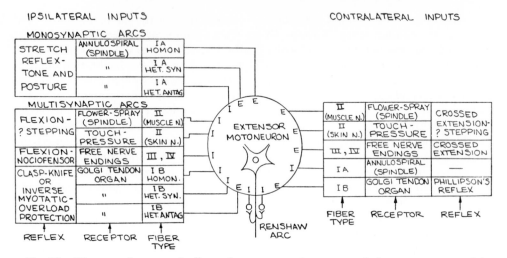

Fig. 16. Diagram of segmental afferent inputs converging on a typical motoneuron supplying an extensor muscle. The influence of each input is indicated as excitatory (*E*) or inhibitory (*I*).

various muscles are systematically studied, the following generalizations are reached. Group IB fibers form disynaptic inhibitory linkages with their homonymous motoneurons and with the motoneurons supplying synergists of the muscle from which they arise. On the other hand, Group IB volleys facilitate, through disynaptic linkages, the motoneurons supplying muscles antagonistic to those from which the afferent volley originates. In other words, the reciprocal connections of Group IB are just the opposite of those typical of Group IA fibers. For this reason, the clasp knife reflex is sometimes referred to as the *inverse myotatic reflex*. The reciprocal connections of the Group IB fibers, however, are somewhat more diffuse than those of the monosynaptic arcs arising in Group IA fibers, for the former may exert, through disynaptic linkages, inhibitory influences on motoneurons supplying muscles which are not direct antagonists of the muscle of origin. For example, a Group IB afferent volley set up in the quadriceps (knee extensor) nerve inhibits, through the disynaptic pathway, the motoneurons supplying the triceps surae (ankle extensor). This phenomenon is in marked contrast to the connections of Group IA fibers which are confined to the motoneurons supplying muscles acting around a single joint.

Summary of Reflex Pathways. At this juncture it is profitable to examine as a whole the segmental afferent inputs to a typical spinal motoneuron. Figure 16 summarizes diagrammatically the various pathways which play upon a spinal motoneuron supplying an extensor muscle. A corresponding diagram of the inputs to a flexor motoneuron would be identical, except that the influence of the multisynaptic paths fed by cutaneous and by Group II, III and IV fibers would be reversed. The striking feature of Figure 16 is the multiplicity of pathways which converge on the final common pathway, the motoneuron. In point of fact, Figure 16 gives but a limited picture of this convergence, for only the segmental inputs are shown. Omitted (for discussion in Chap. 9) are the numerous pathways which arise from other spinal segments and from supraspinal structures and which terminate directly or indirectly upon the motoneuron. Each neuron is thus subjected to a multitude of influences, some reinforcing and some antagonistic, and the balance of these influences at any time determines the membrane potential and hence the excitability of the cell. The motoneuron, the final common path of the arc, thus integrates the messages which impinge upon it.

A persistent problem in neurophysiology has been the apparent hopelessness of explaining complex behavior in terms of what, in axons, appears to be a stereotyped inflexible response —the action potential. Now it can be seen that the system as diagrammed in Figure 16 is a highly flexible machine in which shifts in the intensity and source of afferent bombardment arising from numerous different receptors may alter drastically the participation of the different motoneurons and their subservient muscles in reflex action and thus give rise to an infinite variety of behavioral patterns.

The Fusimotor Fibers and Spindle Regulation.[18, 19, 21] In the preceding sections, attention was focused on the influence exerted by various receptor organs upon the motoneurons. To complete the picture, it is now profitable to consider the influence exerted by certain motoneurons upon a receptor, the muscle spindle. It has already been mentioned that the intrafusal fibers of the muscle spindle receive a motor innervation that typically supplies both contractile poles of the fiber. It is easy to visualize how activation of the fusimotor fibers by inducing polar contraction of the intrafusal fibers might put the noncontractile nuclear bag region under tension and thus produce in the receptor endings a mechanical distortion indistinguishable from that occasioned by passive stretch of the whole muscle. In this way, the fusimotor fibers may initiate spindle discharge in the absence of external stretch or, in the presence of stretch, so increase the sensitivity of the spindle that the frequency of afferent discharge is markedly increased. The fusimotor system thus serves as a biasing mechanism regulating the sensitivity of the receptor.

That the fusimotor fibers constitute a specialized efferent pathway distinguishable from that supplying the extrafusal muscle fibers was first proposed by Leksell.[21] Examination of the myelinated fiber spectrum of a ventral root or of a muscle nerve deafferented by degenerative dorsal rhizotomy reveals that the efferent fibers fall into two distinct size categories (Fig. 17). One group, constituting about 70 per cent of the total, ranges in diameter from about 8 to 13 μ, and thus falls approximately in the A-alpha classification of Gasser. The remaining 30 per cent of the myelinated motor fibers, ranging from about 3 to 8 μ in diameter with a peak cluster at 5 μ, are designated gamma efferents.* The absence of overlap between the two groups makes them relatively easy to distinguish. Figure 17 shows action potentials recorded from the gastrocnemius nerve following stimulation of the S_2 ventral root. In the upper trace, the stimulus was just maximal for the large low threshold alpha fibers. The lower figure shows a trace taken when the stimulus strength was increased sufficiently to recruit the smaller

gamma fibers. The peak conduction velocity of the first deflection was 76 m. per second; that for smaller and later deflection was 27 m. per second. The computed fiber diameters corresponding to these velocities are about 13 μ and 5 μ, respectively—values which agree satisfactorily with the histologic data.

Leksell noted that, when the muscle nerve was stimulated with graded shocks, twitch tension of the muscle was directly related to shock strength only until the alpha spike reached full size; further increase in shock strength caused no further increment in muscle tension, even though such strong shocks resulted in the appearance and growth of the gamma spike. In other words, the gamma fibers appeared to contribute nothing to contractile tension. This conclusion can be tested in another way. When pressure is applied to a nerve trunk, the larger fibers are blocked before the smaller ones are. Leksell found that when the alpha fibers were thus differentially blocked, stimulation central to the block produced little or no contractile response in the muscle, even though electrical recording from the nerve trunk distal to the block showed that conduction in the small gamma fibers was unaltered. It may therefore be concluded that the gamma fibers constitute a discrete efferent system innervating some structure in the muscle other than the ordinary tension-producing extrafusal muscle fibers.

It is now clear that the gamma efferent fibers are distributed *exclusively* to the spindle intra-

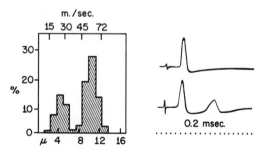

Fig. 17. Diameter spectrum and compound action potential of motor fibers supplying soleus. *Left,* Note distinct bimodal distribution of fiber diameters. Velocity spectrum shown on upper ordinates. *Right upper trace,* Compound action potential elicited by stimulus just maximal for large-diameter, rapidly conducting fibers. *Right lower trace,* Stronger stimulus elicited a second deflection ascribable to activity in the small slowly-conducting fibers. (Histologic data after Eccles and Sherrington, *Proc. roy. Soc.,* 1930, *B106*:326–357; electrical data after Kuffler *et al., J. Neurophysiol.,* 1951, *14*:28–54.)

---

* In some deafferented muscle nerves the gamma cluster is divisible into two subclusters: $gamma_1$ (4 to 8 μ) and $gamma_2$ (1 to 4 μ). The larger fibers are said to innervate nuclear bag fibers; the smaller, nuclear chain fibers.[5]

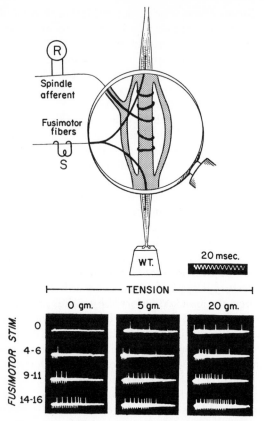

Fig. 18. Effects of tension and fusimotor stimulation on discharge rate of spindle ending. Upward deflections in traces are action potentials of a single isolated spindle afferent fiber. Small deflections below the baseline in some records are shock artifacts produced by stimulating fusimotor fibers. Note that discharge rate depends on both passive tension and fusimotor activity. (After Kuffler *et al., J. Neurophysiol.,* 1951, *14*:29–54.)

but also upon the number of impulses reaching the spindle via the fusimotor fibers. Each spindle receives up to fifteen such fusimotor fibers, which provide a precise mechanism for grading through a considerable range the sensitivity of the receptor to stretch. Also, each individual fusimotor fiber, by branching, participates in the innervation of several spindles, and can thus influence the discharge in a number of afferent fibers from different spindles.

It has already been mentioned that spindle receptors cease firing during muscle contraction. This pause comes about because the intrafusal fibers are arranged in parallel with the extrafusal fibers, so that shortening of the latter removes tension from the spindle. If, however, there is concomitant activation of the fusimotor system sufficient to take up the slack in the intrafusal fibers, the spindle endings may continue to discharge even during contraction. Figure 19 illustrates an experimental demonstration of this phenomenon. The upper trace shows the regular rhythmic firing of an A spindle receptor in response to a maintained 15 gram stretch on the muscle. In the middle trace, the muscle was caused to contract by stimulation of a portion of the ventral root containing only alpha efferent fibers; during the contraction, the spindle discharge ceased. For the bottom tracing, this same sequence was repeated, except that, in addition, a single fusimotor fiber supplying the spindle was stimulated nine times during the early part of the contraction. As a result of fusimotor stimulation, spindle discharge continued throughout the contraction. It may be inferred from such experiments that, in the intact animal, spindle behavior during muscular contraction is determined by the amount of fusimotor activity as well as by the extent of muscle shortening.

REFLEX ACTIVITY OF THE FUSIMOTOR SYSTEM. The discovery of the fusimotor system necessitates reconsideration of the mechanism of the stretch reflex. It will be recognized that the stretch reflex system in the intact animal is composed of a "peripheral loop" of nerve fibers, represented diagrammatically in Figure 20. On the motor side of the loop are the alpha and gamma fibers, both of which influence in unique ways the discharge behavior of the spindle receptors. On the afferent side of the loop, various receptors play back upon and reflexly influence the discharge of both the alpha and gamma systems. It follows that investiga-

fusal fibers, hence the term "fusimotor fibers."[17] Fusimotor activation causes contractions of the intrafusal fibers that are too feeble to add significantly to the total muscle tension but are sufficient to affect profoundly the afferent discharge of the spindle. This effect was demonstrated by Leksell, but more precisely by Kuffler *et al.,*[19] who dissected out for stimulation single fusimotor fibers in the ventral root. Figure 18 shows the effect of fusimotor activity on a single stretch receptor subjected to varying degrees of stretch. At each level of passive stretch the frequency of afferent discharge was accelerated by fusimotor stimulation, and the degree of acceleration increased with the number of fusimotor volleys delivered to the spindle. It is clear therefore that the afferent discharge of the spindle depends not only upon stretch

tions involving the common experimental procedure of dividing ventral or dorsal roots may yield accurate information about the properties of the individual components of the stretch reflex system, e.g., the spindle receptors; but, because the loop is broken, such experiments give a rather distorted picture of the behavior of these components in the intact animal. A measure of this distortion is illustrated in Figure 21, which, in traces *A* and *B,* shows the discharge of a single spindle receptor in a preparation in which the loop was left almost entirely intact. This preparation was accomplished by cutting only a negligibly tiny strand of the dorsal root to sample spindle activity, leaving intact the remainder of the dorsal root and all of the ventral root. Even with the muscle slack and under no measurable stretch, the receptor

discharged a continuous barrage of impulses. When the muscle was stretched, the discharge of the receptor accelerated, but the firing during both the slack and the stretch state was irregular and tended to occur in bursts of varying frequencies. Traces *C* and *D* show the behavior of the same preparation after the loop was interrupted by ventral root section. In the slack state, the spindle was silent. During stretch, the receptor responded with a regularly recurring discharge of impulses quite unlike that in *A* and *B*. Such experiments suggest that, in the intact animal, the fusimotor system maintains a tonic discharge which fluctuates in magnitude as the afferent input to the fusimotoneurons varies.

This "resting" tonic discharge of fusimotoneurons has been studied by Hunt,[12, 17] who dissected out small strands of gamma efferent

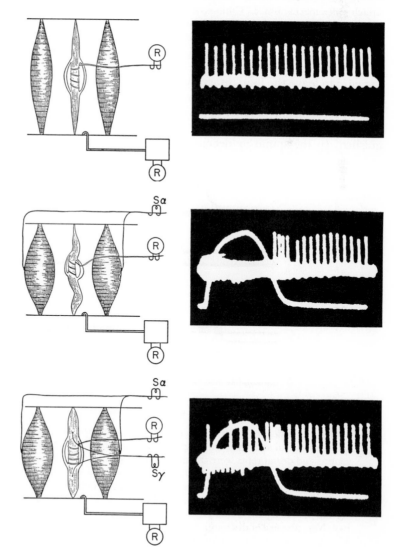

Fig. 19. Effect of fusimotor stimulation on the silent period in spindle discharge during muscle contraction. Thick line in traces, record from spindle afferent fiber; thin line, tension of muscle. *Upper trace,* Sustained tension (15 grams) elicits rhythmic firing of receptor. *Middle trace,* Discharge ceases during muscle twitch because spindles are relieved from stretch. *Lower trace,* Fusimotor stimulation (indicated by shock artifacts extending beneath baseline) takes up "slack" in spindle and permits sustained discharge even during muscle contraction. (After Hunt and Kuffler, *J. Physiol.,* 1951, *113:*298–315.)

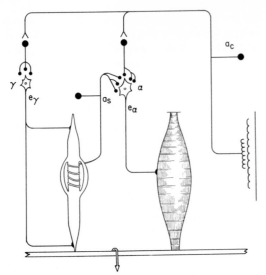

Fig. 20.   Diagram of the "peripheral loop" of the stretch reflex mechanism. a_c, Cutaneous afferent path; a_s, spindle afferent path; e_α and e_γ, alpha and gamma (fusimotor) efferent pathways respectively.

with the limb in a neutral position, many fusimotoneurons are silent, while others maintain a continuous but irregular discharge at frequencies of 10 to 60 per second. That this discharge is highly dependent on segmental afferent inflow is suggested by Hunt's finding that the discharge was abolished by bilateral section of the lumbosacral dorsal roots.*

Various stimuli to the limbs reflexly alter the fusimotor discharge.[12, 17] In this respect cutaneous stimuli are especially effective, light touch, pressure or pin prick causing prominent changes in the discharge frequency of tonically firing units and sometimes driving a resting unit into activity. Generally speaking, such stimuli, particularly when applied to the foot, increase the fusimotor discharge to the ipsilateral flexor muscles but diminish the discharge to ipsilateral extensors. On the side opposite the stimulus, the extensor muscles receive increased fusimotor discharge, whereas the discharge to the flexors is diminished. Thus, in the flexion and crossed extension reflexes, the gamma and alpha motoneurons are affected alike. This arrangement probably acts to compensate for the

fibers from ventral roots or muscle nerves, taking care to leave the loop intact except for the small sampling strand. Fusimotor spikes are usually recognizably smaller in amplitude than alpha fiber spikes and are thus easily distinguished. In the spinal or decerebrate animal

* Other experiments, to be discussed in Chapter 9, indicate that tracts descending from supraspinal structures also influence fusimotor discharge.

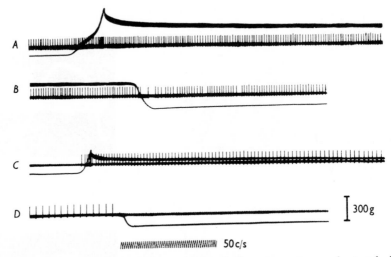

Fig. 21.   Effect of ventral root section on muscle spindle response to muscle stretch. Trace with spikes, electrical activity of single spindle afferent fiber; smooth trace, muscle tension. In *A* and *B* both ventral and dorsal roots were intact except for small strand of dorsal root dissected to sample spindle response. At the beginning in *A,* although the muscle was slack, the unit discharged with an irregular rhythm. When the muscle was stretched 10 mm. as indicated by rise of tension, discharge was moderately accelerated but rhythm remained irregular. *B* is a continuation of *A* showing effect of slackening the muscle again. *C* and *D* show response of same unit to 10 mm. stretch after section of ventral root. Note absence of discharge when muscle was slack and regular rhythmic nature of discharge during muscle stretch. (From Eldred *et al., J. Physiol.,* 1953, *122:*498–523.)

reduction of spindle discharge which might otherwise occur when the reflexly contracting flexor muscle shortens. Fusimotor activity thus provides a mechanism for maintaining a sensory message from the spindles proportional to the amount of external stretch even under changing conditions of muscle contraction.

The distribution of reflexly evoked fusimotor discharge, however, is not stereotyped. Cutaneous stimuli, particularly to proximal portions of the limb, may elicit patterns of fusimotor distribution which do not parallel the flexion and crossed extension patterns. Furthermore, the pattern varies with change in the site of stimulation. For example, the fusimotor discharge to the knee extensor, the quadriceps, in accordance with the flexion reflex pattern, is inhibited by touching or squeezing the ipsilateral foot, but the effect of similar stimulation of the skin on the thigh varies with the locus of stimulation. Touching the skin overlying the quadriceps increases fusimotor discharge to this muscle, whereas touching or squeezing the skin overlying its antagonists, the flexor hamstring muscles, inhibits tonic fusimotor discharge to the quadriceps. The fusimotor arcs, like the flexion reflex, thus display local sign.

Electrical stimulation of cutaneous nerves also markedly influences fusimotoneurons, but the effect varies so much with the afferent trunk employed and with the fusimotoneuron sampled that no generalizations are readily apparent. The unnatural electrical activation of functionally heterogeneous afferent fibers may obscure orderly functional patterns. Electrical stimulation, however, has the advantage that the temporal properties of fusimotor arcs can be determined. Measured central delays are in excess of 2 milliseconds, a fact suggesting that afferent fibers connect to fusimotoneurons through one or more interneurons.[17]

Deep receptors also influence fusimotoneuron activity but, in general, somewhat less prominently than cutaneous receptors do. The stretch receptors of muscle and tendon appear to influence the fusimotoneurons little or not at all.[17] Although muscle stretch sometimes inhibits fusimotor discharge to the stretched muscle,[12] there is reason to doubt that the responsible receptors are muscle spindles or tendon organs. The afferent fibers mediating this inhibition do not reach the spinal cord through the muscle nerve as do the Group IA and IB fibers supplying spindles and tendon organs.

Moreover, electrical stimulation of muscle nerves at intensities adequate only for Group I fibers does not influence fusimotoneurons. It therefore seems that the receptors responsible for fusimotor inhibition during muscle stretch are neither the spindle nor the tendon organs.

In closing it may be stated that, in the present state of knowledge, the physiologic significance of the fusimotor system is not completely clear. It is obvious that the gamma fibers are potentially powerful regulators of spindle function and hence of reflex function. The full measure of their significance in posture and movement cannot be assessed until the conditions governing their activation are further clarified.

CLINICAL SIGNIFICANCE OF REFLEXES

Examination of reflex status is a standard and valuable clinical diagnostic procedure. Clinically, reflexes are categorized as either *deep* or *superficial*. By "deep reflexes"* is meant all stretch or myotatic reflexes of the phasic or "jerk" type, i.e., those elicited by a sharp tap on the appropriate tendon or muscle to induce brief stretch of the muscle. Detailed lists of the commonly tested deep reflexes and the spinal segments which subserve them can be found in textbooks of neurology. The same type of neural arcs may be tested in the limbs and jaw by gauging the resistance to passive movement of the member; this is a test of *muscle tone* which, like the jerk, depends on the stretch reflex arc. An important difference between this test and the elicitation of jerk reflexes is the nature of the afferent discharge. With slow stretch (passive movement) it is asynchronous and prolonged (static stretch reflex), and with brief stretches (tapping) it is synchronous and of short duration. The *superficial* or *cutaneous* reflexes are withdrawal reflexes elicited by noxious or tactile

---

* Deep reflexes are also sometimes inappropriately called "periosteal" reflexes, because neurologists once quite mistakenly believed that the receptive elements were in the periosteum. The term "tendon" reflex, also commonly used interchangeably with "deep" reflexes, is unfortunate, because the receptors are, of course, in the muscle rather than in the tendon and because the jerk reflexes can be elicited by tapping the muscle directly as readily as by tapping the tendon. The clasp knife or inverse myotatic reflex is properly a tendon reflex.

stimulation of the skin, and display the same general properties as the nociceptive flexion reflex described above. Examples are the plantar reflex (plantar flexion of the toes when the sole of the foot is stroked or scratched), the cremasteric reflex (elevation of the testicle when the inner and upper surface of the ipsilateral thigh is lightly scratched), and the abdominal reflex (contraction of the abdominal musculature when the overlying skin is stroked with a dull pin).

Diseases of the nervous system may affect reflexes in one of three ways: (i) the reflexes may be hypoactive or absent, (ii) the reflexes may be hyperactive, or (iii) the pattern of reflex response to a standard stimulus may change to a new one (the so-called "pathologic reflexes"). In evaluating reflexes in man it should be remembered that the motoneurons are subject to a multitude of influences which vary in intensity from patient to patient and in the same patient from time to time. Patients under strong emotional stress may temporarily display brisk myotatic reflexes suggestive of hyperactivity. It is not unlikely that anxiety and tension are associated with increased fusimotor activity.

On the other hand, in a thoroughly relaxed patient the quadriceps jerk, through lack of descending facilitation, is sometimes difficult to elicit. This difficulty may arise because the muscle is sufficiently slack that the tap fails to impart much stretch to the muscle. Spuriously weak reflexes may also occur in older patients in whom structural changes in the muscle and the tendon permit slack in the system. In such instances, myotatic responses can often be elicited by tapping the muscle rather than the tendon, since stretch receptors are sensitive to deformation resulting from tapping the muscle even though little stretch is imparted to the muscle as a whole. Responses so elicited are usually more localized than those induced by tendon tap, because the stimulus affects only a part of the receptive field of the muscle. Even in the absence of such relaxation, the knee jerk is difficult to elicit in some subjects in whom there is no reason to suspect neurologic disease.

It follows from all these considerations that evaluation of reflex performance requires a judicious and cautious approach. If the reflexes appear either equally depressed or equally hyperactive at all levels, repeated examinations, preferably over a considerable period and in a variety of environmental circumstances, may be required to distinguish the spurious from the significant. When the reflex aberrations are asymmetrical— occurring, for example, in one limb and not in another, or on only one side of the body— the examiner is on safer ground, because one part of the body then serves as a control for the others.

Hyporeflexia. It is obvious from the preceding discussion that any process which interrupts or depresses conduction through any part of the reflex arc results in hypoactivity of that reflex in proportion to the severity of damage. The lesion may be in the afferent pathway, as in tabes dorsalis, in which the pathologic process begins in the dorsal root ganglia; or the lesions may affect the efferent limb. Disruption of this portion may result from disease in the gray matter causing injury to the motoneurons, as in anterior poliomyelitis. Disease of nerve trunks commonly affects both the afferent and the efferent limb of a reflex arc; examples are the several varieties of polyneuritis and herniated intervertebral discs or tumors which compress both dorsal and ventral roots in their course through the vertebral canal. Finally, disturbances, such as myasthenia gravis, which interfere with neuromuscular transmission may result in depression or lack of reflexes.

Depressed reflexes, however, do not always indicate an interruption of the segmental arc. It has been mentioned that motoneuron excitability is conditioned by pathways descending the cord from more cephalic spinal and suprasegmental levels as well as by segmental inflows. Even though the segmental arcs are intact after these descending pathways are interrupted by transection of the cord, the reflex responses are severely depressed (spinal shock) in regions innervated by the decentralized spinal segments. With passage of time, some reflexes return (particularly the flexion reflex patterns of the extremities, which may actually become troublesomely hyperactive), but the static stretch reflex often remains permanently depressed. Similarly, cerebellar lesions, by destroying neurons which feed into descending tracts facilitatory to the motoneurons, result in hypoactive stretch reflexes.

Hyperreflexia. Hyperactivity of deep reflexes sometimes results from inflammatory lesions involving the segmental arc, e.g., during the early stages of the intervertebral disc syndrome or of polyneuritis. Persistently hyperactive deep reflexes, however, almost always indicate destruction of descending tracts inhibitory to the segmental stretch reflex mechanism, as in spastic hemiplegia following infarction (from hemorrhage, etc.) in the internal capsule. In this instance, myotatic hyperreflexia is indicated by increased briskness and amplitude of deep reflexes and by increased resistance to passive flexion at the joints (spasticity). In addition, the peripheral distribution of stretch reflex discharge is often increased owing to the occurrence of "crossfiring."

It has already been emphasized that, normally, the stretch reflex discharge returns only to the muscle stretched. When motoneuron excitability is increased (see p. 177), the afferent volley may fire motoneurons that normally are only facilitated (crossfiring). In spasticity, crossfiring is exemplified by *Hoffman's reflex* in which flicking the terminal phalanx of the middle finger results in twitchlike flexion in the other fingers and in adduction and flexion of the thumb. Such a broad field of reflex action resulting from brief stretch of the flexor muscles of one finger joint manifests myotatic hyperactivity.

Another important sign of hyperreflexia, often associated with spasticity, is *clonus.* Clonus occurs when the asynchrony of the motoneuron discharge in a stretch reflex is lost. There then ensues a series of regularly repeated, jerklike contractions superimposed upon a tonic contraction. In the hyperreflexic patient, clonus may be initiated by putting the muscle under moderate but sustained stretch and then tapping the tendon. A jerk response, of course, results; but it is followed by a succession of jerks which continue for a considerable time if the steady stretch is maintained. Figure 22 presents a myograph tracing of a clonic response in a decerebrate cat; the accompanying electromyogram shows that each wavelet of contraction is preceded by a muscle action potential, indicating that the motoneurons are discharging in periodic synchronous bursts. The simplest explanation of clonus is based on the "in parallel" behavior of the stretch receptor. The tap on the tendon initiates a synchronous volley of afferent impulses which fire the motoneurons in concert, causing a jerk contraction. This contraction relieves the spindles of the tension imposed by the sustained stretch, so that they cease firing and the afferent drive to the motoneurons ceases. As a consequence, the muscle relaxes and the spindles are thereby again put under tension which

initiates an afferent volley that again fires the motoneurons so that the sequence is repeated. Even in a healthy subject a slight tendency toward oscillation during a jerk contraction may be observed. If the muscle is under passive tension prior to the tapping of the tendon, the electromyogram displays an asynchronous discharge which indicates that motor units are reflexly firing in response to the sustained stretch. When the tendon is tapped, the electromyogram displays a large synchronous discharge just preceding the muscle contraction, but during the development of contractile tension the asynchronous discharge is in abeyance—the "silent period" already described. As the muscle relaxes and the spindles are again put under tension, firing of motor units resumes and relaxation of the muscle is delayed. Indeed, a second small contraction, the myotatic appendage, may appear on the tension record. When the motoneurons are hyperexcitable, as in spasticity, a series of myotatic appendages appear, constituting clonus which may persist for minutes. Sustained clonus is always a manifestation of hyperreflexia indicating damage within the central nervous system.

Pathologic Reflexes. These are reflex responses which do not occur in the normal person. In a sense, the Hoffman reflex is a pathologic reflex. A better example is the *Babinski sign* or reflex. In the normal adult, stroking the sole

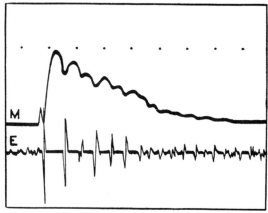

Fig. 22. Clonus. Electrical (*E*) and mechanical (*M*) records of quadriceps muscle. A slight stretch previously applied produced a tonic reflex discharge to the muscle, as indicated by the asynchronous waves in *E*. A tap to the tendon indicated by the first sharp deflection in *M*, elicited a brisk jerk reflex followed by a typical clonic discharge evident in both *M* and *B*. Time above, 100 milliseconds. (After Denny-Brown, *Proc. roy. Soc.,* 1929, *B104*:252–301.)

of the foot causes plantar flexion of the toes; this is the plantar flexion reflex. In certain diseases of the central nervous system, however, the response to plantar stimulation (particularly along the lateral surface and the ball of the foot) is dorsiflexion of the great toe, often accompanied by fanning of the other toes. The Babinski reflex is part of the generalized flexion reflex pattern and is accompanied by flexor contraction at other joints of the limb; the significant deviation in the Babinski reflex is the aberrant pattern. In adults, presence of the Babinski reflex is always a sign of disease, but this pattern is normal in infants, particularly when they are asleep. The Babinski reflex is commonly believed to indicate interruption of the pyramidal tract (see Chap. 12).

Deductions from Examination of Reflexes. In summary, it may be pointed out that the examination of reflexes provides several kinds of information to the thoughtful physician. *First,* unilateral aberration of reflex performance provides a basis for identifying the *side* affected by the disease process. *Second,* the distribution of reflex aberrations along the longitudinal axis of the body often betrays the *segmental level* of the lesion. *Third,* once a segmental defect is established, attention may be turned to identifying the *defective component* in the arc. Loss of reflex accompanied by loss of sensation but without voluntary motor weakness implies injury to the afferent limb. Loss of reflex without sensory defect but with muscular weakness, atrophy, fibrillation or fasciculation suggests injury to the efferent limb. *Fourth,* examination of segmental reflexes often reveals disturbances of *more distant structures* which influence the segmental arcs. Thus, disease of descending pathways inhibitory to the segmental reflex mechanism is brought to the physician's attention by hyperreflexia, as in spasticity.

REFERENCES

1. ADRIAN, E. D. and ZOTTERMAN, Y. *J. Physiol.,* 1926, *61:* 151–171.
2. BARKER, D. *Quart. J. micr. Sci.,* 1948, *89:*143–186.
3. BESSOU, P. and LAPORTE, Y. Pp. 105–119 in *Symposium on muscle receptors,* D. Barker, ed., Hong Kong, Hong Kong University Press, 1962.
4. BOYD, I. A. *Phil. Trans.,* 1962, *B245:*81–136.
5. BOYD, I. A. and DAVEY, M. R. Pp. 191–198 in *Symposium on muscle receptors,* D. Barker, ed., Hong Kong, Hong Kong University Press, 1962.
6. CREED, R. S., DENNY-BROWN, D., ECCLES, J. C., LIDDELL, E. G. T. and SHERRINGTON, C. S. *Reflex activity of the spinal cord.* London, Oxford University Press, 1932.
7. DENNY-BROWN, D. *Proc. roy. Soc.,* 1928, *B103:*321–336.
8. FULTON, J. F. and PI SUÑER, J. *Amer. J. Physiol.,* 1928, *83:* 554–562.
9. GRANIT, R. *J. Neurophysiol.,* 1950, *13:*351–372.
10. HAGBARTH, K. E., *Acta physiol. scand.,* 1952, *26*(Suppl. 94):1–58.
11. HOFFMANN, P. *Arch. Anat. Physiol. (Lpz.), Anat. Abt.,* 1910, 223–246, 1 pl.
12. HUNT, C. C. *J. Physiol.,* 1951, *115:*456–469.
13. HUNT, C. C. *J. Physiol.,* 1952, *117:*359–379.
14. HUNT, C. C. *J. gen. Physiol.,* 1954, *38:*117–131.
15. HUNT, C. C. and KUFFLER, S. W. *J. Physiol.,* 1951, *113:* 298–315.
16. HUNT, C. C. and McINTYRE, A. K. *J. Physiol.,* 1960, *153:* 88–98.
17. HUNT, C. C. and PAINTAL, A. S. *J. Physiol.,* 1958, *143:* 195–212.
18. KUFFLER, S. W. and HUNT, C. C. *Res. Publ. Ass. nerv. ment. Dis.,* 1952, *30:*24–47.
19. KUFFLER, S. W., HUNT, C. C. and QUILLIAM, J. P. *J. Neurophysiol.,* 1951, *14:*29–54.
20. LAPORTE, Y. and LLOYD, D. P. C. *Amer. J. Physiol.,* 1952, *169:*609–621.
21. LEKSELL, L. *Acta physiol. scand.,* 1945, *10*(Suppl. 31): 1–84.
22. LIBET, B., FEINSTEIN, B. and WRIGHT, E. B., JR. *Electroenceph. clin. Neurophysiol.,* 1959, *11:*129–140.
23. LIDDELL, E. G. T. and SHERRINGTON, C. S. *Proc. roy. Soc.,* 1924, *B96:*212–242.
24. LIDDELL, E. G. T. and SHERRINGTON, C. S. *Proc. roy. Soc.,* 1925, *B97:*267–283.
25. LLOYD, D. P. C. *J. Neurophysiol.,* 1943, *6:*317–326.
26. MAGLADERY, J. W., PARK, A. M., PORTER, W. E. and TEASDALL, R. D. *Res. Publ. Ass. nerv. ment. Dis.,* 1952, *30:*118–151.
27. MATTHES, K. and RUCH, T. C. *Quart. J. exper. Physiol.,* 1932, *22:*221–231.
28. MATTHEWS, B. H. C. *J. Physiol.,* 1933, *78:*1–53.
29. McCOUCH, G. P., DEERING, I. D. and STEWART, W. B. *J. Neurophysiol.,* 1950, *13:*343–350.
30. MEGIRIAN, D. *J. Neurophysiol.,* 1962, *25:*127–137.
31. PERL, E. R. *Amer. J. Physiol.,* 1957, *188:*609–615.
32. PERL, E. R. *J. Neurophysiol.,* 1958, *21:*101–112.
33. RENSHAW, B. *J. Neurophysiol.,* 1941; *4:*167–183.
34. RENSHAW, B. *J. Neurophysiol.,* 1946, *9:*191–204.
35. SHERRINGTON, C. S. *Proc. roy. Soc.,* 1893, *52:*556–564.
36. SHERRINGTON, C. S. *J. Physiol.,* 1898, *22:*319–332.
37. SHERRINGTON, C. S. *Quart. J. exp. Physiol.,* 1909, *2:*109–156.
38. SHERRINGTON, C. S. *J. Physiol.,* 1910, *40:*28–121.
39. SHERRINGTON, C. S. *Brain,* 1915, *38:*191–234.
40. SHERRINGTON, C. S. *Nature (Lond.),* 1924, *113:*732, 892–894, 929–932.
41. WOODBURY, J. W. and PATTON, H. D. *Cold Spr. Harb. Symp. quant. Biol.,* 1952, *17:*185–188.

CHAPTER 8

Transection of the Human Spinal Cord: The Nature of Higher Control

By THEODORE C. RUCH

THE principles of reflex action outlined in earlier chapters are applied clinically in dealing with destructive diseases and mechanical injury of the spinal cord. Such injuries are especially common during war. During World War I, spinal transection meant early death; during World War II, however, the prognosis for patients with spinal paraplegia was radically altered. Through application of physiologic principles, many of these men have been rehabilitated and are now self-reliant citizens.

When the spinal cord is severed, all muscles innervated from segments below the transection become paralyzed (paraplegic), and the skin and other tissues are anesthetic. Voluntary motion and sensation are abolished and never recover. Reflexes, although initially abolished, do recover to some degree, and some become overactive. This chapter will be concerned with the higher control of reflex action; sensory changes from complete and partial spinal cord section are discussed in Chapter 15.

CONSEQUENCES OF SPINAL TRANSECTION

Spinal Shock. The disappearance of reflexes was designated "spinal shock" some 100 years ago by Marshall Hall,[13] and the term, despite its inappropriateness, is still used. Spinal shock is not related to surgical shock or to spinal concussion, which results from physical shock to the spinal cord. As Sherrington[31] proved, spinal shock will occur when the cord is functionally sectioned atraumatically, as by cooling or by injection of procaine. If reflexes of segments below a transection have returned, another section just below the first produces no shock effect. In short, it is the *fact* of cord section —not the *act* of transection—which produces spinal shock. The alternative terms are *post-transectional areflexia* or *hyporeflexia*. The state of increased reflex excitability which may supervene can be called *post-transectional hyperreflexia*. A phenomenon following a brain lesion comparable to spinal shock is *diaschisis* (von Monakow).

Areflexia and hyporeflexia. The most conspicuous sign of spinal shock in man and other primates is the suppression of all reflexes, both skeletal and visceral, below the transection. This suppression is usually complete during the first two weeks after the injury. Before the first World War it was believed that the reflexes were permanently abolished, this belief having arisen because intercurrent infections of the bladder or other structures reduced the excitability of the spinal cord. Then, Head and Riddoch[14] proved that some paraplegic patients could be maintained indefinitely by fastidious nursing care, and that in such patients spinal reflexes began to return after two to three weeks. Since World War II, Freeman[5] and others[19] have found that reflexes may reappear within two to three days after the accident.

Return of Reflexes and Hyperreflexia. *Flexion reflex and the Babinski sign.* Contrary to early studies, withdrawal movements in response to plantar stimulation (rather than the knee jerk) are the first reflexes to emerge from the period of areflexia; anal and genital reflexes also recover early. As the withdrawal reflex becomes more brisk, the toes (especially the great toe) tend to become extended upward during the response (the sign of Babinski[9]). In the course of the third and fourth weeks following the injury, the withdrawal response becomes more vigorous, and the zone from which it can be elicited spreads up the inner side of the leg, the knee and the hip. The withdrawal response is brought about mainly by strong contraction of the hamstring muscles of the thigh.

Mass reflex. Several months after spinal transection, the withdrawal reflexes tend to become exaggerated and spread to the visceral autonomic outflow. Thus, if the plantar surface of the foot is vigorously scratched, both extremities may withdraw violently, the patient may sweat profusely, and both the bladder and the rectum may contract. This widespread reflex activation of the musculature in spinal man is referred to as the "mass reflex."[14] Mass reflexes may be evoked unintentionally and, at times, they appear to develop spontaneously without obvious stimulation. Flexor reflex contractions with or without autonomic concomitants are very disturbing to the patient, since they interfere with his sleep and rest.

Extensor reflexes. During the first weeks after a spinal transection, the lower extremities are flaccid: they are limp and do not resist manipulation. Even after the withdrawal reflexes have returned, the limbs usually are still flaccid except when exhibiting flexor spasms. Some months after spinal transection, if there are no complications, a slight degree of extensor posture usually develops, but the extremities seldom become strongly spastic, as in hemiplegia. Strong extensor spasticity occurring soon after the transection generally indicates that the spinal cord is not completely severed and that some degree of functional recovery can be anticipated. However, patients with surgically verified spinal transections may reach a stage in which the tendon reflexes are hyperactive as judged by decreased threshold and clonus. Stretch reflexes and positive supporting reactions sufficiently sustained to permit momentary support of the body have been reported. The lower extremities show both ipsilateral and crossed extension reflexes, but extreme resistance of the extensors to passive stretch is seldom found in spinal man.[18]

Autonomic reflexes. Surprisingly, autonomic reflexes are even more completely suppressed in spinal shock than are somatic reactions. During the first month or two the skin is completely dry, sweating having been wholly abolished, and the skin may be warm and pink owing to separation of the autonomic outflow innervating it from the descending vasoconstrictor impulses. In monkeys, sweating generally does not appear until the third month. In the later stages, this sweating may be so excessive that the patient's clothing and bed linen are constantly wet.[5, 10]

Of the autonomic reflexes, those of the bladder are most important to the patient; these are described in full in Chapter 51.

Completeness of Spinal Transection. In civil life complete spinal transections fortunately are rare. Much more common are partial injuries, and it is important to be able to distinguish between an incomplete and a total transection. Broadly speaking, incomplete transections are marked by an early return of extensor reflexes and are eventually associated with spasticity and great reflex hyperactivity. A patient with a cervical dislocation who appears completely paralyzed below the level of dislocation but who nevertheless exhibits extensor reflexes has an incompletely divided cord, and he has a good possibility of functional recovery if the dislocation can be reduced. Often a patient shows flaccidity and areflexia shortly after the injury but later develops spasticity and active reflexes.

A spinal transection represents the sudden withdrawal of the many excitatory and inhibitory influences which play upon the spinal reflex arcs. A partial interruption of the spinal cord disrupts some but not all of the descending pathways. Since these pathways originate at different levels of the neural axis, transection at higher levels will interrupt some of them and not others. To obtain a complete view of the nature of higher control and the clinical syndromes resulting from destructive lesions of the nervous system, it is necessary to consider the same topic at each level of transection.

NATURE OF HIGHER CONTROL

Spinal transection suddenly interrupts all descending pathways which control spinal reflexes by facilitation and inhibition. The results are necessarily complex. The nature of higher control is the subject of several of the following chapters, but it cannot be fully understood until sections at higher levels interrupting only a few descending pathways are studied.

It might be thought that stretch reflexes, for example, disappear in the higher animal because they have, in course of evolution, been long-circuited through the brain. That these reflexes in higher animals are served by monosynaptic spinal reflex arcs has been proved by Magladery.[24] It is generally conceded that spinal shock results from sudden interruption of control normally exerted on spinal centers by forebrain structures. In the course of evolution, the forebrain has come to dominate lower midbrain and spinal centers more and more, the domination being most complete in man and other higher primates. This evolutionary process is generally referred to as "encephalization." The degree of spinal shock reflects the degree to which a given spinal reflex depends on the brain for facilitation of the segmental afferent input. Generally, the dependence becomes greater as the primate series is ascended, but exceptions do occur. For example, the reflexes of the semiprehensile hind foot of the chimpanzee may be more profoundly disturbed than those of the human foot after spinal transection.

The depression of reflexes comes about because, as will be brought out many times in subsequent chapters, descending pathways converge and summate with the segmental afferent input. Presumably, these descending tracts are discharging continuously, subliminally exciting the motoneurons and keeping many near the point of discharge.[21] As a result, a local afferent volley which has few motoneurons in its discharge zone is able to discharge many neurons lying in its subliminal fringe. If the flow of descending impulses is terminated, the reflex shrinks to its original discharge. This recession explains much of the areflexia and hyporeflexia which follow spinal transection.

Fulton[7] has pointed out that another mechanism may be operative. In addition to or instead of withdrawing facilitation from anterior horn cells, withdrawal of descending impulses might remove an inhibitory influence acting upon the interneurons of an antagonistic reflex arc, necessarily a multisynaptic one. An afferent volley in this arc, e.g., for a flexion reflex, would traverse the uninhibited interneurons with less reduction and would inhibit the motoneurons of the antagonistic extensor reflex. Thus, the flexion reflex should be, and is, augmented while the extensor reflex is inhibited. In passive flexion of a joint to test an extensor stretch reflex, the mere manipulation might prevent one's feeling the weak but recovering stretch reflex.

Ballif *et al.*[1] demonstrated myographically that the knee jerk of a spinal animal, though strong, is inhibited for several seconds by a single ipsilateral stimulus, whereas the knee jerk of a decerebrate animal is inhibited for only a tenth of a second. It is apparent that it is extremely difficult to distinguish between inhibition and lessening of facilitation as mechanisms of spinal shock, and probably both contribute. One of the complexities of the nervous system is that the higher centers can control a spinal reflex by exerting their influence (i) on the motoneurons (ii) on the internuncial neurons of the reflex arc and (iii) on the γ motoneurons which set the sensitivity of the stretch afferent organs and (iv) a combination of the preceding.

Site of Spinal Shock. The immediate change which motoneurons and some interneurons undergo when the spinal cord of a decerebrate animal is sectioned has been shown directly by recording intracellularly at L 5 while the spinal cord was blocked by cooling at Th 10.[2] At each cold block (Fig. 1), most of the cells proved by antidromic firing to be motoneurons underwent a hyperpolarization of from 2 to 6 mV. (mean 3.6 ± 2 mV.). This was reversible by rewarming. These experiments prove that acute spinal shock is evident at the motoneuron as a steady membrane charge but do not establish whether the hyperpolarization derives from withdrawal of facilitation or from increase in tonic inhibition and whether its source is supraspinal or segmental.

In Chapter 9 a strong supraspinal influence on the γ efferent fibers and, hence on the excitability of the stretch afferents will be documented. Some of the depression of the stretch

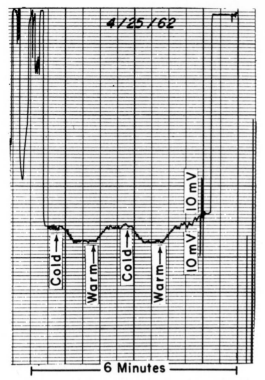

Fig. 1. Intracellular recording from a lumbar motoneuron during alternate cold block and rewarming of the spinal cord in the thoracic region. Large drop in the transmembranal polarization signals penetration of cell. Vertical line at right is the calibration. (After Barnes, Joynt and Schottelius, *Amer. J. Physiol.,* 1962, *203:*1113–1116.)

reflex after spinal transection could result from a reduction in γ efferent discharge. In man, ipsilateral extension jerk elicited by nerve stimulation suffers less than activation of the same muscle by a tendon tap, a difference ascribable to reduced sensitivity of the muscle spindle.[34]

However, in the monkey there is no clear evidence of a reduced γ efferent discharge after spinal transection.[15]

The converse question is: Do hyperactive tendon reflexes after recovery from spinal shock represent heightened fusimotor discharge and resultant increased muscle spindle sensitivity? Meltzer *et al.*[27] could find no increase in the afferent impulses coming from the muscle nerve on the side of a spinal cord hemisection though the ankle jerk was increased 1.5 to 15 times that recorded on the less active side. This activity was therefore ascribed to increased α motoneuron excitability.

The strong inhibitory effects of descending pathway on the γ efferent neurons documented by brain stimulation have yet to be clearly demonstrated by experiments involving transection.

Release of Function. When reflexes below a transection become stronger and more easily elicited, "release of function"* is said to have occurred. The simplest example of release of function is provided by the consideration of what happens to the flexion reflex when the spinal cord of the decerebrate cat is sectioned in the midthoracic region.[29] As will be discussed in greater detail in Chapter 9, a decerebrate cat is a reduced system in which the only descending pathways still affecting the reflex arcs are the vestibulospinal and reticulospinal tracts from the medulla oblongata. What occurs on transection—by surgery, cooling or procaine injection—is a prompt and marked *decrease* in the excitability of stretch and other extensor reflexes and an *increase* in the excitability of the flexion reflex. In other words, the two classes of reflexes are oppositely affected, and the simplest conclusion is that the descending pathways innervate two classes of motoneurons reciprocally. There is the same advantage to reciprocal innervation from the descending pathways as there is to such innervation by the local afferent inputs.

Further evidence of reciprocal effects of spinal transection is seen in the reflex changes in the forelimbs following midthoracic transection in a decerebrate cat. These changes, termed the Schiff–Sherrington phenomenon, are, as indicated in Figure 2, a striking augmentation of the stretch reflex and a decrease in the size of the flexion reflex to equal stimuli. The former is clearly observable without instrumental recording as an increased stiffening of the forelimbs. (The changes are opposite in homologous muscles of the forelimb and hindlimb, and while this must have meaning, the reciprocal changes between flexors and extensors constitute the significant point.)

The diminution of reflexes in these experiments illustrates *spinal shock* resulting from withdrawal of facilitation; the augmentation of reflexes illustrates *release of function* resulting from withdrawal of inhibition. These two phenomena always occur together and are manifestations of a reciprocal relationship of descending pathways to extensor and flexor spinal motoneurons. Descending pathways other than the

* Release of function was first recognized in 1833 by Marshall Hall,[12] who also was the first to describe spinal shock clearly.

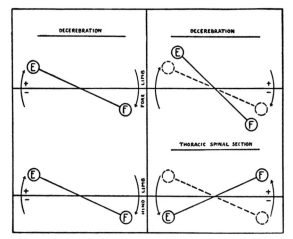

Fig. 2. A schematic diagram of the reciprocal effect of thoracic transection of the spinal cord upon the reflex activity of fore and hind limbs of the decerebrate preparation. *E* and *F* are the extensor and flexor motoneurons. The ordinates are reflex excitability and indicate merely decrease and increase and not absolute amount of change in reflex excitability. (From Ruch and Watts, *Amer. J. Physiol.*, 1934, *110*:362–375.)

vestibulospinal tract act in the same reciprocal fashion but vary in sign, so that a spinal transection which interrupts many descending pathways at once can have quite complex effects. Nevertheless, the effects of transecting lesions, and of certain large brain lesions, can best be interpreted in terms of a kind of algebra of the nervous system in which positive and negative quantities are summated. (For examples, see Chap. 51.)

Synaptic Basis of Release Phenomena. Since the myographic demonstration of the Schiff–Sherrington phenomenon[29] the stretch reflex of the forelimb extensor muscle (triceps) has become a model for investigating release of function, especially by the Italian neurophysiologists, Stella, Cardin, and Moruzzi (see Pompeiano[28]). Even in the reduced nervous system represented by the decerebrate animal they have identified three powerful sources of tonic inhibition of the forelimb stretch reflex—(i) ascending inhibition revealed by postbrachial transection (Schiff–Sherrington phenomenon), (ii) cerebellar inhibition manifested by increase of extensor tone after cerebellectomy or bilateral destruction of the fastigial nuclei of the cerebellum, and (iii) crossed inhibition originating in the proprioceptors of the opposite limb revealed by deafferentation.

The motoneurons' excitability at any one time is the sum of many inhibitory and many

facilitatory influences. The motoneuron effects an algebraic summation of the "plus and minus" inputs. One example of the way the excitability of a reflex can be manipulated up and down is seen in Figure 2. More examples of the "algebra of higher control" will be encountered in subsequent chapters, e.g., Chapter 51.

At the synaptic level release of function presents much the same alternatives as does acute spinal shock. Is the effect a direct disinhibition of α motoneurons or an indirect one by way of disinhibiting γ motoneurons? Is the effect on the motoneurons or upon inhibitory internuncial neurons, or is it by blocking some impinging excitation? The first question can be answered in favor of direct effect (Fig. 3). Pompeiano[28]

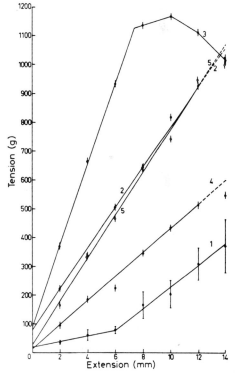

Fig. 3. Initial limb of the stretch reflex recorded from a forearm extensor muscle (caput longis of triceps brachii) after various neural sections. 1. Average value and range of three stretch reflexes in the *precollicular* decerebrate animal; 2. after postbrachial transection of the spinal cord; 3. after deafferentation of the contralateral forelimb C_6 to Th_2; 4. after deafferentation of ipsilateral forelimb; 5. after complete cerebellectomy. Deviation of stretch was 13.1 sec. Record 4 is a pseudostretch reflex representing the increased tension and is due to effect of muscle length on the increased muscular contraction caused by the α motor neuron discharge. (From Pompeiano, *Arch. ital. Biol.*, 1960, *98*: 92–117.)

has shown that if enough inhibitory influences are removed by contralateral deafferentation and postbrachial transection the triceps muscle exhibits tone, even after it is also deafferented. Now if the cerebellum is removed, a large increase in tone occurs which must be independent of the muscles' γ loop interrupted by deafferentation. A similar demonstration has been made for ascending inhibition.

Terzuolo[33] reached the same conclusion by recording monosynaptic reflex discharge intracellularly in extensor neurons during inhibition produced by stimulation of the bulbar reticular system. The fact that inhibitory slowing occurs when the γ loop is rendered ineffective by anterior root section indicates an action on the α motoneurons as do increases in membrane potential ranging from 1.5 to 10.5 mV. (mode 1.5 to 3.5 mV.). Although the inhibitory effect of reticular stimulation is established to be on the motoneurons, it might be either a direct inhibitory bombardment or a blocking of impinging excitatory impulses or both. Analyses of the synaptic phenomenon have indicated a direct postsynaptic inhibition.

Mechanisms of Recovery. The question now arises: Is spinal shock more than mere withdrawal of facilitation and inhibition? Withdrawal of descending influences explains adequately the decrease or release of spinal reflexes. However, there is considerable recovery from the depression of reflexes, and this requires exploration. Why recovery should occur is a puzzle, but clues to a solution are offered by the following experiment.

The effects of interrupting all the descending pathways suddenly are much more profound than those of a gradual interruption. McCouch and Fulton[9, 26] removed the motor cortex of one cerebral hemisphere and noted a depression of reflexes in the contralateral limbs (the corticospinal pathway is crossed). After the reflexes had recovered, the spinal cord was sectioned. The reflexes in the limb contralateral to the brain lesion were only moderately depressed, whereas the spinal shock was profound in the previously normal extremity. The two-stage removal of descending influences had exerted less effect than did the one-stage removal. (For a somewhat similar demonstration, see Chap. 12.) These experiments show that cerebral lesions can depress spinal reflexes. Kempinsky[16] has recently demonstrated what von Monakow deduced from clinical observations and termed

diaschisis—that cerebral lesions will depress the electrical activity in a remote region with which the damaged area is neuronally connected. This "cerebral shock" or diaschisis will be discussed again in Chapter 12. It is theoretically significant that a depression of excitability of motoneurons also follows dorsal root section and that this period of depression is followed by one of increased excitability.[33]

One theory of spinal shock holds that the sudden withdrawal of facilitation decreases the excitability of spinal motoneurons and interneurons more than would be accounted for by the mere withdrawal of excitatory background. In the monkey, depression of reflexes increases for an hour or two after spinal section. Recovery of function is in part interpreted as a return to normal from the "S state" or "shock state" of the neurons. The S state is hypothetical but can be supported by analogy: in certain situations, interruption of axons can cause the cell bodies on which they terminate to undergo microscopically visible disorganization (transneuronal degeneration); degeneration of the muscle cell as a consequence of a sectioning of its motor nerve has already been pointed out. If these transjunctional changes can proceed to the point of visible degeneration, it is not inconceivable that interference with descending fibers terminating on spinal motoneurons can cause changes in them which are not visible under the microscope but which are manifest in a decreased synaptic excitability.

There is good reason to believe that spinal reflex arcs subsequently attain a level of excitability which is more than a return to normal from a hypothetical S state. In part, this hyperactivity reflects a release of function when, as is usually the case, inhibitory as well as excitatory pathways are interrupted by a lesion. Release of function would not be apparent until the S factor had disappeared. But this perhaps does not explain the protracted, month-long increase in excitability following the initial state of depression.

Convincing evidence has been adduced that motoneurons partially denervated by spinal transection[3] or posterior root section[4] become highly sensitive to chemical agents (see law of denervation, Chap. 10). If chemical substances of this kind are present in the synaptic region, they might influence the excitability of motoneurons irrespective of whether neurohumors are involved in transmission at central synapses.

McCouch and his co-workers[26] have described another mechanism which would account for a progressive increase in the excitability of reflex arcs below a spinal transection. These investigators have furnished anatomic and electrophysiologic evidence that, subsequent to spinal transection, the local posterior root fibers sprout new collaterals and produce more synaptic connections with motoneurons and interneurons.[22] This increase in connections would, for reasons already familiar (Chap. 6), increase the magnitude of a reflex response to the same peripheral stimulation. (An analogous sprouting of teledendrons of sensory neurons into denervated skin is described in Chapter 15.)

In patients suffering from neurologic disorders, the "spontaneous" recovery of function can be a difficulty, as in the disturbing flexor spasms of paraplegia; or it can be the sole hope for improvement of the patient, as in hemiplegia. Despite the latter fact, the problem of analyzing the basic mechanism of *shock* and *recovery of function* has been largely left to the future.

HIGHER CENTRAL CONTROL OF AFFERENT INPUT[23]

Within the past decade it has been discovered that descending tracts from the brain influence not only motor neurons but also the γ neurons which regulate sensitivity of the muscle spindle. These receptors make no known contribution to the sensory processes of the cerebral cortex, so that fusimotor control has motor rather than sensory significance. However, central control of the auditory end-organ sensitivity has been demonstrated. Further, higher control is exerted on the first synapse of the somatosensory system, i.e., the synapse between the peripheral afferent neuron with the second order neuron which crosses the spinal cord to ascend in the lateral and ventral white columns to the thalamus and on to the cerebral cortex. In the fundamental observation Hagbarth and Kerr[11] noted that stimulation of the reticular substance of the brain stem, whether inhibitory or facilitatory to motor activity, diminished and sometimes abolished conduction from first to second order neurons. The afferent fibers which enter the spinal cord to ascend in the posterior columns were partially blocked at their first synapse in the medulla oblongata. These observations have been confirmed and elaborated; many brain structures exert control of the first synapse in ascending systems.

The significance of this higher control of ascending pathways is puzzling. Most surprisingly, the controls are exerted mainly by what have been considered motor areas or tracts or both, including what has been considered the highest motor tract of all—the pyramidal or corticospinal tract.

In general, the influences of descending pathways on ascending pathways tend to be inhibitory. For sensation this could be a mechanism of attention, a gating of the afferent inflow, a selection of stimuli by an active rather than a passive brain. These systems are involved in the process of "habituation" by which repeated sensory impulses lose the ability to gain access to the higher levels of the nervous system (Chap. 24). But why should a "classical"* motor tract, the pyramidal, determine transmission in the classical sensory tract? Does this make it a part of the sensory apparatus? Certainly this whole development breaks down the distinction between "sensory" and "motor" as two sequential causally related events. The significance of the descending influences on the transmission through ascending pathways which serve sensation (and the control of movement) must be considered in connection with each brain structure. Because there is no clear indication of the significance of these descending pathways to sensation, they will be discussed mainly in relation to "motor" structures and function.

* "Classical" means something believed for a long time (and now commencing to be considered "not the whole story" or even to be doubted).

REFERENCES

1. BALLIF L., FULTON, J. F. and LIDDELL, E. G. T. *Proc. roy. Soc.*, 1925, *B98*:589–607.
2. BARNES, C. D., JOYNT, R. J. and SCHOTTELIUS, B. A. *Amer. J. Physiol.*, 1962, *203*:1113–1116.
3. CANNON, W. B. and HAIMOVICI, H. *Amer. J. Physiol.*, 1939, *126*:731–740.
4. DRAKE, C. G. and STAVRAKY, G. W. *J. Neurophysiol.*, 1948, *11*:229–238.
5. FREEMAN, L. W. *J. Amer. Med. Ass.*, 1949, *140*:949–958, 1015–1022.
6. FRENCH, J. D. and PORTER, R. W., eds. *Basic research in paraplegia.* Springfield, Ill., Charles C Thomas, 1962.
7. FULTON, J. F. *Muscular contraction and the reflex control of movement.* Baltimore, Williams & Wilkins, 1926.

8. FULTON, J. F. and KELLER, A. D. *The sign of Babinski: A study of the evolution of cortical dominance.* Springfield, Ill., Charles C Thomas, 1932.

9. FULTON, J. F. and McCOUCH, G. P. *J. nerv. ment. Dis.,* 1937, *86:*125–146.

10. GUTTMAN, L. and WHITTERIDGE, D. *Brain,* 1947, *70:*361–404.

11. HAGBARTH, K. E. and KERR, D. I. B. *J. Neurophysiol.,* 1954, *17:*295–307.

12. HALL, M. *Phil. Trans.,* 1833, 635–665.

13. HALL, M. *Synopsis of the diastaltic nervous system; or the system of the spinal marrow; and its reflex arcs.* London, J. Mallett, 1850.

14. HEAD, H. and RIDDOCH, G. *Brain,* 1917, *40:*188–263.

15. HUNT, R. S., MELTZER, G. E. and LANDAU, W. M. *Arch. Neurol. (Chic.),* 1963, *9:*120–126.

16. KEMPINSKY, W. H. *Arch. Neurol. Psychiat. (Chic.),* 1958, *79:*376–389.

17. KUHN, R. A. *Brain,* 1950, *73:*1–51.

18. KUHN, R. A. and MACHT, M. B. *Bull. Johns Hopk. Hosp.,* 1949, *84:*43–75.

19. KUHN, W. G., JR. *J. Neurosurgery,* 1947, *4:*40–68.

20. LANDAU, W. M. and CLARE, M. H. *Arch. Neurol. (Chic.),* 1964, *10:*117–122.

21. LIDDELL, E. G. *Brain,* 1934, *57:*386–400.

22. LIU, C.-N. and CHAMBERS, W. W. *Arch. Neurol. Psychiat. (Chic.),* 1958, *79:*46–61.

23. LIVINGSTON, R. B. Chap. 31 in *Handbook of physiology; Section 1: Neurophysiology,* vol. 1, J. Field, ed., Washington, D. C., American Physiological Society, 1959.

24. MAGLADERY, J. W., PARK, A. M., PORTER, W. E. and TEASDALL, R. D. *Res. Publ. Ass. nerv. ment. Dis.,* 1952, *30:*118–151.

25. McCOUCH, G. P. *Amer. J. Physiol.,* 1924, *71:*137–152.

26. McCOUCH, G. P., AUSTIN, G. M., LIU, C.-N. and LIU, C. Y. *J. Neurophysiol.,* 1958, *21:*205–216.

27. MELTZER, G. E., HUNT, R. S. and LANDAU, W. M. *Arch. Neurol. (Chic.),* 1963, *9:*133–136.

28. POMPEIANO, O. *Arch. ital. Biol.,* 1960, *98:*92–117.

29. RUCH, T. C. and WATTS, J. W. *Amer. J. Physiol.,* 1934, *110:*362–375.

30. SAHS, A. L. and FULTON, J. F. *J. Neurophysiol.,* 1940, *3:* 258–268.

31. SHERRINGTON, C. S. *The integrative action of the nervous system.* New Haven, Conn. Yale University Press, 1906.

32. TEASDALL, R. D. and STAVRAKY, G. W. *J. Neurophysiol.,* 1953, *16:*367–375.

33. TERZUOLO, C. *J. Neurophysiol.,* 1964, *27:*578–591.

34. WEAVER, R. A., LANDAU, W. M. and HIGGINS, J. F. *Arch. Neurol. (Chic.),* 1963, *9:*127–132.

CHAPTER 9

Pontobulbar Control of Posture and Orientation in Space

By THEODORE C. RUCH

ALTHOUGH stretch reflexes are present in the chronic spinal animal, including spinal man, they are poorly sustained. For example, the knee jerk may be brisk, but a protracted stretch of the quadriceps muscles does not give rise to a persistent reflex contraction. In contrast, when the midbrain is so sectioned that the pons and medulla oblongata are left intact and connected with the spinal cord through their descending pathways, the stretch reflexes become hyperactive, *decerebrate rigidity* (Fig. 1 and Chap. 7). The myotatic reflex, which is the basis of decerebrate rigidity, has already been discussed; there remains the question of the higher control of these spinal reflexes. This question is of particular interest because decerebrate rigidity in animals resembles the spasticity associated with hemiplegia in man, a most common neurologic disorder.

Historical Note. Decerebrate rigidity was first clearly described by Sherrington in a paper published in 1898.[19] He noted that, shortly after brain stem sectioning, extensor posture became exaggerated, affecting the four extremities and the neck and tail. He argued that, since this state persisted indefinitely, it could not result from irritation incident to the cut and must therefore be looked upon as a "release" of the lower brain stem from control normally exercised by higher centers in the forebrain. His analysis of the condition is one of the classics of physiology.

In analyzing decerebrate rigidity, Sherrington first asked what forebrain areas must be destroyed to release the rigidity. He reasoned that exclusion of the pyramidal tracts was not responsible, because semisection at the level of the corpora quadrigemina caused the rigidity to appear on the *ipsilateral* side, whereas the pyramidal pathways cross below this level. Sher-

Fig. 1. Cat in decerebrate rigidity. Note hyperextended posture of neck, arching of back (opisthotonos) and extension of tail. Sherrington described the total pattern as "an exaggerated caricature of reflex standing." (From Pollock and Davis, *J. comp. Neurol.,* 1930, *50:*377–411.)

rington concluded that decerebrate rigidity must result from interruption of extrapyramidal projections from some part of the forebrain. Subsequent chapters show that descending systems from the cerebral cortex, the basal ganglia and the cerebellum are involved. It suffices now that impulses in these paths funnel into the structures of the lower brain stem (reticular formation) which will be described in this chapter.

The second question is what brain stem nuclei maintain the rigidity by facilitating the spinal myotatic reflex arcs. The vestibular nuclei are certainly involved (not the red nuclei, as was once supposed),[16] and the lateral reticular formation has been implicated.

RETICULAR FORMATION AND THE STRETCH REFLEX[9]

According to Brodal,[5] "reticular formation" as used by anatomists comprises those areas of the brain stem which are made up of "diffuse aggregations of cells of different types and sizes, separated by a wealth of fibers travelling in all directions. Circumscribed groups of cells, such as the red nucleus or the facial nucleus, formed of relatively closely packed units of a more or less uniform size and type, are not considered to be part of the reticular formation, which forms, so to speak, a sort of matrix in which the 'specific' nuclei and the more conspicuous tracts, e.g., the medial longitudinal fasciculus, are imbedded." Some nuclei with a reticular structure have received names and tend to be excluded when physiologists use the phrase. Finally, the

trend anatomically is to break up the reticular formation into fairly circumscribed cellular areas which can be referred to as nuclei.

The functions of the reticular formation remained obscure for many years. In 1946, Magoun and Rhines[15] reported that stimulation of the reticular substance lying ventromedially in the caudal part of the bulb inhibited the knee jerk, decerebrate rigidity, and movement resulting from stimulation of the motor area of the cerebral cortex. With stimuli of ordinary intensity the inhibitory effect was bilateral, but with weak stimuli it was mainly ipsilateral. These investigators also described a facilitatory region which lay more laterally in the reticular formation and was considerably more extensive, running upward into the midbrain tegmentum, the central gray matter and the subthalamus (Fig. 2).[18] Stimulation of these regions facilitated the knee jerk and augmented the responses to stimulation of the motor area.

At first sight, these reticular areas and their reticulospinal tracts provided an exceedingly simple explanation of decerebrate rigidity and the higher control of posture that was not unlike the action of the brake and accelerator on a car. The reticular facilitatory area was considered to provide a supraspinal facilitation maintaining rigidity. The reticular inhibitory area was believed to be deprived of its input from the cerebellar and cerebral cortex, and hence functionless. However, further analysis revealed that, as previously believed, the vestibulospinal tract also facilitates stretch reflexes. Furthermore, as described in Chapter 7, the net

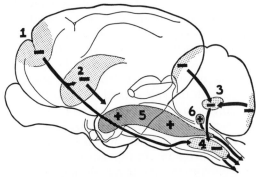

Fig. 2. Reconstruction of cat's brain showing inhibitory and facilitatory systems concerned in spasticity. Inhibitory pathways are: *1,* corticobulboreticular; *2,* caudatospinal; *3,* cerebelloreticular; and *4,* reticulospinal. Facilitatory pathways are: *5,* reticulospinal and *6,* vestibulospinal. (From Lindsley *et al., J. Neurophysiol.,* 1949, *12:*197–216.)

effect of bulbospinal descending pathways in the decerebrate preparation is facilitatory to extensor reflexes and inhibitory to flexor reflexes. If the lateral reticular area were purely facilitatory, loss of its influence could not explain the changes in reflex activity following spinal transection in a decerebrate preparation, because there is a reciprocal decrease of the stretch reflex excitability and increase of flexor reflex excitability.

Further experimentation by Sprague and Chambers[20] has removed this objection by showing that the purely inhibitory and purely excitatory effects of reticular stimulation described by Magoun and Rhines are the exception, not the rule. Generalized inhibition is uncommon in decerebrate cats, and it never occurs in unanesthetized intact cats stimulated through implanted electrodes. Rather, the effect is reciprocal—extensor inhibition-flexor contraction and vice versa—in a given limb. Thus, the reticulospinal tract obeys Sherrington's law of reciprocal innervation.* Threshold stimulation near the midline (the inhibitory area of Magoun and Rhines) tends to inhibit extensor tonus and to cause flexor contraction. Lateral stimulation (the facilitatory area of Magoun and Rhines) tends to facilitate decerebrate rigidity and inhibit flexion. (Reciprocal effects on the opposite limbs are also the rule.)

Gernandt and Thulin[8] recorded monosynaptic and multisynaptic ventral root reflex discharge while stimulating the reticular substance. They found definite reciprocal effects, especially from the medial reticular area. Moving the stimulating electrode position only 0.1 mm. might change the response to the reverse reciprocal effect. Often, an inhibitory or facilitatory effect which was strong at first decayed even though the stimulation was continued. Such decaying responses were followed by a postexcitatory rebound of opposite sign—typical of stimulation of a "mixed" structure. Since Magoun and Rhines originally investigated extensor reflexes extensively and nociceptive flexion reflexes very little, it is quite apparent how the idea of a purely facilitatory and a purely inhibitory area in the reticular formation could

arise. In the light of the subsequent work by Sprague and Chambers and others, it would be appropriate to refer to the "bulbar reticular extensor inhibitory area" and the "lateral reticular extensor facilitatory area."

Alpha and Gamma Mechanisms of Higher Control.   In considering the influence of various brain centers on myotatic reflexes and tonus, one must think of two ways in which such reflexes can be influenced: (i) by facilitation or inhibition of the large α motoneurons which innervate the majority of muscle fibers; (ii) by facilitation or inhibition of the small γ motoneurons which cause contraction of the intrafusal fibers of the muscle spindles, thereby increasing the rate of spindle firing, which in turn influences the amount of the α motoneuron firing that underlies extensor tonus. The reticular system apparently acts mainly through the γ efferents. Since the spindle discharge is only mildly inhibitory to the flexion reflex, the reticular system will affect chiefly extensor myotatic reflexes. This helps us understand how the lateral reticular areas could appear to be purely facilitatory.

Granit and Kaada[10] attached an extensor muscle to a sensitive myograph; a cut-down dorsal root filament, containing a Group I fiber from a muscle spindle in the muscle was placed on recording electrodes. When a point in the brain was stimulated, they could learn: (i) whether the muscle spindle firing was decreased or increased; (ii) whether there was any change in muscle contraction which might account for the change in spindle activity through slackening the muscle spindles. Weak stimulation of the pontile and mesencephalic ("facilitatory") reticular areas augmented the spindle discharge without causing a change in muscle tension.

In similar experiments, the bulbar region, from which Magoun and Rhines obtained inhibition of the knee jerk and decerebrate rigidity, was stimulated. The rate of spindle discharge was dramatically reduced as the result of γ efferent inhibition. An example of such an experiment is shown in Figure 3. Many of the cerebellar and cerebral structures which affect posture do so via the γ efferent system and presumably through the reticular areas. Other descending impulses may act upon the α motoneurons; e.g., elimination of the anterior cerebellum augments decerebrate rigidity although simultaneously paralyzing the γ efferent system.[6] This effect must be exerted directly upon the α motoneurons, probably by the vestibulospinal tract.

Input to Reticular and Nuclear Structures.
If, as pointed out above, the lower brain stem gives rise to descending axons inhibitory as well

---

* Should this prove otherwise, it would be profitable to think of possible nonpostural functions for this system, where nonreciprocal effects would be meaningful. Thus it is possible that the descending reticular system is concerned with awakening the animal or putting it to sleep, as is the ascending aspect of this system (Chap. 23).

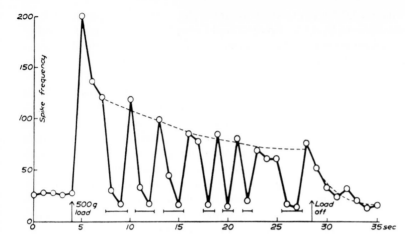

Fig. 3. Discharge frequency of a single fiber from a muscle spindle loaded with 500 grams. The bulboreticular inhibitory system was stimulated intermittently as shown by the lines below the curve. Note accompanying decrease in rate of spindle discharge. (From Granit and Kaada, *Acta physiol. scand.*, 1953, *27*:130–160.)

as excitatory to myotatic reflexes, why are myotatic reflexes hyperactive after decerebration? More specifically, why does the facilitatory pathway remain active while the inhibitory pathway is no longer functional? The reason is that the extensor inhibitory reticular system is dependent for its activity on impulses descending from higher centers (cerebral and cerebellar cortex). In contrast, vestibulospinal pathways facilitating extensors are activated through the labyrinth, and the reticular extensor facilitatory system receives impulses from the ascending afferent systems, including those originating in the muscles. A midbrain transection would remove the input into the reticular inhibitory system, thus leaving the innervated facilitatory system unopposed and the extensor reflexes overactive.

Summary. The brain stem is the origin of descending pathways, vestibular and reticular, that facilitate myotatic reflexes of extensor muscles (and inhibit nociceptive flexor reflexes), so that hypertonus (exaggerated standing) occurs when the effects of this system are unopposed by descending inhibition of myotatic reflexes (and facilitation of flexor reflexes). The actions on stretch reflexes are by two routes: (i) gamma efferent fibers innervating intrafusal fibers, and (ii) alpha motoneurons innervating the ordinary extrafusal motor fibers.

POSTURAL REFLEXES
(STATIC REACTIONS)

Postural reactions, sometimes designated "attitudinal" reflexes,[12, 13] are of three types: (i) local static reactions, (ii) segmental static reactions, and (iii) general static reactions, which include the tonic neck and labyrinthine reflexes. These terms were used by Magnus in his famous book *Körperstellung* (body posture). Some of the underlying reflexes have already been discussed under other names. All are proprioceptive in nature, the local static reactions stemming primarily from gravitational stimuli, segmental reactions arising from the effects of movement of one extremity on the opposite extremity, and general static reactions arising from the actual position of the head in space. Acceleratory reactions, e.g., postrotational nystagmus, are initiated by the semicircular canals and are distinct from the tonic labyrinthine reactions, which are independent of movement or acceleration.

The afferent sources of stimulation are as follows: (i) static reactions originate in the muscles themselves; (ii) segmental reactions develop as a result of afferents from one muscle acting upon fellow muscles of the same segment on the opposite side; and (iii) neck and labyrinthine reactions stem from receptors in the membranous labyrinth (the otolith) and in the neck muscles. Transecting the neural axis of an experimental animal and testing for the presence of the static reactions reveals the general site of the neural structures subserving them.

Spinal Animal. The basic pattern of the local and segmental static reflexes is to be found in the spinal animal. The stretch reflex—the most prominent of the *local static reactions*—is elicitable, though not strongly developed. The crossed extensor reflex may also be obtained, its presence indicating that *segmental static reactions* are also laid down at the spinal level. General static reactions are also seen. When a crossed extensor reflex is obtained in the high spinal preparation, the ipsilateral forelimb also extends. This reaction pattern tends to keep the animal from toppling over and is also a part of the quadrupedal pattern of movement involved in forward locomotion.

Low Decerebrate Animal (Bulbospinal Preparation).* All three types of static reactions are well developed in the decerebrate animal.

LOCAL STATIC REACTIONS. Local static reactions are most conspicuously developed in the extremities, and they have to do primarily with stance—the fixed standing posture that prevents collapse of the extremity under force of gravity. Sir Thomas Browne wrote (1646):

> "For station is properly no rest, but one kinde of motion, relating unto that which Physitians (from Galen) doe name extensive or tonicall, that is an extension of the muscles and organs of motion maintaining the body at length or in its proper figure, wherein although it seem to be immoved is nevertheless [not] without all motion, for in this position the muscles are sensibly extended, and labour to support the body, which permitted unto its proper gravity would suddenly subside and fall unto the earth, as it happeneth in sleep, diseases and death; from which occult action and invisible motion of the muscles in station (as Galen declareth) proceed more offensive lassitudes then from ambulation."†

Magnus put the problem of the local static reaction as follows:[13]

> "A movable limb is at times used as an *instrument* for very different purposes (such as scraping, scratching, fighting, etc.), and moves freely in all joints, whereas at other times it is transformed into a stiff and strong *pillar*, which gives the impression of being one solid column, able to carry the weight of the body. Experiments have shown that this is accomplished by a series of local static reflexes."

In becoming pillar-like, joints must become fixed; this involves simultaneous contraction of opposing muscle groups. The stretch reflex, which is at the basis of the antigravity response, is not of itself sufficient to fix a given joint: opposing muscles must contract simultaneously to ensure fixation of the joint but must relax re-

---

* Preparations made by transecting the neural axis can be designated by the level of the decerebrating transection or by the highest brain stem level maintaining connection with the spinal reflex arcs, e.g., bulbospinal.

† *Enquiries into vulgar and common errors,* 1646, Book 3, Chap. I. Of the Elephant, p. 105.

ciprocally when position of the extremity is changed even slightly.

The basis of this coordinated response involving the entire musculature of an extremity was discovered by Magnus in a decerebellated dog. Here the already exaggerated stretch reflexes are still more pronounced when the pads of the feet are lightly touched. The extremity in these circumstances follows one's finger as if it were a magnet. Although now designated the "positive supporting reaction," the response when first described was termed the "magnet reaction." Close analysis revealed that the reaction starts from a touch stimulus to the skin of the toe pad, i.e., *exteroceptive* stimulus; this, however, is followed by a *proprioceptive* stimulus, i.e., stretch of the interosseus muscles by separation of the toe pads. When the skin of the foot was anesthetized, the exteroceptive phase was abolished, but as soon as the toe pads became separated, the proprioceptive stimulus promptly initiated the response. Once the extremities encountered active resistance, other muscles were stretched, and they in turn reinforced the reaction initiated from the skin and small muscles of the toe pads. The reaction itself transforms the extremity from a flexible and toneless state into a supporting member having the stiffness of a rigid pillar. Although present in normal animals and in man, the reaction is more readily demonstrated in a decerebrate preparation in which all of the static reactions are released and exaggerated.

SEGMENTAL STATIC REACTIONS. The crossed extension reflex is one of the classic reactions of decerebrate animals. One must also recognize intersegmental static reactions. For example, when a hindlimb is caused to extend either through the positive supporting reaction or from a crossed extension reflex, the opposite forelimb also extends, thus demonstrating the influence of the lumbar segments upon the cervical. The same pattern also occurs in reverse—the extension of one forelimb is accompanied automatically by the extension of the opposite hindlimb, all of which is a pattern essential for quadrupedal standing as well as for locomotion.

GENERAL STATIC REACTIONS. Once an animal succeeds in standing, his stance can be modified in accordance with the needs of a given situation. If, for example, a cat lifts its head to look up to a shelf, both forelimbs become automatically extended; if it tries to look under a sofa, both forelimbs become flexed. The general static reactions are due in part to the influence of one muscle group upon muscle groups in other segments, but they are also modified by the tonic neck and labyrinthine reflexes.

Tonic neck reflexes. In order to differentiate neck from labyrinthine reflexes, both labyrinths must be destroyed and sources of stimulation for the static reactions removed, so that only the influence of the neck muscles will be observed when the neck is turned. Rotation of the jaw to the right in such a preparation causes prompt increase in the extensor posture of both limbs on the right side and relaxation of the limbs on the other side. Dorsal flexion of the head of non-hopping animals causes extension of both forelimbs and relaxation of the hindlimbs (cat looking up to shelf); ventral flexion of the head causes relaxation of both forelimbs and extension of the hindlimbs (cat looking under sofa).

These reactions are obviously purposeful. If a cat walking forward in a straight line hears a mouse to its right, mere turning of the head to the right causes the extremities on that side to become extended, and the cat is automatically prepared for a quick takeoff with its left foot. Clear-cut utility is also seen in extension and flexion of the forelimbs when the gaze is directed upward and downward, respectively. Section of the dorsal nerve roots in the anterior cervical region abolishes these reactions. These reactions are prominent in decerebrate cats and have also been clearly demonstrated in labyrinthectomized monkeys following bilateral removal of the motor and premotor areas.

Tonic labyrinthine reflexes. The tonic neck and labyrinthine reactions can be separated by severing bilaterally the upper four cervical sensory roots. The labyrinth itself has two distinct mechanisms, one the otolith and the other the semicircular canals. The static labyrinthine reactions are probably mediated by the otolith, and the reactions to angular acceleration appear to stem primarily from the semicircular canals, but a clear-cut distinction between the functions of the two end organs has never been achieved. The static labyrinthine reactions manifest themselves through changes in resting posture brought about by alterations of the animal's position. When the animal is placed on its back, i.e., in a horizontal supine position, the extremities are maximally extended. Extension is minimal when the animal is prone with its snout tilted 45 degrees to the horizontal plane.

This behavior is contrary to expectation, and its rationale must yet be worked out.

The low decerebrate animal never rights himself, stands or walks spontaneously. That this is not due to "shock" but rather to the loss of the necessary neural apparatus was proved by Bard and Macht,[3] who maintained bulbo-spinal animals for as long as 40 days without observing the spontaneous head or body righting shown by high decerebrate preparations.

High Decerebrate Animal (Midbrain and Thalamic Preparations). The neural apparatus essential for the reactions described below appears to lie in the midbrain, since the reactions are seen if the neural axis is transected just above the red nucleus and the animal is kept alive and in good condition for one or two weeks. If the transection is even higher, yielding a thalamic or decorticate preparation, righting, standing and walking are seen immediately after the operation, and the adjustments are generally brisker and more powerful. The structures lying between the red nucleus and the cerebral cortex apparently facilitate the function of the structures which execute rigidity and walking.

RIGHTING REFLEXES. The second category of general static reactions are the so-called righting reflexes. Once toppled over, the low decerebrate animal exhibits no tendency to regain the upright position. Cats and dogs exhibit no decerebrate rigidity when the midbrain is intact. When the animal is placed on its side, it tends first to right its head and then its body. Through a series of such maneuvers the animal may achieve an upright position, standing essentially normally on all four limbs. The midbrain primate (Fig. 4) shows a similar tendency,

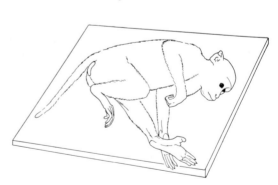

Fig. 4. Thalamic reflex posture in decorticate monkey. Note the lowermost extremities are extended and the uppermost flexed. (From Bieber and Fulton, *Arch. Neurol. Psychiat. (Chic.)*, 1938, *39*:433–454.)

but is unable actually to stand, even though some of the righting reflexes described below are present. The primate differs from the dog or the cat in greater encephalization of motor function in the forebrain.

The classic righting reflex can be demonstrated in the intact cat by dropping it blindfolded with its legs pointed upward. The cat turns with almost incredible speed and lights deftly on all fours. Magnus[12] noted that in every case a rotation of the head initiates the turn. This rotation he considered due to labyrinthine righting reflexes. Rotation of the upper body follows to align it with the head. This Magnus ascribed to neck righting reflexes. These two reactions are followed by rotation of the lower body, completing the turn. Rademaker and Ter Braak[17] have analyzed the muscular movements employed in turning. After its labyrinths have been destroyed, a blindfolded cat fails entirely to turn when dropped, and plummets to the floor on its back. It is not yet clear which part of the labyrinth is responsible for the reaction, but most investigators believe the utricle to be the primary receptor.

The reflexes responsible for the righting tendency have been separated into five principal groups. The reactions are sequential, as are those involved in swallowing.

Labyrinthine righting reflexes.   If all the sensory channels contributing to the righting reflex are obliterated, the animal lies on its side, disoriented, and makes no attempt to bring its head or body into the horizontal position. This "zero" condition is accomplished if both labyrinths are destroyed, the animal is blindfolded, the upper cervical sensory nerve roots are cut, and a weight is applied to the upper surface of the animal's body. If, however, one of these sensory fields is left intact, its contribution can be analyzed. If an animal is blindfolded but its labyrinth is still intact, the head assumes the horizontal position irrespective of the position of the remainder of the body, i.e., the head is given orientation in space. This reaction, like that of a tonic labyrinthine response, disappears if the otoliths are destroyed. The reaction is thus static, having nothing to do with acceleratory responses. The labyrinthine righting reactions are undoubtedly primary and take the lead, as it were, in bringing the body as a whole into the upright position.

Body-on-head righting reflexes.   If a labyrinthectomized animal is blindfolded and is placed in the lateral position on a table, the head also tends to right itself. The reaction can be inhibited by placing a weighted board on the animal's upper surface. The reaction thus is due to asymmetrical stimulation of the receptors of the body surface. These reactions are seen in a thalamic primate as well as in the cat and dog.

Neck righting reflexes.   Once the neck has been turned in response to the labyrinthine and body-on-head righting reflexes, the neck muscle proprioceptors become stimulated, and the body itself then tends to be brought into a horizontal position following the head. This response likewise is seen in the primate and is accompanied by a grasping reflex presently to be described.

Body righting reflexes acting on body.   If the head and shoulders are held in the lateral position, the hindquarters tend to assume the horizontal position independently of the forward segments. This reaction can be inhibited by applying weight to the animal's upper surface.

Optical righting reflexes.   In the normal animal the eyes contribute to the righting reactions, but since the occipital lobes are absent in the thalamic preparation, visual data play no part in midbrain righting. If the labyrinths and neck muscles are denervated and the animal is dropped with its eyes open, righting still occurs, but this reaction fails if such a preparation is blindfolded. The optical cues are particularly important in the primates, for optical righting can still be demonstrated in monkeys after their motor and premotor areas have been completely removed bilaterally (Chap. 12).

Grasp reflex.   The thalamic primate (unlike the cat and dog) has an abnormal distribution of postural reflexes. When the animal is in the lateral position, the lowermost extremities are vigorously extended and the uppermost extremities are flexed (Fig. 4). The uppermost extremities, furthermore, exhibit an involuntary grasp reflex. When the animal is turned to the opposite side, the thalamic reflex pattern is reversed; the extremities previously extended now become flexed and also show a grasp reflex which was previously absent. The grasp reflex seems to be a general static reaction[4] and is well known to clinical neurologists in a slightly modified form termed "forced grasping."

Postural Reactions Depending upon Cerebral and Cerebellar Cortex.   Two groups of reactions important to the postural mechanism clearly depend upon the integrity of the cere-

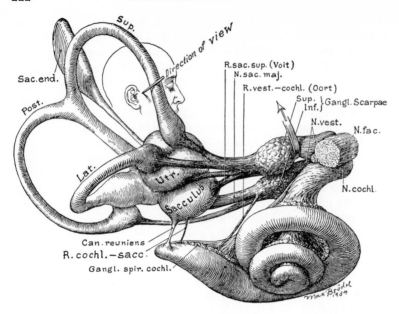

Fig. 5. Structural relations of innervation of human labyrinth. Note orientation of the three nerves supplying the macula sacculi—also Oort's nerve, passing through the cochlea. (From Hardy, *Anat. Rec.*, 1935, *59*:403–418.)

bral cortex[2] and the cerebellum.[20] These are the placing and the hopping reactions.

PLACING REACTIONS. The placing reactions ensure that the foot shall be in a position suitable for normal standing and normal locomotion. These reactions are of two types, visual and nonvisual. When an animal is lowered toward a visible supporting surface, the forelimbs are put down, so that, without further adjustment, the limbs are in a position to support the weight of the body. When the animal is blindfolded, a similar reaction occurs as a result of a combination of exteroceptive and proprioceptive stimuli.[2] (Contact placing, which occurs when the foot touches an object, is described in Chapter 14.)

HOPPING REACTIONS. Hopping reactions are evoked when the body is displaced in a horizontal direction; these maintain the animal in a normal standing posture. If an animal is held so that it stands on one leg and its body is then moved sideways, the leg hops in the direction of the displacement, so that the leg remains more or less under the body. Rademaker has pointed out that the reaction is due to stretching of the muscles and probably is little affected by exteroceptive stimuli.

LABYRINTHINE ACCELERATING REFLEXES

Although technically an organ of special sense, the labyrinth gives rise to reflexes which orient the body in space and which hence are allied to postural reflexes. The labyrinth, often referred to as the vestibular organ, is made up of two principal parts: the semicircular canals and the otolith organs (saccule and utricle), as seen in Figure 5.

Position and structure of labyrinth. The membranous semicircular canals lie within the bony labyrinth. These canals contain endolymph which communicates through fine openings with the endolymph in the utricle. The canals lie in three planes that are, approximately at least, at right angles to the mesial or sagittal plane of the body, and each of the vertical canals makes an angle of about 45 degrees with this mesial plane. The plane of each anterior canal is parallel to that of the posterior or inferior vertical canal of the opposite side of the head, as represented in Figure 6. At one end of each canal, near its junction with the utricle, is the swelling known as the ampulla. Within the ampulla lies the crista acustica, containing hair cells which communicate with the nerve fibers and which therefore are considered to be the receptors of the organ. Sitting astride the hair cells and crista is a gelatinous partition known as the cupula, which rises like a swinging door to the roof of the ampulla, filling the whole cross section of this structure. Once considered a fixation artefact, the cupula is now known to be a real structure of functional importance. It responds in a highly damped fashion to hydrostatic forces acting upon it through the endolymph. The nerve fibers distributed to the hair cells pass into the vestibular branch of the VIIIth nerve.

Function of the Semicircular Canals. The work of Flourens and of the investigators who followed him* made it evident that a primary function of the semicircular canals is to register movement of the body in space; expressed more precisely, the vestibular organ responds to any *change in the rate of movement,* i.e., to acceleration or deceleration. In fast aircraft, for example, very intense acceleratory forces may develop, particularly in the "pull-out" from a dive or in a close turn. In these circumstances the semicircular canals may be so profoundly stimulated that the pilot becomes completely disoriented in space, especially if he should inadvertently turn his head during the high acceleration (Coriolis effect).†

Acceleratory reflexes may be described under two headings: (i) linear acceleration and (ii) angular acceleration.

ACCELERATORY REFLEXES. *Linear acceleration.* If a blindfolded cat is suddenly lowered through the air with its head down, its forelegs become extended and its toes spread (vestibular placing reaction). This is the normal response to linear acceleration. The obvious purpose of the reaction is to facilitate landing after a jump from a high place.

Angular acceleration and nystagmus. During rapid rotation around the vertical axis of the body, a series of reactions affect the muscles of the eyes, neck, limbs and trunk. As the head turns, the eyes turn slowly in the *opposite* direction in order to maintain the gaze at a fixed point and to maintain visual contact with the environment. But, as the body turns farther, the eyes swing rapidly in the direction of the rotation and fix upon a new point, which is held in view as the eyes again move slowly and the rotation continues. This alternate movement of the eyes—a quick refixation phase followed by a slow fixation deviation—is termed *nystagmus.* The direction of the nystagmus is designated clinically by the direction of its quick phase.

When rotation continues for a time at a constant rate, the nystagmus disappears, indicating that acceleration is the stimulus for the response rather than continuous motion. If the acceleration is suddenly stopped, the involuntary eye movements commence once again, but in the opposite direction; i.e., *in postrotational nys-*

tagmus the direction of the quick phase is the opposite of the direction of the preceding acceleration (and of the quick phase during rotation). Combining this rule with a knowledge of the physiologic significance of the eye movements makes it unnecessary to remember the direction of the initial nystagmus. During rotation, the eyes move slowly in the direction opposite that of rotation in order to maintain fixation, and the quick or refixation movement is in the *same direction as the rotation.* Therefore, in postrotational nystagmus the quick phase is opposite to the direction of the prior rotation.

Nystagmus may be horizontal, vertical or rotatory in direction, since the particular response depends upon which semicircular canals or groups of canals are stimulated, i.e., upon the direction of the acceleration. If the head is bent forward at an angle of 30 degrees, the horizontal semicircular canals are in the plane of rotation about the vertical axis of the body and they become responsible for the nystagmus caused by the rotation.

Nystagmus induced by rotation or, more often, by irrigation of the ear with cold water is a clinical test of labyrinthine function. Nystagmus may occur "spontaneously" after a variety of lesions affecting the sense organs or the neural pathways connecting the labyrinth with the motor nuclei innervating the eye muscles. Such nystagmus is of great aid in localizing lesions of the brain.

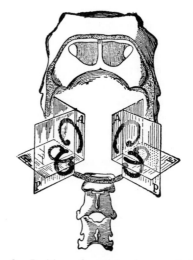

Fig. 6. Position of semicircular canals in birds. The three canals lie in planes at right angles to one another. External or horizontal canals (*E*) on the two sides lie in same plane. Anterior canal of one side (*A*) lies in a plane parallel to that of the posterior canal (*P*) of the other side.

---

* The literature on the semicircular canals and the vestibule is very extensive. The principal bibliography may be obtained from the works by Camis,[6] and by McNalley and Stuart.[11]

†Coriolis, G. G. *Traité de la mécanique des corps solides et de calcul de l'effet des machines,* Paris, 1829.

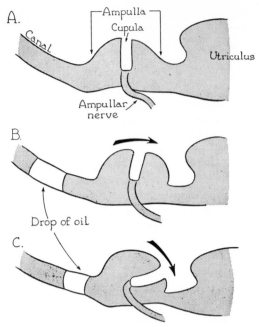

Fig. 7. Ampulla and semicircular canal of living fish (pike) before and during angular acceleration. *A,* Normal relations of ampulla, cupula and utriculus in semicircular canal. In *B,* a drop of oil has been inserted in canal. Note in *C* that cupula, nearly vertical in *B,* bends toward utricle as result of flow of endolymph into ampulla. (After Dohlman, *Proc. Roy. Soc. Med.,* 1935, *28*:1371–1380.)

Mechanism of stimulation of the canals. If the fluid in the semicircular canals moves, the mechanisms for stimulation of the hair cells during and after rotation are easily visualized. While the small diameter of the membranous canals and the consequent capillary forces and frictional resistances argue against fluid movements, direct visualization indicates that movement actually occurs—at least in the semicircular canals of fish. Steinhausen[21] devised an ingenious method of visualizing the semicircular canals in the living animal through the use of dyes, and Dohlman[7] succeeded in introducing a drop of oil into the canal so that he could follow the movement of the endolymph during angular acceleration.

Steinhausen found that the cupula (Fig. 7) bends over toward the utricle when endolymph moves into the ampulla and slowly returns to its resting position after the acceleration stops.

The relations of the canal to the ampullar nerve, the crista and the cupula are shown in Figure 7*A.* In Figure 7*B* one sees a semicircular canal at rest with a drop of oil in the lumen of the canal. In Figure 7*C* the same canal is

shown during angular acceleration; the oil droplet has moved forward, and the cupula is bent over through an angle of some 30 degrees. Dohlman points out that, when the rates of displacement and return of the cupula are actually determined, they coincide precisely with the duration of nystagmus during the acceleration and with that of the postrotational nystagmus which follows. To quote:

"The cupula deviates during, perhaps, the first, or possibly also the second, revolution as long as the rotation is accelerated. On reaching a constant speed the rotation no longer affects the fluid or the cupula in any way. The deviation of the cupula is now, however, gradually diminished by its elasticity; and after about half a minute it has returned to the original position. It is to be expected that the nystagmus *during rotation* should cease when the cupula resumes its normal position, and it does, as Buys showed by nystagmographic registration several years ago.

"When rotation stops we again have, as a result of the effect of retardation on the endolymph, a deviation of the cupula, this time in the opposite direction. A post-rotational nystagmus occurs, and lasts as long as the cupula needs to return once more, through its elasticity, to its starting position. This explains why a post-rotatory nystagmus does not occur until after a longer continued rotation. And it explains why we must have a rotational time of about 20 seconds to obtain the longest nystagmus for any rotational speed. For the cupula has by that time regained its initial position by its elasticity, so that it might be ready for the maximal displacement in the opposite direction through the inertia of the endolymph when the rotation ceases. So the nystagmus *during* rotation, like the *post-rotational* nystagmus, is a consequence of the deviation of the cupula; and its duration depends on the time the cupula requires to reassume its normal position."[7]

In human subjects in whom the membranous labyrinth had been opened to expose the horizontal canal to mechanical stimulation, suddenly applied pressure caused a horizontal nystagmus lasting about 20 seconds.[7]

CLINICAL CORRELATIONS: CALORIC REACTIONS. In 1908, the Swedish neurologist Robert Bárány[1] found that irrigating the external auditory canal with water cooler than body temperature produced about a minute later a nystagmus of variable characteristics depending on the position of the head in space. This procedure has become a useful, if somewhat uncomfortable, clinical test of labyrinthine function, largely replacing the rotation test. Various theories have been proposed to explain the mechanism of caloric nystagmus, and that postulating convection currents appears to be the most satisfactory. During caloric stimulation, the endolymph within the canal is gradually cooled at the point nearest the auditory meatus. This focal chilling causes the endolymph to flow, thus leading to a deviation of the cupula caused by the convection currents. The difference between the two forms of stimulation— rotational and caloric—lies in this: rotation suddenly stimulates both labyrinths, whereas in the caloric test there is a gradual stimulation of only one labyrinth. Thus, caloric stimulation permits the neurologist to determine which labyrinth is affected and to estimate from the duration of the nystagmus the degree of impairment.

Abnormal paroxysmal stimulation of the semicircular canals or of the nerves which innervate them also occurs, the classic syndrome being the one described in the nineteenth century by the French neurologist Menière. Characteristically, the afflicted patient experiences buzzing in the ear (tinnitus), hearing loss and attacks of dizziness during which he is thrown to the ground. Failure or sluggishness of the nystagmic response to caloric stimulation is diagnostic and also indicates that the disturbance destroys function as well as stimulating it. Section of the VIIIth nerve on the affected side relieves the dizziness and improves hearing, because the normal ear hears better when the buzzing in the other ear has ended.

Utricle and Saccule. In summarizing the vast and conflicting literature concerning the discrete functions of the various parts of the labyrinth, McNalley and Stuart[11] drew attention to the work of Ross, who succeeded in recording action currents from individual fibers of the vestibular nerve. He found that the labyrinthine receptors can be divided into three groups, those responding to slow mechanical vibration, those responding to tilting movements (linear acceleration) and those responding to rotatory movements. The semicircular canals are stimulated quite clearly by rotatory movements and probably not by gravity per se;

the cupula projection from the floor of the ampulla would not respond to an increased gravitational force. The otolith organ in the utricle responds to both linear acceleration and tilting; and, in frogs, destruction of the utricle without encroachment upon the semicircular canals has abolished the normal response to linear acceleration and tilting.

Evidence concerning the function of the *saccule* is also conflicting, but it is currently believed to be associated with reception of slow vibrational stimuli rather than being an essential part of the vestibular mechanism.[11]

REFERENCES

1. BÁRÁNY, R. *Med. Klinik,* 1908, *4*:1903–1905.
2. BARD, P. *Harvey Lect.,* 1937–38, *33*:143–169.
3. BARD, P. and MACHT, M. B. In: *Ciba Foundation Symposium on the neurological basis of behaviour,* G. E. W. WOLSTEN-HOLME and C. M. O'CONNOR, eds. Boston, Little, Brown and Co., 1958.
4. BIEBER, I. and FULTON, J. F. *Arch. Neurol. Psychiat. (Chic.),* 1938, *39*:433–454.
5. BRODAL, A. *The reticular formation of the brain stem. Anatomical aspects and functional correlations.* London, Oliver and Boyd, 1957.
6. CAMIS, M. *The physiology of the vestibular apparatus,* trans. by R. S. CREED. London, Oxford University Press, 1930.
7. DOHLMAN, G. *Proc. roy. Soc. Med.,* 1935, *28*:1371–1380.
8. GERNANDT, B. E. and THULIN, C. A. *J. Neurophysiol.,* 1955, *18*:113–129.
9. GRANIT, R., HOLMGREN, B. and MERTON, P. A. *J. Physiol.,* 1955, *130*:213–224.
10. GRANIT, R. and KAADA, B. *Acta physiol. scand.,* 1953, *27*: 130–160.
11. McNALLEY, W. J. and STUART, E. A. *War Med. (Chic.),* 1942, *2*:683–771.
12. MAGNUS, R. *Körperstellung.* Berlin, J. Springer, 1924.
13. MAGNUS, R. *Lancet,* 1926, *2*:531–536; 585–588.
14. MAGOUN, H. W. *Physiol. Rev.,* 1950, *30*:459–474.
15. MAGOUN, H. W. and RHINES, R. *J. Neurophysiol.,* 1946, *9*: 165–171.
16. RADEMAKER, G. G. J. *Das Stehn.* Berlin, J. Springer, 1931.
17. RADEMAKER, G. G. J. and TER BRAAK, J. W. G. *Acta otolaryng. (Stockh.),* 1936, *23*:313–343.
18. RHINES, R. and MAGOUN, H. W. *J. Neurophysiol.,* 1946, *9*:219–229.
19. SHERRINGTON, C. S. *J. Physiol.,* 1898, *22*:319–332.
20. SPRAGUE, J. M. and CHAMBERS, W. W. *Amer. J. Physiol.,* 1954, *176*:52–64.
21. STEINHAUSEN, W. *Z. Hals-, Nas. u. Ohrenheilk.,* 1931, *29*: 211–216.

CHAPTER 10

The Autonomic Nervous System

By HARRY D. PATTON

In the foregoing chapters attention was focused on reflex systems in which the effector organ is skeletal muscle and the response is skeletal movement. Such reflex arcs are termed *somatic reflexes*. Smooth muscle, glands and the conducting tissue of the heart also receive motor nerve supplies which, when reflexly activated, alter the functional state of the innervated organ; such reflexes are termed *autonomic reflexes*.

Autonomic nerve discharge to smooth muscles and glands has an important role in visceral and glandular responses to environmental changes; for example, reflex alteration of arteriolar diameter, mediated over autonomic motor fibers supplying vascular smooth muscle, is at least partly responsible for the shifting of blood from one vascular bed to another in accordance with physiologic demand. Similarly, although not initiating the beat of the heart, reflex discharges over the autonomic nerves sup-

plying the cardiac pacemaker modulate and regulate the rate of beating, so that the varying demands upon the pumping system are automatically met. Numerous examples of the regulation of visceral and glandular structures by autonomic reflex arcs will be encountered in subsequent chapters. This chapter is concerned with the general properties and organization of the autonomic nervous system.

The distinction between autonomic and somatic motor outflows is based on both anatomic and functional grounds. Before entrance upon a detailed description of the autonomic system, a brief account of its unique and distinctive properties is appropriate. Anatomically the autonomic outflow differs from the somatic outflow in the location of the motoneuron soma. In the somatic division, the cell bodies of the motoneurons are located exclusively within the central nervous system, in the anterior spinal

226

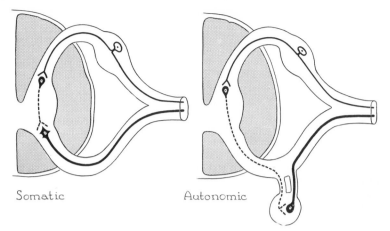

Fig. 1. Diagram illustrating a somatic reflex arc (*left*) and an autonomic reflex arc (*right*).

Somatic

Autonomic

horns or in the motor nuclei of cranial nerves in the brain stem. With one exception, the adrenal medulla, smooth muscle and glands receive direct motor innervation from cell bodies situated in ganglia outside the central nervous system. Thus the typical autonomic reflex chain contains one synaptic junction between the outflow from the central nervous system and the effector organ.

The centrally located penultimate neuron whose axon feeds the ganglion is appropriately termed the *preganglionic neuron;* its axon is typically myelinated and displays the distinctive properties of B fibers (see Chap. 3). The ultimate neuron, originating in the ganglion, is called, somewhat less appropriately, the *postganglionic neuron;* its axon is unmyelinated and displays the distinctive properties described in Chapter 3 under the heading "s.C. fibers." Figure 1 contrasts diagrammatically somatic and autonomic reflex arcs. It should be noted that the afferent sides of these arcs are indistinguishable; indeed, one and the same afferent pathway may feed both autonomic and somatic outflows. The preganglionic neuron may be considered the homologue of the interneuron of somatic arcs. Just as the interneuron, by its numerous intersegmental connections with motoneurons, tends to cause diffuse efferent discharge over several spinal segments, so the preganglionic neuron, by connection with several ganglia, may distribute the postganglionic efferent discharge.

A second fundamental difference between autonomic and somatic reflex arcs lies in the site at which inhibition occurs. In somatic arcs, inhibition is exerted by one neuron upon another, but never by a nerve cell upon an effector (muscle) cell. Relaxation of a skeletal muscle is accomplished by inhibition within the spinal cord of the motoneurons which excite it. This is *central inhibition*. In autonomic reflex arcs, presynaptic fibers may inhibit preganglionic neurons, but, in addition, some autonomic postganglionic fibers inhibit the action of the effector organs which they innervate. The best documented example of such *peripheral* or *neuroeffector inhibition* is the action of vagal impulses upon the heart—the excitability of the pacemaker is so diminished that the heart rate declines. Intense vagal stimulation may result in temporary cardiac standstill.

ORGANIZATION OF AUTONOMIC OUTFLOW

It is convenient to divide the autonomic outflow into two divisions distinguished by the location of their preganglionic cell bodies. The *sympathetic* or *thoracolumbar division* originates from preganglionic neurons in the thoracic and upper lumbar spinal segments, and its axons leave the spinal cord via the corresponding ventral roots. The *parasympathetic* or *craniosacral division* originates from preganglionic neurons in certain cranial nerve nuclei and in the second, third and fourth sacral segments of the spinal cord. The cranial outflow leaves the brain with the appropriate cranial nerves, and the sacral parasympathetic outflow emerges over the S_2, S_3 and S_4 ventral roots.

Sympathetic or Thoracolumbar Outflow. The cell bodies of the preganglionic neurons are found in the intermediolateral gray matter of spinal segments T_1 to L_2 or L_3; the axons of these neurons emerge in the corresponding ventral roots and enter the spinal nerve, where they part from the somatic motor fibers via the *white ramus communicans* to reach the paravertebral sympathetic ganglion chain.

This chain contains one ganglion for each segmental nerve, except in the cervical region where individual ganglia become variably fused to form two or three ganglia—the superior, middle and inferior cervical ganglia. The superior ganglion is the largest and gives rise to the postganglionic sympathetic supply to the head. The inferior ganglion is often fused with the first thoracic ganglion into a dumbbell-shaped structure called the "stellate" ganglion. The remaining thoracic, lumbar and sacral ganglia are variable, small and segmentally arranged.

On entering the ganglionic chain a preganglionic fiber may pursue one of three courses:

(i) It may pass up or down the chain to establish synaptic connections with postganglionic neurons in ganglia belonging to more superior or inferior segments. In this way ganglia of cervical, lower lumbar and sacral segments lacking white rami receive input from the spinal cord. The fibers connecting the ganglia in the chain are largely composed of preganglionic fibers following this course. Each such fiber connects with many postganglionic cells situated in several ganglia; a single white ramus may connect with as many as eight or nine segmental ganglia. Consequently, a discharge of discrete central origin is spread diffusely over several segments in a manner reminiscent of the multisegmental discharge of somatic arcs which contain one or more spinal interneurons. The axons of the postganglionic cells in the paravertebral chain pass through the *gray ramus communicans* to enter the corresponding segmental nerve, where they reach the autonomic effectors of the skin and subcutaneous structures (cutaneous and deep blood vessels, sweat glands, pilomotor smooth muscle). *Each spinal nerve receives a gray ramus from its corresponding ganglion.* In addition to their projections through the gray rami, the cervical and thoracic ganglia send postganglionic bundles to the structures of the thoracic cavity, notably the heart (cardiac accelerator nerves).

(ii) The preganglionic fibers may pass without interruption through the chain into the splanchnic nerves to reach the celiac or other ganglia lying in the prevertebral sympathetic plexus, which invests the abdominal aorta and its major branches down to the iliac arteries. The postganglionic neurons of the prevertebral plexus supply fibers to the smooth muscle of the abdominal and pelvic viscera, to the glands of the gut, to the blood vessels of the abdominal viscera, etc.

(iii) Some preganglionic fibers of the splanchnic nerve directly innervate the secretory cells of the adrenal medulla. The adrenal medulla is the only sympathetic effector organ known to be directly innervated by preganglionic fibers.

Parasympathetic or Craniosacral Outflow. The cranial portion of the parasympathetic outflow originates from preganglionic neurons situated in brain stem nuclei of cranial nerves III, VII, IX and X. The axons of these neurons travel with these nerves to supply postganglionic neurons in ganglia within or near the thoracic and abdominal viscera. The sacral parasympathetic outflow arises from preganglionic neurons, mostly in the third and fourth sacral spinal segments but sometimes also in the second and fifth. The axons of these neurons emerge with the corresponding ventral roots, but separate from the somatic efferent fibers to form the *nervi erigentes,* or pelvic nerves, which supply postganglionic neurons innervating the genitalia and the autonomic effectors of the pelvic cavity. The parasympathetic ganglia containing the postganglionic neurons are usually situated in or near the organ innervated. Unlike the sympathetic ganglionic system, the parasympathetic system contains few or no interconnections between ganglia. Consequently, parasympathetic discharge is more discrete than sympathetic discharge.

AUTONOMIC INNERVATION OF VARIOUS STRUCTURES

The autonomic innervation of some important visceral structures may now be summarized (see also Figure 2). More detailed accounts appear in the monographs by White *et al.,*[16] Kuntz[8] and Mitchell. [11, 12]

LACRIMAL GLANDS

Parasympathetic. *Preganglionic neurons* originate in the superior salivatory nucleus; axons pass with the VIIth nerve, the nervus intermedius, and the greater superficial petrosal and vidian nerves to reach *postganglionic neurons* in the sphenopalatine ganglion. Their axons pass in the maxillary division of the Vth nerve to the lacrimal glands. *Function:* Vasodilation and secretion.

Sympathetic. *Preganglionic neurons* originate in the intermediolateral cell column of the upper thoracic spinal segments; axons ascend the sympathetic chain to reach *postganglionic neurons* in the superior cervical ganglion. Their axons ascend in the carotid plexus, the deep petrosal and vidian nerves, and the maxillary division of the Vth nerve to the glands. *Function:* Vasoconstriction.

EYE

Parasympathetic. *Preganglionic neurons* originate in oculomotor nucleus; axons travel in the oculomotor nerve to reach *postganglionic neurons* in the ciliary ganglion. Their axons traverse the short ciliary nerve to reach the ciliary muscle and the constrictor muscle of the iris. *Function:* Pupillary constriction (miosis), accommodation for near vision.*

Sympathetic. *Preganglionic neurons* originate in upper thoracic segments; axons ascend the sympathetic chain to reach *postganglionic neurons* in the superior cervical ganglion. Their axons pass via the carotid plexus and the ophthalmic division of the Vth nerve to the dilator muscles of the iris, the smooth muscle of the levator palpebrae superioris, the radial fibers of the ciliary muscle and the blood vessels of the retina, orbit, and conjunctiva. In lower mammals, e.g., the cat, fibers also supply the nictitating membrane. *Function:* Pupillary dilation (mydriasis), vasoconstriction, elevation of the lid and accommodation for far vision.*

SALIVARY GLANDS

Parasympathetic. *Preganglionic neurons* of outflow to submaxillary and sublingual glands originate in the superior salivatory nucleus; those of the outflow to the parotid glands originate in the inferior salivatory nucleus. From the former, axons pass in the facial nerve and through the chorda tympani to the submaxillary and sublingual ganglia. Axons from the inferior salivatory nucleus pass via the tympani branch of the IXth nerve to the lesser superficial petrosal nerve and thence to the otic ganglion. Axons of the *postganglionic neurons* pass from the submaxillary and sublingual ganglia to their respective glands and from the otic ganglion via the auriculotemporal branch of the Vth nerve to the parotid gland. *Function:* Vasodilation and secretion.

*During accommodations for near vision the circular fibers of the ciliary muscle contract in response to the parasympathetic innervation. This action releases the tension on the suspensory ligament, permitting the anterior surface of the lens to bulge and thus assume a more nearly spherical shape. During accommodation for far vision not only do the circular fibers of the ciliary muscle relax, but the radial fibers innervated by sympathetic fibers contract. Both actions increase the tension on the suspensory ligament and thus flatten the lens.[13]

Sympathetic. *Preganglionic neurons* originate in upper thoracic segments; axons ascend the chain to reach *postganglionic neurons* in the superior cervical ganglion. Their axons run along the external carotid and external maxillary arteries. *Function:* Vasoconstriction and secretion.

HEART[12]

Parasympathetic. *Preganglionic neurons* originate in the dorsal motor nucleus of the vagus; axons pass through the vagal trunk to reach *postganglionic neurons* in ganglia found in the cardiac plexus and in the walls of the atria. Distribution of the endings is disputed, but they probably reach the coronary vessels, atrial musculature, sino-atrial node and conduction tissue. *Function:* Cardiac deceleration and perhaps coronary constriction.

Sympathetic. *Preganglionic neurons* originate in the intermediolateral column of the upper four or five thoracic spinal segments; axons pass with the corresponding ventral roots and white rami to the sympathetic chain to reach *postganglionic neurons* in the upper four or five thoracic ganglia and in the cervical ganglia. Axons from the cervical ganglia form the superior, middle and inferior cardiac nerves which run to the cardiac plexus, where they are joined by varying numbers of thoracic cardiac nerves from the thoracic ganglia. Some postganglionic neurons arise in ganglia along the course of the cardiac nerves and in the cardiac plexus, and receive their input from preganglionic fibers which run through the chain without synaptic interruption. Distribution of terminals is disputed, but probably extends to coronary vessels, the pacemaker, the conduction system and both the atrial and the ventricular myocardium. *Function:* Cardiac acceleration and perhaps coronary dilation.

LUNGS

Parasympathetic and sympathetic. Origins of innervation are similar to those for the heart except that the sympathetic preganglionic portion originates in the T_2-T_6 segments. Both parasympathetic and sympathetic fibers enter the pulmonary plexus, in which the parasympathetic ganglia are embedded. Parasympathetic fibers of both supplies terminate in bronchi and blood vessels. *Function:* The parasympathetic impulses constrict and the sympathetic dilate the bronchi. Despite demonstrable vascular endings, there is little evidence of significant vasomotor regulation of pulmonary vessels.

ESOPHAGUS

Parasympathetic. Supplied by branches of the vagi. *Function:* Contraction of smooth muscle.

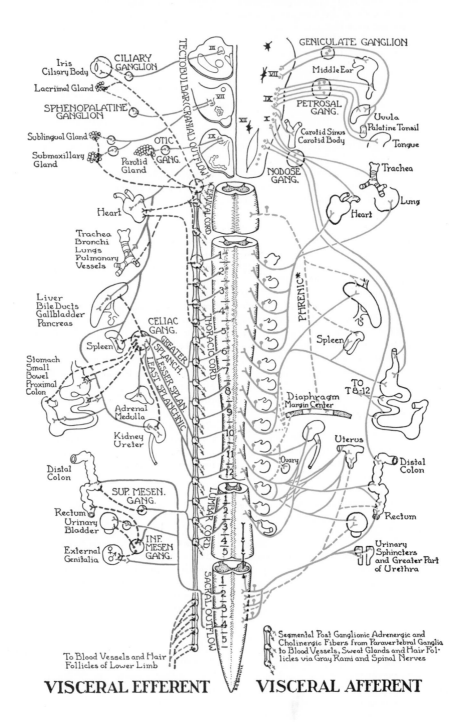

VISCERAL EFFERENT   **VISCERAL AFFERENT**

Fig. 2.   Afferent and efferent innervation of visceral structures. Blue, cholinergic neurons; red, adrenergic neurons; solid lines, efferent preganglionic fibers; broken lines, efferent postganglionic fibers. Afferent fibers from diaphragm are drawn in broken lines to emphasize that it is a somatic structure even though it lies in the visceral cavity.

ABDOMINAL VISCERA, GLANDS AND VESSELS

PARASYMPATHETIC. Vagal *preganglionic* fibers traverse the prevertebral plexus without interruption to reach *postganglionic neurons* in the intrinsic plexus of the visceral organ. *Function:* Stimulation of peristalsis and gastrointestinal secretion.

SYMPATHETIC. *Preganglionic neurons* originate in the lower seven or eight thoracic segments and the upper lumbar segments; axons run via the splanchnic nerves to reach the *postganglionic neurons* in the prevertebral ganglionic plexus. Postganglionic endings are supplied to the visceral blood vessels and the smooth muscle of the viscera. Innervation of the adrenal medulla is preganglionic. *Function:* Vasoconstriction and inhibition of peristalsis; secretion in adrenal medulla; sympathetic supply to the liver causes glycogenolysis.

PELVIC VISCERA

PARASYMPATHETIC. *Preganglionic neurons* originate in the second, third and fourth sacral segments; axons form nervi erigentes which reach ganglia in the walls of the organs innervated. *Postganglionic neurons* supply the uterus, tubes, testes, erectile tissue, sigmoid colon, rectum and bladder. *Function:* Contraction of bladder (see Chap. 51) and lower colon; erection; the significance of uterine innervation is unknown.

SYMPATHETIC. The origin and path of *preganglionic neurons* are the same as those for innervation of abdominal viscera. *Postganglionic axons* run in the hypogastric nerves to the blood vessels, lower colon and rectum, and seminal vesicles. *Function:* Contraction of internal vesical sphincter (see Chap. 51); vasoconstriction; ejaculation of semen; inhibition of peristalsis in lower colon and rectum.

*PERIPHERAL VESSELS AND
CUTANEOUS EFFECTORS*

SYMPATHETIC. These structures receive only sympathetic innervation by *postganglionic* fibers with cell bodies in the ganglion chain. Their axons join the segmental nerves via the gray rami, to be distributed to the skin and deep vessels. *Function:* Vasoconstriction in both cutaneous and deep vessels (existence of an additional system of vasodilator fibers to the vessels of muscle has been postulated from indirect evidence[4]); secretion in sweat glands; excitation of pilomotor muscles.

It will be noted from the foregoing account that some autonomic effectors (e.g., heart, coronary vessels, gut, salivary glands) receive dual innervation, and that others (e.g., adrenal medulla, sweat glands, pilomotor muscles, many vascular beds including those of skin and muscle) receive only sympathetic innervation.

In dually innervated systems, impulses in the two nerve supplies may act antagonistically. For example, parasympathetic impulses decelerate the heart, whereas sympathetic impulses accelerate it. In the gut, the roles of the two innervations are reversed, the sympathetic being inhibitory and the parasympathetic excitatory. In the iris both the parasympathetic and the sympathetic innervation are excitatory to their respective effector organs, but these (the circular and radial muscles) act antagonistically in regulating the diameter of the pupil. At any time, the functional state of the organ receiving antagonistic innervation depends on the balance between the tonic (continuous) discharges delivered over the two sets of nerves. Tonic discharge is regulated by reflex afferent pathways, which generally connect reciprocally with the preganglionic neurons of the two systems, so that the inhibitory discharge is increased when the excitatory discharge increases, and vice versa. Such dual innervations provide for sensitive regulation, a small afferent input being sufficient to produce pronounced functional changes in the organ.

In still other effectors receiving dual innervation, the two supplies act in synergy. One example is regulation of the secretory cell of the salivary gland. Both sympathetic and parasympathetic impulses stimulate secretion, but the respective secretions differ in composition. This difference does not, as was once thought, reflect the existence of two kinds of salivary cells; it is now clear that an individual gland cell receives secretory innervation from both sympathetic and parasympathetic supplies.[10] Regulation of effector systems receiving a single innervation is accomplished through modulation of the tonic excitatory efferent discharge.

GENERAL PRINCIPLES OF AUTONOMIC REGULATION

The many other names for the autonomic nervous system—"visceral," "involuntary," etc. —indicate that it subserves functions different from those mediated by somatic nerves. The autonomic system innervates smooth muscle, cardiac muscle and glands; the components of this system are the regulators concerned with emergency mechanisms, with repair and with the preservation of a constant internal environment. The somatic nerves, on the other hand, control striated muscle and relate the organism to its external environment. When somatic nerves are severed, the muscles they innervate degenerate. Such degeneration usually does not follow section of autonomic nerves. When deprived of autonomic innervation, the organs remain morphologically and physiologically intact, and often function autonomously to a degree.

Claude Bernard pointed out that the blood and lymph which bathe the cells of organisms constitute the *milieu interne,* or internal environment. This internal environment, a product of the organism and controlled by it, was termed the *fluid-matrix* by Walter Cannon, who expressed the belief that the organism's freedom from disturbance "in spite of extensive changes in the outer world, has been brought about by mechanisms, which maintain uniformity of the fluid-matrix." This concept of the steady states maintained in the internal environment, or fluid matrix, and of the importance of constancy of this matrix for continuous efficient action of the organism, ultimately became known as Cannon's doctrine of *homeostasis.*

An animal lacking homeostatic mechanisms must limit its activities or restrict its environment to achieve protection. For example, the frog, which has no temperature-regulating mechanism, must live in the depths of a pond during the winter to survive the cold. In contrast, many mammals can venture out in winter because their body temperature is "thermostatically" regulated to a constant level by autonomic reflex arcs which appropriately vary the diameter of the cutaneous blood vessels (through which heat is lost to the environment), the activity of the pilomotor muscles and sweat glands, and the secretion of the calorigenic product of the adrenal medulla, epinephrine. Another example of homeostasis is the maintenance of arterial blood pressure at relatively constant levels by afferent discharge of the pressoreceptors in the aortic arch and the carotid sinus. These receptors continuously monitor the arterial pressure and, through appropriate reflex connections, alter the tonic autonomic discharge controlling both the heart rate and the diameter of the arterioles.

Junctional Transmission in the Autonomic Nervous System.[1]   Figure 3 shows semidiagrammatically the results of two experiments which emphasize a fundamental contrast be-

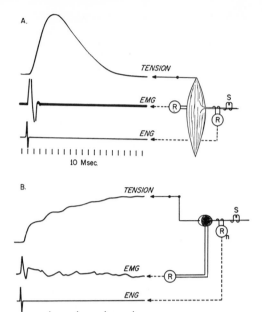

Fig. 3. Neuromuscular transmission in somatic and autonomic effector systems. *A,* Simultaneously recorded electroneurogram, electromyogram and mechanical response of skeletal nerve muscle preparation following single shock to motor nerve. *B,* Simultaneously recorded electroneurogram, electromyogram and mechanical response of nictitating membrane following single shock to postganglionic motor nerve. Note difference in time scales. (Partly after Eccles and Magladery, *J. Physiol.,* 1937, *90:*31–99.)

tween neuromuscular transmission in the somatic and in the autonomic nervous systems. The record in *A* shows the nerve action potential, the muscle action potential and the muscle tension of a skeletal muscle following a single shock to its motor nerve. Each nerve fiber in the trunk responds to the stimulus with a single brief action potential; the resultant compound potential, recorded close to the neuromuscular junction, is brief. Shortly thereafter the action potential of the muscle is recorded as a brief solitary event followed closely by the muscle twitch which is recorded as a change in muscular tension. The arrangement of stimulating and recording electrodes to obtain Figure 3*B* is similar; but the muscle is the smooth muscle of a cat's nictitating membrane, which is supplied by a motor nerve composed of sympathetic axons (from the superior cervical ganglion). As in the somatic motor nerve, the nerve action potential is brief and solitary, but the electromyogram shows a series of somewhat asynchronous deflections, which persist long after the nerve fibers have repolarized. The tension record shows, further, that each muscle action potential is associated with increments of contraction, so that the resulting tension curve is prolonged and bumpy, resembling an unfused tetanus of skeletal muscle.

Persistence of electrical and mechanical activity long beyond the duration of the excitatory nerve impulses is typical of autonomic neuroeffectors and persuasively suggests that the nerve exerts its action on effectors by liberating a chemical transmitter agent which remains and continues to act on the effector after the nerve action has ceased. Observations of this sort led to the theory of humoral transmitters. It has been pointed out that somatic neuromuscular transmission is also accomplished by the liberation of a chemical transmitter (probably acetylcholine) which depolarizes the end-plate, but that transmitter is destroyed rapidly and its action is brief. At autonomic junctions the slow destruction and prolonged action of the transmitter make the chemical nature of transmission much more immediately obvious.

Cholinergic Fibers. Humoral transmission in an autonomic neuroeffector system was first clearly demonstrated by Otto Loewi.[9] Because cardiac inhibition resulting from vagal stimulation far outlasts the period of nerve stimulation, Loewi suspected a humoral transmitter. In the experiment illustrated in Figure 4 fluid perfusing a donor frog heart (*D*) was used to perfuse a second, recipient heart (*R*). When the vagus nerve supplying heart *D* was stimulated, cardiac arrest occurred; shortly thereafter heart *R* also stopped beating, an event implicating an inhibitory chemical agent liberated into the perfusion fluid at the vagal endings in heart *D* and then carried to heart *R*. Loewi noncommittally termed the vagal inhibitory transmitter *Vagusstoff*.

Identification of Loewi's *Vagusstoff* followed from Dale's studies[3] on the pharmacologic actions of choline and its esters. He noted that the acetyl ester of choline is *parasympathomimetic,* i.e., when injected into the blood stream, acetylcholine acts upon autonomic effectors, including the heart, in a manner similar to or mimicking the action exerted on these effectors by their respective parasympathetic nerves. The drug atropine blocks the action of acetylcholine on smooth muscle and similarly blocks the action of parasympathetic nerves on their effec-

tors. The drug eserine, on the other hand, potentiates the action of acetylcholine by inactivating the enzyme cholinesterase, which splits acetylcholine into the relatively inert choline and acetic acid. Eserine also potentiates the effect of parasympathetic nerve stimulation. Such observations provided presumptive evidence that Loewi's *Vagusstoff*—as well as the transmitter at all other parasympathetic postganglionic endings—is either acetylcholine or a closely related substance.

Subsequent investigations have revealed that acetylcholine is also the transmitter agent liberated by autonomic preganglionic fibers, sympathetic as well as parasympathetic. The brief action of the transmitter in ganglia (and at the somatic neuromuscular junction) results from high concentrations of cholinesterase at these sites, so that the liberated transmitter is destroyed within the refractory period of the postjunctional cell.

Nerves which liberate an acetylcholine-like transmitter are called *cholinergic fibers*. In summary, these include somatic motor fibers, all autonomic preganglionic fibers and all parasympathetic postganglionic fibers. In addition, the sympathetic postganglionic fibers supplying sweat glands are also cholinergic (see below).

Sympathetic Postganglionic Mediators. It has already been pointed out that there is reason to suspect that sympathetic postganglionic endings liberate a humoral transmitter which is destroyed relatively slowly and which may act to prolong depolarization in sympathetic effectors. The proof that sympathetic nerve endings liberate a humoral agent under physiologic conditions was first provided by Cannon and his asso-

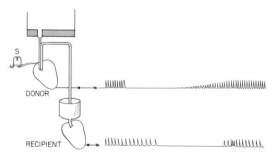

Fig. 4. Loewi's experiment demonstrating humoral mechanism of vagal inhibition of heart. Stimulation of vagus supplying donor heart released chemical inhibitory mediator which not only arrested donor heart but, after diffusion into perfusion fluid, also arrested recipient heart. (After Bain, *Quart. J. exp. Physiol.,* 1932, 22:269–274.)

ciates when they analyzed the mechanism of the cardiac acceleration which accompanies exercise and emotional excitement. Even after the heart was completely denervated by severing of the vagi and the cardiac accelerator nerves, these investigators observed that struggling, excitement or physical exercise induced a prompt (one minute) increase in heart rate of 80 to 100 beats per minute. Such acceleration results partly from the liberation into the circulation of epinephrine by the adrenal medulla. However, adrenal secretion does not entirely account for the response. Cannon found that, after the adrenals were removed or denervated, a moderate (25 to 30 beats per minute) but delayed (three minutes) increase in heart rate followed emotional excitement. Delayed emotional tachycardia persisted in animals subjected to hypophysectomy and bilateral abdominal and cervical sympathectomy. However, complete removal of the abdominal and thoracic sympathetic chains abolished the response.

These experiments implicated an extra-adrenal humoral agent released into the blood stream during exercise or excitement and capable of exerting a sympathetic-like (acceleratory) influence on the heart. Derivation of this substance from sympathetic nerve endings was indicated by experiments in which sympathetic nerves were stimulated electrically. When injected into the blood stream, perfusates of organs collected during stimulation of their sympathetic nerves caused cardiac acceleration and increased blood pressure. Years earlier, Elliott had presciently observed that epinephrine, the secretion of the adrenal medulla, is a *sympathomimetic agent;* i.e., it mimics the action of sympathetic postganglionic stimulation. Although the actions of the sympathetic mediator and of epinephrine were very similar, there were some differences, and Cannon cautiously termed the mediator *sympathin.* It is now known that both the adrenal medulla and the sympathetic postganglionic endings secrete at least two catechol amines—epinephrine and norepinephrine. Although closely related structurally, these two substances do not invariably exert identical actions on effector organs; a full catalogue of their pharmacologic properties can be found in textbooks of pharmacology or in von Euler's monograph.[5] The proportions of epinephrine and norepinephrine secreted appear to vary from nerve to nerve, but norepinephrine is the major

sympathetic postganglionic mediator and probably corresponds to Cannon's sympathin. Adrenal medullary secretion, on the other hand, appears to be principally epinephrine, at least in man.

Nerve fibers secreting epinephrine and/or norepinephrine are called *adrenergic fibers.* Most sympathetic postganglionic fibers are adrenergic. A notable exception is the sympathetic postganglionic innervation of the sweat glands, which is cholinergic and readily blocked by atropine. Other sympathetic postganglionic cholinergic systems have been postulated but are not so well documented.

In passing it may be noted that the discovery of the adrenergic nature of sympathetic postganglionic fibers renders less anomalous the absence of a peripheral synapse in the adrenal medullary innervation. Indeed, the adrenal medullary cells and the sympathetic postganglionic neurons are very similar, since they secrete the same substance and derive from the same embryologic tissues.

Effect of Autonomic Nerve Impulses on Membrane Potentials of Postjunctional Cells.[7] The technique of intracellular recording, so fruitful in studying junctional transmission at muscle end-plates and central synapses, has had limited application to the study of autonomic transmission, principally because the effector cells are generally small and hence tolerate penetration poorly. An exception is cardiac tissue, from which satisfactory intracellular recordings can be obtained. However, a special problem is created when movement of the spontaneously beating heart dislodges the electrode. This accident can be avoided by the ingenious "dangle electrode" technique devised by Woodbury and Brady,[17] who mounted the electrode on a fine flexible wire. Once inside the fiber, the electrode rides freely with the fiber's contractions.

In the spontaneously beating heart, the beat originates in the sinoatrial node, a small nodule of specialized tissue in the wall of the right atrium (see Chaps. 29 and 30). Intracellular recordings from this tissue show rhythmically recurring slow depolarizations (the "pacemaker" potential). When depolarization proceeds to threshold, an action potential is generated (Fig. 5A). No pacemaker potential is seen in recordings from atrial fibers (Fig. 5B). The cause of the pacemaker depolarization is not settled. It

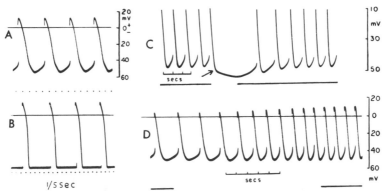

Fig. 5. Intracellular recordings from frog atrial cells beating normally during vagal inhibition and during sympathetic acceleration. *A*, Record from pacemaker cell in normally beating heart; note pacemaker potential (slow depolarization preceding each beat). *B*, Record from atrial fiber in normally beating heart; note absence of pacemaker potential (flat baseline preceding spike). *C*, Records from pacemaker cell during vagal stimulation; gain is high so that peaks of action potentials and zero reference lines are not shown. During vagal stimulation, indicated by break in bottom line, cell becomes hyperpolarized and pacemaker potentials and spikes are in abeyance. Note decreased slope of pacemaker potential in first two beats after recovery. *D*, Records from pacemaker cell during sympathetic stimulation, indicated by break in bottom line. Slope of pacemaker potential increases and rate accelerates. (From Hutter and Trautwein, *J. gen. Physiol.*, 1956, *39*:715–733.)

probably results from a gradual decrease of K^+ permeability during diastole superimposed on a relatively high Na^+ permeability.[14]

Figure 5*C* shows intracellular recordings from pacemaker tissue before, during and after vagal stimulation. During the stimulation period the membrane became hyperpolarized, and the rhythmically recurring depolarizations were abolished. With cessation of vagal stimulation, the pacemaker cell slowly depolarized as the transmitter was destroyed, until threshold was reached and an action potential was generated. During the first few beats, the rate of rise of the pacemaker potential was slow, so that the heart rate remained depressed; also, the duration of the action potential was curtailed. In subsequent beats, the recorded potentials gradually resumed the prestimulation configuration.

It is likely that hyperpolarization during vagal stimulation reflects an increased permeability of the pacemaker membrane to K^+ so that the membrane potential is driven toward the K^+ equilibrium potential. In accord with this hypothesis, acetylcholine increases total membrane conductance[15] and increases K^+ fluxes[6] in atrial pacemaker cells. Also in accord with this interpretation is the shortening of the action potential during vagal inhibitory action (note the first spike after the period of arrest in Fig. 5*C*). This shortening is a manifestation of rapid repolarization which, in pacemaker tissue, as in

nerve and skeletal muscle cells, is the consequence of increased permeability of the membrane to K^+. It will be readily recognized that the action of the vagal transmitter, presumably acetylcholine, is quite different from the action of acetylcholine on the motor end-plate. The discrepancy emphasizes the extremely varied responses of different tissues to a chemical agent.

Figure 5*D* shows the effect of sympathetic stimulation on potentials recorded intracellularly from a pacemaker cell. The firing level remains constant, but the slope of the pacemaker potential increases. As a result, the threshold voltage is reached more rapidly, and the rate of firing increases accordingly. Simultaneously, the "overshoot" of the spike increases, so that the over-all amplitude of the action potential is greater. These events are satisfactorily explained if it is assumed that the sympathetic transmitter increases the permeability of the pacemaker membrane to Na^+ ions and thus permits more rapid depolarization to the firing level and a closer approximation during the spike to the Na^+ equilibrium potential.

DENERVATION HYPERSENSITIVITY[2]

When an autonomic effector is denervated, it becomes increasingly sensitive to chemical agents. This sensitivity is most pronounced

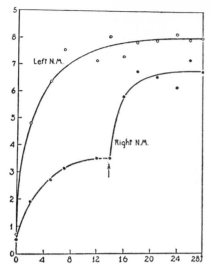

Fig. 6. Contractile responses of denervated nictitating membrane to epinephrine. *Ordinates,* Amplitude of isotonic contraction (cm.) in response to 10 µg. of epinephrine. *Abscissa,* Days after initial denervation. At day 0, left membrane denervated postganglionically, right membrane denervated preganglionically. At day 14 (*arrow*), right membrane denervated postganglionically. (From Hampel, *Amer. J. Physiol.,* 1935, *111*:611–621.)

when the organ is directly denervated by section of its *postganglionic* nerves (Cannon's law of denervation). Such denervation hypersensitivity was first described by Budge, who produced Horner's syndrome in rabbits. *Horner's syndrome,* which results from interruption of the sympathetic supply to the face, consists of pupillary constriction (miosis), drooping of the eyelid (ptosis), and flushing of the face owing to loss of vasoconstrictor tone.

Since the postganglionic sympathetic supply to the face originates in the superior cervical ganglion, which receives a preganglionic sympathetic input from the fibers ascending the cervical chain, Horner's syndrome may be experimentally produced either by dividing the cervical chain to interrupt the preganglionic fibers, or by a transection of the postganglionic fibers emerging from the ganglion. Budge found that, when a preganglionic section on one side and a postganglionic section on the other were performed, the resultant Horner's syndrome was initially symmetrical bilaterally. With the passage of time, however, the pupil on the side of the postganglionic denervation was larger than the one on the preganglionically denervated side, and the discrepancy was intensified when

the animal was frightened or subjected to emotional excitement. Budge could not explain the phenomenon of the paradoxical pupil; but it is now known that denervation hypersensitivity to circulating epinephrine (released into the blood stream during emotional excitement) accounts for the paradoxical pupil as well as for a number of similar phenomena in other denervated organs.

Even skeletal muscle displays the phenomenon of denervation hypersensitivity. Following section of the motor nerve, the muscle fiber membranes become hypersensitive to acetylcholine. Fibrillation in denervated skeletal muscle presumably results from the depolarization of hypersensitive end-plates by minute quantities of circulating acetylcholine or other excitatory chemical substances.

A quantitative study of denervation hypersensitivity is illustrated in Figure 6. The response of the nictitating membrane to a standard dose of epinephrine was measured on successive days following postganglionic denervation on the right side. Both nictitating membranes underwent a gradually increased sensitivity to epinephrine, as evidenced by the amplified responses, but the sensitivity was much more prominent in the membrane postganglionically denervated. On the 14th day the right superior cervical ganglion was removed, and the sensitivity of the related membrane increased, approaching that displayed by the left membrane. If denervation is caused by crushing of the nerves, so that they may regenerate, hypersensitivity occurs but wanes as the regenerating fibers re-establish connections with the muscle cells.

The mechanism of denervation hypersensitivity is not understood. It is probably partly attributable to the demonstrable disappearance from the denervated structure of the enzymes which normally inactivate the transmitter (cholinesterase or monoamine oxidase). This explanation is at best only partial because the increased sensitivity is not specific; the denervated nictitating membrane becomes hypersensitive not only to epinephrine but also to acetylcholine, pilocarpine, calcium, potassium, arterenol, tyramine and several nonphenolic aromatic amines.

Surgery of the Autonomic Nervous System and Denervation Hypersensitivity. To conclude this chapter, an example may be given of the application of the functional and anatomic principles outlined above to a practical clinical problem. To relieve any of a number of disorders, the therapeutic procedure is surgical interruption of the autonomic nerve supply to the diseased organ. The signs of these diseases and the appropriate surgical procedures are discussed in detail by White *et al.*,[16] but for present purposes a single disease may be considered.

Raynaud's disease is a peripheral vascular disease in which there are painful paroxysms of cutaneous vasospasm (usually in the fingers or toes) so intense that gangrene may result. The paroxysms are often precipitated by exposure to cold or by emotional stress. While it is not certain that the vasospasm results from excessive sympathetic discharge, sympathectomy of the affected regions is nevertheless a rational procedure, since impulses in sympathetic fibers regulate vasoconstriction of cutaneous vessels and since interruption of these fibers increases blood flow through the skin.*

The vasoconstrictor pathway to the hand originates in preganglionic neurons situated in spinal segments T_2 to T_7; most of the postganglionic cell bodies are in the stellate ganglion, although a varying small number lie in the second and third thoracic ganglion. The hand can thus be sympathectomized by removal of the stellate, T_2 and T_3 ganglia. This operation has the defect of producing a Horner's syndrome, since the preganglionic fibers ascending the chain to the superior cervical ganglion are interrupted. A more serious objection is that the sympathectomy of the hand is postganglionic, and the denervated vessels become so sensitive to epinephrine that cold exposure or emotional stress (both of which increase adrenal medullary secretion) may precipitate vasospastic attacks

even more severe than those occurring before operation.

A much more successful procedure is preganglionic sympathectomy. The sympathetic chain is divided between the third and fourth ganglia; this interrupts preganglionic fibers originating in segments T_4 to T_7 and ascending the chain. To interrupt the fibers originating in the T_2 to T_3 segments, the segmental nerves are cut at a point central to the entry of the postganglionic fibers via the gray rami. Not only are the consequences of denervation hypersensitivity thus avoided, but Horner's syndrome does not occur because preganglionic fibers passing from the T_1 segment to the superior cervical ganglion are intact.

---

* In chronic Raynaud's disease anatomic changes in the vessels eventually prevent dilation even in the absence of vasoconstrictor nerves. In such cases sympathectomy is of no value. A standard procedure is to perform a diagnostic procaine block of the stellate ganglion. If this procedure does not cause increased blood flow to the hand, as indicated by a rise in skin temperature, surgery is not recommended.

REFERENCES

1. CANNON, W. B. and ROSENBLUETH, A. *Autonomic neuro-effector system.* New York, Macmillan, 1937.
2. CANNON, W. B. and ROSENBLUETH, A. *The supersensitivity of denervated structures.* New York, Macmillan, 1949.
3. DALE, H. H. *J. Pharmacol.* 1914, *6*:147–190.
4. ELIASSON, S., LINDGREN, P. and UVNÄS, B. *Acta physiol. scand.,* 1952, *27*:18–37.
5. VON EULER, U. S. *Noradrenaline.* Springfield, Ill., Charles C Thomas, 1955.
6. HUTTER, O. F. In: *Nervous inhibition.* E. Florey, ed. New York, Pergamon Press, 1961.
7. HUTTER, O. F. and TRAUTWEIN, W. *J. gen. Physiol.,* 1956, *39*:715–733.
8. KUNTZ, A. *The autonomic nervous system.* Philadelphia, Lea and Febiger, 1953.
9. LOEWI, O. *Pflüg. Arch. ges. Physiol.,* 1921, *189*:239–242.
10. LUNDBERG, A. *Acta physiol. scand.,* 1957, *40*:21–34.
11. MITCHELL, G. A. G. *Anatomy of the autonomic nervous system.* Edinburgh, E. and S. Livingstone Ltd., 1953.
12. MITCHELL, G. A. G. *Cardiovascular innervation.* Edinburgh, E. and S. Livingstone Ltd., 1956.
13. MORGAN, M. W., JR., OLMSTEAD, J. M. D. and WATROUS, W. G. *Amer. J. Physiol.,* 1940, *128*:588–591.
14. TRAUTWEIN, W. and KASSEBAUM, D. G. *J. gen. Physiol.,* 1961, *45*:317–330.
15. TRAUTWEIN, W., KUFFLER, S. W. and EDWARDS, C. *J. gen. Physiol.,* 1956, *40*:135–145.
16. WHITE, J. C., SMITHWICK, R. H. and SIMEONE, F. A. *The autonomic nervous system.* New York, Macmillan, 1952.
17. WOODBURY, J. W. and BRADY, A. J. *Science,* 1956, *123*:100–101.

CHAPTER 11

Higher Control of Autonomic Outflows: The Hypothalamus

By HARRY D. PATTON

INTRODUCTION

In the previous chapter it was pointed out that visceral organs, glands and blood vessels—structures important in the maintenance of a constant internal environment (homeostasis)—are regulated by the autonomic nervous system. The preganglionic autonomic neurons are maintained in a continuous but quantitatively variable state of activity by a host of inputs. Some of these inputs are segmental in origin (dorsal roots); others originate in supraspinal structures and descend the neural axis to reach the levels of autonomic outflow.

Some idea of the relative role of supraspinal as contrasted to segmental control of the spinal autonomic outflows (sympathetic and sacral parasympathetic) can be obtained by studying autonomic reflexes in animals subjected to transection of the neural axis at different levels. After the spinal cord is transected above the level of T_1, for example, the spinal autonomic outflows are regulated solely by segmental inputs. The immediate consequence of such a transection is profound depression of all autonomic reflexes,[57] paralleling the depression of somatic reflexes

(spinal shock). Blood pressure drops precipitously, owing to a decrease in the sympathetic discharge to the visceral vascular bed and a consequent diminution in the peripheral resistance to flow.* Temperature regulation is lacking, sweating is absent, and the body temperature changes toward that of the environment. The bladder and bowel are paralyzed, and sexual reflexes (erection and ejaculation) are lacking.

After several weeks spinal shock wanes and the segmental autonomic reflexes reappear. The blood pressure rises from the low levels typical of the spinal shock period and fluctuates in response to noxious stimulation of the skin. (Permanently lacking, however, is the adaptive vasoconstriction which normally prevents gravitational hypotension when the body is moved from a horizontal to a vertical position, because the spinal pathways which connect the pressure-monitoring receptors in the aortic arch and the carotid sinus with the sympathetic outflows are severed.) At the same time vestiges of temperature regulatory mechanisms reappear; sweating returns, and noxious stimulation of the skin may

* Regulation of heart rate remains because it is governed largely by vagal impulses.

elicit troublesomely profuse sweating. Immersion of one extremity in cold water induces vasoconstriction in the contralateral limb, and, conversely, heating one limb is followed by vasodilatation in the other. Nevertheless, even after long recovery periods, temperature regulation remains sluggish, and the smoothly coordinated adjustments of blood vessels, sweat glands, pilomotor muscles and skeletal muscles which make the normal mammalian body temperature independent of environmental temperature are never recovered. Similarly, micturition, defecation and sexual reflexes return and can be elicited by stimulation of the skin of the thigh or genitalia. Micturition in the paraplegic, however, often fails to evacuate the bladder completely. Even ignoring the acute effects of spinal shock, we may conclude that autonomic reflex arcs are highly dependent on supraspinal inputs.

The contribution of medullary structures to the regulation of autonomic reflexes may be inferred from studies on decerebrate preparations in which the brain stem is sectioned at the intercollicular level. Such preparations rarely survive more than a few weeks (and then only with most exacting postoperative care), so that only the acute effects of interruption of suprabulbar pathways can be studied.* The status of autonomic reflexes in such preparations resembles in general that in the spinal preparation. Temperature regulation is lacking, and body temperature fluctuates with environmental temperature. A major difference, however, is that arterial blood pressure is maintained rather well in the decerebrate preparation in contrast to the profound hypotension of the spinal animal. Moreover, both the heart and the visceral vessels respond appropriately to postural changes, so that perfusion pressure remains constant despite changes of the position of the body in space. Retention of these responses is due to the retention of the medullary vasomotor and cardioregulatory centers and their afferent inputs via the IXth (carotid sinus) and Xth (aortic arch) cranial nerves (see Chap. 34). The threshold for the micturition reflex is decreased in the decerebrate cat, an example of release of reflex function from supracollicular inhibition. The released center, however, is in the pons, not the medulla (see Chap. 51).

Finally, if the test section is made at a higher level by removal of the cerebral cortex, residual autonomic function gives some indication of the relative participation of supracollicular brain stem structures in the regulation of autonomic function. Cats and dogs survive decortication surprisingly well and can be kept in good health for long periods. Blood pressure is well maintained, temperature regulation is normal, and the bladder, bowel and sexual functions are essentially those of the intact animal.

The full measure of autonomic reactivity in the decorticate preparation is seen when a mildly noxious stimulus such as lightly pinching the skin is applied. Such stimulation evokes a paroxysm of behavior which, because it stimulates rage, was named "sham rage" by Cannon and Bard. Sham rage is a coordinated reaction pattern with many components mediated by autonomic (principally sympathetic) outflows. Thus, in addition to somatic attitudes of anger (arching of back, spitting, snarling and protrusion of claws), the decorticate animal provoked into sham rage displays piloerection, pupillary dilation, tachycardia and elevated blood pressure. In striking contrast, the decerebrate preparation never shows such explosive behavior.†

The full significance of sham rage is discussed in Chapter 26; for now it need only be emphasized that the presence of sham rage in the decorticate preparation and its absence in the decerebrate preparation indicate that structures lying between the cortex and midbrain influence powerfuly, via descending connections, the lower brain stem and spinal autonomic centers. Moreover, this control is well integrated, so that discharges over both autonomic and somatic pathways are blended into an effective behavioral pattern. This integrative center lies in the hypothalamus.

Prior to and since the discovery of its role in sham rage, the hypothalamus has been subjected to focal lesions and focal stimulation. The results of these experiments indicate that the different areas in the hypothalamus are impor-

---

* "Chronic" decerebrate preparations which will survive a month or more can be obtained if the hypophysis and a small isolated island of the overlying hypothalamus are left intact.[7]

† In response to strong nociceptive stimuli, chronic decerebrate cats show some fragments of affective behavior, e.g., vocalization, protrusion of claws, running movements and acceleration of pulse and respiration. The responses are poorly coordinated, and the threshold for evoking them is high.[7]

tant portions of many of the visceral regulatory mechanisms which maintain the constancy of the internal environment. The remainder of this chapter is devoted to a résumé of these functions.

ANATOMIC ORGANIZATION OF THE HYPOTHALAMUS

The hypothalamus (Fig. 1) consists of those structures in the walls and floor of the third ventricle extending from a position slightly rostral to the optic chiasm caudally to the mammillary bodies. Dorsally the thalamus and subthalamus bound the hypothalamus. On its ventral surface it is connected to the hypophysis by a strand of fine nerve fibers originating in hypothalamic nuclei and running via the median eminence and infundibular stalk into the posterior lobe of the hypophysis. Much of the substance of the hypothalamus is composed of small diffusely arranged cells not clearly segregated into nuclear groups. Nevertheless, the following regions and nuclei, some more clearly delimited than others, can be defined: (i) anterior region, including the preoptic, supraoptic and paraventricular nuclei; (ii) middle region, including the tuberal nuclei and the lateral nuclear masses; and (iii) the posterior region, including the posterior hypothalamic nuclei and the mammillary nuclei.

Many afferent pathways lead into the hypothalamus; they include: (i) the *medial forebrain bundle*, which originates in the ventromedial areas of the rhinencephalon and is distributed to the preoptic region and the lateral hypothalamic and lateral mammillary nuclei; (ii) the *fornix*, which connects the hippocampus with the mammillary nuclei; (iii) the *stria terminalis*, which connect the amygdaloid nuclei with the preoptic and anterior hypothalamic regions; (iv) the *mammillary peduncle*, which feeds impulses ascending from spinal and tegmental structures into the lateral mammillary nucleus; and (v) numerous other, less well defined pathways connecting the hypothalamus with the frontal cortex, the globus pallidus and the thalamus. Branches from the optic tract ending in the supraoptic and ventromedial nuclei have also been described and implicated in the retinal regulation of hypothalamic and hypophysial function.

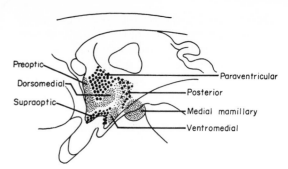

Fig. 1. Hypothalamic nuclei projected on the wall of the third ventricle. (From Peele, *The neuroanatomical basis for clinical neurology*, New York, McGraw-Hill, 1954.)

The efferent pathways include: (i) The *mammillothalamic tract of Vicq d'Azyr*. This pathway links the medial mammillary nucleus with the anterior thalamic nuclei which project to the cortex of the cingular gyrus. (ii) The *mammillotegmental tract* runs from the medial mammillary nuclei to the lateral and medial reticular structures in the tegmentum. (iii) The *periventricular system* arises mainly in the supraoptic, posterior and tuberal nuclei and descends in periventricular gray matter. Some fibers in this system terminate in the dorsomedial thalamic nucleus; others supply the midbrain tegmental reticular nuclei; but most pass into the dorsal longitudinal fasciculus. It is believed that this tract supplies brain stem parasympathetic nuclei and also, through relays, the spinal sympathetic preganglionic neurons. There is also evidence for a dorsolaterally placed descending tract leading from the hypothalamus to spinal levels. (iv) The *hypothalamico-hypophysial* tract leads from the supraoptic nuclei into the posterior lobe of the hypophysis. Some of the fibers originate from the paraventricular nuclei. The role of this tract in regulating water metabolism is discussed later. Fiber tracts leading into the posterior lobe from the tuberal nuclei have also been described.

REGULATION OF BODY TEMPERATURE[59]

It has already been pointed out that experimental animals subjected to transection of the brain stem below the level of the hypothalamus become poikilothermic. The thermoregulatory function of the hypothalamus is even more clearly indicated when discrete portions of the hypothalamus are destroyed experimentally in otherwise intact animals.

Discrete destruction or stimulation of the hypothalamus (or any other subcortical structure) is accomplished with the aid of the stereotaxic apparatus invented by Horsley and Clarke. This consists of an electrode carrier framework which is firmly attached to the animal's head by bars in the ears and clamps fitting against the upper jaw and the inferior orbital ridge. The framework on which the electrode carrier moves is calibrated in millimeters in all three planes of movement: anteroposterior, lateral and vertical. To calibrate the instrument for a given species, wires are introduced into the brain at measured coordinates in each of the three planes. The animal is then sacrificed and serial brain sections are prepared. Measurement on the sections from the distance between the holes made by the reference wires and any subcortical structure yields coordinates for the structure. Using these coordinates one can accurately introduce the uninsulated tip of an insulated electrode into the desired structure with only minimal damage to those overlying it. Stimulation can then be carried out by conventional methods. To produce a lesion a direct current is passed through the electrode tip (positive) through the brain and out through a diffuse electrode (negative) applied to the skin. The high current density at the small uninsulated tip of the electrode causes local electrolytic destruction of tissue in the surrounding region. The size of the lesion varies with current intensity and duration.

The influence of discrete hypothalamic lesions on temperature regulation varies with their location. Lesions in the rostral hypothalamus (level of optic chiasm and anterior commissure), particularly in its lateral reaches, render an animal incapable of regulating its temperature in a warm environment, although it may maintain a normal body temperature in a cold environment. Indeed, so profound is the deficit following rostral hypothalamic destruction that death from hyperthermia often results if the animal is kept at room temperature. Similarly, hyperthermia in man and inability to withstand warm environments have been described as following anterior hypothalamic lesions due to tumors or infarcts.[18, 65] The disturbances are traceable to inadequate operation of the heat loss mechanisms which normally are activated by exposure to a warm environment. In man these are principally cutaneous vasodilatation, which increases radiation of heat to the environment, and sweating, which lowers body temperature by evaporative cooling. In furry animals such as the dog and cat, panting is an important means of heat loss. Following rostral hypothalamic destruction these adaptive changes do not occur when the environmental temperature is elevated, so body temperature rises.

When lesions are placed in the caudal hypothalamus dorsolateral to the mammillary bodies, the animal's ability to maintain normal body temperature in either a warm or a cold environment is seriously impaired; such preparations are essentially poikilothermic. It is probable that the heat loss mechanisms fail in such animals because the lesions interrupt the pathways descending from the rostrally located *heat loss centers,* and that the failure to regulate against cold results from destruction of a caudally located *heat production and conservation center.* In normal animals, exposure to cold elicits cutaneous vasoconstriction, shivering, piloerection and increased epinephrine secretion—all mechanisms which tend to increase the heat content of the body and prevent excessive cooling. Epinephrine and shivering act by increasing metabolism and thus heat production, whereas piloerection* and vasoconstriction conserve body heat by increasing the surface insulation. Following posterior hypothalamic lesions these adaptive mechanisms are defective, and in cold the body temperature inclines toward environmental temperature.

In exceptional instances regulation against heat and cold may be dissociated following posterior hypothalamic lesions. An example is illustrated in Figure 2. In contrast to the intact dog (*46*), which shivered vigorously and maintained normal body temperature when exposed to cold, dog *28* with posterior hypothalamic lesions failed to shiver and suffered profound hypothermia (*left graph*). When exposed to a warm environment, however, dog *28* panted and showed only slightly elevated body temperature, in contrast to dog *72-D* with rostral hypothalamic lesions. The latter animal became markedly hyperthermic without panting after only brief exposure to a warm environment (*right graph*).

The role of hypothalamic structures in initiating thermoregulatory responses is also demon-

---

* The fluffing of body hair to trap an insulating layer of stationary air is an important means of heat conservation in furry animals. In man piloerection has no thermoregulatory importance but persists vestigially in the form of "goose bumps."

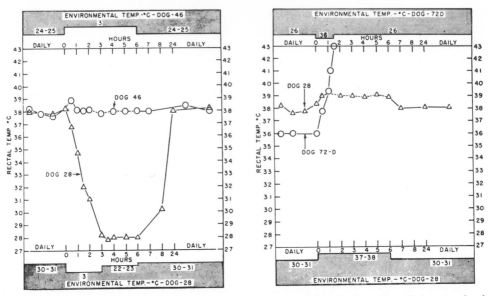

Fig. 2. Effect of hypothalamic lesions on temperature regulation in dogs. Dog *46,* intact animal; dog *28,* posterior hypothalamic lesions; dog *72D,* rostral hypothalamic lesions. Dotted lines joining points indicate, on left, shivering; on right, panting. (From Keller. *Phys. Therap. Rev.,* 1950, *30:*511–519.)

strated by stimulation experiments. In unanesthetized animals electrical stimulation through electrodes permanently implanted in the rostral hypothalamus (level of optic chiasm and anterior commissure) causes panting and cutaneous vasodilation with a resultant drop in body temperature, particularly when the animal is in a cold environment.[4] Cold-induced shivering is inhibited by rostral hypothalamic stimulation, but exposure to cold increases the electrical threshold for inducing panting and vasodilation. These latter observations suggest reciprocal connections between the heat loss and heat production centers. On the other hand, stimulation of the posterior hypothalamus (in the tuberal region between the fornix and the mammillothalamic tract) induces a muscular tremor resembling shivering.[10]

It is thus apparent that the hypothalamus contains two opposing thermoregulatory centers which by their descending connections bring about coordinated and integrated neural discharges to structures involved in maintaining a constant body temperature. In the intact animal these two centers operate reciprocally. When environmental temperature increases and body temperature begins to rise, the anteriorly located heat loss centers are activated and overheating is prevented. Similarly, low environmental temperatures activate the pos-

teriorly placed heat conservation and production center, and the resultant shivering, piloerection, vasconstriction and epinephrine secretion combat excessive cooling of the body. The hypothalamic centers have been likened to a thermostat which operates automatically to prevent large fluctuations of body temperature.

A thermostat requires a receptive mechanism to sample the temperature as well as an executive mechanism to bring about the appropriate regulation. For the hypothalamic thermostat two receptive mechanisms are available: (i) cutaneous thermoreceptors, which vary their rate of firing with changes in skin temperature and which presumably feed impulses into the hypothalamic thermoregulatory centers; and (ii) centrally located thermodetectors, which respond to changes in internal, particularly intracranial, temperature. The properties of cutaneous thermoreceptors are described in detail in Chapter 14. Thermoreceptors are classified as warmth or cold receptors according to the range of temperatures which cause them to discharge. The messages from thermoreceptors are presumed to reach the hypothalamic thermoregulatory centers, where they initiate the appropriate reciprocal actions—i.e., impulses initiated in cold receptors excite the caudally located heat production and conservation center and inhibit the rostrally located heat loss center; impulses from warmth receptors have the reverse action on the hypothalamic centers. In addition, the messages from thermoreceptors presumably feed into other ascending pathways to thalamus and cortex and constitute in part the basis of conscious sensation of temperature, which provides a cue for complex adaptive behavior, such as seeking a more comfortable environment (shelter, shade, etc.).

The existence of centrally located thermodetectors is also well documented. Warming the carotid blood entering the head induces sweating, panting and vasodilation, even though skin temperature (except on the head) is not altered by the procedure. Similarly, cooling the carotid blood induces vasoconstriction, piloerection and shivering. That the thermosensitive regions are contained in the hypothalamus (and indeed are coextensive with the thermoregulatory centers) is indicated by experiments[22, 23, 42] in which local heating of the rostral hypothalamus by diathermy induced sweating, panting and vasodilation. Such local heating does not directly affect skin or body temperature; indeed, inappropriate panting and sweating could be induced by heating the hypothalamus when the body temperature was subnormal (35° C.).

Nakayama *et al.*[50] explored the rostral hypothalamus of cats with microelectrodes. About 20 per cent of the units isolated in the midline rostral to the anterior commissure increased their discharge rates when the adjacent hypothalamus was locally heated by radio frequency currents or by circulating warm water through an implanted electrode (Fig. 3). Within this region no cold-sensitive units were found. It seems clear, therefore, that some of the hypothalamic neurons are directly sensitive to temperature and thus vary in activity in accordance with the temperature of the blood perfusing them.

The relative roles of the cutaneous receptors (sensitive to skin temperature) and the central thermodetectors (sensitive to body core temperature) in initiating and controlling thermoregulatory functions are not entirely clear.[9, 40] Magoun *et al.*[42] found it necessary to elevate hypothalamic temperature to feverish levels (104.5° to 109° F.) to elicit panting and sweating, a fact which suggested that the central receptors constitute a rather crude protective mechanism. Recent studies with more refined techniques[1] suggest that the hypothalamic thermodetectors are much more sensitive than previously supposed. Cooling the anterior hypothalamus only 0.5 to 1.0°C. by passing chilled water through an implanted thermode elicited detectable drops of skin temperature (vasoconstriction) and increases in rectal temperature and rate of oxygen consumption; warming the hypothalamus by similar amounts elicited even more pronounced increases of skin temperature (vasodilation) and decreases in rectal temperature and metabolic rate. Data on human subjects suggest that sweat secretion is related more closely to core temperature than to skin temperature.[9] Studies by Carlson[16] indicate that both cutaneous and central receptors are involved in the activation of shivering induced by cold exposure.

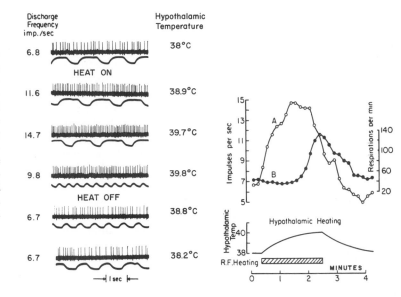

Fig. 3. Extracellular recording from hypothalamic thermodetector cell. *Left,* Preoptic unit (upper) and respiratory (lower) responses to local heating of the anterior hypothalamus with radio-frequency current. *Right,* graphic representation of data from the same experiment. Open circles = frequency of unit discharge; closed circles = respiratory rate. (From Nakayama *et al., Amer. J. Physiol.,* 1963, *204:*1122–1126.)

Behavioral studies indicate that central thermodetectors not only are important in simple reflex thermal adjustments but also regulate complex behavioral responses to altered environmental temperatures (see Chap. 25).

REGULATION OF WATER BALANCE[21]

It was mentioned above that a prominent tract of unmyelinated fibers originates from cells in the supraoptic and paraventricular nuclei and traverses the median eminence and pituitary stalk to terminate in the posterior lobe of the hypophysis. This hypothalamico-hypophysial tract is essential to the formation and release of posterior hypophysial hormones, the most important of which is the *antidiuretic hormone* (ADH). Its function is described in detail in Chapters 44 and 45. Briefly, ADH promotes reabsorption of water from renal tubular fluid into the blood stream and thus limits the amount of water lost from body stores to the urine. Other things being equal, urinary volume is inversely related to the amount of ADH in the blood reaching the kidney. Secretion of ADH is dependent on the integrity of the hypothalamico-hypophysial tract. Injury to the system at the supraoptic nuclear level or to its course through the median eminence and hypophysial stalk, or destruction of the posterior hypophysis itself, causes *diabetes insipidus*, in which excessive volumes of dilute urine are secreted (polyuria). The excessive urinary water loss (up to 20 liters a day in man) results in excessive thirst and ingestion of large quantities of water (polydipsia); the victim is a veritable aqueduct and spends most of his waking hours dashing from water fountain to water closet and back again.

The dependence of ADH secretion on the hypothalamico-hypophysial system has also been demonstrated by stimulation experiments. In rabbits, Harris[32] found that electrical stimulation through electrodes permanently implanted in the tract caused ADH secretion sufficient to block the diuresis induced by a previously administered oral water load.

Neurosecretion.[51] In most neurally regulated secretory systems (e.g., salivary glands, sweat glands, adrenal medulla) nerve fibers terminate on gland cells; nerve impulses initiate the secretory process in the gland cells. The neurohypophysis is an exception to this arrangement. Apart from supporting elements, the posterior lobe is relatively cell-free and its mass is largely composed of terminations of the hypothalamico-hypophysial tract. In some species, the terminal fibers are arranged in parallel rows in close relation to highly vascular connective tissue trabeculae.[11]

The fibers of the hypothalamico-hypophysial tract thus appear to innervate no particular structure but terminate blindly near blood vessels. This perplexing situation has been clarified by Bargmann's discovery[8] that chrome hematoxylin (Gomori stain) applied to sections of posterior hypophysis stains selectively dense intracellular granules which are presumed to comprise either the secretory product of the neurohypophysis or a ground substance to which the active hormone is attached. The material is found in high concentration surrounding the nerve terminals in the neural lobe but also along the entire extent of the hypothalamico-hypophysial tract and within the cells of the supraoptic and paraventricular nuclei. Electron micrographs reveal that the granules are surrounded by a plasma membrane; the nerve terminals in the posterior lobe contain, in addition to secretory granules, many vesicles similar to those found elsewhere in presynaptic fibers.[27] Water deprivation, which is known to increase the secretion of ADH (see below), causes a reduction in the amount of Gomori-stainable material present, particularly in the neurohypophysis but also in the supraoptic and paraventricular cell bodies. It is therefore suggested that the paraventricular and supraoptic nuclei are composed of *neurosecretory* cells capable of elaborating ADH, which then diffuses down in the axons to the terminals to be stored in the posterior hypophysis. Unitary recordings, both extracellular[15] and intracellular,[39] from neurosecretory cells reveal that they are electrically excitable; indeed, their properties do not differ strikingly from those of other neurons. The exact relation of the electrical activity of these cells to the formation and release of ADH is not yet clear.

Regulation of ADH Secretion. Renal excretion of water is closely related to body stores of water. Ingestion of large quantities of water leads to a prompt reduction of tubular reabsorption of water and consequent diuresis. On the other hand, water deprivation leads to accelerated water reabsorption and a scant, concentrated urine. This homeostatic regulation tending to maintain constant water stores and osmotic pressure of blood is achieved by variations in the secretion of ADH in accordance with the blood osmotic pressure. Intracarotid injection of hypertonic solutions stimulates the release of ADH, so that more water is reabsorbed by the kidney. When carotid blood is made hypotonic, ADH secretion declines and diuresis results. These changes are abolished when the internal carotid artery is ligated. Somewhere within the cranial cavity, therefore, cells exist (possibly those of the supraoptic and paraventricular nuclei) which are *osmoreceptors* and which comprise a mechanism for automatic regulation of ADH secretion and hence water excretion in accordance with bodily needs.[63]

However, there may exist mechanisms other than osmoreceptors for regulating ADH secretion. Reduction of total extracellular volume, e.g., by hemorrhage, increases ADH levels and induces oliguria. Conversely, expansion of extracellular volume by transfusing isotonic solutions leads to diuresis. These facts have led to the postulation of "volume receptors" which respond to increased plasma volume and reflexly inhibit ADH secretion. Several possible sites for the hypothetical volume receptors have been suggested; a full discussion of the problem is given in Chapter 45.

Water Intake.   In view of the important role of the hypothalamus in regulating water output, it is perhaps not surprising that it also plays a part in the regulation of water intake. Such a function is indicated by the experiments of Andersson and McCann,[5] who stimulated the hypothalamus of goats through permanently implanted electrodes. Stimulating the region between the columns of the fornix and the mammillothalamic tract induced polydipsic drinking sufficient to cause overhydration up to 40 per cent of the body weight and to cause dilution of renal fluid and polyuria. Microinjections of hypertonic saline in the same regions also induced polydipsia, a response suggesting (but not proving) that the responsible neurons (like the hypothalamico-hypophysial osmoreceptors) are sensitive to the osmotic pressure of the body fluids.

OXYTOCIN SECRETION

In addition to ADH the posterior pituitary elaborates a hormone, oxytocin, which causes (i) powerful contraction of the gravid or estrous uterus and (ii) ejection of milk from the lactating mammary gland. Electrical stimulation of the supraoptic hypophysial tract causes liberation of oxytocin as measured by the responses of both the estrous uterus and the lactating mammary gland.[17, 32] The natural stimuli which trigger release of oxytocin are not entirely clear. In the case of lactation the sensory irritation of the nipples incident to sucking probably constitutes the adequate stimulus. Whether oxytocin is involved in the initiation of spontaneous labor is controversial; in any event, there is no conclusive evidence that the hormone is released at term.

REGULATION OF ADENOHYPOPHYSIAL FUNCTION [33, 34]

Although it is well established that the posterior lobe of the hypophysis receives nerve fibers from the hypothalamus, repeated investigations have failed to demonstrate convincingly that the anterior hypophysial lobe is similarly innervated. Nevertheless, there is considerable evidence that the central nervous system, particularly the hypothalamus, plays some part in the government of adenohypophysial secretion. Since there are no direct neural connections which might mediate this control, it is postulated that certain hypothalamic cell groups elaborate chemical mediators which, reaching the adenohypophysis via the blood stream, stimulate the production and release of hormones. Such hypothalamic cells are thus neurosecretory cells.

Hypothalamico-hypophysial Portal System.[28] Although the hypothalamus and adenohypophysis are not neurally connected, they are connected by a special vascular system which is thought to transmit humoral agents from the hypothalamus to the pituitary. The internal carotid and posterior communicating arteries form a rich vascular plexus over the surface of the median eminence. From this plexus arise myriads of capillary loops which arch up into median eminence, where they are closely related to neurosecretory axons. The capillary loops then coalesce into larger trunks which pass down the hypophysial stalk and drain into the sinusoids of the adenohypophysis. Other branches of the internal carotids penetrate the hypophysis more directly.

Harris[32, 34] believes that a vascular connection with the hypothalamus is essential to the secretory functions of the hypophysis. Severing the pituitary stalk (and consequently the portal vessel) has no permanent effect on adenohypophysial function.[61] According to Harris, it recovers because the severed portal vessels rapidly regenerate. If, however, regeneration is prevented by inserting a paper barrier between the base of the brain and the decentralized hypophysis, or if the gland is transplanted to a remote site, signs of pituitary deficiency ensue (cessation of growth and gonadal, adrenocortical and thyroid atrophy). The interpretation is that such hypophysial transplants, although histologically intact, fail to function because they have lost the direct vascular "pipeline" from the hypothalamic neurosecretory centers.

Adrenocorticotrophic Hormone. Secretion of adrenocortical hormones (with the exception of aldosterone) is entirely regulated by the adrenocorticotrophic hormone (ACTH) secreted by the adenohypophysis (see Chap. 59). Secretion of ACTH with consequent activation of the adrenal cortex may be initiated by a wide variety of seemingly unrelated physiologic and pharmacologic stimuli which are collectively called "biologic stresses." Examples of stresses which activate the pituitary-adrenal axis are exposure to extremes of heat or cold, anoxia, hemorrhage, pain, bacterial toxins, histamine and anesthetic agents. Pituitary-adrenal responsiveness to such stresses is not altered by section of the pituitary stalk,[61] but is abolished by lesions of the median eminence or of the posterior hypothalamus.[30, 47] It is therefore postulated that stress situations induced either by afferent neural input or (in the case of chemical stresses) by direct action stimulate neurosecretory hypothalamic cells to secrete a humoral substance, corticotrophin releasing factor (CRF). CRF is carried by the portal vessels to the hypophysis, where it stimulates secretion of ACTH which, in turn, stimulates adrenocortical secretion.

Additional evidence implicating hypothalamic structures in the regulation of ACTH secretion is provided by experiments involving electrical stimulation of the hypothalamus through implanted electrodes in unanesthetized animals. Stimulation in the tuberal and posterior hypothalamic regions activates the pituitary-adrenal system.[30] Also, extracts prepared from hypothalamic tissue stimulate secretion of ACTH by pituitary cells grown in tissue culture.[31] Although such experiments indicate that the hypothalamus participates in the regulation of ACTH secretion, other mechanisms have been proposed; these are discussed in Chapter 59.

Gonadotrophin Secretion[20] (see Chaps. 62 and 63). Numerous observations suggest neural regulation of pituitary gonadotrophin secretion. In many birds and mammals the sexual cycle may be altered by varying the exposure of the animal to light. For example, a midwinter estrus in the ferret, which normally breeds in the spring, can be induced by exposing the animal to light. Such disturbances in seasonal sexual cycles depend on the visual pathways; ferrets blinded by section of the optic nerve do not have estrus cycles even when exposed to light. Light-induced estrus also fails to occur in ferrets with transected hypophysial stalks. According to Donavan and Harris[19] interruption of the hypothalamico-hypophysial portal system and prevention of vascular regeneration is critical, but this statement has been contested.[62]

Cats and rabbits normally ovulate only after coitus. In estrous cats stimulation of the hypothalamus in the vicinity of the ventromedial nuclei elicits ovulation, and lesions in the ventromedial tuberal region block coitus-induced ovulation.[58]

Thyrotrophin Secretion. Hypothalamic lesions between the levels of the paraventricular nuclei and the median eminence prevent the thyroid hypertrophy which normally results from administration of phenylthiourea.[12, 29] This compound blocks the synthesis of thyroid hormone. The resultant diminution of circulating thyroid hormone stimulates secretion of thyrotrophin, which causes the thyroid gland, although hormonally nonfunctional, to enlarge (see Chap. 60). The effectiveness of hypothalamic lesions in preventing phenylthiourea-induced goiter suggests that the lowered thyroxin blood levels act on neurosecretory cells in the hypothalamus. The latter cells presumably liberate an agent which reaches the hypophysis via the portal vessels and stimulates secretion of thyrotrophin. Conversely, when the thyroxin concentration of fluids bathing the hypothalamus is increased by local intrahypothalamic injection of thyroxin, the neurosecretory elements are depressed, and thyrotrophin secretion diminishes.[64]

Prolactin Secretion. It is well known to the dairyman as well as to the physiologist that maintenance of lactation depends on continued suckling or milking. The breasts of lactating rats undergo involution if the young are allowed to suckle only breasts rendered anesthetic by spinal transection; if suckling of breasts above the level of the transection is permitted, lactation persists.[37] Furthermore, the mammary involution which normally occurs when the litter is removed from a lactating rat can be prevented by the satanic procedure of painting the nipples with turpentine; the irritation thus produced serves as an adequate substitute for that produced by suckling.[36]

The role of the hypothalamus in the regulation of prolactin secretion is difficult to assess. Lactation involves three different hormonal mechanisms: (i) ovarian hormones, regulated by the pituitary gonadotrophins, develop and maintain the secretory tissue and duct systems; (ii) prolactin stimulates milk secretion; and (iii) oxytocin from the posterior pituitary regulates the ejection of milk. Disturbances of lactation following central neural lesions are therefore hard to analyze.

Growth Hormone Secretion. Little is known about the regulation of the secretion of somatotrophin or growth hormone. Growth is usually impaired when the pituitary is transplanted to remote sites, but whether this disorder is due to loss of the vascular connections with the hypothalamus or to other factors is not clear. Recently Bach *et al.*[6] have reported that kittens subjected to lesions of the paraventricular nucleus fail to grow and that the defect can be corrected by administering growth hormone. The hypophysis of the stunted animals showed extensive loss of acidophil cells, which are believed to be the source of growth hormone.

The physiologic stimuli to growth hormone secretion are not known. Using recently developed methods for assaying blood levels of growth hormone, two groups of investigators[38, 53] find that hypoglycemia is a potent stimulus to somatotrophin secretion. The effect is independent of insulin, glucagon and epinephrine. It is not known whether hypoglycemia acts directly on the hypophysis or indirectly through some neural structure (e.g., the paraventricular nucleus) to trigger somatotrophin release.

REGULATION OF FOOD INTAKE[14]

Hetherington and Ranson[35] first demonstrated that animals subjected to small bilateral lesions of the ventromedial hypothalamic nucleus become obese. Careful measurements indicate that the obesity results from increase in food intake, often threefold (Fig. 4). Gastrectomy does not prevent the development of

hypothalamic hyperphagia and obesity; thus there is no evidence that increased afferent input from the gastrointestinal tract drives the animals to increase their food intake. Indeed, behavioral experiments[48] suggest that the animals that were operated upon have no increased food drive and will not work as hard as normal animals for a food reward. For this reason it has been postulated that the ventromedial nucleus is concerned with *satiety* rather than with the initiation of feeding. In other words, the hyperphagic animal doesn't know when to stop eating.

When bilateral lesions are made in the lateral hypothalamus, anorexia results and the animals may die of starvation unless force fed.[2] If, rather than being destroyed, this same region is stimulated through implanted electrodes, food intake increases strikingly (Fig. 5). The lateral hypothalamic region is therefore termed a *feeding center*.

The rather precise adjustment of food intake to energy expenditure and the maintenance of relatively constant body weight thus appears to depend upon the balanced operation of the hypothalamic feeding and satiety centers. Of

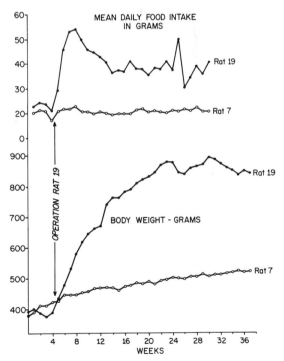

Fig. 4. Food intake and body weight of littermate rats. In rat 19 the ventromedial nucleus of the hypothalamus was electrolytically destroyed at the fourth week.

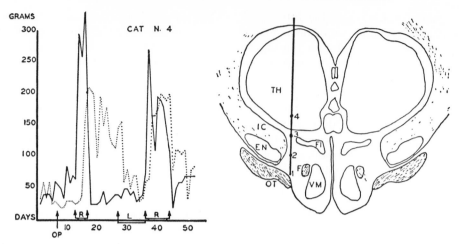

Fig. 5. Effect of stimulating feeding center on food intake in cat. *Solid lines,* meat intake; *dotted lines,* milk intake. *OP,* Implantation of electrodes; *R,* daily stimulation at a point between *2* and *3* in section with marked increase in food intake; *L,* stimulation of a point 2 mm. posterior; 1.5 mm. inferior, and 0.5 mm. lateral to *R* with no effect on food intake. (From Delgado and Anand, *Amer. J. Physiol.,* 1953, *172:*162–168.)

the two, the laterally placed feeding center appears to be dominant, since destruction of both the feeding and the satiety centers results in anorexia and weight loss. Further consideration of the role of the hypothalamic centers in regulating food intake resolves into two questions: what are the efferent connections of the centers and what are the afferent inputs which "inform" the centers of the energy stores of the body? Concerning the first question, little is known except that probably both centers give rise to descending tracts which connect with the cranial and spinal nuclei involved in the complex behavior of seeking and ingesting food. Hyperphagia has been produced by lesions caudal to the hypothalamus in the rostral mesencephalic tegmentum; such lesions presumably interrupt descending pathways from the satiety center. Two additional areas concerned with eating were disclosed by stimulation experiments, one in the premammillary region and one in the mammillary region.[54] In goats, Larsson[41] induced polyphagia by electrical stimulation in the medulla near the dorsal motor nucleus of the vagus; this region might be supposed to receive fibers from the hypothalamic feeding center.

The way in which the hypothalamic centers are activated, although a subject of much speculation, is obscure. Two theories have been advanced. One, proposed by Brobeck,[13] may be termed the *thermostat theory*. Briefly, this theory assumes that the feeding and satiety centers, like the thermoregulatory centers, are sensitive to body temperature; decrease in body temperature is supposed to activate the feeding center and depress the satiety center, whereas increased temperature acts on the centers in the opposite sense. Ingestion of food by increasing heat production [the so-called specific dynamic action (SDA)] leads to satiety, whereas the cooling of the body as heat is dissipated activates the feeding center. The SDA varies with composition of the diet; Strominger and Brobeck[60] found that rats ingest various diets not in proportion to either bulk or total caloric content but rather in proportion to the SDA.

The second theory is the *glucostat* theory, proposed by Mayer.[45] According to this theory, the hypothalamic centers are sensitive to blood glucose levels: hypoglycemia is supposed to excite the feeding center and inhibit the satiety center, whereas hyperglycemia has the reverse actions. In support of this theory, Anand *et al.*[3] found that hypoglycemia decreased electrical activity recorded through electrodes implanted in the ventromedial ("satiety") nucleus and slightly increased the activity recorded from the lateral ("feeding") center. Hyperglycemia resulted in opposite changes in the activity of the two regions. To explain the paradoxical polyphagia of diabetes mellitus (in which, of course, the blood sugar level is high), Mayer suggests that, in the absence of insulin, the failure of sugar to penetrate the receptor cells "tricks" them into behaving as if the blood sugar were actually low. A difficulty with this explanation is that brain cells, unlike cells of other tissues, apparently do not suffer alterations of glucose transport and utilization even in the absence of insulin.

Obesity is induced in mice by gold thioglucose, which destroys cells in the ventromedial nucleus. Other gold-thio compounds, many closely related to gold thioglucose and equally toxic, are ineffective. Mayer and Marshall[46] suggest that the affinity of glucoreceptors in the ventromedial nucleus for the glucose moiety of gold thioglucose causes them to accumulate damagingly high quantities of gold.

REGULATION OF GASTRIC ACID SECRETION

It has been mentioned above that hypothalamic hyperphagia is a disturbance of feeding behavior and does not appear to be directly related to alterations in gastrointestinal function. Nevertheless, the hypothalamus does appear to be involved in gastric secretory activity. According to Porter *et al.*,[24, 52] electrical stimulation of the rostral hypothalamus at the level of the optic chiasm induces a prompt increase in secretion of gastric acid indicated by a drop in pH which reaches maximum in about one hour. The efferent pathway is the vagus nerve, for vagotomy abolishes the response (Fig. 6, *left*). Stimulation of the posterior (tuberal or mammillary) hypothalamus induces a much more delayed gastric acid secretion which is not maximal until three hours after stimulation. This latter secretory response is not influenced by vagotomy but disappears after bilateral adrenalectomy. It is therefore postulated that the hypothalamus is involved in two gastric secretory mechanisms—one neural (vagus) and the other humoral—acting through the adenohypophysis and the adrenal cortex. Insulin-induced hypoglycemia, a strong stimulus to gastric acid secretion, appears to act through both the neural and the humoral channels. Thus lowered blood sugar initiates, via the hypothalamus, not only food-seeking behavior (according to the glucostat theory) but also the secretion of gastric acid to prepare the stomach for the reception of food.

Overactivity of the hypothalamic secretory mechanism leads to injury of the stomach. In monkeys prolonged hypothalamic stimulation (two to four times daily for four to ten weeks) through implanted electrodes often leads to gastric hemorrhage and ulceration.[25] It has long been known that gastric hyperacidity and peptic ulcers occur more frequently in patients under chronic emotional stress; indeed, these abnormalities may be induced in experimental animals by subjecting them repeatedly to conflict

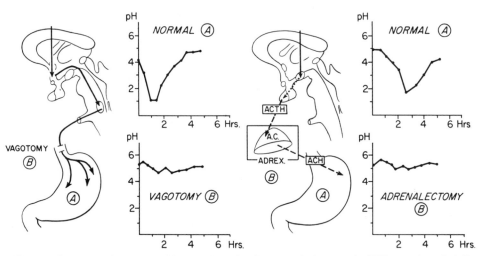

Fig. 6. Diagram of neural and humoral mechanisms regulating gastric HCl secretion. *Left*, Rostral hypothalamic stimulation causes prompt acid secretion (indicated by decreased pH in curve *A*); response is abolished by vagotomy (curve *B*). *Right*, Stimulation of posterior hypothalamus causes delayed acid secretion (curve *A*). Response is not altered by vagotomy but is abolished by adrenalectomy (curve *B*). (From French *et al.*, *Surgery*, 1953, 34:621–632.)

situations. Peptic ulcer is therefore often described as a "psychosomatic disorder." In view of the known role of the hypothalamus in elaborating emotional behavior and in regulating gastric secretory mechanisms, it may be suggested that peptic ulcer is more aptly described as a "hypothalamosomatic disorder."

CARDIOVASCULAR REGULATION IN FEAR, ANGER AND EXERCISE

It has been observed repeatedly in experiments on anesthetized animals that electrical stimulation at various hypothalamic sites induces marked alterations in the cardiovascular system, e.g., changes in blood pressure and heart rate. The significance of these changes is not easy to evaluate in anesthetized or restrained preparations in which the behavior of the animal is suppressed. When Hess developed the technique of permanently implanting stimulating electrodes in the brain it became possible to observe the effects of hypothalamic stimulation on unanesthetized and unrestrained animals. As described in more detail in Chapter 35, such experiments indicate that the hypothalamus plays an important role in the elaboration of emotional or affective behavior. Stimulation at some hypothalamic foci elicits behavior which mimics that displayed by an animal subjected to a threatening situation and which might therefore be called the behavioral pattern of fear. Stimulation at other sites elicits aggressive reactions similar to those displayed by animals angered by natural stimuli or situations.[49] In both fear and anger, changes in heart rate and blood pressure are constantly occurring accompaniments of the total behavioral picture; along with the onset of "fight or flight," to use Cannon's expression, there are concomitant automatic adjustments of the cardiovascular system to support the increased demands for oxygen attending combat or hasty retreat. The cardiovascular changes observed in anesthetized animals during hypothalamic stimulation appear therefore to represent isolated fragments of a total behavioral pattern which is readily recognizable only in the unanesthetized and unrestrained preparation.

Adaptive cardiovascular adjustment occurs, however, in situations other than those eliciting fear or anger. Simple muscular exercise, no matter how motivated, is accompanied by prompt adaptive changes in the heart and vascular tree. Using a variety of ingeniously devised recording instruments which are attached permanently to the heart and great vessels, Rushmer[55] and his colleagues succeeded in monitoring in intact, unanesthetized dogs the cardiovascular response to exercise (walking on a treadmill). Electrical stimulation of the diencephalon in the region of the fields of Forel induces cardiovascular changes which mimic to a remarkable degree those induced in intact dogs by exercise. When bilateral lesions are inflicted on these same regions (Fig. 3, Chap. 35), exercise no longer elicits the cardiovascular adjustments seen in intact dogs.[56]

Pulmonary Edema.[26, 43, 44]   An observation which documents dramatically the vital function of the hypothalamus is that lesions in the preoptic region lead to lung edema and hemorrhage. The edema often develops with an explosive suddenness within one to 24 hours after induction of the lesions and results in the rapid asphyxial death of the animal. Hypothalamic lung edema is apparently a release phenomenon, for caudal hypothalamic lesions, spinal transection or splanchnic nerve sections protects the animals from the effects of preoptic lesions. It has been suggested that the released hypothalamic centers normally regulate the capacity of the systemic venous reservoirs. After destruction of the preoptic region, the unfettered activity of the caudally located centers may result in constriction of venous reservoirs so that an excess volume of blood is dumped into the pulmonary circuit, causing lung hemorrhage and edema.

REFERENCES

1. ADAMS, T. *J. appl. Physiol.*, 1963, *18*:772–777.
2. ANAND, B. K. and BROBECK, J. R. *Yale J. Biol. Med.*, 1951, *24*:123–140.
3. ANAND, B. K., DUA S. and SINGH, B. *Electroenceph. clin. Neurophysiol.*, 1961, *13*:54–59.
4. ANDERSSON, B., GRANT, R. and LARSSON, S. *Acta physiol. scand.*, 1956, *37*:261–280.
5. ANDERSSON, B. and McCANN, S. M. *Acta physiol. scand.*, 1955, *33*:333–346.
6. BACH, L. M. N., O'BRIEN, C. P. and COOPER, G. P. *Prog. Brain Res.*, 1964, *5*:114–126.
7. BARD, P. and MACHT, M. B. Pp. 55–75 in *Ciba Foundation symposium on neurological basis of behavior*, G. E. W. WOLSTENHOLME and C. M. O'CONNER, eds. Boston, Little, Brown and Co., 1958.
8. BARGMANN, W. *Z. Zellforsch.*, 1949, *34*:610–634.
9. BENZINGER, T. H. *Proc. nat. Acad. Sci. (Wash.)*, 1959, *45*:645–659.

10. BIRZIS, L. and HEMINGWAY, A. *J. Neurophysiol.*, 1957, *20:*91–99.

11. BODIAN, D. *Bull. Johns Hopk. Hosp.*, 1951, *89:*354–376.

12. BOGDANOVE, E. M. and HALMI, N. S. *Endocrinology*, 1953, *53:*274–292.

13. BROBECK, J. R. *Yale J. Biol. Med.*, 1957, *29:*565–574.

14. BROBECK, J. R. Chap. 47 in *Handbook of physiology, Section 1: Neurophysiology*, vol. 2, J. Field, ed. Washington, D.C., American Physiological Society, 1960.

15. BROOKS, C. McC., USHIYAMA, J. and LANGE, G. *Amer. J. Physiol.*, 1962, *202:*487–490.

16. CARLSON, L. D. *Proc. Soc. exp. Biol.* (*N. Y.*), 1954, *85:*303–305.

17. CROSS, B. A. and HARRIS, G. W. *J. Endocrin.*, 1952, *8:*148–161.

18. DAVISON, C. *Res. Publ. Ass. nerv. ment. Dis.*, 1940, *20:*774–823.

19. DONAVAN, B. T. and HARRIS, G. W. *Nature* (*Lond.*), 1954, *174:*503–504.

20. EVERETT, J. W. *Physiol. Rev.*, 1964, *44:*373–431.

21. FISHER, C., INGRAM, W. R. and RANSON, S. W. *Diabetes insipidus and the neuro-hormonal control of water balance: a contribution to the structure and function of the hypthalamico-hypophyseal system.* Ann Arbor, Mich., Edwards Brothers, 1938.

22. FOLKOW, B., STRÖM, G. and UVNÄS, B. *Acta physiol. scand.*, 1949, *17:*317–326.

23. FOLKOW, B., STRÖM, G. and UVNÄS, B. *Acta physiol. scand.*, 1949, *17:*327–338.

24. FRENCH, J. D., LONGMIRE, R. L., PORTER, R. W. and MOVIUS, H. J. *Surgery*, 1953, *34:*621 632.

25. FRENCH, J. D., PORTER, R. W., CAVANAUGH, E. B. and LONGMIRE, R. L. *Arch Neurol. Psychiat.* (*Chic.*), 1954, *72:*267–281.

26. GAMBLE, J. E. and PATTON, H. D. *Amer. J. Physiol.*, 1953, *172:*623–631.

27. GERSHENFELD, H. M., TREMEZZANI, J. H. and DE ROBERTIS, E. *Endocrinology*, 1960, *66:*741–762.

28. GREEN, J. D. and HARRIS, G. W. *J. Endocrin.*, 1947, *5:*136–146.

29. GREER, M. A. *J. clin. Endocrin.*, 1952, *12:*1259–1268.

30. DE GROOT, J. and HARRIS, G. W. *J. Physiol.*, 1950, *111:*335–346.

31. GUILLEMIN, R., HEARN, W. R., CHEEK, W. R. and HOUSHOLDER, D. E. *Endocrinology*, 1957, *60:*488–506.

32. HARRIS, G. W. *Phil. Trans.*, 1947, *B232:*385–441.

33. HARRIS, G. W. *Neural control of the pituitary gland.* London, Edward Arnold Ltd., 1955.

34. HARRIS, G. W. Chap. 39 in *Handbook of physiology, Section 1: Neurophysiology*, vol. 2, J. Field, ed., Washington, D.C., American Physiological Society, 1960.

35. HETHERINGTON, A. W. and RANSON, S. W. *Anat. Rec.*, 1940, *78:*149–172.

36. HOOKER, C. W. and WILLIAMS, W. L. *Yale J. Biol. Med.*, 1940, *12:*559–564.

37. INGELBRECHT, P. *C. R. Soc. Biol.* (*Paris*), 1935, *120:*1369–1371.

38. JANSZ, A., DOORENBOS, H. and REITSMA, W. D. *Lancet*, 1963, *1:*250–251.

39. KANDEL, E. R. *J. gen. Physiol.*, 1964, *47:*691–717.

40. KERSLAKE, D. McK. *J. Physiol.*, 1955, *127:*280–296.

41. LARSSON, S. *Acta physiol. scand.*, 1954, *32*(suppl. 115):1–63.

42. MAGOUN, H. W., HARRISON, F., BROBECK, J. R. and RANSON, S. W. *J. Neurophysiol.*, 1938, *1:*101–114.

43. MAIRE, F. W. and PATTON, H. D. *Amer. J. Physiol.*, 1956, *184:*345–350.

44. MAIRE, F. W. and PATTON, H. D. *Amer. J. Physiol.*, 1956, *184:*351–355.

45. MAYER, J. *Physiol. Rev.*, 1953, *33:*472–508.

46. MAYER, J. and MARSHALL, N. B. *Nature* (*Lond.*), 1956, *178:*1399–1400.

47. McCANN, S. M. and BROBECK, J. R. *Proc. Soc. exp. Biol.* (*N. Y.*), 1954, *87:*318–324.

48. MILLER, N. E., BAILEY, C. J. and STEVENSON, J. A. F. *Science*, 1950, *112:*256–259.

49. NAKAO, H. *Amer. J. Physiol.*, 1958, *194:*411–418.

50. NAKAYAMA, T., HAMMEL, H. T., HARDY, J. D. and EISENMAN, J. S. *Amer. J. Physiol.*, 1963, *204:*1122–1126.

51. ORTMANN, R. Chap. 40 in *Handbook of physiology, Section 1: Neurophysiology*, vol. 2, J. Field, ed., Washington, D.C., American Physiological Society, 1960.

52. PORTER, R. W., MOVIUS, H. J. and FRENCH, J. D. *Surgery*, 1953, *33:*875–880.

53. ROTH, J., GLICK, S. M., YALOW, R. S. and BERSON, S. A. *Science*, 1963, *140:*987–988.

54. RUCH, T. C., MAIRE, F. W. and PATTON, H. D. *Abstr. Comm., Congr. int. Physiol.*, 1956, *20:*788.

55. RUSHMER, R. F. *Cardiac diagnosis, a physiologic approach.* Philadelphia, W. B. Saunders, 1955.

56. RUSHMER, R. F. and SMITH, O. A., JR. *Physiol. Rev.*, 1959, *39:*41–68.

57. SAHS, A. L. and FULTON, J. F. *J. Neurophysiol.*, 1940, *3:*258–268.

58. SAWYER, C. H. Pp. 164–174 in *Physiological triggers and discontinuous rate processes*, T. H. BULLOCK, ed. Washington, D.C., American Physiological Society, 1957.

59. STRÖM, G. Chap. 46 in *Handbook of physiology, Section 1: Neurophysiology*, vol. 2, J. Field, ed., Washington, D.C., American Physiological Society, 1960.

60. STROMINGER, J. L. and BROBECK, J. R. *Yale J. Biol. Med.*, 1953, *25:*383–390.

61. TANG, P. C. and PATTON, H. D. *Endocrinology*, 1951, *49:*86–98.

62. THOMPSON, A. P. D. and ZUCKERMAN, S. *Proc. roy. Soc.*, 1954, *B142:*437–451.

63. VERNEY, E. B. *Proc. roy. Soc.*, 1947, *B135:*25–105.

64. YAMADA, T. and GREER, M. A. *Endocrinology*, 1959, *64:*559–566.

65. ZIMMERMAN, H. M. *Res. Publ. Ass. nerv. ment. Dis.*, 1940, *20:*824–840.

CHAPTER 12

The Cerebral Cortex: Its Structure and Motor Functions

By THEODORE C. RUCH

SINCE antiquity, the cerebral hemispheres have been looked upon as the organ of intelligence and conscious sensation. Consequently, the structure of this region of the brain has long aroused curiosity. Ancient writers, and even those of the Renaissance, speculated widely about the localization of consciousness. Some placed the "psyche" in the cerebral ventricles; others drew diagrams suggesting precise localization of various mental faculties in different regions of the forebrain. Neurologists of the seventeenth century, such as Willis and Vieussens, carried out experiments which indicated that the brain substance, not the ventricles, is the seat of consciousness. Willis, moreover, proclaimed the cerebrum the seat of volitional movements and the cerebellum the source of involuntary movements; he also described the gross structure and blood supply of the brain in detail.

Historical note.[21]   Use of the microscope came late in the analysis of the structural organization of the nervous system. The story actually began in February 1776, when an Italian medical student, Francesco Gennari, observed the well defined white line which indicates special structural organization of the occipital lobes of the brain; this line is now recognized as a primary landmark within the so-called visual cortex. In 1840, the French psychiatrist J.-P. Baillarger[24] found macroscopically that six discrete layers can be identified in most areas when thin sections of human cerebral cortex are placed between two plates of glass, but that the relative width of a given layer varies widely from one region to another. He also established that Gennari's white line extends into other cortical areas and corresponds to his own "external band."

In the early part of the present century improved staining methods were brought to bear upon the cortical histology of man and other primates, and this is still a subject of active investigation. This study has taken two main directions: (i) cytoarchitecture and myeloarchitecture, i.e., the cellular and fiber make-up of various cortical areas (Campbell,[12] Brodmann,[8] C. and O. Vogt,[71] and von Economo and Koskinas[19]); and (ii) dendritic and axonic ramifications as studied with silver impregnation methods by Ramón y Cajal[55] and, more recently, by Lorente de Nó[42] and Sholl.[59] Further insight into cortical function has been gained by investigating thalamocortical projections to specific regions and efferent projections from them. Collectively, these studies provide an anatomic framework with which functional studies—ablation, stimulation and the recording of evoked potentials—can be correlated.

STRUCTURE

Through studies of cytoarchitecture (cellular) and myeloarchitecture (dendritic and axonal), the neocortex, as opposed to the archicortex, has been subdivided into areas of specific structure in the belief that structural differences bespeak differences in function. Within each area, the cortex is divided into six more or less distinct layers. The stratification is based on the presence of specific types of cells peculiar to each layer.

The four main types of cells are:

(i) Cells with descending axons, often reaching the white substance, to be continued by a projection or association axon.

(ii) Cells with short axons ramified near the cell body, often within its area of dendritic ramification.

(iii) Cells with ascending axons ramified in one or several cortical layers.

(iv) Cells with horizontal axons.

The six recognized layers are:

I. The molecular or superficial plexiform layer. This layer lies immediately beneath the pia mater and is about 0.25 mm. thick; it is sparsely populated with nerve cell bodies,[59] and is made up of dendrites and axons from neurons lying deeper in the cortex.

II. The external granular layer, or the layer of small pyramidal cells. This layer contains many pyramidal cells, those nearer the lower boundary generally being larger than those above. The apices of these cells are directed toward the external surface. The apical dendrites terminate in the molecular layer and form the basis of intracortical association; the axon arising from the basal side of the cell passes inward to constitute one of the fibers of the medullary portion of the cerebrum. The other cells in this layer belong to the short axon group (Golgi type II or granule cells). This thick lamina of cells is sometimes subdivided into three layers of small, medium and large pyramidal cells.

III. The external pyramidal layer, a layer of larger pyramidal cells. This layer is sometimes difficult to distinguish from layer II.

IV. The internal granular or stellate layer. This layer is composed of many small multipolar cells with short branching axons. These latter are Golgi type II cells and receive endings of specific thalamic afferents to the sensory cortex.

V. The deep layer of large pyramidal cells. Here lie large or medium-sized pyramidal cells, similar in form to those in layer II, with axons which pass into the medulla or white matter of the cerebrum.

VI. The layer of fusiform or spindle-shaped cells. Layer VI consists of cells whose form is more irregular than that of the pyramidal cells. The axons of these irregularly shaped cells pass into the medullary portion of the cerebrum, and their dendrites stretch externally into the layers of pyramidal cells. This layer also contains some Golgi type II cells.

Physiologic Deductions from the Histology of the Cortex.   Ramón y Cajal[55] stressed some anatomic features leading to physiologic generalizations. One to which we have returned is that every part of the cortex receives incoming impulses and gives rise to outgoing impulses; every part of the cortex is, therefore, both the terminal of an afferent path and the beginning of an efferent path. In other words, a cortical point is a reflex center of greater or lesser complexity. Second, there are provisions for the spread of impulses both horizontally through the gray matter and also along association fibers running through the white matter. Thus, efferent discharges from one part of the cortex can be aroused by impulses coming to it from other cortical areas. A given area, in addition to discharging caudally over its own efferents, may transmit impulses to another area and discharge over the latter's efferents. Third, all parts of the neocortex are described as having or departing from a basic structure.

Although the size, shape and density of cell bodies in the cerebral cortex are useful in cytoarchitectural mapping, they offer few clues to function. Study of the plexuses of dendritic and axonal branches that cut across cortical cell layers and determine the synaptic connections through which nerve impulses are transmitted is more useful to physiology.

Layer IV of the cortex is a receptive layer, since the *specific thalamocortical afferents* mainly end there in a compact axon brush; but other layers are also receptive. The *nonspecific thalamocortical afferents* begin to give off horizontal collaterals while still in the white matter; these turn and ascend through the cortex to the outermost layer, ending in terminal branches which

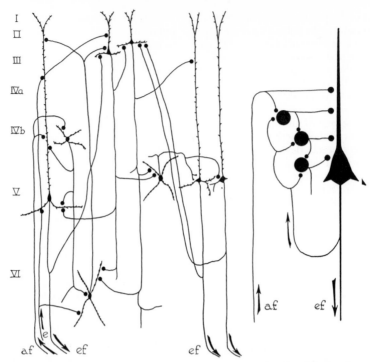

Fig. 1.   Diagram of some intracortical neuron chains. Note that few dendrites and axonal branches have been included. Synaptic junctions are indicated by thickening of axon. *af,* Axon entering cortex; *ef,* axon leaving cortex; *e,* axon of intra-areal cortical association cell whose cell body lies in sixth layer, outside picture. Diagram at right is a simplification of diagram at left. Afferent fiber activates large pyramidal cell, which is origin of efferent fiber and also of a system of cortical internuncial cells; recurrent collateral of *ef* delivers impulses again to internuncial system. This diagram exemplifies the broad plan upon which the cerebral cortex is organized. Roman numerals at left indicate cortical layers. (After Lorente de Nó in Fulton, *Physiology of the nervous system,* 3rd ed. New York, Oxford University Press, 1949.)

also run horizontally. Because of the dual system of branching, the nonspecific afferents terminate in blocks of cortex. Axons linking area to area, or cortex to cortex, are now also thought to terminate in several layers.

The fifth and sixth layers are the main efferent layers. They contain the cell bodies of axons which enter the pyramidal tract. The apical dendrites of the cells in these layers ascend, giving off collaterals, but the basal dendrites may spread laterally or obliquely downward, presenting a much greater area for synaptic contact than the cell body itself. Callosal and association efferent fibers also originate in the deep layers, V and VI.

An impulse traversing one cortical afferent may pass directly or monosynaptically to a cortical efferent, but, through collaterals and cortical cells with short dendrites and axons (cortical internuncials), cortical afferents can effect multisynaptic connection with the efferent neuron, as shown in Figure 1. Moreover, through the recurrent collaterals of cortical ef-

ferents ending on other neurons of the same type, circular chains capable of re-excitation or "reverberation" are formed, an anatomic formation which has important physiologic implications.

Altogether, the cerebral cortex reduced to its absolute skeleton is not unlike the spinal cord. As said by Lorente de Nó,[42] cortical neuron chains "are in no way different from chains of internuncial neurons in any part of the central nervous system." He also points out that, from mouse to man, cortical cells with short axons increase in number more than cells with long ascending or descending axons.

Cajal was first to point out that the large number of cells with short axons was the anatomic expression of the delicacy of function of the brain of man. It is now known that synaptic transmission demands the summation of impulses under strict conditions, and it is evident that the more heterogeneous the origin of the synapses on the cells with descending axons, the more rigid become the conditions for threshold stimulation, and the more accurate the selection of the paths through which the impulses may be conducted. The reduction of the number of cells with short axons, without essential modification of the long links in the chains of cortical neurons, makes the cortex of the mouse the "skeleton" for the human cortex.[31]

Electrophysiologists,[1] by using microelectrodes which can record from single cells throughout the depth of the cortex, have developed a physiology of the cortex comparable to the histologic studies of the cortex made with silver stains. This development brings closer an understanding of cortical function.

CYTOARCHITECTURAL MAPS.   Although cytoarchitectural maps offer few clues to function, major differences between cytoarchitectural fields have been given functional significance. However, every small cytoarchitectural difference does not imply a functional difference nor does each function require a unique cytoarchitecture. Some students of cytoarchitecture have overzealously divided the cortical layers into more and more sublayers and the cortical areas into smaller and smaller subareas. Many of these proposed divisions, almost always based on subjective and nonquantitative criteria, have not been verified by other observers looking at the same sections. Many cytoarchitectural boundaries are not constant from animal to animal, and variations often result from distortions produced mechanically by the cortical folds, which notoriously differ from brain to brain

within a species. It is interesting that the revolt against excessive parcellation was initiated by two psychologists[34] rather than by neuroanatomists.

Experiments on the cerebral cortex are often described in terms of fissures, sulci, gyri and lobes. The fissural pattern for the rhesus monkey, a common laboratory animal, is shown in Figure 2. It can be seen that the simian brain is basically similar to the human, but much simpler. Cytoarchitectural maps also provide a language in which to describe the cortex, a language that is often more compact than description in terms of fissures and convolutions. It is virtually impossible to follow present and past experimental literature based on the monkey without knowledge of Brodmann's map. This map, as modified by the Vogts,[71] and another produced by von Bonin and Bailey[6] are reproduced for reference in Figure 3.*

* In this map the initial letter is drawn from the name of the lobe. The numbers used by Brodmann and others can be remembered more easily if the way they were assigned is understood. His monkey brain was cut horizontally, so the precentral and postcentral regions appeared in the first few sections. These received the low numbers (1–8) as different cytoarchitecture was encountered. It will be noticed that the numbers jump from front to back. The next important group of numbers (9–12) is frontal; 17–19 are occipital; 20–22 are in the temporal lobe in the order of their appearance in serial horizontal sections.

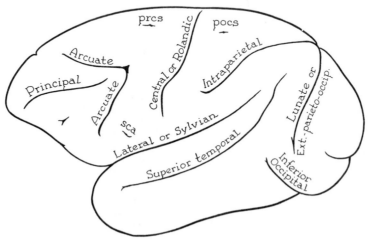

Fig. 2.   Dorsolateral view of the left cerebral hemisphere of *Macaca mulatta* showing pattern and names of sulci. Note following differences from human brain: (i) fewer and less complex sulci, (ii) smaller prefrontal lobe, (iii) ascending course of intraparietal, lateral and superior temporal fissures (also lesser development of posterior parietal region), (iv) lesser development of the superior precentral (*prcs*) and postcentral (*pocs*) sulci. Sulcus subcentralis anterior (*SCA*) may correspond to the human inferior precentral sulcus. (After von Bonin and Bailey. *The neocortex of* Macaca mulatta. Urbana, University of Illinois Press, 1947.)

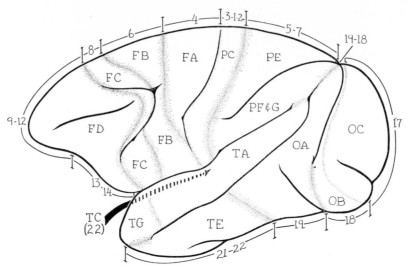

Fig. 3. Cytoarchitectural map of monkey brain relating terminology of Brodmann (*numbers*) to that of von Bonin and Bailey (*letters*). The areas and the relation of the designations are only approximate.

In the interpretation of such maps it should be realized that the boundaries are not sharp; instead, one type of cortex blends into another. The Brodmann terminology can be modified to encompass modern studies. The expression "areas 3–1–2" may be retained, even though the differences between 3 and 1 may not be real and 2 is nonexistent. Similarly, use of "areas 9–12" reflects skepticism of the significance of the subareal differences but describes a region for which there is no other generally accepted term, since some object to the word "prefrontal." In the description below, the letters signify von Bonin and Bailey's terminology. The numbers are those of Brodmann, occasionally modified. Some of the areas concerned with motor function will be discussed in detail; others will be described in later chapters.

FA (*area 4*) is agranular cortex beginning in the depth of the central fissure and extending up its anterior bank onto the free surface of the precentral gyrus. Here the gray matter is thick (3.5 to 5.0 mm.); the presence of the giant pyramidal cells of Betz in the fifth layer constitutes the major basis for determining the anterior border. Since the size necessary to qualify a cell as a Betz cell is not agreed upon, the forward boundary is not definitely established.

FB, together with *FA*, corresponds roughly to Brodmann's *area 6*, although the posterior boundary, as noted, fluctuates markedly. In this area, the cortex is still thick and agranular but lacks giant pyramidal (Betz) cells in the fifth layer.

FC, corresponding to *area 8* as modified since Brodmann, is a transitional band with a poorly developed internal granular layer; it extends around the frontal pole. On the lateral surface, *FC* is largely buried in the two limbs of the V formed by the arcuate fissure, but issues from it laterally. The remainder of the frontal lobe (*FD* or *area 9–12*) is quite uniform in structure, except for an area around the posterior end of the principal fissure.

PB lies almost entirely buried in the depth of the central fissure and is easily recognized. Like other primary sensory areas, *PB* is koniocortex ("dusty cortex," referring to its highly granular nature). *PC*, occupying the free face of the postcentral gyrus, loses the excessive granulation and becomes homotypical; i.e., all six layers are present and none is "overdeveloped." Since area 2 has been shown by von Bonin and Bailey to be nonexistent, the posterior boundary of area *PC* lies somewhat anterior to the superior postcentral fissure. The two terminologies can be made congruent by speaking of *Brodmann areas 3 and 1*.

The remaining areas which figure prominently in discussion of motor function are the two concentric bands surrounding the large and easily identified striate area (the primary visual area), which in monkeys, unlike the situation in man, extends over the free surface of the occipital lobe. The transition from *OC* or *area 17* is sharp, *OB* or *area 18* being homotypical and marked by the presence of very large cells in the third layer. The boundaries between *OB* and *OA* and between *OA* and the parietal lobe are not sharp, and cytoarchitectural analysis is made difficult by the deep fissures in the region. The Vogts and von Bonin and Bailey agree in restricting area 17 mainly to the posterior wall of the lunate sulcus. The general region can be termed *area 18–19* without neglect of major cytoarchitectural criteria.

Corticospinal or Pyramidal Tract.[51]   By definition, the pyramidal tract consists of those fibers which originate in the cerebral cortex and pass to the spinal cord through the medullary pyramids.* It is only accidental and incidental that some of the tract originates in large, conspicuous, pyramid-shaped cells such as the Betz cells. The term "pyramidal tract" in no way implies fibers originating from such cells; in fact, the tract was named before the shape of the cells of origin was known.† Fibers from the cortex to the cranial motor nerve nuclei are functionally similar to those going to spinal segments. Although such fibers obviously do not pass through the pyramids, they should not be confused with those termed extrapyramidal fibers. Some corticobulbar fibers end on intercalated nuclei and are difficult to separate morphologically or experimentally from those that end more directly on the motor nerve nuclei.

It is now believed that all or most of the fibers in the pyramids arise from the cerebral cortex; degeneration in the pyramids is said to be complete after decortication.[47] That the pyramidal tract arises solely in the giant Betz cells is a misconception; the tract also arises from small cells distributed through the third to the sixth layer. In man, the motor area of each hemisphere contains approximately 34,000 Betz cells, enough to account for the 2 per cent of fibers with large diameters ranging from 11μ to 20μ, but not nearly enough to account for the one million axons in each medullary pyramid. Figure 4 shows the distribution of the diameters of the myelinated fibers which constitute the major portion of the pyramidal tract.[35] The remaining fibers in the tract are unmyelinated and recently[16] were estimated to constitute 6 per cent of it. Little is known of their origin and function.

Although many pyramidal tract fibers originate in the primary motor sector (area 4), that the pyramidal tract originates exclusively there is also a misconception. The proportion of fibers originating from the monkey's precentral gyrus

---

*Although recent anatomic evidence that the pyramids may contain ascending fibers has not been contradicted, functional evidence thought to indicate their existence has been thoroughly disproved.[49]

†Some fibers in the pyramids give collaterals to the pontine nuclei and possibly to the reticular formation of the medulla. Should these collaterals reach the cord without synapse they would be corticospinal but not pyramidal. Further, because of this collateralization, it is possible that the distinction between pyramidal and extrapyramidal fibers has been overdrawn.

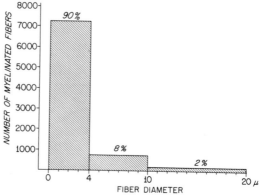

Fig. 4. Myelinated fiber spectrum of pyramidal tract. (After Lassek. *J. comp. Neurol.*, 1942, 76:217–225.)

by the most recent and careful estimates[57] is 31 per cent and that from area 6, contrary to many previous estimates is nearly as large, 29 per cent (Fig. 5). The remainder, 40 per cent, arises from the postcentral gyrus and the posterior parietal lobe. The prefrontal occipital and temporal lobes are now not thought to give origin to any fibers passing through the pyramids. Earlier estimates ascribed a significant share of fibers to these areas because motor and sensory cortical lesions left some 40 per cent of fibers undegenerated. Recent studies indicate that axonal degeneration and disappearance require not a few weeks but a year. Axons late to disappear were ascribed to origins other than the motor and sensory areas.

Extrapyramidal Projections from the Cortex.   Overlapping with pyramidal tract projections in respect to point of origin are projections to a wide range of subcortical structures including the brain stem reticular formation (Table 1, Chap. 13). Through these structures impulses eventually reach the segmental level in the spinal cord and can both *effect* and *affect* movement. Extrapyramidal pathways from the cortex to the spinal cord differ from the pyramidal or corticospinal system in two ways: (i) the chains of neurons are synaptically interrupted in the basal ganglia or in the brain stem nuclei or reticular formation; and (ii) by definition, the pathways do not pass through the medullary pyramids. These systems of neurons can be termed the "cortically originating extrapyramidal system," which can be abbreviated "COEPS." Since the extrapyramidal system also receives subcortical inputs, COEPS is not a synonym for "extrapyramidal system,"

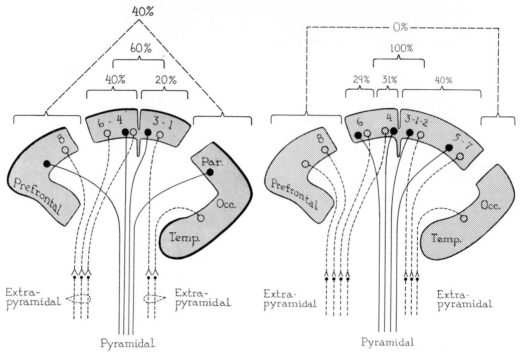

Fig. 5. Summary diagram showing older (left) and newer (right) views of the origins of pyramidal and extrapyramidal systems influencing spinal motoneurons. Note overlapping resulting from extrapyramidal systems originating from sensorimotor areas. Quantitative estimates and other details will vary, depending on technique used. (*Left,* based on data from Lassek,[35] Mettler[47] and others; *right,* based on Russell and De Myer.[57])

but refers to that portion of it which originates in the cerebral cortex. The major COEPS pathways may be summarized as follows.

Corticostriatal and corticopallidal. The existence of a corticostriatal system had long been suspected but could not be demonstrated by the usual degeneration techniques.* Glees,[27] using a silver stain, has observed an unmyelinated corticocaudate and corticoputamen projection in cat and monkey. Dusser de Barenne and his coworkers applied strychnine to the cortex in monkeys and recorded strychnine spikes† in the caudate nucleus. Impulses originating in the cortex can reach the pallidum by way of the putamen or by

---

*A discrete area of cortical tissue is ablated. Some time later, the animal is sacrificed, and lower neural structures are stained and studied histologically for degenerated fibers.

†Strychnine causes a large number of neurons to synchronize their discharges. The result is periodic spikes at the terminus of the neurons in another part of the cortex or in a subcortical nucleus. Since the spikes suffer temporal dispersion at the first synapse, the recording of a spike means a direct connection between the recording and strychninized points. "Strychnine neuronography" is a useful tool for functional anatomy.

direct pathways. Glees traced fibers from area 6 to the external segment of the globus pallidus. From the basal ganglia, impulses can be relayed along the lenticular fasciculus and the ansa lenticularis; and, after traversing a synapse in the field of Forel, the impulses reach the midline tegmentum. A more direct projection from areas 4 and 6 enters the midbrain nuclei including the red nucleus.

Corticothalamic. In general, a specific cortical area sends fibers to the thalamic nucleus from which it receives fibers. This reciprocal arrangement occurs in the motor cortex as well as in the sensory and the association cortex.

Corticoreticular. Rossi and Brodal,[56] using a silver method, found that corticoreticular fibers originate from much of the cerebral cortex but mainly from the sensorimotor region, particularly the motor area. These fibers end predominantly in the pontine reticulum and in the medulla dorsal to the inferior olive. The projection is bilateral and poorly, if at all, organized somatotopically. The terminations of this projection are in the regions from which the reticulospinal tracts originate, providing an extrapyramidal connection of the cortex with spinal motoneurons. Several investigators[2, 3] have shown that single reticular units can be activated by cortical stimulation; the latency (2 to 6 milliseconds) of the response suggests that the connection is a direct corticoreticular neuron.

Some of these connections may be effected by collaterals from the pyramidal tract.

Corticopontine. Each of the four major lobes of the brain projects to the pons, the frontopontine tract being the largest projection. It arises equally from areas 4 and 6. Besides conveying impulses to the cerebellum, this important tract in primates is thought to give off collaterals to midbrain structures, e.g., the substantia nigra. According to Cajal, some corticopontine fibers are actually collaterals of corticospinal fibers.

The COEPS provides not only multisynaptic pathways to the spinal cord but also recurrent or "feedback" pathways from the cortex that pass through the subcortical structures to return to the cortex. There are at least three such potential pathways from the cortex: (i) via the cortico-ponto-cerebellar tract and returning via the dentatothalamo-cortical pathway; (ii) via collaterals from the corticopontine tract and from direct corticospinal fibers to the substantia nigra and thence via nigrostriatal fibers to join the loop described next; and (iii) via cortico-striatal-pallidal projections, thence via the anteroventral nucleus of the thalamus and its projections to the motor areas.

MOTOR FUNCTIONS

Pyramidal Tract. A single point in the motor area of the cortex can be stimulated and the resulting discharge in the pyramidal tract recorded from any point along its course— from the interneurons of the spinal cord, from the motor roots and nerves, or from the muscles. In fact, a point on the motor cortex and the pyramidal fibers to which it gives rise can be treated like the afferent limb of a reflex arc and subjected to the same kind of analysis. Stimulations of two cortical points can be interacted like stimulations of two afferent nerves.

D AND I RESPONSES. The first question to be asked is, what is stimulated when electrodes are applied to the cortical surface of the motor area? The cells of origin of the pyramidal tract? The intracortical neurons which end on these cells? Because too many stages intervene, the response of a muscle or even of a nerve to stimulation of the motor cortex will obviously not give much information.

Patton and Amassian[50, 51] inserted a record-

ing microelectrode into the bulbar pyramid or the pyramidal tract of the cervical spinal cord and stimulated the motor cortex. In the records so obtained (Fig. 6), the first deflection (D wave) is a stable, short-latency (0.7 millisecond), short-duration, positive wave. This wave is followed by a series of positive, irregular or imperfectly rhythmic waves beginning after a longer time (2.0 to 2.5 milliseconds) and lasting for many milliseconds. The first wave was termed the D wave because analysis indicated that it appeared when the electric current excited *directly* the cells giving rise to the pyramidal tract axons. The later deflections were termed the I waves because analysis showed that they were caused by indirect excitation of pyramidal tract neurons. The longer latency of the I waves was accounted for by the time consumed in traversing chains of intracortical neurons.

The experiments leading to this conclusion illustrate how a neurophysiologic analysis can be made. Briefly, the D wave relative to the I waves was more resistant to anesthesia, anoxia, etc.; had a shorter recovery cycle; and persisted when the cortex was removed and the underlying white matter was stimu-

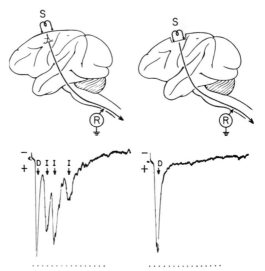

Fig. 6. Pyramidal tract responses to stimulation of motor cortex (*left*) and white matter (*right*) in monkey. Recording electrode in lateral column of spinal cord at C_1. Downward deflection indicates positivity at electrode in pyramidal tract. Time, 1 millisecond. *D* and *I* waves are labeled. (After Patton and Amassian, Chap. 34 in *Handbook of physiology, Section I, Neurophysiology*, vol. 2, J. Field, ed. Washington, D. C., American Physiological Society, 1960.)

lated (Fig. 6). In "penetration experiments," the I waves appeared only when the tip of the stimulating electrode was within the cortex. Further, when the stimulating electrode was moved rostrally, the D wave disappeared, but the I wave persisted for some distance. This observation will help in resolving some of the controversial aspects of localization in the motor cortex.

RATES OF CONDUCTION.   In general, the pyramidal axons are small, less than 2 per cent being of Group I diameter (11 to 22 μ). Maximal conduction velocity in the spinal portion of the tract is, according to Lloyd[41] and Bernhard *et al.*,[5] 60 to 70 meters per second. This difference in velocity suggests that the axons between the cortex and the pyramid are larger than those below the pyramids, the fibers becoming attenuated by collateralization in the spinal cord.

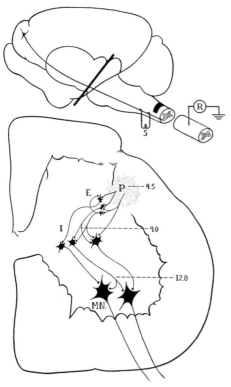

Fig. 7.   Diagram of Lloyd's experiment on activation of spinal nuclei by pyramidal tract discharge. Upper drawing shows positions of stimulating and recording electrodes and of brain ablations to rule out nonpyramidal conduction. Time noted at each level is first detectable facilitation of nuclear neurons. Subtraction gives nuclear delay in *previous nucleus. P,* Pyramidal tract; *E,* external basilar cells; *I,* intermediate nucleus of Cajal; *MN,* motoneuron. (After Lloyd. *J. Neurophysiol.,* 1941, *4*:525–546.)

SPINAL STAGE OF PYRAMIDAL SYSTEM FUNCTION. Knowledge of how the interneurons and motoneurons of the spinal cord are excited is necessary to a complete picture of pyramidal tract activity. In the cat, Lloyd[41] used microelectrodes to record from the nuclear groups of the spinal gray matter while he stimulated the bulbar pyramids (Fig. 7). (All of the medulla except the pyramids had been sectioned below the stimulating electrodes to prevent activation of descending fibers in the extrapyramidal system, and a midcollicular decerebration had been performed to prevent impulses from ascending in sensory tracts and activating the pyramidal tract at the cerebral cortex.)

In view of the great power and promptness of voluntary contractions in intact animals, Lloyd's study revealed a surprising amount of "inertia" in the spinal stage of pyramidal tract function. A single shock discharged only the cells of the external basilar nucleus, which lies in the gray matter just deep to the pyramidal tract fibers. The pyramidal volley arrived 4.5 milliseconds after the pyramids were stimulated and almost immediately discharged a few external basilar cells. This latency largely represents conduction time in the tract. To cause the intermediate nucleus of Cajal to discharge, repeated stimulation was required. By testing the excitability of this nucleus with spinal volleys, Lloyd showed that a nuclear delay of 4.5 milliseconds passed before the external basilar nucleus discharged into the intermediate nucleus. Another 3 milliseconds elapsed before the motoneurons were facilitated, a finding indicating another nuclear delay in the intermediate nucleus. As the repeated stimuli continued, the latency between arrival of an impulse at the spinal segment and motoneuron facilitation was reduced to 1.0 millisecond.

From these studies it can be concluded that two systems of interneurons are involved, one at the cortical stage and one at the spinal stage of pyramidal tract activation. Movements elicited by cortical stimulation will therefore have properties similar to those which interneurons lend to spinal reflex action, and the following phenomena could also be predicted on this basis.

Excitable Properties of the Motor Cortex and Its Efferent Pathways (Pyramidal and Extrapyramidal).   **RECIPROCAL INNERVATION.** In 1889, Sherrington demonstrated that, given a background of reflex muscular contraction, stimulation of a cortical point* might excite flexor motoneurons and inhibit the antagonistic extensor motoneurons—a "flexor point." Conversely, stimulation of a neighboring point might excite the extensor motoneurons and inhibit the antagonistic flexor motoneurons—an "extensor point." The site of the inhibition is in the spinal cord, because the same phenomenon has been demonstrated by stimulating the white matter underlying flexor and extensor points. That reciprocal innervation of muscles by the pyramidal tract has been questioned is understandable because: (i) the flexor and extensor points may overlap somewhat; and (ii) intracortical neurons may spread impulses from one point to another, both giving co-contraction of flexors and extensors.

LATENCY. The latency of cortically induced movements in response to a repetitive stimulus (summation time) may be as long as several seconds, during which time more than 100 volleys pass down the pyramidal tract. In contrast, man can initiate a voluntary response to a signal in less than one fifth of a second. Analytical studies indicate conduction times and nuclear delays in the spinal interneurons measured in milliseconds. Such long latencies of movement in response to cortical stimulation, then, must represent an interaction of excitatory and inhibitory effects resulting from a mixed stimulation of what may be loosely termed "extensor" exciting and "flexor" exciting pyramidal tract fibers.

AFTERDISCHARGE. The movement induced by stimulation of the motor cortex often continues long after the cessation of the stimulation. This afterdischarge is at first sustained ("tonic") and then becomes a series of rhythmic contractions ("clonic"). The same sequence of events is seen in epileptic seizures of the Jacksonian type. Experimentally induced epilepsy is best ascribed to cortical interneurons acting in closed or self-reexciting circuits.

FACILITATION.[18] Bubnoff and Heidenhain[10] recognized that stimulation of one point on the cortex can facilitate (or inhibit) the response of another point. Facilitation is manifested by a greater response to a cortical testing shock

*A cortical point is not a physiologic, anatomic or physical entity, but is simply the point at which electrodes are placed. The current may, for example, excite neurons at a distance from the "point."

when it is preceded by a cortical conditioning shock than when it is given alone. In fact, stimulation of one point may not merely facilitate but actually may discharge pyramidal tract fibers originating from another cortical point. For example, stimulation of neurons in area 6 may cause neurons in area 4 to discharge. Both intracortical spread and arcuate association fibers are involved in this activation. When the discharge of a stimulated area into another falls short of causing the latter to discharge, facilitation occurs. The duration of facilitation in this system is measured in seconds, 13 seconds being a typical figure. Facilitative interaction also occurs at the spinal interneuron pool, and activity at this level as well as at the cortex is important in the interpretation of cortical localization experiments.

EXTINCTION.[18] At intervals longer than those required to demonstrate facilitation, and especially with pulses of long duration, the response to a testing stimulus may be *smaller* when the stimulus follows a conditioning stimulus than when it is delivered alone. Dusser de Barenne and McCulloch[18] called this phenomenon "extinction" to give it a name not limited to a specific mechanism. The unresponsiveness is cortical, not spinal, and is local, becoming progressively less apparent if the electrodes delivering the testing shocks are moved a few millimeters from the conditioning electrodes. *Extinction* was defined as a diminution or absence of response to stimulation of a motor focus following antecedent stimulation of the *same* focus. *Inhibition* is also a diminution or absence of an expected response, but is manifest when the testing stimulus has been preceded by stimulation of *another* cortical point, one from which an antagonistic response may be elicited. Because Betz cells serving antagonistic muscles may not be totally separate, this distinction is not sufficient. In fact, the relationship of extinction to inhibition, suppression, voltage drifts and pH changes in the cerebral cortex is not entirely clear, and whether extinction exists at all has been questioned.[51]

LABILITY.[9] With facilitation, inhibition and extinction resulting from cortical stimulation, it could be anticipated that the motor cortex exhibits a certain lability of response. Not all intensities and frequencies of stimulation give the same result, and apparently identical stimuli do not give identical responses. The names given various manifestations of this "instability of the cortical point"[9] need not concern us. One manifestation of lability is explicable by the immediate history of the point stimulated (intracortical facilitation); another is a change in response as the parameters of the stimulus are changed.

Lilly et al.[40] varied and monitored the pulse duration, amplitude and frequency of cortical stimulation. (i) Combinations of amplitude and duration constituted an intermediate range which excited efferent cells; (ii) stimuli in a second range of durations and amplitude excited both cells and efferent fibers in the white matter; and (iii) strong unidirectional pulses of long duration destroyed cells and, eventually, fibers in the immediate vicinity of the stimulating electrode. (This damage is avoided by using Lilly's reverse pulse stimulator.) It follows that, if stimuli of different parameters excite different structures and if some stimuli injure fibers, quite different results may be obtained by different investigators, or by the same investigator during successive stimulations of the cerebral cortex.

SPREADING DEPRESSION. Electrical, mechanical or chemical stimuli applied to the cerebral cortex were observed by Leão[37] to cause a slowly expanding depression of its spontaneous electrical activity. This depression spreads over the cortex at a rate of 2 to 3 mm. per minute and persists at any one point for two to six minutes. It is also manifested by a decreased cortical excitability to stimulation, a slow change in the steady potential, vascular dilatation and an increase in the electrical resistance of the cortex.[70]

Spreading depression is a marked phenomenon in the rabbit, but it is more capricious in the cat and monkey. Marshall[45, 46] has shown that such depression is an important experimental artifact caused by dehydration and cooling of the cerebral cortex when it is widely exposed. The depression can be prevented by protecting the cortex with mineral oil, or it can be induced by dehydrating the animal by means of an intravenous administration of sucrose. Marshall's analysis suggests that spreading depression is a phenomenon of the pathologic cortex. Spreading depression is significant as a source of error in experiments on the cerebral cortex and may play some role in the general cortical depression that follows epileptic seizures.

Prior to Marshall's analysis, it was believed that stimulation of specific bands of the cerebral cortex (running mediolaterally) gave rise to a widespread diminution of electrical activity and excitability. This phenomenon was given the name "suppression" and was thought to be mediated by circuits passing through the basal ganglia and returning to the cerebral cortex. Experiments by Marshall[45] and by Sloan and Jasper[60] indicate that this suppression is the same as the spreading depression of Leão and that it can be initiated from any point on the cortex, not specifically from the so-called suppressor bands.

Somatotopic Organization of the Motor Cortex. That different parts of the body move when different parts of the precentral gyrus are stimulated has been known for nearly a century, but the nature and detail of this somatotopic representation are still subjects of experiment and controversy. "Representation of the body," "somatotopic organization" and "topographic organization" are synonyms. All mean that the cortical cells which give rise to the descending fibers activating different muscle groups lie in broadly the same relation to one another as do the muscles in the body. On the other hand, according to some authors, movements rather than muscles are represented.

Figure 8 shows the sequence of motor representation expressed in terms of body structures. The body parts are represented "upside down," with the leg area medial, the face area lateral, and the arm area lying between. In man, much of the leg area is buried in the medial longitudinal fissure, and much of the primary motor area for the arm and face lies buried on the anterior wall of the central fissure. In the monkey, more of the motor area lies on the free surface.

An important functional deduction can be made from the amount of cortical space devoted to a given part of the body. The lips and tongue, which are highly mobile and capable of finely graded movement, have larger cortical spaces devoted to them than do the less mobile fingers. The finger and hand areas of the cortex are much greater than the total of those governing the movements of all the other arm muscles. This arrangement suggests that finely graded movements are obtained by the simplest of all methods—the provision of a larger number of efferent neurons. Since the efferent cells, especially the Betz cells, occur in clusters, it is probably not only the number of cells but also the number of interspersed intracortical neurons that determines the variety of movement of which the hand or tongue is capable. In either case, cortical space is required. In view of these considerations, it should not be surprising that the degree of paralysis caused by equal-sized lesions in the motor areas is greater and more persistent in the hand than in the shoulder.

The history of the discovery that movement can be elicited by cortical stimulation is informative because it illustrates how careful clinical observation and astute deductions can interact with the more analytical and controlled animal experiments. In 1870, Hughlings Jackson, the great physiologically minded neurologist, postulated the existence of a somatotopically organized motor area from his observations of the epileptic seizures which originate in that area and now bear his name. In a given patient, a seizure might start in the lips, spread to the face, then to the arm, and then to the leg (the "march of epilepsy"). Hughlings Jackson[31] reasoned that there must exist, somewhere in the brain, structures having a concern with the lip, and further, that the remainder of the musculature must be represented there in an orderly fashion, accounting for the successive and orderly involvement during the epileptic discharge. Independently and experimentally, Fritsch and Hitzig[20] discovered the electrical excitability of the motor cortex in the dog and the monkey, mapped areas for the face, the arm and the leg, and demonstrated some evidence of localization of even smaller body parts.

The trend in both animal and human experiments has been from localization in terms of region (face, arm, leg) to movements of joints and digits, culminating in the suggestion (Marion Hines) that single muscles may be separately represented in the motor cortex. Hughlings Jackson and others following him[74, 75] have expressed the opposite view. Impressed by the fact that a patient can recover the use of a limb after destruction of cortical representation of that limb previously defined by stimulation, they have favored the idea of a widespread overlapping of the representation of muscle groups. Sherrington generalized that the cerebral cortex "thinks" in terms of movements, not muscles; and this view has been found persuasive, particularly by British neurologists and neurophysiologists.

EVIDENCE FROM SINGLE MUSCLE RECORDING. Responses of an individual muscle or its nerve to systematic stimulation of the motor cortex have been studied in efforts to resolve the question.

Just which muscles at a given joint respond to cortical stimulation is difficult to discern with the naked

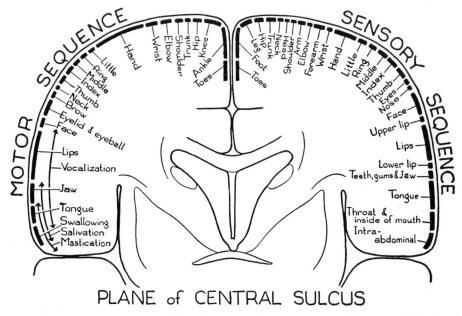

PLANE of CENTRAL SULCUS

Fig. 8.   Diagrammatic representation of sensory and motor sequences as mapped by threshold stimulation of cerebral cortex in man. Length of bars indicates in general way extent of cortical areas devoted to each structure in average patient. This is subject to considerable variation, however. (From Rasmussen and Penfield, *Fed. Proc.,* 1947, 6:452–460.)

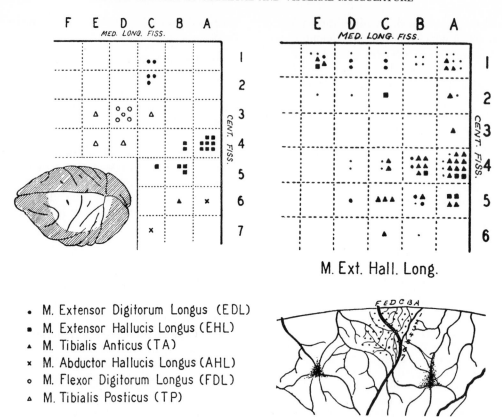

- • M. Extensor Digitorum Longus (EDL)
- ▪ M. Extensor Hallucis Longus (EHL)
- ▲ M. Tibialis Anticus (TA)
- × M. Abductor Hallucis Longus (AHL)
- ∘ M. Flexor Digitorum Longus (FDL)
- ⌂ M. Tibialis Posticus (TP)

Fig. 9. Muscle responses from stimulation of motor cortex. *Lower right,* grid of blood vessels and stimulated points. Broad dark line is caused by vein leaving central fissure to enter longitudinal sinus. Above are two maps of this small cortical area that are related to brain diagram by letters and numbers. *Upper left* shows points from which response was obtained in single foot or ankle muscle. Note that such "solitary" responses cluster. *Upper right* shows points from which extensor hallucis longus was activated. Note, however, that in region *AB45* responses were of short latency; large squares, 0–1.00 second; large triangles 1.01–2.00 seconds. Small circles represent latencies of 2.01–3.00 seconds, and dots, latencies of 3.01 seconds or longer. Responses of several muscles were obtained from *Row 1 A–E,* possibly owing to proximity to supplementary motor area. (From Chang *et al. J. Neurophysiol.,* 1947, *10*:39–56.)

eye. Using monkeys, Chang *et al.*[14] isolated the tendons of 13 muscles acting over the ankle and attached them, eight at a time, to myographs. Part of the foot area in the motor cortex was divided into millimeter squares and systematically stimulated. The response produced in each muscle by a given stimulus was recorded on a two-dimensional plot for that muscle in the space corresponding to the cortical point stimulated. Three major results were obtained: (i) Occasionally, only one of eight muscle responded, and the points for such "solitary responses" by a given muscle always fell in a cluster (Fig. 9, *left*). (ii) When the responses of each muscle were classified according to latency, those with the shortest latency clustered on contiguous points, whereas the points that yielded intermediate and long-latency responses tended to form surrounding rings (Fig. 9, *right*). (iii) When the responses of any two muscles were graded and repre-

sented on the cortical map as greater or less than the other muscle responses, a similar clustering was observed (Fig. 10).

The latency study has been conducted in another way by Bernhard and Bohm,[4] who recorded the latency of impulses in a muscle nerve and correlated it with the point stimulated on the motor cortex (Fig. 11). Again, the lines representing given latencies formed concentric rings. Thus, a given muscle can be thrown into contraction from a fairly wide area of the motor cortex, but into strong short-latency contraction only from a narrow focus.

Both of these studies lead to the concept that Betz and other corticofugal cells activating the motoneuron pool for a given muscle are topographically closely related to one another in the

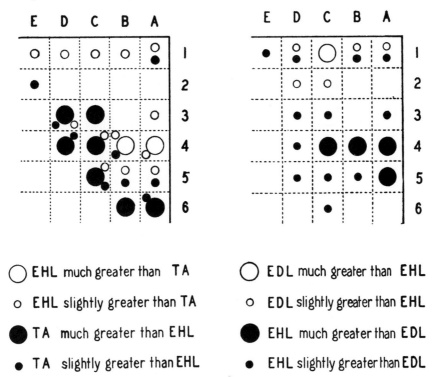

○ EHL much greater than TA   ○ EDL much greater than EHL

o EHL slightly greater than TA   o EDL slightly greater than EHL

● TA much greater than EHL   ● EHL much greater than EDL

• TA slightly greater than EHL   • EHL slightly greater than EDL

Fig. 10. Foci and fields of muscle representation determined by relative strengths of contraction in pairs of muscle to same cortical stimulation. Note that extensor hallucis longus (*EHL*) contractions relative to extensor digitorum longus (*EDL*) contractions were greatest in *4 ABC* and adjoining *5A*, establishing a focus. In the surrounding squares, relative strength of *EDL* contractions was less, establishing a field. Responses of *EDL* exceeded *EHL* only for points in rows *1* and *2*. Note in diagram at left that extensor hallucis longus (*EHL*) and tibialis anticus (*TA*), which in monkeys are slips of the same muscle, are spatially less differentiated than *EDL* and *EHL*. Compare this map with Figs. 9 and 11. (From Chang *et al.*, *J. Neurophysiol.*, 1947, *10*:39–56.)

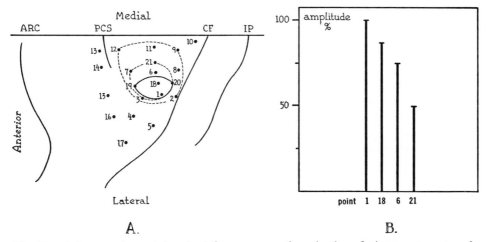

A.   B.

Fig. 11. *A*, Latency (summation time) for monosynaptic activation of triceps motoneurons from different points on left motor cortex, 1 second for inner circle, 3 seconds for next (*dashed*), and 7 seconds for outer circle. Note closeness of isotemp lines inferiorly, suggesting sharp boundary between arm and face. This diagram confirms experiment shown in Figs. 9 and 10. *B*, Amplitudes of monosynaptic discharge from points in a line running vertically through field for triceps. (After Bernhard and Bohm, *Arch. Neurol. Psychiat. (Chic.)*, 1954, *72*:473–502.)

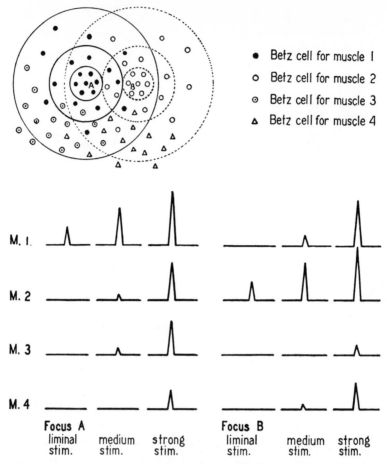

Fig. 12. Diagrammatic representation of hypothetical distribution of Betz and other cells of fifth and sixth layers for individual muscles. A cell group for each muscle has a focal distribution and an overlapping fringe. Each symbol stands for a Betz cell; large concentric circles are spheres of excitation. Expected contraction of muscles to cortical stimulation at different strengths is shown by myograms drawn in lower part of figure, in which magnitude of contraction is determined by number of Betz cells involved in sphere of excitation. Scale is in millimeters; zones *A* and *B* represent about 4 to 8 mm.² (From Chang *et al., J. Neurophysiol.,* 1947, *10:*39–56.)

motor cortex.* In fact, as shown in Figure 12, there appears to be a focus of neurons surrounded by a field for each muscle. The foci for two muscles never overlap, although the field for one muscle may overlap the field and even the focus for another.

For several reasons, the size of the focus and the field for a given muscle, and the degree of overlapping with other muscles, are probably even more restricted than Figures 8 to 11 suggest. Extrapyramidal projections from area 4 and any collateralization of the pyramidal tract axons would obscure a tight grouping of the Betz cells concerned with a given muscle. Further,

* It is remarkable that the axons in the peduncle, the pyramids and the spinal cord are not so related but are considerably intermixed.

transcortical spread of the stimulating current or nerve impulses in intracortical neurons would also obscure discrete localization. That currents of threshold strength can activate neurons 4 mm. away from the electrodes has been proved by Phillips,[54] who used a single cortical unit technique.

EVIDENCE FROM PYRAMIDAL TRACT RECORDING. The common result of cortical stimulation at a single point, especially with strong, long-duration pulses delivered through unipolar electrodes, or with any type of stimulus in an unanesthetized animal, is activation of several muscles, producing a movement of one or more joints. The basic and controversial question is whether this finding means that the motor cortex integrates the activities of various muscles into movements by re-representing the muscle many times and diffusely, contrary to the picture presented above.

The experiments on the D and I waves of the pyramidal tract discharge appear to resolve the controversy and, more important, to explain how the motor cortex organizes the contractions of individual muscles into a pattern which constitutes a skilled coordinated voluntary movement. After location of the point on the cortex giving a large D wave in the axons near the microelectrode tip in the pyramidal tract, the stimulating electrodes were moved several millimeters away from this cortical point until the D response disappeared. A threshold stimulus now elicited only I waves over the intracortical neurons, a D wave occurring only if the intensity was so high that the stimulus spread electrically to the cell body of the primary motor area. A stimulus near threshold can therefore indirectly excite a cell body at a distance of several millimeters.

The conclusion can be drawn that the cells of origin of the corticofugal pathways are highly organized topographically; that the neurons connected ultimately with a given muscle are grouped closely together in the cortex. Thus, the motor cortex is organized in terms of muscles. By definition, the motor cortex thinks in terms of movements, since it produces movement. But the organization of different movements is accomplished, not in the arrangement of Betz and other cells in the deep layers, but in the manifold connections of intracortical neurons with such cells. The neuropil of the cortex thinks in terms of movements, and the controversy over cortical localization can be traced to neurophysiologists' thinking in terms of a morphologically complex structure —the motor cortex—rather than in terms of its various cellular components—single units or classes of like neurons.

EXTENT OF PRIMARY MOTOR AREA. That the mediolateral dimension of the precentral gyrus represents the cephalocaudad dimension of the animal has been known since 1870. By contrast, how the anteroposterior dimension is utilized and what constitutes the forward border of the motor area are still somewhat uncertain. The latter has, in fact, been shifted forward and backward, like the boundaries of some countries. If the mediolateral dimension represents the cephalocaudad dimension of the animal, it is logical that the axial and appendicular dimension should be represented in the remaining anteroposterior dimension of the motor area; and, in fact, this is the most recent view.

In the simunculus based on Woolsey's experiments (Fig. 13), the areas of representation of the fingers, toes, lips and tongue are mainly buried in the central fissure, and the successively more proximal musculature is represented more anteriorly in orderly sequence. The threshold for movement rises and is higher for the axial than for the apical musculature. Note the position of the superior precentral sulcus or "dimple," which corresponds roughly to the anterior border of the motor area by certain cytoarchitectural and functional studies. If the simunculus in Figure 13 is correct, the axial musculature is represented in Brodmann's area 6, which has not previously been considered part of the body representation. In the light of recent experiments on unipolar versus bipolar stimulation, it is possible that Woolsey's studies place the forward boundary too far rostral. That such an expanse of cortex is needed to manage the proximal musculature is improbable.

Other Cortical Motor Areas. With appropriate electrical stimulation, movements can be induced by activating areas other than the primary motor area. In fact, experiments on unanesthetized animals indicate that this is true of virtually the whole of the convexity of the cerebral hemispheres.[39] For each area and type of movement, the question arises whether (or in what degree) the responses from a given point are due to (i) physical spread of current, (ii) spread of impulses over intracortical and intercortical fibers to the primary motor areas, (iii) activation of extrapyramidal fibers (COEPS) originating at the stimulated point, or (iv) activation of pyramidal tract fibers (or equivalent corticobulbar fibers going to the cranial motor nuclei), since, as we have seen, much of the pyramidal tract originates outside the primary motor area.

Whether the first two factors are operative is frequently learned by ablating the primary motor area or by cutting between it and a stimulated area. The consensus is that pyramidal tract efferents are concentrated near the central fissure, and that their concentration diminishes in passing forward. Conversely, the precentral gyrus contributes some fibers to the extrapyramidal system, and this contribution increases in passing forward into areas 6 and 8. With these differences in the kind of efferent projection comes a difference in the kind of movement that results. Tower[66] and Marion

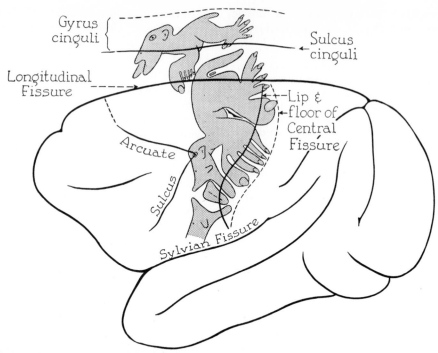

Fig. 13. Somatotopic organization of primary and supplementary motor areas. Note that central and longitudinal fissures are shown "opened out" with dotted line representing floor of a fissure and solid line lip of fissure on brain surface. At bottom of figure is an ipsilateral face area. In bay formed by foot, hand and abdomen is precentral dimple, the anterior border of area 4 (cf. Fig. 2). Much of the primary simunculus and virtually all of supplementary area falls in area 6. (After Woolsey *et al.*, *Res. Publ. Ass. nerv. ment. Dis.*, 1952, *30*:238–264.)

Hines showed that the primary motor area is to some degree the cortical origin of the extrapyramidal system. They sectioned the pyramids of cats, monkeys and chimpanzees, and found that not all ability to move was lost. Although movement lost the delicacy, accuracy and variety that are embodied in the phrase "skilled movement," certain gross movements, such as clutching and climbing, were retained. Moreover, stimulation of the precentral gyrus subsequent to section of the pyramids gave rise to such movements, but not to movements of single muscles or single joints.

However, a recent study emphasizes the lack of change in the type of movement elicited from the motor area after pyramid section[7] except for a threshold change. Experience with the degree of recovery of motor skills by patients after pedunculotomy causes Bucy[11] and others to believe the distinction between COEPS and the pyramidal tract has been overemphasized. The rapidity of conduction over COEPS pathways, the slowness of conduction in some pyramidal tract fibers, the relative

weakness of pyramidal tract effects on spinal mechanisms, and the comparative anatomy of the pyramidal tract tend to play down its role in voluntary movement and suggest some function beyond the activation of motoneuron discharge.[64]

That the corticospinal tract is not the sole agent of volitional skilled movement is true in man as well as in monkeys. The pyramids have not been sectioned surgically, but the corticospinal fibers (along with some extrapyramidal fibers) have been interrupted, occasionally bilaterally, in the cerebral peduncle and in the posterolateral region of the spinal cord. The resulting paralysis has been surprisingly slight and the ultimate recovery surprisingly great. For example, after a posterolateral cordotomy, a patient was still able to play a Beethoven piano concerto. Clearly, the role of the COEPS in the execution of movement is considerable and should be examined in detail. However, as pointed out, it is not always possible to decide whether a given response is executed over the extrapyramidal or the "extraprecentral pyramidal" system. By this latter term is meant pyramidal tract fibers arising elsewhere than in the classic cortical motor area.

SECOND MOTOR AREA. A small motor area in the lateral prolongation of the precentral gyrus onto the lip of the sylvian fissure has been described. The body is represented in reverse order to the representation in the precentral gyrus. Discovered by Sugar *et al.*,[63] the existence of the area has been confirmed[36] but little is known of its function. According to Lauer[36] and Woolsey *et al.*,[77] the area immediately below the main motor representation is an ipsilateral motor face area. This finding correlates with our knowledge that the facial musculature tends to escape paralysis when cortical or capsular lesions are restricted to one side of the brain.

SUPPLEMENTARY MOTOR AREA.[53, 77] In both monkey and man the musculature is represented a third time in the cortex. This representation (Fig. 13), constituting the *supplementary motor area,* is shown in Figure 13 as originally described by Woolsey[77] and in Figure 14 as described by Hughes and Mazurowski[29] from experiments on unanesthetized monkeys. In the latter, the representation occupies the mesial extent of area 6 and the cingular gyrus; it extends forward on the mesial surface of the prefrontal lobe and is bilateral with the ipsilateral representation in the cingular gyrus. The movements from the head region are often "meaningful acts," such as yawning, vocalization or coordinated movements of head and eyes. Also found in the unanesthetized animals is a purely ipsilateral, higher threshold, mirror image (foot-to-foot and tail-to-tail) representation posterior to the projection of the central fissure onto the mesial surface.

In contrast with the primary motor area, the thresholds are higher and more affected by anesthesia, and the responses are in the nature of the assuming and holding of a limb posture rather than quick phasic movements like those induced by precentral stimulation. The postures are often held many seconds after the stimulus has ceased. The responses are often bilateral, and one stimulation tends to facilitate the next.

While the anterior supplementary area gives rise to fibers projecting widely to the frontal and precentral cortex, those reaching the primary motor areas of the same and opposite hemispheres constitute the main projection.

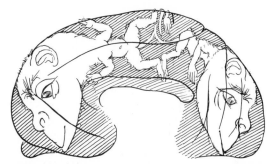

Fig. 14. Anterior (left) and posterior (right) motor simiusculi obtained by stimulation through implanted electrodes in unanesthetized monkeys. Note in top middle of diagram the separate foot and tail areas which are undoubtedly part of the primary motor area on the lateral surface. (From Hughes and Mazurowski, *Electroenceph. clin. Neurophysiol.,* 1962, *14:*477–485)

However, the supplementary area can act independently and in the absence of these connections. Contrary to some reports, it does not contribute fibers to the pyramidal tract, but rather has extensive connections with brain stem structures, inducing motor effects via the extrapyramidal motor system.[17a] Comparable analysis of the posterior supplementary area has been made. The postural nature of the movements, the long after-action and facilitation, and the tendency of widespread areas of musculature to be involved—all are properties associated in reflex action with multisynaptic connections and are to be expected of an area connected with the motoneurons through the extrapyramidal system.

Other Supplementary Areas. An experiment on unanesthetized monkeys was devised to learn the total extent of the free cortical surface which yields movements upon electrical stimulation.[39] As seen in Figure 15, nearly all of the lateral surface of the cerebral cortex was stimulated through as many as 610 implanted electrodes. Most of the cortex was excitable at about the same threshold, but the type of movement varied from region to region.

All regions of the cerebral cortex giving rise to movement on stimulation were termed supplementary motor areas by Crosby.[15] Movements obtained by stimulating the postcentral gyrus are mainly effected through the precentral motor area. A posterior parietal supplementary motor area discharges partly through the pyramidal systems and partly through the extrapyramidal system. The temporal lobe contains two supplementary motor

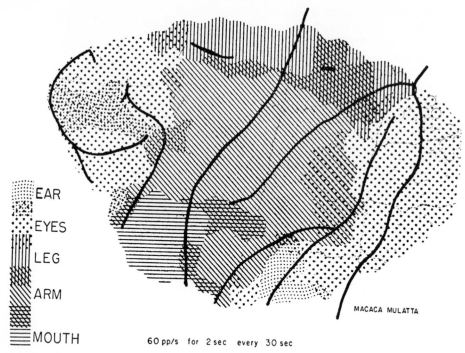

EAR

EYES

LEG

ARM

MOUTH

60 pp/s for 2 sec every 30 sec

MACACA MULATTA

Fig. 15. Map of movements elicited at threshold from cortex of unanesthetized monkey. All of 610 electrodes used yielded same kind of response at about same threshold. Movements elicited by stimulating a given receiving area were appropriate to the corresponding sensation; i.e., eyes and head moved from stimulation of visual areas, ear from acoustic area, somatic musculature from tactile area. To identify fissures compare with Fig. 2. (From Lilly in *Biological and biochemical bases of behavior,* Harlow and Woolsey, eds. Madison, University of Wisconsin Press, 1958.)

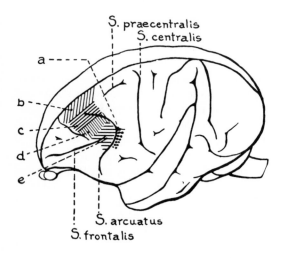

S. praecentralis
S. centralis

a

b

c

d

e

S. arcuatus
S. frontalis

Fig. 16. Subdivisions of frontal eye field and area yielding closure of eyes in monkey (*Macaca mulatta*). Designations: *a*, closure of eyes; *b*, pupillary dilatation; *c*, "awakening"; *d*, conjugate deviation to opposite side; *e*, nystagmus to opposite side. (From Smith, in Bucy, *The precentral motor cortex.* Urbana, University of Illinois Press, 1944.)

areas, one in the lateral region and one in the temporal portion of the preoccipital field. Both regions remain excitable after damage to the primary motor area. They tend to provoke ipsilateral as well as contralateral movements, especially in the facial musculature, the movements on both sides being gross rather than fine.

EYE MOVEMENTS.[62]   Stimulation of area 8 in both man and animals causes responses of the musculature of the orbit and the lacrimal glands. The eyes sweep together (conjugate deviation) so that they often "look away from the stimulating electrodes." Ablation results in lateral deviation of the eyes so that they look toward the side of the lesion and cannot voluntarily move in the opposite direction. Movements obliquely upward and downward also occur, as shown in Figure 16. Fibers from these areas have been traced either directly to the eye nuclei or to coordinating nuclei which distribute impulses to the motor nuclei for the eye. According to Woolsey *et al.*[77] and Crosby,[15] a part of the frontal eye fields is included in the primary motor area representation.

It is significant that autonomic motor responses (lacrimation and pupillary dilatation or constriction) are obtained from foci closely adjacent to, and sometimes overlapping, the foci giving rise to motor effects on the eye musculature. Similar but generally weaker responses of the eye are obtained by stimulating areas 18 and 19 of the occipital lobe. Conjugate deviations elicited by stimulating area 17, the primary visual cortex, are perhaps to be viewed as sensorimotor responses of fixation.

ADVERSIVE MOVEMENTS.   In man, a sustained lateral movement of the eyes and twisting of the neck and upper trunk may constitute an epileptic seizure. Such *adversive seizures* are usually caused by a discharging focus in the general region separating the motor areas from the prefrontal lobe. The exact relationship of this region to the eye fields (area 8), to the forward-lying representation of the axial musculature in the monkey,[77] and to the supplementary motor area is not clear. However, it seems that a broad area, encompassing the anterior part of area 6 and the posterior portion of the prefrontal lobe including area 8, constitutes an extrapyramidal adversive field. It lies in proximity to the pyramidal field for the axial musculature.[77] In patients, Penfield and Jasper[52] observed adversion traceable to a region still farther forward and medial. Their patients, however, were not aware of an epileptic discharge. Adversive movements elicited by stimulation of area 22 of the temporal lobe also have been described.

Use of the term "adversive movements" to describe seizures and experimentally elicited movements does not clearly convey their direction or physiologic significance. The term "orientational movements" may be substituted. Visual and somatosensory impulses initiated externally from the right side pass into the left hemisphere. If such impulses elicited adversive movements by way of area 8, the eyes and the body would twist to the right and thus would be oriented toward the external stimulus. Adversive or orientational movements may therefore be a part of the motor aspect of attention.

AUTONOMIC REACTIONS.[32]   In addition to the autonomic effects of stimulation of the eye fields, there are autonomic reactions to stimulation anterior to the motor area in area 6 or in the premotor area. These are true responses, not nociceptive reflexes activated by stimulation of pain afferents associated with cerebral blood vessels.[73] The arrangement of points yielding autonomic responses coincides closely with the distribution of somatic motor foci. Vasomotor reactions in arms and legs can be obtained by stimulating points on the premotor area opposite the arm and leg areas, respectively. These changes may be associated with fluctuations in the systolic blood pressure and the heart rate. Vasopressor points are usually discrete and separable from vasodepressor points, but their spatial relation varies from animal to animal, and they are highly susceptible to changes in the type of anesthetic used and in the depth of anesthesia. This cortical representation of autonomic function has been confirmed by ablation studies, and aids in explaining autonomic changes often observed in clinical cases of hemiplegia.

CORTICAL EFFECTS ON ASCENDING SYSTEMS

There are two general ways in which the cerebral cortex can influence the afferent input to the brain: (i) by way of the γ efferent motoneurons or fusimotor fibers which contract the intrafusal muscle fibers of the muscle spindle, thereby increasing the discharge of Group IA impulses, and (ii) by acting upon a synapse of an ascending system.

Stimulation of the motor area, unlike stimulation of the reticular area (Chaps. 8 and 9) usually increases the rate of fusimotor discharge although depression can occur.[48] The rate changes are large, e.g., from a resting rate of 10 per second to 60 per second when the cortex is stimulated. The postcentral gyrus activates fusimotor neurons independently of the precentral gyrus; this is not evidence of a control of sensory significance because the postcentral gyrus is a motor area as well as a sensory area.

Cortical maps of fusimotor responses resemble closely the classic maps of movement and muscle representation. The γ motoneurons have discrete areas of cortical representation about like those of α motoneurons (5.0 to 9.5 sq. mm.), and often the two types of motoneurons in a given filament of the ventral root are activated from the same cortical region (Fig. 17). This close tie at the cortex, like that occur-

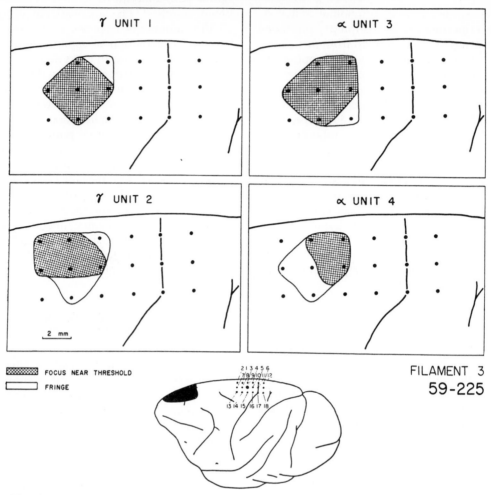

FOCAL AREAS OF L₄ SPINAL MOTORNEURONES
AS DETERMINED BY ELECTRICAL STIMULATION OF CORTEX

Fig. 17. Maps showing cortical areas from which gamma (left) and alpha (right) motoneurons of a single ventral root filament were caused to discharge. Note similarity in size and position of the excitable field for α and γ motoneurons. (From Mortimer and Akert, *Amer. J. phys. Med.*, 1961, *40:* 228–248.)

ring in the extensor muscles (Chap. 7), suggests that a detailed control function rather than a global facilitatory action is executed through the fusimotor system. Furthermore, there exists the temporal coincidence requisite for fusimotor discharge to affect α motoneuron discharge. In fact, in spontaneous movements γ preceded α motoneuron discharge by more than a second (Fig. 18). As pointed out in Chapter 8, the cortical control of spindle discharge is more probably significant to the control of movement than of sensation. While an increasing number of corticospinal tract axons terminate on the α motoneurons in primates, as Mortimer and Akert point out,[48] the fact of cortical con-

trol of the fusimotor system adds a second mechanism—the spindle—to share with the α motoneurons the shaping of the discharge which causes the muscle to contract. The discovery of a new neural mechanism invites speculation in respect to functional significance, but as yet there is little to go on. At this stage it suffices to say that, if a cortically induced movement were not preceded or accompanied by fusimotor activity, the stretch afferent might cease firing as the muscle shortened. Thus there could be little flow of information over Group IA fibers to the cerebellum or to α motoneurons.

A projection from the motor areas of the cerebral cortex to the nucleus of the posterior columns (N. cuneatus and gracilis) has been known since the beginning of the century. It was "rediscovered" and documented in detail in 1957 by three different anatomists.[13, 33, 72] A reticular inhibition of the gracilis nucleus was demonstrated electrophysiologically at about the same time. Magni *et al.*[43] have shown a direct pyramidal tract effect on these nuclei, i.e., not by way of collaterals from the pyramidal tract fibers to the reticular formation. Pyramidal tract stimulation induced a post-synaptic response in the gracile neurons and diminished the response evoked by somatic nerve stimulation supposedly by occlusion rather than by inhibition.

Towe and Jabbur,[65] recording from single units in the nuclei of the posterior columns, showed that 60 per cent of the units in the cuneate nucleus, as judged by its response to cutaneous stimulation, were depressed and 30 per cent were excited; the depression is direct rather than occlusive, and latency studies suggest that it might be exerted by collaterals from the pyramidal tract to the reticular formation. Both depression and excitation are produced by the pyramidal tract because both are retained by sectioning all of the brain stem except the pyramidal tract.[30] Conversely, when the pyramidal tract is sectioned, all facilitations and all but a weak inhibition disappear—the latter supposedly because of an extrapyramidal system.

It is significant that about half of the neurons in the dorsal column nuclei can be *discharged* by cortical stimulation via the pyramidal tract. This does not fit into any simple concept of gating a sensory input. It is further significant that the effect of cortical stimulation comes from the more restricted origin of the pyramidal tract as defined by recent studies (Fig. 5, right). This indicates that the intervention of the cortex on conduction over ascending systems is significant to movement rather than conscious sensation. No hypothesis relating the excitatory effects to sensation has been formulated, whereas a positive feedback to the cerebral cortex has been postulated in the execution of voluntary movements (see Chap. 13).

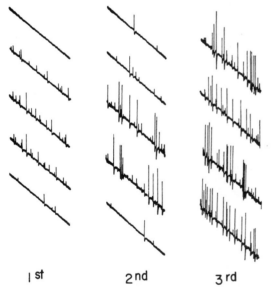

| st   2 nd   3 rd

Fig. 18. Selected sweeps of unit activity recorded from a ventral root filament of L_7 during three consecutive "spontaneous" (nonevoked) movements labeled 1st, 2nd and 3rd. The filament was quiescent prior to the first movement. Small fusimotor discharges preceded by 1.2 seconds the first α motoneuron discharge (seen in the third sweep at left). Note recruitment of α motoneurons in second and third movement. Sweep speed is 100 milliseconds. (From Mortimer and Akert, *Amer. J. phys, Med.,* 1961, *40:*228–248.)

CLINICAL PHYSIOLOGY OF THE MOTOR SYSTEMS

Investigation of the motor systems based on regional cortical ablations, principally by Fulton and Kennard,[22, 26] and on section of the medullary pyramids by Tower[66] and by Hines have profoundly altered the interpretation of such common clinical disorders as *hemiplegia.* Neurologists and neuropathologists were handicapped in learning the neuroanatomic basis of the signs making up hemiplegia because capsular lesions simultaneously and inevitably damage both the pyramidal and the COEP systems. In fact, the same is true of all other naturally occurring damage to the corticospinal neurons in the cortex, brain stem or spinal cord. That all of the signs of hemiplegia should have been ascribed to disruption of the pyramidal tract is an understandable error, but neurophysiologic analysis has now shown that many classic signs of pyramidal tract damage are in fact caused by damage to the extrapyramidal system.

Neurologists confronted with paralysis of voluntary movement ask first: Is this a disease or disturbance of the lower motoneurons—in modern language, motoneuron disease? Or is

Disease of Upper Motor Neurons
(Syndromes Involving Spastic Paralysis)

I. *Movement*
   1. Paralysis   Absence of voluntary movement.
   2. Paresis   Weakness of voluntary movement or deficient motor power.

II. *Postural reflexes*
   1. Spasticity   Resistance to passive movement of a joint, strongest in flexors of arms and extensors of leg. Fundamentally a stretch or myotatic reflex, the mounting resistance to increased force terminating in a collapse of the resistance (lengthening or "claspknife" reaction), distinguishes spasticity from *rigidity*. Spasticity is an example of "release of function."

   2. Exaggerated deep reflexes   Threshold of deep reflexes is low, and presence of myotatic
       Tonic tendon jerk, etc.   appendage causes "dead beat" rather than pendular termination.

       Clonus   A rhythmic series of contractions following the knee or ankle jerks; also elicited by an abruptly applied but sustained passive stretch of extensors.

       Rossolimo's reflex (toes)   Sudden release of fingers (or toes) after bending them downward
       Hoffmann's sign (fingers)   causes them to spring backward, stretching the physiologic extensors and causing a brief, smart contraction in all digits. Spasticity and alteration of deep reflexes are fundamentally the same phenomenon, differing only in the way the stretch reflex is elicited.

III. *Other reflexes*
   1. Babinski sign present*   Normal adult reflex response to scratching sole is downward or
      (Loss of plantar flexion)   plantar flexion of toes. Babinski sign is an upward or dorsiflexion, especially of great toe, with or without fanning. It is caused by contraction of physiologic flexors and is often combined with flexor contraction at knee and hip.

   2. Abdominal and cremasteric   Contraction of abdominal muscles and retraction of testicle to
      reflexes absent   stroking of abdomen and inner side of thigh, respectively, do not occur.

IV. *Muscle*
   1. No atrophy of degeneration   The absence of these signs plus the spasticity, etc., distinguish
   2. No electrical reaction of de-   hemiplegia from flaccid paralysis of motoneuron disease; any
      generation   atrophy is due to disuse and any contracture to holding limb in
   3. No fasciculation or fibrillation   fixed position. (see Chap. 5 for details.)
   4. No contracture

* A clinical nicety is never to speak of a "positive Babinski sign"—a tautology.

it a disturbance of the descending motor tracts —upper motor neuron disease?* Preliminary to an analysis of the clinical syndromes, such as hemiplegia, which are characterized by spastic paralysis, their components may be presented in outline under four categories.

Experimental Analysis. The need to abandon the idea that all elements of the syndrome

*If the paralysis is manifest in the facial musculature, the equivalent of upper motor neuron disease is supranuclear disease.

resulting from lesions at the upper motor levels could be ascribed to interruption of the pyramidal tract became apparent from the critical experiments by Fulton and his colleagues.[22, 23, 25, 26] They have proved that neither the paralysis (see below) nor the reflex changes of hemiplegia can be ascribed solely to damage to the pyramidal tract. These workers removed area 4 in monkeys and chimpanzees, extensively damaging the pyramidal tract while creating relatively little interference with COEPS. *Flaccidity rather than spasticity ensued.* Neither exaggerated deep reflexes nor clonus was in evidence. Although some digital spasticity occasionally occurred several weeks later,[17] it need not have been caused by failure of pyramidal tract function, because even area 4 gives rise to some extrapyramidal fibers.

In additional experiments, Fulton proved further that interruption of COEP fibers is responsible for the spasticity of hemiplegia. Bilateral ablations which included area 6 as well as area 4 caused, in addition to a more profound and enduring paralysis, a typical spasticity and exaggeration of the deep reflexes. In the chimpanzee, these included Rossolimo's and Hoffmann's signs. Toe fanning was added to the Babinski sign, which had followed removal of area 4. The question has recently been raised whether this increased spasticity is due to interference with all of the anterior portions of the motor area or only with its most medial part, the supplementary motor area.[67, 68] Whichever is the case, "pyramidal tract disease" and "upper motor neuron disease" are not synonymous, and the cortically originating portion of the extrapyramidal system must be taken into account in understanding hemiplegia.

As pointed out above, the pyramidal tract consists of those fibers which originate in the cortex and pass to the spinal cord through the medullary pyramids. Therefore, the conclusive experiment is to section the medullary pyramids. The ensuing disturbances throw light on pyramidal tract function; hence, the other clinical signs reflect the functions of the extrapyramidal system.

Pyramidotomy was performed by Tower[66] on monkeys and by Hines[28] on a chimpanzee. The results fully confirmed the cortical ablation experiments. Spasticity was neither an early nor a late consequence of the pyramidal interruption. In the monkeys, there was a definite flaccidity, and in the chimpanzee, a slighter flaccidity. The Babinski sign (in the chimpanzee) and the loss of abdominal reflexes remained as the true pyramidal tract signs. (The status of the cremasteric reflex must be assumed, since the chimpanzee subjected to pyramidotomy was a lady!) Forced grasping, induced by stretching the physiologic extensors of the digits, resulted in a strong plantar flexion that was severe enough to cause an animal to get "hung up" through inability to release its grip on the cage bars.

As pointed out above, interference with the pyramidal tract at all levels from the cerebral cortex to the spinal cord (except at the pyra-

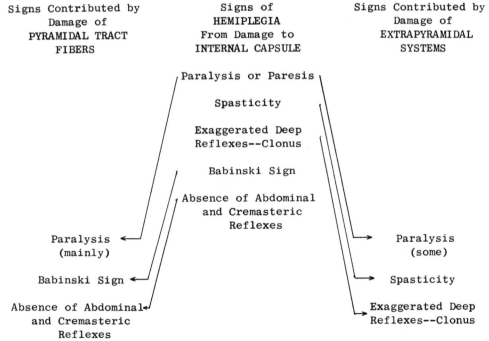

Signs Contributed by Damage of PYRAMIDAL TRACT FIBERS — Signs of HEMIPLEGIA From Damage to INTERNAL CAPSULE — Signs Contributed by Damage of EXTRAPYRAMIDAL SYSTEMS

Paralysis or Paresis

Spasticity

Exaggerated Deep Reflexes--Clonus

Babinski Sign

Absence of Abdominal and Cremasteric Reflexes

Paralysis (mainly)

Babinski Sign

Absence of Abdominal and Cremasteric Reflexes

Paralysis (some)

Spasticity

Exaggerated Deep Reflexes--Clonus

Fig. 19. Contributions of pyramidal tract and extrapyramidal systems to syndrome resulting from damage to internal capsule in man.

mids, which are rarely if ever selectively disrupted by pathologic processes) necessarily involves simultaneous interference with the pyramidal tract and the COEPS. In the light of these experiments, the respective contributions of the pyramidal and COEP systems are those shown in Figure 19.

Much of what is known of the extrapyramidal system has been deduced by subtracting proved pyramidal tract signs from the total and ascribing what is left to the extrapyramidal system. This method may have to be qualified. There is anatomic evidence that corticospinal fibers give off collaterals before reaching the the pyramids. These collaterals enter the pontine nuclei and probably the medial reticular formation, *potentially* reaching descending pathways and exerting an effect on extensor reflexes that is opposite (i.e., inhibitory) to that of the parent corticospinal tract of fibers.

Fulton's and Tower's reinterpretations of corticospinal function afford an explanation, previously lacking, for a typical feature of hemiplegia. The immediate results of disruption of the internal capsule are flaccidity and a reduction in deep reflexes, both of which persist for a varying number of days and gradually give way to the spasticity typical of chronic hemiplegia. Transitory areflexia or hyporeflexia implies the withdrawal of a descending facilitatory influence on segmental neurons. Since the pyramidal tract was traditionally assigned an inhibitory relationship to the segmental postural reflexes, its interruption could not logically underlie the initial flaccidity. However, if in man (as in the monkey) the pyramidal tract is facilitatory to extensor reflexes, the initial flaccidity can be ascribed to its interruption.

Whether in man it is necessary to abandon the idea that the pyramidal tract is the sole servant of voluntary activity cannot be answered with certainty, since neither nature nor the neurosurgeon has selectively sectioned the pyramids. In most clinical studies it is necessary to lump the extrapyramidal systems with the pyramidal systems that originate elsewhere than from the primary motor area. It suffices to say that, in man, section of the cord sector containing the pyramidal tracts, or of the middle two-thirds of the cerebral peduncle containing corticospinal fibers, produces much less interference with volitional movement than does a capsular lesion. The conclusion is that, in man

as in animals, the corticospinal tract from the primary motor area, the corticospinal fibers originating elsewhere in the cortex, and the COEPS work together to produce skilled voluntary movements. This concept is helpful in the interpretation of the recovery of voluntary power after lesions of the motor system.

Recovery of Voluntary Power. Explanation of the recovery of voluntary power that occurs after lesions in the cortical arm or leg area has always presented a problem. In fact, the degree of recovery possible when supposedly all of the cortical arm area is destroyed has led some clinicians to form the view that the arm is represented throughout the length of the precentral gyrus. Such an assumption is no longer necessary now that it is known that: (i) the corticospinal tract originates in substantial degree from areas outside the primary motor area, and (ii) the COEPS supports some voluntary movement. In addition, the amount and complexity of voluntary activity that can be supported by subcortical motor centers have been underestimated in both the monkey[69] and in man, for reasons given below.

Several factors affect the duration and ultimate degree of paralysis. (i) *Extent of cortex removed.* In monkeys, removal of area 6 including the supplementary motor area adds to the depth and duration of voluntary paralysis. Bilateral removal of areas 4 and 6 is more paralyzing than a comparable unilateral lesion. Similarly, retention of one area 6 leaves an animal significant useful movement.* If the parietal lobe, which gives rise to pyramidal tract fibers, is removed, there is a further deficit, only in part attributable to interference with somatic sensation. (ii) *Time between operations.* If bilateral removal of areas 4 and 6—an operation reducing a monkey's motor status virtually to that of a complete decorticate animal—is performed in stages with a long period elapsing between stages, a surprising amount of voluntary ability is recaptured. (iii) *Phylogenetic position.* Clinical signs following isolated ablation of area 4 increase in severity as the primate scale is ascended. Lemurs and New World monkeys exhibit less deficit than do the mangabeys and

*Whether this is an argument for the motor capacity of COEPS or of corticospinal fibers is not entirely clear, since the anatomic and electrophysiologic evidence in respect to the origin of fibers in area 6 is conflicting, as is the evidence in respect to the border of the primary motor area.

macaques, and the chimpanzees exhibit a greater deficit. Motor functions are more highly encephalized (actually "corticalized") in the animals with more highly developed brains. (iv) *Age.* If the removal of areas 4 and 6 is carried out in an infant, the animal is at first little affected by the procedure, a condition which correlates with the late myelination of the pyramidal tract. Serious motor deficits begin to appear as the animal matures, but it may never become as gravely affected as an animal undergoing the ablation as an adult. (v) *Postoperative care.* When small cortical areas are removed in serial operations, passive exercise to prevent contractures and nursing care to prevent bedsores, wasting, etc.,[69] are important factors in recovery. (vi) *Retraining.* The amount of forced usage of the paretic extremity. (vii) *Time after operation.* Given (v) and (vi) above, recovery continues over a much longer postoperative period than is observed in most experiments.

MECHANISMS OF RECOVERY. Even though recovery of function is the first concern of the patient and should be the concern of the neurologist, little research has been devoted to this subject. Definite explanations of the recovery mechanisms cannot be given. One factor is embraced in the term "neighborhood symptoms." Whether the cause of the disorder is a vascular accident or a meticulous surgical ablation, some reversible damage—trauma, dehydration, edema, venous occlusion, free blood, etc.—is done to cortical areas or tracts neighboring on the areas completely destroyed. As these transient lesions abate, what remains functions at more normal levels, and the paresis shrinks in severity and in distribution over the musculature.

Since motor skills can be improved by learning, it is reasonable to believe that usage and training can increase the level at which the undamaged apparatus can perform. This is termed "compensation." That tracts or cortical areas which have previously not controlled a given muscle do so after a lesion—as implied by the term "vicariation"—is exceedingly doubtful. However, performance of the same act with a different set of muscles is a commonplace phenomenon.

The sequence of events—areflexia, hyporeflexia and ultimate hyperreflexia—is typical of both capsular hemiplegia and spinal transection. The hyperreflexia (spasticity) is interpretable as *release of function,* i.e., release from inhibition by a descending pathway. The problem is why this release is not immediately manifest. Release phenomena are manifest within seconds in certain experimental situations, e.g., decerebrate rigidity or the *increase* in the excitability of the hindlimb flexion reflex following spinal transection in a decerebrate preparation. In both instances, no major facilitatory tract is removed by the transection. In primary transection of the spinal cord or in capsular hemiplegia, descending facilitatory tracts as well as inhibitory ones are removed. According to one interpretation, interruption of facilitatory pathways causes some change in the motoneuron's excitability, thus preventing any manifestation of the withdrawal of inhibition until the motoneuron has recovered excitability.

What is Released? Spasticity is a release phenomenon. Two questions must be asked about any release phenomenon. What structures must be damaged to effect the release, and what structures are released? In respect to spasticity and other signs of hemiplegia, the first of these questions has been answered in this chapter. The importance of the second question was first stressed by the philosophical neurologist Hughlings Jackson, who pointed out that a negative event (a lesion) cannot cause a positive event (a phenomenon such as spasticity). Except when irritative, a lesion can be only an antecedent circumstance; the direct *cause* or underlying mechanism of the overactivity must be the structures remaining functional. Releasing the brake of an automobile does not cause the car to go forward; it is the motor which does that. Magoun and Rhines[44] have expressed Hughlings Jackson's idea in a homely fashion, likening the motor systems to a jack-in-the-box. The motor cortex is the lid—but what is the spring that makes the jack jump out of the box?

At first sight, the segmental stretch reflex might seem to be the thing which is released. However, in the higher primates including man, spinal reflexes in themselves are not very strong, or they would not be depressed after spinal transection. For spasticity to develop, some facilitatory tract from the brain stem must remain functional. Just what tract or tracts are responsible is discussed in detail in the next chapter, but they may be previewed briefly as follows. One such tract is the vestibulospinal tract, but it may not be as important in primates as it is in the cat or dog. The second possibility is the reticulospinal tracts descending from the lateral reticular facilitatory area, described by Magoun and Rhines.[44] As will be discussed more fully, the reticular system may be involved in both the maintenance and the release of stretch reflexes. Impulses have been traced by strychnine neuronography from the anterior portion of the motor areas to the bulbar reticular inhibitory area, whence inhibition of the stretch reflexes is exerted by the reticulospinal tracts. Some such fibers may go from the cortex to the caudate nucleus and hence, through poorly defined pathways, to the bulbar reticular inhibitory area. Both of these pathways require verification before they can be fully accepted as the source of the impulses involved in the production of spasticity.

REFERENCES

1. AMASSIAN, V. E. *Electroenceph. clin. Neurophysiol.,* 1953, *5:* 415–438.
2. AMASSIAN, V. E. and DeVITO, R. *J. Neurophysiol.,* 1954, *17:*575–603.
3. v. BAUMGARTEN, R., MOLLICA, A. and MORUZZI, G. *Pflüg. Arch. ges. Physiol.,* 1954, *259:*56–78.
4. BERNHARD, C. G. and BOHM, E. *Arch. Neurol. Psychiat.* (*Chic.*), 1954, *72:*473–502.
5. BERNHARD, C. G., BOHM, E. and PETERSEN, I. *Acta physiol. scand.,* 1954, *29* (Suppl. 106): 79–105.
6. VON BONIN, G. and BAILEY, P. *The neocortex of* Macaca mulatta. Urbana, University of Illinois Press, 1947.
7. BRINDLEY, G. S. and LEWIS, R. P. *J. Physiol.,* 1964, *170:* 25P–26P.
8. BRODMANN, K. *Vergleichende Lokalisationslehre der Grosshirnrinde in Prinzipien dargestellt auf Grund des Zellenbaues.* Leipzig, J. A. Barth, 1909.
9. BROWN, T. GRAHAM, and SHERRINGTON, C. S. *Proc. roy. Soc.,* 1912, *B85:*250–277.
10. BUBNOFF, N. and HEIDENHAIN, R. Chap. 7 in *The precentral motor cortex,* 2d ed., P. C. BUCY, ed. Urbana, University of Illinois Press, 1949.
11. BUCY, P. C. *Brain,* 1957, *80:*376–392.
12. CAMPBELL, A. W. *Histological studies on the localisation of cerebral function.* Cambridge, Cambridge University Press, 1905.
13. CHAMBERS, W. W. and LIU, C-N. *J. comp. Neurol.,* 1957, *108:*23–55.
14. CHANG, H.-T., RUCH, T. C. and WARD, A. A., JR. *J. Neurophysiol.,* 1947, *10:*39–56
15. CROSBY, E. C. In: *Progr. Neurobiol. Proc. 1st. Int. Meet. Neurobiologists.* Amsterdam, Elsevier, 1956.
16. DeMYER, W. *Neurology,* 1959, *9:*42–47.
17. DENNY-BROWN, D. and BOTTERELL, E. H. *Res. Publ. Ass. nerv. ment. Dis.,* 1948, *27:*235–345.
17a. DeVITO, J. L. and SMITH, O. A. *J. comp. Neurol.,* 1959, *111:*261–278.
18. DUSSER DE BARENNE, J. G. and McCULLOCH, W. S. *J. Neurophysiol.,* 1939, *2:*319–355.
19. VON ECONOMO, C. and KOSKINAS, G. N. *Die Cytoarchitektonik der Grosshirnrinde der erwachsenen Menschen.* Berlin, J. Springer, 1925.

20. FRITSCH, G. and HITZIG, E. *Arch. Anat. Physiol. (Lpz.),* 1870, *37:*300–332.
21. FULTON, J. F. *Bull. Hist. Med.,* 1937, *5:*895–913.
22. FULTON, J. F. *Functional localization in the frontal lobes and cerebellum.* Oxford, Clarendon Press, 1949.
23. FULTON, J. F. *Physiology of the nervous system.* 3d ed. New York, Oxford University Press, 1949.
24. FULTON, J. F. *Gesnerus,* 1951, *8:*85–91.
25. FULTON, J. F., JACOBSEN, C. F. and KENNARD, M. A. *Brain,* 1932, *55:*524–536.
26. FULTON, J. F. and KENNARD, M. A. *Res. Publ. Ass. nerv. ment. Dis.,* 1934, *13:*158–210.
27. GLEES, P. *J. Anat. (Lond.),* 1944, *78:*47–51.
28. HINES, M. *Biol. Rev.,* 1943, *18,* 1–31.
29. HUGHES, J. R. and MAZUROWSKI, J. A. *Electroenceph. clin. Neurophysiol.,* 1962, *14:*477–485.
30. JABBUR, S. J. and TOWE, A. L. *J. Neurophysiol.,* 1961, *24:* 499–509.
31. JACKSON, J. HUGHLINGS. *Selected writings of John Hughlings Jackson.* J. Taylor, ed. New York, Basic Books, Inc., 1956, 2 vols.
32. KENNARD, M. A. Chap. 9 in *The precentral motor cortex,* 2d ed., P. C. Bucy, ed. Urbana, University of Illinois Press, 1949.
33. KUYPERS, H. G. J. M. and TUERK, J. D. *J. Anat. (Lond.),* 1964, *98:*143–162.
34. LASHLEY, K. S. and CLARK, G. *J. comp. Neurol.,* 1946, *85:* 223–305.
35. LASSEK, A. M. *J. comp. Neurol.,* 1942, *76:*217–225.
36. LAUER, E. W. *J. Neurophysiol.,* 1952, *15:*1–4.
37. LEÃO, A. A. P. *J. Neurophysiol.,* 1944, *7:*359–390, 391–396; *ibid.,* 1947, *10:*409–414.
38. LEVIN, P. M. Chap. 5 in *The precentral motor cortex,* 2d ed., P. C. Bucy, ed. Urbana, University of Illinois Press, 1949.
39. LILLY, J. C. In: *Biological and biochemical bases of behavior,* H. F. Harlow and C. N. Woolsey, eds. Madison, University of Wisconsin Press, 1958.
40. LILLY, J. C., AUSTIN, G. M. and CHAMBERS, W. W. *J. Neurophysiol.,* 1952, *15:*319–341.
41. LLOYD, D. P. C. *J. Neurophysiol.,* 1941, *4:*184–190.
42. LORENTE DE NÓ, R. In: *Physiology of the nervous system,* 3d ed., J. F. Fulton, ed. New York, Oxford University Press, 1949.
43. MAGNI, F., MELZACK, R., MORUZZI, G. and SMITH, C. J. *Arch. ital. Biol.,* 1959, *97:*357–377.
44. MAGOUN, H. W. and RHINES, R. *Spasticity: The stretch-reflex and extrapyramidal systems.* Springfield, Ill., Charles C Thomas, 1947.
45. MARSHALL, W. H. *Electroenceph. clin. Neurophysiol.,* 1950, *2:*177–185.
46. MARSHALL, W. H. and ESSIG, C. F. *J. Neurophysiol.,* 1951, *14:*265–273.
47. METTLER, F. A. *Proc. Soc. exp. Biol. (N. Y.),* 1944, *57:*111–113.
48. MORTIMER, E. M. and AKERT, K. *Amer. J. phys. Med.,* 1961, *40:*228–248.
49. PATTON, H. D. and AMASSIAN, V. E. *Amer. J. Physiol.,* 1955, *183:*650.
50. PATTON, H. D. and AMASSIAN, V. E. *J. Neurophysiol.,* 1954, *17:*345–363.
51. PATTON, H. D. and AMASSIAN, V. E. Chap. 35 in *Handbook of physiology, Section 1, Neurophysiology,* vol. 2, H. W. Magoun, ed. Washington, D. C., American Physiological Society, 1960.
52. PENFIELD, W. and JASPER, H. *Epilepsy and the functional anatomy of the human brain.* Boston, Little, Brown & Co., 1954.
53. PENFIELD, W. and WELCH, K. *Arch. Neurol. Psychiat.* (*Chic.*), 1951, *66:*289–317.

54. PHILLIPS, C. G. *Quart. J. exp. Physiol.,* 1956, *41:*58–69.
55. RAMÓN Y CAJAL, S. *Proc. roy. Soc.,* 1894, *55:*444–468.
56. ROSSI, G. F. and BRODAL, A. *J. Anat. (Lond.),* 1956, *90:* 42–62.
57. RUSSELL, J. R. and DeMYER, W. *Neurology,* 1961, *11:* 96–108.
58. SHERRINGTON, C. S. *J. Physiol.,* 1889, *10:*429–432.
59. SHOLL, D. A. *The organization of the cerebral cortex.* London, Methuen & Co., 1956.
60. SLOAN, N. and JASPER, H. H. *Electroenceph. clin. Neurophysiol.,* 1950, *2:*59–78.
61. SMITH, O. A., JR., and DeVITO, J. L. *Fed. Proc.,* 1958, *17:* 35, 151.
62. SMITH, W. K. Chap. 12 in *The precentral motor cortex,* 2d ed., P. C. Bucy, ed. Urbana, University of Illinois Press, 1949.
63. SUGAR, O., CHUSID, J. G. and FRENCH, J. D. *J. Neuropath.,* 1948, *7:*182–189.
64. TOWE, A. L. Unpublished observations.
65. TOWE, A. L. and JABBUR, S. J. *J. Neurophysiol.,* 1961, *24:* 488–498.
66. TOWER, S. S. Chap. 6 in *The precentral motor cortex,* 2d ed.,

P. C. Bucy, ed. Urbana, University of Illinois Press, 1949.
67. TRAVIS, A. M. *Brain,* 1955, *78:*155–173.
68. TRAVIS, A. M. *Brain,* 1955, *78:*174–198.
69. TRAVIS, A. M. and WOOLSEY, C. N. *Amer. J. phys. Med.,* 1956, *35:*273–310.
70. VAN HARREVELD, A. and OCHS, S. *Amer. J. Physiol.,* 1957, *189:*159–166.
71. VOGT, C. and VOGT, O. *J. Psychol. Neurol. (Lpz.),* 1919, *25:*279–461.
72. WALBERG, F. *Brain,* 1957, *80:*273–287.
73. WALL, P. D. and PRIBRAM, K. H. *J. Neurophysiol.,* 1950, *13:*409–412.
74. WALSHE, F. M. R. *Brain,* 1942, *65:*409–461.
75. WALSHE, F. M. R. *Brain,* 1943, *66:*104–139.
76. WOOLSEY, C. N. In: *Biological and biochemical bases of behavior.* H. F. Harlow and C. N. Woolsey, eds. Madison, University of Wisconsin Press, 1958.
77. WOOLSEY, C. N., SETTLAGE, P. H., MEYER, D. R., SENCER, W., PINTO-HAMUY, T. and TRAVIS, A. M. *Res. Publ. Ass. nerv. ment. Dis.,* 1952, *30:*238–264.

CHAPTER 13

Basal Ganglia and Cerebellum

By THEODORE C. RUCH

MOTOR FUNCTIONS OF THE BASAL GANGLIA

THE basal ganglia are involved in the control of movement and posture, since abnormal spontaneous movement results from lesions of these ganglia in man. The abnormal functions attendant upon such lesions are well known clinically, but the normal function of the basal ganglia is difficult to visualize. The conventional experimental methods of ablation, stimulation and degeneration in animals have provided tantalizing clues but little definitive information. Certain of the basal ganglia have functions which cannot be classified as motor. These functions will be discussed elsewhere.

Anatomic Considerations. By "basal ganglia" is meant all subcortical motor nuclei of the forebrain including the caudate nucleus, the putamen and the globus pallidus. They discharge to such structures as the corpus Luysi (subthalamic nucleus), the substantia nigra, the red nucleus and the reticular formation in the brain stem, as shown in Table 1. Modern authors include these brain stem structures among the basal ganglia. The caudate nucleus and the putamen, although separated by the internal capsule, are phylogenetically related and are known morphologically as the striatum. Although the putamen and the globus pallidus have been joined under the term "lenticular nucleus," this grouping is not meaningful. It is, however, meaningful to divide the pallidum into a medial (internal) and a lateral (external) portion. The external portion is, in a sense, afferent, since it receives fibers from other structures including the thalamus and the cerebral cortex. These connections are arranged to form a circuit: motor cortex–pallidum–thalamus–motor cortex. The internal division sends a large projection via the ansa and the fasciculus lenticularis to the lateroventral nucleus of the thalamus, which projects to the cerebral cortex. The pallidum also has descending connections with the subthalamic nucleus.

Lying deep to the cerebral cortex and lateral to the cerebral ventricles, the basal ganglia are the highest motor center in birds and lower forms, which possess little cerebral cortex. In these species these nuclei preside over a motor apparatus capable of producing such highly skilled movements as flying. Consistently, the

TABLE 1. *Connections of the Basal Ganglia (after Jung and Hassler[12])*

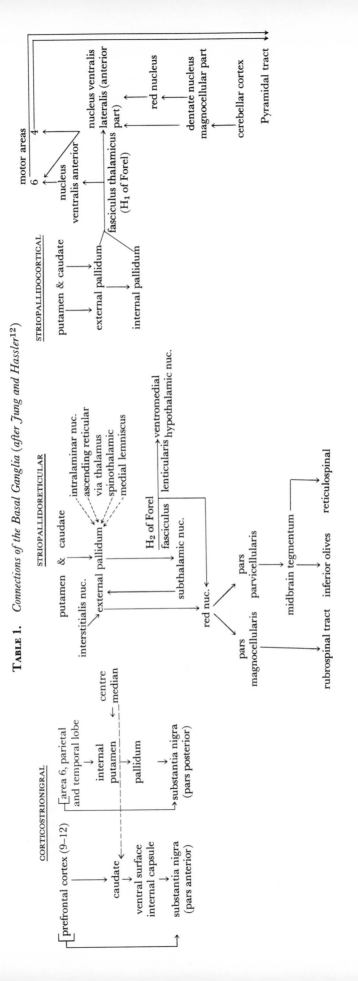

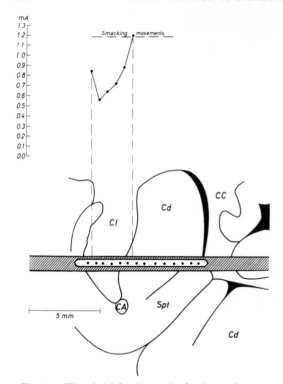

Fig. 1. Threshold for "arrest" of a learned movement from electrical stimulation of the internal capsule and caudate nucleus through a 14-lead implanted electrode (horizontal). Threshold is given on the ordinates. Points deeper within the caudate nucleus, Cd, produced arrest but also produced facial movements typical of stimulating the septal region, Spt., suggesting that arrest was also caused by spread of current. CI is internal capsule, CA is the anterior commissure. (From Laursen, *Acta physiol. scand.,* 1962, *54:*185–190.)

basal ganglia receive fibers from the intralaminar nuclei, the centromedian nuclei and the smaller midline nuclei. These fibers complete a potential subcortical connection of the ascending afferent systems with the basal ganglia. However, this system is not necessarily motor in function. With the development of a whole new apparatus for the control of movement—the cerebral cortex—the evolutionary fate of the basal ganglia becomes an intriguing question.

Motor Responses.[7, 21] The results of early attempts to elicit movement by stimulation of the basal ganglia were mainly negative, and the apparent exceptions actually reflected spread of current to the internal capsule.

In recent experiments stimulation through implanted electrodes in unanesthetized cats left multineuron pathways not depressed and permitted weaker, nonspreading stimuli to be

used. Limb flexion was caused by spread of movement to the internal capsule.[15] Lip-smacking, salivation and swallowing were traced to the adjacent septal region.

Contraversive head and eye movements—i.e., looking away from the side of stimulation—and, with stronger stimulation, running in a circle away from the side of stimulation appear to be the only verified results of caudate stimulation.[7, 15] These have a long latency, are subject to and look like the similar movements of a normal cat, suggesting that the caudate nucleus functions at a high level of integration.

INHIBITORY EFFECTS. If the responsiveness of the basal ganglia is examined against a background of either posture or movements concurrently induced by stimulation of the cerebral cortex, stimulation of the caudate nucleus and the globus pallidus causes inhibition (Fig. 1). Motor reactions initiated by the cerebral cortex "melt away" when even a weak stimulus is delivered to the caudate nucleus.[17, 22] Pallidal stimulation likewise does not induce movement but interrupts a cortically induced movement, thus causing the limb to be held in space.

This sudden inhibition of movement was seen by Laursen[15] but it was due to stimulation of fibers in the internal capsule rather than the caudate nucleus. Laursen trained animals to cross a hurdle in a two-compartment box and could freeze them in any position while crossing. This inhibition was obtained at lowest threshold from the internal capsule; from the caudate nucleus, it was obtained only at strengths causing signs of septal stimulation (Fig. 1), i.e., strong enough to spread to the internal capsule as well.

It is probable that cortically originating fibers give collaterals to the caudate nucleus. A strong immediate arrest of movement from capsular stimulation and weak and delayed arrest from caudate stimulation might be expected. Arrest of movement is also seen from stimulation of the thalamus and the amygdala. Anesthesia may favor the inhibitory and "holding" responses; they were not seen following stimulation of the striopallidum in unanesthetized cats by Forman and Ward.[7]

ACTIVATION BY MOTOR CORTEX. There is some evidence that the basal ganglia are activated by strychnine stimulation of the motor cortex.[5] An anatomic projection from the cortex to the caudate nucleus—a projection which could account for this activation—has been described by Glees.[8] There are also anatomic connections through which the caudate nucleus, when activated, could discharge to the globus pallidus, which in turn is connected with the part of the thalamus that projects to area 4 of the cerebral cortex. Whether this circuit is in fact the route through which the stimulated caudate inhibits movements induced by the cortex has not been proved by critical studies of single unit discharge in the pyramidal tract (see Chap. 12). Much of the functional evidence for the existence of this circuit is based on suppression of the electrical activity of the cortex, a phenomenon of doubtful status (see Chap. 12). Since inhibition is stronger from capsular than from caudate or pallidal stimulation, an effect downstream is suggested. This could be a return loop from the midbrain to the motor cortex or an interaction at the spinal level.

Experimental Lesions. RELATION TO MOVEMENT. Whether the striatum has any function independent of the cortex has been doubted by most investigators,[21] and this is consistent with inability to elicit movement by stimulating the caudate nucleus and putamen.

Cats with neocortex removed were compared with others having, in addition, the striatum removed (so called thalamic cats) so that the independent functions of the striatum could be assessed.[24] Changes on the behavioral level rather than added paresis were noted. Striatal cats groomed themselves, groomed other cats, ate spontaneously, were active and exhibited sex behavior. Cats without neocortex and striatum lacked these abilities, although the component parts of the activity could be elicited. The striatum thus appears to be involved in ordering the component parts of complex movement. As pointed out below, the basal ganglia must participate in movement, since, in man, abnormal spontaneous movements are modified by lesions damaging these ganglia.[6]

Although in themselves of little effect, lesions of the basal ganglia proper combined with lesions of the anterior portions of the motor areas in monkeys and apes induce disturbances of movement reminiscent of those seen in man.[13, 14] This suggests (i) that the basal ganglia in some way modulate the activity of the primary motor areas, either by direct action on them or by convergence at lower levels, and (ii) that the anterior motor areas and the basal ganglia act synergistically, but independently,

to modulate the discharges from the primary motor area.

RELATION TO POSTURE. In Chapter 12 was described a cortex–caudate–reticular mechanism, the interruption of which causes spasticity. This mechanism is part of the cortically originating extrapyramidal system (COEPS). However, the disturbance of postural reflexes occurring in the most common disease of the basal ganglia is clinically termed *rigidity*, and differs from spasticity in its properties and, presumably, in its cause. The actual disturbances of posture and movement resulting from damage to the basal ganglia are best discussed from clinical information.

In recent years the classic consequences of prefrontal lobe lesions at the behavioral level—"hyperactivity" and "recent memory"—have also been ascribed to the caudate nucleus (see Chap. 23). If the evidence is taken at face value, the role of the caudate nucleus encompasses what might be considered most primitive movement—turning of eyes and head and circling—to intellectual functions. If the difficulty of separating caudate function anatomically and physiologically from surrounding and overlying structures is so great, the allocation of role to the other nuclei of the basal ganglia cramped close to one another and interlaced with ascending and descending pathways is understandably greater and our knowledge correspondingly more fragmentary and speculative. For this reason experimental knowledge will be presented in connection with clinical syndromes.

Pathophysiology of Basal Ganglia in Man. The abnormalities resulting from damage to the basal ganglia are more outspoken and more easily examined in man than in experimental animals. Unfortunately, lesions of the human basal ganglia are mainly produced by diffuse pathologic processes, so that clinical cases tell little of functional localization. (The areas of greatest or most common damage may simply be those most easily damaged by the specific agent, not those responsible for the syndrome.) Presumably, the various ganglia do not all have similar functions, because there are two groups of disorders that contrast with one another in many ways.

ATHETOSIS, CHOREA, BALLISMUS. This group of disorders is a spectrum of dyskinesias or abnormal movements having many points of similarity; athetosis and chorea often occur together. These dyskinesias have in common marked—even violent—voluntary-like movement with *no typical changes in muscle tonus.* * Paradoxically, these movements are involuntary, i.e., not willed by the patient and beyond his control.

In *chorea*, meaning "dance," a wide variety of rapidly performed, jerky, but well coordinated movements occur ceaselessly. They are not willed by the patient and serve no purpose. Their coordinated, purposive look led Hughlings Jackson to speak of "some method in their madness."

In *athetosis*, the limbs indulge in ceaseless, slow, sinuous, writhing movements which are especially severe in the hand and are involuntary. They are reminiscent of certain oriental dances and bear less resemblance to coordinated voluntary movements than do those of chorea; antagonistic muscles may contract simultaneously. The brain damage is said to be greatest in the striatum.

In *ballismus*, the movements are violent and flinging (ballistic) and are caused by contractions of the proximal limb muscles. If the movements are confined to one-half of the body, as is commonly the case, the condition is called *hemiballismus*.

Clinical and neuropathologic observations, animal experiments and neurosurgical attempts to relieve chorea and athetosis have not yielded any consistent picture of the underlying mechanism of these diseases and what lesions produce them. There is some evidence that human athetosis is relieved by lesions of the premotor area and of the anterior columns of the spinal cord. Bucy[2, 3] has suggested that athetosis represents an abnormal discharge over the COEPS.

Perhaps the clearest production of involuntary movement is shown by monkeys (but not cats) in which the subthalamic nucleus of Luysi is partially destroyed.[29] Clinically, lesions in this nucleus are believed to cause hemiballismus. However, the involuntary movements (hyperkinesis) obtained in monkeys are of the choreic type; i.e., they occur in irregular sequences of movement varying in amplitude and duration. Sometimes the movement is slower and more sinuous (athetoid) and only occasionally is it the repetitive, flinging, ballistic type. The latter is the type associated with pathologic disturbance of this nucleus in man. As in man, the hyperkinesis does not occur if

---

*In the contrasting disease, parkinsonism, tonus is severely disturbed, and involuntary movements are generally less conspicuous.

nearby structures are damaged, e.g., the internal pallidum, fasciculus lenticularis (H_2) and thalamicus (H_1) or the internal capsule. The subthalamic nuclei have ascending connections with the internal pallidum and could affect corticospinal and COEPS discharge by way of the ventrolateral thalamic nucleus. The descending efferents are thought to be rubrospinal. The spinal pathway mediating the abnormal movements following experimental lesions of N. subthalamicus has been narrowed down to the posterolateral columns of the spinal cord deep to the dorsal spinocerebellar tract.[4] Lesions here abolished choreiform movements, which failed to return with partial recovery of voluntary movement. The movements are probably executed over the corticospinal tracts but the rubrospinal and pontine reticular spinal tracts passing through this region of the spinal cord must also be suspected. However, lesions of the red nucleus do not abolish N. subthalamicus hyperkinesis, whereas cortical intervention does. For this category of involuntary movement, the point of interaction between the extrapyramidal system and the pyramidal system appears to be the cortical motor areas.

PARKINSON'S DISEASE (PARALYSIS AGITANS). As the second part of the formal name suggests, paralysis agitans is, like the previous group, often marked by an involuntary movement— in this case a *tremor*. Unlike athetosis, chorea and ballismus, Parkinson's disease results in a definite and disabling reduction in voluntary and associated movements (poverty of movement) and also in a definite disturbance in the postural sphere, *rigidity*. Observations on Parkinsons's disease and related animal experiments can be taken as exemplifying two important clinical signs, rigidity and tremor. The pallidum and the substantia nigra are often said to be the most consistent sites of damage in this syndrome. However, there is good reason to believe that the lesions in the pallidum are not the responsible ones.

Although nearly a century and a half have elapsed since Parkinson described the syndrome, none of its three major components can yet be clearly explained in terms of mechanism or responsible neural structure. Since the major components tend to occur in different proportions in different patients, and since the brain damage is diffuse, it is presumed that several structures may be involved.

Poverty of movement. Parkinson's disease contrasts with chorea and athetosis in that initiation of voluntary movement is difficult and there is a resultant immobility. Absent are the small restless movements, the play of emotional expression on the face, and the movements associated with intentional movements, such as arm-swinging during walking seen in normal persons. Despite the formal name for the condition, there is no real paralysis, and in this fact, as well as in the type of tonus change, Parkinson's disease differs from spastic paralysis resulting from capsular lesions. Magoun and Rhines[16] ascribe the poverty of movement to interference with the descending reticular facilitatory system; however, such interference might be expected to induce accompanying flaccidity rather than rigidity. Some think that movement is damped by the rigidity, since movement improved in amplitude, speed and endurance when injection of procaine hydrochloride into the muscles had caused them to become flaccid.[28] However, the tendency for hypokinesia and rigidity to occur in different proportions in different patients suggests that rigidity is not the sole basis for the poverty of movement.

Rigidity. In Chapter 12 rigidity was distinguished from spasticity. A rigid limb affords resistance throughout the entire extent of a passive movement. The resistance does not develop suddenly, does not mount with the application of additional force, and does not collapse terminally in a lengthening reaction. Sometimes, however, the response to passive movement is a series of catches and gives—so-called "cogwheel" rigidity. The rigidity is manifest in both extensor and flexor muscles, being stronger in the latter. To the examiner the resistance has a dead, leadlike feel, as opposed to the live vibrant resistance felt in the spastic limb. The rigid limb therefore exhibits a more marked plasticity than does a spastic limb. The rigidity of extrapyramidal disease is dependent upon the integrity of the myotatic reflexes; it disappears in muscles deprived of afferent innervation by posterior root section.[18] However, the tendon reflexes are not exaggerated or marked by clonus. It is interesting that Jendrassick's maneuver (clenching of hands), used to bring out or enhance a weak tendon jerk, does not affect such reflexes in Parkinson's disease (Fig. 2). In all these respects, the rigidity resulting from extrapyramidal lesions at the level of the basal ganglia differs from the spasticity caused by interference with the COEPS.

Section of the pyramidal tract at the spinal level in Parkinson's disease does not augment rigidity but rather decreases it slightly.[20] Thus interruption of the pyramidal tract appears to cause neither rigidity nor spasticity. Contrary to expectation from results of animal experiments, in man section of the efferent outflow from the pallidum (ansa lenticularis) or destruction of the medial pallidum itself may virtually abolish rigidity.[6] Moreover, surgical destruction of the lateroventral nucleus, which receives impulses from the pallidum and projects to areas 4 and 6 of the cerebral cortex, also may abolish rigidity. It thus seems that the globus pallidus should not be considered a structure which, when damaged, releases the mechanisms underlying rigidity; rather it should be considered contributory to the mechanism underlying rigidity. It is not clear how this system of fibers operates in the intact animal—whether through the midbrain motor nuclei or by influencing descending pathways

Fig. 2. Electromyograms of deep reflex jerks in biceps brachii in a case of hemiparkinsonism. Left side of records shows size of reflex before reinforcement by hand-clasping; right side shows reflex during hand-clasping. The reflex in limb exhibiting parkinsonism is unchanged by reinforcement. (After Hassler, *Dtsch. Z. Nervenheilk.*, 1956, *175*:233–258.)

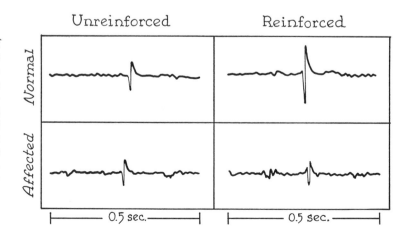

(COEPS) at the level of the cerebral cortex. Hassler,[10] who ascribes the Parkinson syndrome to destruction of the substantia nigra, suggests that loss of *ascending* collaterals from the nigra to the pallidum permits overactivity in the pallidothalamic system of neurons. As with spasticity and decerebrate rigidity, descending influences may cause the rigidity of Parkinson's disease by acting upon the alpha motoneurons or upon the fusimotor fibers. Marked inhibition of spindle discharge follows stimulation of the lateroventral nucleus of the thalamus; this effect is exerted through the cerebral cortex.[27] This finding cannot be correlated in any simple way to the demonstrated effects of lateroventral thalamic lesions on Parkinson's disease.

Tremor. The tremor, which is initially most obvious distally in the limb, is fine, highly regular and rapid (four to eight cycles per second). It occurs during rest and stops when the limbs are used voluntarily. It is therefore variously termed "tremor of rest" or "static tremor." Electromyography shows that antagonistic muscles are alternately activated and that the rate is surprisingly constant over long periods in a given muscle group. Both in its sinusoidal regularity and its occurrence at rest, the tremor of Parkinson's disease contrasts with the intentional tremor of cerebellar disease (see below). In the later stages of the disease, which is rather common in people who contracted influenza during World War I, the tremor becomes more

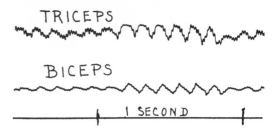

Fig. 4. Synchronous electromyograms of triceps and biceps in a monkey exhibiting tremor consequent to ventrolateral midbrain lesion. Note alternating contraction in antagonistic muscles. (From Ward *et al., J. Neurophysiol.,* 1948, *11*:317–330.)

violent, shaking the whole body and thus greatly disturbing and exhausting the patient.

Production and control of tremor. Pathologic or neurosurgical damage to the motor areas,[2] the internal capsule, the cerebral peduncle (Fig. 3)[3] or the posterolateral region of the spinal cord[19, 20] abolishes or diminishes tremor, at least transiently. The relationship is well established, but different authors interpret it quite differently. Bucy,[2] for example, considered the tremor to result from an oscillatory continuous discharge of the pyramidal tract unmodulated by a cortex-to-cortex circuit through the basal ganglia, the oscillating discharge being superseded by impulses mediating smooth movement when the pyramidal tract is involved in voluntary movement. However, no experimental lesion of the striopallidum link in the modulating circuit has ever produced a static tremor. On the other hand, Ward[25, 26] and others[9, 22] have produced a Parkinson-like tremor in monkeys by placing lesions in the ventrolateral midbrain reticular area between the red nucleus and the substantia nigra. The tremor is about eight cycles per second, and antagonistic muscles contract alternately (Fig. 4). As seen in Figure 5, the tremor, as in Parkinson's disease, disappears upon voluntary movement and tends to be increased during emotional excitement; it disappears during sleep. Other signs of Parkinson's disease were masked facies, sluggish movements and rigidity. On the basis of these experiments, Ward postulates that the lesion giving rise to the tremor of clinical Parkinson's disease lies in the mesencephalic tegmentum. Effective lesions in the ventrolateral midbrain have included the substantia nigra in some series[9] and the anterior fibers of the brachium conjunctivum destined for the

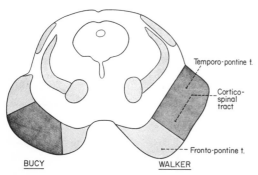

Fig. 3. Cross sections through the human midbrain. On right is shown a pedunculotomy performed by Walker and on the left one performed by Bucy. Involuntary movements were greatly diminished and recovery of voluntary power included independent movements of fingers in Bucy's case. (After Bucy, Chap. 11 in *Pathogenesis and treatment of parkinsonism,* W. S. Fields, ed. Springfield, Ill., Charles C Thomas, 1958.)

MOVEMENT DISORDER – MONKEY

Effect of Voluntary Movement on Tremor at Rest

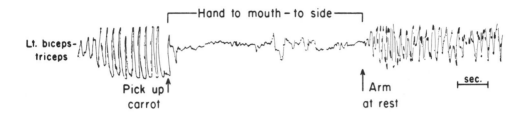

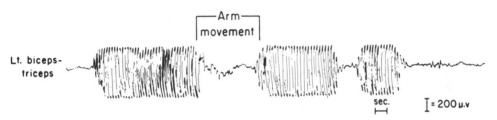

Fig. 5. Electromyographic records of arm tremor in monkey with bilateral lesions of ventromedial midbrain region. Note absence of tremor while a carrot is grasped and placed in mouth, and while arm is being returned to animal's side. (From Schreiner *et al.*, in *Pathogenesis and treatment of parkinsonism*, W. S. Fields, ed., Springfield, Ill., Charles C Thomas, 1958.)

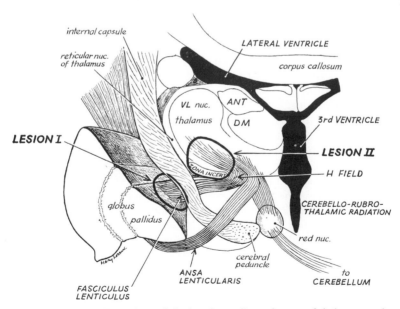

Fig. 6. Diagram in three dimensions of the basal ganglia and some of their connections, showing the sites of operation for relief of parkinsonism. Lesion I, originally used by Cooper, consisted of interrupting pallidothalamic connections. This lesion is less effective in respect to tremor than Lesion II in the gateway of pallidal and cerebellar pathways to the ventrolateral nucleus of the thalamus. (From Lin, Okumura and Cooper, *Electroenceph. clin. Neurophysiol.*, 1961, *13*:631–634.)

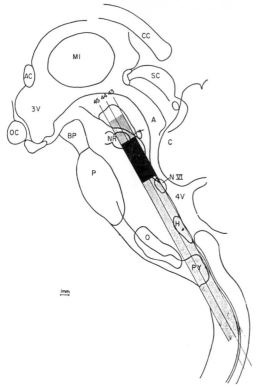

Fig. 7. Sagittal section through brain stem showing tremorogenic zone demarcated by electrical stimulation. Black area between Horsley-Clarke coordinates 43 and 45 yields tremor most consistently. Pertinent abbreviations are: *NR*, nucleus ruber; *VI*, nucleus of abducens nerve; *H*, nucleus of hypoglossal nerve; *O*, inferior olive; *PY*, pyramids. (From Jenkner and Ward, *Arch. Neurol. Psychiat.* (*Chic.*), 1953, *70*:489–502.)

thalamus and pallidum in most. Although interruption of these fibers can produce resting tremor and may be contributory, it is not necessary for the production of tremor.

Since, according to Hughlings Jackson's principle, the tissue destroyed cannot directly cause an overactivity (tremor), Ward concluded that the lesion, by interrupting descending pathways, has permitted some lower brain stem mechanism to oscillate. The oscillatory discharge is, by exclusion of major descending systems, in the reticulospinal tract. Stimulation of the reticular substance below the level of the lesion causes rapid oscillatory movements (15 to 25 per second).[11] As seen in Figure 7, the region yielding this tremor is the medial reticular substance lying between the red nucleus and the VIth cranial nerve. Presumably, impulses inhibiting these tremorogenic neurons come from higher levels and funnel through the ventrolateral midbrain area—perhaps from

the substantia nigra, but this assumption has not yet been verified. The role of the pyramidal tract is envisioned as the supplying of a facilitatory, nonoscillatory background which is necessary for tremor just as a tonic background is favorable to clonus. Stimulation of other regions besides the reticular core causes tremor, e.g., brachium conjunctivum, nucleus ruber and amygdala.[1]

A search for single units discharging synchronously with the tremor revealed none in the reticular formation, in contrast with 15 per cent of cells synchronously discharging recorded from the sensorimotor area of the cortex.[9] Chlorpromazine produces static tremor, but, judging from neuropathologic lesions it causes, its action is too wide to have localizing value. However, the tremor produced by drugs or lesions and stimulation of the reticular system is abolished by decerebration.[1] Thus levels above the midbrain may be necessary for tremorogenesis either independently or by way of the reticular formation. Since sleep inhibits tremor, it is worthy of note that ascending reticular impulses may produce a nonspecific activation of brain structures favorable for tremor.

Abolition of tremor by damage to the projections from the cortical motor areas as a consequence of a stroke causing hemiplegia was known by Parkinson himself. Neurosurgical interference with the motor areas,[1] internal capsule, cerebral peduncle (Fig. 3), or the posterolateral column of the spinal cord abolishes or diminishes tremors whereas the paresis lasts. Further insight into tremor again has come from clinical observations.

The substantia nigra and the globus pallidus are usually considered the most common sites of damage resulting in paralysis agitans, but, quite empirically, it was learned by Cooper in 1952 (see Ref. 4 and Fig. 6) that destruction in the region of the globus pallidus decreases both tremor and rigidity, and restores mobility to many patients with Parkinson's disease. Destruction of the ansa lenticularis or the ventrolateral nucleus of the thalamus (Fig. 6) has proved even more effective. Experimental Parkinson's disease from midbrain lesions is also relieved by pallidectomy.[22]

The sites of the operations which reduce tremor, rigidity and hypokinesis are on a known neural loop: motor areas → putamen → pallidum → ventrolateral nucleus of the thalamus

→ motor areas. Into this feed contributions from the brachium conjunctivum, nigra-pallidal fibers and possibly parallel fibers from the ventrolateral reticular formation. Lesions at all these three input sites are suspected of causing tremor. Interruption of the loop or of the pyramidal tract—an offshoot from it— relieves the tremor. Thus, a second hypothesis of tremor is that an oscillation of a feedback system occurs when not driven by the cortex or by cerebellar, nigral or reticular inputs. It would be necessary to think of the input outside the loop as inhibitory since high gain in a feedback system causes oscillation.

A reverberating circuit, of which cortex-to-cortex might be a complex example, is one means of producing an oscillation. Sensory motor unit discharge in phase with the tremor lends some support to this idea. Oscillation can also be produced by subjecting spinal motor neurons to evenly balanced excitation of flexor and extensor neurons, much like the teeter board analogy that will be used to explain rhythmic respiration (Chap. 41). A strong bias, as represented by decerebrate rigidity, should be unfavorable to this kind of oscillator—and is—but so should the rigidity of parkinsonism.

Another familiar oscillation occurs when there is a strong bias rhythmically interrupted, as in clonus.

Parkinsonian tremor presents a bewildering series of paradoxes and uncertainties, to which can be added the empirical fact that atropine-like compounds relieve Parkinson's disease, an action suggesting that excessive acetylcholine or acetylcholine-sensitivity may be involved. However, acetylcholine mediation of synaptic transmission in the brain has never been proved.

It is paradoxical that destruction of the very structures showing maximum pathologic alterations in Parkinson's disease often lessens the disability. This paradox could be resolved by the possible (but unpopular and unsubstantiated) hypothesis that the circuit consisting of the globus pallidus, the ansa lenticularis and the ventrolateral thalamus is the site of a discharging lesion. Such a discharge might act on the cerebral cortex or upon the brain stem tegmentum. To account for a symptom-free interval of as long as 30 years, and to account for the efficacy of anticholinesterase drugs on the basis of degeneration hypersensitivity, it is necessary to postulate further that an irritative-destructive process begins long after the original influenzal infection. In short, although the disappearance or reduction of tremor by pallidectomy

does not establish the pallidum as the site of the discharging oscillatory lesion, the possibility that this is the case must be considered.

CEREBELLUM

Orientation. The cerebellum, like the cerebral hemispheres, is a suprasegmental structure, but it has no long, direct pathway to the spinal cord comparable to the pyramidal tract. Thus, the cerebellum can influence motoneurons only through its connections with the motor systems of the brain stem and with the cerebral cortex. It is therefore not surprising to find that the cerebellum does not execute detailed movements;* none disappears when it is extirpated. Its chief function lies in the *control* or regulation of movement, especially voluntary skilled movements, but also such brain stem functions as walking. The cerebellum also regulates posture and tonus; it must also regulate visceral activities, since many of them are altered by cerebellar stimulation or ablation.[43]

Consistent with widespread regulation or control is the cerebellum's richness of efferent and afferent connections,[57] as seen in Figure 8.

*Cerebellar stimulation does produce coordinated rotations of the head or flexions and extensions involving the whole limb. Such stimulation also facilitates and inhibits movements. The distinction between a strong facilitation and a weak movement is not great. The above distinction may therefore be more conventional than real. In fact, Sprague and Chambers[61] found that contact placing reactions are lost after cerebellectomy.

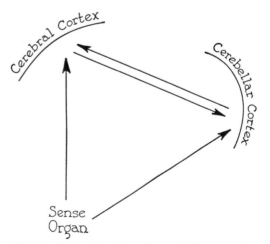

Fig. 8. Basic plan of cerebrocerebellar control system. Arrows indicate the pathways of impulse conduction, not neurons.

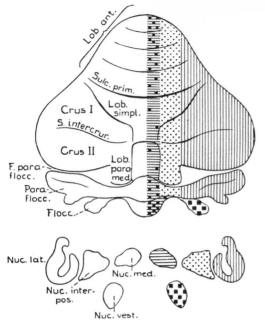

Fig. 9. Diagram of primate corticonuclear zones. Note that medial or vermal zone of cerebellum (*horizontal lines*) projects to nucleus medialis, i.e., fastigial nucleus, and to the vestibular nuclei; intermediate or paravermal zone (*stipple*) projects to nucleus interpositus; and lateral zone (*vertical lines*) projects to nucleus lateralis or dentate nucleus. (From Jansen and Brodal, *Avh. norske VidenskAkad., Kl. I,* 1942, No. 3.)

It is reciprocally connected* with the cerebral motor and sensory areas.[48, 50, 57] It projects to the brain stem structures giving rise to descending motor pathways. Control requires information. Functional studies indicate that the cerebellum receives an afferent input not solely from the proprioceptive and vestibular systems, but from many sensory systems, including those for vision and audition.[59] Certain areas of the cerebellar cortex are somatotopically organized, although not in the detail found in the cerebral

*"Reciprocal connection," not to be confused with "reciprocal innervation," means that A sends fibers to B and B sends fibers to A.

cortex. Furthermore, there is evidence of functional localization reflecting differences in the efferent and afferent projections; however, thought on this matter is now in a state of flux.

Anatomic Organization.   The cerebellum, like the cerebrum, consists of a cortex and deep nuclei. Unlike the cerebral cortex, the three-layered cortex of the cerebellum has a uniform structure showing no cytoarchitectural subdivisions. The efferent cells of the cerebellar cortex, the Purkinje cells, send their axons to the deep nuclei in such a manner that the cerebellum can be divided into longitudinal corticonuclear zones (Table 2 and Fig. 9). The efferent path is then continued by neurons of these nuclei, the axons leaving the cerebellum via the inferior and superior peduncles to reach various nuclei of the thalamus, midbrain and medulla.[38] Some cortical areas also project directly to the vestibular nuclei of the medulla (Fig. 9). The corticonuclear zones were delimited anatomically by Jansen and Brodal,[51] and this description was modified recently by Cohen *et al.*[38] The functional significance of these zones has been stressed by Chambers and Sprague.[37] This way of dividing the cerebellum may be termed the longitudinal or zonal, in contrast to the transverse or lobular division.

The afferent pathways to the cerebellum terminate chiefly in the cortex (the granule and Purkinje cell layers) and to a lesser extent in the deep nuclei. The regions of termination of the various afferent pathways are shown in Figure 10, in which the lobular organization of the cerebellum is illustrated. Although knowledge of afferent projections has influenced the concept of a lobular organization, this concept is based to a greater extent on comparative anatomy and embryology.†[41, 42, 43, 53]

Knowledge of the connections of the cerebellum is essential for the understanding of its functional organization. Comparative anatomy

†The afferent pathways can also be related satisfactorily to the longitudinal corticonuclear zones.

TABLE 2.   *Corticonuclear Zones of the Cerebellum*

Medial zone	Vermal cortex	Fastigial nuclei
Intermediate zone	Paravermal cortex (incl. paramedianus?)	Interpositus or intermediate nuclei‡
Lateral zone	Hemispheric cortex lobulus ansiformis and paraflocculus	Dentate nucleus

‡ Globosus and emboliformis nuclei of man.

and embryology have demonstrated that the cerebellum has two major divisions separated by the posterolateral fissure—the flocculonodular lobe and the corpus cerebelli. Phylogenetically, the flocculonodular lobe develops early, and it receives its connections chiefly from the vestibular system. This lobe is relatively the same in various animals and is sometimes called the *archicerebellum.* The corpus or body of the cerebellum first appears as a medial (vermal) area consisting of a cortex and deep nuclei, which are presumably the homologue of the fastigial nuclei. This area, the *paleocerebellum,* is connected primarily with the vestibular mechanism and the proprioceptors and exteroceptors of the body and head. In mammals the paleocerebellum also receives corticopontile connections. The body of the cerebellum shows great development, especially in its lateral parts (*neocerebellum*), which consist of intermediate and lateral areas with their respective nuclei (Fig. 10). The lateral area receives its chief connections from the cerebral cortex via the pontine nuclei and additional connections from the upper brain stem via the inferior olive. The intermediate area shares the afferent connections of the lateral area and many of those of the vermis. These connections are the ventral

and dorsal spinothalamic tracts, the tectocerebellar tracts and the connections with the trigeminal and other sensory systems innervating the face.

The flocculonodular lobe projects back to the vestibular nuclei. The vermal area of the corpus cerebelli projects to the same vestibular nuclei, to the reticular formation of the medulla, and to the pons, midbrain and thalamus. The lateral and intermediate areas project to the reticular formation of the midbrain and to the red nucleus and the thalamus. Thus all areas of the cerebellum except the flocculonodular lobe project to the origin of the pyramidal and extrapyramidal systems in the cerebral cortex via the ventral thalamic nuclei. All cerebellar areas likewise send projections to the subcortical extrapyramidal systems, that from the vermal area going chiefly to the medulla (reticulospinal paths).

The concept of lobular parcellation now seems inadequate in the light of some of the newer information on afferent and efferent somatotopic organization. For example, the representation of the body surface extends behind the fissura prima into the declive and the simplex lobule; moreover, a second spinothalamic projection area exists, and there is a

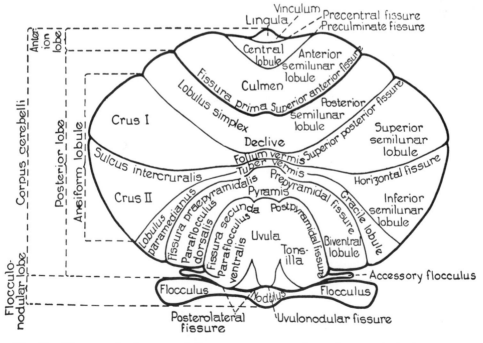

Fig. 10. Diagram of primate cerebellar cortex to summarize various terminologies, based principally on lobes and afferent projections to cerebellar areas (*right*). (From Larsell, *Anatomy of the nervous system,* 2d ed. New York, Appleton-Century-Crofts, 1951.)

representation of the body surface in the posterior part of the posterior lobe. Under the system of lobular division, the anterior lobe—that part of the corpus cerebelli rostral to the primary fissure—has often been treated as a unit. In primates, however, this lobe consists of three zones—vermal, intermediate and lateral—each having different fiber connections and functions. Such a subdivision exists in the posterior lobe, lying between the primary and posterolateral fissures. In each instance, the lateral (and probably the intermediate) area should be referred to as the hemisphere. Even the flocculonodular lobe is subdivided into a vermal portion, the nodulus, and a lateral portion, the flocculi.

FUNCTIONAL ANATOMY OF THE CEREBELLUM

Localization and Projection. If the cerebellar cortex is explored, millimeter by millimeter, with a recording electrode while a point on the skin is touched, a cerebellar point will be found at which the so-called evoked potential is maximal (see Chaps. 15 and 23). Stimulation of an adjacent point on the skin evokes a maximal potential at an adjacent point on the cortex. In this fashion, a *somatotopic* map of the cerebellar cortex has been produced, and the cortex is said to be somatotopically or topographically organized. Elicitation of movements by cerebellar stimulation has confirmed such maps. If the evoked potential technique is applied to the cerebral and the cerebellar cortex, recording from one while stimulating the other (and then reversing the procedure) reveals many specific connections between them.

MULTIPLICITY OF INPUTS. By varying the type of stimulus to the body, or by stimulating different sense organs such as the eye or the ear, one can determine the kind of sensory input received by a central area. Until 1942, when Snider and Stowell[59] performed experiments of this type, the afferent input into the cerebellum was thought to be exclusively vestibular and proprioceptive. These workers demonstrated that tactual, visual, auditory and even visceral impulses reach the cerebellar cortex. Subsequently it was learned that the portion of the cerebellar cortex responding to peripheral stimulation is reciprocally connected with the cerebral cortical area which responds to the same type of stimuli. Thus the vermal and intermediate parts of the anterior

lobe, which receives somesthetic input, are connected with the postcentral gyrus, the somatosensory area of the cerebral cortex; the cerebellar visual area (vermis of the posterior lobe) is interconnected with the cerebral cortical visual area; etc. Finally, after it was discovered that the cerebral cortex contains two somatosensory areas (see Chap. 15), the classic postcentral one (somatic area I) was found to be interconnected with the anterior projection field of the spinocerebellar tract in the anterior lobe and the second (somatic area II) with the posterior or paramedian projection of the spinocerebellar tracts.[47]

Beginning with Adrian's work[30] in 1943, demonstrations of a comparable reciprocal connection—cerebellum to cerebral cortex and vice versa—between all zones of the anterior lobe and the motor areas of the cerebral cortex became available. All these experiments also revealed an element of topographic organization.

One role of the cerebral-cerebellar connection has recently been disclosed. When the major somatic sensory pathways to the *cerebral* cortex are functionally intact, the evoked potential in cerebellar cortex elicited from cutaneous stimulation is very large. Section of the dorsal columns, medial lemniscus and cerebral peduncles or lesions of the N. ventralis posterior lateralis reduce the cerebellar-evoked potential. There must be, therefore, a loop that conducts impulses from the somatosensory pathways, through cerebral cortex to cerebellar cortex, employing the reciprocal element connecting the two cortices. Thus, the cerebellum has a direct (spinocerebellar) and an indirect posterior column to cerebral cortex pathway from the skin (Kennedy and Grimm, unpublished).

To summarize: (i) The cerebellum receives afferent inputs other than vestibular and proprioceptive. (ii) The anterior lobe is reciprocally connected with somatosensory area I of the cerebral cortex. (iii) The posterior lobe (paramedian lobule) is reciprocally connected with the second somatosensory cortex. (iv) The motor area of the cerebral cortex and the entire anterior lobe are reciprocally connected. (v) In all these areas there is considerable somatotopic organization. The general plan of reciprocal connections can be diagrammed as in Figure 8.

It can be deduced from this information that

the cerebellum (since it has an input from exteroceptors) is concerned with adjustments of the body to the external world as well as to the internal proprioceptive world. Secondly, the cerebral motor cortex and the cerebellum must work closely together in effecting and controlling movements.

Somatotopic Organization.   Evidence of a somatotopic organization of the cerebellar cortex comes from electrophysiologic studies of afferent inputs and stimulation of the cerebellar cortex and anatomic studies of the projections of the spinocerebellar tracts. This organization is, however, relative rather than absolute.* The body surface of the cat is projected into its anterior cerebellum, so that the tail is predominantly "localized" in the lingula, the hindleg in the simplex. Furthermore, the axial portions of the animal are represented along the midline in the vermis, and the apical portions more laterally, in the intermediate cortex. Similarly, as shown in Figure 11, the tail areas in the somatosensory and motor areas of the cerebral cortex are reciprocally connected with the lingula—and so on through the cerebral and cerebellar areas for the hindlimb, forelimb and neck–face. In the second representation of the body surface, found in the posterior part of the corpus cerebelli, there is also a topographic localization.

FUNCTIONS OF THE CEREBELLUM

Equilibration.   Since part of the cerebellum developed from the vestibular structures of the medulla oblongata, it is not surprising that regulation of the mechanism underlying upright posture is a cerebellar function. One such mechanism is equilibration, or balancing, and its regulation is served mainly by the flocculonodular lobe.

FLOCCULONODULAR LOBE.   The disturbances resulting from ablation of this lobe reflect its vestibular afferent and efferent connections. Dow[40] performed isolated ablations in this area

* In electrophysiologic mapping experiments conducted on *un*anesthetized cats by Combs,[39] stimulation of a point on the skin or of a cutaneous nerve resulted in bilateral activation of all folia of the vermal and intermediate anterior lobe. For reasons which will be brought out in the discussion of similar experiments on the cerebral cortex, this finding is not incompatible with the existence of a focus of representation as revealed in experiments involving use of barbiturate anesthetics.

and observed conspicuous disturbances of equilibrium without either changes in the basic postural reflexes or difficulties in volitional movements. After such a lesion, a monkey can feed itself manually without tremor or deviation of the hands, but it is unable to stand, even on a broad base, without swaying and falling. For this reason, the monkey generally sits, propping itself up in a corner to secure support from two sides of the cage or maintaining equilibrium by clutching the cage wall or floor. The syndrome is therefore one of *disequilibration*. The vestibular concern of the flocculonodular lobe is further documented by the fact that development of motion sickness in dogs is prevented by ablation of this area but not by removal of any other in either the cerebellar or cerebral cortex.[64, 65]

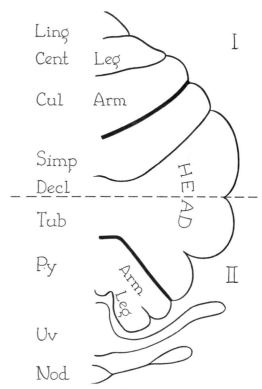

Fig. 11.   Summary diagram showing somatotopic organization of cerebellar cortex and nature of cerebrocerebellar relationships. The latter are indicated by the Roman numerals (referring to cerebral somatosensory areas) and horizontal dashed line. For meaning of abbreviations, see Fig. 10. Much of data obtained on cats and extrapolated to primate cerebellum. Representation in paramedian lobule, behind lower heavy line indicating prepyramidal fissure, is bilateral. (After Hampson *et al., Res. Publ. Ass. nerv. ment. Dis.*, 1952, *30:*299–316.)

OTHER CEREBELLAR AREAS REGULATING STAND-
ING. The stretch reflexes are the raw materials
of standing, but these basic reflexes must be
controlled. Equilibration is only one phase of
this control, the phase in which the vestibular
system is important. Vision, too, is a factor, as
can be quickly learned by standing on one foot
and comparing the amount of swaying with
the eyes closed and with them open. Proprioception is another factor, since interruption of
spinal proprioceptive pathways, as in locomotor
ataxia, makes standing without swaying difficult, especially when the eyes are closed (Rom-
berg's sign).

Although the flocculonodular lobe is unquestionably important in equilibration, it is not
the only cerebellar structure regulating standing. Recent evidence suggests that the medial
zone of the vermis throughout the whole of the
cerebellum is concerned with standing. Chambers and Sprague[36] found that lesions confined
to the anterior zone of the vermal area produce
difficulties in standing like those caused by posterior (medial) vermal lesions affecting the
nodular area. Since the medial vermal cortex
projects to the fastigial nucleus, which in turn
sends many fibers to and receives many fibers
from the vestibular nucleus of the medulla oblongata, this finding is anatomically reasonable. Furthermore, the spinocerebellar tract,
carrying proprioceptive and tactual impulses
from the body, projects heavily to the anterior
portion of the vermis. Such sensory impulses
would be helpful in maintaining equilibrium.
Finally, visual and auditory impulses are projected to the vermal structures, centering on
the declive, the folium and the tuber vermis.[52, 59] It may be predicted that one function
of this projection will prove to be the visual element in the maintenance of the body's orientation in space.

In summary, standing—whether on two legs
or four—depends upon three afferent inputs:
vestibular, somesthetic and visual. All these are
heavily represented in the most medial vermal
regions of the cerebellar cortex that control the
musculature of the entire body. The higher
control of equilibration and standing seems to
be served by the medial vermal region of the
corpus cerebelli and by the flocculonodular
lobe.

Tonus.   More fundamental to standing than
equilibration is the control of the myotatic reflexes. As discussed in Chapter 6, these include

two-neuron-arc spinal reflexes regulated by impulses descending from the vestibular nuclei
and from the brain stem reticular system. Normally, such reflexes serve to prevent collapse of
the joints by the pull of gravity. A decerebrate
animal, in which descending influences from
the cerebellum and cerebrum are interrupted,
can stand, but its legs must be adjusted under
it. If pushed slightly from the side, the animal
does not adjust the strength of its extensor reflexes sufficiently to prevent toppling. The intact animal has a greater capacity for promptly
adjusting its muscular contractions to the vicis-
situdes of gravitational forces. The cerebellum
is concerned with reflex tonus of the musculature and presumably functions to control that
tonus.

Inhibition of extensor tonus is the predominant effect of threshold stimulation of the medial anterior lobe. This inhibition of rigidity is
especially evident when the vermal area of the
anterior lobe of a decerebrate cat is stimulated.
Consistently, when decerebration is combined
with ablation of this lobe, as in the anemic
method of decerebration,[54] the release of extensor myotatic reflexes is greater than that
following simple transcollicular decerebration.
These effects in decerebrate animals prove also
that much of the postural influence of the medial anterior lobe is exerted on the brain stem
—understandable since the major outflow from
the lobe is the fastigiobulbar tract to the vestibular and reticular nuclei of the medulla.
There is little doubt that the loss of the anterior
lobes is responsible for the extensor spasm, the
opisthotonos and the hyperactive positive supporting reaction seen during the *initial* stages
after decerebellation. However, in the dog and
cat, the medial anterior lobe is not purely inhibitory to extensors, but usually activates the
flexors reciprocally. Moreover, after stimulation of the lobe has ceased, a contrary effect
often appears—contraction of extensor muscles
and inhibition of flexor motoneurons. The response obtained depends somewhat on the parameters of the stimulus. This and the rebound
phenomena indicate that the anterior cerebellum contains oppositely acting components,
each of which acts reciprocally on flexor and
extensor motoneurons.

The release of extensor reflexes is greater and
more enduring in the pigeon than in the dog or
cat, and is less in the monkey than in the cat.
In man, a medial anterior lobe syndrome de-

noted by release of extensor reflexes has never been identified. All these facts lead to the conclusion that the extensor-inhibiting postural function of the medial anterior lobe has changed during phylogeny.

A factor in the complex effects of ablation of the anterior lobe was disclosed by Sprague and Chambers[60] when they destroyed only one fastigial nucleus, the main outflow from the anterior lobe (and from the remainder of the vermis). Whereas bilateral nuclear lesions have effects similar to those of an ablation of the anterior lobe, destruction of one fastigial nucleus causes spasticity in the contralateral extensor muscles and in the flexor muscles of the ipsilateral limbs. Another complicating observation was that lesions of the vermian cortex of the anterior lobe exert effects opposite to those of lesions of the underlying fastigial nucleus. The cortex presumably inhibits the nucleus, which, in turn, is inhibitory to contralateral extensors and ipsilateral flexors. With the cerebellum, as with many other structures, what is seen on stimulation or ablation reflects the predominant rather than the *sole* function of the structure.

Suprasegmental influences on myotatic reflexes can be exerted on either the alpha motoneurons or the gamma fusimotor neurons. The cerebellum acts through both avenues. Granit and Kaada[46] have shown that the afferent discharge from a muscle spindle is *decreased* by stimulation of the vermal portion of the anterior lobe, an action which would decrease muscle tonus. This finding corresponds to the known predominant effect (inhibition) of such stimulation on myotatic reflexes. Stimulation of the intermediate portion of the anterior lobe increased the spindle discharge, a finding which correlates with studies described later in this chapter. The tonus changes exerted through gamma efferents occurred at a lower threshold of anterior cerebellar stimulation than did direct effects upon alpha motoneurons. However, the anterior cerebellum also acts upon alpha motoneurons. Functional ablation of it by cooling resulted in extensor hypertonus without increased gamma efferent discharge. Knowledge of the higher control of tonus via the gamma efferent is a new development which may in the future explain some of the puzzling features of abnormal tonus states (Chap. 6).[43]

One hypothesis to account for the severe *hypo*tonia seen in clinical cases of cerebellar damage is that hypotonia is caused by injury to the lateral corticonuclear zone of the whole cerebellum. Since these areas are developed progressively in primates, including man, this theory might explain why hypotonia rather than hypertonia is typical of the human cerebellar syndrome. Unfortunately, lesions in experimental animals have rarely been confined to the lateral zone but have included portions of the medial and intermediate zones, and thus an element of extensor reflex release has been introduced.

It is not certain whether lesions confined to the lateral portion of the cerebellum in the dog or cat result in hypotonia after the initial stage of hypertonus.[32, 37] Hypotonia is much more marked in the primate. After unilateral cerebellar ablations sparing the anterior vermis and the fastigial nucleus in baboons, Botterell and Fulton[31] observed hypotonia, which was more severe and enduring when the dentate nucleus was damaged.

The lateral and intermediate portions of the cerebellum, unlike the vermis, do not project to the reticular and vestibular areas of the brain stem known to be concerned with facilitating and inhibiting the basic, spinal, myotatic reflexes. How, then, can these cerebellar areas influence muscular tonus?

The efferent projection of the lateral lobes of the cerebellum is to the dentate nucleus, from which fibers pass to the thalamus, some with a synapse in the red nucleus (Fig. 12). At this point, an influence on posture could be exerted by way of the rubrospinal tracts or the neighboring descending systems of the reticular facilitatory area. A synapse in the lateroventral nucleus of the thalamus interrupts the ascending pathways to the cerebral cortex. Fibers from this nucleus project to the motor areas of the motor cortex. Physiologic experiments teach that the pyramidal tract arising in the motor area is facilitatory to the extensor monosynaptic reflex arcs serving stretch reflexes. It is reasonable to assume that the fibers reaching the cerebral cortex from the lateral cerebellum provide the input drive for this tonic pyramidal influence on extensor reflexes. If this drive were eliminated by a lateral cerebellar lesion, the effect would be hypotonia.

It would be going too far to ascribe the hypotonia of the human cerebellar syndrome entirely to injury to the lateral hemispheres, since the more medial cerebellar regions connect with the motor area through the fastigial and interpositus nuclei as well as with the brain

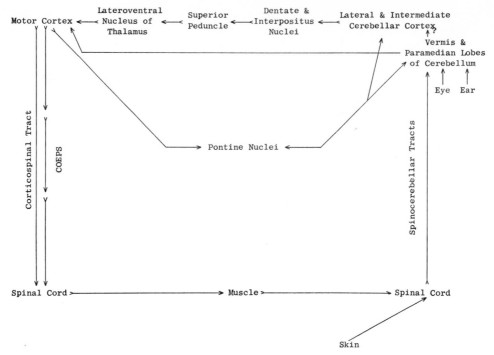

Fig. 12.   Feedback loops from and to motor cortex. Long loop involves a return of proprioceptive information from muscle to motor cortex by way of cerebellum. This loop assumes existence of connections between paleocerebellum and neocerebellum. A second potential loop is shorter and entirely within brain. It may or may not receive information from periphery, depending on connection of neocerebellum with vermis and paramedian lobes, which receive proprioceptive and exteroceptive sensory information. Note that short loop is informed of events in periphery only if there are connections between the medial and the more lateral cerebellar regions. Also note that arrow connecting vermis and paramedian lobe is questioned. This pathway is known functionally but not anatomically.

stem. However, the influence of the medial cortex upon pyramidal tract discharge seems to be mainly inhibitory,[38, 61] and the net effect exerted through the brain stem connection is inhibitory to extensor tonus. Damage to either system would not produce hypotonia. Altogether, it is probable that damage in the greatly expanded lateral hemisphere is responsible for the hypotonia consequent to cerebellar injury in man.

Control of Volitional Movements.   Because these controls are displayed best in man when cerebellar disease has disrupted them, the detailed descriptions may be deferred. It suffices to say that the signs of such defects are errors in the rate, range, force and direction of volitional movements (ataxia) and coarse, irregular oscillations, especially at the termination of a movement.

Anatomic considerations strongly suggest that the lateral and paravermal zones of the cerebellum are particularly concerned with the control of voluntary movement of the limbs.

The lateral zone has developed commensurate with manipulatory ability in the primate series, and the afferent and efferent connections of these lobes form a cerebello-cerebellar circle. However, the paravermal cortex also projects to the motor cortex via the interpositus nucleus and, unlike the lateral zone, is somatotopically highly organized. The most recent evidence from animal experiments indicates that ablation of the paravermal cortex induces ataxic movement; the influence of the more lateral region is less clearly established—a situation which may mean simply that the influence is more subtle. Paradoxically, lesions of the dentate nucleus, through which the lateral cortex exerts its influence, produce the most striking effects on volitional activity.[31, 45] Regardless of the relative roles of the lateral and the paravermal cortex, it is clear that they, together, control voluntary movement through the projections ultimately reaching the cortex, whereas the midline structures influence mainly the basic postural reflexes.

Before the ways in which the cerebellum and the cerebral cortex interact in the control of voluntary movement are discussed in detail the manifestations of cerebellar disease in man should be examined. Not only are certain disturbances more pronounced in man than in animals, but the examination of movement can be more detailed and enlightening in man than in experimental animals. However, it should be remembered that knowledge of which cerebellar regions have been destroyed or damaged is less certain.

Clinical Correlations. DISTURBANCES OF GAIT AND STATION. A specific type of tumor (medulloblastoma) occurring in young children induces disorders almost exactly like those which Dow[40] produced in monkeys by ablating portions of the flocculonodular lobe. Arising from the roof of the fourth ventricle, often at the base of the nodulus, these tumors produce few obvious signs of incoordination of movement as long as the child lies in bed. However, he is unable to balance and walk. Disturbances of gait and station, unaccompanied by hypotonia, also occur when the more anterior vermal region is affected by tumor or degeneration. Such cases are rare. In fact, as a result of the sheltered position of the anterior and flocculonodular lobes and their proximity to vital brain stem structures, the usual case of cerebellar disease probably reflects mainly damage to the cerebellum as a whole.

DISTURBANCES OF TONUS. The common procedure of passive flexion or extension of a joint, or simply shaking a limb, is generally used to demonstrate disorders of tonus. A *pendular knee jerk* is a manifestation of hypotonia. Through default of the myotatic appendage, the limb is not lowered but falls as an inert body does, and swings back and forth (Fig. 13). Failure of the antagonistic flexors to respond with a stretch reflex as the leg passes the midposition is also

a factor. The mechanism of cerebellar hypotonia is not known with certainty. As pointed out earlier, the neocerebellum is connected with the motor areas of the cerebral cortex and can facilitate their action. From the Fulton–Tower–Hines analysis of pyramidal tract function, default of the cerebellar discharge to the motor cortex could, like interruption of the pyramidal tract, result in flaccidity. Default of the cerebellar connection with the upper brain stem, which contains the reticular facilitatory area, is another possibility.

DISTURBANCES OF VOLUNTARY MOVEMENT.[49, 50] Deficiencies in force (asthenia), rate, direction (dysmetria) and steadiness (tremor) of movement are typical effects of cerebellar lesions on volitional movement. Starting, stopping and changing the direction of motion are especially disturbed.

The weakness of voluntary movements is not accompanied by loss of any specific movement, and, although severe subjectively, it is not easily demonstrable objectively. This *asthenia* is explicable by the hypothesis that the cerebellum facilitates the motor cortex. As with many cerebellar signs, the facilitation could be at the segmental level by way of the cerebellar connections with the brain stem.

In patients with cerebellar lesions, simple movements are slow to start (Fig. 14), a condition presumably reflecting the lack of facilitation. Figure 14 also shows that movements are slow to stop, so that hypermetria—overshooting the mark—occurs in a finger-to-nose test. (However, the finger can also undershoot—hypometria.) The rebound phenomenon, i.e., inability to restrain an arm exerting tension when it is suddenly released by the examiner, is a failure to stop a willed muscular contraction

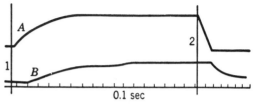

Fig. 14. Myograms of voluntary contraction by a patient with unilateral cerebellar lesion. *A*, normal; *B*, affected hand. Vertical lines *1* and *2* mark signals to start and stop gripping. Note slower start, weaker contraction, and delayed relaxation in the lower record. (From Ruch, Chap. 5 in *Handbook of experimental psychology*, S. S. Stevens, ed. New York, Wiley, 1951.)

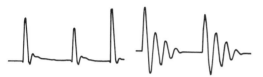

Fig. 13. Excursion of leg in knee jerk in normal person (*left*) and in patient with cerebellar lesion (*right*). Note that in three knee jerks at left leg falls "deadbeat," whereas in two knee jerks at right leg oscillates after initial upright excursion due to the knee jerk itself. (From Holmes, *Lancet*, 1922, *202*:1177–1182.)

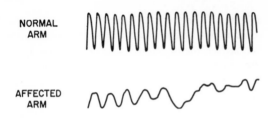

NORMAL ARM

AFFECTED ARM

Fig. 15. Tracings of rapidly alternating supination and pronation of arms illustrating adiadochokinesis. By contrast with normal arm, affected arm even initially made slow, low-amplitude movements, which rapidly deteriorated further. (From Holmes, *Lancet,* 1922, *203*:59–65.)

quickly. As shown in Figure 15, a patient with cerebellar disease is unable to perform alternating movements (supination and pronation of forearms) rapidly and with equal excursions (adiadochokinesis). This sign again reflects a defect in starting and stopping a movement.

A cerebellar tremor is "intentional" (i.e., occurs during voluntary movement rather than rest), terminal (most marked at the end of a movement), and coarse and irregular, as seen in Figure 16. In all these respects, cerebellar tremor contrasts so greatly with the regular oscillatory tremor of rest seen in Parkinson's disease that "tremor" may be a poor term. The term "ataxic tremor" is descriptive.[34] In visualizing the cerebellar tremor, one can imagine the arm drifting from the intended path and being corrected too late and too vigorously, so that the hand overcorrects and then overshoots the intended path. This overcorrection continues through slowness in stopping a movement and in initiating a return toward the course. As this sequence is repeated, the result is an irregular tremor which mounts in severity as the

movement progresses. The whole appearance somewhat resembles the first attempt to steer a boat. There are also typical disturbances in speaking, writing, standing and walking, but they present no new features.

The effort of neurophysiologists is to reduce the many manifestations of cerebellar disease to one or two basic defects. A unitary explanation of cerebellar symptoms must take into account the cerebellocerebral relationships.

Cerebellocerebral Relationships. The principal fact is the one we started with. The cerebral cortex cannot execute coordinated movements without help. This is true even though the cerebral cortex has at its disposal rich information from proprioceptors and exteroceptors. Although the cerebellum also has rich somatosensory inputs, it is presumed to contribute to cortically induced movement something over and beyond sensory information. It is surely significant that the cerebellum is reciprocally linked with the cerebral motor cortex, the connections potentially forming a loop.

It has long been known that stimulation of the neocerebellum can make the motor cortex more excitable,[55] and that some of this effect is exerted through connections between the two structures rather than by convergence on the reticular substance or spinal levels. Electroencephalographic waves are augmented. Surprisingly, the influence of the midline paleocerebellar areas on corticomotor excitability is better documented.[43] These areas have a topographic organization, and their influence on the motor cortex, like their influence on the limb reflexes, is often *inhibitory* but can be facilitatory. Snider and Magoun[58] have found facilitatory areas lying just lateral to the vermis

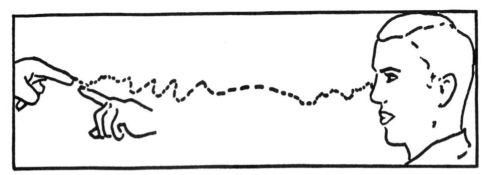

Fig. 16. Record of tremulous movement obtained by having patient move his finger from his nose to touch the finger of the examiner, represented at the left. Note irregularity and coarseness of tremor and that it is most marked near termination of the movement. (From Ruch, Chap. 5 in *Handbook of experimental psychology,* S. S. Stevens, ed. New York, Wiley, 1951.)

in the anterior lobe and the paramedian lobule. The occurrence of inhibitory or occlusive interaction in the cerebral cortex has been shown by recording from the pyramidal tract while interacting cerebellar and motor area stimulation.[63] It is clear that the cerebellum exerts both facilitatory and inhibitory influences on movement initiated by the cerebral motor cortex. This helps us to understand why the clinical manifestations of cerebellar injury present contrary elements—slowness to start and overshoot.

Altogether, the available data on the functioning of reciprocal cerebellocerebral connections does not permit more than speculation. Since the function of the neocerebellum is the control of discrete limb movement, and since control systems developed in engineering often employ a feedback loop, considerable *a priori* significance is attached to the potential neural loop afforded by the reciprocal cerebellocerebral connections. Wiener [66] and others[44] have commented on the similarity between servomechanisms and the neural control of movements. This parallel is illustrated in Figure 17.

A command to take a new position activates a motor which effects the movement to a degree dependent upon the difference between the present position and the desired position. A signal from the response is returned to the comparator, where present position is again related to intended position and a new order is issued to the power source. Thus the error, i.e., difference between present and intended position, is progressively reduced. Such systems are subject to overshoot and oscillation in making rapid transients if underdamped, or to a sluggish response if overdamped. Unfortunately for the sake of simple analogy, the signs of cerebellar disease appear to be overdamping at the initiation of movement and underdamping at its end.

The cerebellum might serve as a comparator, comparing the order from the cortex with the resulting limb position; however, the cerebral cortex itself, with its extensive exteroceptors, would be a more logical candidate for the task of comparing the goal with the present position. Perhaps the cerebellum should be considered analogous to the feedback stabilizing or controlling network, which determines whether the system is too slow in its control or is prone to oscillation.

It has been suggested[56] that the motor cortex is handicapped in planning movements in time because nerve impulses cannot be stored to be discharged after a fixed delay. However, if the motor cortex discharged in a circular pathway involving the cerebellum, a programming of movement in time might be possible. The cerebellum might provide an accelerating or facili-

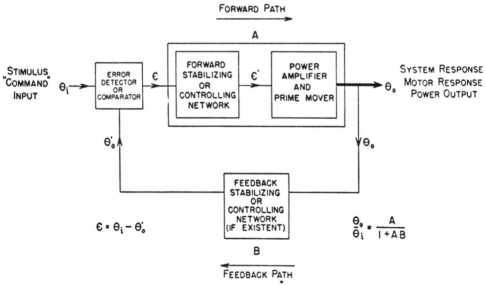

Fig. 17. Diagram illustrating the analogies between a physiologic control system and the basic elements of a servosystem. The "command" is a low energy input such as the sight of an object. The forward path might represent the corticospinal pathways. Θ reflects achieved movement, which is compared with intent of stimulus, and a modified order goes over the forward path. (From Frank *et al.*, *Ann. N. Y. Acad. Sci.*, 1948, *50*:187–277.)

tating mechanism to impart velocity without overshoot. Default of such a function would account for the slowness of movements to start in a patient with cerebellar disease (Fig. 13). A programming circuit with the correct delay characteristics would be helpful in decelerating movement to prevent overshoot or a jerky stop. Movements so roughed in could be further refined by afferent sensory reports, either via the cerebellum or to the cerebral cortex by way of the spinothalamocortical fibers. Whatever its resemblance to servomechanisms, the cerebellum has the requisite facilitatory and inhibitory relationship to the motor cortex and to the brain stem mechanisms to aid both systems in starting and stopping movements in the manner necessary to effective, well directed movement.

REFERENCES

Basal Ganglia

1. ARONSON, N. I., BECKER, B. E. and McGOVERN, W. A. *Confin. neurol. (Basel)*, 1962, *22*:397–429.
2. BUCY, P. C. Chap. 15 in *Precentral motor cortex*, 2d ed. Urbana, Ill., University of Illinois Press, 1949.
3. BUCY, P. C. Chap. 11 in *Pathogenesis and treatment of parkinsonism*, W. S. FIELDS, ed. Springfield, Ill., Charles C Thomas, 1958.
4. CARPENTER, M. B., CORRELL, J. W. and HINMAN, A. *J. Neurophysiol.*, 1960, *23*:288–304.
5. DUSSER DE BARENNE, J. G. and McCULLOCH, W. S. *J. Neurophysiol.*, 1941, *4*:311–323.
6. FIELDS, W. S. *Pathogenesis and treatment of parkinsonism.* Springfield, Ill., Charles C Thomas, 1958.
7. FORMAN, D. and WARD, J. W. *J. Neurophysiol.*, 1957, *20*:230–244.
8. GLEES, P. *J. Anat. (Lond.)*, 1944, *78*:47–51.
9. GYBELS, J. M. *The neural mechanism of Parkinsonian tremor.* Brussels, Editions arscia, S.A., 1963.
10. HASSLER, R. *Dtsch. Z. Nervenheilk.*, 1956, *175*:233–258.
11. JENKNER, F. L. and WARD, A. *Arch. Neurol. Psychiat. (Chic.)*, 1953, *70*:489–502.
12. JUNG, R. and HASSLER, R. Chap. 35 in *Handbook of physiology; Section I, neurophysiology*, vol. 2, J. FIELD, ed. Washington, D. C., American Physiological Society, 1960.
13. KENNARD, M. A. *J. Neurophysiol.*, 1944, *7*:127–148.
14. KENNARD, M. A. and FULTON, J. F. *Res. Publ. Ass. nerv. ment. Dis.*, 1942, *21*:228–245.
15. LAURSEN, A. M. *Acta physiol. scand.*, 1962, *54*:175–184; 185–190.
16. MAGOUN, H. W. and RHINES, R. *Spasticity: The stretch-reflex and extrapyramidal systems.* Springfield, Ill., Charles C Thomas, 1947.
17. METTLER, F. A., ADES, H. W., LIPMAN, E. and CULLER, E. A. *Arch. Neurol. Psychiat. (Chic.)*, 1939, *41*:984–995.
18. POLLOCK, L. J. and DAVIS, L. *Arch. Neurol. Psychiat. (Chic.)*, 1930, *23*:303–319.
19. PUTNAM, T. J. *Arch. Neurol. Psychiat. (Chic.)*, 1940, *44*:950–976.
20. PUTNAM, T. J. and HERZ, E. *Arch. Neurol. Psychiat. (Chic.)*, 1950, *63*:357–366.
21. RIOCH, D. McK. and BRENNER, C. *J. comp. Neurol.*, 1938, *68*:491–507.
22. SCHREINER, L. Chap. 5 in *Pathogenesis and treatment of Parkinsonism*, W. S. FIELDS, ed. Springfield, Ill., Charles C Thomas, 1958.
23. TOWER, S. S. *Brain*, 1935, *58*:238–255.
24. WANG, G. H. and AKERT, K. *Arch. ital. Biol.*, 1962, *100*:48–85.
25. WARD, A. A. Chap. 4 in *Pathogenesis and treatment of Parkinsonism*, W. S. FIELDS, ed. Springfield, Ill., Charles C Thomas, 1958.
26. WARD, A. A., JR., McCULLOCH, W. S. and MAGOUN, H. W. *J. Neurophysiol.*, 1948, *11*:317–330.
27. WARD, A. A. and STERN, J. Personal communication.
28. WALSHE, F. M. R. *Brain*, 1924, *47*:159–177.
29. WHITTIER, J. R. and METTLER, F. A. *J. comp. Neurol.*, 1949, *90*:319–372.

Cerebellum

30. ADRIAN, E. D. *Brain*, 1943, *66*:289–315.
31. BOTTERELL, E. H. and FULTON, J. F. *J. comp. Neurol.*, 1938, *69*:63–87.
32. BREMER, F. *Arch. int. Physiol.*, 1922, *19*:189–226.
33. BROOKHARDT, J. M. Chap. 51 in *Handbook of Physiology; Section I, neurophysiology*, vol. 2, J. FIELD, ed. Washington, D. C., American Physiological Society, 1961.
34. CARREA, R. M. E. and METTLER, F. A. *J. comp. Neurol.*, 1947, *87*:169–288.
35. CASEY, K. L. and TOWE, A. L. *J. Physiol.*, 1961, *158*:399–410.
36. CHAMBERS, W. W. and SPRAGUE, J. M. *J. comp. Neurol.*, 1955, *103*:105–129.
37. CHAMBERS, W. W. and SPRAGUE, J. M. *Arch. Neurol. Psychiat. (Chic.)*, 1955, *74*:653–680.
38. COHEN, D., CHAMBERS, W. W. and SPRAGUE, J. M. *J. comp. Neurol.*, 1958, *109*:233–266.
39. COMBS, C. M. *J. Neurophysiol.*, 1954, *17*:123–143.
40. DOW, R. S. *Arch. Neurol. Psychiat. (Chic.)*, 1938, *40*:500–520.
41. DOW, R. S. *Biol. Rev.*, 1942, *17*:179–220.
42. DOW, R. S. *J. Neurophysiol.*, 1942, *5*:121–136.
43. DOW, R. S. and MORUZZI, G. *The physiology and pathology of the cerebellum.* Minneapolis, University of Minnesota Press, 1958.
44. FRANK, L. K., HUTCHINSON, G. E., LIVINGSTON, W. K., McCULLOCH, W. S. and WIENER, N. *Ann. N. Y. Acad. Sci.*, 1948, *50*:187–278.
45. FULTON, J. F. *Functional localization in the frontal lobes and cerebellum.* Oxford, Clarendon Press, 1949.
46. GRANIT, R. and KAADA, B. R. *Acta physiol. scand.*, 1952, *27*:130–160.
47. HAMPSON, J. L. *J. Neurophysiol.*, 1949, *12*:37–50.
48. HENNEMAN, E., COOKE, P. M. and SNIDER, R. S. *Res. Publ. Ass. nerv. ment. Dis.*, 1952, *30*:317–333.
49. HOLMES, G. *Lancet*, 1922, *202*:1177–1182, 1231–1237; *203*:59–65, 111–115.
50. HOLMES, G. *Brain*, 1939, *62*:1–30.
51. JANSEN, J. and BRODAL, A. *Avh. norske VidenskAkad., Kl. I*, 1942, No. 3.
52. KOELLA, W. P. *J. Neurophysiol.*, 1959, *22*:61–77.
53. LARSELL, O. *Arch. Neurol. Psychiat. (Chic.)*, 1937, *38*:580–607.
54. POLLOCK, L. J. and DAVIS, L. *Brain*, 1927, *50*:277–312.

55. ROSSI, G. *Arch. Fisiol.*, 1912, *10:*389–399.
56. RUCH, T. C. Chap. 5 in *Handbook of experimental psychology*, S. S. STEVENS, ed. New York, John Wiley & Sons, 1951.
57. SNIDER, R. S. *Arch. Neurol. Psychiat. (Chic.)*, 1950, *64:*196–219.
58. SNIDER, R. S. and MAGOUN, H. W. *J. Neurophysiol.*, 1949, *12:*335–345.
59. SNIDER, R. S. and STOWELL, A. *J. Neurophysiol.*, 1944, *7:*331–357.
60. SPRAGUE, J. M. and CHAMBERS, W. W. *J. Neurophysiol.*, 1953, *16:*451–463.

61. SPRAGUE, J. M. and CHAMBERS, W. W. *Arch. ital. Biol.*, 1959, *97:*68–88.
62. THOMAS, D. M., KAUFMAN, R. P., SPRAGUE, J. M. and CHAMBERS, W. W. *J. Anal. (Lond.)*, 1956, *90:*371–385.
63. TOWE, A. L. and CASEY, K. L. *Physiologist*, 1959, *2:*22.
64. TYLER, D. B. and BARD, P. *Physiol. Rev.*, 1949, *29:*311–369.
65. WANG, S. C. and CHINN, H. I. *Amer. J. Physiol.*, 1956, *185:*617–623.
66. WIENER, N. *Cybernetics or control and communication in the animal and the machine.* New York, John Wiley & Sons, 1948.

SECTION IV

SENSORY FUNCTIONS OF THE NERVOUS SYSTEM

CHAPTER 14

Somatic Sensation

By THEODORE C. RUCH

INTRODUCTION

ALL knowledge comes to us through our sense organs. Our simplest motor acts are initiated through sense organs; our most complex ones are controlled by means of them. Pain is a matter of immediate interest in many clinical conditions, and testing other forms of somatic sensation is a considerable part of the neurologic examination. In the next chapter it will become clear that the distinction between sensation and perception is a valuable clue to the level of nervous system damage. Under the broad heading of sensation come complex phenomena which are immensely important to the individual experiencing them: hunger, nausea, vertigo, sexual sensations, feelings of fatigue, and a host of ill-defined discomforts originating in the deeper structures of the body. Many of these have only recently become the object of physiologic inquiry.

Sensation, Perception and Affect. A sensation has several parameters (dimensions) or attributes. The first of these is *quality,* the subjective difference which enables us to name sensations—warmth, cold, taste, etc. A sensory modality* or simply a "sense" often includes submodalities which may or may not blend into one another. Thus, red and green are submodalities of vision, and sweet and sour, of taste. Submodalities are unlike enough subjectively so that we give them different names. At each level from the sense organ to the cerebral cortex neurophysiologists seek to discover func-

---

* Modality is a traditional word of obscure meaning which is not greatly clarified by the dictionary. Perhaps the simplest synonym for "a modality of sensation" is simply "a kind of sensation."

tional and structural mechanisms underlying modalities and submodalities of sensation.

Intensity is obviously a fundamental parameter of sensation; without some finite strength of the stimulus, the subjective threshold is not exceeded and no sensation occurs.

Locus is a third basic parameter. A sensation appears to come from some part of the body or the external world (*projection,* see p. 315). How the brain can know locus is one of the problems that neurophysiologists are intensely investigating.

Pure sensation is an abstraction and probably occurs only the first time a baby experiences that sensation. Thereafter past experience, the blending of sensations, the comparison of one sensation with another, etc., transform sensation into perception: The fusion of cold and pressure yields a perception of wetness. A perception may involve simply a temporal pattern of a single modality.

The comparison of two stimuli simultaneously or successively presented in respect to intensity, quality or position is in psychological parlance a *judgment,* or in physiologic and clinical parlance a *discrimination.* The discrimination of spatial aspects of a stimulus, its location, size, shape, etc., is particularly important in clinical neurologic diagnosis and is discussed at length in this and the next chapter.

Finally, the subjective response to afferent impulses has another aspect. Besides the quality, intensity and locus of a sensation or perception, we feel that some sensations are pleasant, others unpleasant. Technically this aspect of sensation is known as *affect.* In certain neurologic disorders, the affect becomes more intense and the quality of sensation less vivid, suggesting different brain mechanisms for the two phenomena.

The preceding paragraphs are diagrammed in Figure 1.

In broad outline, knowledge of our environment involves: (i) the sensor–transducer function of the peripheral terminals of a sensory neuron, (ii) conduction along nerves and central tracts and transformation of signals at at least two synaptic stations, and (iii) appreciation of the quality, intensity, locus and affective quality of the stimulus and the combination of these data into recognition of the object. As pointed out in Chapter 4, the sense organs of the skin through the phenomenon of the adequate stimulus (or, better stated, because of the

property of differential sensitivity) analyze the energy flux between the environment and the skin. Nerve impulses carry this information to the cerebral cortex.

Determination and Classification of Sensory Modalities. Touch was, until nearly this century, treated as a single, unitary sense which appreciated many aspects of the stimulus object.[3] Thus, warmth or coldness, pressure, etc., were thought of as subqualities of the single sense of "feeling" or "touch." About 1890, it was discovered that the skin is not everywhere uniformly sensitive to all aspects of a stimulating object. If the skin is marked off in millimeter squares and systematically explored with very small objects—blunt (pressure), sharp (pain), warm and cold—it is found that some spots give rise to sensations of warmth but not of cold or pain, while others respond only to a cold stimulus and with a sensation of coldness; still other areas respond only with sensations of pressure or pain. Cutaneous sensibility is therefore *punctiform* or pointlike in its distribution. This was one of the fundamental experiments in the physiology of sensation. On the basis of such experiments, touch was easily divided into several separate senses—pressure or touch, warmth and cold.

The senses and sensory receptors are classified in several ways, all of which are useful. Since parts of each system are in common use, it is well to become familiar with all.

Sherrington's classification.[31] This classification of receptors is much used in physiologic literature and is based on the source of the stimulus and the location of the receptor. The proprioceptors, found in muscles, tendons and

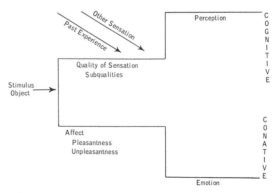

Fig. 1. Diagram of two aspects of the subjective consequences of a stimulus at two levels of psychological (or neural) complexity. Judgment is another step above perception.

joints, and in the labyrinth, give information concerning the movements and position of the body in space. The exteroceptors, of the skin, give information on changes in the immediate external environment. The interoceptors transmit impulses from the visceral organs. The teleceptors, or distance receptors, inform us of changes in the more remote environment, and are the sense organs of the eyes, ears and nose. (By usage, labyrinthine receptors are often not included in the proprioceptive group.)

Clinical classification of sensation. The clinical classification of sensation is strongly influenced by anatomy. The following list shows how the modalities of sensation are designated by clinicians; in the right-hand column a sample term to illustrate clinical terminology of the sensation and its disturbances is given.

I. *Special senses* served by the cranial nerves
   1. Vision . . . . Hemianopia
   2. Audition . . . . None
   3. Taste . . . . Ageusia
   4. Olfaction . . . . Anosmia
   5. Vestibular . . . . None
II. *Superficial or cutaneous sensations* served by the cutaneous branches of spinal and certain cranial nerves
   1. Touch–pressure . . . . .Hypesthesia
   2. Warmth . . . .⎱
   3. Cold . . . .⎰ Hypothermesthesia
   4. Pain . . . . .Hyperalgesia
III. *Deep sensations* served by muscular branches of spinal nerves and certain cranial nerves
   1. Muscle, tendon, and joint sensibility, or position sense . . . . .Bathesthesia
   2. (Deep pain)
   3. (Deep pressure)
IV. *Visceral sensations* served by fibers traversing the autonomic nervous system
   1. Organic sensation, e.g., hunger, nausea, etc.
   2. Visceral pain

The parentheses indicate that the position of deep pain and pressure in the scheme is anomalous. Thus, the phrase "deep sensation," as ordinarily used, does not include muscular pain and sometimes does not include deep pressure.

Other classifications. Sensory receptors are sometimes designated by the agent which most easily stimulates them, e.g., chemoreceptors, mechanoreceptors, etc. The term *nociceptors* was applied to pain receptors by Sherrington because they respond to a variety of stimuli which have in common the property of being noxious or damaging to the tissues. Finally, a useful dichotomy applicable to both motor and sensory phenomena is *somatic* and *visceral* for sensations arising in structures derived from the somatopleura and visceropleura, respectively. Somatic sensation (or *somesthesia*)

is a convenient name for superficial and deep sensation together.

Adequate Stimulus (Differential Sensitivity or Specificity). Traditionally, physiologists speak of the *law of the adequate stimulus* to describe the fact that sense organs typically have a low threshold for one form of energy though may be stimulated by other forms if sufficiently strong (Chap. 4). The use of the word "law" in this connection is unfortunate since, sometimes it is biologically useful to have a narrow band pass filter and for other biological functions a wide band pass, or funnel-like sensitivity may be desirable. It is therefore pertinent to inquire of each receptor the degree of specificity of its response to the energy spectrum. Some cutaneous sense organs are quite specific, others less so, but the truly nonspecific ending postulated as the end organ serving pain has escaped electrophysiologic variation.

It is important to make the distinction between the sense organ's sensitivity to various modes or intensity of energy and the ultimate ending and psychological effect in the brain. Also important is the distinction between physiologic and anatomic specificity of sense organs.

Whatever the mechanism of specificity, most sense organs respond differently to different forms of energy, analyzing the complex energy pattern of the external world, and translate them into a pattern of nerve impulses which are combined in the cerebral cortex to give an analog of the external world.

"Specific Nerve Energies" (Nonspecific Sense Organ Discharge). Complementary to the principle of the adequate stimulus is another law enunciated by Johannes Müller,[26] known as the "doctrine of specific nerve energies." Although a sense organ can be stimulated by other than its adequate stimulus, and a sensory system can be stimulated centrally, the *response* is of the same subjective quality regardless of *kind* of physical stimulus. Thus, the excitation of the visual system whether by pressure on the eye, by electrical stimulation or by irritative stimulation of the visual pathway (by a pathologic process) gives rise to *visual* sensation only. Müller's principle implies that the modality or submodality of sensation depends upon *what* end organ or *what* nerve fiber is stimulated and not upon what energy stimulated them. The phrase "specific nerve energy" was an unfortunate choice to convey the idea of a nonspecific sense organ discharge. Actually Müller favored the idea that the subjective quality distinguishing one sense modality from another or simply "modality specificity" is determined centrally, a concept subsequently supported by the elicitation of visual sensation by stimulation of the cortical visual area in conscious human patients and of somatic sensation by stimulation of the cortical somatosensory area. Müller's law is broadly analogous to a "place theory" in the language applied to the auditory system (see Chap. 18).

Coding and Pattern Theories.   In contrast to the idea of specifically sensitive endings and private lines (fiber coding) to specific cortical loci is a growing belief by some that spatial pattern of fibers and temporal (frequency) patterns determine *quality* of sensation. Weddell,[35, 36] who has demonstrated the profuse division and interdigitation of the originating branches of single axons and the absence of morphologic specialization of receptors in hairy skin and the artifactual nature of some complex endings in nonhairy regions, is the chief exponent of this point of view. Certainly some cutaneous sense organs are sensitive to more than one kind of energy; i.e., they are partially nonspecific. Weddell argues that all cutaneous organs could be nonspecific and by firing in different frequency or temporal patterns and in varying combinations with the endings of interdigitating axons could convey information of quality and locus to the brain, making unnecessary the concept of specific sense organs.

The simplest modality coding would be the firing of sense organs at different impulse frequencies in response to different energies. If these frequencies were preserved in ascending to the brain, they could be given different subjective interpretations. This would require only that the axon form a synaptic connection with a second order neuron that could respond only to a high frequency discharge and another that would respond only to a low frequency discharge. Such coding usurps the dimension usually allocated to intensity signaling. The specificity of end organs will be discussed in more detail later in this chapter.

Intensity.   The discharge from a field of sense organs is a quantity, the number of afferent axons times the frequency of firing. The latter, in turn, is proportional to the log of the stimulus strength. The importance of these two factors is different in rapidly adapting sense organs and those which maintain a plateau discharge. Gray[11] points out that the most sensitive and rapidly adapting mechanoreceptors in cat's pad may fire only once to an impact, which precludes frequency coding. In multifiber preparations there is a continuous relation between the number of fibers contributing to the action potential and the skin displacement by the stimulator. Fifty fibers were fired by a 20 μ displacement at a single point on the pad. The interdigitation of terminals (multiple innervation of a single spot) seems to be the means by which the strength of a stimulus to rapidly adapting fibers can be coded.

Conversely, in sense organs capable of yielding a steady discharge, frequency is available for coding the strength of stimulus, and the frequency is the log of the stimulus strength.

In passing through the synaptic junctions of the somatosensory pathways the logarithmic relationship of intensity to frequency is changed to a power function according to Mountcastle *et al.*,[25] who have measured the relationship between joint angle of a cat's limb and the firing rate of single cell in the thalamic nucleus which receives impulses from the deep-lying receptors. This finding correlates with some twenty years of research by psychologists on the relation between stimulus and sensation. Stevens and his co-workers[32] have amassed overwhelming evidence that the magnitude of sensation relates to intensity of stimulation not as a log function but as a power function:

$$\Psi = K \, \Phi^2$$

in which psychological magnitude (Ψ) is a constant times some power of the magnitude (Φ) of the physical stimulus. This is a rather unusual relationship between input and output in contrast to the law of diminishing returns represented by a logarithmic relationship. It is, however, extensively demonstrated, as seen in the next chapter.

Neurohistology   of   Cutaneous   Sensation.[12, 24, 35, 36, 37]   Hairy skin contains only fine free nerve endings and nerve baskets about the roots of the hair, and together these must serve touch, cold and warmth, once thought to be served by specialized encapsulated endings of various sorts. No encapsulated endings of any kind are found in hairy skin and the same is true of the cornea, which clearly is sensitive to both touch as well as pain.[23] Glabrous skin, such as the lips and finger tips, does contain in addition to free nerve endings encapsulated end-organs and "organized" endings made up of whorls of unmyelinated terminal fibers. That differential sensitivity is based on morphologic differentiation is now in doubt (i) because glabrous and adjacent hairy skin do not differ greatly in sensitivity and (ii) because the specialized endings do not, as once thought, fall into four morphologic categories corresponding to the four cutaneous senses, but present many gradations. Unencapsulated nerve endings connected with C-fibers can be specifically and exquisitely sensitive to cold, warmth and touch. Functions ascribed to the capsule of an end-organ where it exists are now viewed quite differently. For example, the capsule of the pacinian corpuscle may not give the sensory ending specificity and sensitivity, as once thought, but rather protection from strong stimuli.

A free nerve ending is formed by the repeated dichotomizing of an axis cylinder, which loses its medullary sheath, but not the sheath of Schwann until the very end. The fine naked branches of the axis cylinder ramify among the cells of the deeper layers of the epidermis; other free nerve endings are found subepidermally. Knowledge of these terminations comes from intravital staining with methylene blue. The free nerve endings are not disposed in the skin like trees in the forest with trunks widely separated and branches touching; instead, the arrangement is pseudoplexiform. The ramifications of a parent axon are said to interconnect and form a true nerve net. Nets derived from different parent axons overlap, interdigitate, but do not form a syncytium; i.e., they are not interconnected protoplasmically. Nerve fibers from the superficial plexus branch repeatedly over a wide area and end in fine, unmyelinated, beaded terminals disposed beneath and among the cells of the deeper layers of the epidermis. The type of ending associated with hairs exhibits a similar interdigitating pattern. An afferent axon may serve 100 hairs scattered over several square centimeters of skin and, conversely, a single hair is served by 2 to 20 axons. More organized receptors in hairless skin also receive multiple innervation.

The ramifications of an axon can be followed to some degree histologically, but electrophysiologic studies are more certain.

Receptive Fields. Tower[33] in 1940 first mapped the *receptive field* of a single afferent axon. A single fiber of a long ciliary nerve was discharged by stimuli applied over an area forming roughly a quadrant of the cornea and the adjacent sclera and conjunctiva. The receptive fields for different axons varied between 50 and 200 sq. mm. The branches of a single axon can be followed anatomically over areas of this size.[35] Within this field there were, of course, silent points, and stimulation of these would sometimes cause a different sensory fiber to discharge.

The receptive field of a single afferent fiber for light brushing of the skin of the cat's leg varied between 2 by 2 mm. to 18 by 10 mm.[34] Single axons (3 to 11 μ) connected with an ending sensitive to pin prick but not light touch yield larger zones, 3 by 3 mm. on foot pad and ten times larger on hairy areas. In all cases the receptive field was round or oval (with the long axis running down the leg), and was never irregular or patchy. A receptive field for the axon, as Tower first showed, is not uniformly sensitive but exhibits a spatial gradient. In passing from the center to the periphery, the threshold is higher, the latency is longer by as much as 5 milliseconds, and the discharge less prolonged. The ending studied was rapidly adapting and connected with axons conducting at the average rate of about 75 meters per second.

The receptive field gradient obtained for unmyelinated fibers whose endings respond to weak mechanical stimulation and yield a steady discharge is even more striking. The latency at the center of the field was 15 to 35 milliseconds and at the periphery 270 milliseconds. Presumably some type of summation between branches of axons underlies the receptive field gradient, but the mechanism of such summation is unknown. For the possible significance of the response gradient in localization of a stimulus see the next chapter.

The size of the receptive field is an additional method for categorizing different kinds of sensory inputs.

Free Nerve Endings Associated with C-Fibers.[7, 8, 21] The free nerve endings—unassociated with hair follicles—and their small unmyelinated C-fibers, once considered to respond only to strong damaging stimuli and to subserve pain, play a much greater potential role in sensation. This was first shown by Douglas and Ritchie in an experiment in which the impulses in large-diameter, low-threshold fibers are caused to collide, leaving a C-fiber volley to reach the recording electrodes (see Fig. 2 for explanation). By this method it was proved that the endings of many C-fibers in skin nerves respond to stimuli of the most innocuous character, e.g., brushing the skin with absorbent cotton. At somewhat greater pressure with the cotton swab a second, slower C-wave occurs. Similarly, temperature decreases of 3 °C. caused a C-fiber discharge and a fall of 10 °C., less intense than a painful cold stimulus, activated three-quarters of the C-fibers. Knowledge of the C-fiber ending's behavior was increased by studying single axons from them electrophysiologically. Iggo[21] succeeded in recording from single C-axons (conducting at 0.6 to 1.4 meters per second) by incredibly skillful "cutting down" techniques. In agreement with the results of Douglas and Ritchie, levels of stimulation far less than those which would be expected to arouse pain induced impulses in C-fibers. All C-fibers cannot, therefore, subserve

pain; some are clearly cold (and others warm) fibers, judged by the criteria of threshold and specificity.[23]

Some single C-fibers responded to more than one form of energy, again at levels not likely to produce pain and considerably below those responses in myelinated fibers for energies other than the adequate stimulus. In fact, the requisite stimulus intensity was little below that of the specific receptor served by large unmyelinated fibers. In contrast to A-fibers, C-fibers have slow firing rates and tend to respond for long periods after cessation of the stimulus (after discharge). While most C-fiber endings responded to some kind of innocuous stimuli, such as slight hair displacement or light pressure on the skin, some responded only to strong (? painful) stimuli.

It is, of course, not known from animal experiments whether the C-fiber equipped with wide band-pass endings transmits impulses to the brain resulting in conscious sensation. However, there is presumptive evidence that it does.

SOMATIC SENSES

Temperature Senses.[38] Rather than a single temperature sense there are two: one for cold and one for warmth. Three pieces of evidence support this statement: (i) The skin contains receptors which fire more rapidly as the temperature increases and others which fire more rapidly as the temperature decreases. (ii) There is a clear subjective difference between warmth and cold. (iii) Temperature sensibility is distributed in a punctate or "spotty" fashion. When the skin is explored millimeter by millimeter, spots (or more accurately, small areas) are found which respond only with a sensation of cold (Fig. 3). Other spots, fewer in number, respond only to warmth, and the intervening areas are sensitive to neither. On the forearm, cold spots average about 13 to 15 per square centimeter and warm spots only one or two per square centimeter. It was once believed that beneath each type of spot lay a distinctive type of end-organ. Failure to prove this by mapping spots and identifying histologically an underlying sense organ early cast doubt on the morphologic specificity of sense organs. Thus, the areal nature of the cold and warm spots suggested that a highly branching fiber or group of fibers serves the temperature receptors. It has

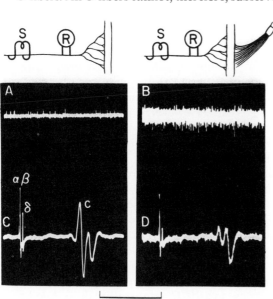

Fig. 2. Action potentials of myelinated and unmyelinated fibers of a sensory nerve twig before (*A*) and after (*B*) skin was stroked with cotton gauze. In *C* and *D* the unit nerve impulses seen in *A* and *B* have been shunted out so that the C wave is emphasized and the alpha, beta and delta waves (seen at left of each record) are reduced; also an antidromic volley was sent down the nerve to collide with the impulses in it. Note that the C wave of the antidromic volley in *C* is greatly reduced by collision after stroking. (After Douglas and Ritchie. *J. Physiol.*, 1957, *139*:385–399.)

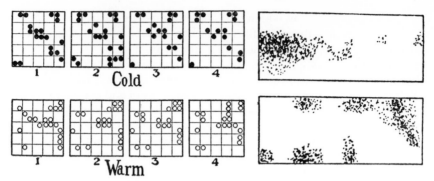

Fig. 3. Maps of thermal sensitivity of skin. *Left:* Results of four successive mappings (left to right) of same area on upper arm. Each small square equals 4 mm.² Observe high degree of similarity in independent mappings and that sensitive spots occur in groups. (From Dallenbach, *Amer. J. Psychol.,* 1927, *39:*402–427.) *Right:* Maps of distribution of sensibility to cold in 12 mappings of an area on volar surface of forearm. Each rectangle corresponds to area on skin 4 by 10 mm., and each represents a different subject. Subjects were permitted to report neutral and three degrees of coldness. Score for each point is crudely given by depth of shading. (From Jenkins, *J. exp. Psychol.,* 1939, *25:*373–388.)

since been proved that only branching, free nerve endings are found in the spaces between hair shafts.

Whether there is a morphologically specialized temperature ending even in hairless skin and mucous membranes is also doubtful. The

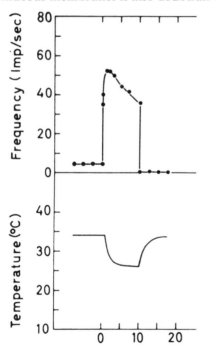

Fig. 4. Frequency of discharge of a single "cold fiber" (upper) in man and the cutaneous temperature (lower), both plotted against time in seconds. Note that the response has a much higher frequency to a smaller temperature change than in the next figure. (From Hensel and Bosman, *J. Neurophysiol.,* 1960, *23:* 564–568.)

strongest evidence for a specialized cold ending, Krause's end bulb, has been disproved. (The evidence for the warmth ending of Ruffini was never strong.) What were long thought to be Krause's end bulbs in the conjunctivum are seen in number only in older persons and are believed by Weddell[35] to be regenerating fibers which have met an obstruction, proliferated and twisted to form so called *sterile end bulbs* like those found in the proximal stumps of divided nerves. It appears certain that in hairless skin no encapsulated or specialized organs exist. However, it must be remembered that *the absence of a microscopic anatomic specificity does not disprove functional specificity.* For example, the threshold energy for warmth sensation is one-thousandth of that for heat-induced pain, though both are served by free nerve endings.

Some skin receptors served by myelinated fibers are sensitive only to cooling—the classic cold receptor (Fig. 4). In man,[17] as in the cat, they respond to lowered temperature with a large increase in firing rate, specifically in man an increase of 45 impulses per second in response to a 10°C. temperature drop. Another and perhaps more numerous group exhibit both mechanical and temperature sensibility (Fig. 5). They are, however, only weakly responsive to cooling, the discharge increase being about one-ninth that of a specific cold receptor. Because they respond vigorously to pressure, they can be classed as mechanoreceptors with some cold receptive ability. They differ from other mechanoreceptors by firing spontaneously at neutral skin temperature in the absence of

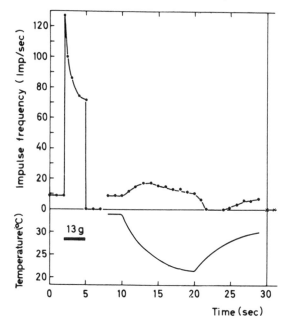

Fig. 5. A plot of discharge frequency of a non-specific, mechanothermal sensitive sense organ in man. Contrast the high frequency response to pressure (13 g) left to the low frequency discharge to large drop in temperature (nearly 20° C.) at the right. (From Hensel and Bosman, *J. Neurophysiol.*, 1960, *23*:564–568.)

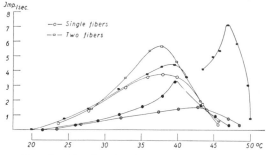

Fig. 6. Graphs showing relation between frequency of discharge and temperature for different single and dual warm fiber preparations. Steady discharge after adaptation has occurred is graphed. An occasional fiber (one in 13) had a maximum above 45° C. and was undoubtedly a heat fiber. (From Dodt and Zotterman, *Acta physiol. scand.,* 1952, *26*:345–357.)

known mechanical stimulation. Their role in sensation is unknown. Their existence may explain why a cold object resting on the palm of the hand seems heavier than a warm one of the same size and weight (Weber's illusion).

The less numerous warmth fiber has not yet been identified electrophysiologically in man but has been in animals (see Fig. 6). Moreover, a "heat" receptor has been discovered by Iggo. It is excitable by radiant heat. As seen in Figure 6, it starts firing in the range at which the warmth fibers are decreasing their firing rate and above that at which tissue damage starts. Figure 7 shows increased frequencies of response with high temperature. It is sufficiently heat specific to demarcate it from the postulated nonspecific nociceptive receptor. It may, however, contribute to a subjective pain response as well as serve thermal sensibility, which persists after blocking of myelinated fibers.

In the cat, dog and rat highly sensitive cold and warm fibers conducting with C-fiber velocity are abundant. Responses to a temperature decrease of 0.3° C. have been detected in single fiber preparations and three-quarters of C-fibers respond at 10° C. A "cold" C-fiber can main-

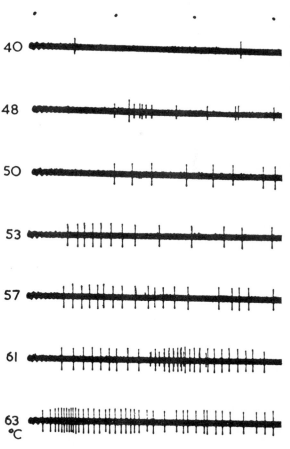

Fig. 7. Responses in a C-fiber (1 meter per second conduction velocity) when a heated brass rod was applied to the skin. The discharge at 40° and 48° C. save one are from a nearby mechanoreceptor; the rod alone did not stimulate the "heat" receptor. The dots at the top give time in seconds. (From Iggo, *Quart. J. exp. Physiol.,* 1959, *44*:362–370.)

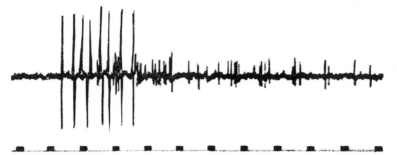

Fig. 8. Oscillographic record from a "cut-down" lingual nerve showing a volley of large fiber potentials (touch) and of small fiber potentials (cold). Stimulus was a current of air strong enough to deform surface of tongue visibly. (From Zotterman, *Skand. Arch. Physiol.*, 1936, *75*:105–120.)

tain steady firing at a temperature as high as 38°C.[22] However, in the monkey, which is expected to be more like man, only a few such fibers are found (Iggo[22]). Fibers highly cold-sensitive (0.5° C. threshold) conduct at rates of 3.6 to 15 meters per second and hence are among the smallest myelinated fibers. They maintain a discharge in response to a sustained temperature drop and are not stimulated by the usual mechanical stimuli. They originate in a single, restricted spot on the skin and have a small receptive field measuring 0.25 to 0.6 sq. mm.

These experiments agree with nerve-block experiments on man showing that most, though not all, impulses underlying thermal sensation are conducted in myelinated fibers.

Contrary to past teachings, there are no morphologically specialized endings for thermal receptors either in smooth or hairy skin. Regardless of the lack of morphologic specificity, physiologically specific receptors have been found for which the adequate stimulus is: cold but not warmth or heat, warmth but not cold or heat, or heat alone. However, a receptor which responds strongly to pressure and weakly to cold is fairly commonly encountered in man. Extrapolation from experiments on the monkey suggests that C-fiber involvement in combined thermal and mechanical sensitivity is not a major factor in man.

The adequate stimulus for both warmth and cold is heat. Cold is not a positive quantity, and temperature does not have the dimension of energy. The threshold stimulus for cold receptors is a fall in temperature at the rate of 0.004°C. per second and, for warmth receptors, a rise of 0.001°C. per second, both continuing for three seconds.[22] The thermal sense organs record not the temperature of objects, but the temperature of the skin at the depth at which the receptors are situated. Hence they are stimulated by internal heat as well as by the

heat of the environment. The patient with Raynaud's disease who experiences a vasospasm in the fingers complains bitterly of the cold even in a warm room. A metal object and a wooden object of the same temperature do not seem equally cold to the touch because the metal object conducts heat from the skin more readily. A most important factor is the temperature of the skin. Objects having a temperature close to the physiologic zero, i.e., the temperature of the skin, elicit neither warmth nor cold sensations. On the other hand, even warm air falling on the warmer skin during fever arouses distressing sensations of cold. Since thermal sense organs play a role in the regulation of body temperature, it is important to know the exact nature of the temperature stimulus.

Hensel and Zotterman[38] recorded "cold" impulses from the lingual nerve along with the surface and intracutaneous temperature of the tongue during cooling with cold water (Fig. 8). A drop in water temperature from 37° to 13°C. caused a maximum discharge within one to two seconds which fell exponentially to a plateau rate of 25 impulses per second in about 70 seconds, at which time the temperature at the level of the receptor was no longer changing. Such steady discharges were recorded after 70 minutes of cooling. Thus, while temperature change is a powerful stimulus to the rapidly adapting cold receptor, it is not a necessary condition for stimulation, since discharge to steadily maintained cooling occurred. The actual stimulus therefore is either a temperature gradient (energy flow) from within out or the absolute temperature. The latter would imply that excitation depends on some internal physiologic process, such as a chemical reaction, inversely dependent on temperature. The direction of temperature gradient and heat flow is of no importance. From experiments comparing responses from one surface of the tongue when comparable gradients from within out were maintained during cooling of first the upper and then the lower surface, Hensel and Zotterman[38] concluded that temperature *per se* rather than a temperature gradient is the actual stimulus to the cold receptor. By combining frequency of firing and recruitment, as few as ten cold fibers can show a linear relation of impulses per second to temperature between 38° and 27° C.[38]

Touch–Pressure. Touch is one of the four fundamental cutaneous sense modalities. Whether touch forms a single sense modality, like warmth or cold, or whether there are subqualities, served by distinct neural mechanisms, is uncertain. That there are several functional types of mechanoreceptors is certain.

The existence of at least two physiologically specific mechanoreceptors was first proved by Adrian and Zotterman[1] by recording action potentials from single cutaneous fibers while stimulating the skin. One receptor was rapidly adapting, the discharge lasting only 0.2 second to a sustained touch, and the second was slowly adapting, maintaining after an initial period of rapid adaptation, a sustained discharge for many seconds. It is now possible to describe these receptors from similar studies conducted on monkey skin, both hairy and glabrous, and from heroic experiments on man.

The rapidly adapting receptors which fire only while the skin is being touched or a hair is being bent have a low threshold (5 to 20 mg. tested by von Frey hairs), are connected with myelinated fibers (2 to 8 μ from hairy skin and 6 to 11 μ from smooth skin) and have large receptive fields, 1.5 to 5 sq. cm. at threshold. In man, bending a hair by 5°, which is the sensory threshold, may elicit only one impulse. Some receptors are temperature-sensitive, but they give only three to five responses to a large and rapid decrease of the skin's temperature and are therefore classed as mechanoceptors. The rapidly adapting fibers from smooth skin have higher thresholds and are unaffected by temperature.

The second touch receptor discovered by Adrian and Zotterman has been found in man.[17] After an initial period of rapid adaptation, it maintains a steady discharge with little further decrease in frequency. The plateau frequency is related to amount of pressure and attains rates as high as 330 impulses per second. The pressure which will just discharge the end-organ is in the same range as the sensory threshold of the same region. The receptor does not fire spontaneously or in response to cooling and its steady response to pressure is unaffected by temperature. It has a spotlike receptive field of about 1 to 2 mm. in diameter in hairy and adjacent nonhairy skin. In the monkey, Iggo[22] finds a receptor similar in its spotlike distribution and firing characteristic. Its afferent fibers are large, in the 6 to 9 μ range. It is a specific mechanoreceptor. In the cat, 64 of 77 fibers examined were fired either from one or from two spots, the spots being usually within 1 to 5 mm. of each other even when a cluster of 3 to 8 spots fired a single axon.[20]

A nonspecific skin receptor of man[17] differs by being sensitive to cooling as well as to pressure, by discharging spontaneously at a low rate (one impulse per second) and having a maximal discharge rate which is a fraction of that attained by the specific touch receptor. In the monkey[22] this receptor has fieldlike distribution leading to afferent fibers 5 to 13 μ in diameter. Receptors with a fieldlike distribution found in glabrous skin are similar except that the threshold is higher by 5 to 20 times.

The sensory response to these nonspecific receptors is thought to be a touch–pressure sensation. While the functional significance of sensitivity to both cold and pressure is not known, it is suggestive that impulses arising from such receptors appear to enter ascending sensory systems having characteristics which can be broadly termed "nonspecific."

Pain. The sensory mechanism for pain is in many ways unique. The sensory end-organs for pain are spread through virtually all of the tissues of the body, so that three kinds of pain are recognized and designated: (i) superficial or cutaneous pain; (ii) deep pain from muscles, tendons, joints, and fascia; and (iii) visceral pain. The first two together form somatic pain. The pain endings are unique also in exhibiting only to a limited degree the phenomenon of the adequate stimulus. Several kinds of energy are adequate to elicit pain—electrical, mechanical, extremes of heat and cold, and a wide variety of chemical stimuli. The pain ending therefore is not specialized to react to a single form of energy, but reacts to extreme degrees of several kinds of stimulation. Sherrington pointed out that the property common to all stimuli adequate to excite pain endings is the threat of damage to the tissues. Hardy *et al.*[13] have proved this quantitatively for heat energy. Thus, increasing degrees of heat first stimulate warmth endings and then, at 44.9°C., commence to stimulate pain endings. At about 44° to 45°C., irreversible damage to the skin, demonstrable histologically, occurs, and accompanying release of chemical substances such as

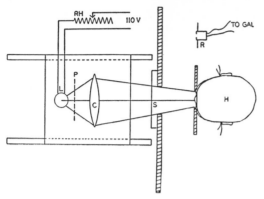

Fig. 9. Radiant energy apparatus for measuring warmth and pain sensibility. Light from 1000 watt lamp, *L,* is focused by condensing lens, *C,* through fixed aperture of 3.5 sq. mm. on forehead of subject, which is blacked by India ink. Intensity of radiation is controlled by means of rheostat, *RH,* and duration by shutter, *P,* which automatically limits exposure to 3 seconds. Shutter, *S,* is hand-operated. (From Hardy et al., *J. clin. Invest.,* 1940, *19*:649–657.)

histamine is expected. One explanation of the wide stimulus spectrum of the pain end-organ is that various noxious stimuli release a chemical substance in the skin and that this substance stimulates the end-organs. The evidence for this will be presented in the next chapter under the heading *Hyperalgesia.*

In Sherrington's classification of the senses, pain was termed *nociceptive,* meaning sensitive to noxious agents. The function of the pain sense is protective, whereas the other modalities of sensation are primarily informative or gnostic. Other differences are that pain is unpleasant or, in other words, possesses a considerable *affect;* that pain leads to more precipitate action; and, finally, that certain types of pain tend to radiate and to be poorly localized.

Because pain is so unlike other forms of sensation, it was long considered not a separate form of sensation but rather a response elicited by intense stimulation of other kinds of sensory end-organs. This overstimulation or intensive theory is refuted by considerable evidence, including the fact that stimulation of certain areas causes only pain. That overstimulation of touch and pressure organs does not cause pain was proved by Cattell and Hoagland.[5] Intense stimulation of an end-organ increases the frequency of its discharge. Stimulating the skin of a frog with puffs of air at a high frequency produced high rates of discharge (300 per second). When such stimuli were applied to an unanesthetized frog, it exhibited no sign of pain.

MEASUREMENT OF PAIN SENSIBILITY. For purposes of clinical examination, pain is elicited by pricking the skin with a pin or needle. The subject reports whether the pricks "feel" different on the two sides of the body, or he is asked to distinguish between the point and the head of a pin. Thresholds can be determined more quantitatively with a thistle glued to a von Frey hair (see below). In such tests touch receptors are stimulated along with the pain receptors, and the results are not sufficiently quantitative.

Hardy et al.[15] employed radiant heat (Fig. 9) in increasing intensities to obtain a threshold for pain. If precautions are taken to ensure that skin temperature is stabilized, or its variations corrected for, thresholds of a single individual are remarkably invariable. As with cold sensation, pain from radiant heat seems to depend on actual skin temperature and not on the rate of change. In contrast with other sensory channels, the threshold is not dependent on size of area stimulated. Spatial summation between fibers supplying a given area, or between the branches of a single fiber, apparently does not occur. Hardy et al.[16] found that they could discriminate only 21 steps (j.n.d.) between threshold and maximum pain, and the range of energy was little more than 2:1. The grossness of the j.n.d. is experimental justification for speaking of pain as a nondiscriminative modality of sensation.

Visceral pain, deep pain and special forms of pain are discussed in Chapter 16.

For many decades the nociceptive receptor was thought to be a free nerve ending responsive to several forms of energy if sufficiently strong and connected with unmyelinated or the smallest unmyelinated axons. Despite the ability to record from such axons in cutaneous nerve it has not been possible to identify electrophysiologically a pain ending responsive to a variety of stimuli and *only* at strong intensities. Among the endings innervated by C-fibers are some that have the required high threshold such as the so-called "hot" fibers or those sensitive only to pricking or squeezing the skin but not to light touch. An occasional fiber is found which is sensitive to both extreme cold and heat. However, all these are too modality-specific to qualify as the hypothetical wide bandpass pain receptor. The free nerve endings connected with C-fibers, so abundant and so suited to reception of noxious stimuli of several kinds have other occupations (touch, warmth, cold reception) and can no longer be associated exclusively with pain. Pain is a sensory modality in search of a sense organ.

Deep Sensibility. Although one gives it little thought, a person with closed eyes knows the direction of a movement, active or passive, and is aware of the position of his arms and legs. It was not until 1826 that Charles Bell[3] explicitly described the "sixth" sense—muscle sense. "For example," he said, "between the brain and the muscles, there is a circle of nerves; one nerve conveys the influence from the brain to the muscle; the other gives the sense of the condition of the muscle to the brain." The forms of deep sensibility exclusive of pain and deep pressure are known by several synonyms, all of which are in common use: muscle sense or, more completely, muscle, tendon and joint sensibility; kinesthesia (Bastian); proprioception (Sherrington); and, operationally and clinically, position sense and the appreciation of passive movement (Head). Some, for inadequate semantic reasons, prefer kinesthesia (sense of movement) to proprioception (or self knowledge) because the receptors from joints seem more important to cortical awareness of passive movement of the limb or the position in space than are the muscle receptors, originally implicated by Goldscheider.

Four types of sense organs are found in muscles, tendons and joints: (i) the muscle spindle; (ii) the Golgi tendon organ; (iii) the joint organs, the pacinian corpuscle, etc.; and (iv) free nerve endings. The analysis previously presented suggests that muscle, tendon and joint receptors as a group record three aspects of the state of the muscle: active contraction, passive stretch (length of fiber) and tension, whether produced by passive stretch or active contraction.

Browne *et al.*[4] found that application of procaine to the joint capsule ends the appreciation of passive movement of the metatarsal-phalangeal joint and appreciation of the position of the great toe in space. Significant clinically is the fact that some normal subjects appreciated only very large displacements (10 to 30 degrees). Impairment of the appreciation of passive movement, whether occurring naturally or induced by application of procaine to the capsule, was not associated with any defect in appreciation of active movement. The former function is capsular; the latter is muscular or tendinous. The joint capsule contains end-organs of the nonadapting type which vary the discharge rate according to joint position.

THE NEUROLOGIC EXAMINATION OF SENSATION

So far, sensory function has been discussed mainly from a biologic point of view with brief mention of how it is examined clinically. In the following pages are described normal psychological processes of a higher order, relating them to the sensory examination of neurologic patients.

Clinical Examination of Deep Sensibility. Deep pressure and deep pain are elicited by firm, massive pressure over muscles or tendons. Muscles and tendons possess an exquisite pain sensibility; this is discussed in a subsequent chapter.

The "appreciation of passive movement" of a single joint is commonly tested in the neurologic examination. If a finger or toe is grasped by the side (to minimize cues from pressure) and moved up or down, a patient with normal sensibility states the direction of quite small angular displacements. A roughly quantitative estimate of the threshold can thus be obtained.

The "sense of position" is tested in a variety of ways. A limb is placed in an unusual position and the patient, with eyes closed, is asked to duplicate the posture with his other limb. Another maneuver—the finger-to-finger test—consists of passively moving the arm to be tested and bringing it to rest with finger extended. The patient is then asked to touch the extended forefinger with the forefinger of the other hand. By interposing a piece of cardboard between the two fingers and marking their positions, a quantitative estimate of the error can be obtained. Recently, another method for quantitation of position sense was described by Cohen[6] (Fig 10). In animals something akin to the sense of position is tested by determining whether a false or abnormal position—not extreme enough to be painful—is corrected, a test which is valid only when motor ability is normal. A similar procedure applicable to animals is the "proprioceptive placing" reaction (Chap. 9).

The appreciation of muscle tension is studied by determining the ability to detect difference in weight of objects by lifting them. Two weights are usually presented, and the subject is asked to state which is the heavier. This classic laboratory procedure in psychology has proved useful in studying neurologic patients and has been adapted to monkeys and chimpanzees in the study of cortical localization of sensory functions.

Vibratory Sensibility. The appreciation of vibration, or pallesthesia, is tested crudely by placing the base of a vibrating tuning fork upon the skin. A thrill or feeling of vibration is normally experienced, but only a sense of continuous contact is felt in the presence of certain neurologic lesions. Electrically driven vibratory devices yield thresholds in terms of the just perceptible amplitude of vibration. The greatest sensibility occurs at 200 to 400 cycles per second and can be as low as 0.064 μ displacement.[29] Vibratory sensibility is often erroneously considered a separate sense modality rather than a special excitation of the sense organs for pressure and possibly proprioception. Because application of the fork over bone intensifies the stimulus in a purely mechanical fashion, vibratory sensation has been mistakenly called "osseous sensation." The lowest threshold is found not over bone but on the finger tips. Vibratory sensibility has a punctate distribution with vibration-sensitive spots corresponding to pressure-sensitive spots. Deep sense organs are also involved. In fact, the deep-lying pacinian corpuscle is especially suited for the detection of vibration, following one-for-one in the range from 150 to above 700 cycles per second, rates at which no other somatic end-organ can follow.[19] (The pa-

cinian corpuscle cannot follow below 150 because of its rapid adaptation.) The presence of pacinian corpuscles in interosseous membranes and other structures related to bone may contribute to making regions over bone especially sensitive to vibration.

Vibratory sensibility is certainly not a separate sense. It is certainly not bone sensibility, nor does it seem to be associated exclusively with either deep or superficial pressure receptors. Vibratory sensibility is a perception of a temporal pattern of pressures, somewhat like the flicker phenomenon in vision (Chap. 20). This interpretation is supported by the behavior of vibratory sensibility in various clinical neurologic conditions.

The underlying impulses must be conducted in the posterior columns of the spinal cord since defective vibratory appreciation is typical of spinal cord lesions but surgical section of the anterolateral columns leaves it unimpaired. If spinal cord damage is sufficient to affect position sense, vibratory appreciation is always affected. In contrast, lesions of the cerebral cortex rarely affect vibratory sensibility unless they penetrate deeply; in such cases damage to the thalamus may be responsible (Fig. 11). Though not subject to any simple explanation, this difference in vulnerability of vibratory sensitivity at the spinal and cerebral levels makes vibratory sensibility helpful in clinical diagnosis.

The vibratory sensibility changes with age, beginning to diminish at or just about fifty years. It is an accurate indicator of sensory loss in diabetes and pernicious anemia.

Localization or Topognosis.[3] Every somatic sensation has in addition to its quality and its intensity a localization upon the body surface. The accuracy of localization has been extensively investigated in both normal persons and neurologic patients. Weber (1852) touched the skin with a pointer dipped in powdered charcoal to mark the point stimulated; the subject, with his eyes closed throughout, tried to touch the same spot with another pointer. The measured discrepancy between the two marks gave the error of localization, which was found to vary greatly in different regions of the body surface.

Usually only localization of light pressure is tested clinically; it is sometimes forgotten that all sensations can be localized, though with quite different accuracy. (The explanation for this will be given in the next chapter.) Localiza-

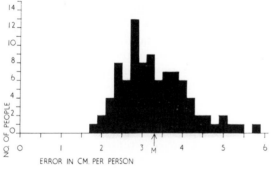

Fig. 10. Accuracy of position sense in 91 normal young adults. Subjects touched with forefinger a reference point on a target at arm's length. After closing eyes and returning arm to side, subjects attempted to touch the point again. Test was repeated until 48 different points were tried. *Abscissa,* mean error on 48 points. (From Cohen, *J. Neurophysiol.,* 1958, *21*:550–562.)

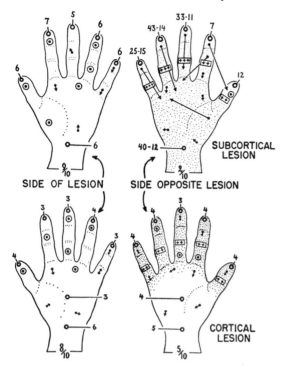

Fig. 11. Example of Fox's chart used for recording sensory examination of neurologic patients with subcortical (*upper*) and cortical lesions (*lower*). Degree of loss of position sense in phalangeal joint is indicated by +, + + and + + +; accurate localization of point touched is designated by circle and dot; displacement of an erroneous localization is indicated by arrow. Areas of hypesthesia are indicated by stipple. Fraction at wrist is a measure of stereognosis and shows number of successfully identified objects in series of ten presenting increasing difficulty. Numbers connected by line with heavy circle give threshold of vibration in arbitrary unit at point indicated; a large number signifies large amplitude of vibration. (After Fox and Klemperer, *Arch. Neurol. Psychiat. (Chic.)*, 1942, *48*:622–645.)

tion may be severely impaired by damage to central pathways when mere awareness of the stimulation is preserved. Testing topognosis is, therefore, part of the neurologic examination (Fig. 11).

Projection of Sensation. This is a phenomenon related to localization.* The ultimate event in the sensory process occurs in the brain, but in no case are we aware of this. On the contrary, our sensations are projected either to the

---

*The distinction between projection and localization is that the former has more to do with the envelope or layer, external or internal, from which a sensation appears to come. Localization has more to do with where on these envelopes the sensation is localized (see Chap. 16).

external world or to some peripheral organ in the body, i.e., to the place where experience has taught us that the acting stimulus arises. Sound seems to come from the bell, light from the lamp, etc. Pain, muscle sense, labyrinthine sensations, hunger, thirst, sexual sense, etc., are projected to the interior of the body. The temperature senses may be projected either to the air or to the skin, according to circumstances.

An aspect of sensation important to clinical neurology and which deserves to be called the *law of projection* is that stimulation of sensory pathways at any point central to the sense organ gives rise to a sensation which is projected to the periphery and not to the point of stimulation.

Numerous examples of this law can be cited. An amputee may experience projected sensations so elaborate that they amount to a feeling that the limb is still present and executing movements, often painful—the phenomenon of "phantom limb." Irritation of a dorsal spinal root by a ruptured intervertebral disc of the fifth lumbar segment often gives rise to a sensation of pain over the buttock and down the back of the thigh, which is the region innervated by the affected root. Stimulation of the cerebral cortex in conscious human patients at the time of intracranial operation gives rise to sensations which appear to come not from the head but from the skin of some part of the body. In all these cases the cerebral cortex interprets the nerve impulses as though they had come from the sense organ. For further implications of the phenomenon of projection, see the section on referred pain (Chap. 16).

Two Point Sensibility. If the blunt points of a compass are applied simultaneously to the skin with sufficient distance between them, they are perceived as two separate points of contact. If the points are brought progressively closer together in successive applications, they eventually give rise to a sensation of a single point applied to the skin. The smallest distance between points at which they are still perceived as two separate contacts is the *two point threshold*. A two point threshold can be determined for all forms of sensation, but only thresholds for light pressure and occasionally pain (prick) are tested clinically. The two point threshold is a smaller distance for touches than for warmth or cold stimuli. The ability of the skin to resolve two points is only one three-thousandths of that of the eye. Regional differences are pronounced (Fig. 12) and broadly parallel the accuracy of localization. They do not, however, parallel regional variations in the intensity threshold. In

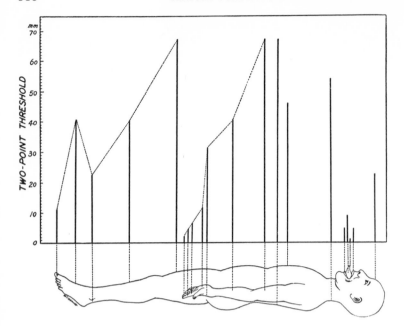

Fig. 12. Regional variation in two point threshold for touch. Length of vertical lines is approximately equal to magnitude of two point threshold. (Data from Weber cited by Sherrington in Schäfer, *Text-book of physiology*. Edinburgh, Young J. Pentland, 1900.)

the neurologic examination corresponding areas on both sides of the body must be tested.

Size, Shape, Figure Writing, Etc. The ability of the cutaneous and proprioceptive sensory systems to appreciate the spatial aspect of objects is demonstrable by a variety of simple maneuvers. Objects of graded size, such as coins, placed successively in the hand are discriminated. The direction and length of a line drawn upon the skin are recognized. Touch and pressure are mainly responsible for such discrimination. Geometric patterns of warmth produced without contact (radiation) are virtually unrecognizable. Perhaps the most convenient test of the spatial aspect of skin sensibility is the "figure writing" test introduced by Foerster. While the patient's eyes are closed, numerals between 0 and 9 are written on his palm or another smooth surface of his body with a blunt, pointed object, using a slow, even movement. Although mistakes are rarely made by a normal person after the first few trials, certain neurologic patients do little better than chance. The manner of recording the observation is as follows:

As written	1	2	7	4	8	6	9	5	3	0
As reported	1	2	6	3–2	6	6	1	7	7	0

Figure writing, left hand. J. P., a white youth aged 18. Tests were conducted subsequent to a right occipital craniotomy which disclosed an aneurysm of the posterior cerebral artery with a hemorrhagic cyst in the anterior portion of the occipital lobe. The resection included the midportion of the posterior parietal lobe.

STEREOGNOSIS. The appreciation of the form of three-dimensional objects by palpation without the aid of vision is termed *stereognosis* or the knowledge of (geometric) solids. A key, a coin or a pencil may serve as a test object— "recognition of common objects." A series of standardized objects or geometric forms of graded difficulty, as employed by Fox (Fig. 11), is desirable because it allows a rough quantitative statement of ability. Stereognosis is not a "sense" despite the common clinical usage. It is a complex perception or concept based upon the synthesis of the several modalities of somatic sensation.

Touch and kinesthesis perhaps yield the most information, but all senses may be involved. For example, the roundness of a cyclinder is recognized by the even pressure on the pulp of the fingers when it is rolled, kinesthetic sense giving information on the diameter and weight of the object. It is soon appreciated that the object rolls in one direction but not the other. As the finger slides along the smooth surface, an end is discovered which proves to be a flat, smooth surface, the circular border of which confirms the original impression. And when the identical impression is gained from the opposite end, the data are synthesized into the conclusion that the object is a cylinder. Additional data with regard to smoothness and temperature complete its recognition as a metal cylinder.

It is not difficult to understand how stereognosis becomes defective when either tactual or kinesthetic sense is blunted, although one can partly substitute for the other. This situation is more properly termed stereoanesthesia. After lesions of the posterior parietal lobe, stereognosis seems to be affected out of proportion to the deficit in the basic sensations—so-called pure astereognosis. At some point difficult to define, disturbances of the higher levels of sensation merge into agnosia and aphasia (see Chap. 23).

REFERENCES

1. ADRIAN, E. D. *The basis of sensation.* London, Christophers, 1928.
2. BELL, C. *Phil. Trans.,* 1826, Pt. 2, pp. 163–173.
3. BORING, E. G. *Sensation and perception in the history of experimental psychology.* New York, D. Appleton-Century Co., 1942.
4. BROWNE, K., LEE, L. and RING, P. A. *J. Physiol.,* 1954, *126*:448–458
5. CATTELL, McK. and HOAGLAND, H. *J. Physiol.,* 1931, *72:* 392–404.
6. COHEN, L. A. *J. Neurophysiol.,* 1958, *21*:550–562.
7. DOUGLAS, W. W. and RITCHIE, J. M. *Physiol. Rev.,* 1962, *42*:297–334.
8. DOUGLAS, W. W., RITCHIE, J. M. and STRAUB, R. W. *J. Physiol.,* 1960, *150*:266–268.
9. FIELD, J., ed. *Handbook of physiology; Section I: Neurophysiology,* vol. 1. Washington, D.C., American Physiological Society, 1959.
10. GELDARD, F. A. *The human senses.* New York, John Wiley & Sons, 1953.
11. GRAY, J. In: *Biological receptor mechanisms.* Cambridge, The University Press, 1962.
12. HAGEN, E., KNOCHE, H. SINCLAIR, D. C. and WEDDELL, G. *Proc. roy. Soc.,* 1953, *B141*:279–287.
13. HARDY, J. D., GOODELL, H. and WOLFF, H. G. *Science,* 1951, *114*:149–150.
14. HARDY, J. D. and OPPEL, T. W. *J. clin. Invest.,* 1937, *16:* 533–540.
15. HARDY, J. D., WOLFF, H. G. and GOODELL, H. *J. clin. Invest.,* 1940, *19:*649–657.
16. HARDY, J. D., WOLFF, H. G. and GOODELL, H. *J. clin. Invest.,* 1947, *26*:1152–1158.
17. HENSEL, H. and BOSMAN, K. K. A. *J. Neurophysiol.,* 1960, *23:*564–568.
18. HENSEL, H., IGGO, A. and WITT, I. *J. Physiol.,* 1960, *153:* 113–126.
19. HUNT, C. C. *J. Physiol.,* 1961, *155:*175–186.
20. HUNT, C. C. and McINTYRE, A. K. *J. Physiol.,* 1960, *153:*88–98; 99–112.
21. IGGO, A. *Quart. J. exp. Physiol.,* 1959, *44:*362–370.
22. IGGO, A. *Acta neurovegetativa,* 1962, *24:*225–240.
23. IRIUCHIJIMA, J. and ZOTTERMAN, Y. *Acta physiol. scand.,* 1960, *49:*267–268.
24. LELE, P. P. and WEDDELL, G. *Brain,* 1956, *79:*119–154.
25. MOUNTCASTLE, V. B., POGGIO, G. F. and WERNER, G. *J. Neurophysiol.,* 1963, *26:*775–806.
26. MÜLLER, J. *Handbuch der Physiologie des Menschen für Vorlesungen,* Coblenz, J. Holscher, 1834–1840, 2 vols. Translated selections in: Rand, B. *The classical psychologists.* Boston, Houghton Mifflin, 1912.
27. OPPENHEIMER, D. R., PALMER, E. and WEDDELL, C. *J. Anat. (Lond.),* 1958, *92:*321–352.
28. PERL, E. R. *Ann. Rev. Physiol.,* 1963, *25:*459–492.
29. PLUMB, C. S. and MEIGS, J. W. *Arch. gen. Psychiat.,* 1961, *14:*611–614.
30. ROSENBLITH, W. A., ed. *Sensory communication.* New York, John Wiley & Sons, 1961.
31. SHERRINGTON, C. S. *The integrative action of the nervous system.* New Haven, Yale University Press, 1906.
32. STEVENS, S. S. See Rosenblith, No. 30.
33. TOWER, S. S. *J. Neurophysiol.,* 1940, *3:*486–500.
34. WALL, P. D. *J. Neurophysiol.,* 1960, *23:*197–210.
35. WEDDELL, G. In: Brazier, ed. *Brain and behavior,* Vol. I, Washington, D.C. American Institute of Biological Sciences, 1961.
36. WEDDELL, G. See Rosenblith, No. 30.
37. ZANDER, E. and WEDDELL, G. *J. Anat. (Lond.),* 1951, *85:* 68–93.
38. ZOTTERMAN, Y. Chap. 18 in *Handbook of physiology. Section 1. Neurophysiology,* Vol. 1, J. FIELD, ed. Baltimore, Williams & Wilkins, 1959.

CHAPTER 15

Neural Basis of Somatic Sensation

By THEODORE C. RUCH

CHAPTER 14 described the stimuli and physiologic characteristics of the sense organs and the end results of somatic sensation:perception and affect; this chapter takes up the sensory pathways in sequence, beginning with the peripheral nerve trunk and ending with the thalamic and cortical organization.

The clinical examination for neurologic diseases involves two questions: which sensory functions are lost? and, equally important, which are retained? What is lost and what is retained is called a *dissociation of sensation*. Pathologic lesions at each level of the nervous system produce characteristic dissociations. From a knowledge of these dissociations the level and location of a lesion are deduced. Four kinds of dissociation are taken into account: (i)

topographic dissociations, in which certain regions of the body show altered sensitivity and other regions remain normal; (ii) *modality dissociations*, in which one or a group of sensations are lost or impaired while others are preserved; (iii) an *affect-quality dissociation*, in which the affect is exaggerated; and (iv) *dissociations of levels of sensation*, in which the more complex sensory functions, e.g., perception, are lost but the simpler ones are retained.

PERIPHERAL NERVE AND
SPINAL ROOTS

A "peripheral nerve field" is the area of skin supplied by one cutaneous nerve. Charts showing the fields for the major cutaneous nerves are used clinically to record the distribution of sensory disturbances. Not shown on such charts, however, is the overlap between peripheral nerve fields. Each major nerve field has a central zone of skin, the *autonomous zone*,[71] innervated *only* by the parent nerve and, therefore, completely anesthetic when the nerve is sectioned. Between this zone and the surrounding fully innervated skin is the *intermediate zone* of overlap, where sensation is now served only by branches from neighboring nerves. The sensation elicited by stimulation in this zone of overlap has three abnormal aspects: (i) sensory dissociation, only pain and possibly pressure being appreciated; (ii) hypesthesia, responses to light pressure stimuli showing a gradual transition from anesthesia to normal threshold; and (iii) hyperpathia, pain sensations being abnormally unpleasant.

After nerve section, sensibility is recovered by a remarkable circumferential shrinkage of the anesthetic area, i.e., the intermediate zone extends day by day into the anesthetic area. This shrinkage starts within the first few days after nerve section, long before regenerating fibers could possibly reach the skin. Pollock[50] reasoned that the shrinkage is due to an ingrowth of fibers from the adjacent peripheral nerve fields, because the recovery was not lost after a resectioning of the regenerating nerve. Weddell *et al.*[71] have demonstrated by intravital staining that unmyelinated fibers do grow out from the intermediate into the autonomous zone.

Shortly after nerve section, pain (and, to some degree, touch sensibility) elicited from the intermediate area is qualitatively altered. Although a stronger stimulus is needed to arouse sensations of pain (hypalgesia), once the threshold is exceeded the pain is peculiarly strong and unpleasant (hyperpathia). This phase passes, but at about the time the sensation served by the regenerating nerve returns to the anesthetic area, the abnormal pain responses tend to reappear.

Epicritic and protopathic sensibility.[10, 20, 67, 70] Head grouped the abnormal sensations found in the intermediate zone, in the autonomous zone during later stages of nerve regeneration, and in regions of special sensitivity, e.g., glans penis, under the name *protopathic sensibility;* and for it he postulated a special set of fibers having a wide peripheral nerve field and quick regeneration. He also postulated a second set of fibers for each modality to carry out fine intensity and spatial discriminations e.g., serving two-point threshold; for these he coined *epicritic sensibility*. The more highly evolved epicritic system was believed to inhibit the phylogenetically older protopathic system, except when absent, as after nerve section.

Few now accept Head's theory. Some of his observations were in error and others have different explanations, e.g., the thinning out of fibers in the intermediate zone. Nevertheless, the terms are still used by clinical neurologists. Perhaps, in a very broad sense, the terms can be used to characterize two kinds of sense organs and sensory pathways with different physiologic properties.

Dermatomes.[23, 24, 27, 59] The area of skin supplied with afferent fibers by a single posterior root is a *dermatome*. Because the dermatomes are important to clinical neurology, they have been mapped repeatedly (Fig. 1). Such charts, which are used in recording the results of a sensory examination, show the dermatomes as contiguous fields. Actually the dermatomes of adjacent roots overlap greatly, so that always two and sometimes three roots supply a single point on the skin. The dermatomes are therefore considerably larger than those shown on most clinical charts. The size of a dermatome is somewhat smaller for pain than for temperature and smaller for temperature than for touch, which is just the reverse of the dissociation in the border surrounding a peripheral nerve injury. Dermatomes, or *sensory root fields,* must not be confused with peripheral nerve fields. The two are quite different in shape, and often the fibers of one dermatome are conducted to the spinal cord in two peripheral nerves.

The dermatomes cannot be demarcated by sectioning a single posterior root and mapping the resulting area of anesthesia, since, owing to overlap, none may be found. The classic method for mapping dermatomes is that of *remaining sensibility*. Sherrington sectioned three roots above and three below the intact root to be studied, producing an island of sensitivity in a sea of anesthesia. Mapping the hyperesthesia induced in the skin surface by injection of 5 per cent saline solution into the interspinous ligaments[27] is another method of dermatomal mapping. Finally, mapping zones of hypesthesia produced by pressure on posterior roots has yielded results at variance with those obtained by the classic procedure.[23, 24]

According to Sherrington,[59] dermatomes are the distorted remnants of what was originally an orderly metameric arrangement that has survived with clarity only in the trunk. There, the dermatomes consist of a series of 12 narrow (overlapping) bands running from the vertebral column to the midventral line. The bands slope downward as they pass around the body to the ventral surface, because, as a result of his upright posture, man's front has blossomed while his back has regressed. In the limbs, the segmental organization is less clear because a number of metameres have been combined to form the limb. The apparent complexity of the dermatomes is clarified if man is placed in the

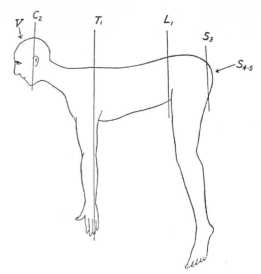

Fig. 2. Key dermatomal boundaries in man in quadruped position. First spinal dermatome is shown as C_2 because first cervical segment lacks posterior root. (After Monrad-Krohn, *The clinical examination of the nervous system,* 3rd ed., London, H. K. Lewis, 1926.)

posture of his forebears as in Figure 2, which brings out the neurologically important fact that the perianal region—once ornamented by a tail—and not the foot is the most caudal part of the body and hence is innervated by the lowermost posterior roots.

According to Sherrington's observation, the dermatomes of the arms, when viewed from the side, are "rays" which originate at a mid-dorsal line, as brought out in Figure 3, and terminate in the midventral line. Thus, the dermatomes, as the name suggests, are not bands but cuts or slices. In the arm, a dermatome consists of the surface of a wedge which passes through the arm in the same plane as, but diverging from, the plane established by the mid-dorsal and midventral line of the limb from which the dermatome takes origin. For example, the same dermatome includes the back and front of the middle finger. Dermatomes anterior to the mid-dorsal and the midventral plane are *preaxial;* those posterior are *postaxial.*

Keegan and Garnett[24] present a different kind of dermatomal map based upon the distribution of dermal hypesthesia caused by nucleus pulposus material extruding from a ruptured intervertebral disc and pressing on individual posterior roots. In this map (Fig. 3), the dermatome extends as a band from the backbone down the arm or leg to its tip, and this pattern is repeated serially much as on the trunk. It is surprising that a difference of opinion exists on such a fundamental matter as the shape of the dermatomes.

The dermatomal pattern is significant in several ways to both clinical medicine and physiology: (i) in distinguishing peripheral nerve injury from root in-

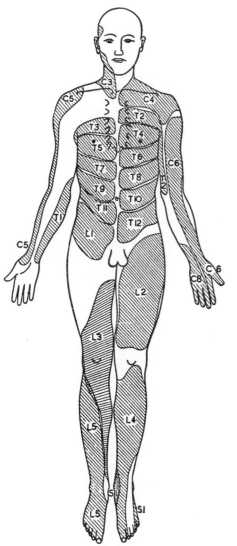

Fig. 1. Dermatomes of man determined by method of "remaining sensibility." Half the dermatomes are shown on left and remainder on right in order to display the overlap. (Data of Foerster, *Brain,* 1933, *56:*1–39, redrawn by Lewis, *Pain,* New York, Macmillan, 1942.)

jury; (ii) in localizing the level of spinal cord injury; (iii) in determining the levels for root sections or cordotomy for relief of pain; (iv) in treating herpes zoster, which is often distributed on the skin according to dermatomes; (v) in recognizing the origin of visceral pain, which is often referred to a dermatome; and (vi) in studying the lamination of spinal tracts and the projection of the body surface upon the cerebral cortex (see below).

Conduction of Sensory Nerve Impulses. With the discovery that afferent nerve axons fall into several groups of different fiber size and conduction rates, attempts were made to associate modality of sensation with fiber groups. The order of failure of different sensory modalities during cocaine and ischemic nerve block was studied. These attempts, with one exception, have been in a sense unsuccessful because of the high degree of overlap. However, the early observations in which pain was associated with small myelinated delta fibers and the even smaller unmyelinated C fibers have been of considerable importance in understanding clinical pain phenomena.

Double Pain Response.[27, 47, 51]   Evidence for the existence of a fast and a slow system of pain fibers comes from several sources: (i) *Psy-cholgic studies*. Several investigators have described under the names *double pain, delayed pain, echo pain* or *first* and *second pain* the fact that the pain sensation from a brief stimulus is often experienced as two pulses or peaks of pain. You can demonstrate this for yourself by flicking the dorsum of a finger against a light bulb. (ii) *Latency studies*. If the two pain pulses are due to rapidly and slowly conducting fibers, the interval between pulses should be greater when stimuli are applied to the distal end of an extremity than when they are applied to the proximal end. They are,[27] and the delays are compatible with the difference between C and delta rates of conduction. During asphyxial block, the reaction time to second pain remains unchanged for 36 minutes while first pain fails or appears after a prolonged latency after 18 to 24 minutes.[59a]

CLINICAL CORRELATIONS.   *Tabes dorsalis and peripheral neuropathy.*[62]   Neurosyphilitic damage to the posterior roots may result in loss of touch, proprioception, etc., without destroying pain. However, such pain is often felt after a delay of 1 or 2 seconds and may well be especially disagreeable—hyperpathic. This was not understood until the existence of the "slow" pain fibers was discovered. The latencies of the pain re-

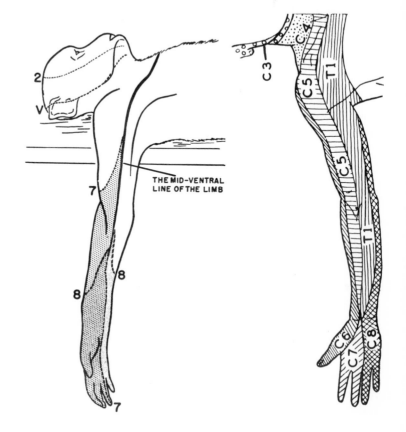

Fig. 3. Diagrams of monkey and man contrasting two concepts of the cervical dermatomes. According to Sherrington, the dermatomes converge on a mid-ventral and mid-dorsal line (not shown). Note also the overlap. Human dermatomes as determined by hypesthesia resulting from a ruptured intervertebral disc begin at midline of chest and back (not shown). This is not a species difference since Foerster's diagram of man resembles that of the monkey; both were obtained by the same method. (After Sherrington, *Phil. Trans.,* 1898, *B190:*45–186; and Keegan and Garnett, *Anat. Rec.,* 1948, *102:*409–437.)

THE MID-VENTRAL LINE OF THE LIMB

sponse in most tabetic patients and of *second* pain in normal persons are approximately the same.[47] Further, the delay in the pain response in the tabetic patient is about 1 second after stimulation of the knee, but nearly 2 seconds after stimulation of the toes. That light touch, position sense and vibratory sensibility are affected early in both tabes dorsalis and nutritional neuropathy is explicable on the grounds that the impulses mediating these sensory functions travel in fast-conducting fibers of the A group while pain impulses are conducted in fibers of small diameter. Pain fibers in tabes also seem to fire spontaneously, causing tabetic crises, as though the pathologic factor which is progressively killing fibers causes bursts of impulses to be generated in the ones remaining viable.

Hyperpathia.[62, 63] Dissociations of pain from other modalities are often associated with a qualitative change in pain, its disagreeableness (affect) being heightened—the phenomenon of *hyperpathia* or *dysesthesia*. From time to time it is suggested that the unmyelinated fibers serve a kind of pain different from the more rapid one. One can easily verify for himself that the qualities of the two flashes of pain elicited from normally innervated skin are similar if not identical, although the second tends to be more prolonged. Hyperpathia tends to occur when pain sensibility persists after the other modalities of sensation are blocked (nerve ischemia, tabes,[62] neuropathy,[63] nerve degeneration). Head, as noted earlier, postulated a central inhibitory interaction between pain and other modalities of sensation. However, Landau and Bishop[25] believe, from experiments involving asphyxial nerve block, that the slow pain impulses (C fibers) give rise to dull, burning, disagreeable pain when not preceded by the delta pain impulses.

SENSORY PATHWAYS OF THE SPINAL CORD

The axons of afferent neurons, on entering the spinal cord, may (i) connect with spinocerebellar neurons; (ii) without synaptic interruption or crossing, ascend in the ipsilateral posterior column to the medulla; or (iii) synapse with a neuron which sends an axon across the spinal cord to ascend in the contralateral anterolateral region of the cord. Of the various somatic and visceral modalities of sensation, some are conveyed exclusively in the posterior columns, others in the anterolateral columns, and still others in both pathways. The possibil-

ity of a third pathway is discussed later in the chapter.

Anterolateral Tracts.[*18, 22, 65, 69, 72] Impulses conducted in the anterolateral tracts subserve the following kinds of sensation and perception:

Partially anterolateral:
1. Pressure and touch

Exclusively anterolateral:
1. Pain from skin, muscles, tendons, joints and viscera
2. Warmth
3. Cold
4. Sexual sensations
5. Tickle, itch and feelings of muscular fatigue

Upon entering the spinal cord, sensory fibers are regrouped so that (i) the fibers for cutaneous and deep sensibility are no longer separate and (ii) the fibers serving the same quality of sensation are sorted out and grouped together. Thus, pain fibers from cutaneous, muscular and visceral nerves are collected together in the anterolateral tract, and the muscle sense impulses from the deep branches pass into the posterior columns. Both temperature senses go together.

Several of these modalities of sensation inform us of the body's condition; this is in part true even of thermal sensation. Phylogenetically, the anterolateral tracts represent an ancient system of fibers concerned with "self-reception" and little with the external world. However, this aspect should not be overemphasized since some of the ascending fibers are not only truly spinothalamic but also are connected with the cerebral cortex and do convey information about the external world (see below).

Functional anatomic details—origin and decussation. Each posterior root branches into a fan of rootlets which enter the spinal cord. At the point of entry, the fibers of each filament sort out according to size. The *medial division* contains the large myelinated fibers which, instead of entering the posterior horn, swing across its tip to enter the posterior columns (Fig. 4). The unmyelinated and small myelinated fibers are grouped into a *lateral division* which swings laterally and, bifurcating, forms the tract of Lissauer (*dorsolateral fasciculus*) at the tip of the posterior horn. This is not really a tract since the fibers ascend only one to three segments before terminating in the substantia gelatinosa Rolandi, a cell column capping the poste-

---

* This term is preferable to "spinothalamic tract" since our knowledge is based on cord sectioning which also severs the many other tracts in the area.

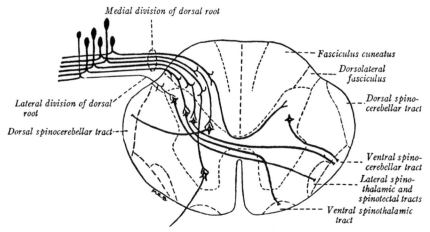

Fig. 4. Schematic cross section of spinal cord showing destination of fibers of medial and lateral divisions of dorsal root and position of ascending tracts. (From Ranson and Clark, *Anatomy of the nervous system,* Philadelphia, W. B. Saunders Co., 1959.)

rior horn. This column is named for its discoverer and for its seemingly uniform texture (due to the smallness of the cell bodies and the absence of large myelinated fibers traversing it) (see Fig. 5). The axons of its fine cells cross the cord and ascend in the lateral spinothalamic tract or other tracts in this region.

Some fibers of the medial division terminate, either immediately or after ascending several segments, upon large pericornual cells in the posterior horn. The axons of these cells decussate in the ventral gray commissure to ascend in the ventral portion of the anterolateral column (ventral spinothalamic tract). This scheme may be too rigid; both divisions of the posterior root probably contribute to both the lateral and the ventral spinothalamic tract.

Clinical correlations: Syringomyelia. The proximity of the anterior gray commissure to the central canal makes the decussating fibers liable to interruption by a widening of the central canal (syringomyelia). This produces a clinical syndrome consisting of loss of pain and of warmth and cold sensations on *both sides* of the body at the level of the segments affected. Touch, pressure and deep sensibility are not affected. Syringomyelia is, therefore, a good example of modality dissociation.

LAMINATION. The ascending tracts of the anterolateral region (spinobulbar, spinotectal and spinothalamic) are laminated. This means that the contributions of successive dermatomes form more or less distinct layers or laminae of fibers. A tract so arranged is said to be "topographically organized." The lamination is in

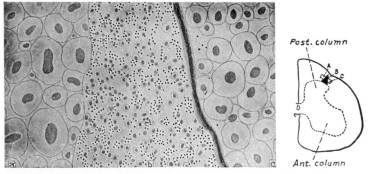

Fig. 5. Silver stained cross-section through white matter at tip of dorsal horn of spinal cord as shown in insert at the right. *a,* In the slide are the large fibers of the medial division of dorsal root after entering fasciculus cuneatus. *b,* Unmyelinated fibers appearing as fine dots and fine myelinated fibers of lateral division after entering fasciculus dorsolateralis (Lissauer). *c,* Second order fibers of dorsospinocerebellar tract. (From Ranson and Clark, *Anatomy of the nervous system,* Philadelphia, W. B. Saunders Co., 1959.)

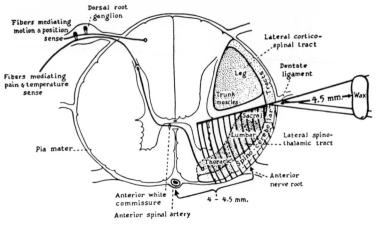

Thoracic II.

Fig. 6. Diagram illustrating cordotomy. Cross section of spinal cord shows lamination of spino-thalamic tract, position of pyramidal tract in relation to it, and presence of other tracts in lower quadrant. A piece of bone wax is mounted 4.5 mm. from tip of knife as a depth gauge. Heavy curved lines in ventral quadrant indicate sweep of knife. Note that a desire to spare lateral corticospinal tract would result in sparing of sacral dermatomes. (From Kahn and Rand, *J. Neurosurg.*, 1952, *9*:611–619.)

the form of imperfect annular rings with the fibers from the most caudal regions lying superficially because the long fibers from sacral segments are pushed outward by the accretion of crossing fibers at each successive segment (Fig. 4). Some other influence pushes the longer sacral fibers laterally and dorsally away from the margin of the ventral horn where they originally lay. This results in the arrangement seen in Figure 6. The physiologic significance of such lamination is the preservation of the topographic organization of fibers whereby the dermatomes of the body surface may ultimately be projected onto the cortical sensory areas.

Clinical correlations: Cordotomy.[22, 65, 72] Lamination explains certain features of the symptoms produced by spinal cord tumors. Extramedullary tumors, those originating outside the spinal cord, tend to cause hypalgesia in the caudal dermatomes first, because the pressure from the outside blocks first the peripherally lying fibers from the sacral segments. As the cord is pressed further, the sensory border creeps up. Intramedullary tumors, on the other hand, may leave a characteristic region of intact sensibility in the anogenital region because they spare the peripherally lying fibers derived from the lowest sacral roots.

The separation of sensory impulses to travel in the anterolateral and posterior columns of the spinal cord allows surgical interruption of the pain pathway without production of a disabling anesthesia and ataxia. As shown in Figure 6, a small knife is inserted into the spinal cord just below the dentate ligament and pyramidal tract and is drawn downward through the anterolateral columns. Such anterolateral cordotomies are performed to relieve unbearable pain not tractable to medical control. The operation is effective for superficial, deep and visceral pain, although, for the last, bilateral operations are required. Despite the fact that the ventral spinocerebellar and various descending motor tracts—vestibulospinal, tectospinal, ventral corticospinal tracts, etc.—are partially sectioned, little motor disturbance is apparent. Bilateral cordotomy rarely interferes permanently with bladder function or with sensations of bladder fullness. However, sensations of the sexual orgasm are usually lost.

Posterior White Columns.[18, 60] These columns (more correctly funiculi), lying between the posterior horns, are formed by the ascending and descending branches of the fibers making up the medial division of the posterior horns. Some of the ascending fibers reach the medulla before synaptic interruption; others transmit impulses to the second order neurons which form well defined ascending tracts passing to the cerebellum. By collaterals, impulses also reach the motoneurons and possibly the propriospinal system.

The sensory functions of the posterior columns are known from the study of residual sensation in patients subjected to anterolateral cordotomy for relief of pain. In some of these operations, the ventral region of the spinal cord near the midline has been intentionally included; the most posterior segment of the funiculus is spared because it contains the pyramidal tract.

The sensory impulses conducted in the posterior columns serve the functions listed below. Note that the list includes processes of a perceptual nature, some of which involve more than one modality of posterior column sensibility. A clinical or laboratory test of each sensory or perceptual function, described in Chapter 14, is also mentioned.

- A. Muscle, tendon and and joint sensibility (proprioception, kinesthesia)
  1. Passive movement—threshold angular movement for appreciation that movement has occurred
  2. Threshold of tension—discrimination of lifted weights
  3. Position of limb in space—finger-to-finger test
- B. Touch and pressure
  1. Light touch—absorbent cotton
  2. Light pressure—von Frey hairs
  3. Massive pressure—weight discrimination with supported hand
- C. Perceptual functions
  1. Topognosis or localization—spot finding test
  2. Two-point discrimination—compass test
  3. Spatial functions—figure writing
  4. Appreciation of vibration—tuning fork test or pallesthesiometer
  5. Stereognosis—recognition of common objects by palpation

The sensations served by the posterior columns are gnostic,* discriminative, "epicritic" and spatial. They give knowledge of the position of the limbs in space and knowledge of objects making up the external world. For this knowledge, fine discrimination of the weight, size and texture of objects handled is required. However, intensity, spatial and temporal discriminations are not exclusively the attributes of posterior column sensibility; nor are there some fibers serving localization and others serving intensity discrimination. These are functions common to all forms of sensation. But the sensory axons of the posterior column have modality-specific receptors and small receptive fields, and are topographically organized so they perform such functions as localization, resolution of two stimuli or discrimination of intensity very accurately.†

*From "gnosis" meaning "knowledge."

†Note that one should not speak of a "sensation," much less a "two-point threshold," ascending the posterior columns.

About touch, two views are held: (i) The anterolateral pathway is functionally equivalent to the posterior column pathway, or (ii) the posterior column system, phylogenetically newer, is capable of a higher degree of perceptual function. After anterolateral cordotomy, including all of the ventral region, the disturbance of perceptual proprioceptive and tactual function (localization, two-point discrimination and figure writing) is minimal,[18] but the threshold for light pressure is markedly elevated.[73] The posterior columns are rarely sectioned surgically, but experiments on animals suggest that the spinothalamic tract may serve more perceptual function than previously suspected. On the other hand, current electrophysiologic and anatomic studies are revealing many details consistent with the characterization of the posterior column system as providing the brain with knowledge of the external world and the anterolateral system as providing information about the state of the organism itself.

SENSORY SYSTEMS OF THE BRAINSTEM

At the upper border of the medulla oblongata, impulses derived from the fifth and other mixed cranial nerves are added to the ascending sensory systems. Here, the ascending systems undergo some rearrangement.

Trigeminal Nerve. Pain, temperature and touch-pressure sensibility of the face and buccal cavity are served by trigeminal neurons. Their cell bodies are located in the semilunar (gasserian) ganglion and their central processes enter the pons. Approximately half of the fibers of large diameter bifurcate, giving one branch to the main sensory nucleus located in the pons and one branch to the elongated spinal nucleus which extends through the medulla to meet the substantia gelatinosa Rolandi. The other half of the large fibers connect only with the main nucleus. All but a few of the fine fibers connect only with the spinal nucleus. Pain and temperature impulses pass exclusively by way of the spinal nucleus. Harrison and Corbin[19] recorded tactual impulses from the spinal tract of the trigeminal nerve. As in the spinal cord, a small and functionally unimportant component of the touch-pressure system pursues the same course as the impulses for pain and temperature.

TABLE 1. *Sensory Connections of Spinal and Cranial Nerves*

SPINAL NERVE	TRIGEMINAL NERVE	FACIAL, GLOSSOPHARYNGEAL AND VAGUS NERVES
Lateral division		
Tract of Lissauer	Descending fibers	Tractus solitarius
Substantia gelatinosa Rolandi	Spinal nucleus	Nucleus of tractus solitarius
Spinothalamic tract	Ventral secondary tract	Unknown
Medial division		
Posterior columns	Ascending fibers	
Nn. gracilis and cuneatus	Main sensory nucleus	
Medial lemniscus	Dorsal secondary tract	

The proprioceptive innervation of the striate muscles of the face and the orbit has long been a neurologic puzzle. Recent studies suggest that the mesencephalic extension of the trigeminal nucleus contains the cells of origin for afferent fibers coming from the muscles of mastication (which also receive motor fibers from the trigeminal nerve). If so, this is the one known instance in which cell bodies of afferent neurons are found *within* the substance of the central nervous system. Although proprioceptive end-organs have been demonstrated in eye muscles, the location of cells or origin of the fibers supplying them is unknown.

SECOND ORDER NEURONS.[28, 33, 69] As shown in Table 1, the second order neurons carrying somatosensory impulses ascend by way of the medial lemniscus and the dorsal secondary trigeminal tract, and the spinothalamic and ventral secondary trigeminal tract. These are joined by other, less well worked out systems of secondary neurons from the vagus, etc., and all terminate in the thalamus. In addition to these well organized tracts, there are others which are less well organized. When impulses from the teeth were traced through the brain stem, electrical activity was recorded from no less than five areas (Fig. 7).[33] Three of these lie within the reticular area.

Clinical correlations: Trigeminal neuralgia. This consists of paroxysmal attacks of excruciating pain projected to an area innervated by one or more divisions of the trigeminal nerve. Vasomotor and secretory disturbances may accompany the pain; the facial musculature undergoes clonic contractions—hence the common name *tic douloureux.* The area of skin affected is often apparently hyperesthetic and hyperalgesic, but measurements of threshold indicate a *decreased sensitivity,* suggesting a central overresponse rather than true hyperesthesia. In cases of severe trigeminal neuralgia, the trigeminal neurons are severed central to the ganglion (retrogasserian neurectomy) to avoid regeneration. Although effective, this operation sacrifices touch sensitivity, which results in an unpleasant feeling of numbness over the face, and keratitic changes in the cornea due to loss of protective pain reflexes may ensue.

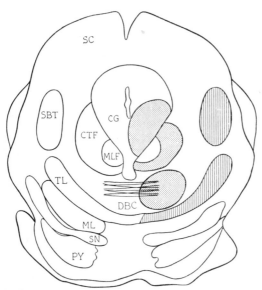

Fig. 7. Brainstem areas conducting impulses from tooth pulp. Vertically lined areas are the classic pain pathways, the spinobulbothalamic tract (*SBT*) and the trigeminal lemniscus (*TL*) adjacent to the medial lemniscus (*ML*). Dotted areas are three additional regions from which tooth pulp impulses were recorded: one in the central gray (*CG*), one in the central tegmental fasciculus (*CTF*), and one in the reticular substance lateral to decussation of the brachium conjunctivum. Section is at the level of the superior colliculi (*SC*). (After Melzack, Stotler and Livingston, *J. Neurophysiol.,* 1958, *21:*353–367.)

THALAMOCORTICAL SYSTEMS

All sensory tracts except the olfactory are interrupted by a synapse in the thalamus of the diencephalon before proceeding to the cerebral cortex. The thalamus is therefore the gateway to the cerebral cortex through which passes most information gained from the external world and from our bodies.

From anatomic, electrophysiologic and behavioral techniques combined with surgery, three kinds of pathways to the cerebral cortex have been demarcated. These are potentially but not necessarily sensory pathways. They are as follows: (i) the classic somatosensory pathways—the posterior column and *true* spinothalamic systems—which traverse relay nuclei and end in the primary areas of the cerebral cortex, (ii) "by-passing" tracts sometimes derived from relay nuclei but often traversing other thalamic nuclei and ending adjacent to classic cortical sensory areas, and (iii) multineuron pathways (or collaterals from the above) which synapse before reaching the thalamus, sometimes more than once, and employ different thalamic nuclei than (i) and (ii) above; they may or may not reach the cerebral cortex. These latter pathways are often revealed only by silver stains for degenerating axons.

Classic Somatic Sensory Pathways via Relay Nuclei.[13, 53, 68] These fall into three groups: (i) axons passing up the posterior columns to synapse in the nuclei of gracilis and cuneatus with second order fibers that enter the medial lemniscus, (ii) axons originating at the spinal level and passing uninterrupted to the thalamus—the "true spinothalamic tract," and (iii) the homologous elements added to this system from the trigeminal nerve (see Table 1). The course of these pathways, which consist primarily of myelinated fibers, has been determined by placing lesions in the spinal cord or in the gracile or cuneate nuclei and tracing, with the Marchi method, the resulting degeneration of myelin.

All of these fibers end in the posterior ventral portion of the nuclear masses lateral to the internal medullary lamina. Those areas receiving impulses from the face end medially in a nucleus appropriately called n. ventralis posteromedialis (or for its shape, the "arcuate" nucleus [see Fig. 8]). The second order fibers receiving impulses from the body end more laterally in the n. ventralis posterolateralis. A tendency for the spinothalamic fibers to end slightly more posteriorly has been described, but there is virtual fusion of the two systems (and hence, of modalities). By contrast, the contributions from various parts of the body tend to remain distinct, i.e., the posteroventral nuclei have a topographic organization. This is shown by cutting the spinal cord at various levels and identifying the distribution of Marchi degeneration in the thalamus. In a spider monkey (Fig. 8), which has a prehensile tail (a fifth hand), successive groups of dermatomes between the caudal segments and the cervical ones are represented in a lateral-to-medial sequence in n. ventralis posterolateralis; the sequence is completed by the face representation still more medially. An even finer topographic organization was proved by Mountcastle and Henneman,[38, 39] who searched the thalamus in half-millimeter steps for electrical activity during stimulation of points on the body surface. They obtained a finely detailed map of the thalamus with the head posteromedial, the tail anterolateral, the back superior and the feet inferior. In short, the body surface is *projected* onto the thalamus, specifically onto the posteroventral nucleus.

Projection in the nervous system is roughly analogous to the projection of a lantern slide, nerve fibers taking the place of light "rays." There is considerable distortion. Certain parts of the body are "blown up"

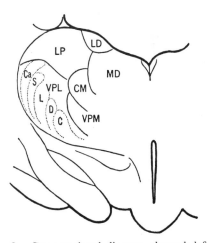

Fig. 8. Cross-sectional diagram through left half of thalamus, showing areas of nucleus ventralis posterolateralis (*VPL*) in which spinothalamic tract fibers from different levels of spinal cord terminate. From Marchi degeneration studies on monkey with prehensile tail. Comma-shaped areas enclosed in fine dots show termination of spinothalamic tract fibers. Order of termination from lateral to medial is: *Ca,* caudal; *S,* sacral; *L,* lumbar; *D,* thoracic; *C,* cervical. For abbreviation of thalamic nuclei see legend of Fig. 10. Note that degeneration was not found in nucleus ventralis posteromedialis (*VPM*), "face" and "taste" nucleus. (After Chang and Ruch, *J. Anat.* (*Lond.*), 1947, *81:* 140–149.)

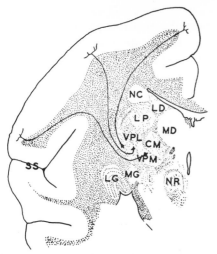

Fig. 9. Schematic frontal section through thalamus and postcentral gyrus of cerebral cortex to show topographic arrangement of projection fibers from posteroventral nuclei. Nucleus ventralis posteromedialis (*VPM*) projects to inferior end of postcentral gyrus near sylvian fissure (*SS*), whereas nucleus ventralis posterolateralis (*VPL*) projects to middle and superior thirds of postcentral gyrus. (From Walker, *The primate thalamus,* Chicago, University of Chicago Press, 1938.)

or enlarged, an arrangement which is functionally significant (see below). The essential feature of a topographically organized system is that the spatial relations existing peripherally are preserved. A detailed organization is often described as a "point-to-point" projection, i.e., a point on the body surface is projected to a point on the thalamus or cortex. A point in this case should be considered a point of maximal electrical response.

The topographic organization manifested in the thalamic terminations of sensory systems is preserved in the thalamocortical projections but is inverted from side to side (Fig. 9). The medially situated arcuate nucleus (VPM), receiving impulses from the face, projects laterally near the sylvian fissure. The lateral part of the posterolateral nucleus (VPL), receiving impulses from the leg, projects near the midline. The projection of impulses from the arm is intermediate in both thalamus and cortex. Thus, the body surface is projected upon the postcentral gyrus with its spatial relations preserved; the lateromedial relationship is opposite in the thalamus and cortex. This information was gained by truncating the axons of thalamocortical projection fibers by a restricted lesion of the cortex and observing the "retrograde degeneration reaction"—chromatolysis, eccentric placement of the nucleus and blurring of the

cell outline. In most thalamocortical neurons this goes on to complete degeneration, disappearance and gliosis. Thalamic nuclei receiving input *directly* from the great ascending system and sending output to the cerebral cortex are termed *relay nuclei.*[59] For other thalamic nuclei and their connections refer to Figure 10.

Ipsilateral nature of projections. All of the cortical projection from one half of the thalamus passes to the cerebral cortex on the same side; none crosses in the corpus callosum to the opposite cortex. Thus, any representation of one lateral half of the body surface in the ipsilateral cortex must come about because some fibers either do not cross at levels below the thalamus or cross twice, once at a spinal level and once at a brain stem level. A slight ipsilateral projection to the relay nuclei has been demonstrated electrically.[39] Other systems discussed below have a large ipsilateral component.

EVOKED POTENTIAL MAPPING OF SENSORY CORTEX.[53, 77] Recording action currents evoked in the postcentral gyrus of the cerebral cortex by cutaneous stimulation reveals a detailed *dermatomal* projection.[77] Tactual stimulations were applied to the skin, and a recording electrode connected to an oscilloscope was moved systematically over the cortex in millimeter steps. Maximal *evoked* potentials* in response to stimulation occurred in the areas receiving projection fibers from the posteroventral nucleus, cytoarchitectural areas 3, 1 and 2. Short latency potentials with clear topographic localization were recorded from areas 4 and 6. Electrical responses were confined to the contralateral cortex, except that stimulation of the face gave rise to ipsilateral cortical responses as well.

The main conclusion reached from these experiments was that "the parts of contralateral body surface are represented in an orderly sequence. In the case of the lower extremity this sequence clearly reflects the metameric origin of the dermatomes; the arrangement is in the order of spinal innervation, not in the order— hip, thigh, knee, leg, ankle, foot, toes." Thus, the order may be termed "dermatomal" or "metameric," as opposed to "regional," the

*Cortical potentials induced by stimulation of end-organs or afferent pathways are, by convention, termed *evoked potentials.* The earliest response is surface-positive and brief in latency and duration. Later waves will be discussed in a subsequent chapter. *Evoked potentials* are sometimes called *slow potentials* to distinguish them from spike-like potentials from single cortical units (*fast potentials*).

term "segmental" being ambiguous. The dermatomal law is borne out by the fact that a fast fiber component of the splanchnic nerve reaches the trunk area of the cortex, the region which had been predicted on the basis of the segments at which the splanchnic nerve impulses enter the spinal cord. The observation also suggests that one should speak of the "somatovisceral" area rather than of simply the "somatosensory" area.[1, 2, 3]

Another result has been to demonstrate that the extent of cortical area devoted to a given region parallels the tactual acuity and innervation density of the region. Thus, a wider strip is devoted to the distal than to the proximal portions of the limbs or to the trunk dermatomes. Representation of T_{1-12}, dermatomes for the chest and abdomen, is compressed into a cortical strip only 2.5 mm. wide. In contrast, the cortical area for the thumb and forefinger dermatome (C_8) is several times larger.

The large numbers of sense organs and cortical neurons devoted to the relatively small skin areas of thumb and fingers underlie the low two-point threshold and small error of localization of stimuli in those regions, and topographic organization of thalamocortical projections explains why a cortical lesion may, for example, affect the arm but spare the leg. However, although such organization is clinically important, is there sufficient point-to-point representation of the body surface on the cortex *physiologically* to contribute the neural substrate for topognosis and two-point discrimination?

Somatic area II.[76] The sensory representation of the body in the postcentral gyrus is duplicated in reverse order, i.e., face, arm, leg, in passing from the foot of the postcentral gyrus to the bottom of the sylvian fissure. This so-called "somatic area II" is less well organized topographically and the evoked potentials are of longer latency and more susceptible to anes-

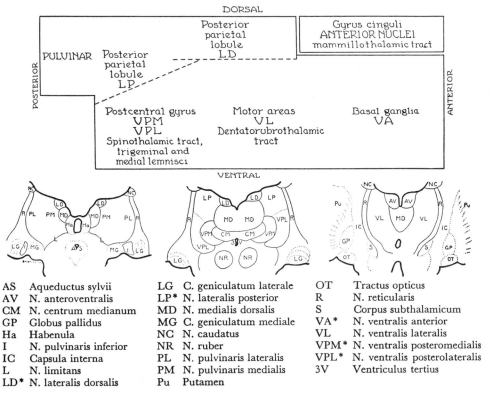

AS	Aqueductus sylvii	LG	C. geniculatum laterale	OT	Tractus opticus
AV	N. anteroventralis	LP*	N. lateralis posterior	R	N. reticularis
CM	N. centrum medianum	MD	N. medialis dorsalis	S	Corpus subthalamicum
GP	Globus pallidus	MG	C. geniculatum mediale	VA*	N. ventralis anterior
Ha	Habenula	NC	N. caudatus	VL	N. ventralis lateralis
I	N. pulvinaris inferior	NR	N. ruber	VPM*	N. ventralis posteromedialis
IC	Capsula interna	PL	N. pulvinaris lateralis	VPL*	N. ventralis posterolateralis
L	N. limitans	PM	N. pulvinaris medialis	3V	Ventriculus tertius
LD*	N. lateralis dorsalis	Pu	Putamen		

Fig. 10. Correlation of longitudinal and cross-sectional views of thalamus. *Top:* Lateral nuclear mass of macaque thalamus in schematic parasagittal section. Cortical projection is given above abbreviation; afferent connection, below it. (Data from Walker, *The primate thalamus,* Chicago, University of Chicago Press, 1938, and after Ranson, *Anatomy of the nervous system,* 1943.) *Bottom:* Cross sections of chimpanzee thalamus at three levels—*left,* posterior; *middle,* midthalamus; *right,* anterior. (From Fulton, *Physiology of the nervous system,* 3d ed., New York, Oxford University Press, 1949.)

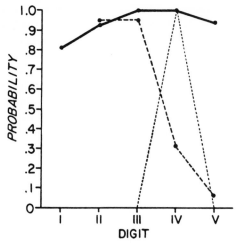

Fig. 11.   Size of the field from which three differ-ent cortical units could be fired. *Solid line,* unit with a large receptive field; *dotted line,* unit with receptive field confined to one finger; *dashed line,* unit with large field, showing rapid decline of discharge probability near edge of field. (From Towe and Amassian, *J. Neuro-physiol.,* 1958, *21*:292–311.)

thesia than those in the postcentral gyrus. Here, ipsilateral as well as contralateral cutaneous stimulation evokes potentials, and the second area may be more important in lower animals than in primates. Ablation experiments leave the function of somatic II in doubt.[43] With the discovery of an additional sensory area, the classic primary area is now often termed so-matic area I or simply somatic I.

RECEPTIVE ZONE OF THALAMIC AND CORTICAL NEURONS.[36, 53]   There is considerable diver-gence within the sensory pathway so that the receptors at a single spot on the skin will excite many cells in the postcentral gyrus, especially in the unanesthetized animal. This divergence is orderly, however, and a single postcentral neuron has a homogeneous receptive field rather than a mosaic of skin patches from which it can be excited. The fields tend to be round on the hand or foot and elliptical on the arm or leg with the long axis of the field running parallel to the extremity.[51] They are quite large, even on the hand, where they average about 3 sq. cm. in area; on the shoulder (monkey), they average about 25 sq. cm. and are still larger on the back. These figures are calculated to be 15 to 100 times the area of the receptive field for a second order neuron.[36] As in the periphery, the neuron is maximally excited when the stimulus falls in the center of the receptive field and the number of discharges decreases as the stimulus

is moved toward the edges of the field; the firing probability decreases and the latency be-comes longer.[36, 66] Thus, we see that progres-sively in the central pathway, as in the periphery, canalization has been eschewed in favor of divergence.

This brings out another property of synapses in the sensory system—a tendency to fire in trains of impulses in response to a single volley input. This tendency was shown by Amassian and DeVito[6] to be established at the first syn-apse, i.e., in the cuneate nucleus, but it is char-acteristic of the thalamus and the cerebral cortex as well. Characteristic, also, is lability of latency as a function of stimulus intensity ap-plied to the input.

Towe and Amassian[66] have found in somatic area I a few cortical units with large receptive fields, e.g., a cortical neuron almost equally re-sponsive to stimulation of all the five digits (Fig. 11). Such large receptive fields may be-long to the spinothalamic system and smaller ones to the posterior column–medial lemniscal system.

By-pass Systems.   Ablation of the cerebral cortex immediately in front of and behind the postcentral gyrus produces retrograde degener-ation in nuclei other than the classic relay nuclei (VPM and VPL).[13, 59] The nucleus pro-jecting to motor areas of the procentral gyrus (strongly to area 4 and weakly to area 6, as seen in Figures 10 and 12) is the n. ventralis lateralis,* which lies just anterior to the relay nuclei. The input to this nucleus is derived from the cerebellum via the dentatorubro-thalamic tract. It would be easy to dismiss a system ending in a motor area as being con-cerned not with conscious sensation, but with the control of movement; however, evidence for a discriminative sensory function of this area will be presented below.

Evoked surface-positive responses to periph-eral stimulation, recorded from the precentral gyrus of monkeys, were found to have about the same latency as postcentral responses.[57] Malis et al.[29] proved that this activity is not "relayed" from the postcentral gyri since it persisted after their removal. The electrophysiologic evidence proving whether this system is sensory or sim-ply afferent is incomplete. Does the rapid con-

*This nucleus is a relay nucleus in Walker's classifica-tion but is considered a part of a by-pass system because of the afferent input and cortical projec-tion.

duction in the spinocerebellar fibers make up for a delay in cerebellar detour? Are there other pathways to the motor area (see below)? Does the rapidity of Betz cell discharge after a stimulus to the projections of the lateroventral input mean that this system controls Betz discharge and is unrelated to sensation? Other evidence is necessary to answer these questions.

A second subset of somatosensory projections to the cerebral cortex apart from the projection of the relay nuclei to the primary sensory area has been disclosed from lesions placed *behind* the precentral gyrus in the posterior parietal lobe (areas 5 and 7). In this case, retrograde degeneration was found in the n. lateralis dorsalis and n. lateralis posterior and in the pulvinar, all of which are lateral to the internal medullary lamina and posterior to the n. ventralis lateralis. The nn. lateralis posterior (Fig. 12) and dorsalis project to areas 5 and 7. The pulvinar projects more posteriorly. Comparison of Figures 10 and 12 shows that the anterior-posterior relation of these projections is the same in the thalamus and cortex. Walker's[68] interpretation was that these nuclei receive afferent input from the relay nuclei. It is now known that some posterior thalamic nuclei receive input *directly* from both the anterolateral and the posterior column spinal pathways (see below). It will be seen that these posterior parietal areas are concerned with discriminative function, just as is the postcentral gyrus.

NONLEMNISCAL, NONSPINOTHALAMIC RELAY PATHWAYS.[11, 31, 32] In the last century, Sherrington and others observed that the pathways of the anterolateral column, while ascending the spinal cord and brainstem, not only acquire fibers but also lose them. In the cat, this loss of fibers is so great that few anterolateral fibers ever reach the thalamus directly. In monkeys and man, however, there is a substantial classic spinothalamic tract, i.e., fibers coursing without interruption to relay nuclei and eventually to somatic area I. Until recently, "spinothalamic" and "anterolateral columns" were often equated and other ascending systems in these columns were ignored. The extent and termination of anterolateral pathways is now more fully appreciated because of the development of the Nauta stain for degenerating axons.

Many anterolateral fibers terminate in the brainstem, raising the question of whether they serve brainstem control of reflexes or continue on to the thalamus and cortex; if they continue on, do they perform any sensory function and, if so, what kind? Because these fibers are in a sense a new territory of neurophysiology, they will be described without regard to sensory function. Quite possibly, within this system lies the answer to the question of the affective aspect of sensation as exemplified by pain. Unthinkingly, pain has been identified with the spinothalamic tract to the extent that many

Fig. 12. Diagram of connections and projections of main thalamic nuclei. Geniculate bodies and nuclei with purely subcortical connection are not shown. Details of connections indicated by dotted lines are not known. Numbers along cerebral cortex designate Brodmann areas. (Based upon Walker and LeGros Clark. From Ruch, Kasdon and Walker, unpublished.)

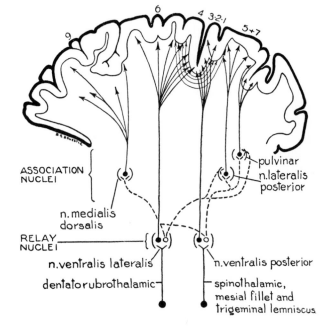

HINDFOOT

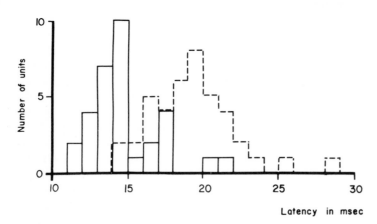

Fig. 13. Histogram of mean latencies for discharge of single units in somatosensory area II. Solid line, posterolateral tract intact; dashed lines, comparable data for dorsal column pathway. In both pathways units with small receptive fields were tested. (From Andersson, *Acta physiol. scand.,* 1962, *56:*Supplement 194.)

other components of the anterolateral column system which have different endings in the brainstem have been ignored. Mehler et al.[32] and Bowsher,[11] applying the Nauta technique to monkeys, describe the *anterolateral* (as opposed to the spinothalamic) system as follows:

Spinobulbar pathways. Many anterolateral fibers terminate in or give collaterals to the lateral reticular nucleus and to the medial reticular formation. Some of these are collaterals from spinothalamic axons ascending to the thalamus. Also, an independent spinoreticular tract terminating most strongly in the medial reticular "core" is probable.

Spinomesencephalic system. In man and monkey, axons from the anterolateral columns terminate in the mesencephalon, specifically in the deep layers of the superior colliculus (spinotectal fibers) and in the adjacent lateral aspect of the central gray substance; both pathways have been implicated in pain.

Spinoposterothalamic pathway. At the junction of the mesencephalon and the diencephalon, a group of fibers from the anterolateral columns splits off as it passes just medial to the medial geniculate body, terminating in the pars magnocellularis of that body and in the suprageniculate nucleus. Thus, some components relay in nuclei other than the classic ventral posterior relay nuclei. Some fibers from the medial lemniscus also end here.[11]

Spinal connections to medial nuclei. Another component splits off from the spinothalamic tract and pursues a medial course to synapse in the rather ill-defined nuclei making up the intralaminar group. According to Bowsher,[11] these fibers end in n. fascicularis and n. cen-

tralis lateralis but not in the large, easily identified center median or any other intralaminar nucleus. This pathway, preponderant in primitive mammals, has been termed the "paleospinal" pathway by Bishop[9] to distinguish it from the "true" or "classic" spinothalamic pathway that terminates more laterally in relay nuclei associated with the medial lemniscus. The later pathway he terms the "neospinalthalamic" tract, which, by convention, is what is meant when one speaks of the spinothalamic pathway without any modifier. The systems described above as synapsing elsewhere than in nn. ventralis posteromedialis and lateralis are "spinothalamic" but are not ordinarily included when one speaks of the spinothalamic tract, and they have different functional properties. The above description is based on the degeneration seen in the medial thalamus following interruption of the anterolateral columns of the spinal cord; to these must be added systems which synapse in the brain stem and continue on to thalamic areas which may or may not transmit impulses directly or indirectly to the cerebral cortex.

The multisynaptic and direct paleospinothalamic systems ending in the intralaminar nuclei will be discussed in Chapter 22.

Soon after introducing in this country the technique of single cortical neuron analysis of somatosensory function, Amassian discovered a somatosensory projection to an association area in the cat.[4] The same single unit was found to respond to large areas of the body surface, two legs or perhaps all four legs, and to more than one modality. This contrasts with the modality-specific cells of the postcentral gyrus.

In 1957, Whitlock and Perl[46, 74] discovered in the cat and monkey that peripheral stimuli evoke potentials in the magnocellular portion of the medial geniculate body when both posterior columns and one lateral column are sectioned. Natural stimuli such as a transient mechanical stimulus or a strong stimulus of almost any kind were also effective in evoking a response.[46] Responses also could be recorded somewhat posteriorly in adjoining tissue. Since posterior thalamic neurons have large, bilateral and often patchy receptive fields,[48] no topographic organization could be established. The same cell in this general posterior region responded to a wide variety of stimuli, including different somatic (though not joint movement) and auditory stimuli. They are neither "space-specific" nor "modality-specific." There is little reason to associate this region especially with pain, as Poggio and Mountcastle[48] have attempted. Much anatomic and physiologic evidence, of which only a part concerns us now, leads to the conclusion that the whole posterior region of the thalamus receives a wide variety of sensory inputs and projects to the "association areas" lying between the somesthetic, visual and auditory areas of the cerebral cortex.

It is concluded, therefore, that the posterior region of the thalamus contains two by-pass systems. One is indirect by way of relay nuclei to by-pass nuclei and is probably more heavily a posterior than an anterior column system. The second system involves posterior nuclei only and receives many more anterolateral than posterior column impulses.

Other Ascending Systems. Recent studies indicate the existence of a third sensory system which ascends in the *lateral columns* immediately adjacent to the posterior horn. This system, unlike the nearby dorsal spinocerebellar system, is not destined for the cerebellum but reaches somatic areas I and II. It is called the posterolateral tract or Morin's tract after its discoverer. Some axons in the region are ipsilaterally and monosynaptically excited and have restricted receptive fields. They respond specifically to light touch but not to stimulation of muscle nerves. Another group responds broadly in respect to place and modality. Both groups relay in the lateral cervical nucleus and terminate in sensory area I and sensory area II. Those with restricted fields have a latency shorter than the posterior column systems, as shown in Figure 13. Mark and Steiner[30] have identified a rapidly conducting system of fibers to the cerebral cortex which appear to run in the posterolateral position in the cord.

Kennedy and Towe[26] have recently discovered a fast pathway to the cat's motor and sensory cortex. This pathway conducts from bulb to cortex in 1.5 milliseconds (including one synapse), which is considerably more rapid

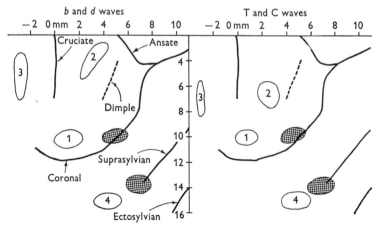

Fig. 14. Foci of maximal cortical response from the fast lemniscal system (cross hatching) demonstrated in two ways—ipsilateral ventral bulbar (left) and contralateral forepaw stimulation (right). The response in area 1 is centered on the coronal sulcus and that in area 2 on the suprasylvian. The numbered areas are maximal zones for slower lemniscal components. The *b* wave from ventral bulbar stimulation and the T wave potential evoked by peripheral stimuli are clearly the same and differ from the later *d* and C wave associated with slow lemniscal elements (From Morse and Towe, *J. Physiol.*, 1964, *171*:231–246.)

than other fibers in the medial lemniscus. Morse and Towe[34a] have shown that this pathway traverses the posterior columns, the rostral part of the cuneate nucleus, probably the posteroventral nucleus of the thalamus and projects caudolaterally to somatosensory areas I and II (Fig. 14). The fast lemniscal system is believed to convey touch impulses and the slow lemniscal system impulses from hair stimulation. This type of modality separation is different from that suggested by other investigators.

The fast posterolateral and the fast lemniscal pathways do not appear to be parts of the same system.

CORTICAL FUNCTION IN SENSATION

Anatomic and electrophysiologic studies give detailed knowledge of topographic organization of sensory systems and of what kind of sensory end-organ sends impulses to what region of the cortex, and experiments depending on human or animal behavior in a sense validate deductions from electrophysiology.

Electrical Stimulation.[44] The cortical sensory area was stimulated electrically in conscious patients by Cushing in 1909 and later by Foerster and by Penfield.[44] Stimulation of the area for the foot gives rise to sensations which seem to come from the foot; stimulation near the face area causes sensations localized to the face (see the *law of projection*). Sensations can often be elicited by stimulating the motor areas of the precentral gyrus even though the postcentral gyrus has been ablated, and these sen-

sations are similar in quality to those elicited by stimulation of the postcentral gyrus. Ease of elicitation correlates well with the density of thalamocortical projection fibers. Sensations of the spinothalamic category—pain, warmth and cold—are rarely reported, the usual responses being a sense of numbness, tingling and, especially, a sensation of movement unaccompanied by actual movement. The sensations are not clearly formed, but the same is true of those aroused by stimulation of a sensory nerve. No evidence of zonal localization of modalities has been obtained.

Ablation Experiments. Through special techniques developed by psychologists, an animal's sensory status after a cortical ablation can be inferred from his overt behavior (see Chap. 24). The ability to discriminate weight, roughness and geometric forms after the formation of various cortical lesions has been studied[56] objectively and quantitatively. Ablation of the postcentral gyrus (areas 3–1) reduces ability to discriminate roughness and weight in the chimpanzee (Fig. 15) and, to a lesser degree, in the monkey. Significantly, a parietal lobectomy (areas 5 and 7) interferes much more with the ability to discriminate weight and roughness than does ablation of the postcentral gyrus. Obviously, the posterior parietal lobule does not depend solely upon sensory impulses related through the short association fibers from the postcentral gyrus. Besides the direct pathway between relay nuclei and areas 3–1 (Fig. 12), there is growing evidence for the anatomic substrate demanded by these experiments, namely "by-pass" systems by which impulses from the

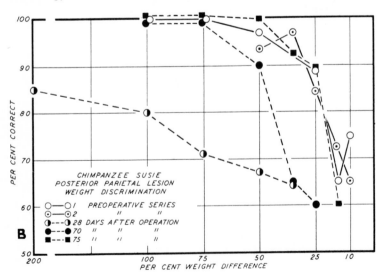

Fig. 15. Discrimination of lifted weights before and after ablation of the posterior parietal lobule contralateral to the arm tested, secondary to ipsilateral parietal lobectomy. Note the decreased ability shown in the first postoperative series. The improvement between the second and the third postoperative curve (filled circles and squares) is due to retraining, the lapse of time being insignificant. (From Ruch, Fulton and German, *Arch. Neurol. Psychiat.*, (*Chic.*), 1938, *39*:919–937.)

ascending sensory systems reach the cortex. As indicated above, fibers pass from relay nuclei via posterior thalamic nuclei to areas 5 and 7. Others by-pass the relay nuclei entirely; e.g., the anterolateral and posterior column systems synapse directly in the posterior thalamic region. The possibility that the spinothalamic components to the posterior thalamic nuclei are involved in weight discriminations becomes more likely because posterior column section, although interfering seriously with the discrimination of weights at first, has little permanent effect.[17] The anterolateral or the posterolateral tracts must support this recovery of function.

It may be concluded from much recent anatomic and physiologic investigation that the conventional pathway, from the thalamus to sensory area to the posterior-lying "association" area, is not the only course open to sensory impulses (see also Chap. 21). These and parallel experiments on auditory systems have led to the abandonment of the idea of "association areas" (Chap. 23).

Ablation of the parietal lobe also does not end ability to discriminate weights or roughness, except transiently. After an extensive lapse of time and retraining, impairment in ability to discriminate small differences in weight is all that remains. When discovered, the second somatic area was naturally suspected of underlying the recovery of discrimination function after parietal lobectomy. This was not borne out by later experimentation.[24a, 43] Although precentral lesions do not have great effects alone, when combined with extensive postcentral lesions they appear to increase the impairment.[24a] Further, indirect lines of evidence suggest that the so-called "motor areas" may serve discriminative functions and are, in fact, sensorimotor areas. For example, section of the medial lemniscus and spinothalamic tract in the midbrain leaves some weight discrimination and other proprioceptive functions.[60] When the lesion includes the dentatorubrothalamic tract, the impairment is much greater. However, as noted earlier, posterior column section in the monkey fails to abolish weight discrimination permanently. This result of posterior column section in the cervical region would seem to minimize the importance of the cerebellar "by-pass" because the fibers from the arm to the dorsospinal cerebellar pathway run in the posterior column up to the medulla (external cuneate nucleus) and therefore would be sec-

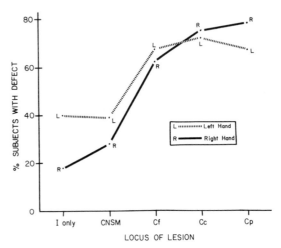

Fig. 16. Graph showing that missile wounds in the contralateral precentral (C_f), postcentral (C_c), and the posterior parietal (C_p) sectors cause sensory defects in about the same number of patients. I, lesions of the ipsilateral side only; CNSM, lesions sparing contralateral C_f, C_c, and C_p. (From Semmes *et al.*, *Somatosensory changes after penetrating brain wounds in man.* Cambridge, Mass., Harvard University Press, 1960.)

tioned. The posterolateral and anterolateral pathway systems may be involved. If so, their strong ipsilateral component may provide bilateral discrimination of weight and roughness. That in man, the three sectors—precentral, postcentral and posterior parietal lobule—are involved in sensation is shown in Figure 16, where it can be seen that penetrating wounds in the three regions produced somatosensory disturbances in about the same percentage of cases.[58]

Clinical Studies: Cortical Function in Man.[20, 21, 44, 56, 58, 70] The status of sensation can be learned in much greater detail in man than in animals, especially when refined, quantitative methods borrowed from the psychologists are used, as by Head[20] and more recently by Semmes et al.[58] However, interpretation may be confused by increased intracranial pressure, lesions which do not respect cytoarchitectural zones, lack of histologic verification of the lesion, especially when it is progressive, unconscious selection of cases, and failure to include control patients. Studies in man often show only the *kind* of sensory function carried on by the cerebral cortex and leave unanswered many of the questions on cortical localization and the "corticalization" of sensory functions.

Cortical lesions do not produce anesthesia

for any modality of sensation except as a transitory phenomenon. Persisting anesthesia implies subcortical damage, as shown in Figure 11 of the previous chapter, because the thalamus subserves sensation; deep lesions are more effective because they may injure the thalamus or because they interrupt projection fibers to a larger area of cortex. Cortical lesions are manifested by an increase in the threshold for elicitation of sensation, and in severe cases only the fact and kind of stimulation can be recognized. The modalities of sensation are not equally affected. Pain recovers most quickly and almost completely; pressure, warmth and cold recover next. Light touch and proprioceptive sensation are most severely and permanently damaged. Discrimination of intensity is subnormal for all modalities.

Perceptions having a strong spatial element —topognosis, two-point discrimination, figure writing and stereognosis—are especially affected by cortical lesions, and deficiencies in them may well be the first sign of damage to the parietal region. On the other hand, perception of temporal patterns (vibratory sensibility) is relatively little influenced by cortical lesions unless they extend into the white matter (Chap. 14, Fig. 11). Tactual and proprioceptive sensations, and the perceptions built upon them, are affected in much the same way by parietal and posterior column lesions. This is not true of vibratory sensibility, which is greatly blunted by posterior column lesions but not by cortical lesions. The defects of stereognosis represent more than the default of a necessary sensory channel. They occur, especially from parietal lesions, in a marked degree when sensation is not greatly disturbed. If sensation is disturbed, the term to use is "astereognosis through anesthesia," or "stereoanesthesia."

Because spatial and discriminative functions are severely damaged by cortical lesions, Head and others have given the impression that sensation has a thalamic and perception a cortical representation. Intensity and spatial functions have even been assigned different areas in the parietal lobes. To separate sensation and perception is not in accord with modern psychologic teaching or with the close interrelation between the thalamus and cerebral cortex. Apparently the discrimination of fine spatial functions and of differences in intensity requires a multitude of neurons arranged in dense, spatially organized fields. The cortex possesses such fields and the thalamus does not. Why else do regions with a high degree of spatial discriminative ability, e.g., the forefinger or the fovea of

the retina, have a wide expanse of the cortex devoted to them? Thus, even if the thalamus is capable of some form of sensation, it apparently does not possess the extensive apparatus necessary for fine discrimination and accurate localization, since only very few functional cells are left when the cortex is removed. Crude sensation of the type ascribed to the thalamus is "crude" in the sense that it is poorly located and capable only of coarse discrimination. Here, as in the discussion of epicritic and protopathic sensation, the same facts are open to two theories, one assuming qualitative difference and a different neural substrate, the other stressing quantitative and topographic differences in the neuronal organization of tracts and projection fields.

It is possible to argue that lamination and topographic organization at the thalamus and cortex represent mere engineering conveniences and are not functionally significant. Two facts would support this belief. The posterior parietal lobe is poorly organized topographically; yet damage to it can interfere with spatial discriminations, even though the highly organized apparatus of the postcentral gyrus remains intact. Moreover, the single cortical unit technique applied to the association area of a cat under chloralose anesthesia (a cortical excitant) shows that the same cell in the somatic association area can be fired from all four limbs and from superficial, deep and visceral nerves.[4] Topographic organization appears to be progressively less in ascending through the various levels of the nervous system. Some of the modern speculation based upon work of communication engineers suggests that this very dispersal rather than canalization may make more accurate discriminations possible. This question will be treated in detail below.

NEURAL BASIS OF SPECIFIC SENSORY FUNCTIONS

In the preceding chapters the dimensions of a sensation—e.g., quality and intensity, the nature of perception and judgment, and the connative (affective) aspects—were defined and clinical tests were described. The neural pathways for somatic sensation as known from anatomy and electrophysiology have been described; in this section, the neural basis for various aspects of sensation will be discussed.

Quality.   The ability to experience the several modalities of sensation is subjective so that knowledge of the role of the thalamus and cortex depends on clinical studies. Even studies of the hemidecorticate man do not give a clear answer because sensation may be served by ipsilateral pathways to the intact cortex. Thus, in the side of the face contralateral to an hemispherectomy, touch and pinpricks are quite well appreciated (and to some degree localized), but over the body all forms of sensation are lost except the appreciation of heavy touches and pinpricks. Loss of a hemisphere including the thalamus leaves some pain sensibility. Lesions less in extent than a hemispherectomy leave appreciation of the kind of stimulation (quality) intact while interfering with other aspects of the sensation such as localization. Thus, pain conventionally considered a thalamic function could be due either to the ipsilateral pathways to the intact hemisphere or to midbrain.

Pain and Affect. Neither pain nor affect is a single, simple thing. Pain varies from the bright, localized, mildly unpleasant experience of a pinprick to insufferable, excruciating perversion of pain and affect, better described as suffering rather than pain. An understanding of the pain-hyperpathia-suffering continuum spans the distance between the oldest, most primitive remnants in the nervous system to the frontal lobe, which has undergone perhaps the greatest phylogenetic development of any part of the brain. A guiding principle in understanding pain goes back to Hughlings Jackson, Henry Head and C. J. Herrick. According to this principle, when evolution builds a new story on the nervous system it never quite abandons the older ones but merely conceals them by an inhibitory overlay until disease comes along and allows the primitive mechanism free play. Livingston[28] has likened the physician's approach to pain to a chess game; if so, the opponent is often an ancestral ghost. The evolutionary approach to pain was ably developed by Bishop,[9] and much of a second guiding principle to understanding pain is based on his work and that of Collins.[14, 15] This principle may be stated as follows: Fiber size is not only related to the evolutionary development of a sensory system but also is maintained from the periphery throughout the sensory system.

Bilateral anterolateral cordotomy may control pain completely (but often does not control perversion of pain). Therefore, it would appear that the posterolateral spinal pathway is not concerned with pain, a view consistent with its rapid conduction rate. By contrast, mesencephalic spinothalamic tractotomy has been unsuccessful. Cutting the spinothalamic tract at this site would leave open the fine-fibered spinobulbar reticular pathway described earlier. The pain remaining is especially unpleasant and is described as the causalgic or "burning" type.[9] Because this pathway is multisynaptic to the site of thalamic synapse it is somewhat difficult to determine, but the strong development of the medial reticular system suggests a medial location. At the midbrain level pain impulses from the feet are carried in the central gray and in the spinothalamic tract. Section of each separately abolishes pain for a few days, so there are two pathways for pain.[33] Electrodes have been implanted in each of the two pathways in cats and connected with different lever-switches under the animals' control. Stimulation through either pathway causes unmistakable signs of pain and the cats quickly learn to open whichever circuit the experimenter has closed; i.e., a subjective discrimination must have taken place. The two pathways must therefore serve two kinds of pain sensation.

That a component of the anterolateral pathway terminates in the tectum of the midbrain lends substance to several observations linking it with pain. Painlike responses to skin stimulation are retained when a lesion is placed just below the thalamus.[69] Stimulation in the tectal region in man causes subjective pain sensation, and the objective signs from similar experiments in animals persist after destruction of the posteroventral thalamus.[61]

Head[20] believed that affect was served by a midline structure of the thalamus. The medial coursing multisynaptic pathways discussed would, from their anatomic position near or in the central gray substance reach the medial thalamic structures. Another significant group of fibers split off from the classic spinothalamic tract just as it enters the thalamus and takes a medial course terminating in the intralaminar nuclei. Attempts[48] to implicate a pathway through the posterior thalamic nuclei and sensory area II in nociception have less force than the more direct experiments of Perl and Whitlock,[46] which show that impulses from gentle cutaneous stimulation reach this region.

Pain is only slightly and transiently affected by cortical lesions, and clear-cut pain experiences are not elicited by stimulating the human cerebral cortex. In contrast to stimulation of the spinothalamic tract or the lateral nuclear mass of the thalamus, stimulation of the sensorimotor cortex will not motivate behavior, as will peripherally induced pain.[16]

Clinical correlations: Thalamic syndrome. In a classic "thalamic syndrome," spontaneous pain and subjective over-response to pleasant and unpleasant stimuli are prominent features. This syndrome is usually caused by occlusion of a small blood vessel (thalamogeniculate branch of the posterior cerebral artery) which supplies the posterolateral portion of the lateral nuclear mass of the thalamus.

The syndrome consists of unilateral symptoms:[68] (i) fleeting hemiplegia or hemiparesis, (ii) sensory disturbances of the cortical type, and (iii) over-response or hyperpathia. Attacks of "spontaneous" or central pain of a severe, agonizing nature are common. Pinprick or strong stimulation produces an intensely disagreeable, irradiating, diffuse sensation which is quite intolerable. One of Head's patients, a clergyman, complained that his trousers produced such disagreeable sensations that he was forced to remove them! Pleasantness of a sensation is also magnified, and emotional responses to music give rise to excessive "feelings" on one side of the body! Sensory over-response differs from hyperesthesia because the threshold is often elevated, but once it is attained the experience is overly intense. Little definite can be said about the thalamic syndrome. Spontaneous pain and over-response have in common with the hyperpathia produced by disturbances at lower levels a reduction of touch and deep sensibility paralleled by a heightened response to painful stimuli. Perhaps all have a common explanation in the hypothesis that affective activity of the midline nuclei is normally held in check when the ventral posterior nucleus is activated.

Neural Basis of Intensity Appreciation.

From psychological experiments in which the differences between small weights were estimated by lifting them, Weber discovered in the nineteenth century that the smallest discriminable difference (just noticeable difference, j.n.d.) is a constant fraction of the weights themselves, the so-called "Weber fraction." This fraction is approximately 1/30; i.e., 31 grams is discriminated from 30, 62 grams from 60, and so on. This is usually stated as $\Delta I/I = C$, in which ΔI means a just discriminable increment of intensity.

Fechner's name is linked to Weber's because by mathematical manipulation he derived a relationship between stimulus and sensation. By assuming that discriminable increments are equal units of sensation, he derived the Weber-Fechner law:

$$\text{Sensation} = K \log I + C$$

Although a logarithm function describes the relationship between stimulus intensity and frequency of sense organ discharge (see Chap. 4), it does not apply to sensation when measured in other ways nor to the frequency of response of thalamic and cortical neurons.

The measurement of sensation—psychophysics—is performed by means of three procedures:

1. *Discriminability scales* are scales of equal (just noticeable) differences.

2. *Category scales* are obtained, for example, by assigning a series of tones to a given number of equally spaced categories.

3. *Magnitude scales* are exemplified by the method of "magnitude estimation." The observer simply assigns a number to the intensity of his subjective impression relative to a standard. This is a ratio scale like the decibel scale used in expressing sound intensities.

The different results yielded by these three methods are shown in Figure 17. The j.n.d. scale approximates a logarithmic function and the magnitude scale is a power function which approximates a straight line because its exponent value is nearly one (0.95). The method of magnitude estimation has been applied to a large number of sensory processes, each time yielding a power function though of a variable magnitude.

Plotted on log-log coordinates, the power function becomes a straight line whether the

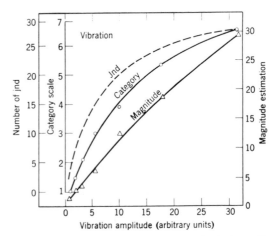

Fig. 17. Three psychophysical methods quantifying apparent intensity of the amplitude of a vibration applied to the finger tip. Note that the axes of the graph are linear. (From Stevens, In: *Sensory communication.* W. A. Rosenblith, ed., New York, John Wiley & Sons, 1961.)

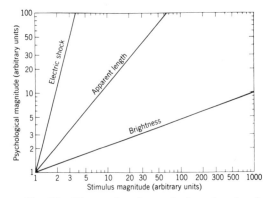

Fig. 18. The results of magnitude estimation for three sensory functions plotted on log-log coordinates. The slope of the line corresponds to the exponent of the power function relating psychological to physical magnitude. (From Stevens, In: *Sensory communication.* W. A. Rosenblith, ed., New York, John Wiley & Sons, 1961.)

exponent is less or more than one (Fig. 18). This permits easy comparison of the effect of, say, doubling stimulus intensity on subjective response for any number of stimuli.

Data gained by such a subjective procedure as assigning a number to the strength of a sensation naturally cause skepticism. However, the validity of the data is shown by several experiments, e.g., cross-modality comparisons. If a subject is asked to equate throughout the intensity series the loudness of a noise with the amplitude of a tactual vibration, the relationship between the two modalities is linear (Fig. 19). The slope of the line is close to that predicted from the ratios of exponents of the loudness and vibration function.

Another cross-modality comparison is *ratio matching*. The subject may be asked to adjust one loudness to another so that they bear the same relation to each other as two presented brightnesses bear to each other, i.e., C is to D as A is to B. If both energies are plotted relative to threshold, i.e., using a decibel scale for light as well as sound, the relationship is indicated by an approximately 45° line, showing nearly perfect cross-modality matching.

In another remarkable experiment the subject is asked to squeeze a hand dynamometer in proportion to loudness of a noise. When the force of the grip is plotted against loudness a straight line results. In fact, when grip is scaled against different sensory stimulation, the obtained exponent agrees well with the predicted exponent.

Parenthetically, it is worth knowing that functions far removed from sensation lend themselves to scaling procedures. For example, a group of students asked to apply a number to the seriousness of various kinds of juvenile delinquency produced a scale which agreed well with a similar one produced by judges of the juvenile court.

In summary, the relationship between physical energy and sensation seems best described not by a logarithmic function as in the Weber-Fechner law, but by a power function of a ratio of a given response to threshold. In a nicely mnemonic equation, Steven's law states

$$\Psi = K\,(\Phi - \Phi_\theta)^n$$

The psychological magnitude *psi* is related to a power of the magnitude of the physical stimulus *phi* less the threshold effective stimulus. The magnitude range of the exponent *n* for natural environmental stimuli has ranged between 0.33 for visual brightness and 1.6 for warmth; for electrical stimulation, 3.5.

Psychologic and physiologic correlation. The discharge frequency of a thalamic or cortical neuron is held to be an analog of stimulus intensity. The nature of this relationship—logarithmic versus a power function—can be determined and tested quantitatively most nearly ideally by using joint receptors. The frequency of impulses from these receptors returns, after an accelerated discharge during and just after joint movement, to an almost steady state

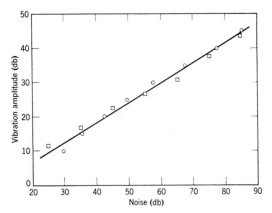

Fig. 19. Equal sensation functions obtained by adjusting loudness to match tactual vibration (circles) and vice versa (squares). Note that the stimuli are expressed on a logarithmic (decibel) scale. (From Stevens, In: *Sensory communication.* W. A. Rosenblith, ed., New York, John Wiley & Sons, 1961.)

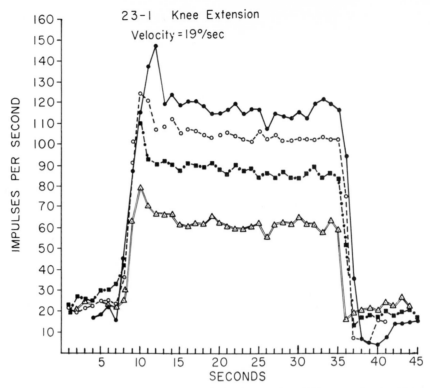

Fig. 20. The response frequency of a single thalamic neuron to different maintained joint angles reached by a constant velocity of joint rotation. Movement toward extension started at the 7th second, those toward flexion at the 35th second. (From Mountcastle, Poggio and Werner, *J. Neurophysiol.*, 1963, *26*:807–834.)

which is independent of the velocity of the previous movement (Fig. 20).

When the frequencies of response in certain thalamic cells for different joint angles are plotted in the same way as the psychophysiologic data in Figure 18, a similar straight line relationship is found (Fig. 21).

There is here a very close correlation between a psychologic (magnitude estimation) and a physiologic measurement (frequency of thalamic neuron response) of the central analogs of stimulus intensity. Not only are they both power functions, but the size of the exponent for joint position (average 0.7) falls in the same range as mechanoreception studied psychologically, 1.0. This is perhaps the most successful cross-correlation between electrical events and psychologic phenomena yet achieved.

Neural Basis of Localization and Two-point Discrimination. Weber assumed that the two-point threshold for a given region was fixed by the size of the skin area to which terminals of a single nerve fiber are distributed (so-called Weber's sensory circles). When one unexcited

sensory brush remained between the two on which the compass rested, the points were, according to Weber, appreciated as two. The size of cutaneous receptive fields is to some degree correlated with the size of the two-point threshold in the same region. But Weber's notion of two excited receptors and an intervening unexcited one, each with a private path to the cerebral cortex, is now recognized to be incorrect. The ramifications within the skin of a single posterior root fiber do not occupy discrete areas but overlap. It is implicit in Weber's concept that the three neurons making up the sensory pathway from receptor to sensory cortex constitute a simple chain having no cross-connections with other chains at the synaptic levels. Even in the most highly organized somatosensory system each peripheral axon excites a large number of cortical cells and this divergence occurs at each synaptic station, as shown in Figure 22. There being no point-to-point projection, maxima may be discriminated. One factor sharpening these peaks is a peripheral axon's greater frequency of firing from the center of its receptive field than from the periphery (lower left). The same is true of the much larger receptive field of a cortical neuron. That inhibition of a cortical unit can follow a volley to a somatosensory input which does not itself fire that unit was first clearly demonstrated by Towe and Amassian[66] in 1957 (see Fig. 23). This established the existence of a true inhibition not due to neuron sharing. As in the auditory and visual systems, an excitatory receptive field is surrounded by an inhibitory one. However, inhibitory fields of postcentral neurons are even larger than the excitatory fields and can include the whole area from elbow to wrist.[51] A highly suggestive observation is that adjacent or nearby cells often act reciprocally—one excited, the other inhibited. It is difficult to visualize the summation of excitatory fields and inhibitory surrounds of overlapping receptive fields of such large dimensions as giving sharp peaks. The problem of the two-point threshold is much the same as that of visual acuity, in which a start has been made on understanding spatial discrimination.

Amassian[5] attaches great weight to the fact that at each synapse sensory units, unlike motoneurons, tend to fire in bursts or trains of impulses. This is true of the posterior column as well as of the anterolateral system. Possibly, the temporal features of cortical activity play a role in "coding" the locus of a stimulus over and above the intensity information conveyed by frequency. In any case, a complete explanation of cortical function must include an explanation of the propensity of afferent neurons to fire repetitively. Amassian further points out that tactual acuity (discrimination of grades of sandpaper) carried out in the absence of the postcentral gyrus casts doubt on the dependence of acuity on topographic organization. He concludes from a detailed review that "At present, it appears unlikely that discriminative abilities are any more dependent on topographically organized cortex than they are on nontopographically organized cortex. . . . It is most unlikely that two portions of the body stimulated at various intensities could induce an identical temporal pattern of activity in a population of

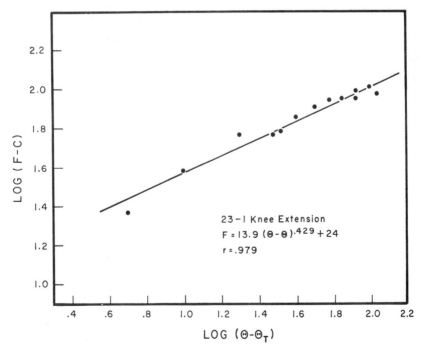

Fig. 21. Discharge frequency of a thalamic neuron plotted against joint angle. Frequency was obtained after the discharge had reached steady state. The same transformation used by Stevens was used here: subtraction of spontaneous rate (C) from obtained frequency (F), subtraction of threshold angle Θ from each angle plotted, and conversion of the stimulus continuum to a ratio scale. Both Θ variables are expressed on a log-log scale as in Figure 19. The Pearson coefficient of correlation of .979 indicates how well the straight line fits the data. (From Mountcastle, Poggio and Werner, *J. Neurophysiol.*, 1963, *26*: 807–834.)

central neurons. The major problems facing such studies are to identify those particular relationships between unit responses of different neurons which persist in the face of a change in stimulus intensity and to prove that such a pattern of activity engenders specific responses of the organism. The need for a statistical interpretation became apparent when it was discovered that stimulation of a given set of fibers led to discharge of neurons A.B.C., etc., with probabilities P_a, P_b, P_c, etc."

The paradox of the nervous system is that in ascending the sensory pathways both di-

mensions of a sensory input have remained relatively unrestricted in space (overlap, divergence–convergence) and time (repetitive firing); at least the former is greater in cortical than in subcortical levels and in the newer "association" than in the older primary sensory areas.

The optimists can argue that even the human brain has just taken the first step toward a one-to-one relationship between points and points on the cortex in the posterior column system and has a great evolutionary future before it. Others, however, including communica-

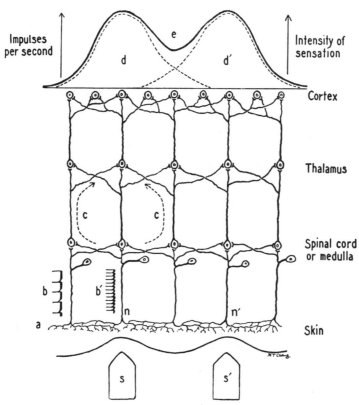

Fig. 22. Schematic diagram illustrating some neural factors involved in localization and in discrimination of two points; s and s′ are the points of compass used in determining a two point threshold; a is plexus of interlocking terminals; b and b′ show rate of discharge from sensory neuron stimulated at periphery of terminal brush and second neuron stimulated at center of its distribution. Arrows c illustrate that tendency of excitation to spread in first synaptic layer results in intensification by facilitation of core neuron in next synaptic layer; d and d′ represent graphically frequency of corticopetal impulses arriving upon (and hence activity of) each cortical cell when due to s and s′ respectively; e represents summed activity pattern; d, d′ and e are termed *modal excitation fields.** In the diagram an attempt has been made to combine the views of Weber, Bernstein, Lorente de Nó, Tower, and Marshall and Talbot but not the surround inhibition of Towe and Amassian, Mountcastle and Powell and others.

*In a frequency curve in which classes are arranged along the abscissae from small to large and the number falling within each class is graphed, the mode is that class which contains the largest number of frequencies or members.

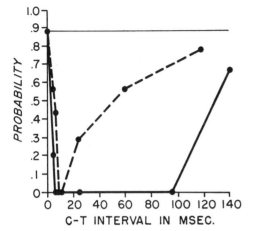

Fig. 23. Demonstration of inhibition by conditioning—test shocks applied to the digits showing that inhibition decreases with greater spatial separation on the skin. Note that stimulation of the middle finger, which almost never failed to cause firing, fails to fire for nearly 100 msec. (solid line) when preceded by a shock to the index finger. Stimulation of the thumb caused shorter-lasting inhibition. Probability of stimulation of thumb or index finger firing the unit was nearly zero. (From Towe and Amassian, *J. Neurophysiol.,* 1958, *21:* 292-311.)

tion engineers, see virtues in the "sloppiness" of the nervous system. Certainly the engineers faced with the problem of conveying the maximum amount of information over the minimum number of lines quickly abandoned the door bell model.

Much ingenious experimentation and sophisticated thinking will be required before we learn what, if anything, is gained by the lack of spatial and temporal constraint in sensory pathways.

REFERENCES

1. AMASSIAN, V. E. *J. Neurophysiol.,* 1951, *14:*433–444.
2. AMASSIAN, V. E., *J. Neurophysiol.,* 1951, *14:*445–460.
3. AMASSIAN, V. E. *Res. Publ. Ass. nerv. ment. Dis.,* 1952, *30:* 371–402.
4. AMASSIAN, V. E. *J. Neurophysiol.,* 1954, *17:*39–58.
5. AMASSIAN, V. E. *Int. Rev. Neurobiol.,* 1961, *3:*67–136.
6. AMASSIAN, V. E. and DeVITO, R. V. *J. Neurophysiol.,* 1954, *17:*575–603.
7. ANDERSON, J. A. *Acta physiol. scand.,* 1962, *56:* Suppl. 194.
8. v. BEKESY, G. *J. acoust. Soc. Amer.,* 1957, *29:*1059–1069; *ibid.,* 1958, *30:*399–412.
9. BISHOP, G. H. Chap. 5 in *Neural physiopathology.* R. G. Grenell, ed. New York, Harper & Row, 1962.
10. BORING, E. G. *Sensation and perception in the history of experimental psychology.* New York, D. Appleton-Century Co., 1942.
11. BOWSHER, D. *J. comp. Neurol.,* 1961, *117:*213–222.
12. BROOKHART, J. M., LIVINGSTON, W. K. and HAUGEN, F. P. *J. Neurophysiol.,* 1953, *16:*634–642.
13. CLARK, W. E. LeG. and BOGGON, R. H. *Phil. Trans.,* 1935, *B224:*313–359.
14. COLLINS, W. F. and RANDT, C. T. *J. Neurophysiol.,* 1958, *21:*345–352.
15. COLLINS, W. F., NULSEN, F. E. and RANDT, C. T. *Arch. Neurol. (Chic.),* 1960, *3:*381–385.
16. DELGADO, J. M. R., ROBERTS, W. W. and MILLER, N. E. *Amer. J. Physiol.,* 1954, *179:*587–593.
17. DeVITO (LOGAN), J. *Study of sensory pathways in monkeys.* Ph.D. Thesis, University of Washington, 1954.
18. FOERSTER, O. *Bumke u. Foersters Handb. Neurol.,* 1936, *5:*1–403.
19. HARRISON, F. and CORBIN, K. B. *J. Neurophysiol.,* 1942, *5:* 465–482.
20. HEAD, H. *Studies in neurology.* London, Oxford University Press, 1920.
21. HOLMES, G. *Brain,* 1927, *50:*413–427.
22. HYNDMAN, O. R. and WOLKIN, J. *Arch. Neurol. Psychiat. (Chic.),* 1943, *50:*129–148.
23. KEEGAN, J. J. *Arch. Neurol. Psychiat. (Chic.),* 1943, *50:*67–83.
24. KEEGAN, J. J. and GARNETT, F. D. *Anat. Rec.,* 1948, *102:* 409–437.
24a. KRUGER, L. and PORTER, P. *J. comp. Neurol.,* 1958, *109:* 439–467.
25. LANDAU, W. and BISHOP, G. H. *Arch. Neurol. Psychiat. (Chic.)* 1953, *69:*490–504.
26. KENNEDY, T. T. and TOWE, A. L. *J. Physiol.,* 1962, *160:* 535–547.
27. LEWIS, T. *Pain.* New York, Macmillan, 1942.
28. LIVINGSTON, W. K. In *Basic research in paraplegia.* J. D. French and R. W. Porter, eds., Springfield, Ill., Charles C Thomas, 1962.
29. MALIS, L. I., PRIBRAM, K. H. and KRUGER, L. *J. Neurophysiol.,* 1953, *16:*161–167.
30. MARK, R. F. and STEINER, J. *J. Physiol.,* 1958, *142:*544–562.
31. MEHLER, W. R. In *Basic research in paraplegia.* J. D. French and R. W. Porter, eds., Springfield, Ill., Charles C Thomas, 1962.
32. MEHLER, W. R., FEFERMAN, M. E. and NAUTA, W. J. H. *Brain,* 1960, *83:*718–750.
33. MELZACK, R., STOTLER, W. and LIVINGSTON, W. K. *J. Neurophysiol.,* 1958, *21:*353–367.
34. MORIN, F. *Amer. J. Physiol.,* 1955, *183:*245–252.
34a. MORSE, R. W. and TOWE, A. L. *J. Physiol.,* 1964, *171:* 231–246.
35. MOUNTCASTLE, V. B. *J. Neurophysiol.,* 1957, *20:*408–434.
36. MOUNTCASTLE, V. B. Chap. 22 in *Sensory communication.* W. A. Rosenblith, ed., New York, John Wiley & Sons, 1961.
37. MOUNTCASTLE, V. B., COVIAN, M. R. and HARRISON, C. R. *Res. Publ. Ass. nerv. ment. Dis.,* 1952, *30:*339–370.
38. MOUNTCASTLE, V. B. and HENNEMAN, E. *J. Neurophysiol.,* 1949, *12:*85–100.
39. MOUNTCASTLE, V. B. and HENNEMAN, E. *J. comp. Neurol.,* 1952, *97:*409–439.
40. MOUNTCASTLE, V. B., POGGIO, G. F. and WERNER, G. *J. Neurophysiol.,* 1963, *26:*807–834.
41. MOUNTCASTLE, V. B. and POWELL, T. P. S. *Bull. Johns Hopk. Hosp.* 1959, *105:*173–200, *idem,* 201–232.
42. NORRSELL, V. and VOORHOEVE, P. *Acta physiol. scand.,* 1962, *54:*9–17.
43. ORBACH, J. and CHOW, K. L. *J. Neurophysiol.,* 1959, *22:* 195–203.

44. PENFIELD, W. and RASMUSSEN, A. T. *The cerebral cortex in man: a clinical study of localization of function.* New York, Macmillan, 1950.

45. PERL, E. R. *Ann. Rev. Physiol.,* 1963, *25:*459–492.

46. PERL, E. R. and WHITLOCK, D. G. *Exp. Neurol.,* 1961, *3:* 256–296.

47. POCHIN, E. E. *Clin. Sci.,* 1938, *3:*191–196.

48. POGGIO, G. F. and MOUNTCASTLE, V. B. *Bull. Johns Hopk. Hosp.,* 1960, *106:*266–316.

49. POGGIO, G. F. and MOUNTCASTLE, V. B. *J. Neurophysiol.,* 1963, *26:*775–806.

50. POLLOCK, L. J. *J. comp. Neurol.,* 1920, *32:*357–378.

51. POWELL, T. P. S. and MOUNTCASTLE, V. B. *Bull. Johns Hopk. Hosp.,* 1959, *105:*133–162.

52. RANSON, S. W., DROEGEMUELLER, W. H., DAVENPORT, H. K. and FISHER, C. *Res. Publ. Ass. nerv. ment. Dis.,* 1935, *15:*3–34.

53. ROSE, J. E. and MOUNTCASTLE, V. B. Chap. 17 in *Handbook of physiology. Section 1. Neurophysiology,* vol. 1, J. Field, ed. Washington, D. C., American Physiological Society, 1959.

54. RUCH, T. C. Chap. 19 in *Physiology of the nervous system,* 3d ed., J. F. Fulton, ed. New York, Oxford University Press, 1949.

55. RUCH, T. C. Chap. 4 in *Handbook of experimental psychology,* S. S. Stevens, ed., New York, John Wiley & Sons, 1951.

56. RUCH, T. C., FULTON, J. F., and GERMAN, W. J. *Arch. Neurol. Psychiat. (Chic.),* 1938, *39:*919–937.

57. RUCH, T. C., PATTON, H. D. and AMASSIAN, V. E. *Res. Publ. Ass. nerv. ment. Dis.,* 1952, *30:*403–429.

58. SEMMES, J., WEINSTEIN, S., GHENT, L. and TEÛBER, H.-L. *Somatosensory changes after penetrating brain wounds in man.* Cambridge, Mass., Harvard University Press, 1960.

59. SHERRINGTON, C. S. *Phil. Trans.,* 1898, *B190:*45–186.

59a. SINCLAIR, D. C. and STOKES, B. A. R. *Brain,* 1964, *87:* 609–618.

60. SJÖQVIST, O. and WEINSTEIN, E. A. *J. Neurophysiol.,* 1942, *5:*69–74.

61. SPIEGEL, E. A., KLETZKIN, M. and SZEKELY, E. G. *J. Neuropath. exp. Neurol.,* 1954, *13:*212–220.

62. STEIN, M. H. and WORTIS, H. *Arch. Neurol. Psychiat. (Chic.),* 1941, *46:*471–476.

63. STEIN, M. H., WORTIS, H. and JOLLIFFE, N. *Arch. Neurol. Psychiat. (Chic.),* 1941, *46:*464–470.

64. STEVENS, S. S. Chap. 1 in *Sensory communication.* W. B. Rosenblith, ed. New York, John Wiley & Sons, 1961.

65. SWEET, W. H. Chap. 19 in *Handbook of physiology, Section 1.* vol. 1. J. Field, ed. Washington, D. C. American Physiological Society, 1959.

66. TOWE, A. L. and AMASSIAN, V. E. *J. Neurophysiol.,* 1958, *21:*292–311.

67. TROTTER, W. and DAVIES, H. M. *J. Psychol. Neurol. (Lpz.),* 1913, *20,* Erganzungsheft *2:*102–150.

68. WALKER, A. E. *The primate thalamus.* Chicago, University of Chicago Press, 1938.

69. WALKER, A. E. *Res. Publ. Ass. nerv. ment. Dis.,* 1943, *23:*63–85.

70. WALSHE, F. M. R. *Brain,* 1942, *65:*48–112.

71. WEDDELL, G., GUTTMANN, L. and GUTMANN, E. *J. Neurol. Psychiat.,* 1941, *N.S. 4:*206–225.

72. WHITE, J. C. and SWEET, W. H. *Pain. Its mechanisms and neurosurgical control.* Springfield, Ill., Charles C Thomas, 1955.

73. WHITE, J. C., SWEET, W. H., HAWKINS, R. and NILGES, R. G. *Brain,* 1950, *73:*346–367.

74. WHITLOCK, D. G. and PERL, E. R. *J. Neurophysiol.,* 1959, *22:*133–148.

75. WHITLOCK, D. G. and PERL, E. R. *Exp. Neurol.,* 1961, *3:* 240–255.

76. WOOLSEY, C. N. and FAIRMAN, D. *Surgery,* 1946, *19:*684–702.

77. WOOLSEY, C. N., MARSHALL, W. H. and BARD, P. *Bull. Johns Hopk. Hosp.,* 1942, *70:*399–441.

78. ZOTTERMAN, Y. *J. Physiol.,* 1939, *95:*1–28.

Pathophysiology of Pain

By THEODORE C. RUCH

In the previous two chapters the pathologic physiology of pain as seen in disturbances of the nervous system has been stressed. The present chapter will deal with the pain arising from pathologic processes at the periphery: visceral pain, muscle and joint pain and cutaneous hyperalgesia. In a sense, all pain is pathologic, but these forms of pain are especially so. This chapter will also deal with the physiologic mechanisms involved in psychosomatic pain states.

Characteristics of Pain. Pain is often described as pricking, stabbing, tearing, stinging, burning or throbbing. These descriptions reflect the duration of the sensation or identify it with an agent which has caused such pain in the past. Many agents (needle prick, pinching, traction on a hair, heat, electric current, etc.) cause indistinguishable "pricking" pains when briefly and focally applied.[28] The same stimuli prolonged cause a "burning" pain, even though heat is not involved. What Lewis[28] called the time–intensity curve of pain makes pains seem different and often suggests a possible origin. A needle prick produces a flash of pain. The impact of the pulse wave over sensitive pain organs will cause a throbbing pain, etc. Figure 1 gives additional examples.

Sharp pain elicited from the skin is called "bright." Heavy, diffuse, aching pain from the deeper layer of the skin or the subjacent receptors, as is elicited by sustained pinching of the web between the fingers, is called "dull." The autonomic responses to deep and visceral pain—sweating, nausea, fall in blood pressure causing pain to be sickening—differ from those

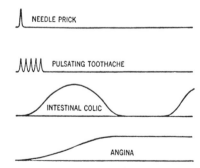

Fig. 1. Time-intensity curves of some common forms of pain. (From Lewis, *Pain,* New York, Macmillan, 1952.)

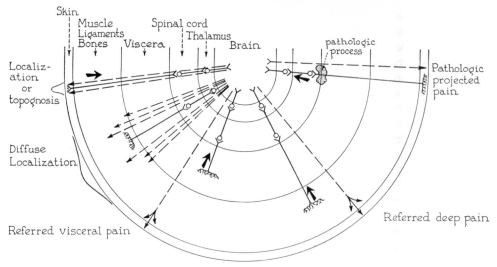

Fig. 2. Highly schematic representation of the projection of pain to points distant from the actual stimulation. Note that the place from which the pain seems to come (projection) may be incorrect in respect to two dimensions, depth and distance.

to cutaneous pain. Thus, pain is a protean phenomenon differing in quality and time course, depending on how it is elicited.

Localization, Projection and Reference of Pain. These words are related but should not be used indiscriminately. The basic concept is *projection* (see Chap. 14), a psychologic process which makes sensation seem to come from some layer of the body or from the external world. *Localization* (topognosis) reflects slight random errors in the projection of the sensation to the skin (Fig. 2). The clarity and extent of the projection can vary. Deep and visceral pain are often described as diffuse and poorly localized. *Projected pathologic pain* accurately describes the fact that impulses set up anywhere along the pain pathway from nerve to cortex give rise to a sensation projected to the peripheral region served by the end-organs of that pathway. Thus, the pain from a ruptured intervertebral disk is projected, not referred. (Note that it is the stimulus that is pathologic; the projection is normal, the brain merely having been tricked.) *Referred pain* is pain projected to an area distant from and usually superficial to the point of end-organ stimulation. Referred pain can be described as a systematic error in the projection of pain; examples will be given below.

CUTANEOUS HYPERALGESIA

In many pathologic states of the skin, light innocuous contacts not normally painful, such as friction from clothes, arouse pain. Often the pain is an especially intense, unpleasant, burning sensation which is diffuse, poorly localized or prolonged. This condition, called *hyperalgesia*, can be caused by a large number of agents (heat, abrasions, ultraviolet light, freezing, etc.). Two forms of hyperalgesia appear to exist. In *local* or *primary hyperalgesia*, the threshold is lowered; the response is intense, often burning in character, is accompanied by vasodilation (reddening) and extends beyond the area of damage, though not so far as in *secondary hyperalgesia*. In secondary hyperalgesia the threshold is actually elevated, but the response, once it occurs, is unpleasant. The zone of secondary hyperalgesia extends beyond the injured area and the surrounding zone of vasodilation. Secondary hyperalgesia is akin to referred pain.

Primary Hyperalgesia. Although it is common experience that some time after an injury the skin becomes reddened and hypersensitive to pain, it was not until 1933 that a major study of this phenomenon was conducted.[29] Pain resulting from brief stimulation of a hyperalgesic area has a burning quality. It is translated into actual pain when the area is heated. Cooling reduces the hyperalgesia.

Because the hyperalgesic state develops after a painless interval, Lewis and Hess[29] reasoned that it is not caused by persisting damage of nerve endings dating from the trauma. Echlin and Propper[15] demonstrated a sense organ basis for hyperalgesia. They applied equal stimuli to intact and scraped frog skin and recorded from

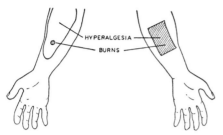

Fig. 3. Arm to right illustrates primary hyperalgesia confined to area of lesion; arm to left, secondary hyperalgesia extending well beyond burn. (From Hardy *et al.*, *J. clin. Invest.*, 1950, *29*:115–140.)

the cutaneous nerves. After scraping, the stimulus elicited more of the slowly conducted impulses typical of pain, and the threshold was lower. In minor injuries, hyperalgesia is confined to the traumatized area (Fig. 3), but, with greater injury, it gradually spreads out somewhat, especially along lymphatic channels. This pattern would result from the diffusion of a substance which causes both pain and vasodilatation, part of the inflammation process. Histamine is such a substance. Lewis and Hess[29] believed that some other, unidentified, substance is involved, because hyperalgesia is not combined with itching, the main response to histamine injected intradermally.

Primary hyperalgesia caused by the local release of chemical substances from damaged cells and coincident with the area of damage (and the wheal) may be termed *local primary hyperalgesia* in contrast with what may be termed *circumferential hyperalgesia*.* In the former, the peripheral nerves are involved only in transmitting pain impulses to the central nervous

* Considerable confusion in terminology has arisen because two terms, "primary hyperalgesia" and "secondary hyperalgesia," have been used to describe three events. In the light of new evidence we are adding a subclass to primary hyperalgesia— "circumferential hyperalgesia"—rather than treat this phenomenon as an alternate mechanism of secondary hyperalgesia as in the previous edition of this book.

system; in the latter, they cause the release of a "pain substance."

Surrounding an injury, there appears after some delay an area of vasodilatation called the "flare" (Chap. 32).

Early work which shows that the flare is mediated by fibers with cell bodies in the dorsal root ganglion has been reconfirmed in man.[12] The flare persists indefinitely after section central to the ganglion, and for a time after section peripheral to the ganglion, and then progressively disappears as the sensory fibers degenerate. Flare and vasodilatation from posterior root stimulation are ascribed to the release of a chemical substance. In the flare, this release is supposedly based on an axon reflex, some of the widely branching terminal axons being sensory and some motor, the latter releasing a mediator in the vicinity of blood vessels, causing vasodilatation and sensitizing neighboring sense organs. (However, the possibility that the chemical substance is a chemical interposed between strong, tissue-damaging stimulation and sensory ending discharge which is released by backfiring into the receptive terminals, has never been disproved.)

A necessary link in the chain of evidence is that the substance released by antidromic stimulation will lower the threshold to noxious stimuli. This has been shown in two ways.

Habgood has demonstrated release of a chemical substance by antidromic stimulation of frog's cutaneous nerve. He arranged two pieces of frog skin, each with a cutaneous nerve attached, in such a way that their undersides were in contact and the two nerves were available for stimulation and recording (Fig. 4). When one nerve was stimulated antidromically, the dromic discharge caused in the other nerve by a standard stimulus applied to its piece of skin was increased (sensitization). Often actual discharge was produced in the second nerve (induced discharge). Sensitization and induced discharge also occurred during stimulation and recording from adjacent nerve twigs. Pharmacologic analysis suggested that histamine (not acetylcholine) was the chemical agent involved.

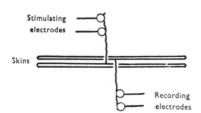

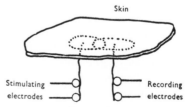

Fig. 4. Double skin preparation (*left*) and double nerve preparation (*right*) used to prove the release of a chemical by antidromic stimulation of a cutaneous nerve. (From Habgood, *J. Physiol.*, 1950, *111*:195–213.)

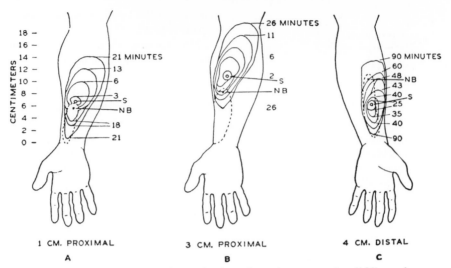

Fig. 5. Development of secondary hyperalgesia as shown by concentric solid lines when a cutaneous nerve is stimulated at point *S* proximal (*A, B*) and distal (*C*) to a nerve block (*NB*). Broken line marks area of anesthesia supposedly due to nerve damage. Figures give rate of development and spread of hyperalgesia. (From Hardy *et al.*, *J. clin. Invest.*, 1950, *29*:115–140.)

Chapman *et al.*[12] perfused and collected fluid from the skin through two hypodermic needles during vasodilatation evoked by noxious stimulation of the skin. The perfusate obtained at a distance 4 cm. from the point of stimulation was reinjected into normal skin and produced a wheal, flare and pain of a burning quality. This strongly supports a humoral interpretation of circumferential hyperalgesia.

While histamine has the requisite vasodilating and pain-producing abilities and has been considered the mediator of hyperalgesia, the experiments of Chapman *et al.*[12] point to a polypeptide similar to bradykinin.

Bioassay (rat duodenum, uterus and blood pressure) indicated this similarity (but not identity) to oxytocin and to vasodilator polypeptides, bradykinin and others. For this reason the substance has been termed "neurokinin." Neurokinin was obtained from perfusate collected beneath a thermal injury, and from the dermatome of a cut posterior root stimulated at its peripheral end. Neurokinin was not produced from noxious stimulation in an area of skin denervated by nerve section, but was in the dermatome of the posterior root, sectioned a year previously. Though obtainable in the region of noxious stimuli immediately after extirpation of the ganglion, it gradually disappeared from the perfusate accompanied by a step-by-step decrease in the size of the flare until both disappeared in about 10 days. Thus, the re-

covery of neurokinin was affected by a variety of procedures in exactly the same way as the flare, which is compatible with the neurokinin being responsible for the flare and hyperalgesia.

Secondary Hyperalgesia. Prolonged electrical stimulation causes, after a painless interval, hyperalgesia extending two or three inches beyond the point of stimulation (Fig. 3). The main characteristics distinguishing secondary from primary hyperalgesia are: (i) The painful area extends far beyond the borders of the irritation and beyond the area of vasodilatation into normal-appearing skin. (ii) The secondary form never lasts more than 48 hours, whereas primary hyperalgesia may last for days. (iii) The threshold only seems lower in secondary hyperalgesia because the subjective response is greatly augmented.[18] (iv) Secondary hyperalgesia extends beyond the area of flush (erythema), but the pain and vascular phenomena in primary hyperalgesia are usually coincident, at least initially.

Hardy *et al.*[19] stimulated a nerve *proximal* to a procaine block. They obtained hyperalgesia mostly proximal to the block (Fig. 5). Repeated pinpricks within the hyperalgesic area caused its borders to shrink, an occurrence suggestive of central inhibition. After the pricking was stopped, the zone expanded again. Hardy and his co-workers concluded therefore that secondary hyperalgesia occurs because a barrage of impulses from the injured area facilitates centrally the afferent pathways from adjacent skin areas. They postulated an interneuronal system between first-order pain neurons and spinothalamic tract fibers. However, this system has not been proved anatomically or physiologically. It is unwise to postulate a set of fibers to explain each physiologic phenomenon, and dichotomizing of first-order neurons would seem to make such interneurons unnecessary. Quite possibly hyperalgesia is explicable along the same lines as referred pain, discussed in detail below (see Fig. 13). Also, the point of interaction may well lie in the thalamus or cortex rather than in the spinal cord.

Itch. Itching rivals pain in the amount of discomfort it causes. According to Rothman,[39] it is a temporal pattern of pain which tends to follow stimuli as an afteraction. Bishop[6] induced it with repeated shocks by "sparking" from electrodes not quite touching the skin, each stimulus being too weak to be felt by itself. As shown in Figure 6, itch is distributed in a punctate fashion; this is true of chemically induced itch[40] as well as of that induced by electrical and mechanical stimulation.[2, 6, 7, 41] In sensory dissociations resulting from neurologic lesions or operations, pain and itching are lost together.

Itching disappears entirely in cases of complete analgesia, but is not affected in cases of touch anesthesia.[5] According to Zotterman,[54] the impulses underlying itching are conducted in C fibers, since only these continue to discharge in the afterstimulation period when itching occurs. The latent period for itch following mechanical stimulation is consistent with this view.[42] However, C-fiber conduction rates no longer identify an afferent input with pain.

Some itching is explained by the release of a chemical substance, perhaps histamine, which stimulates nerve endings. Histamine injected into the skin certainly causes intense itching, and histamine is liberated into the skin by the types of injury which cause itching (mechanical damage, electrical stimulation, sunburn, etc.). On the other hand, as the concentration of intradermally injected histamine is reduced, itch disappears before reddening and whealing, and yet in pruritus, violent itching occurs without visible skin change.[2] Arthur[2] and Shelley[40, 41] argue that, unlike histamine, a proteinase produces a prompt and sustained itching without evident whealing or other gross tissue damage. More than two substances may be required to explain the itch in various pathologic states of the skin.

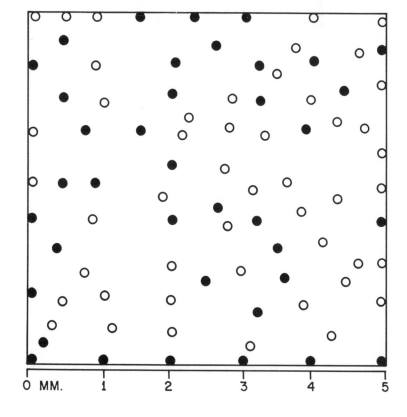

Fig. 6. Map of itch points on flexor surface of wrist. *Solid circles,* Points at which itching was reported. *Unfilled circles,* Sites at which itching was not experienced. Stimulus, 5 millisecond square-wave pulses; rate, 25 impulses per second; intensity, 1.5 V. (After Shelley and Arthur. *Arch. Derm.* (*Chic.*), 1957, 76:296–323.)

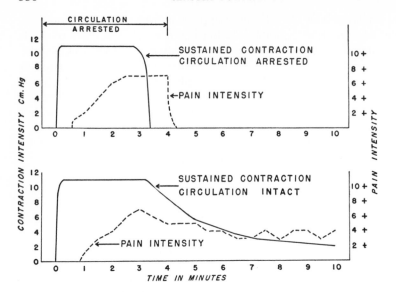

Fig. 7. Time course of sustained muscle contraction and resulting pain with arrested and intact circulation. In both experiments contraction was maintained as long as possible. (From Dorpat, *Mechanisms of muscle pain*, M.D. thesis. University of Washington School of Medicine, 1952.)

DEEP PAIN

The impulses underlying deep pain originate in muscles, tendons and joints, and, with occasional exceptions, traverse the muscle branches of mixed nerves. The quality of deep pain is dull, aching or boring. It seems to come from below the skin, but is difficult to localize, for it tends to radiate. Deep pain is accompanied by a definite autonomic response and is especially disagreeable, even sickening. The deep structures vary in sensitivity. According to Inman and Saunders,[23] the periosteum has the lowest threshold to irritating chemicals, followed in order of ascending threshold by ligaments, fibrous capsules of joints, tendons, fascia and the body of muscle. Feindel *et al.*[16] applied the methylene blue staining technique to deep pain fiber plexuses. Fine, beaded, naked fibers like those in skin form networks of varying density, being sparsest in connective tissue septa of muscles, denser in fascia, and still denser in periosteum. The density of innervation, then, seems to agree with the sensitivity of the structures.

Adequate Stimuli for Deep Pain. Mechanical forces excite deep pain endings. After trauma or infection these become so sensitive that the slightest touch or movement may be distressing. The endings are also sensitive to chemicals used experimentally or occurring in the body. Prolonged, continuous contraction of muscles, as in holding surgical retractors, causes muscles to ache and become sore. Rhythmic contraction, as in walking, or sustained contrac-

tion interrupted at frequent intervals causes no pain unless the muscle is ischemic. The pain which results from activity of ischemic muscle is called angina if it occurs in the heart and intermittent claudication if it occurs in the leg.*

Lewis' experimental analysis[28] of muscle pain is one of the classics in human physiology. It illustrates how much can be accomplished with minimal equipment but with close observation and reasoning. He had a subject grip an ergograph at the rate of once each second. When the circulation to the forearm was arrested by an inflated sphygmomanometer cuff around the upper arm, the standard exercise caused pain within 24 to 45 seconds which became severe in 60 to 90 seconds. Muscle tension is not the direct cause of such pain, because the pain is continuous while the contractions are intermittent. Under standard conditions, the time of onset of pain is remarkably constant, as is the onset of claudication in a patient. In ergographic experiments, Park and Rodbard[35] found the severity of pain to be exactly related to the amount of work, i.e., the product of the number of contractions times the square root of the load and the cube root of duration. When exercise is stopped but occlusion is continued, the pain continues undiminished (Fig. 7). When blood is readmitted to the limb, the pain disappears within a few seconds. Since the pain stimulus

*"Angina," a Latin word, refers to the sense of suffocating contraction which accompanies the pain from the heart. "Claudication" refers to the limping which accompanies the pain.

appears to be "stored up," Lewis and his co-workers concluded that the stimulus is a chemical substance arising out of the contraction process.

This substance seems to be eliminated from the muscle by metabolism rather than by being washed out in the blood. Intact circulation does not prevent the development of pain in muscles during sustained contraction (Fig. 7) or during rhythmic contraction when the blood is insufficiently oxygenated. However, oxygen lack in itself is probably not the direct and sufficient pain stimulus.

Lewis termed the hypothetical metabolite "factor P." It seems to be a normal product of muscle metabolism in both the resting and active states and to stimulate the pain endings only when it accumulates in fairly large quantities. Exercise facilitates this accumulation because it induces greater metabolic activity and thus greater release of factor P. For example, if a muscle with an occluded blood supply is exercised, but not to the point of pain, continued arrest of circulation to the resting muscle will eventually cause pain.[33] Cessation of pain requires only that the concentration of factor P be reduced below the critical threshold level, not that it be completely removed from the muscle. If a muscle performs measured work until pain starts and is rested only until pain stops before the experiment is repeated, the time to onset of pain is much shorter for the second trial.[28] This means that the factor P produced during the second trial is added to an accumulation remaining from the first trial, even though pain induced by the first trial had stopped.

Of the many agents which may constitute factor P (anoxia, pH changes, lactic acid, potassium, histamine) lactic acid or any of the intermediary substances of the Krebs cycle can be ruled out since subjects with hereditary absence of muscle phosphorylase (McArdle's syndrome) experience severe pain on exercise of ischemic muscles. Potassium, in the opinion of Dorpat,[14] is most likely the one. Both activity and ischemia release potassium from the muscle fiber, and intra-arterial injection of it provokes a severe pain in muscle resembling ischemic muscle pain. However, the same is true of intra-arterial injection of 1 to 2 μgm. of bradykinin, the site of pain stimulation supposedly being the free branching terminal of perivascular nerves around capillaries.

The pain-inducing nature of sustained muscle contraction is particularly important because many pains and aches in organic disease and anxiety states result from it. The underlying mechanism is probably diminished blood flow caused by compression of blood vessels within the muscles.[14] Muscle temperature *decreases* momentarily at the beginning of exercise, probably because the blood, which is warmer than the arm, is prevented from entering it.

Causes of sustained muscle contraction. Sustained contractions of skeletal muscle likely to cause pain may arise from higher centers or from reflexes of somatic or visceral afferents. Such reflexes are important (i) as diagnostic signs (Kernig's sign, stiff neck of meningeal irritation, abdominal rigidity of appendicitis), and (ii) as secondary sources of pain and discomfort.

Nociceptive impulses experimentally induced from a restricted focus in the head often give rise to a pain confined and fairly well localized to the traumatized focus, and also to a second, more generalized, pain ("headache"). According to the following analysis, the second pain results from tension of the neck muscles.[42] A single injection of 0.6 ml. of 6 per cent saline solution into the right temporal muscle caused intense local pain accompanied by sweating, salivation, lacrimation, nausea and contraction of the temporal and neck muscles. However, it caused no discomfort in the neck. Additional injections were made before temporal muscle pain had subsided. Pain in the neck began after the second injection and increased with each subsequent injection. At the end of 40 minutes, the neck pain was rated at nearly half the intensity of the local pain. With other stimuli—an irritating substance injected into the conjunctival sac or excessive activity of the external ocular muscle to overcome a tendency to double vision caused by a vertical prism set before one eye—the neck pain outlasted and, in the latter case, exceeded the local (frontal) pain (Fig. 8). The neck pain was promptly relieved by massage. It is not known how much the building up of the reflex muscle contraction is due to a change in the interneuron pools of the spinal cord, since no clear experimental demonstration of such long-lasting facilitatory effects has been made. The muscle contraction may be due to a vicious circle: deep pain→sustained reflex contraction→deep pain→reflex contraction→ etc. The success of such single procedures as osteopathic treatments, ethyl chloride sprays and procaine hydrochloride injection of trigger zones may depend on the breaking of the circle.

Muscle pain in anxiety states. Headache associated with a mild emotional disturbance such as that caused by an uncongenial job was found to be accompanied by tension of the neck and scalp muscles which disappeared along with the pain after psychiatric and drug therapy.[42] According to Holmes and Wolff,[21] in many instances of backache local dysfunction is minimal and mus-

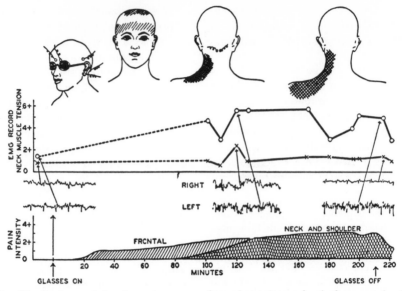

Fig. 8.   Distribution and time intensity course of muscle tension and pain from sustained contraction of external ocular muscle induced by vertical prism in front of left eye. Note neck pain and muscle tension, middle record, is on this side. Dips in upper EMG record are due to involuntary movements of head and neck. (From Simons *et al., Res. Publ. Ass. nerv. ment. Dis.,* 1943, *23*:228–244.)

cle tension produced by emotional tension is the cause of *secondary pain* in the back. Muscle tension could readily be induced by provoking hostility in the patient and relieved by appropriate psychiatric treatment. Thus, the sustained muscle contraction which causes pain reduces down to a familiar pattern representing a segmental reflex discharge and facilitation of this reflex from the brain.

Referred Muscle Pain.   By a mechanism entirely different from that operating in secondary pain, the stimuli arising from a restricted focus in muscle can give rise to pain which ap-

pears to come from points distant from the point of stimulation. In short, muscle pain shows the phenomenon of referred pain in the same way as visceral pain does (see below). Lewis and Kellgren[30] injected small quantities of 5 per cent saline solution, which is highly irritating, into deep structures. Localization of the resulting pain was fairly accurate when injections were made into fascia or tendons lying near the surface and into the periosteum of superficial bones such as the tibia. Pain from the same kinds of deeply situated structures,[25] and also pain from the belly of a muscle, were diffuse and often

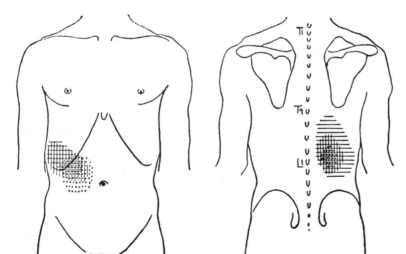

Fig. 9.   Reference of deep pain elicited by injections of hypertonic saline into three muscles supplied with pain fibers from T_9: multifidus muscle (*horizontal lines*), intercostals (*vertical lines*) and rectus abdominis (*dots*). (From Kellgren, *Clin. Sci.,* 1938, *3*:175–190.)

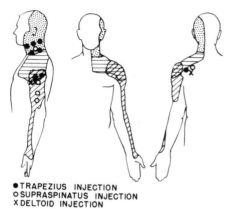

● TRAPEZIUS INJECTION
○ SUPRASPINATUS INJECTION
✕ DELTOID INJECTION

Fig. 10. Sites of cutaneous hyperalgesia resulting from injecting 5 per cent sodium chloride solution into muscles. Points of hypersensitivity to radiant heat (Hardy–Wolff apparatus) resulting from injecting into a given muscle are shown by location of the symbols for each muscle. Dermatome C_3 dots, C_4 horizontal lines, C_5 diagonal lines. (From Klingon and Jeffreys, *Neurol.* (*Minneap.*), 1958, *8*:272–276.)

were referred to a distant area of the skin surface in a regular, reproducible fashion (Fig. 9). Deep somatic pain was referred to the dermatomes supplied by the posterior roots which conduct pain impulses from the muscle stimulated. Pain from the muscle itself is initially diffuse and tends to shrink down to a small area of pain and muscle tenderness related to the origin and insertion of the muscles rather than the point of saline injection. The referred pain for deep muscle stimulation is accompanied by rigidity and tenderness of muscles, and the skin may become hyperesthetic. Such points of cutaneous hypersensitivity occur on the arm and neck when the deep muscles of the back of the shoulder are stimulated (Fig. 10). However, as in referred pain the impulses from the cutaneous hyperalgesic point and from the muscles stimulated enter the spinal cord by the same posterior root.

VISCERAL AND REFERRED PAIN

Neuroanatomists, following Langley, define the sympathetic nervous system as an efferent system. Langley was fully aware that sympathetic nerves and the white rami carry sensory fibers from the viscera. He chose to "rule them out" by definition because, except in origin, they resemble ordinary somatic afferents, whereas the sympathetic efferents are distin-

guished from somatic efferents by a peripheral synapse. Because so much autonomic surgery is performed to control pain, the modern tendency is to alter Langley's definition and to speak of "sympathetic," "autonomic" or, better still, "*visceral*" *afferents*. Pain impulses arising within the abdominal and thoracic cavities may reach the central nervous system by three channels: (i) the parasympathetic nerves, (ii) the sympathetic nerves, and (iii) the somatic nerves innervating the body wall and the diaphragm. The last of these channels makes visceral sensation a somewhat larger question than autonomic afferent innervation.

Visceral Pain.[28, 33, 48, 49] It is noted by surgeons operating with local anesthesia that visceral organs can be handled and even cut, crushed or burned without causing sensation, as long as traction on the mesentery and stimulation of the body wall are avoided. And it is true that the viscera are sparsely innervated. However, Kinsella[26] has shown that a broad, firm, manual pressure on the appendix elicits pain when restricted stimuli affecting only a few fibers of the sparse innervation are ineffective. If account is taken of the principle of the adequate stimulus and the fact that pathologic states may lower the threshold of pain fibers, the viscera are unquestionably sensitive. The viscera are not normally exposed to the forms of stimulation that are adequate for skin receptors and therefore have not evolved sensitivity to them. The adequate stimuli for visceral afferents are those arising from their own environment and especially from their own activities and pathologic states. Such adequate stimuli include: (i) sudden distension against resistance; (ii) spasms or strong contractions, especially when accompanied by ischemia; (iii) chemical irritants; and (iv) mechanical stimulation, especially when the organ is hyperemic (stomach). The pain from such stimulation is not, as is often stated, due to traction on the mesentery. Normal contractions and relaxations of visceral organs apparently do not discharge pain fibers, although normal activities may become painful when the blood supply is inadequate.

Most visceral reflexes and organic sensations are served by afferents in the parasympathetic nerves (see Chap. 17), but *impulses serving visceral pain are conducted mainly in the sympathetic nerves.* The major exceptions to this rule, given in detail below, lie in the pelvic regions and in the esophagus and trachea. Because sympathetic nerves

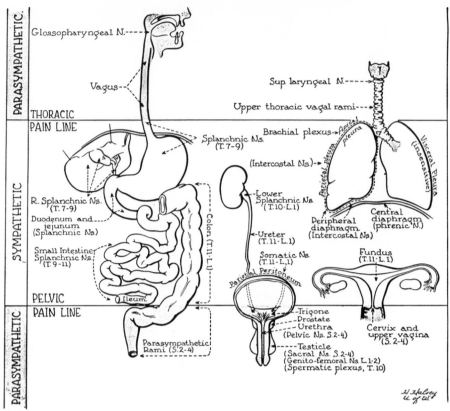

Fig. 11. Summary diagram of pain innervation of various viscera. Pain afferents from structures between thoracic and pelvic pain lines traverse sympathetic nerves, and structures above and below these lines traverse parasympathetic nerves. (Data from White, *Res. Publ. Ass. nerv. ment. Dis.,* 1943, *23*:373–390.)

are not essential for visceral regulatory reflexes, sympathectomy for the relief of pain does not produce serious visceral dysfunction.

Pain pathways can be interrupted at several points, as can be seen by tracing a typical pathway from an abdominal organ. The axons of free nerve endings in the walls of a viscus follow the artery to the abdominal aorta, where they traverse the collateral ganglia without synapse and enter the splanchnic nerve. The ganglion of the sympathetic chain is entered and traversed, again without synapse; and, by way of the white ramus, the fibers reach the spinal nerve close to the spinal ganglia. The cell body of the viscerosensory fiber is situated in the spinal ganglion, and the central process enters the spinal cord by way of the dorsal root. There it forms reflex connections with somatic motoneurons and preganglionic fibers and ascending connections with the neurons of the spinothalamic tract. A visceral organ can therefore be denervated of pain fibers by (i) stripping the artery supplying it (periarterial neurectomy), (ii) removal or alcohol injection of the sympathetic chain of ganglia at appropriate levels, (iii) rhizotomy of several posterior roots, and (iv) section of the spinothalamic tract (cordotomy). Impulses from a

single visceral organ enter the spinal cord by several roots, necessitating extensive root sections. Cordotomy is often the operation of choice because somatic as well as visceral structures are frequently involved.

Visceral pain fibers are not confined to the sympathetic nerves. Many pain impulses reach the spinal cord via the pelvic nerve; others reach the brain stem via the vagus nerve. Sympathetic surgery for the relief of hypertension permits study of this question in man (Fig. 11). Below an imaginary line, which may be termed the *pelvic pain line,* pain impulses from the bladder neck, prostate, urethra, uterine cervix and the lower end of the colon are conducted to the spinal cord by way of the parasympathetic pelvic nerve. This explains why hypogastric neurectomy fails to relieve bladder pain. Note that the portions of the urogenital system falling above this line (bladder fundus, kidney, ureters, ovaries, fallopian tubes, uterus and testes) are served with pain afferents by way of sympathetic nerves. (The testes have migrated below the pelvic pain line, carrying with them a sympathetic innervation derived from the tenth thoracic cord segment.) Above the pelvic pain line, the pain fibers from the abdominal and most of the thoracic viscera pursue sympathetic nerves, although they have equal opportunity to join the vagus nerve.

It has long been taught that no visceral pain impulses are conducted in the vagus. By means of implanted electrodes, Bradford Cannon[10] stimulated the vagus in cats below the recurrent laryngeal branches. No pain responses were observed. However, other observations[17, 46, 51] suggest that a "thoracic pain line" may be drawn, with the esophagus and trachea giving fibers to the vagus nerve. Finally, it is to be noted that somatic nerves are also concerned with innervation of the visceral cavities.

Impulses arising in visceral structures may give rise to pain localized to more superficial structures of the body, often those at a considerable distance from the disturbed organ. Such pain is said to be *referred*. Why visceral pain is referred is not known, but what determines where the pain is referred is known. Pain is referred to the dermatomes supplied by the posterior roots through which the visceral afferent impulses reach the spinal cord. This may be called the "dermatomal rule." Thus, referred pain from the heart (angina pectoris) seems to come from the chest and from a thin strip along the inner aspect of the upper arm. The highest root carrying pain fibers from the heart is the first thoracic posterior root, and the upper border of the corresponding dermatome extends out along the inner aspect of the arm.

Pain is only one of four associated signs of visceral disease. Irritation of the viscera by a pathologic process is manifested in four ways: (i) pain; (ii) hyperalgesia, hyperesthesia or tenderness; (iii) autonomic reflexes—sweating, piloerection or vasomotor changes; (iv) somatic reflexes, muscular rigidity.

Types of Pain from Viscera. Two main types of "visceral" pain must be recognized: (i) quasivisceral pain aroused by stimulation of the inner surfaces of the body wall, and (ii) pain actually arising from the viscera. Either type may be unreferred or referred. Quasivisceral pain is an important factor in visceral disease. Spread of inflammation, exudation, pressure, friction or an invasion of the body wall by a pathologic process causes pain impulses which reach the spinal cord via the somatic nerves supplying the walls of the visceral cavities. Moreover, the thoracic and abdominal cavities are deeply penetrated by a somatic nerve—the phrenic—in which one fiber in three is sensory and many are unmyelinated. Table 1 summarizes the role of the somatic afferent fibers.

Unreferred parietal pain. Capps and Coleman[11] studied this kind of pain in conscious patients. Taking advantage of the space for maneuvering afforded by collections of exudate in the body cavities, these workers stimulated various internal structures. A wire was passed into the space by means of a trocar, and pressure or friction was applied to visceral and parietal structures. The peritoneum was insensitive to this kind of stimulus, but stimulation of the inner body wall caused a sharply localized pain. This pain seemed to come from the body wall over the site of stimulation, presumably because one posterior root innervates superimposed areas on the internal and external surface of the body wall. The lower right quadrant pain in the second stage of appendicitis falls in this category.

Referred parietal pain. Experimental stimulation of the margin of the diaphragm, innervated by the lower six intercostal nerves, was referred to the anterior abdominal wall, which is innervated by the same thoracic nerves (Fig. 12, *right*). Pain from stimulation of the central zone of the diaphragmatic pleura or peritoneum was invariably referred to the point of the shoulder and neck (Fig. 12, *left*). This reference is well recognized clinically. Thus, impulses ascending the phrenic nerve and entering the spinal cord via C_{3-4} are referred to the dermatomes of these roots.[20] Because the diaphragm has migrated caudally, carrying its nerve supply with it, the discrepancy between the points of origin and of reference is dramatic.

Referred visceral pain. Unlike referred somatic

TABLE 1. *Role of Somatic Afferent Fibers in Sensibility of Visceral Cavities*

Somatic afferent fibers	Phrenic nerve	Central zone of diaphragm Portions of pericardium Biliary tract
	Thoracic and upper lumbar spinal nerves	Parietal pleura Parietal peritoneum Borders of diaphragm Roots of mesentery

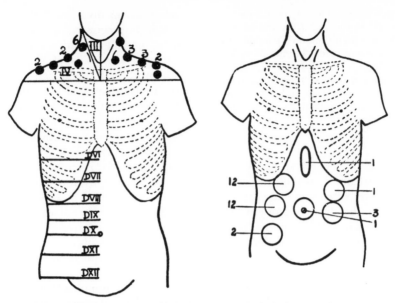

Fig. 12.   Superficial reference of pain from diaphragm. *Left:* Reference of pain from stimulating *central zone* of diaphragm. Black dots and attached numbers represent position and frequency of reference in a series of observations. Pain is also referred to corresponding territory on dorsal surface of neck and shoulders (not shown). Roman numerals identify 3rd and 4th cervical and 6th to 12th thoracic dermatomes (*D*). *Right:* Reference of pain from visceral disease affecting *margins* of diaphragm. Circles represent points of reference, numbers the frequency of reference; in two cases pain was referred to back. Margins of diaphragm are innervated by lower six thoracic posterior roots. Compare their cutaneous distribution shown in figure at left with zones of reference shown in figure at right. (From Capps and Coleman, *An experimental and clinical study of pain in the pleura, pericardium and peritoneum.* New York, Macmillan, 1932.)

pain, this type of pain results from impulses arising in the viscera and conducted over visceral nerves, usually sympathetic. Frequently, the pain seems to come from the superficial layers of the body, often at a considerable distance from the diseased organ. Despite the error of reference, the localization may be quite definite, and its apparent location obeys the dermatomal rule. Angina pectoris and the pain from myocardial infarction are perhaps the classic examples of a referred visceral pain. The pain from a renal stone descending the ureter does not move but has a fixed reference (to the groin although the upper end of the ureter is beneath the last rib). An inflated balloon in the gut, which embryologically is a midline structure, gives rise to pain which has the same reference whether the stimulated portion of the gut is on the left or right side of the body. Stimulation of the central end of the splanchnic nerve in conscious patients gives rise to referred pain.[47] There seems little justification for Morley's contention[34] that pain from the viscera is referred only when the body wall is involved.

Unreferred visceral pain (splanchnic pain). In anginal pain there is, in addition to the superficially referred pain, a deep, substernal, agonizing component. Such pain is therefore unreferred although it is poorly localized. Ross[38] in 1888 hypothesized the double nature of visceral pain and named the unreferred component "splanchnic pain." This category of pain is less well substantiated. It should be recognized, however, that gastrointestinal tract pain, although referred elsewhere than the point of stimulation, appears to come from much deeper within the body than does the referred parietal pain.

Referred Pain.   The reference of pain from the central zone of the diaphragm, innervated by a somatic nerve, provides a clue to the nature of referred pain. So, too, does the common observation that pain arising in the teeth cannot be localized to the correct tooth, even though the sensory innervation of the teeth is somatic (trigeminal). Referred pain is therefore not a phenomenon associated exclusively with the viscera, and the reference of visceral pain is therefore not due to any unique properties of the visceral pain pathways. Lewis and Kellgren[30] induced pain in observers with experience of angina pectoris by injecting hypertonic saline into the first thoracic interspinous ligaments. The subjects recognized the similarity of the two types of pain. The common denominator of referred visceral pain and referred muscular pain is that they both originate deep to the skin and in a general sense are deep pain. Faultiness of localization perhaps represents the failure to evolve a topographically organized neural apparatus for localization. The faulty projection of deep pain to the surface is the result of (i) infrequency of deep pain, and (ii) inability to use vision to verify the source of stimulation. Thus, learning appears to be an important factor in referred pain.

Habit reference. Evidence that reference of sensation is a learned phenomenon can be found in the clinical observation that a pain may be referred not to its usual point of reference but to the site of a previous surgical operation, trauma or localized pathologic process. Experimentally this was demonstrated repeatedly in Jones' study[24] of gastrointestinal pain resulting from distension by balloons. Aberrant projections of pain, for example those falling to one side of the midline when the balloon was in the upper level of the gastrointestinal tract, were explicable as references to pre-existing surgical scars.

Habit reference had the status only of a clinical observation until recently, when it was suspected of being the cause of a bizarre pain phenomenon and was subjected to formal experimental proof by Reynolds and Hutchins.[22, 37] During high-altitude flying some individuals suffer severe pain localized to the teeth (aerodontalgia). After every possible dental cause for the pain had been excluded, it was discovered that the pain stimulus was the expansion of air trapped in the maxillary sinus. Some individuals referred this pain to the face; others referred it to the teeth. The latter group had a high incidence of traumatic dental work on the side of reference, suggesting habit reference of pain. To test this hypothesis, dental work was done without anesthesia on one group of young men and with anesthesia in another group. Two weeks later, the ostium of the maxillary sinus was pricked with a pin. Over 90 per cent of the no-anesthesia group referred this pain to the dental area where the work had been done. This

response could still be elicited two months after the dental trauma. The anesthesia group did not refer the pain to the teeth.

Habit reference, secondary hyperalgesia and referred pain are subject to two explanations, one peripheral and the other psychologic. With the above experiments as an example, the first explanation is that the traumatized teeth were the source of a subthreshold discharge of pain impulses which was facilitated by impulses from the sinus. The other interpretation is, as the term "habit reference" implies, that a projection of pain is learned and that the pain impulses from the sinus, conducted in an overlapping pathway, were simply given the previously learned reference for impulses in that path.

Mechanism of Referred Pain. To account for the dermatomal reference of pain, MacKenzie[31] suggested that sensory impulses from the viscera were unable to pass directly to the brain, having no connection with the spinothalamic tract, but created an "irritable focus" in the segment at which they entered the spinal cord. Afferent impulses from the skin were thereby magnified, causing pain which was literally cutaneous pain. Stated in modern language, MacKenzie's theory of irritable focus amounts to the suggestion that visceral impulses facilitate somatic pain impulses normally coming from the skin in insufficient quantities to excite the spinothalamic tract fibers. Hyperalgesia and referred pain would be the consequence. Wiggers,[49] Hinsey and Phillips,[20] and others have stated the MacKenzie theory very clearly in modern physiologic terms. It can be called the *convergence–facilitation* theory to distinguish it from the convergence–projection theory.

Convergence–projection theory. Although facilitation may well be essential for hyperalgesia of dermatomal distribution, it is not essential for reference of pain. An adequate explanation of referred pain is that some visceral afferents converge with cutaneous pain afferents to end upon the *same* neuron at some point in the sensory pathway—spinal, thalamic, or cortical—and that the system of fibers is sufficiently organized topographically to provide the dermatomal reference. The first opportunity for this is in the spinothalamic tract. The resulting impulses, upon reaching the brain, are interpreted as having come from the skin, an interpretation which has been learned from previous experiences in which the same tract fiber was stimulated by cutaneous afferents. The same explanation

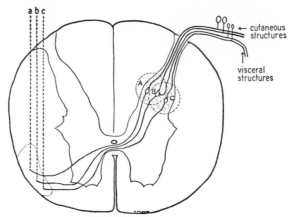

Fig. 13. Convergence–projection mechanism of referred visceral and somatic pain based upon Sherrington's neuron–pool concept. *A, B* and *C* represent a neuron pool consisting of all the spinothalamic tract fibers originating in one segment of spinal cord. *A* is field of neurons having connections only with afferent fibers from cutaneous sense organs. *B* is field of overlap constituted by neurons which receive impulses from *both* visceral and cutaneous afferents, and impulses in *B* will give rise to pain referred to skin. *C* are those neurons of pool which connect only with afferent fibers from visceral cavities, and give rise to unreferred or true splanchnic pain. Only one neuron in each category is represented; others are indicated by "ghost cells." *a, b* and *c* are fibers in spinothalamic tract having cell bodies in fields *A, B* and *C,* respectively.

serves equally well for referred parietal or diaphragmatic pain.

The pain fibers in the posterior roots outnumber the spinothalamic tract fibers, so that several pain fibers must converge upon one tract fiber. Therefore, it is likely that a share of the afferent pain fibers coming from the diaphragm converge with cutaneous pain fibers entering the same segment to end upon the spinothalamic tract neurons. According to the doctrine of specific nerve energies, impulses in a spinothalamic tract fiber are identical whatever their origin. On all previous occasions when these particular spinothalamic neurons have been activated, stimulation of the body surface, verified by other senses, was responsible. Thus, when impulses of visceral origin reach the cerebral cortex, the interpretation is made which experience has built up—that of a pain arising from cutaneous pain neurons.

Figure 13 illustrates the convergence–projection theory of referred pain applied to visceral sensation. The spinothalamic tract fibers originating at one segment of the spinal cord are regarded as a pool of neurons. The visceral pain afferents entering the posterior root of that segment come into synaptic relation with one group of cells, and the cutaneous pain afferents synapse with an overlapping field in the pool. Those spinothalamic tract neurons within the field of overlap, when stimulated by visceral afferents, give rise to pain referred to the cutaneous surface. In Figure 13, certain spinothalamic tract fibers are "private" to visceral afferent neurons. These fibers are responsible for "splanchnic" or unreferred visceral pain. Facilitation of cutaneous nerve impulses within the overlap probably accounts for hyperalgesia, but facilitation is not involved in referred pain. Thus is avoided the unphysiologic and unnecessary supposition that cutaneous pain afferents are perpetually discharging at an amount inadequate to discharge spinothalamic fibers unless facilitated.

Attempts to demonstrate facilitation within pain systems in man, by means of radiant heat, have failed. Unfortunately, pain fibers are too small to be studied easily by bioelectric methods, but in such studies on other somatosensory systems the evoked cortical response to peripheral stimulation has given little indication of facilitation in sensory systems.[1] One afferent volley tends to block another either by occlusion or by what resembles inhibition in reflex arcs. Clinical experience also teaches that the effect of a cutaneous pain or a strong stimulus (e.g., mustard plasters) is to reduce visceral pain, not facilitate it.

The crucial experiment to decide the role of facilitation versus simple convergence and projection would seem to be injection of procaine into the area to which the pain is projected. Such experiments have been carried out on man and animals for a variety of referred visceral and somatic pain, but with conflicting results. Unfortunately, no agreement has been reached, despite extensive investigations. It seems certain that visceral and somatic pain are referred after injection of procaine into the projection site or surgical deafferentation of it so that the convergence–projection mechanism is substantiated. Why in other situations the pain is alleviated is not clear. If, as the convergence–projection theory holds, the reference of pain is a psychologic phenomenon, several factors must be considered: (i) the subjective nature of the pain and its tendency to be reduced by any form of therapy, (ii) procaine injection does not produce a blankness, as does a visual field defect, but a feeling of numbness which may suppress the projection to the area, and (iii) the strength and persistence of the referred pain. In view of the conflicting nature of the evidence, perhaps it is best to accept both mechanisms as operative.

The only evidence that facilitation is a necessary feature of referred pain lies in the experiments of Weiss and Davis[44] and others, in which procaine injection into the skin over the area of reference ended the referred pain or caused it to migrate. However, studies by Carmichael, on anginal pain, and by Livingston, on diaphragmatic pain, have shown that procaine injection of an area of reference has no effect upon the reference. White *et al.*[47] denervated the thoracic wall by section of the intercostal nerves in dogs and observed that ischemia of the myocardium continued to produce pain; Wolff[53] also found that superficial anesthesia in most instances did not prevent the superficial reference of deep pain experimentally produced.

Rigidity and Deep Tenderness. This phenomenon is a special example of the sustained muscle contraction and resulting soreness which were discussed in connection with deep pain. Unlike referred pain, the rigidity which accompanies visceral disease is distributed regionally rather than segmentally. It appears to be a sustained reflex comparable to the flexion reflex of the limbs to nociceptive stimuli. Like referred pain, rigidity is typical of pain stimulation arising from the deep somatic tissues as well as that from diseased viscera, and is readily produced experimentally by hypertonic saline injections.

In fact, the rigidity of visceral disease is most marked when the body wall is involved (parietoskeletal reflex). Pain from some hollow organs is not accompanied by rigidity, whereas that from others is accompanied by a marked rigidity and a resulting deep tenderness that outlasts and outweighs the original pain.

McLellan and Goodell[32] described an experiment in which the ureter of a female patient was stimulated electrically near the kidney (Fig. 14). Pain with typical references anteriorly along the border of the rectus muscle at the level of the umbilicus was reported. This pain subsided quickly, but the muscles of the abdominal wall on the side of stimulation remained contracted, and, after about half an hour, the "side commenced to ache." This ache became severe and lasted six hours; the side was tender the next day. The course of this pain is shown in Figure 14. Similar experiments on the kidney pelvis yielded a similar result. The initial transient pain was referred to the back at the junction of the ribs and vertebral column, and the back muscles ached and became tender. If, in visceral disease, the source of pain continues, it is clear that the resulting pain may be a mixture of referred visceral pain and pain arising from sustained skeletal muscle contraction. Since the muscle ache and tenderness may be at a considerable distance from the site of the projected pain, rigidity and tenderness are an additional source of confusion in diagnosis.

Specific Applications. Although a detailed

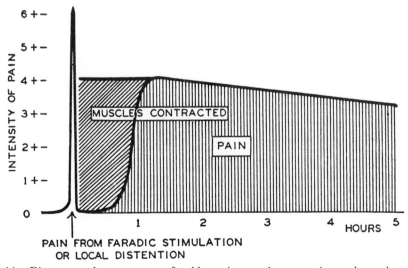

Fig. 14. Diagram to show sequence of sudden pain, muscle contraction and muscle ache from stimulation of ureter or kidney pelvis. (From McLellan and Goodell, *Res. Publ. Ass. nerv. ment. Dis.,* 1943, *23*:252–262.)

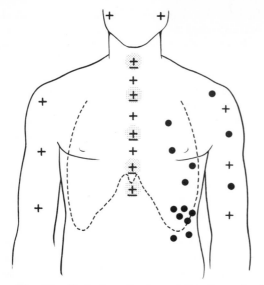

Fig. 15. Projection of pain and the diagnosis of coronary artery disease. The "false" pain indicated by black circles seems real to the patient but is "false" in leading to a diagnosis of coronary or other serious disease. The ±'s may be "false" in relation to coronary disease, but indicative of other serious organic disease. (From Macmillan, *N. Carolina med. J.,* 1952, *13*:9–11.)

consideration of pain characteristics of specific viscera is beyond the scope of a textbook of physiology, a few examples illustrating the mechanisms of visceral pain will be given.

Pains in the chest. As in Figure 15, these may be grouped as (i) due to angina pectoris or myocardial infarction, (ii) due to one of several disorders of the chest and abdomen, and (iii) "false" pains that have no diagnostic significance. The need to recognize (i) and (ii) is obvious. It is also extremely important to recognize the false pains, both in cardiac and other patients lest a cardiac neurosis be created.

Gastrointestinal pain from distension. Pain arising from the gastrointestinal tract has been investigated by Jones[24] in normal subjects (medical students), and by Ray and Neill[36] in patients during sympathectomy operations. Pain induced by inflation of a balloon at various levels in the upper end of the gastrointestinal tract (i) is usually anterior (but sometimes goes through to the back), (ii) is usually projected to the midline, and (iii) moves caudally as the stimulus is moved through the tract. As the position of the balloon moves through the esophagus, the point of projection moves with it (Fig. 16). Thus, esophageal sensation in this respect, as in others, is transitional between that typical of the exterior and that of the interior of the body. In contrast, the lower esophagus, the stomach and the duodenal cap all project to the region overlying the xiphoid (Fig. 17). The duodenal projections extend from the xiphoid to the umbilicus and are deep, resembling "a gas pain." The upper, middle and lower jejunum and the ileal projections are grouped around the umbilicus, and variations of several feet in the position of the balloon make no appreciable difference in the localization. The pain is well localized and sharp or cramplike. When the balloon is in the large bowel, the pain differs by being more diffusely localized and less intense; it is more often localized to one side of the midline and is always localized below the umbilicus, but with less correlation between locus of the balloon and locus of the projection. At three points, the hepatic and splenic flexures and the sigmoid, the loci of the balloon and of the projected sensation coincide. In part this correlates with the fixation of the colon and could be explained on the basis of unreferred somatic pain. However, Ray and Neill[36] found that these lateral projections are lost after sympathectomy.

Heart burn (pyrosis). This term describes a hot, burning, almost painful sensation deep to the sternum, popularly ascribed to regurgitation of acid gastric contents into the esophagus. However, such sensations are described when free gastric acidity is absent, and

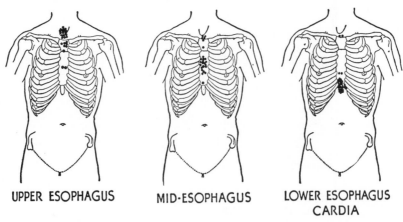

UPPER ESOPHAGUS   MID-ESOPHAGUS   LOWER ESOPHAGUS CARDIA

Fig. 16. Reference of pain produced experimentally by distension of esophagus at various levels with balloon. (From Jones, *Digestive tract pain: diagnosis and treatment; experimental observations.* New York, Macmillan, 1938.)

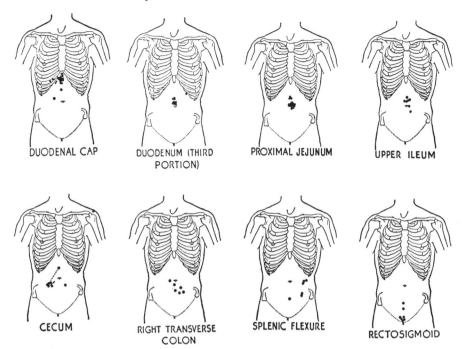

DUODENAL CAP   DUODENUM (THIRD PORTION)   PROXIMAL JEJUNUM   UPPER ILEUM

CECUM   RIGHT TRANSVERSE COLON   SPLENIC FLEXURE   RECTOSIGMOID

Fig. 17. Reference of pain produced experimentally by distension of small and large intestine at various levels. Note rapid downward progression of reference points as distending balloon progresses along duodenum and also that pain from jejunum and ileum are referred to about the same point. Note also shift of reference point from right center to left center combined with downward progression in passing from cecum to rectosigmoid. (Selected records from Jones, *Digestive tract pain: diagnosis and treatment; experimental observations.* New York, Macmillan, 1938.)

Jones[24] induced exactly the same burning sensation with mere inflation of a balloon inserted into the lower end of the esophagus. Actually, cold water or 0.1 normal NaOH was a more effective stimulus than 0.1 normal HCl. Often accompanying heart burn is what is popularly known as "acid regurgitation," in which a burning sensation seems to run up the esophagus with or without regurgitation of gastric contents into the mouth. X-ray observation shows that this sensation is accompanied by reverse esophageal peristalsis and that periods of heart burn are accompanied by constriction of the lower esophagus. Jones concluded that both phenomena result from abnormal neuromuscular activity and that the chemical constituency of any regurgitated fluid is of little importance.

Stomach pain. Pain from the stomach does not lend itself to study by the balloon technique. However, Wolf and Wolff[51] have studied the sensitivity of the gastric mucosa in a modern Alexis St. Martin, much as the sensitivity of skin has been studied. To mechanical and thermal stimulation, the gastric mucosa responded as does skin, but was not so sensitive. Nocuous stimuli such as pinching, electric shocks and strong chemicals did not arouse pain in normal mucosa, but did so if the mucosa was engorged or inflamed. Since the engorgement underlying such hypersensitivity could be produced by stress situations or psychologic probing, the experiments clearly illustrate a psychosomatic mech-

anism. Physiologically, this phenomenon seems to resemble primary cutaneous hyperalgesia, but whether secondary hyperalgesia is involved is not known.

Peptic ulcer pain. A variety of clinical and experimental facts, including the observations referred to in the previous paragraph, suggest that acidity is the immediate precipitating cause of pain in end-organs rendered excessively excitable by ulceration. Local vascular and inflammatory factors play a critical role. Mechanical factors such as hyperperistalsis are insufficient to evoke pain in the absence of acid, but play a subordinate role. The effect of surgical section of the vagus in ending pain is so immediate and dramatic some have thought that the vagus carries the pain impulses. However, direct evidence disproves such a theory, and the immediate relief must be interpreted to mean that the vagotomy immediately changes some factor in the equation of acid + local sensitivity = pain.

Appendicitis. The two stages in acute appendicitis illustrate two of the types of visceral pain described above. The first stage, consisting of pain localized diffusely to the midline at the epigastric level and not accompanied by muscular rigidity, is a classic example of unreferred visceral pain. The second stage, with pain much less diffuse, localized to the lower right quadrant and accompanied by rigidity and deep tenderness, illustrates referred parietal pain.

Gallbladder pain. Consistent with the studies of Ray and Neill,[36] gallbladder pain is localized to the right and above the umbilicus. It is a pain involving purely sympathetic innervation. Because the pain fibers from the gallbladder, pancreas, duodenum and stomach enter the spinal cord within a few thoracic segments, the references of pain are similar enough to make diagnosis difficult.

Pain Reaction versus Pain Perception.   No discussion of the difficulties attending the interpretation of pain is complete without the recognition that different individuals evaluate the degree of pain quite differently. Chapman *et al.*,[13] using the Hardy–Wolff type of apparatus, measured the pain threshold of a normal and a psychoneurotic group of subjects. No clear difference was found in threshold. There seems little justification for the belief of psychoneurotics that they are "so sensitive to pain." When the test was conducted so that it measured the stimulus necessary to cause a reaction to pain—flinching, blinking or withdrawing—as opposed to mere detection of pain, there emerged a clear difference in the average threshold for reaction. On the average, the psychoneurotic group reacted more readily to pain. However, the amount of overlap was so great that it is perhaps more correct to say that *some* psychoneurotics react more to pain. Clearly, evaluation of pain at this level requires an understanding of the highest levels of cortical function. This subject will be discussed in the chapter on the cerebral association areas.

Pain as a Feeling State.[4, 8]   The subject of pain extends considerably beyond pain as a sensation and the distortions of it seen in neurologic disease. In speaking of the "significance of pain" to the individual, one is dealing with emotion and the whole background of life experience which has contributed to giving pain emotional significance. Deflection of attention away from pain is a powerful factor in the end result of a painful stimulation. Whatever the agent used to control pain, it is necessary to examine whether it interferes mechanically and chemically with the pain pathways at some point, acts on some overt result of painful stimuli such as muscular contraction, or acts on the mechanisms of attention or emotion. Severing the connections of the prefrontal areas with the brain (prefrontal leukotomy) decreases the suffering from intractable pain but does not necessarily elevate the pain threshold or the subjective sensation of pain as nearly as that can be made out.

The lessened response to or evaluation of pain is described under a number of terms.

The unattentive, withdrawn element of the prefrontal leukotomy syndrome is a factor because when attention is focused on the source of painful stimuli, a sensation of pain and even suffering is reported accompanied by external signs of pain. The relief of pain by opiates and placebos thought to be opiates presents similar problems. The effectiveness of the placebo in about 35 per cent of subjects indicates that pain is elaborated in some way centrally where it is amenable to control by situational factors—in this case the belief in the supposed drug's effectiveness, the physician, etc. Morphine itself appears to relieve pain not by elevating the pain threshold or altering the subjective pain sensation. Much the same terms are used to describe the effect of morphine and of frontal leukotomy —an effect on anxiety or fear and upon attention by way of a "bemused state."

The concept that various agents and procedures and the make-up of the individual can alter the subjective response to pain without altering the pain sensation or its threshold seems well established. The study of the mechanism involved has only just begun. Clearly, evaluation of pain at the highest level requires an understanding of the highest levels of cortical function as well as the more primitive parts of the brain, which will be discussed in the next and subsequent chapters.

REFERENCES

1. Amassian, V. E. *Res. Publ. Ass. nerv. ment. Dis.,* 1952, *30:* 371–402.
2. Arthur, R. P. and Shelley, W. B. *J. invest. Derm.,* 1955, *25:*341–346; and In *Pain and itch: nervous mechanisms,* Wolstenholme, G. E. W. and O'Connor, M., eds. Boston, Little, Brown and Co., 1959.
3. Association for Research in Nervous and Mental Disease. *Pain. Research Publications,* vol. 23. Baltimore, Williams & Wilkins, 1943.
4. Barber, T. X. *Psychol. Bull.,* 1959, *56:*430–460.
5. Bickford, R. G. *Clin. Sci.,* 1938, *3:*377–386.
6. Bishop, G. H. *J. Neurophysiol.,* 1943, *6:*361–382.
7. Bishop, G. H. *J. invest. Derm.,* 1948, *11:*143–154.
8. Beecher, H. K. *Pharmacol. Rev.,* 1957, *9:*59–209.
9. Bonica, J. J. *The management of pain.* Philadelphia, Lea & Febiger, 1953.
10. Cannon, B. *Amer. J. Physiol.,* 1933, *105:*366–372.
11. Capps, J. A., with collaboration of G. H. Coleman. *An experimental and clinical study of pain in the pleura, pericardium and peritoneum.* New York, Macmillan, 1932.
12. Chapman, L. F., Ramos, A. O., Goodell, H. and Wolff, H. G. *Arch. Neurol. (Chic.),* 1961, *4:*617–650.

13. Chapman, W. P., Finesinger, J. E., Jones, C. M. and Cobb, S. *Arch. Neurol. (Chic.)*, 1947, *57*:321–331.
14. Dorpat, T. L. *Mechanisms of muscle pain*. M.D. Thesis, University of Washington, 1952.
15. Echlin, F. and Propper, N. *J. Physiol.*, 1937, *88*:388–400.
16. Feindel, W. H., Weddell, G. and Sinclair D. G. *J. Neurol. Psychiat.*, 1948, *11*:113–117.
17. Grimson, K. S., Hesser, F. H. and Kitchin, W. W. *Surgery*, 1947, *22*:230–238.
18. Habgood, J. S. *J. Physiol.*, 1950, *111*:195–213.
19. Hardy, J. D., Wolff, H. G. and Goodell, H. *J. clin. Invest.*, 1950, *29*:115–140.
20. Hinsey, J. C. and Phillips, R. A. *J. Neurophysiol.*, 1940, *3*:175–181.
21. Holmes, T. H. and Wolff, H. G. *Res. Publ. Ass. nerv. ment. Dis.*, 1950, *29*:750–772.
22. Hutchins, H. C. and Reynolds, O. E. *J. dent. Res.*, 1947, *26*:3–8.
23. Inman, V. T. and Saunders, J. B. deC. M. *J. nerv. ment. Dis.*, 1944, *99*:660–667.
24. Jones, C. M. *Digestive tract pain: diagnosis and treatment; experimental observations*. New York, Macmillan, 1938.
25. Kellgren, J. H. *Clin. Sci.*, 1938, *3*:175–190.
26. Kinsella, V. J. *The mechanism of abdominal pain*. Sidney, Australasian Medical Publishing Co., 1948.
27. Klingon, G. H. and Jeffreys, W. H. *Neurology, (Minneap.)*, 1958, *8*:272–276.
28. Lewis, T. *Pain*. New York, Macmillan, 1942.
29. Lewis, T. and Hess, W. *Clin. Sci.*, 1933, *1*:39–61.
30. Lewis, T. and Kellgren, J. H. *Clin. Sci.*, 1939, *4*:47–71.
31. MacKenzie, J. *Brain*, 1893, *16*:321–354. See also his *Symptoms and their interpretation*, 2d ed. London, Shaw and Sons, 1912.
32. McLellan, A. M. and Goodell, H. *Res. Publ. Ass. nerv. ment. Dis.*, 1943, *23*:252–262.
33. Moore, R. M. *Surgery*, 1938, *3*:534–555.
34. Morley, J. *Abdominal pain*. New York, William Wood & Co., 1931.
35. Park, S. R. and Rodbard, S. *Amer. J. Physiol.*, 1962, *203*:735–738.
36. Ray, B. S. and Neill, C. L. *Ann. Surg.*, 1947, *126*:709–724.
37. Reynolds, O. E. and Hutchins, H. C. *Amer. J. Physiol.*, 1948, *152*:658–662.
38. Ross, J. *Brain*, 1888, *10*:333–361.
39. Rothman, S. *Res. Publ. Ass. nerv. ment. Dis.*, 1943, *23*:110–122.
40. Shelley, W. B. and Arthur, R. P. *Arch. Derm. (Chic.)*, 1955, *72*:399–406.
41. Shelley, W. B. and Arthur, R. P. *Arch. Derm. (Chic.)*, 1957, *76*:296–323.
42. Simons, D. J., Day, E., Goodell, H. and Wolff, H. G. *Res. Publ. Ass. nerv. ment. Dis.*, 1943, *23*:228–244.
43. Sinclair, D. C., Weddell, G. and Feindel W. H. *Brain*, 1948, *71*:184–211.
44. Weiss, S. and Davis, D. *Amer. J. med. Sci.* 1928, *176*:517–536.
45. White, J. C. *Res. Publ. Ass. nerv. ment. Dis.*, 1943, *23*:373–390.
46. White, J. C., Garrey, W. E. and Atkins, J. A. *Arch. Surg.*, 1933, *26*:765–786.
47. White, J. C., Smithwick, R. H. and Simeone, F. A. *The autonomic nervous system; anatomy, physiology, and surgical application*, 3d ed. New York, Macmillan, 1952.
48. White, J. C. and Sweet, W. H. *Pain. Its mechanisms and neurosurgical control*. Springfield, Ill., Charles C Thomas, 1955.
49. Wiggers, C. J. Chap. 6 in Levy, R. L., ed. *Diseases of the coronary arteries and cardiac pain*. New York, Macmillan, 1936.
50. Williams, A. F. *Thorax*, 1950, *5*:40–42.
51. Wolf, S. and Wolff, H. G. *Human gastric function*, 2d ed. New York, Oxford University Press, 1947.
52. Wolff, H. G. *Harvey Lect.*, 1944, *39*:39–95.
53. Wolff, H. G. and Wolf, S. *Pain*. Springfield, Ill., Charles C Thomas, 1949.
54. Zotterman, Y. *J. Physiol.*, 1939, *95*:1–28.

CHAPTER 17

Taste, Olfaction and Visceral Sensation

By HARRY D. PATTON

TASTE[43, 56]

In the previous chapter, the pain aroused by noxious stimuli in visceral and deep structures was discussed. Scattered through the mesentery and within the walls and mucosa of the viscera are end-organs which mediate other sensations. The adequate stimulus for these receptors is usually either mechanical (distension or contraction) or chemical. The sense of taste falls into the latter category.

Four distinct gustatory submodalities are recognized: sweet, salt, bitter and sour or acid. The complex sensations aroused by mixed gustatory stimuli are a fusion of these four primary modalities along with various somatosensory and olfactory components. Application of pure solutions to various regions of the tongue reveals differences in sensitivity. The tip of the tongue is sensitive to all four modalities, but mostly to sweet and salt. The lateral margins of the tongue are most sensitive to sour or acid stimuli, but may also respond to salt. The basal portion of the tongue is sensitive to bitter stimuli.

The zonal distribution of sensitivity complicates determination of thresholds, because the threshold for a modality varies with the region of the tongue. For example, Kiesow reported the following thresholds (grams per cent) for quinine sulfate:

Base of tongue	0.00005%
Tip of tongue	0.00029%
Right edge of tongue	0.00020%
Left edge of tongue	0.00021%

Similar regional variations in threshold can be demonstrated for other pure stimuli.

Receptors. The taste buds are ovoid structures on the tongue, palate, anterior faucial pillars, pharynx and larynx. They are most numerous on the circumvallate and fungiform papillae of the tongue. The mid-dorsal region of the tongue lacks taste buds. Strangely, the larynx, particularly the laryngeal surface of the epiglottis and the medial and lateral surfaces of the arytenoids, is significantly populated with taste buds. Stimulation of these regions by solutions applied through a laryngoscope elicits taste sensations. Each bud is composed of a number of elongated receptor cells (about 10 μ in diameter) clustered together into a barrel-shaped structure about 50 μ in transverse diameter (Fig. 1, upper left). The apical tips of these cells project through the surface epithelium forming the gustatory pore; here sapid substances dissolved in the saliva come into contact with the membrane of the receptor cell. Electron micrographs reveal that the tips of the cells project through the pore as a number of filiform microvilli each 0.1 to 0.2 μ in diameter and 2 μ or more long (see Fig. 1, upper right). The space between the microvilli is filled with a dense homogeneous osmophilic material. The cytoplasm contains numerous mitochondria and large numbers of dense spherical granules.

The taste bud is innervated from its base. Here myelinated nerve fibers 1 to 6 μ in diameter approach the basement membrane, lose their myelin and form a plexus. The fibers of this plexus fall into two size groups: (i) 0.5 to 1.0 μ and (ii) less than 0.5 μ. Some of the latter measure only 50 millimicrons. The fibers of the plexus penetrate the basement membrane and occupy positions in invaginations of the receptor cell membrane, the relationship being similar to

that between axon and Schwann cell in the plexus (see lower half of Fig. 1). The larger fibers often lie between the boundaries of two receptor cells, forming intimate contact with both; smaller fibers are buried more deeply and have long mesaxons. The cytoplasm of both large and small fibers has numerous vesicles similar to those seen in presynaptic terminals; their significance is unknown.

The receptor cells appear to have a brief life cycle, degenerates being constantly replaced with new cells formed by mitotic division of adjacent epithelial cells. After injecting colchicine, which blocks mitotic division, Beidler[10] found numerous arrested mitotic figures in surrounding epithelium but none in the taste buds. After 8 to 10 hours the buds degenerated (presumably because they were not rejuvenated by addition of new receptor cells) and nerve responses to chemical stimulation of the tongue disappeared. In unpoisoned animals the chromosomal material of the dividing cells can be tagged with radioisotopically labeled thymidine, which can be detected radioautographically. After such an injection, the number of tagged cells in taste buds increases sharply, reaching a peak in about 100 hours, suggesting that the receptor cells are all of relatively recent origin. If this picture of rapid turnover is correct, it raises the perplexing question of how connections of nerve terminals and receptor cells are maintained.

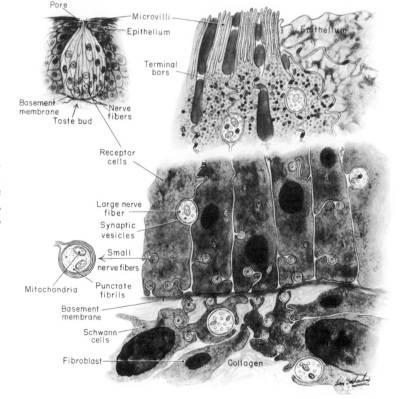

Fig. 1. Structure and innervation of the taste bud. (From de Lorenzo, In: *Olfaction and taste,* Y. Zotterman, ed., New York, The Macmillan Co., 1963.)

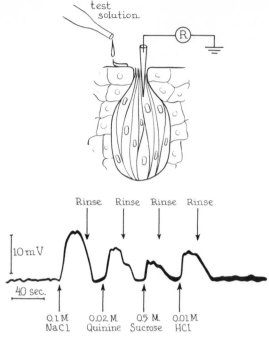

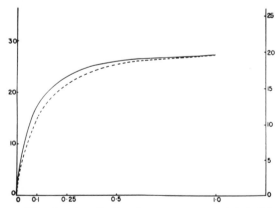

Fig. 2.   Intracellularly recorded responses of taste receptor cells to gustatory stimuli. (After Kimura and Beidler, *J. cell. comp. Physiol.*, 1961, *58*:131–139.)

GENERATOR POTENTIALS.   A microelectrode introduced through the gustatory pore may be positioned to record steady potentials of -50 to -95 mV. relative to an indifferent electrode on the neck muscles.[33, 53] The potential differences appear abruptly as the electrode is slowly advanced into the pore and disappear equally abruptly with further minute advance of the electrode. For these reasons, their occurrence is assumed to signal penetration of a receptor cell, and their magnitude to measure the transmembrane potential of the cell. Application of sapid substances to the surface of the tongue elicits a positive-going potential shift (Fig. 2) the magnitude of which varies with concentration of the stimulating solution (Fig. 3). The electrode records no all-or-nothing spikes; presumably the potential shifts are isolated graded generator potentials developed across the receptor cell membrane. How these generator potentials excite the nerve terminals nestled in the folds of the receptor cell membrane is not known, but a linkage between the two events is strongly suggested by the close correspondence between the amplitude-intensity curves of the receptor potential and of the integrated response of the nerve trunk (see below) supplying the tongue (Fig. 3).

Figure 2 shows that the same receptor cell responded to salty, sweet, bitter and sour test solutions although sensitivity was greatest for NaCl, which, in 0.1 molar solution, elicited a 10 mV. depolarization. Such promiscuous but "sensitivity-specific" behavior is commonly found and presents a serious difficulty for the long-cherished hypothesis that taste submodalities are mediated by separate specifically sensitive receptor cells.

Nerve Fiber Discharges.   Taste-evoked conducted spikes can be recorded from single fibers teased from one of the nerve trunks supplying taste buds, usually the chorda tympani (see below). Figure 4 shows the response of such a fiber to application of varying concentrations of NaCl to the tongue. Generally such units, like other receptor units, signal increased intensity of stimulation by increased rate of firing and increased number of units firing. With prolonged stimulation the discharge adapts. Gustatory fibers, like the receptor cells which they supply, show only crudely quantitative selectivity in their responsiveness to solutions which give rise to markedly different taste sensations. For example, the NaCl-sensitive unit shown in Figure 4 also responded to HCl and to KCl.

A frequently used and convenient additional method of measuring the total neural response to gustatory stimulation is to record from the whole chorda tympani trunk using an integrating amplifier. Such amplifiers add together the asynchronous impulses in individual nerve fibers and give an approximate meas-

Fig. 3.   Amplitude of receptor potential (solid line) and of integrated chorda tympani response (dashed line) to varying strengths of NaCl. *Abscissa,* concentration of NaCl; *ordinates,* amplitude of integrated response (right) and of receptor potential (left). Scales arranged so that asymptotes of two curves coincide. (From Kimura and Beidler, *J. cell. comp. Physiol.,* 1961, *58*:131–139.)

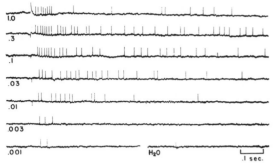

Fig. 4. Response of single afferent fiber in rat chorda tympani to NaCl applied to tongue. Numbers under records give molar concentration of solution. *Lower right record,* Control with water as stimulus. (From Pfaffmann, *J. Neurophysiol.,* 1955, *18:*429–440.)

ure of the magnitude of response of a population of units. Integrated records provided the data for construction of the dashed curve in Figure 3.

Neural Mechanism of Submodality Discrimination. The nonspecific sensitivity of receptor cells (and hence of the afferent fibers which serve them) to stimuli easily discriminated subjectively is puzzling. A single gustatory unit indiscriminately responsive to each of several substances cannot distinctively signal by its discharge which of these substances elicited the discharge. This is true even if the unit shows (as most do) some quantitative variation in sensitivity to various substances, because concentrations for each substance could still be found which would produce identical discharge rates. Pfaffman[43] suggests that the frequency pattern of the discharge of a *population* of receptors constitutes the basis for discrimination. Erickson,[24] using an ingenious combination of electrophysiologic and behavioral techniques, has tested this theory. In a number of single fibers teased from the chorda tympani he measured the discharge rate elicited by NH_4Cl, KCl and NaCl solutions on the tongue. The correlation between sensitivities to NH_4Cl and KCl was +0.83; i.e., fibers which had high sensitivity to NH_4Cl tended to have high sensitivity to KCl. Sensitivities to NaCl, however, were poorly correlated with those to KCl (−0.09) or to NH_4Cl (−0.11). If the population discharge pattern determines submodality discrimination, it might therefore be predicted that animals would find the discrimination between NH_4Cl and KCl more difficult than the discrimination between either of these substances and NaCl. Behavioral tests showed this to be the case. Rats were trained to avoid drinking KCl by giving them a painful shock each time they sampled the solution. When animals so trained were presented a free choice to drink KCl, NH_4Cl or NaCl, they avoided not only KCl but also NH_4Cl, but their consumption of NaCl solution was little altered.

Taste Pathways. At least two cranial nerves are involved in the transmission of taste impulses from the tongue. The taste buds of the posterior one-third of the tongue are innervated by the *glossopharyngeal nerve;* those from the anterior two-thirds by the chorda tympani branch of the *facial nerve.* Also, a few fibers in the vagus may supply the buds of the larynx and pharynx. The trigeminal nerve mediates general somatic sensation from the tongue, but apparently contains no gustatory afferents.

Taste fibers entering the glossopharyngeal nerve continue with it into the brain. The course of taste fibers leaving the tongue in the chorda tympani is complicated, apparently being subject to individual variation. Of the four known peripheral pathways for these fibers, only two need be described here. The first is a direct route via the chorda tympani until it joins the facial nerve and thence in this nerve to the brain. The second pathway is via the chorda tympani through its anastomoses with the otic ganglion. The taste fibers pass through this ganglion to the greater petrosal nerve and in it to the geniculate ganglion of the facial nerve. The former is the usual route, but the petrosal nerve may be important in a few people.

That taste fibers in both the facial and glossopharyngeal nerves are small may be inferred from the small amplitude and slow conduction of impulses aroused by gustatory stimulation. Zotterman[55] assigned taste fibers a diameter of less than 4 μ. In the "demotored" chorda tympani of the cat, 18 per cent of the fibers are unmyelinated (less than 1.5 μ), and myelinated afferents range from 1.5 to 6.0 μ.[26]

The afferent fibers of the VIIth, IXth and Xth nerves, after entering the medulla, form a well-defined common descending tract, the *tractus solitarius.* In this respect, taste fibers behave like the pain and temperature fibers of the trigeminal nerve, which descend in the neighboring spinal trigeminal tract (Fig. 5). Most of the taste and viscerosensory fibers terminate in the gray matter adjacent to the solitary tract, *nucleus tractus solitarius.*[45] The fibers of the three nerves terminate at different levels in the nucleus. Fibers from the facial and glossopharyngeal nerve terminate in the rostral part of the nucleus, only vagal fibers entering the caudal portion. Consequently, secondary taste neurons are concentrated in the rostral part of the nucleus.

The axons of the secondary neurons pursue a course up the brain stem in close relation to the medial lemniscus and the ventral secondary quintothalamic tract. The gustatory fibers relay in the most medial part of the nucleus ventralis posteromedialis (arcuate nucleus). Lesions of

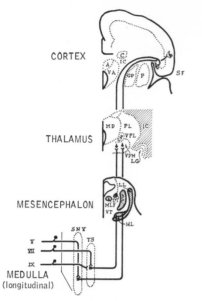

Fig. 5. Summary diagram, highly schematic, representing taste and somatosensory pathways from face. *A,* Anterior thalamic nucleus; *BC,* brachium conjunctivum; *C,* caudate nucleus; *CM,* n. centrum medianum; *DT,* dorsal secondary trigeminal tract; *GP,* globus pallidus; *IC,* internal capsule; *LG,* lateral geniculate body; *LL,* lateral lemniscus; *MD,* n. medialis dorsalis; *ML,* medial lemniscus; *MLF,* medial longitudinal fasciculus; *P,* putamen; *PL,* n. lateralis posterior; *SF,* sylvian fissure; *SNV,* spinal nucleus of 5th nerve; *TS,* nucleus of tractus solitarius; *VA,* n. ventralis anterior; *VPL,* n. ventralis posterolateralis; *VPM,* n. ventralis posteromedialis (arcuate nucleus); *VT,* ventral secondary trigeminal tract.

this nucleus in the monkey severely impair the animal's ability to discriminate between quinine solutions and water.[15, 41] Single units isolated in the medial arcuate nucleus are driven by gustatory stimulation of the tongue; these cells are distinct from more laterally situated cells which respond to thermal or mechanical stimuli to the tongue.[12, 14]

In the cortex the taste-receiving area lies in close association with the representation of other modalities from the tongue.[13, 14, 34, 39] In monkey and chimpanzee, taste deficits follow lesions which destroy the cortex buried in the sylvian fissure at the foot of the fissure of Rolando.[9, 40, 47] Benjamin[12] believes that the claustrum may be involved in taste perception.

Biologic Value of Taste.[44, 46] Superficially, taste appears to be an unimportant sensory modality. Richter,[46] however, has shown that taste plays a critical role in nutrition and in the maintenance of a constant internal environ-

ment for the organism. He demonstrated that rats suffering from dietary or endocrine deficiencies select foodstuffs or liquids containing the substances required to correct their deficiencies. For example, an adrenalectomized rat shows a marked appetite for saline and, if allowed to do so, will selectively drink sufficient sodium chloride not only to maintain life but to gain weight; adrenalectomized animals not offered saline die within a few days. Similarly, a parathyroidectomized animal displays an increased appetite for solutions containing calcium, and this appetite can be abolished by parathyroid implants. Vitamin-deficient rats will also eat selectively those foods containing the necessary vitamins. Taste provides the sensory cue by which these vitally important discriminative selections are made. Animals with their peripheral taste nerves sectioned are no longer capable of regulating their diets to correct deficiencies, but tend to eat and drink indiscriminately.

OLFACTION[36, 56]

The olfactory mucosa occupies an area of 2.5 sq. cm. in each nostril, including the upper third of the septum and the superior concha. Little of the air entering the nostrils in quiet respiration reaches the olfactory crypt. Rapidly diffusing molecules of volatile substances may, however, reach the mucosa, and sniffing creates currents which aid in carrying molecules upward into this secluded location.

Absolute olfactory thresholds vary considerably, depending on the methods of measurement, but agree in indicating very high sensitivity. For example, artificial musk can be detected at a concentration of only 0.00004 mg. per liter of air and mercaptan at 0.00000004 mg. per liter of air.

Relative thresholds can be measured more easily and yield consistent results. Although variations from person to person occur because of differences in the construction of the nasal passages,[23] ranges of normal values have been obtained, and repeated determinations on a man give constant values. In women, the individual results are also consistent, but acuity increases just before and during the menstrual period.

The first apparatus for testing olfaction in the human was designed by Zwaardemaker. It consists of two concentric tubes. The inner wall of the outer tube is porous so that it may be saturated with an odorous solution. The inner tube, graduated in arbitrary units of length termed *olfacties,* may be inserted into the outer tube to any depth. This controls the area of odorous material exposed. The tube is held to one nostril and the subject inhales through it. Unfortunately, this procedure does not control the force of inhalation, which can affect the threshold. To overcome this, Elsberg[23] designed an apparatus by which the odorous material is pumped into the nostril while the subject holds his breath. With this apparatus, the minimum identifiable odor (MIO), or threshold, is determined as the least quantity of air saturated with the olfactory substance which can be smelled when injected with uniform force.

These olfactory testing methods have some application in clinical neurology. In 74 per cent of patients with tumors in or around the frontal lobes, the MIO was found to be elevated.[23] No changes were found in patients with lesions below the tentorium. Through lack of sufficient postmortem verification of the lesions, such studies have failed to contribute much to the understanding of how the various parts of the olfactory system function.

Receptors. The olfactory mucosa is composed of two intermingled vertically oriented cell types: (i) the sustentacular cells and (ii) the receptor cells (Fig. 6). The former are columnar cells with filamentous processes (microvilli) abutting the nasal cavity. The receptor cells are bipolar neurons which serve both as receptors and ganglion cells. At their dendritic extremities they expand and present toward the nasal cavity 6 to 12 cilia. The expanded portion (called the olfactory rod) contains vacuoles and mitochondria as well as numerous vesicles resembling those seen in presynaptic terminals. At its basal extremity the receptor cell dwindles; its membrane is continuous with that of the axon from which it derives. Each axon gives rise to only one receptor cell.

The olfactory nerve fibers pass through the cribriform plate to enter the olfactory bulb. The individual axons, which average 0.2 μ in di-

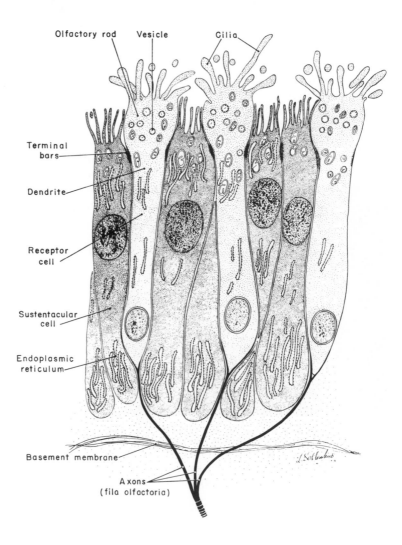

Fig. 6. Structure and innervation of the olfactory mucosa. (From de Lorenzo, In: *Olfaction and taste,* Y. Zotterman, ed., New York, The Macmillan Co., 1963.)

Olfactory rod   Vesicle   Cilia

Terminal bars

Dendrite

Receptor cell

Sustentacular cell

Endoplasmic reticulum

Basement membrane

Axons (fila olfactoria)

ameter, bear a unique relation to the Schwann sheath: each Schwann mesaxon surrounds not a single axon (cf. Fig. 10, Chap. 3) but a cluster of closely packed axons, the membranes of which are separated by spaces only 100 to 150 Å wide.[27, 56]

GENERATOR POTENTIALS.[35]   The small size of olfactory receptors precludes intracellular recording. An electrode placed on the surface of the olfactory mucosa records a slow negative potential (electro-olfactogram) when a jet of odorous air is directed over the mucosa (Fig. 7). The amplitude of the potential increases approximately logarithmically with increasing odor intensity. The potential persists after application of cocaine to the mucosa in doses sufficient to block impulse traffic in the olfactory nerve fibers. These similarities to unitary generator potentials (see Chap. 4) suggest that the electro-olfactogram reflects the local graded potential of a population of primary olfactory receptors under the electrode. Since the potential is a mass response, it provides little information about the excitatory process in individual receptor cells; nevertheless, as shown in Figure 7, different odorants elicit potentials of different configurations and durations.

RECEPTOR SPIKES.[30]   Spike activity of individual olfactory receptors may be recorded extracellularly with microelectrodes positioned in the olfactory mucosa (Fig. 8). A minute (0.2 ml.)

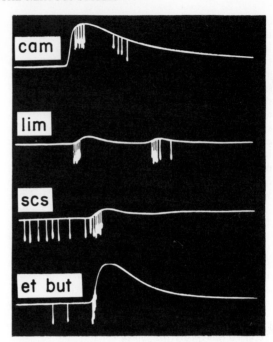

Fig. 8.   Electro-olfactogram and receptor spike discharges recorded during stimulation of frog olfactory mucosa with brief jets of odorous air. From above downward stimuli were: camphor, limonene (two puffs), carbon disulfide and ethyl butyrate. Sweep lengths 10 seconds. (From Gesteland *et al.* In: *Olfaction and taste,* Y. Zotterman, ed., New York, The Macmillan Co., 1963.)

puff of odorized air evokes bursts of spikes lasting for 1 to 4 seconds and reaching frequencies up to 20 per second. Increasing the volume of the jet increases both the amplitude of the electro-olfactogram and the number and frequency of spikes. Individual units are only crudely odor-selective; most show especially strong responses to one or more odorants and weaker responses to others (Fig. 8). Just how such receptors signal to the brain the many subjectively discriminable odor submodalities is not clear.

Olfactory Bulb and Central Olfactory Pathways.   The axons issuing from the olfactory receptors enter the cranial cavity through the cribriform plate of the ethmoid bone. On the ventral surface of the frontal lobes near the midline they enter the olfactory bulb. The bulb, like the retina, is a part of the brain proper. In lower animals it is prominent and possesses a cavity which communicates with the ventricular system of the brain. In man, the central cavity is obliterated by a mass of neuroglia. Next to the neuroglia is a deep layer of myelinated fibers passing from the bulb to the olfactory tract (Fig.

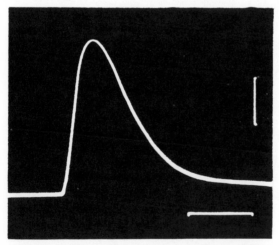

Fig. 7.   The electro-olfactogram recorded from surface of olfactory mucosa of frog. Stimulus was a brief jet of air containing butanol. Upward deflection signifies negativity of mucosal surface to distant electrode. Horizontal bar, 2 seconds; vertical bar, 1 mV. (From Ottoson In: *Olfaction and taste,* Y. Zotterman, ed., New York, The Macmillan Co., 1963.)

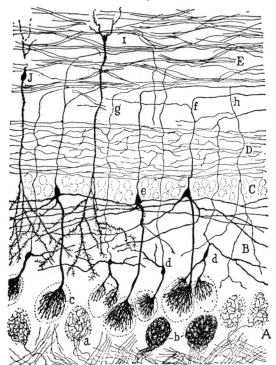

Fig. 9. Olfactory bulb of a kitten, Golgi stain. Surface of bulb is at bottom; core white matter at top. *A,* Layer of glomeruli; *B,* external plexiform layer; *C,* layer of mitral cells; *D,* internal plexiform layer; *E,* layer of granule cells and white matter; *I, J,* granule cells; *a, b,* glomerular terminals of primary olfactory fibers; *c,* glomerular terminal of mitral cell dendrite; *d,* tufted cells; *e,* mitral cell; *h,* recurrent collateral of mitral cell axon. (From Ramón y Cajal.)

9). Superficially there is a layer of unmyelinated fibers which are the terminations of the olfactory nerve. Situated between the two fiber layers is a mass of gray matter which contains three types of neurons, the tufted cells, the mitral cells and the granule cells. The tufted cells are the most superficial. The mitral cells form a compact layer just beneath them. The dendrites of both types of cells course toward the periphery of the bulb and break up into rounded, bushy terminals, the olfactory glomeruli, which form synapses with the primary olfactory fibers. The axons of the mitral and tufted cells join the deep myelinated fiber layer of the bulb to pass into the olfactory tract. The axons of the tufted cells probably leave the tract to reach the opposite olfactory bulb via the anterior commissure; they do not degenerate if the olfactory tract is severed. The mitral cells are thus the secondary olfactory neurons. The granule cells are most deeply situated and send short axons toward the surface of the bulb.

The olfactory tract courses caudally on the base of the frontal lobes. Both tract and bulb are derivatives of the brain, and the fibers of the tract are capped dorsally by gray matter continuous with the gray matter of the bulb; the tract is really a gyrus in which the gray matter has been greatly reduced. The site of termination of the tract fibers is not entirely settled. The most careful studies[19] indicate the following direct connections: (i) the opposite bulb (via the anterior commissure), (ii) the prepyriform area and parts of the amygdaloid complex, and (iii) the olfactory tubercle. Contrary to the usual statement, there appear to be no direct connections with either the hippocampus or the septal area.[17] Unlike all other sensory modalities, olfaction does not seem to have a thalamic representation.

Olfactory Discrimination. An amazing variety of odors can be distinguished even by man, in whom olfaction is much less acute than it is in lower animals. It is therefore interesting to inquire how the centrally transmitted message varies when the mucosa is excited by psychologically discriminable odorants. An estimated 26,000 receptors converge upon a single glomerulus. Also, each glomerulus receives axons from some 24 mitral cells and 68 tufted cells.[5] This extreme convergence and divergence allows for a complex variation of pattern in the centrally directed message.

Fine electrodes thrust into the central white matter of the bulb satisfactorily record spike activity of individual secondary units (axons of mitral and/or tufted cells).[3] In the anesthetized animal breathing odorous air, each inspiration is accompanied by a burst of activity in secondary axons; this ceases when charcoal-filtered air is substituted for odorous air. For each mitral unit isolated there is one odor which will stimulate it at a concentration too low to affect other units in touch with the electrode. The selective sensitivity is usually greatest for one substance, but chemically related substances may also be effective.[4]

Electrodes in different parts of the bulb record differential activity with different odorants.[2] In rabbits the anterior part of the bulb responds briskly to inhalation of substances with a fruity odor, e.g., amyl acetate, whereas a posteriorly situated electrode records little. The posterior part, however, responds readily when oily-smelling substances, e.g., benzene or pentane, are added to inspired air. Adrian[2] suggests that such spatial differences (as well as certain observable temporal differences) may constitute a basis for odor discrimination.

The spatial arrangement of the projection of the olfactory mucosa onto the bulb can be mapped because receptors whose axons are interrupted rapidly undergo retrograde degeneration.[20] By making discrete lesions of the bulb and mapping the areas of atrophy in the mucosa, one can map the spatial pattern of projection. Such studies first led to the conclusion that there is no topographic organization of the projection onto the bulb.[20] Subsequently, Le Gros Clark[18] repeated these experiments and found mucosal degeneration was not completely diffuse following discrete bulbar lesions, but tended to appear in patches, the boundaries of which were sometimes sharp. It is evident, however, that there is no point-to-point projection of mucosa onto the bulb in the sense that each local area of sensory epithelium is represented centrally in an orderly sequence of equivalent areas having the same spatial relationship. The reason for this is the plexiform distribution of the primary fibers after they reach the surface of the bulb. Normal material shows olfactory fibers randomly approaching and entering individual glomeruli from different directions.

VISCERAL SENSATION

Since the afferent fibers of the autonomic and

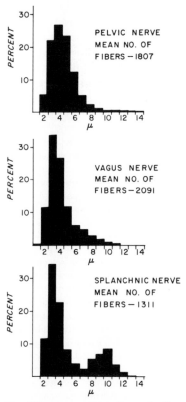

Fig. 10. Histogram of myelinated afferent fibers in "demotored" autonomic trunks supplying viscera. Abscissae show fiber diameters in μ; ordinates, percentage incidence of fibers at each diameter. (From Griffin, Griffin and Patton, unpublished studies.)

somatic nervous systems are similar except in course, the terms "sympathetic visceral afferents" and "parasympathetic visceral afferents" do not imply any functional peculiarity of these afferents as compared with somatic afferents (see Chap. 16). Actually, the sensory innervation of the visceral cavities is derived from both the autonomic and the somatic nervous system.

The number of visceral afferent fibers traversing somatic pathways cannot be estimated, but about 10,500 myelinated visceral afferents traverse autonomic pathways. To this should be added an uncounted but large number of unmyelinated (type C) visceral afferents reaching the spinal cord by both pathways. Figure 10 shows the size distribution of myelinated, visceral, autonomic afferents in the cat. The data were obtained by enumerating and measuring osmic acid-stained fibers remaining after section had caused degeneration of the efferent fibers. In all three nerves there are prominent peaks at 3 to 4 μ (A delta fibers). The splanchnic nerves show a second smaller peak at 10 μ (A alpha fibers). The vagal afferents shown are almost wholly derived from thoracic and cervical structures. Compound action potentials elicited by stimulating the vagus just above the diaphragm show only a C elevation, and sections of "demotored" supradiaphragmatic vagus show few or no myelinated afferents. Vagal afferents from abdominal viscera are thus nearly all unmyelinated.

Reflex Afferents. Not all of the visceral afferents are truly sensory. Many form reflex connections in the cord and bulb without projections to the higher sensory centers. Such fibers do not mediate conscious sensation. The origin of visceral afferents and the reflex and sensory functions which they subserve are shown diagrammatically in Figure 11. The afferent limbs of the reflex arcs controlling vital visceral phenomena—cardiac reflexes, aortic reflexes, Hering–Breuer reflex, micturition, etc.—are without exception found in *parasympathetic nerves.* True, stimulation of the central end of the splanchnic nerve will elevate blood pressure and initiate polysynaptic reflex discharges in adjacent ventral roots, but these appear to be pain reflexes. Gentle stimulation of the mesentery[29] or weak stimulation of the central end of the splanchnic nerve, although adequate to excite the large afferent fibers, does not elicit reflex discharge. This occurs only when stimuli are sufficiently strong to excite smaller A delta fibers.[7] The sympathetic afferent fibers, although abundant, are not essential to the reflex regulation of the visceral organs. Reflexes from parasympathetic afferents are regulatory reflexes operative under normal conditions of life, whereas the reflexes from sympathetic afferents occur in response to strong stimuli and in pathologic conditions. The contrast between sympathetic and parasympathetic motor function (Cannon) applies equally well to afferent function. The sympathetic afferents are "dispensable."

In this chapter, the visceral sensory afferents are discussed. Visceral reflex afferents are described in the chapters dealing with the organ systems which they serve.

SENSORY VISCERAL AFFERENTS AND THEIR CENTRAL PATHWAYS

Somatic and Sympathetic Afferents. Noxious stimulation (pinching, burning, application of hypertonic NaCl or acid) of the diaphragm sets up a shower of small centripetally conducted spike potentials in the phrenic nerve.[28] Light tactile stimulation is without effect. When the nerve is subdivided, individual spikes can be recorded and conduction velocities estimated from spike size and duration. Such studies indicate that the active fibers are of A delta or C size. Similar small spikes appear in the splanchnic nerve when the intestine is pinched.[29] Passage of strong peristaltic waves and spastic contractions of the intestinal wall induced by local application of acetylcholine also excite splanchnic A delta and C fibers. It thus appears that

visceral and cutaneous pain are conducted by similar fibers.

Light mechanical stimulation of the mesentery elicits in the splanchnic nerve large spikes with conduction velocities in the alpha range.[29] These fibers supply the pacinian corpuscles of the mesentery.[50] However, some of the large splanchnic afferents must end in other kinds of receptors, because there are more large splanchnic afferents than pacinian corpuscles.[7] The sensory function of mesenteric pacinian corpuscles is not entirely clear. They are rapidly adapting receptors and are exquisitely sensitive to mechanical distortion; the air vibration induced by the spoken voice is often sufficient to excite a brief shower of spikes.

Both A alpha and A delta groups project to the cerebral cortex and hence presumably subserve conscious sensation. Stimulation of the splanchnic nerve evokes typical surface-positive potentials in the contralateral postcentral gyrus.[6] The splanchnic receiving zone lies between and overlaps the areas for the arm and leg in the somatosensory cortex. A similar topographic projection of splanchnic impulses obtains in the lateral part of the posteroventral thalamic nucleus.[38] This accords with expectation in a topographically organized system. There appears to be no special cortical or thalamic area devoted to visceral as opposed to somatic sensation.

Weak stimuli liminal for A alpha fibers evoke a smooth cortical wave with a latency of 8 to 12 milli-

Fig. 11. Diagram showing origin and function of visceral afferent fibers.

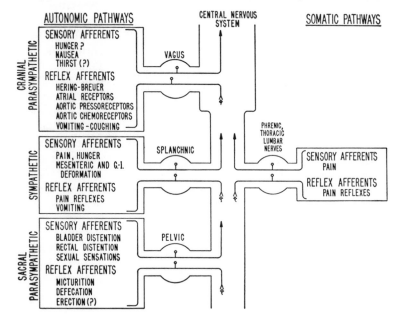

seconds. Mechanical stimulation of the mesentery produces a similar response, although the latency may be slightly greater (15 milliseconds). Stronger shocks recruiting A delta fibers into the afferent volley produce a double wave, the second wave (latency about 20 milliseconds) being superimposed on the rising limb of the first. Thus, at least some of the impulses carried by A delta afferents reach the cortex. The spinal pathway for the large afferent fibers is via the dorsal columns; shocks strong enough to excite A delta fibers evoke electrical activity in the contralateral anterolateral column.[7]

Conduction of visceral afferent impulses to the cortex is conditioned by activity in somatic afferents. A shock to the splanchnic nerve which produces a maximal cortical response when delivered alone may produce little or no response if it is preceded by a shock to somatic afferents.[8] Blockage of conduction of splanchnic impulses may also occur with antecedent tactile stimulation of the skin. Blocking interaction is readily demonstrated at the thalamic level. It may explain the efficacy of cutaneous irritation (mustard poultices) in relieving visceral distress.

Vagus Nerve. The evidence for a specific cortical projection of vagal afferents is much less clear. Dell[22] recorded short-latency (8 to 10 milliseconds) cortical responses to vagal stimulation. The responsive cortical area was in the inferior part of the face somatosensory area. In the thalamus responses of 5 to 6 milliseconds latency were recorded in the midline nuclei medial to the face somatosensory relay nuclei. Other investigators have failed to record specific cortical responses to vagal stimulation.[48, 49]

In conscious humans, stimulation of the postcentral cortex within the sylvian fissure elicits sensations referred to the pharynx.[42] Nausea, "sinking sensations of the stomach," belching and vomiting may result when the island of Reil is stimulated. It is, however, quite possible that the primary effect is motor and that the sensations are secondary.

Most of the myelinated vagal afferents appear to subserve purely reflex functions.[37] Sensations aroused by irritation of the pharynx or the lining of the respiratory tree (the adequate stimulus for the gag and cough reflexes) may be subserved by myelinated afferents since these structures are clearly supplied with some of the larger afferent fibers of the vagus. However, we have seen that the abdominal viscera have few if any myelinated vagal afferents. Specific cortical projection of impulses traversing C fibers has never been clearly demonstrated by electrical recording methods. This may be due to the small size of potentials conducted in small fibers, or it may indicate that sensations mediated by C fibers are elaborated at subcortical levels.

Pelvic Nerve. Stimulation of the central end of the pelvic nerve evokes small primary cortical responses in the most medial part of the leg somatosensory cortex to which tactile impulses from the sacral segments project. Whether these responses represent the neural substratum of bladder or genital sensation, however, is open to question; cortical stimulation in conscious patients produces neither micturition nor sensations referable to the bladder.[42] Similarly, electrical stimulation of cortex does not elicit sexual sensations, although contralateral nonerotic sensations projected to the genitalia occur when the postcentral gyrus is stimulated on the mesial surface of the hemisphere.

Erickson[25] reported the case of a female patient in whom a tumor arising from the falx and compressing the paracentral lobule produced seizures characterized by erotic sensations and intense desire for intercourse. The patient described the sensations as more intense on the side opposite the tumor. She was first diagnosed as a nymphomaniac, and an unsuccessful attempt was made to induce artificial menopause by ovarian irradiation. Subsequent discovery and removal of the tumor abolished the symptoms.

Summary. Two features are notable in the cortical projections of autonomic visceral afferents. First, despite their common origin in visceral structures, the three nerves have quite separate cortical receiving zones. This is because they enter the nervous system at different levels: sacral, thoracic, and bulbar. The orderly segmental pattern of afferent inflow is preserved in cortical localization which respects neither functional similarity nor anatomic propinquity of the organs represented.[48] Secondly, relatively small areas of cortex are devoted to the viscera. This corresponds to the poverty of spatial discrimination in visceral sensations as compared, for example, with cutaneous tactile sensation, vision, or audition, which have extensive cortical receiving zones. Precise spatial discrimination apparently requires large numbers of cortical cells.

ORGANIC SENSATIONS

In the previous chapter it was emphasized that visceral pain is chiefly mediated by afferent fibers traveling with sympathetic and somatic nerves. The remaining sensations from visceral organs (hunger, thirst, bladder fullness, sexual sensations, etc.) are termed "organic sensations." Organic sensations signal body needs and lead to behavior which satisfies those needs. They are mediated by both sympathetic and parasympathetic afferents.

Hunger. Hunger, defined generically as all those processes which lead to the ingestion of food, has at least three components: appetite, hunger sensations or pangs, and a third, unnamed, physiologic state or hunger-drive which leads to the ingestion of food.

APPETITE. The term "appetite" refers to a food preference which "arises from the experience of previous pleasures; a wishing, longing or yearning for something especially desirable" (Cannon). Associated with appetite are conditioned gastrointestinal reflexes. The sight, smell or taste of favored food elicits copious secretions of saliva and gastric juice, whereas similar presentation of food for which the subject has little liking is a much less potent stimulus. Since most obesity appears to result from strong appetites and their free indulgence, it often is primarily a psychologic problem. Although previous experience is most important in determining appetite, genetic factors obviously determine food preferences of different species; for example, lions do not eat tomatoes, nor do monkeys eat meat. Appetite as reflected by food preference patterns may also be altered by dietary or metabolic deficiencies, as discussed in the previous section on taste. The preference pattern is invariably of a type which combats or offsets the deficiency. The mechanism of such homeostatic changes of appetite is poorly understood.

HUNGER SENSATIONS. Although appetite may determine *what* we eat under situations of free choice, it does not determine *when* or *how much* we eat. In the human, frequency of eating is largely determined by social custom and by appetite. There is, however, a physiologic mechanism for signaling that it is time to eat—*hunger sensations*. These are described as "a very disagreeable ache or pang or sense of gnawing or pressure which is referred to the epigastrium." Hunger pangs recur periodically and with a fair degree of regularity. Prior to 1911, hunger sensation was considered to be a sensation of the depletion of bodily stores of foodstuffs in blood or tissues. Cannon discovered that hunger pangs

are sensations derived from contractions of the empty stomach.

Frequency and amplitude of hunger contractions are greatest in the empty stomach. They disappear promptly with ingestion of food and are temporarily stopped by sham chewing or swallowing, by smoking, by alcohol, or by tightening the belt. Strong emotional states also abolish them. Sleep, however, does not inhibit them. Restlessness and dreams are associated with their occurrence, as was proved by a simultaneous recording technique (Carlson). Newborn infants are restless before feeding time as though disturbed by unpleasant sensations, and random activity of rats interpretable as food seeking is associated with onset of hunger contractions. Recent observations suggest that hunger sensations do not cause the increased random activity, but that both are manifestations of some more deep-seated phenomenon. For example, lowering the blood sugar level by injection of insulin increases hunger contractions, spontaneous activity and food intake. In prolonged fasts hunger sensations disappear after the first few days, but the hunger contractions persist. This appears to be due to some central adaptive process.

Hunger contractions, both spontaneous and insulin-induced, are abolished by vagotomy.[51] It is thus difficult to test the time-honored hypothesis that the afferent path of hunger sensations is vagal. At least part of the impulses traverse sympathetic pathways. Grossman and Stein[31] stated that sympathectomy abolishes hunger sensations although the contractions persist. This is not surprising, since hunger pangs are disagreeable sensations allied to pain, which is, of course, mediated via sympathetic pathways.

HUNGER DRIVE. Although hunger contractions signal to the nervous system emptiness of the stomach (and possibly hypoglycemia), they are not essential for the maintenance of food intake sufficient to support caloric balance. Neither vagotomy (Bash, Morgan) nor gastrectomy (Tsang) seriously affects food intake, food seeking activity or weight maintenance. In vagotomized humans, insulin-induced hypoglycemia no longer elicits hunger contractions, but usually creates a desire for food.[31] Finally, cessation of hunger contractions (which occurs with the ingestion of a few mouthfuls of food) does not correlate with termination of eating. Rather, eating normally continues until sufficient calories have been ingested to maintain requirements. Mature rats fed diets diluted with cellulose or kaolin eat increased quantities and maintain constant caloric intake and weight.[1] Similarly, fat-fortified high caloric diets lead to decreased bulk intake until constant caloric intake is achieved.*[52] Thus it must be concluded that *hunger as a physiologic state leading to ingestion of food and in amounts adjusted to energy expenditure is something different from hunger as a sensation.* Hunger as a drive is discussed in Chapters 11 and 25.

Thirst.[54] Thirst, like hunger, appears to consist of a sensory component and a physiologic state or drive. The sensory component is mediated by the glossopharyngeal and vagus nerves which signal the dryness of throat which accompanies dehydration. Salivary secretion, for example, decreases markedly with advancing dehydration; with water deficits of 8 per cent of the body weight (computed from weight loss during dehydration), salivary flow drops to near zero. The resulting dryness of the mucous membranes is sensed. This sensation can be abolished by anesthetizing the mucous membrane or by administering drugs which stimulate salivary flow.

The presence or absence of a sensation of oral and pharyngeal dryness does not, however, govern the frequency or amount of drinking. Neither section of the IXth and Xth nerves nor removal of the salivary glands affects water intake. Drugs (e.g., pilocarpine) which stimulate salivary secretion prevent oral dryness but do not alter the amount of water drunk by dehydrated humans. Obviously, then, there is a thirst drive or "urge to drink" which is relatively independent of the sensory component of thirst.

The mechanism of the thirst drive is entirely unknown, but experiments show that the intensity of the drive is directly related to the water deficit. A dehydrated dog, when offered water, at once drinks enough to replace its water deficit and bring the body fluid content to the threshold of diuresis. In other words, in a few moments all the water the body will hold is metered with some accuracy through the pharynx.[11] The same behavior is exhibited by dogs with an esophageal fistula which prevents ingested water from reaching the stomach; hence receptor activation in the stomach is not the cue to stop drinking. In fact, when enough water to replace the deficit is introduced into a

dehydrated dog's stomach through the distal end of the fistula, it still sham drinks that amount if water is offered immediately. If the interval between prewatering and presentation of water is 20 minutes or more, the dog does not drink. Two satisfactions thus appear to be involved, a temporary one produced by passage of an appropriate quantity of water through the throat, and a more lasting one following absorption and distribution of water from the stomach.

Dehydrated man is more deliberate in replacing water deficits than is the dog, rabbit or burro; within 30 minutes after breaking a water fast, man replaces only about 80 per cent of the water deficit. Nevertheless, dehydrated man has a strong urge to replace water deficits, and this urge is unaffected by drugs. Dehydration in both man and animals is accompanied by anorexia, but ingestion of moderate amounts of food does not alter the thirst drive. The diet of choice during water deprivation is carbohydrate, because its oxidation yields a mol of water for every mol metabolized, and because its other combustive product, CO_2, requires no water for excretion.

Nausea.[16] Nausea is an unpleasant sensation vaguely referred to the epigastrium and abdomen and often culminating in vomiting. However, vomiting does not always follow nausea, nor is nausea a necessary antecedent of vomiting. Vomiting produced by mechanical irritation of the pharynx and the "projectile vomiting" of children with tumors in or near the fourth ventricle may occur without nausea. In animals, the salivation, swallowing and rhythmic licking preceding vomiting are often taken as signs of nausea. With some emetic agents, e.g., cardiac glycosides, a conditioned vomiting response may be established, suggesting that such drugs cause true nausea as well as vomiting.

Stimulation of the vomiting center in the dorsolateral reticular formation of the medulla consistently produces vomiting in decerebrate cats.[16] The vomiting is projectile in nature, stimulus-bound (i.e., persists only during the stimulus), and can be repeatedly initiated. This is probably comparable to the projectile vomiting, often unassociated with nausea, that is seen with cerebellar tumors. Spontaneous nausea and vomiting occur in response to a wide variety of stimuli. Emetic drugs initiate nausea and vomiting either by central action alone or by combined peripheral and central action. Central action is not directly upon the vomiting center in the reticular formation, but upon a

---

*Such readjustment of bulk intake to maintain constant caloric intake requires several days. Caloric balance is thus a relatively long-term regulation and does not account for the amount ingested in any one feeding period.

"chemoreceptor trigger zone" situated near the fasciculus solitarius and the area postrema, dorsal to the vomiting center.

Lesions of the trigger zone abolish vomiting induced by intravenous or oral apomorphine, whereas combined vagotomy and abdominal sympathectomy have no effect.[16] Trigger zone lesions do not prevent vomiting induced by orally administered copper sulfate, whereas combined vagotomy and abdominal sympathectomy greatly elevate the threshold and prolong the latency of emesis. The effectiveness of intravenous copper sulfate is not altered by peripheral denervation. Neither copper sulfate nor apomorphine causes vomiting when the vomiting center is selectively destroyed and the trigger zone is left intact. Thus, whereas apomorphine acts solely via the trigger zone, copper sulfate acts both peripherally and centrally.

The emetic effectiveness of digitalis glycosides is greatly reduced by destruction of the trigger zone, but large doses produce delayed vomiting even when the gut is denervated and the trigger zone ablated.

Impulses from the abdominal cavity which cause nausea and vomiting traverse both vagal and sympathetic pathways, although the former predominate. Copper sulfate, mustard, Escherichia coli peritonitis, staphylococcus enterotoxin and distension of the biliary tract elicit nausea and vomiting which are ameliorated by vagotomy but abolished only by combined vagotomy and abdominal sympathectomy. Vomiting which results from experimental intestinal distension (simulating intestinal obstruction) is abolished by sympathectomy, but anorexia (presumably indicating nausea) persists until the vagi are sectioned.

MOTION SICKNESS. The term "motion sickness" is a misnomer; continuous movement at uniform velocity in one direction does not induce nausea. Only when the speed or direction of motion is repeatedly varied does nausea occur; hence, the term "acceleration sickness" is more appropriate. The responsible receptors are in the vestibular apparatus; section of the VIIIth nerve or labyrinthectomy renders susceptible animals immune to acceleration. Also, nausea may be invoked by irrigating the ear with hot or cold solutions which stimulate vestibular receptors by inducing convection currents in the endolymph. Finally, nausea and vomiting commonly accompany the attacks of vertigo in acute labyrinthitis and Menière's disease.

When the provocative acceleration is linear, as in an elevator or a vehicle accelerating in a straight line, the responsible impulses arise largely from the saccular macula. Angular accelerations (spinning) stimulate principally the cristae of the semicircular canals, and the resultant nausea is accompanied by nystagmus. Many accelerations producing nausea have angular as well as linear components, e.g., in swings, ships, airplanes and automobiles, but linear components constitute the major share of the movement. Susceptibility to nausea from such motions is affected by the position of the head. For example, horizontal position reduces susceptibility to wave accelerations simulating the conditions in boats.

The belladonna alkaloids, the barbiturates and certain antihistaminic drugs are useful in combating acceleration sickness. All are central nervous system depressants and produce drowsiness. Whether their effectiveness is due solely to such general action or whether they have a specific action on the central neural apparatus of vomiting has not been settled.

REFERENCES

1. ADOLPH, E. F. *Amer. J. Physiol.,* 1947, *151:*110–125.
2. ADRIAN, E. D. *Brit. med. Bull.,* 1950, *6:*330–332.
3. ADRIAN, E. D. *Année psychol.,* 1951, *50:*107–113.
4. ADRIAN, E. D. *Brit. med. J.,* 1954, *1:*287–290.
5. ALLISON, A. C. and WARWICK, R. T. T. *Brain,* 1949, *72:* 186–197.
6. AMASSIAN, V. E. *J. Neurophysiol.,* 1951, *14:*433–444.
7. AMASSIAN, V. E. *J. Neurophysiol.,* 1951, *14:*445–460.
8. AMASSIAN, V. E. *Res. Publ. Ass. nerv. ment. Dis.,* 1952, *30:* 371–402.
9. BAGSHAW, M. H. and PRIBRAM, K. H. *J. Neurophysiol.,* 1953, *16:*499–508.
10. BEIDLER, L. M. In *Olfaction and taste.* Y. Zotterman, ed. New York, The Macmillan Co., 1963.
11. BELLOWS, R. T. and VAN WAGENEN, W. P. *Amer. J. Physiol.,* 1939, *126:*13–19.
12. Benjamin, R. M. In *Olfaction and taste.* Y. Zotterman, ed. New York, The Macmillan Co., 1963.
13. BENJAMIN, R. M. and PFAFFMANN, C. *J. Neurophysiol.,* 1955, *18:*56–64.
14. BLOMQUIST, A. J., BENJAMIN, R. M., and EMMERS, R. *J. comp. Neurol.,* 1962, *118:*77–88.
15. BLUM, M., WALKER, A. E. and RUCH, T. C. *Yale J. Biol. Med.,* 1943, *16:*175–191.
16. BORISON, H. L. and WANG, S. C. *Pharmacol. Rev.,* 1953, *5:* 193–230.
17. BRODAL, A. *Brain,* 1947, *70:*179–222.
18. CLARK, W. E. LE GROS. *J. Neurol. Psychiat.,* 1951, *14:*1–10.
19. CLARK, W. E. LE GROS and MEYER, M. *Brain,* 1947, *70:* 304–328.
20. CLARK, W. E. LE GROS and WARWICK, R. T. T. *J. Neurol. Psychiat.,* 1946, *9:*101–111.
21. COHEN, M. J., LANDGREN, S., STRÖM, L. and ZOTTERMAN, Y. *Acta physiol. scand.,* 1957, *40* (Suppl. 135):1–50.
22. DELL, P. *J. Physiol. Path. gén.,* 1952, *44:*471–557.

23. Elsberg, C. A. In *Medical physics*. O. Glasser, ed. Chicago, Year Book Publishers, 1944.

24. ERICKSON, R. P. In *Olfaction and taste*. Y. Zotterman, ed. New York, The Macmillan Co., 1963.

25. ERICKSON, T. C. *Arch. Neurol. Psychiat. (Chic.)*, 1945, **53**: 226–231.

26. FOLEY, J. O. *Proc. Soc. exp. Biol. (N. Y.)*, 1945, *60*:262–267.

27. GASSER, H. S. *J. gen. Physiol.*, 1956, *39*:473–496.

28. GERNANDT, B. *Acta physiol. scand.*, 1946, *12*:255–260.

29. GERNANDT, B. and ZOTTERMAN, Y. *Acta physiol, scand.*, 1946, *12*:56–72.

30. GESTELAND, R. C., LETTVIN, J. Y., PITTS, W. H., and ROJAS, A. In *Olfaction and taste*. Y. Zotterman, ed. New York, The Macmillan Co., 1963.

31. GROSSMAN, M. I. and STEIN, I. F., JR. *J. appl. Physiol.*, 1948, *1*:263–269.

32. KARE, M. R. and HALPERN, B. P., eds. *Physiological and behavioral aspects of taste*. Chicago, Univ. of Chicago Press, 1961.

33. KIMURA, K. and BEIDLER, L. M. *J. cell. comp. Physiol.*, 1961, *58*:131–139.

34. LANDGREN, S. Chap. 23 in *Sensory communication*. W. R. Rosenblith, ed. New York, John Wiley and Sons, 1961.

35. OTTOSON, D. *Acta physiol. scand.*, 1956, *35* (Suppl. 122): 1–83.

36. OTTOSON, D. *Pharmacol. Rev.*, 1963, *15*:1–42.

37. PAINTAL, A. S. *Ergebn. Physiol.*, 1963, *52*:74–156.

38. PATTON, H. D. and AMASSIAN, V. E. *Amer. J. Physiol.*, 1951, *167*:815–816.

39. PATTON, H. D. and AMASSIAN, V. E. *J. Neurophysiol.*, 1952, *15*:245–250.

40. PATTON, H. D., RUCH, T. C. and FULTON, J. F. *Fed. Proc.*, 1946, *5*:79.

41. PATTON, H. D., RUCH, T. C. and WALKER, A. E. *J. Neurophysiol.*, 1944, *7*:171–184.

42. PENFIELD, W. and RASMUSSEN, T. *The cerebral cortex of man.* New York, The Macmillan Co., 1950.

43. PFAFFMANN, C. Chap. 20 in *Handbook of physiology, Section 1: Neurophysiology*, vol. 1. J. Field, ed. Washington, D.C., American Physiological Society, 1959.

44. PFAFFMANN, C. In *Olfaction and taste*. Y. Zotterman, ed. New York, The Macmillan Co., 1963.

45. PFAFFMANN, C., ERICKSON, R. P., FROMMER, G. P. and HALPERN, B. P. Chap. 24 in *Sensory communication*. W. A. Rosenblith, ed. New York, John Wiley and Sons, 1961.

46. RICHTER, C. P. *Harvey Lect.*, 1943, *38*:63–103.

47. RUCH, T. C. and PATTON, H. D. *Fed. Proc.*, 1946, *5*:89–90.

48. RUCH, T. C., PATTON, H. D. and AMASSIAN, V. E. *Res. Publ. Ass. nerv. ment. Dis.*, 1952, *30*:403–429.

49. SACHS, E., JR., BRENDLER, S. J. and FULTON, J. F. *Brain*, 1949, *72*:227–240.

50. SHEEHAN, D. *J. Anat. (Lond.)*, 1932, *67*:233–249.

51. STEIN, I. F., JR. and MEYER, K. A. *Surg. Gynec. Obstet.*, 1948, *86*:473–479.

52. STROMINGER, J. L., BROBECK, J. R. and CORT, R. L. *Yale J. Biol., Med.*, 1953, *26*:55–74.

53. TATEDA, H. and BEIDLER, L. M. *J. gen. Physiol.*, 1964, *47*: 479–486.

54. WOLF, A. V. *Thirst*. Springfield, Ill., Charles C Thomas, 1958.

55. ZOTTERMAN, Y. *Skand. Arch. Physiol.*, 1935, *72*:73–77.

56. ZOTTERMAN, Y., ed. *Olfaction and taste*. New York, The Macmillan Co., 1963.

CHAPTER 18

Audition and the Auditory Pathway

By ARNOLD L. TOWE

MECHANICAL PROPERTIES OF THE EXTERNAL AND MIDDLE EARS

The auditory system transmits information about pressure variations in the air to the central nervous system through a mechanism consisting of (i) the external and middle ears, (ii) the cochlea and (iii) the auditory nerve and pathways to various central neural structures. The first stage is an effective mechanical impedance-matching device which transmits pressure variations from the air to the cochlear fluid with little energy loss. The second stage is the site of excitation of nervous tissue, a process depending upon both an external and an internal energy source. Energy for the subsequent nerve conduction and synaptic transmission is supplied entirely by the metabolizing organism. For our purposes, schematic diagrams (Fig. 1*A, B*) suffice to portray the functional anatomy of the auditory mechanism; knowledge of the detailed anatomy of the middle and inner ear should be obtained from special works on anatomy and histology. The mechanical principles of energy transmission can be outlined without recourse to detailed anatomy. Figure 1*B* illustrates the sequence of events in the ear when a wave of compression reaches the ear. The tympanic membrane is displaced inward, deflecting the middle ear bones and thereby compressing the fluid of the cochlea. Inward movement of the stapes is accompanied by a downward deflection of the basilar membrane and outward movement of the membrane sealing the round window. The displacement of the basilar membrane is "measured" by the nervous tissue attached to it and signaled to the central nervous system.

Resonance. Longitudinal waves enter the external auditory meatus, where they lose their energy to the walls of the tube and the tympanic membrane. Some of this energy is reflected

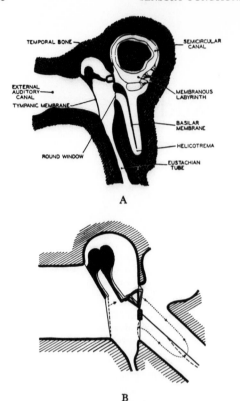

A

B

Fig. 1. *A,* Highly schematic diagram of middle and internal ear in which cochlea is shown as though uncoiled. Oval window (unlabeled) lies just above round window and opens into vestibule and scala vestibuli, which is separated from scala tympani by basilar membrane. (After Békésy. Redrawn for Stevens and Davis, *Hearing: its psychology and physiology,* John Wiley & Sons, Inc., 1938. Reprinted by permission.) *B,* Highly schematic diagram of auditory portions of middle and inner ear showing position of ossicles and various membranes at rest and following inward displacement of tympanic membrane (*shadow lines*) by a sound wave. Dotted lines and arrows represent path of sound waves. (Reprinted by permission from Stevens and Davis, *Hearing: its psychology and physiology,* New York, John Wiley & Sons, Inc., 1938.)

back to the air but some appears as motion of the membrane. The external meatus behaves as a closed tube, so that sound pressures are greater at the closed end than at the open end. A resonance curve may be constructed by plotting the pressure difference between the two ends against the applied frequency. The curve thus obtained is not sharply peaked but, largely as a result of the damping effect of the nonrigid tympanic membrane, is broad and rounded. The maximum increase in pressure occurs when the applied sound has a wave length four times the effective length of the external meatus

(about 12 decibels* at 3400 to 4000 cycles per second). The curve falls off on either side of the resonant frequency, being above 5 db over the interval from 2000 to 6000 cps.[65] The resonant frequency is nearly 3000 cps above the major speech frequency.

The tympanic membrane completely separates the air-filled external and middle ears. It is shaped like a shallow funnel with its apex, or umbo, somewhat below the center and directed inward. The handle of the malleus is directed downward and attaches to the umbo. Radial fibers radiate from the umbo, except in a pie-shaped wedge under the handle of the malleus, and circular fibers interfuse the membrane. This membrane acts like a pressure receiver, being insensitive to velocity changes but exceedingly sensitive to pressure changes. Its specific behavior varies with the applied frequency. At low frequencies the membrane vibrates like a rigid body about a horizontal axis at its upper edge. At frequencies exceeding 2400 cps the drum membrane vibrates in segments, the particular pattern depending upon the applied frequency. However, measurement of maximum membrane displacement shows that it approximates the amplitude of motion of the air molecules at nearly all frequencies. At the threshold of hearing, this ranges from 10^{-5} cm. for low frequencies to 10^{-9} cm. at 3000 cps.[66]

Impedance Matching. The unique problem solved by the middle ear is one of transferring sound energy from a gas to a liquid without significant loss.† This feat is accomplished by the drum membrane–ossicular chain system (Fig. 1*B* and Fig. 2), which amplifies the applied pressures by means of a lever arrangement and a "hydraulic press" action. Movements of the drum membrane are communicated to the tip of the malleus. The malleus and incus rotate as a unit about an axis through the short process of the incus and along the tympanic side of the

*The standard unit of sound intensity is the decibel (db), 1/10 bel. The bel is the logarithm of the ratio of the applied power or energy to some reference power or energy; measurement of the "absolute" energy level is difficult. The reference usually taken in auditory work is the power necessary for a 1000 cycle per second (cps) pure tone to be just audible; this is about 10^{-16} watts per cm.[2] Thus, $N_{db} = 10 \log_{10} P/P_o$, where P = applied power and $P_o = 10^{-16}$ watts per cm.[2]

†An air-water interface reflects about 99.9 per cent of the sound energy back to the air, a 30 db loss in transmission.

malleus. Because, when measured to this axis, the manubrium is a longer lever than the long process of the incus, the force appearing at the stapes is greater than that at the tympanic umbo by about 1.3 to 1.

The area of the drum membrane averages about 64 sq. mm., and the stapedial footplate measures about 3.2 sq. mm. If the two structures moved as simple pistons, the resulting pressure amplification could readily be estimated. However, neither structure behaves so simply. As mentioned above, the mode of vibration of the tympanum varies with frequency, the effective area being 60 to 75 per cent of the total. Because the annular ligament fixing the stapedial footplate into the oval window is narrowest at its posterior margin, the stapes rotates about a vertical axis near its posterior border.[5] Hence, the ratio of effective areas could vary from ear to ear between 13 to 1 and 16 to 1. Since the force delivered to the stapes is amplified by the lever action described above, the total pressure gain would range from 17 to 21 for the average ear. This gain, equivalent to about 25 db at the oval window, signifies a long step toward matching the impedance of the inner ear mechanism to the air. At all frequencies, however, some energy is reflected, and some is lost to frictional resistance. The energy flow through the system can be calculated when the impedance is known; at the threshold of hearing, the impedance is large for low frequencies and minimal around 1000 cps, increasing again at higher frequencies. This relationship means that the ear is most sensitive in the region of 1000 cps.

When the phase shifts of the reflected portion of a sound wave are measured,[60, 64] it becomes clear that the stiffness (elastic reactance) of the ear mechanism is large at low frequencies, whereas the mass of the system (mass reactance) predominates at high frequencies. Somewhere between 300 and 3000 cps these two reactances, which are 180° out of phase, just cancel, and the only limitation becomes the frictional losses. Thus, transmission losses are least in the region of 1000 to 2000 cps.

Overloading and Damping.   Contraction of either or both of two small muscles in the middle ear, the *tensor tympani* and *stapedius*, will increase the stiffness of the middle ear mechanism, thereby decreasing the energy flow of low frequencies. The tensor tympani has a long tendon inserted onto the manubrium of the malleus; this tendon can pull at right angles to the plane of motion of the malleo-incudal system. The stapedius muscle inserts onto the neck of the stapes and likewise pulls at right angles to its main axis. This muscle thus tends to rotate the stapes out of the oval window, opposing the action of the tensor tympani, which indirectly forces the stapes into the oval window.

Reflex contraction of these muscles can be produced by (i) clicks, tones and noises, (ii) irritation of the external meatus, pinna or face and (iii) bodily movements, especially swallowing and yawning. This *acoustic reflex* begins in the stapedius muscle about 15 milliseconds after sound stimulation and a bit later in tensor tympani, although the latency varies markedly with sound intensity. To prolonged intense sound, the reflex contraction attains an initial maximum and then gradually lessens, falling to prestimulation tension in a half hour or more. The reflex is bilateral. Johannes Müller proposed that this reflex acts as a protective mechanism like blinking of the eyelids and constriction of the pupils; increasing tension in the system disturbs the impedance match for lower frequencies such that less energy (as great as 40 db loss) is transmitted to the inner ear mechanism. With the exception of explosive changes, which develop full effect before this reflex can come into play, the damping protects the system from being "shaken apart." However, this mechanism is more than a mere emergency device called forth under exceptional conditions; Carmel and Starr[16] have shown it to be a dynamic system almost constantly in operation. It comes into play during bodily movements and vocalization, and can readily be sensitized by prior auditory experience. Its failure in Bell's palsy and perhaps

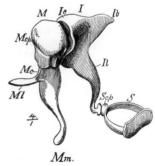

Fig. 2. Bones of middle ear in functional connection. *M*, Malleus; *Mcp*, head; *Mc*, neck; *Ml*, processus gracilis; *Mm*, manubrium; *I*, incus; *Ic*, body of incus; *Ib*, short process; *Il*, long process; *S*, stapes. (From Helmholtz, *Die Lehre von den Tonempfindung*, Braunschweig, F. Wieweg & Son, 1896.)

in acute myesthenia gravis may be the source of the frequent complaint of hyperacusis.

Static Pressure Matching. By connecting the middle ear cavity with the pharynx and thus with the exterior, the *eustachian tube* provides a means of adjusting the air pressure in the middle ear. In this way the pressures on the two sides of the tympanic membrane can be kept equal. Normally, the soft, slitlike pharyngeal orifice is closed; it is opened by the tensor palati muscle during swallowing, yawning and sneezing. Without thinking, man swallows whenever the sensations from the tympanic membrane warn him of inequality in the pressures upon its two sides. In upper respiratory infections, however, the auditory tube may be blocked by inflammation or collection of mucus. As the trapped air is partially absorbed, the tympanum is pushed inward; the resulting pressure sensations and impairment of hearing are quite discomforting.

In severe changes of atmospheric pressure, such as those encountered in flying,[3] the adjustment of air pressure within the middle ear can present serious problems. In ascent, with the ambient pressure decreasing, the excess pressure in the middle ear can force the eustachian tube open, even if it is not opened by swallowing. In descent, however, swallowing is the sole mechanism for equalizing pressure. If muscular action is absent, as may occur in sleeping passengers or in unconscious wounded who are transported by air, the tubes remain closed or are held closed by the higher pressure in the nasopharynx. Weak solutions of phenylephrine hydrochloride (Neo-Synephrine) or ephedrine are frequently sprayed into the nostrils to shrink the tissue around the eustachian orifice, thus aiding in pressure equalization. If negative pressures of 60 to 80 mm. Hg develop within the middle ear, pain is severe and deafness, tinnitus and vertigo supervene. At pressures of 80 to 90 mm. Hg, muscular contraction may not open the tube, and at negative pressures between 100 and 150 mm. Hg the eardrum may rupture. Such rupture is marked by the sensation of a loud explosive sound, piercing pain, nausea and even shock. Short of rupture, pressure differences may produce traumatic inflammation of the middle ear.[3] The eardrum is sometimes pierced with a fine needle to allow pressure equalization; small defects of the tympanum so produced quickly close and heal.

AUDITION

Before studying the inner ear mechanisms we should become familiar with some basic phenomena of hearing. We live in an auditory world rich in variety and complexity; but ours is not the only such world. Many insects which prowl unobtrusively about us carry on boisterously at frequencies too high for our ears to detect. The vocalizations of fish and cetaceans,* although at "our" frequencies, are reflected at the water surface. Bats utilize their "auditory radar" system almost entirely when flying and feeding; they emit short scanning runs from 100,000 down to 20,000 cps a dozen or more times each second while flying. Although primates are best described as "visual" animals, they possess a remarkable auditory capability. To analyze this capability, the physiologist uses quite simple kinds of auditory stimuli; to employ richer auditory stimuli has its analogy in studying the digestive physiology of a Dagwood sandwich.

Physical and Psychological Dimensions of Sound.[50] Sound waves are longitudinal; i.e., they depend upon molecular motion parallel to the direction of energy transmission. Alternate waves of condensation and rarefaction move through a medium with specifiable velocity according to the characteristics of the medium and independently of the intensity of the wave. The simplest sound wave, a sinusoid, can vary in amplitude, frequency and phase (provided some time referent is used). The perceived *pitch* of such a wave is largely determined by its frequency; the *loudness* of such a wave is determined both by its amplitude and by its frequency. Such simple waves are produced by tuning forks or electronic oscillators, but rarely occur in the natural environment. Most sound sources produce compound waves consisting of a fundamental frequency and overtones of various amplitudes and phase angles. The overtones bear a simple arithmetic relationship to the fundamental frequency (or first harmonic); a single string vibrates not only as a whole but also in halves, thirds, fourths, etc. It is the fundamental frequency, with its greater amplitude, that determines the pitch of the sound; however, overtones can also be heard with their own pitches. The relative amplitudes of the various harmonics yield a unique wave-form for each sound

*Some cetaceans emit sounds as high as 150,000 cps.

source, giving the sound its *timbre* or *quality*. It is this property of complex sound which enables us to distinguish between different musical instruments, human voices or other sound sources, even when they emit at equal fundamental frequency and intensity. No matter how complex, a wave-form is "musical" if its pattern is regularly repeated through several cycles; nonperiodic vibrations, which constitute the vast majority of sound waves emanating from the natural environment, are "noise." However, even noise has a crude sort of pitch, for some frequencies in the jumble have a greater amplitude than others. When many frequencies are represented about equally, as in the thermionic emission of a vacuum tube, the resulting sensation is termed "white noise" (by analogy to white light). In studying the ear, it is usually convenient to use sinusoidal waves or clicks of various forms.

Loudness.[51] That loudness depends upon both the amplitude and the frequency of a sinusoid is revealed in the audibility curve (Fig. 3). Loudness is a perceptual response to the *intensity* (or energy flux density) of a sound wave, which is proportional to the square of amplitude. The weakest intensity of any sinusoid which can just be heard depends strongly upon the frequency of the sinusoid. Figure 3 shows this dependency for the human ear; at each frequency, two threshold intensities can be found, one for hearing and one for feeling. Between these two extremes, loudness varies as the logarithm of intensity. At the threshold of audibility, measured under delicate experimental conditions, the effective pressures at the tympanum and the consequent movements of the tympanum are extremely minute. Displacements of the tympanum *less* than the dimensions of a hydrogen atom (10^{-8} cm.) are effective. Why pressure variations and vibrations of the blood vessels of the tympanum and cochlea do not produce distracting sounds is puzzling in view of this extreme sensitivity; such sources become audible only in anechoic chambers.

The striking feature of the audibility curve is the degree to which it depends upon frequency. Hearing is keenest in the 1000 to 4000 cps range, decreasing sharply for higher and lower frequencies. On the other hand, the threshold for feeling discomfort* is fairly constant at about

*Sound waves, when sufficiently intense, will stimulate somesthetic sense organs. The resulting sensations include touch, tickle, pressure and even pain.

10^{-3} watts per cm.² The fundamental and major overtones of the human voice are all at lower frequencies than the peak sensitivity of the ear. About 100 times greater sound energy is required to just hear middle C (256 cps†) than two octaves higher (1024 cps). The audibility curve is determined to a large extent by the energy losses in the middle and inner ear and to a small extent by the resonance properties of the external ear. The purely resistive losses occur in the range of the resonant frequency of the external meatus; thus, several factors combine to make the ear most sensitive in a range slightly above vocalization frequencies.

Audiometry. Because the auditory threshold varies so sharply with frequency, the rough-and-ready clinical methods of testing hearing—whispering and the ticking watch—merely sample hearing. A more comprehensive clinical index of hearing ability is found in the *audiogram,* which plots a patient's auditory threshold for several different frequencies relative to "normal." The normal or mean threshold value, determined for each frequency from measurements on a large number of "normal young adults," differs by 15 to 20 db from the "absolute" auditory threshold because the audiogram measure-

†Musical instruments are usually tuned to middle C at about 262 cps.

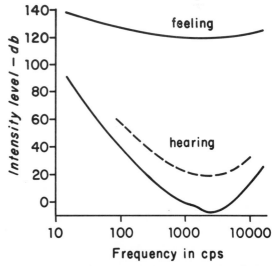

Fig. 3. Audibility curve in man, showing threshold under ideal conditions and under conditions in which audiometer tests are administered. Energy which excites factual and pain receptors is about a million million times energy at threshold of hearing at 1000 cps. (After Licklider, Chap. 25 in *Handbook of experimental psychology,* S. S. Stevens, ed. New York, John Wiley & Sons, 1951.)

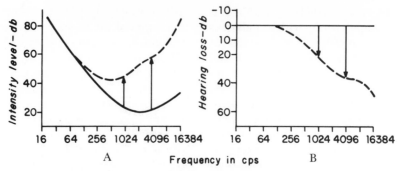

A   Frequency in cps   B

Fig. 4.   Left graph shows threshold of hearing for audiometer curve (solid line) and audibility curve for aged person with high tone hearing loss (dashed line). Right graph shows same data plotted as *audiogram* with normalized audiometer curve; this form of plotting hearing loss relative to "normal" is convenient.

ments (dashed line in Fig. 3) are made in less than ideal conditions. Figure 4*A* shows a deviant audiogram for one patient in relation to the normal. It is apparent at 1024 cps that sound intensity must be raised 22 db above the normal value (an increase of about 160 times the energy) to be just audible to this patient. The standard *audiogram* plot of the same information about this patient is shown in Figure 4*B*; it is based on a normalized auditory threshold curve and hence displays more clearly the deviation of hearing loss from normal.

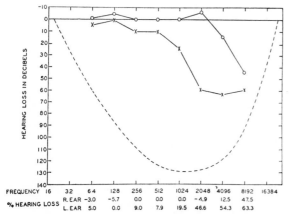

Fig. 5.   Graphic representation of hearing ability (audiogram) of individual suffering from high-tone deafness. Circles indicate auditory sensitivity of right ear; crosses, that of left ear. Figures at bottom show calculation of per cent hearing loss, with broken line, the threshold of feeling, representing complete loss of hearing. For convenience, normal threshold of hearing is taken as zero (or reference point) on a decibel scale. In absolute physical units threshold energy varies considerably throughout audible range of frequencies. (Reprinted by permission from Stevens and Davis, *Hearing: its psychology and physiology,* New York, John Wiley & Sons, Inc., 1938.)

The audiometer consists of an electronic oscillator arranged to produce 10 to 12 different frequencies at octave intervals on one or both of a pair of earphones. Wearing the earphones in an otherwise quiet environment, the patient flashes a light whenever he hears a sound. The examiner steadily decreases the intensity of an intermittently sounded tone until the patient no longer signals its occurrence consistently. The sound intensity at this point is read from the intensity dial (calibrated in decibels above and below the normal for that frequency, but sometimes scaled in sensation units), and is entered on the audiogram. This fixes one point on the patient's audibility curve; the procedure is repeated for the remaining frequencies. Then the other ear is tested. In interpreting such curves, the following facts should be noted. Hearing loss may be stated either in terms of decibels loss or in terms of percentage loss of useful hearing. If at any point the patient's threshold coincides with the broken line of Figure 5, representing the threshold of feeling, the loss of hearing is complete. If the threshold falls halfway between the 0 line and the broken line, the loss in that ear is 50 per cent.

THE COCHLEA

The ear of man is a mechanoreceptor with a long phylogenetic history. The hydrozoan statocysts represent an "ear" in the most general sense. True hearing organs first appear with the chordotonal organs and scolophores of the arthropods and become progressively elaborated in the terrestrial vertebrates, reaching a pinnacle of development in the bats. Man does not possess such an elaborate pinna or the capability of directing it, and his directional sensitivity is of a lower order.

Structure. The manner in which the ear analyzes complex sound waves into component frequencies was originally deduced by Helmholtz from the structure of the inner ear. He was struck by the fact that the ear contains a very large number of neurosensory units arranged along a membrane interposed in the path of the sound wave. He viewed this membrane as a system of tuned elements that resonated so that a given unit would be the one most vigorously stimulated by sound waves of a given frequency. This arrangement would result in a different nerve fiber discharging more actively for each frequency within the audible range, and the discharge of this unit, transmitted over the auditory pathway, would be recognized by the cerebral cortex as a given pitch. Although significant advances have been made in the theory of auditory receptor excitation, Helmholtz set the basic philosophy that the functional anatomy and the physiology of the inner ear are inextricably bound together.

The auditory portion of the inner ear, like the middle ear, is housed in a system of cavities and tunnels known as the osseous labyrinth (Figs. 1 A and 6). The cochlear portion of the osseous labyrinth consists of a fluid-filled tube about three centimeters long that is coiled in a spiral about a central pillar (modiolus). Except for a small opening in the apical end (helicotrema), the tube is completely divided into two canals by a stout connective tissue membrane (basilar membrane) and a bony shelf (spiral lamina) extending from the modiolus. At the base of the tube, the cochlear partition consists mainly of spiral lamina, the basilar membrane being narrowest at this end. Farther up around the spiral the bony lamina becomes smaller and the basilar membrane widens until the helicotrema is reached at the apex. The latter opening serves to equalize slowly developing pressure differences between the two divisions of the cochlea.

Sound waves enter the part of the cochlea *above* the basilar membrane (*scala vestibuli*) by way of the oval window in the vestibule—hence its name (Fig. 1 B). The passageway below the basilar membrane (*scala tympani*) communicates with the middle ear by way of the round window, which is closed by the *secondary tympanic membrane*.

Within the osseous labyrinth lies the membranous labyrinth, a portion of which extends into the cochlea to contribute *Reissner's membrane,* the basilar membrane and the *organ of Corti* (thus forming the cochlear duct, or *scala media*). In a sense, the scala media occupies the lower third of the scala vestibuli; Reissner's membrane is so delicate that the two scalae probably function as a single tube in the transmission of sound. In fact, the term "scala vestibuli" is often loosely used to include the cochlear duct.

The membranous labyrinth, floating in the *perilymph* of the osseous labyrinth, contains a special fluid, the *endolymph*. Endolymph is similar to intracellular fluid in its ionic content but is rather low in protein.[48] The endolymph apparently does not occupy the tunnel of Corti or the space of Nuel (Fig. 6); its very high K^+ content should render the cochlear nerve fibers traversing these spaces inexcitable or unstable. The perilymph is similar to spinal fluid in having a high concentration of Na^+, but it has twice the concentration of protein.

Sensory epithelium of the cochlea. The fibers of the cochlear branch of the VIIIth nerve, which number 25,000 to 30,000 in man, arise in bipolar cell bodies lodged within the modiolus (*spiral nucleus*) and arborize around the sensory *hair cells* of the organ of Corti. These hair cells are in a position to be affected by sound waves and, in turn, generate nerve impulses in the fibers of the auditory nerve. The general arrangement and relations of these cells are indicated in Figure 6. The hair cells are divided by a supporting arch (rods of Corti) into a single row of *inner hair cells* and three or four rows of *outer hair cells*. Up to 120 stereociliar type hairs arise from the surface of each cell, project through the *reticular lamina* and make contact with the overlying *tectorial membrane*. While the cilia of the inner hair cells form a continuous double row running the length of the cochlea, those of the outer hair cells form a distinctive "long-horned W" pattern from two or three rows of cilia, with the "horns" pointing toward the spiral lamina.[22] In man, there are about the same number of hair cells as cochlear nerve fibers; however, this does not mean a one-to-one pattern of innervation. The 3- to 5-μ fibers of the cochlear nerve lose both their myelin and their Schwann sheaths as they emerge from the spiral lamina to radiate outward and arborize around the bases and sides of the hair cells. Two distribution pat-

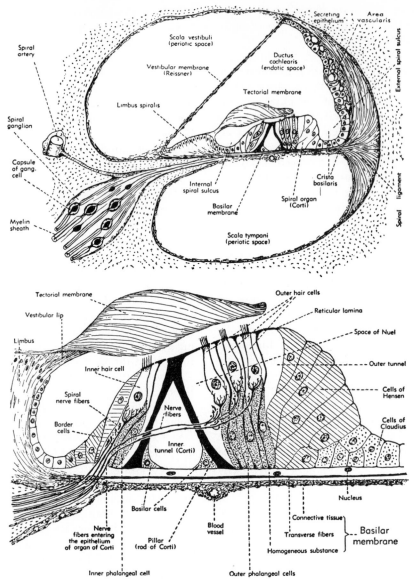

Fig. 6. *Upper*, Vertical section of human cochlea showing organ of Corti and adjacent structures. *Lower*, Organ of Corti and basilar membrane in greater magnification. (From Rasmussen, *Outlines of neuro-anatomy*, 3d ed., Dubuque, Ia., William C. Brown Co., 1943.)

terns are recognized. Each *radial fiber* makes contact with two or three hair cells, and each hair cell receives endings from two or three radial fibers.[24] Although radial fibers are distributed to most hair cells, they form the major innervation of the inner hair cells. Another group of fibers, the *spiral fibers*, turn sharply after emerging from the habenula perforata to form a small internal spiral bundle, a tunnel bundle and a large external spiral bundle. These fibers extend about a quarter of a turn through the organ of Corti, arborizing around *many* different hair

cells. Fernandez[24] believes that the internal spiral fibers are *efferent;* their cell bodies lie in the superior olivary complex of the opposite side of the brain stem.

The inner hair cells are histologically quite distinct from the outer hair cells. They excite radial fibers and receive an efferent supply from the internal spiral fibers. On the other hand, the outer hair cells, which possess a much denser array of nerve endings, excite largely external spiral fibers. Studies with the electron microscope have revealed several different types

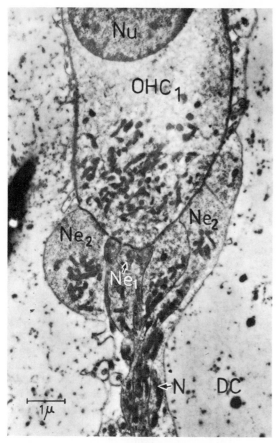

Fig. 7. Electron micrograph of outer hair cell of guinea pig (OHC₁), showing its nucleus (Nu) and the supporting cells of Deiter (DC). Two types of nerve endings, the small (Ne₁) and larger, vesicular (Ne₂), can be seen arising from the nerve fibers (N). (From Engström in *Neural mechanisms of the auditory and vestibular systems,* G. L. Rasmussen, and W. F. Windle, eds., Springfield, Ill., Charles C Thomas, 1960.)

of "synaptic" endings around each cell.[46, 47, 49] Chemical transmission between hair cell and nerve fiber is suggested by the marked accumulations of mitochondria and vesicles at the base of many hair cells, and similar thoughts are provoked by the structure of the "synaptic" membrane regions (Fig. 7). However, the functional significance of these various terminal structures is as yet only speculative.

Excitation in the Cochlea. The cochlea as a whole is a device whereby sound waves, transmitted through the fluid of the inner ear, are translated into nerve impulses. It is apparent from the arrangement of the cochlea that the vibration imparted to the basilar membrane by a pressure variation in the scala vestibuli is one

stage in this process. This is shown directly by the observation that excessive vibrations produced by loud sounds may dislodge the organ of Corti from the basilar membrane. Moreover, the segment of the basilar membrane undergoing the widest excursion shifts progressively with frequency.[51] As this shift occurs, different auditory fibers undergo maximal excitation. Because nerve impulses remain canalized as they pass through the fibers of the auditory system, ultimately each tone results in a peak of activity in some patch of auditory cortex.[2, 67] The doctrine of specific nerve energies (Chap. 14) holds that which patch of cortex is involved determines which pitch is experienced. This view of cochlear function is the "place theory" of hearing, somewhat irreverently known as the "pitch-is-which" theory. It differs from the "frequency" theory, which accords the pattern of firing in auditory fibers a more important role than which particular fibers are firing.[61]

Although theories regarding the manner in which the basilar membrane responds to different sound frequencies differ widely enough to require separate categories—resonance, traveling wave, standing wave, telephone—yet they have much in common. Békésy[11] has shown it possible to obtain results consistent with any of these theories merely by varying the amount of stiffness and the rate of change of stiffness with distance along the membrane. It is thus essential to know the physical properties of the cochlear partition. Helmholtz had been led by several histologic features to regard the basilar membrane and its burden of receptors and supporting elements as a series of tuned resonators. However, Békésy[6, 12] has shown that the membrane is under slight transverse tension; the most liberal calculations show that no resonance theory could account for more than four and one-half of the ten and one-half octaves available to the human ear.[64]

Several theories of cochlear mechanics invoke traveling waves like pressure pulse waves in blood vessels; the basilar membrane introduces enough elasticity into an otherwise rigid tube to justify the analogy. From measurements of the travel time for pulses along the membrane and from study of phase displacements at selected positions on the basilar membrane, Békésy[11] concluded that the basilar membrane indeed does support traveling waves. Such a conclusion

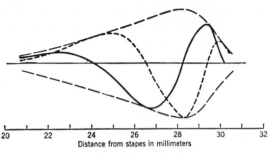

Fig. 8. Diagram illustrating traveling wave theory of basilar membrane movement. Solid and short dash lines represent same sound wave at two instants of time. Long dash line is described by connecting the peaks at successive instants of time. Scale at bottom represents distance along basilar membrane. (After Békésy, *J. acoust. Soc. Amer.,* 1947, *19:*452–460.)

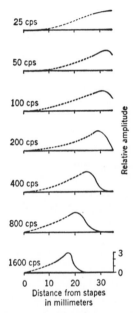

Fig. 9. Displacement amplitude along basilar membrane for different frequencies (constant amplitude) of stapes vibration. Solid lines were obtained by measurement, dotted lines by extrapolation from other observations. (From Békésy and Rosenblith, Chap. 27 in *Handbook of experimental psychology,* S. S. Stevens, ed., New York, John Wiley & Sons, Inc., 1951.)

does not preclude resonance altogether, but means that adjacent regions are strongly coupled and cannot resonate independently.

A positive pressure pulse at the oval window spreads instantaneously (20 μsec.) throughout the cochlea, bulging the secondary tympanic membrane. The relatively stiff regions near the base of the basilar membrane move downward toward the scala tympani in phase with the

stapes, while the more elastic apical regions lag significantly. Thus, the displacement of the membrane "moves" toward the apex. With sinusoidal driving pressures, the stiffer basal region "wags" the more apical regions, yielding a wave-form illustrated in Figure 8. The region of maximal displacement of the membrane, revealed by the envelope of the traveling wave, varies with the driving frequency (Fig. 9). Low frequencies displace the entire membrane in a whiplike manner while high frequencies damp out a short distance from the stapes. Thus, high tones are represented at the base of the cochlea and low tones throughout the cochlea but with maximal effectiveness near the apex.

Movements of the basilar membrane slide the tectorial membrane over the reticular lamina, thereby stressing the cilia of the underlying hair cells. By this mechanism, the force displacing the cochlear partition is greatly amplified at the cilia. A simple upward movement of the cochlear partition displaces the tectorial membrane toward the supporting cells of Hensen. Because of the relative tilts of the inner and outer hair cells, this radial displacement pulls on the cilia of the inner hair cells and pushes or bends the cilia of the outer hair cells. But the movements of the cochlear partition are not quite so simple (Fig. 10); the mean vector of the shearing force has both radial and longitudinal components which change in magnitude not only with the phase of the applied sinusoid but also according

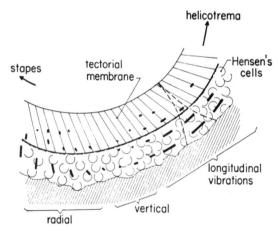

Fig. 10. Section of cochlear duct as seen from above through Reissner's membrane, showing distribution of radial and longitudinal vibrations along organ of Corti for stimulation with a tone. Maximal displacement of cochlear partition occurs along central zone of transition (vertical). (From Békésy, *J. acoust. Soc. Amer.,* 1953, *25:*770–785.)

to site on the basilar membrane relative to the applied frequency. Vertical movements predominate in the region of maximal membrane displacement (see envelope in Fig. 10). Longitudinal movements develop more distally, where the rate of change of displacement with distance along the membrane is greatest; radial movements predominate toward the stapes. We have come a long way from a simple system of tuned resonators.

Electrical activity of the cochlea. Accompanying the mechanical responses of the cochlear partition are several characteristic electrical changes. Even in the unstimulated condition, however, the cochlear duct maintains a potential some 80 mV. above ground.[8, 9] The electrical energy for this latter potential, the *endocochlear potential,* is supplied continuously by the *stria vascularis* that overlies the spiral ligament on the lateral aspect of the cochlear duct[19, 57] (Fig. 6). A small potential exists in the perilymph, grading from 3 mV. in the apical half of the scala vestibuli through ground potential halfway down the scala tympani to −2 mV. at the round window.[11] The cellular elements of the cochlea have typical intracellular potentials (−20 to −80 mV.). But the entire fluid-filled scala media and the tectorial membrane are about 80 mV. positive to the perilymph. Thus, the voltage drop across the reticular lamina, from endolymph to hair cells, can be as high as 180 mV. This voltage is highly dependent upon an adequate oxygen supply, but is not a consequence of the "intracellular" ionic composition of the endolymph. It can be increased or decreased through several millivolts by static displacements of the basilar membrane,[9, 55] especially by longitudinal displacement near the limbus.[7]

When a sinusoidal or a complex sound wave is applied to the eardrum, a potential which "faithfully mirrors" the applied wave-form can be recorded from the region of the ear. Because this *cochlear microphonic* (Fig. 11) was first recorded from the auditory nerve,[62, 63] it was initially mistaken for a series of auditory action potentials. Analysis soon showed that these voltage variations originate in the cochlea and spread decrementally along the nerve and throughout the tissue surrounding the cochlea. The cochlear microphonic appears with no apparent threshold and negligible latency. It increases linearly with increase in the pressure of the applied sound wave to a maximum of 2 mV. and decreases with further increase in sound pressure. Unlike nerve action potentials, the cochlear microphonic is highly resistant to drugs, anesthesia, cold and fatigue. At death it drops rapidly to a low level, but it sustains this level for hours.

When recorded at the round window, the cochlear microphonic is nearly inverted from its configuration at the oval window. If a microelectrode is passed vertically through the organ of Corti during sound stimulation, the microphonic is seen to go through a 180° phase shift at the reticular lamina;[55] this coincides exactly with the 160 mV. drop in voltage from endolymph to hair cells. Radial displacements of the basilar membrane have been shown most efficacious in producing the microphonic,[7, 10] and it is well established that the outer hair cells are responsible for this potential change during such displacement.[10, 19] Thus, the behavior of the cochlear partition during sound stimulation determines the characteristics of the microphonic potential at each position along the membrane. The microphonic shows the increas-

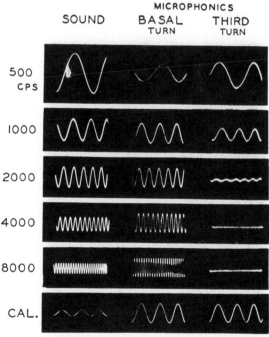

Fig. 11. Microphonic electrical records from base and from a point near apex of guinea pig cochlea in response to sound waves of various frequencies. Note that basal turn responds to all frequencies as demanded by traveling wave theory, and that amplitude of sound waves need not be altered greatly (10 db) to give equal responses. Note absence of response to high frequencies at third turn. (From Tasaki, *J. Neurophysiol.,* 1954, *17:* 97–122.)

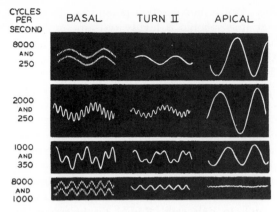

PAIRED ELECTRODES, SCALAE VESTIBULI AND TYMPANI, IN EACH TURN

Fig. 12. Simultaneous recordings of cochlear microphonic made at three sites along the cochlea of the guinea pig. When an 8000 cps and a 250 cps tone are sounded simultaneously, the 8000 cps tone appears only near the base, while the 250 cps tone affects the entire membrane, but the apex maximally. From the bottom trace, it can be seen that neither a 1000 cps nor the 8000 cps tone produces any microphonic at the apex. In the middle records, it is shown that complex microphonics appear everywhere except in the region where the lowest frequency has maximal effect. (From Tasaki, Davis and Legouix, *J. acoust. Soc. Amer.,* 1952, *24*:502–519.)

tude with increasing sound pressure; its amplitude is proportional to the root mean square value of the applied sinusoid. The summating potential appears most prominently where the traveling waves reach their maximum amplitude on the cochlear partition and where they are steep and short. They are best produced by longitudinal displacement of the tectorial membrane over the medial part of the reticular lamina.[7, 10] Summating potentials may grow to 10 mV. or even greater, bringing the endocochlear potential down below 70 mV.; this is several times the maximum amplitude attained by the cochlear microphonic.

Békésy[9] has calculated that the mechanical energy of the sound wave cannot supply all the electrical energy of the microphonic potential. Maximum displacements of the basilar membrane at the threshold of hearing are of subatomic magnitude. In order to secure maximum energy transfer, a very good impedance match must be attained; the middle ear matches the air to the fluid-filled cochlea and translation of vertical displacement of the basilar membrane into a shearing force at the reticular lamina provides a second internal match. It is possible but

ing latency and phase shift with distance from the stapes expected on the traveling wave hypothesis.[56] It is generated over the entire cochlear duct when low sound frequencies are used, but is restricted to the basal region when high frequencies are used (Figs. 11 and 12). This distribution has made it possible to check very simply the concept of *tonal localization in the cochlea* developed through a variety of ingenious and painstaking methods; the results are in essential agreement and are summarized in Figure 13. Because of its close relation to inner ear behavior, the cochlear microphonic has become a valuable tool in analyzing middle ear and inner ear function.

However the cochlear microphonic results from stimulation of outer hair cells, a different sort of response has recently been associated with stimulation of inner hair cells.[18, 19] Moderate to strong stimulation decreases the voltage difference between the cochlear duct and the vestibule, and this decrease is maintained as long as sound stimulation persists. It is therefore termed a *negative summating potential* (Fig. 14). Like the cochlear microphonic, it shows no threshold and negligible latency. Unlike the microphonic, it continues to increase in ampli-

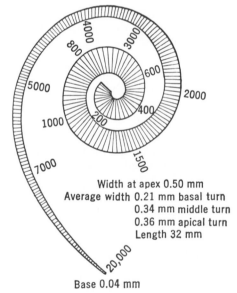

Width at apex 0.50 mm
Average width 0.21 mm basal turn
0.34 mm middle turn
0.36 mm apical turn
Length 32 mm

Base 0.04 mm

Fig. 13. Schematic diagram of human cochlear duct, showing areas of maximal displacement of the partition for pure tones of different frequencies. The 200 cps tone, although displacing the entire cochlear partition, has maximum effect near the apex. The 20,000 cps tone has maximum effect at the base, and damps out completely near the base. (From Stuhlman, *An introduction to biophysics,* New York, John Wiley & Sons, 1943.)

AP, CM AND SP FROM BASAL TURN

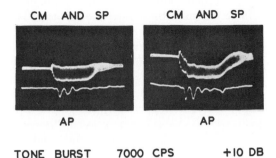

TONE BURST   7000 CPS   +10 DB

Fig. 14. Cochlear microphonic and summating potentials (upper) and simultaneously recorded auditory nerve action potential (lower) from basal turn of guinea pig cochlea in response to moderate (left) and 10 db stronger (right), 7000 cps tonal burst. Action potential shows successive, synchronized volleys of activity. (From Davis in *Neural mechanisms of the auditory and vestibular systems,* G. L. Rasmussen and W. F. Windle, eds., Springfield, Ill., Charles C Thomas, 1960.)

by no means proved that these shearing forces serve to "valve" the energy stored in the endocochlear potential for excitation of the auditory nerve terminals.

Auditory nerve action potentials. The foregoing discussion has shown that, both mechanically and electrically, the cochlea behaves as an acoustic analyzer. The analysis is coded in terms of all-or-none activity in single auditory nerve fibers and is transmitted to the central nervous system. Tasaki[54] recorded the response of single auditory nerve fibers to tonal "pips" of different frequencies and intensities, and found that at threshold a fiber is excited only by a narrow band of frequencies (Fig. 15). This band widens as the sound intensity is increased, expanding rapidly into lower frequencies (gradual cut-off) and almost not at all into higher frequencies (sharp cut-off). This pattern of responsiveness is precisely that expected on the traveling wave hypothesis; high frequencies affect a limited stretch of basilar membrane near the stapes, whereas low frequencies affect the entire membrane. A sufficiently intense low frequency sound excites a large number of auditory fibers ranging over half or more of the cochlear partition. For sinusoids below 1000 cps the individual spikes are synchronized with the sound wave. Excitation occurs when the cochlear duct goes negative, i.e., when the basilar membrane is displaced toward the tectorial membrane. Such a movement bends the cilia of the hair cells

toward the supporting cells of Hensen, exciting the fibers innervating the outer hair cells. The discharge pattern of the fibers innervating the inner hair cells, driven by the constant current of the negative summating potential (by bending cilia of inner hair cells toward the apex of the cochlea), is probably quite different but has not yet been recognized.

The whole nerve response, seen best following click stimulation (Figs. 16 and 19), seems to be dominated by the activity of fibers from the basal turns of the cochlea. It consists of two distinct components, N_1 and N_2, each about one millisecond in duration. The latency of the first component varies with the sound intensity (and frequency) from 1.0 to 2.3 milliseconds. Neither component grows linearly with increasing sound pressure; N_1, with the lower threshold, grows in such a way as to suggest the activity of two different sets of receptor elements with quite different thresholds. The nerve response is very sensitive to anoxia, cold and various drugs, and can be reduced or precluded by the activity of efferent inhibitory fibers (see below). The precise mechanism for excitation of the fibers whose activity makes up the whole nerve response is not known; electron microscopic studies and the latency to the action potential support a chemical mediator concept although current thinking still favors electrical excitation of the nerve terminals.

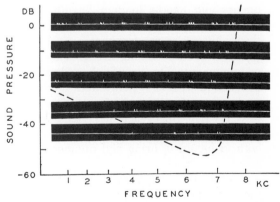

Fig. 15. Single auditory nerve responses to tone "pips" of different frequencies and intensities. Each strip of record shows a short burst of repetitive discharges in the single fiber in response to a tone which is increased in frequency between pips. Each strip of record represents a different sound level, lower record representing weakest intensity used. Dashed line encloses "response area" for this fiber. (From Tasaki, *J. Neurophysiol.,* 1954, *17*:97–122.)

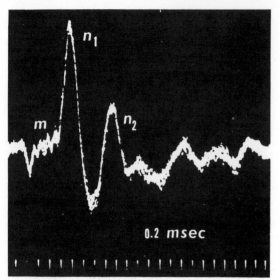

Fig. 16. Auditory nerve response in cat following 0.1 millisecond click stimulation. The cochlear microphonic (m) is evident at the beginning of N_1. Ten superimposed traces. (Courtesy D. Humphrey, University of Washington.)

After examining the mechanics of transmission and the consequent nerve fiber activity, we are still left with the two major theories—the place theory and the frequency theory. Volleys of all-or-none discharges follow in phase with an applied sinusoid up to 2000 cps—about three octaves above middle C and covering the entire range of speech frequencies. A frequency theory must handle pitch in terms of discharge frequency and handle loudness in other terms, such as number of active fibers. The place theory allows for the fact that a pure tone, if intense, will throw a long stretch of the basilar membrane into vibration. Such a vibration has a maximum at some region, and the nerve fibers leading from this region discharge at the highest rate. The place theory handles pitch in terms of which fibers are active and loudness in terms of both frequency of firing and number of fibers active.

Routes of Conduction.[61]   Sound waves in the ear reach the organ of Corti by three routes, the first of which may be termed the *physiologic* or *ossicular route*. The vibrations are transmitted from the tympanum through the ossicular chain and oval window to the scala vestibuli and scala media, and thence through the organ of Corti and basilar membrane to the scala tympani and, finally, to the round window. This route has already been discussed at some length; the

important role of the round window is discussed below.

The second route of conduction through the middle ear may be termed the *air route*. This begins at the tympanum and passes via the air in the middle ear to the round window, scala tympani, etc. The air route is principally by way of the round window, because this window is covered by only a thin membrane, whereas the oval window is stoppered by the stapes, especially when the chain is ankylosed ("frozen"). But transmission through the round window is inefficient because it lacks the impedance matching device of the ossicular chain; most of the sound energy is reflected.

When the ossicular chain is broken, the air route conducts less well than might be expected from the acoustical matching value of the chain (30 db). The hearing loss from interruption of the chain varies between 30 db for low tones and 65 db for the middle range. Two factors are involved. One is that the tympanum, weighted by the interrupted ossicular chain, becomes an obstacle to sound transmission to the air of the middle ear. The second is that the sound waves transmitted through the round window and scala tympani push the basilar membrane upward during the phase of positive pressure while the same wave conducted by the now unhindered oval window and scala vestibuli pushes the membrane downward. If this interference is prevented experimentally by leading the sound through a tube to only one window, the hearing loss is 30 db. Fortunately, the sound paths are not equally long, and therefore the sound waves are not 180° out of phase. The cancellation is thus imperfect, and the net loss due to this factor is about 12 db.

More common than interruption is a fixation of the ossicular chain, resulting from adhesions in the wake of a middle ear infection or from a pathologic change in the temporal bone that seals the stapes into the oval window (otosclerosis). Understanding of the resulting deafness and its surgical relief hinge on an appreciation of the physiologic significance of the round window.

The function of the round window apparently is to provide "give" in the otherwise rigidly encased cochlea. Deformation rather than mere compression is required for stimulation of skin receptors and also of hair cells. For deformation to occur, the basilar membrane must actually move, no matter how slightly, and the membrane closing the round window must bulge to permit this. The volume displaced in hearing is of the order of 10^{-8} to 10^{-9} cm^3.

In otosclerosis, hearing is severely impaired partly because the ossicular route of conduction is lost. Further, the air route of conduction to the round window cannot function to best advantage because "give" is lacking. Such "give" is successfully provided in Lempert's *fenestration* operation by drilling a small window into the horizontal semicircular canal, which is in continuity with the vestibule of the cochlea. A flap of skin is placed over this fistula, and hearing is significantly improved (usually within 20 to 30 db of normal) as long as the new passage remains patent.

The third route by which sound can be conducted to the inner ear is by means of bone conduction—the *osseous route*. Sound waves reach the inner ear through the bones of the skull; the middle ear is, as it were, "short-circuited or bypassed." Unlike the ossicular and air routes, bone conduction plays little, if any, part in hearing ordinary sounds because so much energy is lost in the passage of a sound wave from air to the bone of the head. However, if a tuning fork which is unheard when sounded in air is held with its base against the skull (better acoustical matching), it can be heard clearly. Bone conduction is important in distinguishing between types of deafness, and it is employed for one type of hearing aid. Conduction by this route must be ruled out in testing an ear with sounds louder than 50 to 60 db above the threshold for 1000 cps, for at this level bone-conducted sound may reach the normal ear. Ear plugs are, of course, useless, but hearing of bone-conducted sound can be eliminated by introducing a *masking* sound into the ear. Suitable adjustment of the intensity and phase of a sinusoid conducted via the *ossicular* route can completely cancel the perception of the same sinusoid via the *osseous* route.[4] Thus, the mechanism of excitation in bone conduction must be the same as that in air conduction, viz., fluid movements near the stapes. These movements develop because inertia prevents the stapes and cochlear fluid from following exactly the oscillations of the head bones, and the resulting differential movements deflect the basilar membrane and the secondary tympanic membrane.

Types of Deafness.[61] Deafness, including partial impairment of hearing, is classified into three main types according to where the block occurs. *Conduction deafness* is any interference

with the passage of sound waves through the external or middle ear. Common causes are collections of pus, exudates or wax; adhesions of the ossicles to the bony walls; thickening of the tympanum as a result of infection; and new growths of bone that bind the stapes. The Weber and Rinné diagnostic tests are based on the greater interference with air and ossicular routes of conduction characteristic of conduction deafness. Because it "by-passes" the middle ear, bone conduction is little affected. The deafness is never total because some sound is conducted through the skull. Also, in these patients, audiograms tend to be "flat"; i.e., the loss is about equal for all frequencies. The patient, paradoxically, seems to hear best in noisy surroundings, because voices are raised and he is not disturbed by the lower intensity background noise —it is unheard. He tolerates hearing aids and is greatly benefited by them.

The second type of hearing impairment, once termed *perception deafness,* is now known as *nerve deafness.* The defect is not in the cortical process of sound perception but is caused by a degeneration of sensory cells of the inner ear, tumors of the auditory nerve, etc. Because the damage is in the portion of the hearing mechanism common to air and bone conduction (hair cells and auditory nerve), a failure of both routes is diagnostic. The hearing of high tones (4000 cps) is typically the most impaired (hence "high tone deafness"). This distorts the *timbre* of sounds, making it hard for the patient to discriminate sound sources and interfering with the perception of consonants. For some reason, as the intensity of a tone is increased, the perceived intensity (loudness) increases more rapidly than it does when hearing is normal. The loud sounds may be just as unpleasant as they are to the normal ear, making the patient intolerant of loud speech or hearing aids. Since this is the deafness of old age, the familiar phrase, "Don't shout, young man," is understandable. Nerve deafness may be temporary when caused by fatigue or partial trauma, as in exposure to prolonged loud sounds ("boilermaker's deafness"), or permanent when caused by degeneration through exposure to very intense sounds, senility, disease or toxic agents. The problem of acoustic trauma is one of growing medical and legal importance.

The third type of deafness, *central deafness,* is rare. It may result from interference with the pathway of nerve impulses to the cerebral cortex, but is more often a manifestation of aphasia (Chap. 23) or of a psychogenic disorder. Recent studies[26, 27] on suppression of auditory nerve discharge may have some bearing on these latter disorders.

PHYSIOLOGY OF THE CENTRAL AUDITORY PATHWAYS

Information about the state of the cochlear partition is continuously transmitted to the central nervous system via the VIIIth cranial nerve. The peripheral ramifications of the bipolar cells in the spiral ganglion, rather varied and complex, have already been discussed. The central axons of the bipolar cells enter the pons at its junction with the medulla, bifurcate and connect with both the ventral and the dorsal cochlear nuclei. In the nerve, the fibers from the base and apex twist like a rope, but do not inter-

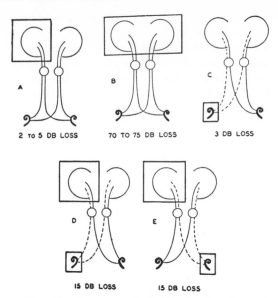

Fig. 18. Summary diagram of series of experiments demonstrating bilaterality of auditory pathway in dog. Number below each diagram is hearing loss in decibels, and a box around symbol for cerebral cortex or cochlea indicates destruction of it. Observe that in *D* hearing depends on *uncrossed* fibers of left lateral lemniscus, whereas in *E* hearing depends upon crossed fibers of right lateral lemniscus; hearing loss is equal in the two cases. (Experiments by Mettler *et al., Brain,* 1934, *57:*475–483; diagram after Stevens and Davis, *Hearing, its psychology and physiology,* New York, John Wiley & Sons, Inc., 1938.)

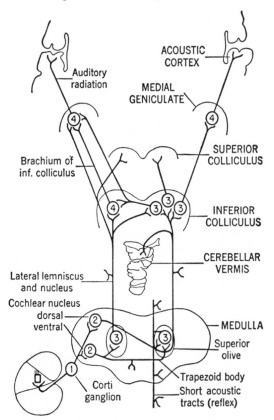

Fig. 17. Afferent acoustic pathways. Numbers in circles represent first, second, third and fourth neuron of chain. Drawing summarizes work of several investigations, mainly on cat. (From Davis, Chap. 28 in *Handbook of experimental psychology,* S. S. Stevens, ed., New York, John Wiley & Sons, Inc., 1951.)

mingle randomly; synaptic terminals are so distributed that the cochlear nuclei become "uncoiled" reflections of the cochlea. The ventral cochlear nucleus of higher mammals developed from the more dorsally situated nucleus magnocellularis of the terrestrial amphibians and reptiles, while the newer dorsal cochlear nucleus finds its homologue in the nucleus angularis that developed in reptiles in close association with the magnocellular nucleus. These nuclei project to the more medially placed superior olivary complex, which appeared in the amphibians and developed rapidly in reptiles and birds. In the submammalian forms, fibers arising from the superior olivary complex, forming the lateral lemniscus, end chiefly in the mammalian homologue of the inferior colliculus. With the rapid encephalization in mammals, the system stretched out through the medial geniculate body of the thalamus to reach the cerebral cortex. This latter addition failed to develop crossing fibers; Figure 17 shows the extensive crossing fibers at lower levels. Action potentials can be recorded from both the ipsilateral and contralateral lateral lemnisci when one cochlea is stimulated.[34] From the size and timing of the activity, the ipsilateral fibers apparently equal the contralateral in number, and the same number of synapses is involved. Chow[17] has shown that the number of fibers progressively increases at each stage of the auditory system. For each fiber in the spiral ganglion, two issue from the cochlear nucleus, 14 issue from the medial geniculate and some 340 occur in the auditory cortex.

The bilaterality of the auditory system was well demonstrated physiologically in the ingenious experiments by Mettler *et al.*[35] (Fig. 18). After various components of the auditory pathway in dogs had been interrupted, the degree of hearing loss was determined by the conditioned reflex method. By removing one cerebral cortex in combination with one or the other cochlea, Mettler and his coworkers discovered that the "acoustic values" of the ipsilateral and contralateral pathways are equal. Nearly complete bilaterality of representation also characterizes the auditory system of man. Unilateral cortical lesions affect hearing only slightly, and, since both auditory areas are seldom attacked by the same pathologic process, deafness is rarely produced by cortical lesions.

In addition to the specific projection to the auditory cortex outlined above, a more diffuse route can be traced through the reticular formation. Although several major stages in this system are undefined, the ascending reticular system is clearly implicated by the observation that sounds continue to arouse decerebellate cats after the specific auditory system has been severed. It has even been possible to evoke a "normal" auditory primary evoked response in the cortex of the cat after complete transection of the brachium of the inferior colliculus.[28]

Centrifugal Auditory Pathway. Anatomically, it is known that a bundle of fibers originates in the superior olivary complex and terminates in the cochlea of the same side (about 20 per cent) and the opposite side (80 per cent). This pathway, called the bundle of Rasmussen or the bundle of Oort, consists only of about 500 fibers in the cat.[40] Nonetheless, it has a rather powerful influence on cochlear output. By applying electric shocks to this olivocochlear bundle of Rasmussen in the cat, Galambos[27] was able to alter the response of the auditory nerve to click stimuli (Fig. 19). When the muscles and ossicles of the middle ear were removed

and the animal was curarized, the suppression began 20 to 30 milliseconds after the first shock of the train of stimuli and continued as long as 500 milliseconds beyond stimulation. The outer hair cell response (cochlear microphonic) was unaltered during these maneuvers, but the auditory nerve response was suppressed (strong clicks) or totally abolished (weak clicks). It is evident that the central nervous system can modulate its input via this system; malfunction of the system could result in significant alteration from normal hearing.

Cochlear Nuclei.[25, 42]   In the cat, each auditory nerve fiber which enters the brain stem, radial and spiral fiber alike, bifurcates to send one branch rostrally into the anterior part of the ventral cochlear nucleus and another branch caudally through the posterior part of the ventral cochlear nucleus and then dorsally into the overlying dorsal cochlear nucleus. Each fiber forms synaptic endings on a multitude of neurons. Fibers terminate in an orderly sequence such that those from the apex of the cochlea end first while those from the base of the cochlea penetrate farthest into the nuclei before bifurcating and terminating. Several different types of synaptic structures are recognized, but their functional significance is still unknown. These nuclei receive fibers from other regions of the brain stem as well as from the cochlea and display a complex and in some regions a laminar arrangement. The laminar dorsal cochlear nucleus projects into the tuber vermis of the cerebellum and into the contralateral inferior colliculus, while the ventral coch-

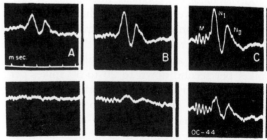

TENSOR AND STAPEDIUS CUT; CURARIZED; STAPES DISARTICULATED

Fig. 19.   Suppression of auditory nerve response to click stimulation by shocks to olivocochlear bundle. *A,* Response to weak click totally abolished by 100/sec. shocks to medulla. *B, C,* Stronger clicks, showing incomplete suppression. *M,* Hair cell response. N_I and N_{II}, Auditory nerve response. (From Galambos, *J. Neurophysiol.,* 1956, *19*:424–437.)

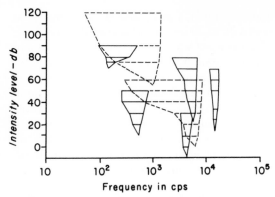

Fig. 20. Auditory response curves from cochlear nucleus of cat, showing both narrow (solid lines) and broad band (dashed lines) receptive areas. The "best frequencies" for each neuron are the lower "peaks" of the response curves. Note that most neurons respond to lower, but not higher, pure tones as the intensity level is increased. (After Rose *et al., Bull. Johns Hopk. Hosp.,* 1959, *104:*211–251.)

lear nucleus sends fibers to the superior olivary complex bilaterally.

Neurons in these nuclei behave much as the single auditory nerve fibers studied by Tasaki.[54] Rose *et al.*[42] found that at sufficiently weak stimulus intensities, only one frequency excited the neuron. As the intensity was increased, the range of excitatory frequencies increased toward the low frequencies but hardly at all to higher frequencies (Fig. 20). These frequency-intensity graphs define the *response area* or "receptive field" of a neuron, and the frequency at minimum or threshold intensity is termed the *best frequency* for the neuron. It is evident in Figure 20 that some neurons have wide and some narrow response areas; both types are found in all subdivisions of the cochlear nuclei. When prolonged tones were employed, the neurons responded with an initial high frequency of spike discharge and then a gradual decline in discharge rate to a steady, low value (from 200 spikes per second down to 20 to 30 spikes per second). Similar response properties have been found in the nucleus magnocellularis and nucleus angularis of the pigeon,[52] in spite of the marked histologic differences in cochlear structure (birds possess neither rods of Corti nor reticular lamina, and but a primordial tectorial membrane "improperly" located).

When a penetrating microelectrode traverses first the dorsal and then the ventral cochlear nuclei, the *best frequencies* of the neurons isolated along the way show an orderly sequence from high to low, with a sudden jump to high again

as the ventral nucleus is entered. Three such *tonotopic organizations* can be found in the cat, oriented from high frequencies dorsomedially to low frequencies ventrolaterally, one in the dorsal cochlear nucleus, one posteriorly in the ventral nucleus and another anteriorly in the same nucleus. This corresponds well with the orderly termination of auditory nerve fibers in these nuclei; a full tonal spectrum is found in each division. This is not simple duplication of representation, however. The dorsal division receives a heavy input from central brain stem structures and shows certain inhibitory phenomena not commonly seen in the ventral divisions. Evidently considerable "processing" of auditory information goes on at these primary auditory relays.

Superior Olivary Complex.[25] The superior olive itself, its accessory nucleus, the pre-olivary nuclei, trapezoid body and the cells of origin of the olivocochlear bundle of Rasmussen constitute this complex. It receives fibers primarily from the ventral cochlear nucleus, some bilaterally and some unilaterally. Curiously, when the cochlear nuclei are destroyed on one side, terminal degeneration in the accessory superior olive is confined to the dendrites toward the lesion.[53] The complex gives rise to the lateral lemniscus, but also sends fibers into motor nuclei in the brain stem and the ubiquitous reticular formation. These nuclei have been regarded as supporting reflex functions but recently have assumed a more important place in the main stream to the cortex. Little is known of the physiology of this complex; trapezoid neurons show narrow response areas and may not be tonotopically arranged.[32]

Inferior Colliculus. A main or central nuclear mass overlaid by an external nucleus constitutes the main feature of this nucleus, although other subdivisions are recognized. Input fibers arrive directly from the contralateral dorsal cochlear nucleus and from both superior olivary nuclei; a large amount of "intercommunication" occurs within the various subdivisions of the nucleus and across the midline, and more input fibers arrive from rostral sites. Output fibers are sent not only to the medial geniculate body, but also to the superior colliculus and down into lower brain stem nuclei. However, the main body of the lateral lemniscus by-passes the inferior colliculus; the latter is probably more involved in auditory reflex activity than in perceptual analysis.

Response areas of the different neurons in the inferior colliculus are uniformly narrow.[32] A tonotopic organization has been found in these nuclei[43] which is inverted between the external nucleus and the central mass. Moving in a general dorsoventral direction, starting caudolaterally and moving toward the rostroventral aspect of the nuclear mass, one finds best frequencies arranged from high to low in the external nucleus and from low to high in the central mass. Rose *et al.*[43] found some neurons to behave like a portion of those in the dorsal cochlear nucleus—with increasing sound intensity, the number of spikes in the response first increases but then decreases, as though the higher sound intensities call into play some inhibitory mechanism. Similar observations have been made in the inferior colliculus of the bat.[30] Intracellular recordings have shown that active inhibitory effects do occur in this structure; Nelson and Erulkar[38] found both excitatory and inhibitory postsynaptic potentials, depending upon which ear was stimulated, upon whether clicks or tones were used, and upon the frequency and intensity of the tones. Continuous tones often produced slowly rising depolarizations; at the cessation of the tone, such depolarizations declined equally slowly.

Medial Geniculate Body.[25] The medial geniculate body consists of an apparently nonauditory superior lobe* and an inferior lobe, containing a medial magnocellular division and a lateral, crescent-shaped principal division. Large fibers from the lateral lemniscus and the brachium of the inferior colliculus enter the *principal nucleus* to arborize around many cells; thin fibers spread throughout the *magnocellular nucleus,* each fiber likewise ending on many cells. Corticogeniculate fibers end chiefly in the principal nucleus. The axons of the small, densely-packed neurons in the principal nucleus form the auditory radiation to the cerebral cortex. Thus, the pars principalis of the medial geniculate body constitutes the primary relay en route to the cerebral cortex; the pars magnocellularis is still largely an unknown.

Exploration of the medial geniculate region with microelectrodes has shown only the principal nucleus to be activated by sound stimulation.[41] Neurons in this nucleus have narrower response areas than elsewhere along the audi-

tory pathway,[33] even though many wide response areas can also be found here. According to Katsuki and coworkers,[32, 33] the response areas of individual neurons become progressively narrower as one moves from the primary auditory nerve fibers through the cochlear nuclei, the superior olivary complex, inferior colliculus and finally to the medial geniculate. The initial response latency to clicks or tonal pips averages 12 milliseconds at the medial geniculate, no matter which ear is stimulated. In terms of threshold sound intensity, however, the contralateral ear is slightly favored.[29] Although a tonotopic organization within the pars principalis probably exists, it has not been clearly defined.

Primary Auditory Cortex. The *auditory cortical field* shows a variety of architectonic configurations (see Chap. 12). It consists of a central field surrounded by a band of tissue divisible into three sectors (Fig. 21). The central field, AI, receives direct projections from the pars principalis of the medial geniculate body; input to the surrounding sectors seems to be indirect, either through collaterals from the geniculocortical projection fibers or through other thalamic nuclei.[44] The specific projection fibers from the pars principalis end heavily in layer IV and to some extent in layer III, each fiber making contact with a large number of neurons. The nonspecific thalamic afferents and cortical association fibers end throughout the upper two-thirds of the cortex. Area AI consists of a very dense array of medium to small, more-or-less rounded polymorphic cells, in such profusion that the normal cortical lamination is blurred and layers II, III and IV seem to be "fused." This contrasts sharply with the bordering sectors, which show distinct lamination and an increasing pyramidalization; layer III possesses larger cells than layer II. The transition between sectors is gradual.

Neuron response properties. About two in every three neurons isolated with a microelectrode in the primary sector, AI, respond in some way to sound stimulation. Although stimulation of either ear is effective, cortical neurons show a 5 to 20 db higher threshold to ipsilateral stimulation than to contralateral stimulation. As at all other levels of the auditory pathway, two response patterns occur—either an initial burst of spikes with failure to continue, or a burst of spikes at onset of a tone followed by a rapid decline in firing frequency to a lower level that is

---

* The commissural fibers forming Gudden's tract interconnect the superior lobes and have no known auditory function.

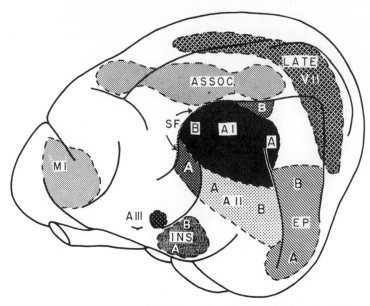

Fig. 21.   Lateral view of left cerebral hemisphere of cat showing the four central areas of auditory cortex, with the cochlear represented anteroposteriorly from base (B) to apex (A) in AI and AII and from apex to base in the suprasylvian fringe area (SF). The posterior ectosylvian area (EP), like the insula (INS), displays the cochlea from apex to base in a more vertical arrangement. Auditory responses appear late in motor (MI) and associate cortex and very late in visual II. (From Woolsey in *Neural mechanisms of the auditory and vestibular systems,* G. L. Rasmussen and W. F. Windle, eds., Springfield, Ill., Charles C Thomas, 1960.)

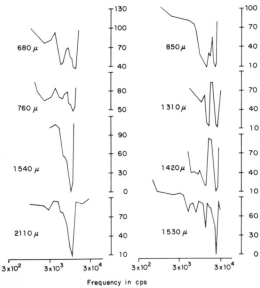

Fig. 22.   Auditory response curves from area AI of the cat. Left series shows response curves for neurons recorded at successively lower depths in the cortex; note similarity in "best frequencies" and compound nature of curves. Right series, taken from penetration more posteriorly, shows higher "best frequencies." (After Hind, Chap. 14 in *Neural mechanisms of the auditory and vestibular systems.* G. L. Rasmussen and W. F. Windle, eds., Springfield, Ill., Charles C Thomas, 1960.)

maintained as long as the tone is sounded. The latter "sustained" response pattern characterizes neurons in the cochlear nuclei, but the "onset" pattern occurs with increasing frequency at successively higher levels and is the rule in auditory cortex. The response areas of cortical neurons are wider than in the medial geniculate body but not so wide as in the cochlear nucleus.[31, 33] They remain narrow from threshold intensity to about 60 db above threshold and then broaden sharply; often two or even three smaller "peaks" are evident (Fig. 22), especially when both ears are stimulated.[31]

Area AI is tonotopically organized; in subprimate forms, the best frequencies are arranged in a rostrocaudal direction from high to low (from base to apex of cochlea), but the reverse is true of primates. When the microelectrode penetrates down through the cortical layers, the best frequencies of the neurons isolated are about the same[31] (Fig. 22). However, even though a high degree of order is present at all levels of the auditory pathway, including the auditory cortex, the system also specializes in diversity. Occasionally wide deviations from the "normal" best frequency for a region occur. Response areas can be altered markedly in configuration by continuous background or "masking" tones, although the best frequency remains as such. The threshold intensity at the best frequency varies widely from one neuron to the next, being bounded near the audibility curve on the low side but ranging to 40 or even 60 db above that value. The entire auditory pathway specializes in inhibitory phenomena; neurons are excited by some frequencies and inhibited by others—or are inhibited by the same frequencies but at a different intensity. Thus, when a simple sinusoidal sound wave impinges on the ear, neurons at all sites in the auditory pathway respond in various degrees. Activity is canalized; it is maximal at a region in each auditory nucleus that is determined by the frequency of the sinusoid, and the magnitude of "maximal" is determined by the amplitude of the sinusoid. Around this region of maximal response, neuron activity rapidly falls off. Farther away, neurons are actively "turned off" or made unresponsive to particular tones. The response of the auditory pathway to simple sounds is thus highly canalized and consistent with the place theory of hearing.

Auditory areas. In 1942 Woolsey and Walzl[67] studied the *primary evoked response* (see Chap. 22) that is produced in the cortex of the cat by focal electrical stimulation along the edge of the osseous spiral lamina. They found two complete representations of the cochlea on the ectosylvian and sylvian gyri, one in the cortex heavily innervated by the medial geniculate body (called AI; see Fig. 21) and a second more laterally disposed (AII). The representations became evident when they observed that slight changes in the site of cochlear stimulation changed the point of maximal electrical activity on the auditory cortex. Stimulation near the base of the cochlea caused activity in the anterior part of AI, while stimulation at the apex caused activity posteriorly; intermediate cortical regions were activated by stimulation of intermediate cochlear regions. The order of representation of the cochlea was reversed in AII. Tunturi[58] soon verified the AI "map" by employing tonal stimuli (Fig. 23) and also identified a third auditory response area (AIII) sharing cortex with the second somatosensory area.[59] Two additional representations of the cochlea have been found, immediately adjacent to the primary auditory area, AI (Fig. 21). The place theory, which asked for only one representation of the cochlea in the cortex, finds itself with an embarrassing richness of tonotopic "maps."

At first it seemed that the auditory areas immediately adjacent to AI were brought into activity by fiber projections from AI,[1, 14] and such interconnections have been demonstrated.[21] But ablation of AI had no effect on tonal discrimination either in cat[36] or monkey;[23] complete bilateral destruction of all auditory areas seemed necessary to interfere permanently with the ability to distinguish small changes in frequency of a tone. These "fringe" areas have been shown to possess independent afferent projections.[21] Further, it appears that with different training methods,[15] animals can relearn frequency discriminations after ablation of all these cortical auditory areas. Nor does the cortex appear to play any role in discrimination in changes in intensity of a tone.[39] However, the ability to locate a sound in space is severely impaired following bilateral ablations of AI, AII and Ep but little affected if the ablation is unilateral.[37] Clinical evidence is in dispute on this point.

The function of AI may lie in some "higher" auditory activity. AII seems essential to pattern discrimination, whereas AI is not.[20] If tones A and B are used to make two tonal patterns, ABA and BAB, the transition between them is easily discriminable by a cat before operation. After removal of the three main auditory areas, pattern discrimination, unlike single frequency discrimination, is lost and cannot be relearned. Impairment in the understanding of speech is evident in cases of human temporal lobe dam-

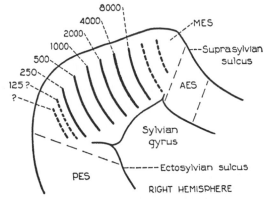

Fig. 23. Tonal localization in dog's primary auditory area. *AES,* Anterior ectosylvian area; *PES,* posterior ectosylvian area; *MES,* middle ectosylvian area. Bands indicate point at which strychnine spikes occurred with lowest intensity. Bands indicated by dashes were not determined experimentally. (After Tunturi from Bremer, *Some problems in neurophysiology,* London, Athlone Press, 1953.)

age,[13, 45] and quantification of the deficit shows that the ear contralateral to the lesion suffers more deficit. Patients with cortical damage often make mistakes in the perception of nasal sounds,[45] whereas patients with peripheral auditory damage less often show such a defect.

REFERENCES

1. ADES, H. W. *J. Neurophysiol.*, 1943, *6*:59–63.
2. ADES, H. W., METTLER, F. A. and CULLER, E. A. *Amer. J. Physiol.*, 1939, *125*:15–23.
3. ARMSTRONG, H. G. *Principles and practice of aviation medicine.* 3rd ed. Baltimore, Williams & Wilkins, 1952.
4. BÉKÉSY, G. VON. *Ann. Physik.*, 1932, *13*:111–136.
5. BÉKÉSY, G. VON. *Acta oto-laryng.* (*Stockh.*), 1939, *27*:281–296.
6. BÉKÉSY, G. VON. *J. acoust. Soc. Amer.*, 1948, *20*:227–241.
7. BÉKÉSY, G. VON. *J. acoust. Soc. Amer.*, 1951, *23*:29–35.
8. BÉKÉSY, G. VON. *J. acoust. Soc. Amer.*, 1951, *23*:576–582.
9. BÉKÉSY, G. VON. *J. acoust. Soc Amer.*, 1952, *24*:72–76.
10. BÉKÉSY, G. VON. *J. acoust. Soc. Amer.*, 1953, *25*:786–790.
11. BÉKÉSY, G. VON. *Experiments in hearing*, N.Y., McGraw-Hill, 1960.
12. BÉKÉSY, G. von and ROSENBLITH, W. A. Chap. 27 in *Handbook of experimental psychology*, S. S. Stevens, ed. New York, John Wiley & Sons, 1951.
13. BOCCA, E. *Laryngoscope* (*St. Louis*), 1958, *68*:301–309.
14. BREMER, F. *Some problems in neurophysiology.* London, Athlone Press, 1953.
15. BUTLER, R. A., DIAMOND, I. T. and NEFF, W. D. *J. Neurophysiol.*, 1957, *20*:108–120.
16. CARMEL, P. W. and STARR, A. *J. Neurophysiol.*, 1963, *26*:598–616.
17. CHOW, K. L. *J. comp. Neurol.*, 1951, *95*:159–175.
18. DAVIS, H., DEATHERAGE, B. H., ELDREDGE, D. H. and SMITH, C. A. *Amer. J. Physiol.*, 1958, *195*:251–261.
19. DAVIS, H., DEATHERAGE, B. H., ROSENBLUT, B., FERNANDEZ, C., KIMURA, R. and SMITH, C. A. *Laryngoscope* (*St. Louis*), 1958, *68*:596–627.
20. DIAMOND, I. T. and NEFF, W. D. *J. Neurophysiol.*, 1957, *20*:300–315.
21. DOWNMAN, C. B. B., WOOLSEY, C. N. and LENDE, R. A. *Bull. Johns Hopk. Hosp.*, 1960, *106*:127–142.
22. ENGSTRÖM, H., ADES, H. W. and HAWKINS, J. E., JR. *J. acoust. Soc. Amer.*, 1962, *34*:1356–1363.
23. EVARTS, E. V. *J. Neurophysiol.*, 1952, *15*:443–448.
24. FERNÁNDEZ, C. *Laryngoscope* (*St. Louis*), 1951, *61*:1152–1172.
25. GALAMBOS, R. *Physiol. Rev.*, 1954, *34*:497–528.
26. GALAMBOS, R. *Ann. Otol.* (*St. Louis*), 1956, *65*:1053–1059.
27. GALAMBOS, R. *J. Neurophysiol.*, 1956, *19*:424–437.
28. GALAMBOS, R., MYERS, R. E. and SHEATZ, G. C. *Amer. J. Physiol.*, 1961, *200*:23–28.
29. GALAMBOS, R., ROSE, J. E., BROMILEY, R. B. and HUGHES, J. R. *J. Neurophysiol.*, 1952, *15*:359–380.
30. GRINNEL, A. D. *J. Physiol.*, 1963, *167*:38–66.
31. HIND, J. E. Chap. 14 in *Neural mechanisms of the auditory and vestibular systems*, G. L. Rasmussen and W. Windle, eds. Springfield, Ill., Charles C Thomas, 1960.
32. KATSUKI, Y., SUMI, T., UCHIYAMA, H. and WATANABE, T. *J. Neurophysiol.*, 1958, *21*:569–588.
33. KATSUKI, Y., WATANABE, T. and MARUYAMA, N. *J. Neurophysiol.*, 1959, *22*:343–359.
34. KEMP, E. H., COPPÉE, G. E. and ROBINSON, E. H. *Amer. J. Physiol.*, 1937, *120*:304–315.
35. METTLER, F. A., FINCH, G., GIRDEN, E. and CULLER, E. *Brain*, 1934, *57*:475–483.
36. MEYER, D. R. and WOOLSEY, C. N. *J. Neurophysiol.*, 1952, *15*:149–162.
37. NEFF, W. D., FISHER, J. F., DIAMOND, I. T. and YELA, M. *J. Neurophysiol.*, 1956, *19*:500–512.
38. NELSON, P. G. and ERULKAR, S. D. *J. Neurophysiol.*, 1963, *26*:908–923.
39. RAAB, D. H. and ADES, H. W. *Amer. J. Psychol.*, 1946, *59*:59–83.
40. RASMUSSEN, G. L. *J. comp. Neurol.*, 1946, *84*:141–219.
41. ROSE, J. E. and GALAMBOS, R. *J. Neurophysiol.*, 1952, *15*:343–357.
42. ROSE, J. E., GALAMBOS, R. and HUGHES, J. R. *Bull. Johns Hopk. Hosp.*, 1959, *104*:211–251.
43. ROSE, J. E., GREENWOOD, D. D., GOLDBERG, J. M. and HIND, J. E. *J. Neurophysiol.*, 1963, *26*:294–320.
44. ROSE, J. E. and WOOLSEY, C. N. *J. comp. Neurol.*, 1949, *91*:441–466.
45. DE SA, G. *Laryngoscope* (*St. Louis*), 1958, *68*:309–317.
46. SMITH, C. A. *Ann. Otol.* (*St. Louis*), 1961, *70*:504–527.
47. SMITH, C. A. *Trans. Amer. otol. Soc.*, 1961, *48*:35–60.
48. SMITH, C. A., LOWRY, O. H. and WU, M-L. *Laryngoscope* (*St. Louis*), 1954, *64*:141–153.
49. SMITH, C. A. and SJÖSTRAND, F. S. *J. Ultrastruct. Res.*, 1961, *5*:523–556.
50. STEVENS, S. S. and DAVIS, H. *Hearing: its psychology and physiology.* New York, John Wiley & Sons, 1938.
51. STEVENS, S. S., DAVIS, H. and LURIE, M. H. *J. gen. Psychol.*, 1935, *13*:297–315.
52. STOPP, P. E. and WHITFIELD, I. C. *J. Physiol.*, 1961, *158*:165–177.
53. STOTLER, W. A. *J. comp. Neurol.*, 1953, *98*:401–431.
54. TASAKI, I. *J. Neurophysiol.*, 1954, *17*:97–122.
55. TASAKI, I., DAVIS, H. and ELDREDGE, D. H. *J. acoust. Soc. Amer.*, 1954, *26*:765–773.
56. TASAKI, I., DAVIS, H. and LEGOUIX, J-P. *J. acoust. Soc. Amer.*, 1952, *24*:502–519.
57. TASAKI, I. and SPYROPOULOS, C. S. *J. Neurophysiol.*, 1959, *22*:149–155.
58. TUNTURI, A. R. *Amer. J. Physiol.*, 1944, *141*:397–403.
59. TUNTURI, A. *Amer. J. Physiol.*, 1945, *144*:389–394.
60. WAETZMANN, E. *Akust. Z.*, 1938, *3*:1–6.
61. WEVER, E. G. *Theory of hearing.* New York, John Wiley & Sons, 1949.
62. WEVER, E. G. and BRAY, C. W. *J. exp. Psychol.*, 1930, *13*:373–387.
63. WEVER, E. G. and BRAY, C. W. *Proc. nat. Acad. Sci.* (*Wash.*), 1930, *16*:344–350.
64. WEVER, E. G. and LAWRENCE, M. *Physiological acoustics.* Princeton, N.J., Princeton University Press, 1954.
65. WIENER, F. M. and ROSS, D. A. *J. acoust. Soc. Amer.*, 1946, *18*:401–408.
66. WILSKA, A. *Skand. Arch. Physiol.*, 1935, *72*:161–165.
67. WOOLSEY, C. N. and WALZI, E. M. *Bull. Johns Hopk. Hosp.*, 1942, *71*:315–344.

CHAPTER 19

The Eye as an Optical Instrument

By FRANK W. WEYMOUTH*

THE eye is the peripheral organ of vision. By means of its physical structure (Fig. 1), rays of light from external objects are focused upon the retina and there set up nerve impulses that are transmitted by the fibers of the optic nerve and the optic tract to the visual area in the cortex of the brain. Here is aroused the reaction we call seeing. In studying the physiology of vision we must first consider the eye as an optical instrument that is physically adapted to form an image on its retina and that is provided with certain physiologic regulatory mechanisms.

FORMATION OF AN IMAGE

The image on the retina is formed by virtue of the refractive surfaces of the cornea and the lens. The curved surfaces of these transparent bodies act substantially like a convex glass lens, and the physics of the formation of an image by such a lens is used to explain the refractive processes in the eye.

*Deceased. Chapter revised by Theodore C. Ruch.

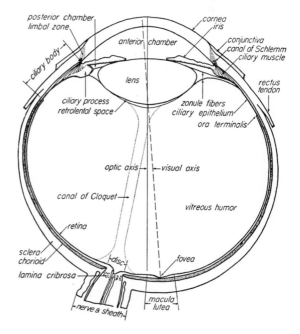

Fig. 1. Horizontal section of human eye. (From Walls, *The vertebrate eye.* Bloomfield Hills, Mich., Cranbrook Institute of Science, 1942.)

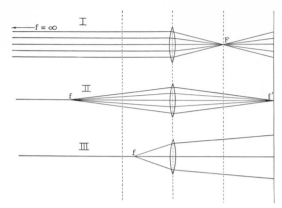

Fig. 2. Refraction of light by convex lens. *I*, Refraction of parallel rays; *II*, refraction of divergent rays; *III*, refraction of divergent rays from a luminous point nearer than principal focal distance. *F*, Principal focus; *f*, luminous point; *f'*, focused image of *f*.

Image Formation by a Convex Lens. The most common artificial lens is a piece of glass with polished spherical surfaces surrounded by air. Such lenses are of two types, the converging lens with convex surfaces (thick in the middle) and the diverging lens with concave surfaces (thin in the middle). The *principal axis* of a lens with two spherical surfaces is a line passing through the centers of curvature that is therefore perpendicular to these surfaces where it pierces them. Real images that may be caught on a screen are formed only by convex (converging) lenses.

Light from a point on the principal axis so distant that the rays are parallel when they strike the lens will converge at a point, the *principal focus*, on the principal axis behind the lens (*F* in Fig. 2, I).* The distance between the principal focus and the lens is the *principal focal distance*. This distance, which is a measure of the refractive power or "strength" of the lens, depends upon the curvatures of the lens surfaces and the refractive index of the glass. Absolutely parallel rays emanate from an infinitely distant source of light; practically, however, objects not nearer than about 20 feet give rays which diverge so little that they may be considered to be parallel. On the other hand, if a luminous object is placed at *F* in Figure 2, the rays that pass through the lens will emerge as parallel rays. If

*In all such diagrams, the curvatures and thickness of the lens are greatly exaggerated. Statements concerning the course of rays are strictly true only for an ideally thin lens and for a small area about the principal axis.

a luminous point (*f* in Fig. 2, II) is placed in front of the lens at a distance greater than the principal focal distance but not far enough to give practically parallel rays, the cone of diverging rays from this source will focus at *f'*, which is farther away than the principal focus. Conversely, the rays from a luminous point at *f'* will be brought to a focus at *f*. Such points as *f* and *f'* are spoken of as *conjugate foci*. All luminous points within the limits specified have corresponding conjugate foci at which their images are formed by the lens. Lastly, if a luminous point is placed nearer to the lens than the principal focal distance, as at *f* in Figure 2, III, the cone of strongly divergent rays, although refracted, is still divergent after leaving the lens, and consequently is not focused and forms no real image of the point.

Any lens contains an *optical center*, or nodal point, on the principal axis; in Figure 3, *DE* is the principal axis, and *o* is the optical center. All other straight lines passing through the optical center, i.e., rays coincident with the principal axis or any secondary axis, are not bent in passing through the lens. Moreover, the conjugate focus of any luminous point not on the principal axis will lie somewhere upon the secondary axis drawn from this point through the optical center.

The exact position of the image of such a point can be determined by the construction illustrated in Figure 3, I. *A* represents a luminous point throwing a cone of rays upon the lens; the limiting rays of this cone are

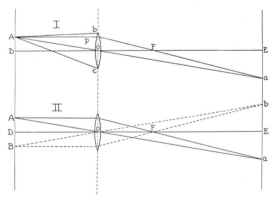

Fig. 3. Formation of image by convex lens. *I*, Relation of a point (*A*) to its image (*a*). *Ab* and *Ac* are limiting rays of cone of light reflected by *A*; *Ap*, ray parallel to optic or principal axis (*DE*) of lens; *F*, principal focus; *o*, optical center. *II*, Relation of luminous object and its image points. *A*, *B*, luminous points; *a*, *b*, images of points.

represented by Ab and Ac. Ray Ap is parallel to the principal axis and will therefore pass through the principal focus, F. If the focal distance is known, the line Ap can be extended, as indicated, to pass through F after leaving the lens. The point at which the prolongation of this line cuts the secondary axis, Ao, marks the conjugate focus of A and gives the position, a, at which all the rays are focused to form the image.

To calculate the position of the image of any object in front of the lens, the same method may be used, a construction being drawn to determine the images of two or more limiting points, as shown in Figure 3, II. If AB is an arrow in front of a lens, the image of A is formed at a on the secondary axis Ao and the image of B at b along the secondary axis Bo. The images of all the intervening points will, of course, lie between a and b, so that the entire image is that of an inverted arrow. This image may be caught on a screen at the distance indicated by a construction drawn to scale.

The principal focus of a convex lens in air may be determined experimentally, or it may be calculated from the formula

$$\frac{1}{F} = \frac{1}{f_1} + \frac{1}{f_2}$$

where F represents the principal focal distance, and f_1 and f_2 the conjugate focal distances for an object farther away than the principal focus. That is, if the distance between the object and the lens, f_1, is known, and the distance of its image, f_2, is determined experimentally, the principal focal distance of the lens, F, may be determined from the formula.

Image Formation by the Eye. Although the refractive surfaces of the eye act essentially like a convex lens, they are more complex. As indicated in Figure 4, the eye contains three refractive surfaces. The light is refracted at the anterior surface of the cornea, where the rays pass from the air into the denser medium of the cornea; at the anterior surface of the lens, where they again enter a denser medium; and at the posterior surface of the lens, where they enter the less dense vitreous humor. The relative refractive effects on these various surfaces depend upon the curvatures and the indices of refraction* of the various media of the eye and therefore differ.[6, 8]

Index of refraction $= \dfrac{\text{velocity in air}}{\text{velocity in x}} = \dfrac{\text{sine i}}{\text{sine r}}$

The following illustrate the data on the index of refraction:

*The index of refraction is the ratio of the velocity of light in air (or, more exactly, in vacuum) to the velocity of light in the substance considered; this index is commonly measured by the ratio between the sine of the angle of incidence and the sine of the angle of refraction.

air	= 1.000
water	= 1.333
aqueous and vitreous humors	= 1.336
crystalline lens (index of an equivalent thin lens)	= 1.413

Because the difference between the index of refraction of air and that of the cornea is greater than the difference between the indices for the lens and its surroundings, light is more strongly bent on entering the eye than in passing through the lens.

In a lens system like the eye, composed of media with different indices of refraction separated by surfaces of varying curvatures, it is possible, but laborious, to trace accurately the entire path of the light. However, the course of light rays through the eye can be followed with sufficient accuracy by means of a simplification, the *reduced eye*.[4] All refraction is presumed to occur at a single interface between air and the contents of the eye, here assumed to be homogeneous and to have the same index of refraction as water, 1.333. The interface (c in Fig. 5) corresponding to the surface of the cornea has a radius of 5 mm., and its center of curvature is the optical center or nodal point (n) of the system. The retina lies 15 mm. posterior to the nodal point and 20 mm. from the cornea; this is also the principal focal distance of the system, so that distant objects are focused on the retina of the reduced eye at rest. The anterior principal focus, i.e., the point at which rays parallel within the eye would converge on emerging, lies 15 mm. in front of the cornea. The anterior and posterior focal distances are different because the light travels in air outside the eye and in denser media inside the eye. If the interior focal distance, 20 mm., is divided by the index of refraction of the reduced eye, the result will equal the anterior focal distance, $20/1.333 = 15.0$.

As mentioned above, the surfaces and distances in the completely relaxed ideal eye are

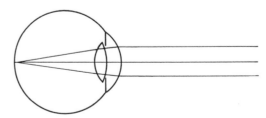

Fig. 4. Chief ocular interfaces at which light rays are refracted. Rays are refracted at air-cornea, aqueous-lens and lens-vitreous interfaces.

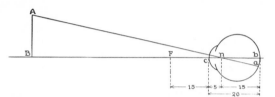

Fig. 5. Diagram of reduced eye with dimensions and construction required for location and size of retinal image. *AB*, Object; *ab*, image; *n*, nodal point; *F*, principal focus (anterior); *c*, corneal surface.

so related that the posterior focal point coincides with the retina and images of distant objects are focused on it. The formation of the image on the retina can therefore be shown by a construction like the one presented in Figure 5. Secondary axes are drawn from the limiting points of the object—*A* and *B*—through the nodal point. Where these axes meet, the retinal image of the object will be formed. That is, all the rays of light from *A* that penetrate the eye will be focused at *a*, and all those from *B* at *b*. The image on the retina will therefore be inverted and smaller than the object. The angle formed at the nodal point by the lines *An* and *Bn* (angle *AnB* or *anb*) is known as the *visual angle;* it varies inversely with the distance of the object from the eye.

Retinal Image and Spatial Perception. The apparent position of objects is related to the position of their retinal images, as produced by these physical processes. Stimulation of retinal point *a* in Figure 5 indicates an object at *A,* the point in the outside world from which light would normally come to focus on *a*. If point *a* is stimulated in some other manner, as by finger pressure on the eyeball producing a phosphene, the sensation is projected, i.e., appears to come from the direction of *A*. This relation occurs in the congenitally blind just as it does in persons who have "used" their retinas for years.[16]

It is clear that the relation of the direction in which an object is "seen" to the part of the retina stimulated is innate; it is present as soon as a child's behavior indicates a recognition of up and down, right and left. Salamanders in which an eye has been rotated through 180° during an early larval stage snap down for food held above the nose and never learn to correct this confusion. In man, when an abnormal position of an eye causes the stimulation of its retina to indicate an object position disagreeing with that indicated by other sources of information, including the other eye, the afferent impulses

from the divergent eye are, after a period of confusion, excluded from consciousness. The nonconforming eye is then said to be amblyopic and is, for certain purposes, blind. However, when the images in both eyes have been reversed by lenses, experimental subjects have, after some confusion, performed tasks in a manner indicating proper orientation in space. When the inverting lenses were then removed, a second period of disorientation followed. In man there seems to be a certain plasticity of brain function which is poorly understood, but which is clinically important in ambylopia.

Size of Retinal Image. The size of the retinal image may readily be calculated from the size of the actual object and its distance from the eye. As can be seen from Figure 5, the triangles *AnB* and *anb* are similar; consequently, we have the following equality of ratios:

$$\frac{AB}{ab} = \frac{An}{an}$$

or

$$\frac{\text{object size}}{\text{image size}} = \frac{\text{object distance from nodal point}}{\text{image distance from nodal point}}$$

Suppose it is desired to find the size of the retinal image of a tree 40 meters high at a distance of 2 km. Reducing all measurements to meters and substituting in the above equation, we have

$$\frac{40}{\text{image}} = \frac{2000}{0.015}$$

$$\text{image} = \frac{0.6}{2000} = 0.0003 \text{ m. or } 0.3 \text{ mm.}$$

The image of the tree is thus about the size of the fovea.

ACCOMMODATION

Accommodation of Eye for Objects at Different Distances. In the *emmetropic* or ideal refractive state, parallel rays from distant objects are brought to a focus on the retina when the eye is at rest. In other words, the structures are usually so correlated that the retina lies very near the second principal focus of the relaxed eye's combined refractive surfaces. When objects are brought closer to the eye, however, the rays proceeding from them become more and more divergent. Were the eye to remain unchanged, the rays would strike the retina before coming to a focus; in consequence, each luminous point in the object, instead of forming a point upon the retina, would form a circle, known as a *diffusion circle*. Thus, the retinal image as a whole would be blurred. Up to a certain point, the eye *accommodates* itself to focus rays from nearer objects so that blurring does not occur.

That a change in the curvature of the lens is the essential factor of accommodation for near objects is demonstrated by a simple and conclusive experiment utilizing the Purkinje images. The eye to be observed is relaxed, i.e., gazes into the distance. A lighted candle is held to one side and the observer takes a position on the other, where he can see the light of the candle reflected from the observed eye. With a little practice, and under the right conditions of illumination, the observer can see three images of the candle reflected from the eye as from a mirror. One image, the brightest, is reflected from the convex surface of the cornea (image *a*, Fig. 6 *A*). A second, larger and much dimmer, is reflected from the convex surface of the lens (image *b*); this image is larger and fainter because the reflecting surface is less curved. The third image (*c*) is inverted and is smaller and brighter than the second. This image is reflected from the posterior surface of the lens, which acts as a concave mirror in this instance. If the observed eye now gazes at a near object (Fig. 6 *B*), the first image (*a*) does not change at all, the third image (*c*) also remains practically the same, but the middle image (*b*) becomes smaller and approaches nearer to the first. This result can only mean that in the act of accommodation the anterior surface of the lens becomes more convex. In this way, its refractive power is increased and the more divergent rays from the near object are focused on the retina. Helmholtz demonstrated that the curvature of the posterior surface of the lens also increases slightly, but this change is so slight that the increased refractive power is referred chiefly to the change in the anterior surface. The means by which the change is effected was first satisfactorily explained by Helmholtz.

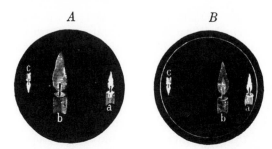

Fig. 6. Effect of accommodation on Purkinje images. *A*, eye at rest; *B*, eye accommodated for near objects; *a*, image reflected from air-cornea interface; *b*, from aqueous-lens interface; *c*, from lens-vitreous interface.

The structures involved (Fig. 7) and their action as envisioned by Helmholtz will be described briefly. The tiny *ciliary muscle* lies in a thickened anterior portion of the vascular layer, called the *ciliary body*, which lies as a collar between the anterior margin of the functional retina and the root of the iris surrounding the lens. Some of the smooth fibers making up the ciliary muscle take a radial course, originating in the sclera near the margin of the cornea and inserting in the chorioid* near the posterior margin of the ciliary body. Other fibers, tending to lie more central to these, have a circular course like that of the fibers of a sphincter muscle.

The lens is suspended by the *zonula*, which consists of delicate transparent membranes and fibers bridging between the ciliary body and the elastic capsule covering the lens. *When the ciliary muscle is relaxed, the zonula is under tension* and pulls

---

* The spelling *chorioid* is preferred to *choroid* as etymologically more correct and closer to the intended meaning, "resembling the chorion."

Fig. 7. Detail of anterior segment of human eye. Ciliary process has been distorted in cutting of section. Scleral roll is a narrow shelf of scleral tissue, on under side of which radial or meridional fibers of ciliary muscle originate. (After Bloom and Fawcett, *A textbook of histology*, Philadelphia, W. B. Saunders Co., 1962.)

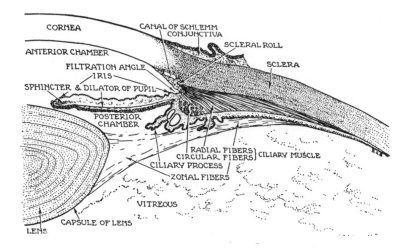

on the equator of the lens so that the lens is flattened. When the ciliary muscle contracts, it pulls the ciliary body toward the lens, relaxing the zonula. The tension which held the lens in its flattened shape having been reduced or abolished, the elasticity of the capsule, like the rubber of a toy balloon, tends to mold the plastic lens into a more convex form.

Although other theories have been proposed both before and since the time of Helmholtz, his view of the mechanism, with minor changes resulting from recent work,[8] is still the most adequate.

Other mammals accommodate in the same way as man, but not all vertebrates do. In most bony fish, for example, the mechanism is wholly different. The lens moves backward and toward the retina, thus focusing the eye for more distant objects.[2, 22]

Near and Far Points of Distinct Vision. When an object is brought closer and closer to the eye, a point is reached at which even the strongest contraction of the ciliary muscle will not result in a clear image of the object. The rays from it are so divergent that the refractive surfaces cannot bring them to a focus on the retina. Therefore, each luminous point makes a diffusion circle on the retina, and the whole image is indistinct. The nearest point at which an object can be distinctly seen, with full accommodation, is called the *near point*. The distance between the near point and the eye increases with age, slowly in early life, most rapidly in the early 40's, and very slowly after 50. The rate of this decline is shown in Figure 8. Recession of the near point is usually ascribed to

a progressive loss of the plasticity of the lens, so that, although contraction of the ciliary muscle reduces the tension of the zonula, the lens is less and less capable of being molded into a more convex form. The progressive loss starts as early in life as the near point can be satisfactorily measured; this process is one of many showing that senescence begins practically at birth. This decline in the power of accommodation is little noticed until it begins to interfere with reading, usually between the 40th and 50th years, when the condition is called *presbyopia* or old-sightedness (p. 408).

In the normal eye, parallel rays are brought to focus on the retina from infinity. If large enough, objects at distances greater than 20 feet are seen distinctly without accommodation— i.e., with the eye at rest. Practically, then, a distance of 6 meters (20 feet) is the *far point* of the normal eye.

Refractive Power and Amplitude of Accommodation. The refractive power of a lens is usually expressed in terms of its principal focal distance. A lens with a focal distance of 1 meter is taken as the unit and is designated as having a refractive power of 1 diopter, 1 D. Compared with this unit, the refractive power of lenses is expressed in terms of the reciprocal of their principal focal distances measured in meters; thus, a lens with a principal focal distance of 1/10 meter is a lens of 10 diopters (10 D.), and one with a focal distance of 5 meters is 1/5 diopter (0.2 D.).

The reduced eye at rest has a refractive power of 66 2/3 D. This value is the reciprocal of the focal distance in air when measured in meters (1/0.015 = 66 2/3 D.), or the reciprocal of the focal distance within the medium of the eye multiplied by the refractive index of that medium (1.333/0.020 = 66 2/3 D.). This power is somewhat greater than that—about 58 D.— derived from measurements of the eye. The cornea contributes about twice as much to this power as does the lens. Thus, the loss of the lens, as in cataract operations, does not lessen the refractive power as much as does the abolition of the action of the cornea occurring, for example, when the eye is opened under water.

In accommodation, greater curvature of the lens increases the total refractive power of the eye. Thus when a 20 year old emmetrope, with a near point of 1/10 meter, accommodates, the eye not only brings to a focus parallel rays (66-2/3 D.) but overcomes in addition the diver-

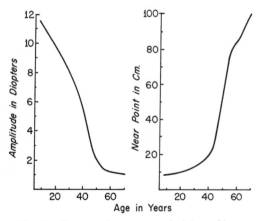

Fig. 8. Decrease in accommodation and increase in distance to near point of vision with age. (Based on data gathered by Duane[6] in over 4000 subjects.)

gence of light from the near point (10 D.). It is as though the eye were left at rest, and a glass lens of 10 D. were placed before the cornea. The amplitude of accommodation may thus be expressed by the number of diopters added to the refractive power of the eye by the action of the ciliary muscle. Figure 8 shows the amplitudes of accommodation at various ages corresponding to the near points plotted in Figure 8. Both of these charts are derived from data collected by Duane.[5, 6]

OPTICAL DEFECTS AND ABNORMALITIES

Optical Defects of the Emmetropic Eye. As in other optical systems, spherical, chromatic and other aberrations are present in the eye, but they seldom appreciably affect vision. There are several reasons why these aberrations rarely distort the retinal image. First, the shape and structure of the cornea and the lens and the location of the iris near the nodal point reduce aberrations. In addition, several physiologic factors favor clear vision. The most severe distortions fall on the peripheral retina, where visual acuity is low and more distinct images cannot be appreciated; the important "finder" function of this part of the retina is not thereby impaired. Another factor is the lesser sensitivity of the retina to the wavelengths at the ends of the spectrum—the extreme reds and blues— where chromatic aberration is most marked. Thus, since scattered light and diffraction fringes are of low intensity, they tend to fall below the retinal threshold. For these reasons, what may be called the "physiologic image" is commonly better than the physical image.

Ametropia. As pointed out above, emmetropia is that refractive state of the eye in which, without accommodation, parallel rays focus on the sensitive layer of the retina, or in which the far point is infinitely distant; a person with such eyes is often called an "emmetrope." Any deviation from the condition of emmetropia is called *ametropia*. Obviously, emmetropia does not require any particular total refractive power or size of eye so long as there is a proper proportion between the axial length and the refractive powers of the cornea and lens.

Only recently have accurate measurements been available for a sufficient number of living eyes to permit analysis of the interrelations among the various optical elements.[10, 17] As with other human measurements, all values vary from person to person, the distribution for nearly all elements following a normal frequency curve. The deviations from emmetropia, as measured by the lens needed to bring parallel rays to focus in the resting eye, give a distribution more peaked than normal and with a scatter far less than would result from a chance association of the refractive elements. Correlations of the axial length, the refractive power of the cornea and the lens, and the other optical elements tend to reduce ametropia. In consequence, emmetropia is surprisingly common. Thus, if emmetropia is construed as embracing values from −0.5 to +0.5 D., about 25 per cent of young adults are emmetropic; if the range is expanded to include values between −1 and +1 D., about 65 per cent fall in this category.[14, 17]

At one time those biologic variations constituting ametropia excluded the afflicted from occupations requiring good vision. Now, most defects can be remedied by eyeglasses and are hardly noticed.

Ametropia may result from an unusually large or small value for any optical element, or from some combination of these elements not resulting in the compensatory correlations mentioned above. Analysis of Stenström's data[17] indicates that: (i) unusual values for the axial length are the most common cause of ametropia, (ii) about half as common is variation in the corneal refraction, and (iii) less important are separation of the cornea and lens or other optical elements. Ametropia of necessity falls into two types. In one, parallel rays come to a focus before reaching the retina; in the other, they reach the retina before coming to a focus. In the first, the axial length is relatively too long for the refractive power—this is called *myopia*.[9] In the second, the axial length is too short—this is called *hyperopia* (hypermetropia). The frequency distribution of the refractive state in adults shows, as stated above, a crowding of cases toward emmetropia (the mean is about 0.5 D. hyperopic), with some extreme cases of myopia and hyperopia, so that the form of the curve is distinctly peaked.[3, 11, 14, 19, 20]

MYOPIA. During growth (from about six to 20 years, but particularly at puberty) in a small proportion of persons, the increase in length is relatively more rapid than the decrease in refractive power. As a result, they become myopic.

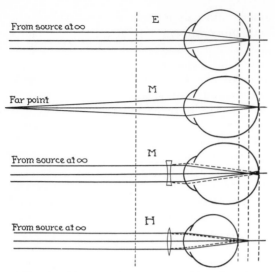

Fig. 9. Diagram of emmetropia (*E*) (reduced eye to scale), myopia (*M*), and hyperopia (*H*). Dotted lines in two lower diagrams show effect of proper correcting lenses.

In myopia, without accommodation, parallel rays of light come to a focus in the vitreous and diverge again to form diffusion circles on the retina. In any degree of myopia there is some point, nearer than that giving parallel rays, from which the light is sufficiently divergent to come to a focus on the retina of the unaccommodated eye; this is the myopic far point. The distance of this far point may be only a few centimeters, and all more distant objects will appear in some degree blurred—the more so the more distant they are. This condition is represented by diagram *M* in Figure 9. The obvious remedy is to use concave lenses for distant vision. By this means, the rays can be made divergent enough that the focus will be thrown accurately on the retina. Since the myopic eye at rest can focus rays of some degree of divergence, it can in full accommodation focus on very near objects; i.e., its near point is nearer than that of an emmetropic eye with equal amplitude of accommodation. This situation has led to the term "nearsightedness."

HYPEROPIA. This condition is represented in diagram *H* of Figure 9. In the eye at rest the retina is reached before the light has come to a focus, and each point source of light is represented by a diffusion circle. A converging lens of the proper strength will obviously bring light rays to the eye with that additional amount of convergence needed for their focus on the sensitive layers of the retina. The uncorrected hyper-

ope may see distant objects clearly only by use of his accommodation. Clear vision is accomplished at the expense of eyestrain arising from constant excessive accommodation without corresponding convergence of the two eyes. Further, since some accommodation is used to see even far objects, less is available for viewing near things. Consequently, the near point is more distant than it is in an emmetrope with equal amplitude of accommodation. The extra effort required for near work limits the amount of effective reading or other close work and leads to headaches or other evidences of eyestrain.

The term "farsightedness" for hyperopia is misleading. The "far" refers only to the excessive distance to the near point. The hyperope sees distant objects no better than does an emmetrope. In fact, when the farsighted person sees them as well, it is at the cost of some eyestrain.

PRESBYOPIA. A decline in the amplitude of accommodation is termed presbyopia and, as indicated earlier, is a consequence of aging. The near point of distinct vision recedes farther and farther from the eye until near work is difficult or impossible. Because his near point is initially more distant, the uncorrected hyperope will experience difficulty with near work earlier than will the emmetrope, and the myope will experience reading difficulty late in life, or perhaps never. A myope with a near point of 20 or 30 cm. can see near objects even if no accommodation remains; those people who can read fine print at 80 or 90 are, in all cases, myopes. All properly corrected eyes will become presbyopic at about the same time, at an age of approximately 45; after that age, an additional convex lens will be necessary for comfortable reading.

Astigmia or Astigmatism. In an ideal eye, the refractive surfaces of the cornea and lens would be spherical surfaces with equal curvatures along all meridians. In many eyes, however, the corneal surface is not spherical. In such a case there is a meridian of least curvature and a meridian of greatest curvature at a right angle to the first. Rays from a luminous point, refracted in passing through such a surface, will not form a point image; rays falling along the meridian of greatest curvature will tend to reach a focus before those falling along the meridian of least curvature do, and may already be diverging when the latter reach a focus.

The effect is illustrated by Figure 10, which represents the refraction of rays from a distant luminous point by a lens in which the curvature is greater along the vertical than along the horizontal meridian. The rays along the vertical meridian are brought to a focus (*G*) while those along the horizontal meridian are still converging. A screen placed at this point will reflect an image having the shape of a horizontal line (*a–a'*). The rays along the horizontal meridian are brought to a focus at *B*, but those from the vertical meridian, having passed through the focus at *G*, are by this time spread out vertically. A screen placed at this point will show the image as a vertical line (*b–b'*). In between, the image of the point may be elliptical or circular, as represented in the diagram.

Astigmia may be due to a toric cornea or to the decentering of the cornea or the lens. Such conditions, producing the image forms just described, are called *regular astigmia*. Regular astigmia may be corrected by a cylindrical lens or by a combination of spherical and cylindrical lenses of such strength and so placed that they equalize the refraction in the meridians of greatest and least curvature. Since in a markedly astigmatic eye the image of a point is an ellipse or line, the image of a line, which may be considered a series of points, will be a series of small image lines. If these image lines have the same direction as the entire image, this image will be dark and clear (except for a slight blurring at the ends); but if the image lines are transverse, the entire image will appear broad, gray and indistinct. Because of this, a chart like Figure 11 may be used to detect astigmia and to locate the axes of least and greatest curvature. If the lines appear to differ in clearness, astigmia is present, and the two axes at right angles correspond to the blackest and grayest sets of lines.

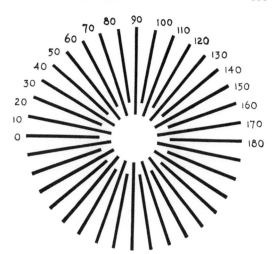

Fig. 11. Lancaster-Regan chart used to test for astigmia.

Related to astigmia is the characteristic image defect of rays about a central point when a point image might be expected. This defect is a result of the peculiar structure of the crystalline lens, since it is absent in aphakics (individuals whose lenses have been removed). The stars, which furnish accurate point sources of light, do not give rise to point images in the human eye, but rather to radiate figures, the exact form of which varies from eye to eye. The "star" form is thus not characteristic of the heavenly bodies but of our eyes.

OPTICAL EFFECTS OF OTHER FACTORS

Iris and Pupil. The iris has important optical and sensory functions, and, because its innervation is exposed to lesions in several locations, the size and reactions of the pupils are important diagnostically in a surprising variety of conditions. The iris, the colored portion of the eye, arises from the anterior surface of the ciliary body and lies between the cornea and the lens, being in contact with the latter. As seen through the cornea, the iris is slightly magnified. It is pierced by a central opening, the pupil. The stroma of the iris contains, besides the visible pigment, a rich network of blood vessels and black pigment on the interior surface. Because of the abundant pigment the iris is impervious to light and forms an excellent diaphragm. Between the layers mentioned lie the muscles of the iris, the larger and better developed sphinc-

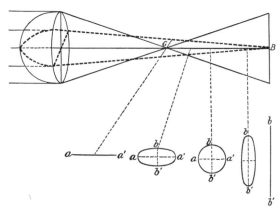

Fig. 10. Diagram of conoid of light emerging from an astigmatic lens. Lower figures represent cross sections of light at points indicated; note that image of distant point of light is never a point.

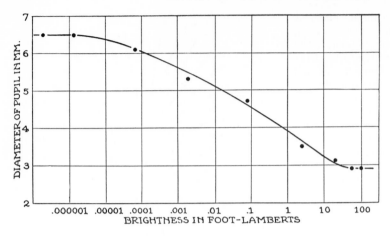

Fig. 12. Relation of pupil diameter to illumination. Data obtained by infrared photography. (From Wagman and Nathanson, *Proc. Soc. exp. Biol.* (*N. Y.*), 1942, *49:*466–470.)

ter near the pupillary margin and the smaller and less completely differentiated dilator near the posterior surface next to the pigment layer.

The iris exerts its principal effect in producing clear images. By constricting, it excludes the periphery of the lens, where spherical and chromatic aberration are greatest. The constriction also increases the depth of focus; i.e., the diffusion circles produced by cones of light from points just too near or too far to be in focus are reduced in area. Both these effects are greatest during near work. Constriction of the pupil occurs in conjunction with accommodation and convergence in near vision. The illumination must be adequate at such a time, since constriction reduces the amount of light falling on the retina, a factor which strongly affects the acuity of vision (see Chap. 20).

LIGHT REFLEX. An increase in light intensity causes the pupil to constrict, and a decrease in light intensity permits it to dilate. An increase of light in one eye leads to changes in the size of both pupils. The reaction of the pupil illuminated is called the *direct* light reflex and that of the opposite pupil the *consensual* light reflex. Over a considerable range of ordinarily encountered illumination, a person's pupils have a nearly constant average or habitual size. A slight increase in light intensity causes a slight constriction of the pupil, which then gradually dilates again as the retina adapts to the new higher level of illumination, and in a short time the pupil has resumed its habitual size.

When the new intensity is above this normal range, the change in pupillary size persists. This is illustrated by Figure 12, which shows the pupil diameter at illuminations over a range of a millionfold.[21] It will be seen that at both ends of this huge range of illumination, the pupil

reaches a constant size representing its limit of dilation or constriction. These diameters are approximately 2.9 mm. and 6.5 mm.; there is, therefore, a fivefold change in area. Obviously, such a small change in area is utterly inadequate to compensate for the enormous range of experimental intensities or even for the smaller range of intensities met during daily variations in light. (This compensation is accomplished by retinal adaptation; see Chapter 20.) A fivefold alteration of area, however, helps the eye adjust to the sudden moderate changes in illumination to which it is constantly exposed. If the amount of light decreases, dilation of the pupil, although far less effective than retinal adaptation, is more prompt and gives, within 15 or 20 seconds, an appreciable improvement in the ability to see in dim light. If the amount of light increases, the still more rapid constriction of the pupil, in 3 or 4 seconds, shields the retina from light too intense for the existing level of sensitivity.

Intraocular Pressure. The position of the refracting surfaces relative to each other and to the retina must be maintained with great exactness. That minute variations in the axial length will cause ametropia is often not realized. When refraction was carefully measured in 1000 school children 12 years and older, 47 per cent showed ametropia of 0.50 or 0.25 D.[11] The change in axial length necessary to produce these degrees of ametropia is 0.187 mm. or less. Clearly if there is to be any constancy in refraction, even of an individual eye, the constancy of the size and shape of the globe must be assured.

The fixed distance of the refractive surfaces from the retina is maintained because the inelastic scleral envelope is under a constant intraocular pressure of 20 to 25 mm. Hg. This pressure results from a balance between the production and the escape of intraocular fluid. The volume of vitreous humor is relatively constant, although it may absorb or lose water to some extent. The chief changes occur in the aqueous humor.

The mechanism maintaining intraocular pressure is complex and, although much studied, is not completely agreed upon; the following appears to be the most satisfactory view. The aqueous consists of about 1 per cent solids, about one-eighth the solid content of the serum. All the constituents of the serum are found in the aqueous. The proteins are present in little more than traces, but the electrolytes appear in amounts about equal to those in the serum, the anions being clearly more abundant. According to some studies,[15] the total osmotic activity is above that of the blood. The material of the aqueous is derived from the blood —chiefly from that in the ciliary body, although to some extent from that in the iris—partly by secretion and partly by diffusion; and the aqueous escapes by leakage into the canal of Schlemm, nonselectively, at a rate of 5 or 6 ml. a day.[13] From the canal of Schlemm and the connecting canaliculi, the aqueous reaches the venous system through the aqueous and intrascleral veins.[1, 18] It is claimed that the hypertonicity results from secretion of the electrolytes. Interference with the outflow leads to a rise in the intraocular pressure which may damage the fibers of the optic nerve where they pass out of the globe (glaucoma).

Nutrition of the Lens and Cornea.   The eye contains the largest nonvascular mass in the body. No blood vessels are found in the cornea, the aqueous, the lens or the vitreous after the early fetal period of rapid growth; obviously, blood vessels would seriously interfere with the optical function of all these structures. None of these tissues has a high metabolic rate, the rates of the aqueous and vitreous being negligible; but interference with the oxygen supply of the cornea, for example, is promptly followed by loss of transparency.

Like other organs of epithelial origin, the lens continues to grow throughout life, and, even though its metabolic rate is low, must maintain an interchange with the blood. This exchange is carried on through the intraocular fluid which, as pointed out above, contains at least a trace of all the constituents of the blood.

The transparency of the cornea, so necessary to its optical function and impaired in so many pathologic conditions, has attracted much study. Histologically the stroma of the cornea is not strikingly different from that of the opaque white sclera. The corneal stroma, however, differs in its osmotic relations, since it is covered by closely investing semipermeable membranes, epithelium on the exterior and endothelium on the interior surface. The normal transparent cornea is markedly dehydrated. When excised and placed in water, the cornea swells to three or four times its normal thickness and becomes opaque. When placed in contact with a hypertonic solution, the uninjured surface of the cornea loses water rapidly enough to remain dehydrated and transparent. Under normal conditions, the water of the cornea is derived from the vascular margin. It slowly diffuses toward the center and is lost through both surfaces to the hypertonic tears and to the aqueous.[12] This slow circulation of fluid from the periphery together with the diffusion from the aqueous supplies the slight metabolic needs of the cornea. In addition, oxygen reaches it directly from the external air.

CHIEF INSTRUMENTS FOR EYE EXAMINATION

Among the instruments designed for study of the eye, three have proved outstandingly useful. The *ophthalmoscope* makes visible the interior of the eye and is of value to the internist or surgeon as well as specialists on the eye. The *retinoscope,* or skiascope, provides an objective and accurate method of determining the refraction of the eye. The *ophthalmometer,* designed to measure corneal curvature, has been a valuable source of data on optical constants, but its usefulness in modern practice is limited. Because ophthalmoscopic inspection of the eye is an important part of the general physical examination, this instrument will be described here briefly. Descriptions of the retinoscope and the ophthalmometer may be found in ophthalmologic manuals.

Ophthalmoscope.   Light entering the eye is largely absorbed by the black pigment of the retina and the chorioid. In leaving the eye, the part that is reflected, chiefly by the blood vessels, approximately retraces the path by which it entered. Merely holding a light near the eye does not, therefore, enable us to see into it, since to see this emerging light an observer must place his head where it blocks the entering light. If, however, the light could enter the observed eye as though it proceeded from the observer's own eye, then the returning rays might be utilized to give a view of the retina and its blood vessels, or the *fundus,* as it is called.

The principle of the ophthalmoscope is well repre-

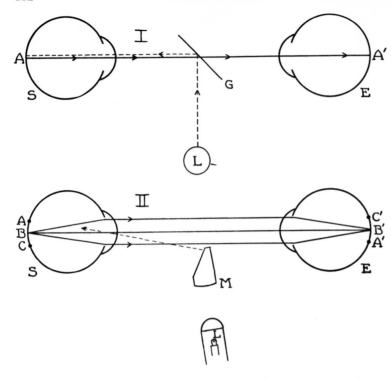

Fig. 13. Course of light in ophthalmoscope; *S,* eye of subject; *E,* eye of examiner. Entering light is indicated by dotted line; emerging light by solid line. *I,* Diagram of original model devised by Helmholtz; *L,* light; *G,* unsilvered glass; *A,* illuminated point in observed eye; *A′,* image in examiner's eye. *II,* Diagram of ophthalmoscope with May prism; *L,* electric bulb in handle; *M,* May prism. *A, B* and *C,* three illuminated points in observed eye, here assumed to be emmetropic; *A′, B′* and *C′,* images in examiner's eye, also emmetropic.

sented by the original form, shown schematically in Figure 13, *I. S* represents the observed eye and *E* the eye of the examiner. Between these two eyes is placed a piece of glass inclined at an angle. Some rays from a source of light falling upon this glass are reflected to enter eye *S;* these rays then emerge from eye *S* along the same course, pass through the glass and enter eye *E.* The glass plate used by Helmholtz was soon replaced by a mirror, either one with a small hole in the center or one with a small area of silvering removed to permit the returning light to reach the examiner's eye. The source of light was later placed in the handle of the instrument, and at present light is thrown into the observed eye not by a mirror but by a prism of special form. This prism directs the light into the lower half of the pupil while the returning rays emerge through the upper half and reach the examiner's eye over the top of the prism (Fig. 13, *II*).

Irrespective of the manner in which the light reaches the fundus, this surface becomes a luminous object sending out rays of light. If eye *S* is emmetropic, any three objects on the retina, *A,B,C,* are at the principal focal distance, and the rays sent from each are in parallel bundles after emerging from the eye. These rays enter the examiner's eye as though they came from distant objects. If his eye is also emmetropic, or is made so by suitable glasses, these bundles of rays will be focused on his retina without an act of accommodation. In fact, in looking through the ophthalmoscope, he must gaze, not at the eye before him, but through the eye and into the distance, as it were, in order to relax his accommodation. In this way he will see the illuminated portion of the retina; the images of the objects seen will be inverted on his own retina and therefore will appear erect. If the observed eye is myopic, its

retina is farther back than the principal focus of its refracting surfaces; consequently the emerging rays converge and cannot be focused on the retina of the examiner's eye. By inserting a concave lens of proper power between his eye and the mirror, the examiner can render the rays parallel and thus bring out the image. Just the reverse happens if the observed eye is hyperopic. In such an eye the retina is nearer than the principal focal distance of the refractive surfaces; consequently the light emerges in bundles of diverging rays which cannot be brought to focus on the retina of the examiner unless he exerts his own power of accommodation or interposes a convex lens between his eye and the mirror.

The battery of lenses in the ophthalmoscope is valuable in estimating the degree to which objects lie above or below the general level of the fundus. For example, the head of the optic nerve normally occurs in a slight conical pit, the *physiological depression* or *cup* (Fig. 14). When intraocular pressure is greatly elevated, as in glaucoma, this depression may be transformed into an excavation. Conversely, in papilledema caused by increased intracranial pressure, the physiologic cup may be eliminated and the nerve head swollen. The difference in the power of the lenses required to bring the center of the optic disc into sharp focus as compared with that required for its margin may be recorded in diopters. Thus, the progress of cupping may be followed and the depth estimated from the fact that 3 D. correspond to about 1 mm. The usefulness of the ophthalmoscope is twofold. First, it renders conditions within the eye as visible as they would be in a superficial structure; second, the blood vessels of the retina are a sample of those in all parts of the body and reveal certain general circulatory conditions.

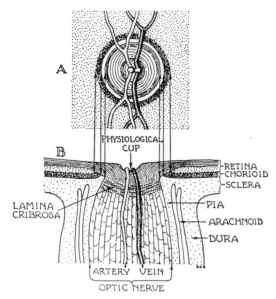

Fig. 14. Ophthalmoscopic appearance of optic disc (*A*) correlated with histologic section through it (*B*). Arrows indicate corresponding points on the two views. Pigmented ring is emphasized in *A* to show manner of its formation.

EXTERNAL MUSCLES OF THE EYE

The dioptric and neural mechanisms for accurate vision at the central portions of the retina are rendered more useful by a provision for training this area upon objects requiring close examination. The gaze can be transferred quickly from point to point or it can be fixed steadily on a single detail. Two kinds of movements are executed so that light from an object will always fall upon the fovea in each eye, making possible fusion of the images: (i) convergence-divergence movements occurring when the eyes are fixed upon near or far objects, and (ii) conjugate movements in which the eyes sweep from side to side, etc., in unison.

Eye Movements. Each eyeball is moved by six extrinsic, striated muscles which are innervated by three cranial nerves. By means of these muscles the eyeballs execute various movements best considered as *rotations* of the eyeball around various axes. These axes are: (i) the horizontal, which corresponds with the visual axis; (ii) the transverse; (iii) the vertical; and (iv) the oblique axes, which include all axes of rotation making oblique angles with the horizontal axis. Rotations around the oblique axes move the eyeballs obliquely upward or downward. The share of the individual eye muscles in producing rotation of the eyeball around the various axes is shown in Figure 15, which indicates the paths traversed by the visual axis when each muscle separately moves the eyeball.

The eyes can be moved sufficiently to fix on objects within a circular area having a diameter equal to 100° of visual angle. Rotations to the left and right are approximately equal in extent, but vertical upward movements are more limited (40°) than vertical downward movements (60°). The range of eye movements is tested with a *tangent screen* and is an important diagnostic sign in neurology.

In *conjugate deviations* the eyes move in a way to keep the visual axes of the two eyes parallel or else to converge them upon a common point, the medial rectus of one eye acting with the lateral rectus of the other. In movements of convergence, the medial recti of the two eyes are associated. Normally, it is impossible to diverge the visual axes beyond the parallel. A movement of this kind would produce useless double vision (diplopia).

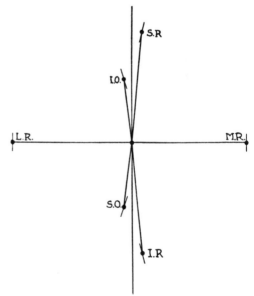

Fig. 15. Hering's diagram showing actions of individual eye muscles. Lines radiating from primary fixation point show path which visual axis would describe on screen placed in front of eyes when they are rotated by each muscle acting singly. Short line through terminus of each line represents tilt of eyes from vertical imparted by action of each eye muscle in executing each movement. Abbreviations are: *I.O.* and *S.O.,* inferior and superior oblique; *I.R.* and *S.R.,* inferior and superior recti; *L.R.* and *M.R.,* lateral and medial recti. (From Martin and Weymouth, *Elements of physiology.* Philadelphia, Lea & Febiger, 1928.)

The smooth intrinsic and striate extrinsic muscles of the eyeball and lids are controlled by a group of nuclei centered about the midbrain. These are closely interconnected to integrate the activities of the various muscles. Provision is made for the simultaneous activation of one muscle and inhibition of the motoneurons supplying its antagonist (reciprocal innervation). Provision is also made for associating the activities of two or more muscles. Even simple upward or downward movement requires unison contraction by two muscles. Reading requires simultaneous conjugate movements and a slight convergence. Transference of the gaze from a far to a near point involves the "fixation triad": (i) constriction of the pupil, (ii) accommodation of the lens, (iii) convergence. The strong linkage of these explains one form of "muscle strabismus" (see below).

Coordination of Eye Muscles—Strabismus. Useful binocular vision requires a beautifully balanced or coordinated action of the opposing muscles to move the eyeballs in absolute unison. The visual axes must unite upon the object or point looked at. In looking about or in reading, the individual readjusts his eyes continually to bring point after point at the junction of the visual axes. When he looks at a distant object, the visual axes should be parallel. If this balance does not exist, a condition designated as *heterophoria* is present.

In heterophoria a constant contraction of one or more muscles is required, even in far vision, to prevent diplopia. When the eye at rest tends to drift toward the temporal side because of the unbalanced pull of the lateral rectus, the condition is known as *exophoria*. If there is a tendency to drift to the nasal side, the condition is described as *esophoria*. A tendency to drift upward is *hyperphoria* and downward is *hypophoria*. A lack of resting balance of this kind may also make itself felt in near work, such as reading and sewing, since it will require an increasing activity of the muscle overbalanced by its antagonist. The resulting muscular strain causes much distress. When muscular effort no longer brings the visual axes to bear upon the same point, a condition of squint or *strabismus (exotropia, esotropia, hypotropia,* or *hypertropia*) exists. Since both eyes cannot fix, double vision would result were it not for suppression of the image; this, however, leads to a reduction of visual ability (see below) in the squinting eye.

Severe defects of long standing and those caused by actual muscle weakness may be remedied by surgical operations upon the muscles or by the use of proper prisms with bases adjusted to direct light upon the fovea. Recognition of the physiologic causes operative in a "functional" type of strabismus permits a more fundamental treatment. *Convergent concomitant strabismus* in which one eye turns inward is usually due to uncorrected hyperopia in early childhood. For a hyperope to focus on near objects, excessive accommodation is necessary. Because accommodation and convergence are closely linked in the midbrain region, this convergence is appropriate to the excessive accommodation and in excess of that required to converge on the object. Early correction of the hyperopia, forced use of the squinting eye, and orthoptic training in binocular vision often render operative treatment unnecessary.

REFERENCES

1. ASCHER, K. W. *Amer. J. Ophthal.*, 1942, (3) *25*:31–38.
2. BEER, T. *Pflüg. Arch. ges. Physiol.*, 1894, *58*:523–650.
3. BROWN, E. V. L. *Arch. Ophthal.* (*N. Y.*), 1942, n.s. *28*:845–850.
4. DONDERS, F. C. *On the anomalies of accommodation and refraction of the eye. With a preliminary essay on physiological dioptrics,* tr. by W. D. MOORE. London, New Sydenham Society, 1864.
5. DUANE, A. *Ophthalmoscope,* 1912, *10*:486–502.
6. DUANE, A. *Amer. J. Ophthal.,* 1922, (3) *5*:865–877.
7. DUKE-ELDER, W. S. *Text-book of ophthalmology,* vol. 1. St. Louis, C. V. Mosby Co., 1939.
8. FINCHAM, E. P. *Brit. J. Ophthal.,* 1937, Suppl. *8*:5–80.
9. von HELMHOLTZ, H. *Treatise on physiological optics,* J. P. C. SOUTHALL, ed. Rochester, N. Y., Optical Society of America, 1924–25.
10. HIRSCH, M. J. and WEYMOUTH, F. W. *Amer. J. Optom.,* 1947, *24*:601–608, and *Arch. Amer. Acad. Optom.,* 1947, Monogr. 39.
11. KEMPF, G. A., JARMAN, B. L. and COLLINS, S. D. *Publ. Hlth. Rep.* (*Wash.*), 1928, *43*:1713–1739.
12. KINSEY, V. E. and COGAN, D. G. *Arch. Ophthal.* (*N. Y.*), 1942, n.s. *28*:449–463.
13. KINSEY, V. E. and GRANT, W. M. *Brit. J. Ophthal.,* 1944, *28*:355–361.
14. KRONFELD, P. C. and DEVNEY, C. *v. Graefes Arch. Ophthal.,* 1931, *126*:487–501.
15. ROEPKE, R. R. and HETHERINGTON, W. A. *Amer. J. Physiol.,* 1940, *130*:340–345.
16. SCHLODTMANN, W. *v. Graefes Arch. Ophthal.,* 1902, *54*:256–267.
17. STENSTRÖM, S. *Acta ophthal.* (*Kbh.*), 1946, Suppl. *26.*
18. THOMASSEN, T. L. and BAKKEN, K. *Acta ophthal.* (*Kbh.*), 1951, *29*:257–268.
19. TRON, E. *v. Graefes Arch. Ophthal.,* 1934, *132*:182–223.
20. TRON, E. J. In *Modern trends in ophthalmology,* F. RIDLEY and A. SORSBY, eds. New York, Paul B. Hoeber, Inc., 1940.
21. WAGMAN, I. H. and NATHANSON, L. M. *Proc. Soc. exp. Biol.* (*N. Y.*), 1942, *49*:466–470.
22. WALLS, G. L. *The vertebrate eye and its adaptive radiation.* Bloomfield Hills, Mich., Cranbrook Institute of Science, 1942.

CHAPTER 20

Vision

By THEODORE C. RUCH

In the previous chapter the eye was portrayed as an optical instrument focusing light rays from objects at various distances and regulating the amount of light falling upon the retina. However, the formation of a physical image on the retina is of no value unless that image is translated into a pattern of nerve impulses from which the cerebral cortex can reconstruct a reasonably accurate perception of the external world. In this perception, color, fineness of detail and sharpness of contour all play a part.

The eye contains not one but two end-organs, each specialized for quite different visual functions although closely knit anatomically. One system of receptors, the cones, is specialized to function in daylight when the surroundings are brightly illuminated. Objects are then seen clearly with much detail and many grades of color. The pupil constricts, sharpening the image. Visual acuity is at its best. The second system of receptors, the rods, is specialized for twilight and night vision. Then, low threshold is desirable. By a chemical process in the retina, the eye becomes many times more sensitive to light (dark adaptation) and dilation of the pupil admits more light to the eye. The human retina is extraordinarily able to use the slightest light energy afforded by the environment, nearly attaining the theoretical lower limit of sensitivity—sensitivity to 1 quantum of light. But specialization in one direction has meant loss of capacity in another. The apparatus for night vision does not record the color of objects or fine details and sharp boundaries.

415

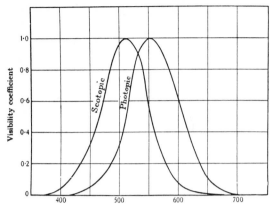

Fig. 1. Visibility or luminosity of a bright spectrum as seen by cones (photopic) and of a dim spectrum as seen by rods (scotopic). Ordinates are the reciprocal of the energy which is just visible for each wavelength of light (scotopic) or which matches a moderately bright standard light (photopic). Curves were adjusted to a common scale by making maximum of each curve equal to one. On an absolute scale of intensities, rod curve would fall far below that for cones, which are much less sensitive than rods. (From Rawdon-Smith, *Theories of sensation*, Cambridge, Cambridge University Press, 1938, after Hecht and Williams, *J. gen. Physiol.*, 1922, *5*:1–34.)

Yet perception of objects as dark, indistinct masses makes the difference between blindness and visual orientation to the environment at night.

The retina itself is specialized into the fovea centralis for color and detail vision, and the periphery for light and dark vision. The fovea contains only cones, and in the periphery rods predominate. The neural pathways give further evidence of a double function. The "duplicity" theory is, then, the organizing principle to be used in describing vision. Originally, this theory referred only to the existence of two types of receptor cells, but it is now applied to the central mechanism of vision as well.

Visual Stimulus. The eye is sensitive to a narrow band of wavelengths, the visible spectrum (723 mμ to 397 mμ) lying between the long, infrared heat waves and the short, ultraviolet "chemical" waves. The wavelengths within this range are not equally effective in stimulating the retina. The wavelength influences the intensity of light necessary to elicit a sensation and also determines the hue or chroma. The curve which expresses that relation is the *visibility curve* (Fig. 1). Before any curve or other quantitative data can be under-

stood, the nature of the visual stimulus and the units in which it is measured must be defined.

In the audibility curve, the base line is frequency; in the visibility curve, it is wavelength, i.e., the inverse of frequency, since the speed of light is divided by frequency to obtain the wavelength. A wavelength is stated in Ångstrom units (1 Å = 1/10,000,000 mm.) or, more usually, in millimicrons (1 mμ = 1/1,000,000 mm.). The unit for the ordinate must express the intensity of the light. As in audition, the physical unit most useful is one with a psychologic reference. The basic unit is the *international candle,* which is the total luminous energy emitted in all directions by a standardized candle with a flame 1 inch high. To state the amount of light *falling upon* an object, the illumination (a more usual requirement), the distance between the object and the candle must be defined because the total energy becomes less per unit area as it spreads over a larger sphere. The *foot-candle* is the amount of light falling on a square foot of area placed 1 foot from the standard candle. But not all of the light is reflected by the surface and only reflected light can be seen. The *brightness* of an object, which is the amount of light reflected from it, is measured in *millilamberts.* This is the amount of light reflected by an ideal surface 1 foot square illuminated by 0.93 foot-candle. Since the size of the pupil of the eye affects the amount of light entering the eye, another unit, the *photon,* has been devised which takes this factor into account. Photons are the number of millilamberts × sq. mm. of pupil area. In experiments this is easily calculated because an artificial pupil—a screen with an aperture smaller than the pupil—is usually employed.

The visibility curve is affected by the distribution of energy among the different wavelengths of the particular light source employed—daylight, carbon lamp, etc.—but can be calculated for an equal energy spectrum. Also, light is filtered by the cornea, lens and vitreous body. When all physical factors are properly accounted for, the visibility curve becomes an index of the manner in which the retina utilizes light of different wavelengths. The visibility curve expresses one fundamental parameter of visual sensation, luminosity, whether aroused by colored or uncolored light.

Intensity Functions. The intensity of the physical stimulus must be distinguished from the intensity of the resulting visual experience. Although these two intensities are related causally, intervening photochemical and neural processes may considerably alter the correlation between the two. *Luminosity, brilliance* and *apparent brightness* always refer to the response; *brightness* is restricted to the intensity of the physical stimulus. Three main intensity functions are distinguished: the *absolute threshold,* the least that can be seen; the *difference threshold,* the least discriminable difference between two intensities; and the *critical flicker fusion frequency.*

The principal factors affecting the absolute threshold will be discussed in detail later, but may be enumerated as follows: (i) intensity of light, (ii) wavelength of light, (iii) size of illuminated area, (iv) duration of exposure, (v) state of the retina (dark adaptation, etc.), and (vi) the region of retina stimulated. Much the same factors influence the difference threshold, which is basically similar to the absolute threshold. The Weber fraction is not constant for brightness discrimination. The curve of $\Delta I/I$ rises sharply for weak and strong stimuli and is constant for the middle range of intensities only if small changes are ignored (by coarse plotting). The absolute threshold under the most favorable conditions appears to approach the theoretical minimum, the receptors being sensitive to 1 quantum of light according to the calculations of Hecht.[17]

As few as 54 quanta of light incident upon the cornea are perceptible. An estimated half of these are reflected or absorbed by the ocular media. Of the 27 quanta reaching the retina, perhaps only 5 are absorbed by the visual purple of the rods. These rods, spread over a retinal area containing an estimated 500 rods, are so few that at threshold a given rod must rarely receive more than 1 quantum of energy. According to Einstein's photochemical equivalence law, 1 quantum of energy will break down one molecule of visual purple. Thus, the evolution of the eye has progressed to the theoretical maximum of sensitivity. The threshold for a foveal cone is estimated to be no more than 5 to 7 quanta.

The *critical fusion frequency (c.f.f.) for flicker,* once determined by rotating a sectored disc in front of a light source at a speed controlled by the observer, is now determined by electronically controlled flashes. With low frequencies intermittent flashes of light are seen, but at a certain rate for each intensity the light seems steady—the critical fusion frequency. The higher the intensity of the light, the higher the c.f.f. For the middle range of intensities, c.f.f. = log I + k (Ferry-Porter law). When the light falls on the periphery of the retina, the duality of the visual mechanism produces a sharp inflection in the curve relating c.f.f. to log I (Fig. 2). For the fovea, the curve shows no inflection. The first

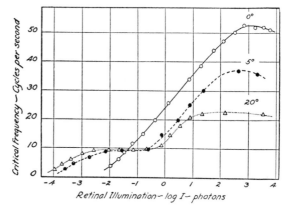

Fig. 2. Curves showing relation between critical fusion frequency (c.f.f.) and logarithm of intensity for three retinal locations: fovea, and 5° and 20° from fovea. (From Hecht and Verrijp, *J. gen. Physiol.,* 1933–34, *17:*251–268.)

part of the duplex curve is interpreted as a response of the rods and the second as a response of the cones.

PHOTOCHEMICAL BASIS OF VISION[10a]

Visual Purple—Rhodopsin. The change taking place in the rods and cones which translates physical energy, light, into nerve impulses involves a photochemical step, i.e., light waves set up chemical changes in rods or cones which, in turn, give rise to nerve impulses. The retinal rods contain a red pigment which is bleached by light (Boll, 1877), *visual purple* or *rhodopsin.* The cones probably contain another pigmented substance.

Solutions of visual purple are also bleached when exposed to light. Visual purple is, therefore, an unstable substance readily altered by light energy. That this photochemical property of rhodopsin accounts for the visibility curve was first suggested by Kühne (1878), who studied the effectiveness of different wavelengths in bleaching rhodopsin. According to Draper's law, the photochemical effect of a given wavelength is proportional to its absorption. The absorption spectrum of visual purple from the frog's retina has been accurately determined (Fig. 3). Moreover, a fair degree of success has been attained in superposing the absorption spectrum and the visibility curve of the human eye. The success of one such attempt is shown in Figure 4. The visibility curve for rod function appears, therefore, to be determined by the photochemical properties of rhodopsin. If so, rhodopsin must be the photochemical intermediary standing between the light stimulus and the optic nerve impulse.

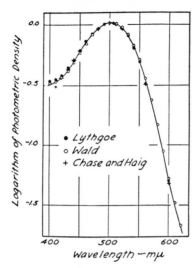

Fig. 3. Absorption spectrum of the visual purple from frog. Data obtained by three independent observers were made equal at 500 mμ. Ordinates show degree to which each wavelength is absorbed, with 0.0 representing maximal absorption. (From Hecht, *Amer. Scientist,* 1944, *32*:159–177.)

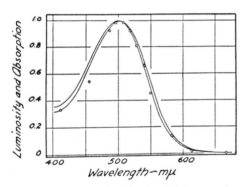

Fig. 4. Relation of subjective brightness of spectrum (luminosity, circles) to absorption curve of visual purple (frog). Visibility curve is corrected for transmissional losses, quantum effectiveness, etc., and therefore is not identical with that shown in Figure 1. Two solid lines give absorption spectrum calculated by assuming that 20 and 5 per cent of light are absorbed by visual purple. (From Hecht *et al., J. gen. Physiol.,* 1942, *25*:819–840.)

The same in vitro demonstration has not yet been made for cone pigment, although the intermediation of a rhodopsin-like photosensitive substance *iodopsin* (visual violet), is strongly suspected.[33] Others are inferred by stimulating curves and will be discussed under Color Vision.

Dark Adaptation. The retina possesses to a remarkable degree the ability to become sensi-

tive to dim light* and thus to make maximum use of weak light reflected from objects. This is especially true of the periphery of the retina. When one passes from daylight into a dark room, vision is at first very imperfect, but it rapidly improves "as the eye becomes accustomed to the dark." This change is known as *dark adaptation.* Loss of the sensitivity attained through dark adaptation occurs upon re-exposure of the eyes to light and is called *light adaptation.*

A curve of dark adaptation is plotted by repeatedly determining the weakest flash of light which is visible. The rate of dark adaptation for rods is initially rapid, although not so rapid as the rate of light adaptation. Dark adaptation is about 60 per cent accomplished in the first five minutes and virtually completed in 20 minutes, after which the curve is asymptotic. A curve with this simple form is obtained by starting from levels of illumination too low to stimulate the cones and by observing with the peripheral portions of the retina where there are few cones. It is therefore the rod adaptation curve.

When both cones and rods are stimulated, the curve is made up of two curves (Fig. 5). First there is an initial rapid fall in threshold which tends to strike a plateau. After about seven minutes of darkness, a further drop occurs which is less rapid but is quantitatively much greater. Analysis shows that the curve

* The change from full sunlight to the least light perceptible at night is a change of approximately 10 billion to 1.

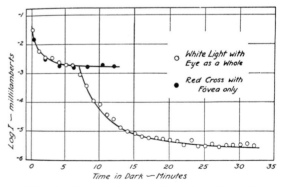

Fig. 5. Curve of dark adaptation obtained by plotting visual threshold against time spent in darkness. Initial limb of curve for whole eye (*circles*) is due to cones; lower portion is due to rods. To obtain complete curve for cones alone (*black dots*), stimulation of the more sensitive rods was avoided by employing red light and foveal fixation. (From Hecht, *A handbook of general experimental psychology,* C. Murchison, ed., Worcester, Clark University Press, 1934.)

before its breaking point is due to dark adaptation of the cones. Dark adaptation is therefore not a phenomenon peculiar to the rods. Cone adaptation is much more rapid than rod adaptation but produces less reduction of threshold.

Factors Influencing Dark Adaptation.

The extent and rapidity of dark adaptation are critical in many military and civilian activities including the viewing of the fluoroscopic screen and x-ray films. Several factors are involved.

AVOIDANCE OF LIGHT. The most effective means of securing dark adaptation is to prevent unnecessary exposure to light. Obvious as this is, it has often been overlooked.

Miles'[24] introduction of red goggles as an aid to the acquisition of dark adaptation illustrates effective application of physiology to a practical situation. A tedious 20 to 30 minute wait in a completely dark room evidently is avoided by wearing the goggles, which allow cone vision to continue while the rods are adapting to dark. As the visibility curve shows, wavelengths longer than 640 mμ stimulate the rods only very weakly. Thus, red goggles, by passing only longer wavelengths, prevent light adaptation of the rods.

Other factors influencing dark adaptation are:

PREADAPTATION ILLUMINATION. The more intense the illumination and the longer the time during which the eye is light-adapted, the longer the period necessary to attain complete dark adaptation.[19, 35] This phenomenon appears explicable on the basis of a slow and a fast resynthesis of rhodopsin (see p. 420).

NYCTALOPIA.* This is a rare organic and often hereditary abnormality in which rod function is seriously disturbed or, in extreme cases, absent. Dark adaptation is correspondingly reduced in extent and greatly slowed. The result is *night blindness*. Color vision is normal. There is no evidence that vitamin A therapy will affect the congenital form of nyctalopia.

VITAMIN A DEFICIENCY. Severe vitamin A deficiency experimentally induced interferes with the mechanism of dark adaptation, and irreversible changes can be produced. Dark adaptation of cones as well as of rods is affected. The measurement of dark adaptation has not proved useful in detecting vitamin A deficiencies in the degree present in the population.

ANOXIA AND METABOLIC FACTORS. McFarland and Evans[23] have shown that the visual threshold of the completely dark-adapted eye is elevated 2.5 times by anoxic anoxia resulting from exposure at 15,000 feet. Glucose neutralized the effects of anoxia and insulin intensified them. Hyperventilation at sea level relieved visual threshold[36] and CO_2 added to air doubled it. Such changes, although small in relation to the whole range of dark adaptation, are significant in night flying. Because these changes occur more rapidly than

* "Hemeralopia," the term for inability to see in bright light, is sometimes used instead of "nyctalopia."

photochemical changes, it is believed that the anoxic effects are exerted on the synaptic apparatus of the retina.

Curve of Light Adaptation.

After a period of darkness, light of moderate intensity at first seems intense, dazzling and even painful, but after a few minutes the eye becomes less sensitive. In other words, the sensitivity gained by dark adaptation is lost when the eye is stimulated by light. Light adaptation is simply the absence of dark adaptation, and the expression is somewhat misleading. It is an active process, since the first intense stimulation results from bleaching of the rhodopsin accumulated during dark adaptation, resulting in intense visual stimulus. It takes much less time to lose dark adaptation than to acquire it. Light adaptation is largely completed in just a few minutes.

Mechanism of Rod Stimulation and Dark Adaptation.[17, 33]

Rhodopsin is the intermediary in the excitation of rods by light and changes in its concentration are believed to be the basis of dark adaptation. The simplest possible photochemical mechanism employing rhodopsin is as follows:

$$\text{Light} \longrightarrow \text{rhodopsin} \longrightarrow \text{excitatory decomposition product} \longrightarrow \text{nerve impulse}$$

During dark adaptation rhodopsin is regenerated. Until recently it seemed possible to account for the principal features of excitation and dark adaptation on the basis of a simple equation from photochemistry.[33] In brief, light was conceived of as breaking down photosensitive material (rhodopsin) at a rate dependent on the light intensity and the amount of photochemical substance present. It now seems that bleaching a small amount of rhodopsin causes the threshold to rise enormously; for the human eye, the bleaching of 0.006 per cent of the visual purple decreases the visual sensitivity 8.5 times, and a 0.6 per cent bleaching lowers the sensitivity an estimated 3300 times.[34] Nevertheless, bleaching and regeneration of rhodopsin follow the same time courses as light adaptation and dark adaptation (Fig. 6), and this is true of the faster adaptation of the cones.[28, 30] However, the concentration of rhodopsin is proportional to the *logarithm* of the sensitivity. Whether a neural factor must be introduced into the equation to gain quantitative agreement is still to be learned.

Photochemical Cycle of Retina.

Using a

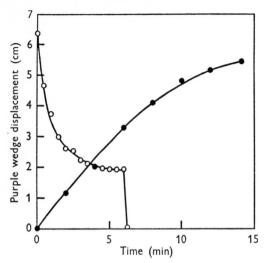

Fig. 6. Time course of bleaching (o) and subsequent regeneration (●) of rhodopsin in the human eye. Sudden drop at 6 minutes was caused by flash of very bright light. (From Campbell and Rushton, *J. Physiol.,* 1955, *130:*131–147.)

spectrographic technique to follow the changes in the photochemical substances, Wald[32, 33] established the broad outlines of the photochemistry of the visual cycle.* Three main reactions were observed (Fig. 7). The first is a rapid reaction:

$$\text{Rhodopsin} \underset{\text{dark}}{\overset{\text{light}}{\rightleftharpoons}} \text{Retinene} + \text{Protein.}$$

Visual purple, which has a high molecular weight (270,000), is a conjugated protein, i.e., a protein molecule united to a pigment group (*retinene*), and is related to the carotene compounds. Rhodopsin is stable unless exposed to light, when it bleaches owing to a dissociation into protein and retinene. In the dark it is reconstituted (Fig. 6). Because the rate and extent of decomposition depend on the intensity of light and the duration of exposure, this phase is believed to be the photochemical basis of light and dark adaptation. Retinene is reduced to vitamin A by the conjoint action of an enzyme (alcohol dehydrogenase) and the coenzyme DPN. Rushton and his colleagues[31] have been able to measure rhodopsin in the human retina. The changes in the density of rhodopsin in passing through the fovea and the optic nerve head into the peripheral retina conform to the known density of rods. Proceeding much more slowly

* Several intervening substances have been partially defined biochemically.

is a thermolabile reaction in which rhodopsin is re-formed with vitamin A as an intermediate step. Vitamin A from blood is also a source for restoring the retinal level of vitamin A and rhodopsin. These reactions therefore form the photochemical cycle, which may be divided into a photodynamic and a thermolabile phase. In Figure 7 the length of line connecting the substances indicates roughly the speed of the reaction.

The effect of preadaptation illumination on the rate of dark adaptation is explained by a "slow" and a "fast" synthesis of rhodopsin. If the completely dark-adapted retina, charged with rhodopsin, is light-adapted by a *short exposure to intense light,* much retinene and little vitamin A are produced. Therefore, subsequent dark adaptation is rapid because rhodopsin is re-formed by the "fast route" from retinene. Exposure to weaker adapting lights for a seven-minute period is followed by a slowed adaptation curve, because more retinene has gone to vitamin A and must be resynthesized by the slower route.

In addition to the visual functions which seem interpretable on the basis of photodynamic action there are certain processes which depend on the neural mechanisms of the retina.

Electrical Activity of Retina. Depending on the size and placement of the recording electrodes, four types of changes in potential are obtained from the retina: (i) a steady corneoretinal potential, (ii) phasic potentials produced by light (electroretinogram), (iii) unit responses from the level of the bipolar cells, and (iv) action potentials of ganglion cells and optic nerve

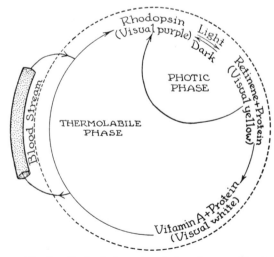

Fig. 7. Retinal photochemical cycle according to Wald. Length of arrows suggests speed of reaction.

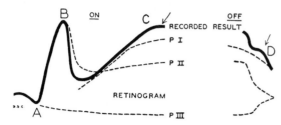

Fig. 8. Compound electric potential (heavy line) recorded from retina (electroretinogram, ERG) in response to stimulation by light. Upward deflections indicate electropositivity. *A, B, C, D,* are potential waves of ERG, and broken curves, *P I, P II, P III,* are one analysis (Granit) of compound potential into its components. (From Bartley, *Psychol. Rev.,* 1939, *46:*337–358.)

fibers. The steady potential recorded between the front and back of the eyeball is produced by the retina, probably across Bruch's membrane of the chorioid. In penetration experiments with ultramicroelectrodes, Brown and Wiesel[7] recorded a 30 to 60 mV. potential across the membrane with the chorioidal side negative. When recorded from the tissues about the eyes, the steady potential can be used to measure eye movements.

ELECTRORETINOGRAM (ERG). This is a complex of potential changes, shown in Figure 8 as recorded and as analyzed into components by Granit. The significance of the ERG is that it can be recorded for clinical purposes by electrodes applied to the cornea; otherwise it is a phenomenon to be explained rather than being explanatory. However, its components can now be interpreted more fully in light of recent experiments by Brown and Wiesel[7, 8] involving intraretinal or "depth" recording with ultramicroelectrodes.

The A wave, a small, sharp, downward cornea-negative wave, represents a photopic response. It is more marked in cone-rich retinae and in response to red light, which has little effect on rods; penetration experiments show it to be largest near Bruch's membrane. It has been demonstrated directly that the A wave probably comes from the outer segments of the receptors and is identical to Granit's P_{III} (see below). The C wave is also maximal near Bruch's membrane and probably originates in the cells of the pigment layer. It is abolished by iodate, which severely damages the pigment layer, while the A and B waves and the neural layers of the retina escape unimpaired.

The B wave waxes in the dark and wanes in

the light; it is strongest at intermediate retinal depths, centering on the outer plexiform layer. It is derived from activity in the inner nuclear or ganglionic layer and disappears when the retinal circulation is blocked. Penetration experiments show that Granit's P_{II} is made up of a B wave and a separate D.C. component; the latter starts abruptly, maintains a steady plateau during the stimulus period, and afterwards declines, at first abruptly and then more slowly.

THE RECEPTOR POTENTIALS. Brown and Watanabe[6] confirmed the deductions about the origin of the A wave. They recorded intraretinally from the pure cone fovea of the monkey, which lacks much of the nuclear layer and all of the ganglionic layer. In addition, they obtained records before and after pressing on the optic nerve head, which presumably leaves the retinal structure with a blood supply only from the choriocapillaries. With the B wave progressively eliminated by these procedures, as seen in Figure 9, the A wave emerges until it is seen as a sharply developing potential which holds steady (for seconds) and then rises abruptly

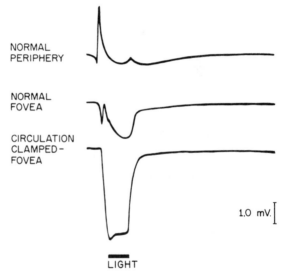

Fig. 9. The A wave of ERG isolated by depth recordings in the region of the receptor cells of the monkey. Note in top record, normal periphery, the small, positive downward potential and the large upward B deflection; in lower record of the fovea, clamping the retinal circulation reduces activity in ganglion and bipolar cells, eliminating the B wave, and allowing the A wave to emerge, presumably in nearly pure form. Stimulus duration applies to bottom record only. The records are arranged so that waves are in the same direction as in Figure 8. (After Brown and Watanabe, *Nature (Lond.),* 1962, *193:*958–960.)

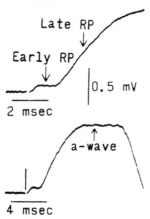

Fig. 10. Time course of the early and late RP (receptor potential), at slow sweep speed (below) and at more rapid sweep speed (above). The initial negative wave is lost in the shock artifact. Stimulus is shown by a break in the base line, marked by a vertical line in lower record. (From Brown and Murakami, *Nature* (*Lond.*), 1964, *201*:626–628.)

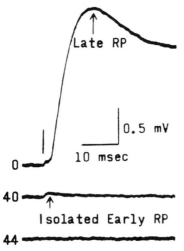

Fig. 11. Selective effect of anoxia on the late RP, isolating the early RP. Retinal circulation is clamped and respiratory movements are paralyzed. Artificial respiration was turned off before the upper record was taken (0 time). The second record was made 40 minutes later and the early RP is undiminished. At 44 minutes it disappears, proving that the potential is not due to light acting on the electrode. Vertical line gives time of stimulation. (From Brown and Murakami, *Nature* (*Lond.*), 1964, *201*:626–628.)

when the stimulation ceases. The A wave seen in the ERG is therefore the leading edge of this receptor potential; the remainder is obliterated by the rapidly rising B wave (see below). The A potential, with a latency of 1.7 milliseconds, is interpreted not as a generator potential but as

a depolarization of the presynaptic terminals. With finer analysis of the A wave under precise conditions, by intraretinal recording Brown and Murakami[5] discovered a small negative-positive potential, termed *early RP* (latency 50 μsec.), as opposed to the balance of the A wave termed *late RP* (Fig. 10). The early RP is seen in pure form after a combined ischemic and respiratory anoxia (Fig. 11). It strongly resembles the microphonic potential of the cochlea and, like it, is linearly proportional to energy intensity. It has been identified in the ERG.[9a] A preliminary interpretation is that the early potential is triggered by the nearly instantaneous isomerization of rhodopsin. Wald holds this to be the chemical reaction that initiates visual excitation.

NEURAL BASIS OF RETINAL FUNCTION

Functional Anatomy of Retina.[25] The neural layers of the retina are three strata of densely packed cell bodies and two intervening synaptic layers consisting of intertwining dendritic and axonic brushes (Fig. 12). The retinal layer nearest the chorioid is made up of pigmented cells which probably produce and store photochemicals such as visual purple. The layer next to the pigment cells contains two kinds of neurons, one bearing a cone-shaped process and the other a rod-shaped process. The rods and cones, packed closely together, are the structures actually sensitive to light. The axons of the rod-bearing and cone-bearing neurons end upon the dendrites of the middle layer of bipolar cells, which in turn give axons to the dendrites of ganglion cells. The axons of the ganglion cells sweep to a point just slightly to the nasal side of the center of the retina. There they pierce the chorioid and sclera in the company of the blood vessels and make up the optic nerve. It is an instance of nature's lack of wisdom that light must pass through blood vessels, nerve fibers, and cell bodies to reach the rods and cones. The rod and cone neurons are the receptor cells. The bipolar and ganglion cells are, respectively, second and third order neurons; this makes them part of the brain. Like other parts of the brain, they form complex synaptic relations.

To study human and monkey retinas, Polyak employed the Golgi technique, which fully impregnates only occasional neurons so that the cell body, dendrites and axon of single neurons can be distinguished. The distinctness of the rod and cone systems is not maintained at the level of the bipolar cells. Many bipolar cells synapse with both rod and cone neurons, and this is not an occasional variation. The rod and cone systems are thus incompletely separated in their pathways to the brain. This finding obviously embarrasses the theory of specific receptors and private pathways for each phenomenon, but its exact significance is yet to be realized. Polyak recognized two types of bipolar cells. The most common type is variously termed the *diffuse, polysynaptic* or *rod and cone* bipolar cell because of its widely spread dendritic branches through which it receives impulses from a group, sometimes large, of rod and cone neurons. The bipolar cell termed the *individual, monosynaptic, cone* or *midget* bipolar cell connects only with cones, sometimes only one (fovea). The third order neurons also fall into two categories: (i) *diffuse* ganglion cells which connect with a great number of bipolar cells, and (ii) *monosynaptic* or *individual* ganglion cells which establish synaptic connections, by way of midget bipolar cells, with only one or two cones.

NEURAL BASIS OF AREAL INTERACTION. Thus, there are two systems of neurons in the retina. One, identified exclusively with cones, is highly canalized and spatially organized so that each cone in it has a private path in the optic nerve. The other system, one of mixed rods and cones, is marked by the convergence of many receptors

on bipolar cells and of many bipolar cells upon ganglion cells. Convergence is, as pointed out in connection with spinal reflexes, the neural substrate for an interaction of streams of impulses that results in facilitation and inhibition phenomena. An arrangement of this sort, therefore, affords a basis for the receptors of a retinal region to interact at the bipolar and ganglion cell. Interaction is further provided for by a system of intraretinal association neurons. These include (i) *horizontal* cells, (ii) *centrifugal* bipolar cells, and (iii) possibly some of the *amacrine* cells. The horizontal cells are named for their axons, which run horizontally for long distances in the outer plexiform layer. They appear to connect various points of the layer of rod and cone neurons.

REGIONAL VARIATIONS OF RETINA.[25] By confining the stimulus to the fovea, cone function can be studied in isolation; by confining the stimulus to the extreme periphery, rod function almost free of cone activity can be studied. However, there are important differences between foveal and peripheral vision besides the ratio of cones to rods, e.g., the synaptic relationships.

The retina extends through roughly 180°. In the center of this hemisphere (in line with the visual axis) is a yellow pigmented area, the *macula lutea*, within

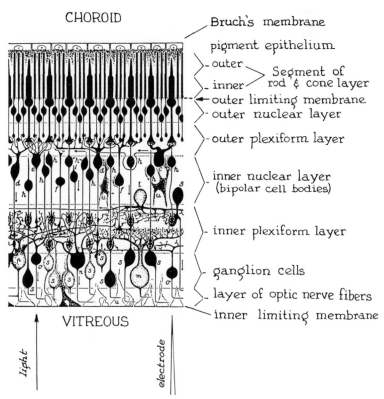

CHOROID

Bruch's membrane
pigment epithelium
outer
inner
Segment of rod & cone layer
outer limiting membrane
outer nuclear layer
outer plexiform layer
inner nuclear layer (bipolar cell bodies)
inner plexiform layer
ganglion cells
layer of optic nerve fibers
inner limiting membrane

VITREOUS

light

electrode

Fig. 12. Primate retina based on Golgi impregnation, showing principal cell types and their synaptic relations. Various cell types are: *c,* horizontal cells; *d, e, f,* diffuse or polysynaptic bipolar cells; *h,* individual cone (midget) bipolar cell; *i, l,* "amacrine cells"; *m, n, o, p, r, s,* ganglion cells, of which *s* is the individual or monosynaptic ganglion cell. (From Polyak, *The retina,* Chicago, University of Chicago Press, 1941.)

which is a round pitlike depression 1500 μ in diameter, the *fovea centralis,* which in turn encompasses a slighter depression containing the finest cones, the *foveola.* In man an area of 1200 μ, or 2° of arc, is rod-free, the rods appearing just within the margin of the fovea. It contains approximately 34,000 cones varying from 1 μ (12 to 15') to 3.3 μ (40') in diameter.

The fovea is specialized for detail vision in four ways: (i) the cones are more slender and densely packed, especially in the foveola; (ii) it is rod-free; (iii) blood vessels and nerve detour around it, and the cellular layers are deflected to the side, reducing the scattering of light; and (iv) the cones have a "private line" to the optic nerve.

In passing peripherally, two principal changes occur. The cone-to-rod ratio rapidly decreases in the first 5° of arc. A few cones (6 to 8 per 100 μ linear distance) occur even in the extreme periphery. Another difference is an increased convergence of receptor elements on single ganglion cells. The ideal ratio of one cone to one ganglion cell is probably approached in the fovea centralis. In the periphery (beyond 10° from the fovea), there are as many as 250 rods and cones per ganglion cell.

RETINAL SUMMATION AND INHIBITION

Summation Effects in Man. When the objects are small the threshold for the human fovea is inversely proportional to the area of the test object (Ricco's law). Such areal effects represent mutual facilitation between units occupying the field of stimulation, just as fibers within a nerve trunk facilitate one another synaptically.

Graham and Granit[12] used the flicker technique to show summation between retinal areas by throwing two illuminated half circles upon the retina and varying their separation. The two areal stimuli facilitated one another to a degree depending on their proximity. Under special conditions, one of which is foveal position, stimulation of one area reduces the sensitivity of the other—a form of inhibition.

Summative interactive phenomena are less pronounced in the fovea than in the periphery, where the degree of convergence and lateral connection is greater. Facilitation appears to be the mechanism by which the periphery of the retina attains a higher degree of sensitivity (higher c.f.f.) than the fovea,[10] even though the peripheral cones are less sensitive. When the test object has a very small area, the c.f.f. drops very sharply as the stimulus passes from central fixation to 3 to 5°. In fact, under these conditions, the c.f.f. is lower throughout the periphery than at the fovea, because use of a small area reduces the amount of intra-areal facilitation.

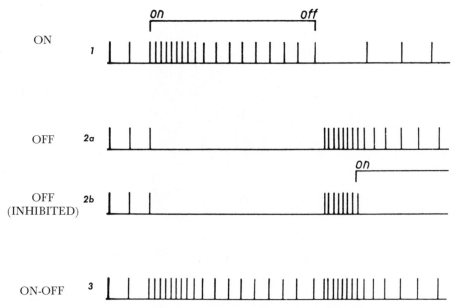

Fig. 13. Diagram of discharges of three optic nerve fibers with different discharge patterns. Beginning and end of stimulus indicated by horizontal bar. In *2b* note inhibitory effect of light on discharge of "OFF" fiber, which otherwise would have fired as in trace *2a*. This diagram collects observations by Adrian and Mathews, Hartline and Granit. (From Granit, *Receptors and sensory perception,* New Haven, Yale University Press, 1955.)

But with large test patches permitting intra-areal summation, the peripheral sensitivity is greater than the foveal.

Thus, the retinal periphery has two means of increasing its ability to respond to weak stimuli: (i) photochemical reactions (rhodopsin) and (ii) summative neural mechanisms. Both are operative in dim light, but only the latter is operative in daylight. The second mechanism is probably also a factor in endowing the scattered rods of the extreme periphery with good perception of movement. Neural interactions of an inhibitory nature occur in the foveal regions and are significant to detail vision.

Ganglion Cell Responses. Recording singly from a number of ganglion cells reveals that optic nerve axons send three kinds of signals to the brain. Certain axons may respond to the onset of light—the "ON fibers." Others, if responding prior to the stimulus, cease to fire during it and resume firing when it ends—the so-called "OFF fibers." (This should be understood as "OFF fiber behavior"; it depends upon function, not some fixed mechanism.) A third type of fiber behavior is firing at the start and after the end of a stimulus—the "ON-OFF" fibers. These three types are shown in Figure 13, which illustrates the ways the receptor cells manipulate the ganglion cells. The slowing of the background spontaneous discharge after an "ON" response (record 1, Fig. 13) suggests a concealed inhibition of the ganglion cell which shows up sharply by a total inhibition of the "OFF" response by light (2*b*, Fig. 13). Such concealed inhibition is often seen in spinal reflexes. A purely inhibitory ganglionic response is seen when the stimulus is strong (Fig. 14). The inhibition continues after the cessation of the stimulus. With weaker stimuli the inhibition begins one discharge later, is less complete (slowing of discharge) and is followed by a definite OFF response. The strong stimulus (first and last record in Fig. 14) blocks the concealed excitation of the ganglion cell after, as well as during, the stimulus. A somewhat weaker inhibition of the ganglion cell allows the concealed excitatory influence to manifest itself after the stimulus ceases. The OFF response may therefore be likened to so-called postinhibitory rebound[11] in spinal reflexes. The OFF response is greater than the spontaneous discharge prior to stimulus because the stronger light has stimulated the excitatory as well as inhibitory receptors to the ganglion cell.

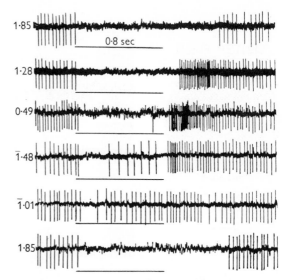

Fig. 14. Responses of a ganglion cell, showing lability of response to changes in light intensity. The response at stimulus strength 1.28 would be labeled OFF but at $\bar{1}.01$ would be labeled ON. (From Brown and Wiesel, *J. Physiol.*, 1959, *149*:537–562.)

Intracellular recording from ganglion cells by Brown and Wiesel[8] indicates that increased discharge frequencies are accompanied by depolarization of the cell membrane. Inhibition of impulses was linked with hyperpolarization, indicating a direct inhibition of ganglion cells rather than cessation of excitation.

Alternate but not exclusive explanations of the OFF effect can be made in terms of persisting membrane changes more deserving of the term "rebound." The OFF effect may be a mixture of persisting membrane phenomena and afterdischarge of a delay path.

Receptive Fields of Ganglion Cells. The receptive field of a retinal ganglion (or bipolar) cell is defined as that portion of the visual field from which the discharge of a given ganglion cell can be increased or decreased. These fields can be mapped out in the intact eye with the aid of penetrating electrodes, punctate light sources and direct observation of electrode positions.

In 1953, Kuffler discovered that the receptive field has an annular organization in which the center and periphery are mutually antagonistic. If the center increases discharge as in Figure 15, top, stimulation of the periphery causes discharge only when the light goes off. In another cell, the center of the receptive field may be inhibitory (Fig. 15, bottom), giving a response only when the discharge ceases, while the pe-

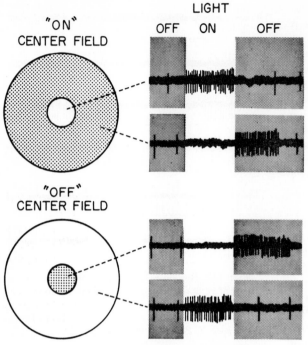

"ON" CENTER FIELD

"OFF" CENTER FIELD

LIGHT
OFF   ON   OFF

Fig. 15. The topographic organization of receptive fields of ganglion cells of the retina (left) and the ON and OFF discharge. Each dashed line could be viewed as an exploring spot of light in one of the many positions in the center or the peripheral zone of the receptive field, which would give a discharge from the ganglion cell as shown in the corresponding record. Note that in the upper diagram, where the center produces a discharge when the light is on, none is produced by stimulation of the peripheral zone until the light goes off. (Hubel, *Scientific American*, 1963, *209*:54–62.)

riphery gives an ON response during the discharge. From an ON center ganglion cell, Kuffler recorded a faster and faster discharge by increasing the size of a light spot (Ricco's law), indicating mutual facilitation between the receptors corresponding to the center of the receptive field. However, when the spot grew large enough to reach and encompass the periphery, the discharge was reduced in frequency and even eliminated. An annular ring of light of appropriate size is strongly inhibitory to an ON center ganglion cell. Figure 16 shows that in a similar experiment the receptive fields of cells in the inner nuclear layer resemble those of ganglion cells.

The size of the field varies with the state of dark adaptation and with the strength of stimu-

lus. As predicted by the greater convergence upon ganglion cells in the periphery than in the fovea, the receptive fields are correspondingly larger in the periphery. In the monkey, the arc of the receptive field ranges from 4 minutes to 2 degrees. Penetration experiments prove that small ganglion cells and cells in the inner nuclear layer have similarly round fields with concentric excitatory and inhibitory areas (Fig. 16). Since what are presumably bipolar cells exhibit hyperpolarization, part of the ganglion cell inhibition is indirect, i.e., shutting off of stimulation. That the concentric rings for a given ganglion cell must represent a mixture of receptors which are excitatory and inhibitory to the cell is required for the interpretation of OFF and ON effects given above. Such evidence has been

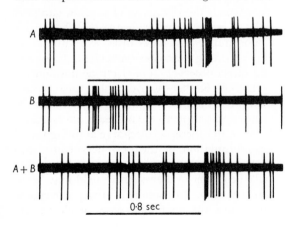

A

B

A + B

0·8 sec

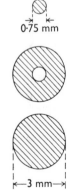

0·75 mm

3 mm

Fig. 16. Records from a cell in the inner nuclear layer of the retina demonstrating the mutual inhibitory relationship between the center (predominantly excitatory) and the periphery (predominantly inhibitory) of the receptor field of the retina. The stimulus pattern for each record is shown at the right. (From Brown and Wiesel, *J. Physiol.*, 1959, *149*:537–562.)

obtained from experiments on goldfish, which, unlike the cat, have color vision.

Goldfish eyes show OFF, ON, and ON-OFF ganglion receptive fields concentrically arranged which have the advantage that the OFF effect has a maximum spectral sensitivity at 650 mμ wavelength and the ON a maximum at 500 mμ. Figure 17 shows the result of traversing the receptive field with the OFF-650 mμ and the ON-500 mμ stimuli and determining the sensitivity at each point. There is a central zone of higher sensitivity yielding OFF response; the higher threshold ON responses are obtained from the central as well as the peripheral zone of the receptive field.

It is easy to see that a suprathreshold stimulus of intermediate wavelength (550 to 600 mμ) restricted to the center of the receptive field would produce more inhibition than excitation because the inhibitory units are more sensitive. No ON response would occur because of the stronger inhibition; it would be classed as an OFF-center field. In the periphery of the field the excitatory process is more strongly driven so that an ON effect occurs. Whether the discharge increases at the end of stimulation depends on what mixture of excitatory and inhibitory units are excited, which in turn depends on wavelength and position in the border between center and periphery.

The interaction of predominantly excitatory and inhibitory zones and the size and shape of receptive fields have a great importance to visual acuity and the perceptions of movement. This will be discussed in connection with the visual pathways (Chap. 22).

VISUAL ACUITY AND DETAIL VISION[10a]

Biologically, visual acuity is the sharpness with which detail and contours are perceived and constitutes the basis for form or object vision. From the point of view of testing, it is often measured by finding the smallest distance by which two lines may be separated without appearing as a single line. This distance is the *minimum separable.* Visual acuity is thus the *resolving power* of the eye, i.e., its ability to resolve two lines, and is akin to the two-point threshold of the skin. Lines or contours of solid fields placed closer together than the minimum separable blur into one another and may, if sufficiently close, appear homogeneous. Thus, if visual acuity is low, the fine details of environment are blurred and the intricate patterns of detail and contour give way to structureless masses with fuzzy outlines. Tests of visual acuity are simply standardized and quantified means of sampling a basic physiologic function—detail vision. Visual acuity can also be expressed in terms of the *minimum visible,* the narrowest line or the finest thread that can be discriminated from a homogeneous background. Weymouth[38] has shown that the *minimal angle of resolution* (M.A.R.) is a better designation for many purposes than is the minimum separable.

Dioptric Factors. The minimum separable varies with many conditions which are of two main kinds—dioptric and stimulus factors. The first have to do with the physical formation of a sharply focused image on the retina (Chap. 19). Under this heading come: (i) the "normal" errors of dioptric mechanisms: spherical and chromatic aberration, diffraction by imperfections in the ocular media and scattering of light by reflection from the retina. (ii) Errors of refraction: myopia, hyperopia and astigmatism. (Detection of such errors is the main purpose for clinical tests of visual acuity. (iii) Pupillary

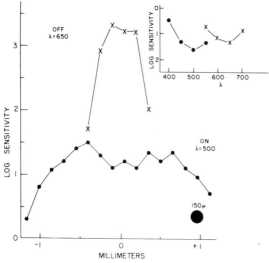

Fig. 17. Topographic organization of a "color-coded" ganglion cell receptive field. The curves are sensitivity profiles of an OFF center ganglion cell obtained by determining thresholds along a line cutting across the receptive field. Solid dots represent sensitivity of ON responses. The crosses designate a similar curve for a wavelength yielding response at terminations of the stimulus. Abscissae are retinal distance and the ordinates the reciprocal of threshold energy or sensitivity. Large dot is the stimulus size. (From Wagner, *et al., J. opt. Soc. Amer.,* 1963, *53:*66–70.)

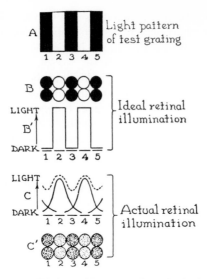

Fig. 18. Diagram illustrating hypothetical mechanism of detail vision or visual acuity. *A* is test grating; *B* and *C′* are receptors with intensity of the illumination represented by shading; *B′* and *C* are plots of intensity of illumination, with dotted line in *C* representing algebraic summation of two underlying curves. For further explanation, see text.

size: constriction increases visual acuity by minimizing factors (i) and (ii), although undue constriction hinders detail vision by increasing diffraction. (iv) The composition of the light: monochromatic light increases visual acuity by decreasing chromatic aberration. (v) Random variations of fixation: these occur even when control of eye muscles is normal and cause a slight shifting (30′ of visual angle) of the image on the retina, thus blurring it.

Ratliff and Riggs[26] have recorded such movements by attaching a mirror to a contact lens. While the eyes are supposedly fixated no less than four types of movement are being made, varying from rapid movements (30 to 70 per sec.) averaging 17.5′ of visual angle to slow drifts and rapid jerks averaging 5′ of visual angle. Such movements have proved to be not a hindrance to vision but an actual necessity.[11] An optical stabilizing of the retinal image, counteracting movement, results not in more detailed vision but in an actual fading of the image. Consistently stabilizing the eye and moving the stimulus slightly has dramatic effects on the rate of discharge of a cortical neuron in the visual cortex.[25a] As indicated earlier, something appears to be gained by the introduction of variability into the system.

Stimulus Factors. With the printed page

as the stimulus, there are four ways in which the stimulus can be altered to make its recognition more difficult.[22] The letters may be reduced uniformly in size; the ink may be bleached to the white of the background or the background may be darkened; the light falling on the page can be diminished; and, finally, the time allowed for observation can be shortened. The four factors influencing visual acuity are, then, size of detail, brightness contrast, illumination, and exposure time. All must be considered in attaining efficient vision in the school room or industry.

Retinal Grain. A third group of factors influencing visual acuity involves the anatomic and physiologic grain of the retina. Just as one factor in obtaining detail in photography is fineness of the grain in the film, so retinal grain is a factor in visual acuity. The dense packing together of exceedingly minute receptor elements is undoubtedly based upon the need for a finely grained receptive mechanism. The minimum separable, converted from seconds of visual angle to retinal distance and the diameter of a cone are of about the same order of magnitude. This suggests that two white lines on a black field could not be seen as two unless an unstimulated row of cones separated the stimulated ones ("ideal retinal illumination," Fig. 18). Yet we know this is not true. The eye distinguishes the lines even though optical imperfections and eye movements have caused the edges of the light bands to spread randomly over the intervening cones (diagrams *C* and *C′*, Fig. 18). If the lines are brought closer together, the curves representing the random distribution of light will be drawn together until the summated stimulus on the center cones equals that on the neighboring cones. So long as there is a discriminable difference in intensity of illumination between the shaded cone and its neighbors, a dark stria is visible. Visual acuity therefore resolves into the discrimination of a light-dark pattern. With these facts in mind, the retinal factors influencing visual acuity may be enumerated.

RETINAL REGION. Visual acuity is far from uniform over the entire retina. The fovea centralis is a region specialized for high visual acuity and is employed for accurate inspection of fine detail. The zone immediately surrounding the fovea possesses the next greatest capacity for detail vision, etc. The falling off in acuity in passing from fovea to periphery is quite abrupt (Fig. 19). With the foveal visual acuity taken as

1, the acuity at the edge of the macula (2.5°) has fallen to one-half; at 7.5° from the fovea it is one-fourth, and in the extreme periphery it is only one-fortieth. This curve, difficult to characterize, tends to become a straight line if plotted as the minimal angle of resolution, as in Figure 20;[38] at least two factors operate to produce this result. Extrafoveal cones are both larger in diameter and fewer per unit area, being "diluted" by rods. Secondly, more cones converge on a single ganglion cell in the periphery than in the central zones; as shown in Figure 21, visual acuity falls off more rapidly than intercone distance. On the other hand, the sep-

aration of ganglion cells in minutes of visual angle, plotted against degrees of eccentricity, forms a straight line. This confirms the deductions made from Figure 21.

Figure 20 also shows the marked difference between the visual acuities of the rod and cone mechanisms. With light below cone threshold, the fovea has the lowest visual acuity. In training for night vision, observers are taught to use the parafoveal regions of the retina. The acuity of rod vision increases throughout 10° owing to the increasing proportion of rods. Rod vision by night is inferior to cone vision by day within a 30° zone surrounding the fovea, not because the

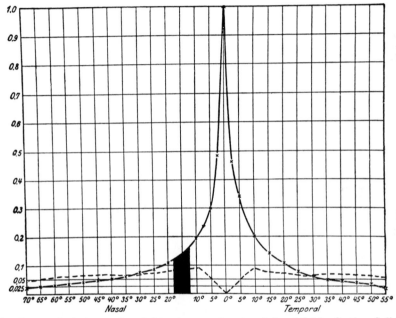

Fig. 19. Curve of relative acuity of vision in central and peripheral fields of retina. Solid line represents acuity of cone vision (light-adapted eye), and dotted line represents acuity of rod vision (approximate). Black area is the blind spot. (After Wertheim, *Z. Psychol.*, 1894, *7*:177–187.)

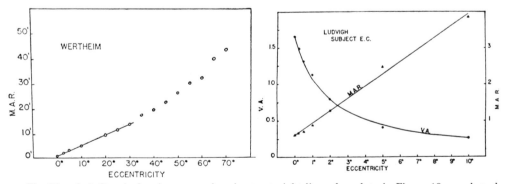

Fig. 20. *Left,* Graph showing approximation to straight line when data in Figure 19 are plotted as minimal angle of resolution. *Right,* Graph of data obtained by Ludvigh to show value of expressing visual acuity as minimal angle of resolution. (From Weymouth, *Amer. J. Ophthal.*, 1958, *46*:102–113.)

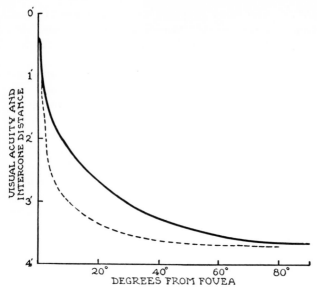

Fig. 21. Comparison of visual acuity and cone density for central and peripheral portions of retina. Dotted line shows visual acuity in minutes of visual angle. Note that the lower the curve the larger is the minimum separable. Heavy line shows cone gradient of retina in terms of intercone distance for periphery and cone width for rod-free areas, plotted on same ordinate as visual acuity. Failure of curves to correspond proves that factors other than density and diameter of cones determine minimum separable. (After Polyak, *The retina*, Chicago, University of Chicago Press, 1941.)

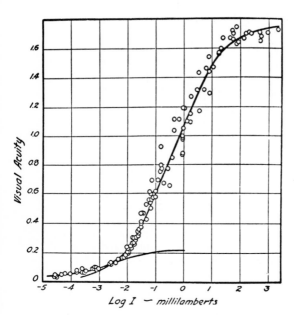

Fig. 22. Curves showing relation between visual acuity and level of illumination. Circles represent experimental determinations by König of visual acuity (reciprocal of minimum separable on ordinate) for a wide range of intensities of illumination (abscissa). Two solid lines, one for rods (lower) and one for cones (upper), show the success with which a normal probability integral can be fitted to data. According to Hecht's theory, curve represents number of receptor units whose threshold is attained by a given intensity of illumination, thresholds of receptors being distributed according to normal probability curve. (From Hecht, *A handbook of general experimental psychology*, C. Murchison, ed., Worcester, Clark University Press, 1934.)

rods are "diluted" by inactive cones but because many rods converge ultimately upon a single ganglion cell. This is a second indication that the number of "lines" available to carry information to the brain, as well as the anatomic grain of the receptor elements, is important.

FUNCTIONAL GRAIN AND CONTOUR VISION. Hecht explains the familiar effect of illumination on visual acuity in terms of "functional retinal grain." He assumes that cone thresholds are distributed according to a normal frequency curve like heights or weights of individuals. By integrating* such a curve, the S-shaped line in Figure 22 is obtained, and agreement of the theoretical curve and the experimental data justifies the assumption.

Figure 23 shows why dim lighting results in fuzzy, blurred contours. For convenience of illustration, Hecht's theory of cone thresholds is adopted. Circles represent the anatomic grain of the retina; the filled circles, the cones active at successively higher levels of illumination, A, B and C. The central vertical line demarcates a shadow cast upon the retina by a black object; the heavy line represents the boundary between lighted and shaded cones. A progressively sharper definition is obtained as more active cones are available to "draw" the contour, which is therefore sharpest at high illumination. (The same diagram also illustrates

---

*This can be done graphically by adding the low threshold cones to those of the next lowest threshold to get the second part on the curve, and so on for each class.

the difference in contour vision in peripheral [*A*], paracentral [*B*] and central [*C*] regions of the retina under conditions of bright illumination, the unfilled circles then being considered rods [inactive] and the filled circles cones.)

Clinical tests of visual acuity. Visual acuity is usually measured by the familiar chart on which the letters in each line are smaller than those in the previous line.

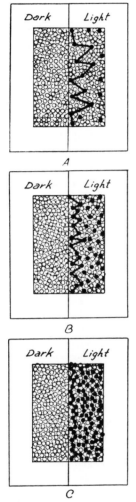

A

B

C

Fig. 23. Diagrams illustrating relation between level of illumination and perception of contours. *A, B, C* represent increasing levels of illumination of right-hand side of field, left-hand field being shielded by the shadow of an object. Filled circles represent active units and unfilled circles inactive units, rods and cones, retinal ganglion cells, or cells of striate cortex. Where many units are active, contour is quite sharply defined, but when few units are active contour is fuzzy. Same diagram serves to compare contour vision of peripheral (*A*), intermediate (*B*), and macular (*C*) regions of retina, with filled circles representing active cones, and unfilled circles inactive rods.

The chart is always viewed from the virtual far point of vision (6 m., or 20 ft.), so that accommodation is not needed. The number at the end of each row of type is the distance at which a whole letter of the size found on that line subtends an angle of 5′ on the retina, and each stroke of the letter subtends a visual angle of 1′. Snellen (1876), in making the chart, believed that the components of a letter should be separated by a distance equal to the minimum separable for the letter to be perceived by the normal eye. The situation is more complex than this. For example, the letters differ considerably in legibility; if B, the hardest letter to distinguish, is taken as 1, G and H are next hardest at 0.92, and L is the easiest at 0.71. However, the shortcomings of the test appear to compensate for one another, and the test serves its purpose very well. The chart must be well lighted; each eye is tested separately.

If at 20 feet the individual reads the letters of the line marked 20 feet, visual acuity is stated as 20/20 and is considered normal. If an individual can read only the line marked 100 (which a normal eye can read at 100 feet), his visual acuity is given as 20/100. Lines of test type smaller than the 20/20 line are provided and are rated 20/15, 20/13 and 20/10. Such ratings mean that the individual has better than normal acute vision and *do not mean that the individual is hyperopic.* As pointed out in the previous chapter, the hyperope does not see better than the emmetrope at a distance, but sees with less need for accommodation when objects are at a distance. To reduce the visual acuity to a fraction by saying that a person with 20/40 vision has 50 per cent normal visual acuity is like saying that a temperature of 80° is twice as hot as 40°. In some Snellen test charts the lines of type are labeled in terms of percentage of useful vision.

COLOR VISION[10a]

The sensations of color or hue resulting from the stimulation of the retina by the successive wavelengths of the visible spectrum and the *extraspectral* color, purple, form the *chromatic series.* It is paradoxical that the series of whites and grays—which in common parlance denotes a lack of color—is most conveniently considered a form of color vision, the *achromatic series.*

Achromatic and Chromatic Series. Objects reflecting to our eye all the visible rays of sunlight give us a white sensation. Black, on the contrary, is the sensation caused by withdrawal of light. In order to see black one must have a retina. In the region of the blind spot one sees not black but nothing. Thus, it is not improbable that black is a sensation connected with a definite retinal activity.

In the chromatic series many different colors (technically hues) may be detected—some observers record as many as 160. We generally give specific names only to those that represent quite distinct sensations. The limiting wavelengths (mμ) of the commonly named colors are: red, 723–647; orange, 647–585; yellow, 585–575; green, 575–492; blue, 492–455; indigo, 455–424; violet, 424–397.

Color saturation. The term "saturation" means the amount of color or freedom from dilution by white sensation. Pale or pastel shades is the nontechnical name for unsaturated colors. However, even monochromatic light does not produce a color experience entirely free from white sensation, since the monochromatic rays induce the retinal processes underlying white as well as those underlying its own special color (see below).

Laws of color vision. There are a number of laws which any theory of color vision must explain. Some of these are more in the province of psychology than physiology. We must, therefore, content ourselves with a brief statement of the main laws of color vision.

(i) *Color mixture or fusion.* When two or more wavelengths fall upon the same retinal area, the resulting sensation is often quite different from any aroused by the individual wavelengths. (ii) *Primary colors.* Color fusion experiments show that three wavelengths may be selected from the spectrum, one from the red end, one from the blue end, and one from the middle, whose combinations in different proportions will give a sensation of white, of any intermediate color shade, or of extraspectral purple (obtained by mixing the two ends of the spectrum). It is customary to designate these three wavelengths as primary colors.* (iii) *Complementary colors.* For any given color there is a complement which combines with it to produce white. Because the colors of the spectrum differ in saturation, widely differing intensities may be necessary. Colors that are closer together in the spectral series than the complementaries give on fusion some intermediate color. Thus, red and yellow, when fused, give orange. Colors farther apart than the distance between the complementaries give some shade of purple. (iv) *After-images.* After one stops looking at a color, he may continue to see it for a short time (positive after-image) or he may see its complementary color (negative after-image). This is a retinal phenomenon. (v) *Color contrasts.* If a piece of blue paper is laid upon a yellow paper, the color of each of them is heightened—color contrast.

Theories of Color Vision. Many theories have been proposed to explain the facts of color vision. None of them is entirely successful. The oldest and simplest theory is that of Young and Helmholtz.

YOUNG-HELMHOLTZ THEORY. Proposed by Thomas Young[39] in 1801 and later modified by Helmholtz, this theory assumes three fundamen-

*There are many combinations of three wavelengths with which the spectrum can be matched.

tal color sensations—red, green and violet. Corresponding with these are three classes of cones containing three different photochemical substances. Decomposition of each of these substances stimulates different nerve fibers, and the impulses are conducted to different systems of nerve cells in the visual cortex. The theory, therefore, assumes specific nerve fibers and specific cortical cells, corresponding respectively to the red, green and violet photochemical substances.†

When these three cone types are equally excited, a sensation of white results. All other color sensations, including yellow, are compounded by combined stimulation of the three receptors in different proportions. It is assumed, furthermore, that each photochemical substance is acted upon to some degree by all of the visible rays of the spectrum, but that the rays of long wavelengths at the red end of the spectrum affect the red substance most strongly, etc.

The theory of Helmholtz accords with the doctrine of specific nerve energies, since each photochemical substance serves simply to excite a nerve fiber and the quality of the sensation aroused depends on the ending of this fiber in the brain.

Negative after-images are explained as follows: If we look fixedly at a green object, the corresponding photochemical substance is chiefly acted upon. When the same cones are subsequently exposed to white light, the red and violet substances, having been previously less acted upon, now respond in greater proportions to the white light, and the after-image takes a red-violet—that is, purple—color. Many objections have been raised to the Young-Helmholtz theory. It fails to explain some of the subjective phenomena of color vision in normal and "color-blind" persons, and why, in the periphery, yellow and, farther out, white or gray are perceived in otherwise color-blind zones. Finally, recent neurophysiologic and anatomic information suggests that the theory is oversimplified.

Photochemistry of Color Vision. Cone pigment has proved more elusive than rod pigment. The high threshold for cones suggests that the pigment is less concentrated in cones than rods. Trichromatic theories of color vision require three pigments. A violet-sensitive substance—

†Helmholtz's hypothesis of zonal representation of color in the cerebral cortex has not proved justified. Le Gros Clark, however, has made the interesting suggestion that the three layers of the lateral geniculate body are related to the three receptors of the trichromatic theory.

iodopsin—was extracted from the chicken retinae by Wald in 1937 and since has been synthesized by adding an isomer of retinene to a preparation of the outer segments of rods and cones. The absorption spectrum of iodopsin fits reasonably well with the photopic sensitivity curve of the fowl when shifting of the curve by oil droplets in the eye of the fowl is taken into account.

By spectroscopic analysis of the retina *in vivo* and *in vitro,* its photochemical substances can be studied without chemical extraction. Rushton[28, 30] obtained the first direct spectral sensitivity evidence of cone pigments by an ophthalmoscopic procedure directed to the human fovea.

Brown and Wald[8a] made precise physical measurements of the spectral sensitivity of the receptor substances in the green and red range, finding maxima at 535 and 565 mμ respectively. The blue substance inferred from psychological experiments proved elusive. Recently, the tiny cones of the human and monkey retina were studied microspectroscopically *in vitro.*[23a] The existence of the blue receptor substance was unquestionably demonstrated. Further, because *single* cones were studied it was learned that each cone contains one specific photochemical substance, though the possibility that the red receptor may contain some green pigment could not be wholly ruled out. It seems safe to speak of blue and green receptors. Finally, Wald[34a] has been able to gain evidence for the blue pigment in man and to obtain good correlation between spectra determined psychologically and physically. Figure 24 shows the degree of fit, which is remarkable, since colored degradation products will distort the curve (green curve) as will any bleaching of some green pigment in determining the absorption spectrum of the red pigment.

The trichromatic theory of color vision (see below) is strongly supported by the proof that three pigments exist in the retina and, with one reservation, three color cones. How the discharges from these cells interact with others of

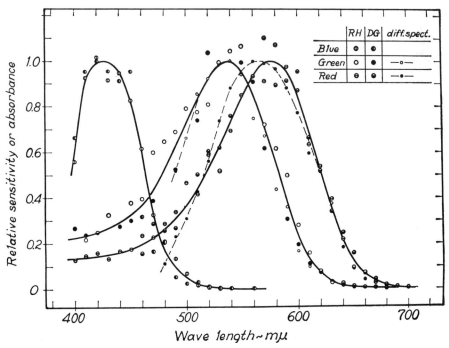

Fig. 24. Comparison of action spectra of color pigments of the human retina obtained by psychological methods (solid lines) with difference spectra obtained by physical methods (red and green only). Sensitivity spectra are adjusted to the same height. The curves for green and red would be of about the same height, but that for blue would be much less. (From Wald, *Science,* 1964, *145*:1007–1016.)

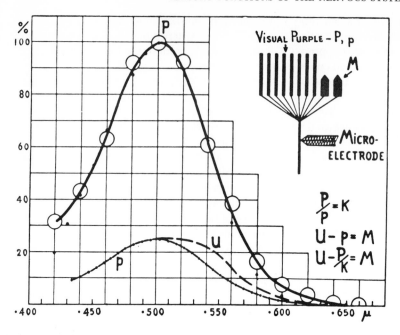

Fig. 25. Average sensitivity curve (large circles) of receptors connected with single ganglion cell of cat's retina when dark-adapted. Black dots are Lythgoe's curve for the absorption of light by visual purple. U is experimentally obtained curve from which curve P in appropriate magnitude (p) is subtracted to give sensitivity of specific color receptor. (From Granit, *J. Neurophysiol.*, 1945, *8*:195–210.)

their kind or of opposite kind is a question which must be answered at each stage of the visual system.

Responses to Color—Ganglion and Geniculate Cells. Granit's[15] pioneer studies of the spectral sensitivity of ganglion cells were carried out on cats, which, though not entirely color-blind, are nearly so. The monkey has color vision comparable to man's, but its ganglion cell spectra have not been determined. However, the cells of the geniculate body on which the ganglion cells end exhibit definite color specificity. Maxima were found at 580, 540, and 450 millimicra wavelengths, agreeing very well with the results of Marks, *et al.* for single monkey cones.[23a] It is of importance to color vision that in many cases cones of different spectral sensitivity converge on the same geniculate cell and are mutually inhibitory.

Specific Color Receptors. The spectral sensitivity of the ganglion cell can be determined by recording from it with microelectrodes while subjecting the eye to different wavelengths of light (Granit). The three curves corresponding to the three pigments indicated by color mixture experiments and by direct observation of bleaching are not found. All units studied exhibited sensitivity to a wide band of wavelengths. The curve of sensitivity obtained in the dark-adapted eye agreed closely with the absorption curve of visual purple (Fig. 25). Un-

der conditions of light adaptation, a curve resembling the photopic visibility curve was obtained. A structural basis for this is that both rods and cones converge through bipolar cells upon the same ganglion cell. The shift from the scotopic to the photopic curve presumably means that rods cease to function at the intensities that stimulate cones. Granit terms this response the *scotopic and photopic dominator response*. The conscious response is presumably achromatic.

In addition to these dominator responses, some units in the light-adapted eye respond to a *narrow* band of wavelengths, narrower than the spectral sensitivity of cone pigments known directly (iodopsin) or indirectly by ophthalmoscopic bleaching experiments. This is termed the modulator response; it may represent the activity of individual cones. The sensitivity curves tend to vary slightly, but cluster into three groups (Fig. 26): red-yellow (580 to 600 mμ), green (520 to 540 mμ), and blue (450 to 470 mμ). The visibility curve reconstructed from these curves agrees satisfactorily with that of the human eye. This direct evidence therefore indicates that Helmholtz's trireceptor theory may be true in the statistical sense that the cones fall into three groups within which the receptors of narrow band sensitivity have similar, though not identical, sensitivity. Apparently many ganglion cells discharge in response to several

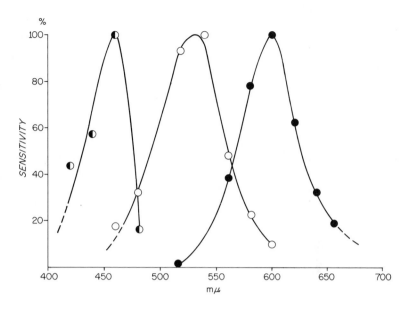

Fig. 26. Sensitivity curves for blue (*left*), green (*middle*), and red (*right*) color receptors. These were obtained by selective adaptation and by averaging curves of several individual receptors, which varied from average by amount indicated by upper contours. (From Granit, *J. Neurophysiol.,* 1945, *8*:195–210.)

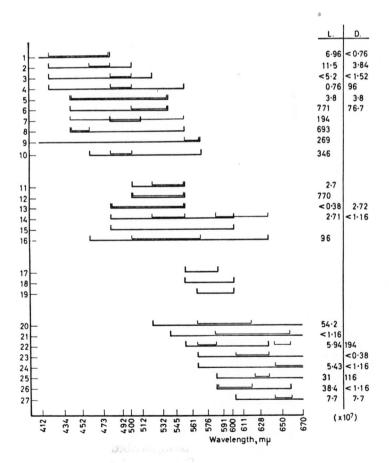

Fig. 27. Spectral sensitivity of 27 single cortical units. The wide bracket shows band of wavelengths eliciting responses at high intensities and narrow bracket at low intensities. (From Andersen, Buchman and Lennox-Buchtal, *Vision Res.,* 1962, *2*:295–307.)

receptors, each sensitive to a narrow band, which collectively give the ganglion cell a sensitivity (visibility) curve like that of the whole eye. Such units, which are numerous, probably give rise to a sensation of white. Other ganglion cells connected with single receptors serve color discrimination.

Spectral Sensitivity of Cortical Neurons. A single cortical neuron, like a retinal ganglion cell, can respond in two ways: broad band responders yielding a burst or train of impulses and narrow band responders yielding one or two impulses. Most frequently single cortical neurons responded to white light selectively or to many monochromatic lights distributed throughout the spectrum (Fig. 27). Most significantly, some could respond to a narrow spectral band when tested with diffuse flashes of monochromatic light. Near threshold a third of the units with restricted response were discharged by only one filter (< 15 mμ). At high intensities the most selective unit found was responsive to a 30 mμ band; the more usual was to a 60 to 100μ band. Some units responsive only to blue, green, red and yellow wavelengths were found, but usually the sensitivity spread into the wavelengths for other colors. This selective spectral sensitivity is not fixed. In repeated trials the frequency most often responded to could shift from one band to another and back again without change in stimulus conditions. Under chloralose anesthesia a unit which has responded to a narrow band can irreversibly lose its selectivity and respond to all wavelengths and to white light. The narrowest effective band was smaller than that so far recorded from the lateral geniculate body, or for the modulator response of the retinal ganglion cell. The sharpening of the band sensitivity is probably a cortical function in which inhibition favored by diffuse illumination plays a part. A similar problem and explanation will be encountered in the study of visual acuity.

Clinical Correlations: Color Blindness and Anomalies. The discovery of color blindness (1794) is credited to the British chemist and physicist, John Dalton (of the gas law), who was himself "color-blind."

CLASSIFICATION OF COLOR BLINDNESS. The conventional classification of color blindness derives from the Young-Helmholtz theory of three specific receptors, color blindness being ascribed to an alteration in one of them. Defects in color

vision are no longer described in terms of red, green and violet blindness, because, for example, the individuals Helmholtz called red blind are actually red-green blind. They see the spectrum as yellow and blue (see p. 437). Instead are employed the more noncommittal categories suggested by von Kries: protanopia, deuteranopia and tritanopia, implying merely a defect in the first (*protos*), second (*deuteros*) or third (*tritos*) receptor. The suffixes -anomaly and -anopia distinguish color weakness and color blindness, respectively. The conventional classification is as follows:

I. TRICHROMATS

1. normal color vision
2. protanomaly
3. deuteranomaly

II. DICHROMATS

1. protanopia
2. deuteranopia
3. tritanopia

III. MONOCHROMATS

This classification, like the parent Young-Helmholtz theory, characterizes adequately the objective phenomena of color mixture in the color-blind and is not meant to describe the appearance of the spectrum. The normal and color-weak trichromats require three primary colors to match all colors in the spectrum, but they use the colors from the red and green parts of the spectrum in different proportions. In matching yellows by mixing red and green wavelengths, they employ quite different ratios; the protanomalous requires more of the red, and the deuteranomalous more of the green. Their defect may be slight or may be nearly as severe as in dichromatism.

Dichromats are so named because they can match the spectrum as they see it with only two primary colors, a red and a blue for the deuteranope and a green and a blue for the protanope. These two conditions are believed to be reduction systems representing the loss of one of the three Young-Helmholtz color receptors. Tritanopia is an extremely rare form of color blindness in which a wavelength from the long end and one from the middle of the spectrum suffice to duplicate the spectrum. The monochromat duplicates the spectrum with only one wavelength by adjusting its intensity. Apparently, only grades of light and dark are seen.

Luminosity of spectrum in color blindness. To the

deuteranope-deuteranomalous the luminosity of the spectrum (visibility curve) is virtually normal; to the protanope-protanomalous it is distinctly abnormal, the spectrum being shortened. The longer (red) wavelengths are not even appreciated as light; it is as though they did not reach the retina. This explains why a protanope can confuse a red with a black and appear at a funeral wearing a red tie. The point at which the spectrum seems brightest is shifted from 552 mμ to approximately 540 mμ. No intermediate forms link the protanope to the normal (Fig. 28), and the visibility curves for protanopes and protanomalous are identical. The term *scoterythrous* has been suggested for this state. The visibility curve of the deuteranope shows no such abnormality; hence, it is a form of pure color blindness, whereas protanopia is a *color plus light blindness.*

Color confusions. The color-blind person is satisfied with the appearance of his visual world, rarely misnames a colored object or even a color, and is often tardy in discovering his abnormality. His deficiency is usually first noticed because he confuses certain colors, and tests of color vision depend on these confusions. The protanomalous and deuteranomalous find difficulty in distinguishing the red-green range, and the tritanomalous finds difficulty in distinguishing the blue-yellow range; the dichromat fails entirely.

Subjective phenomena.[17, 37] How does the spectrum appear to the color-blind? To the dichromat, protanope and deuteranope, the spectrum is divided into two halves by a band of gray in the neighborhood of 493 to 497 mμ (greenish blue), the so-called neutral point above which all wavelengths seem yellow and below which all wavelengths seem blue (Fig. 29). The colors gain in saturation in passing away from the neutral point. Dalton described the spectrum as follows: "My yellow comprehends the red, orange, yellow and green of others; and my blue and purple (dark blue?) coincide with theirs." The few cases of monocular color vision examined confirm this description of the spectrum. So, too, the color confusions of deuteranope and protanope are only subtly different. From the point of view of their subjective experiences, protanopes and deuteranopes both are red-green color-blind, but in slightly different ways. Protanopia is characterized by a shortening of the spectrum and a decreased luminosity of the longer (red) wavelengths.

An explanation of why the spectrum appears to be made up of yellow and blue, rather than green and blue and red and blue, is as follows: In protanopia the "red receptor" is supposed to have the same wavelength sensitivity as the "green receptor," but retains its central "red" reaction unaltered. Therefore, neither green nor red is ever separately experienced, their receptors being always excited together, resulting in a color mixture. The spectrum corresponding to the whole red and green range appears as yellow or orange,

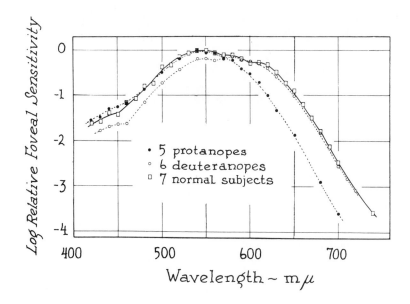

Fig. 28. Luminosity curves of color blind and normal subjects. Downward in the graph represents loss of sensitivity, the log of the reciprocal of threshold energy. (From Hsia and Graham, *Proc. nat. Acad. Sci.,* (*Wash.*), 1957, *43*:1011–1019.)

• 5 protanopes
○ 6 deuteranopes
□ 7 normal subjects

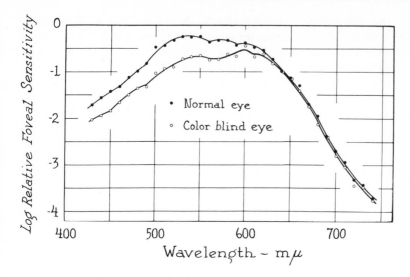

Fig. 29. Luminosity curves of the fovea in a unilaterally color blind (dichromatic) subject. Downward on the graph indicates less sensitivity in log units, which occurs in the blue-green region of the spectrum. (From Graham and Hsia, *Proc. nat. Acad. Sci. (Wash.)*, 1958, *44:* 46–59.)

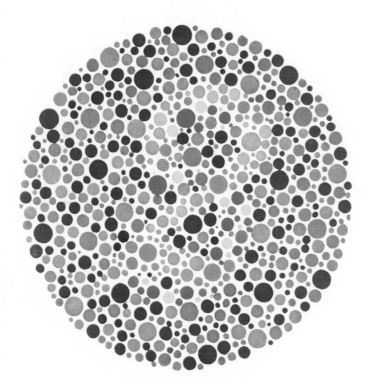

Fig. 30. Hidden-figure chart for detection of color blindness. Normal eye sees figure 5, color blind eye sees figure 2. (Copied by permission from Ishihara's *Series of plates designed as tests for color blindness,* Tokyo, Kanehara & Co., 1920.)

the hues resulting from mixing red and green wavelengths. Deuteranopia may consist of a change in the cone normally most sensitive to the green wavelength so that it has the same sensitivity as the red-sensitive cone.

Classified on the basis of etiology, color disability may be (i) *acquired* through a variety of retinal, cerebral, systemic and toxic disorders, including avitaminosis, or (ii) *congenital* because

of inherited lack of some mechanism vital to color vision. Red-green blindness and weakness are strongly sex-linked. According to one study it is present in some degree in 8 per cent of boys and 0.5 per cent of girls. It passes from father by way of a daughter to a grandson. The lesser incidence among females is presumably due to the necessity for the disability to be received from both parents if it is to be exhibited. Total color blindness seems to be inherited as a simple recessive trait. Difficulty with blue and yellow is usually acquired; too few individuals born with this form have been discovered to learn much of its genetics.

Tests of color blindness. For the purpose of explaining the principles involved, the simplest of the many tests for color vision is Holmgren's. A number of skeins of wool are used, and three standard colors are chosen: standard I, a pale, pure green skein, which must not incline toward yellow-green; standard II, a medium purple (magenta) skein; and standard III, a vivid scarlet skein. The subject is given skein I and is asked to select quickly from the pile of assorted colored skeins those that have approximately the same color. Those who are dichromatic will see the test skein as a gray with some yellow or blue shade and will select, therefore, not only the green skeins, but the grays or grayish-blue skeins. To ascertain whether the individual is a protanope or a deuteranope, standards II and III may then be employed.

With standard II (medium purple) the protanope will select, in addition to other purples, only blues or violets; the deuteranope will select as "confusion colors" only greens and grays.

With standard III (red) the protanope will select as confusion colors greens, grays or browns less luminous than the standard color, and the deuteranope will select greens, grays or browns of a greater brightness than the standard.

The second test of color vision in common use is the Ishihara or some other version of Stilling's (1876) pseudo-isochromatic charts. This test, familiarly known as the "hidden digit" test, consists of a book of plates containing digits made up of spots of color set in a field composed of spots of the confusion color (Fig. 30). Spots of several shades are used because the luminosity of certain hues is altered for color deviates. In constructing the original tests, Stilling was guided in choice of colors by a red-green blind painter and a blue-yellow blind school teacher. In the Ishihara test one number is seen by the normal eye and another by the color-weak eye. By appropriate choice of colors and chroma levels, the test can be made qualitatively and quantitatively diagnostic.

REFERENCES

1. ANDERSEN, V. O., BUCHMANN, M. B. and LENNOX-BUCH-THAL, M. A. *Vision Res.*, 1962, *2:*295–307.
2. BARLOW, H. B. *J. Physiol.*, 1953, *119:*58–68; 69–88.
3. BARLOW, H. B., FITZHUGH, R. and KUFFLER, S. W. *J. Physiol.*, 1957, *137:*338–354.
4. BRINDLEY, G. S. *Physiology of the retina and the visual pathway.* London, Edward Arnold, Ltd., 1960.
5. BROWN, K. T. and MURAKAMI, M. I. *Nature (Lond.)*, 1964, *201:*626–628; *ibid.*, 1964, *204:*739–740.
6. BROWN, K. T. and WATANABE, K. *Nature (Lond.)*, 1962, *193:*958–960.
7. BROWN, K. and WIESEL, T. N. *Amer. J. Ophthal.,* 1953, *46* (No. 3, Pt. 2): 91–98.
8. BROWN, K. and WIESEL, T. N. *J. Physiol.*, 1959, *149:*537–562.
8a. BROWN, P. K. and WALD, G. *Nature (Lond.)*, 1963, *200:* 37–43.
9. CAMPBELL, F. W. and RUSHTON, W. A. H. *J. Physiol.*, 1955, *130:*131–147.
9a. CONE, R. A. *Nature (Lond.)*, 1964, *204:*736–739.
10. CREED, R. S. and RUCH, T. C. *J. Physiol.*, 1932, *74:*407–423.
10a. DAVSON, H., ed. *The eye*, vol. 2, *The visual process.* New York, Academic Press, 1962.
11. DITCHBURN, R. W. and GINSBORG, B. L. *J. Physiol.*, 1939, *119:*1–17.
12. GRAHAM, C. H. and GRANIT, R. *Amer. J. Physiol.*, 1931, *98:* 664–673.
13. GRAHAM, C. H. and HSIA, Y. *Proc. nat. Acad. Sci. (Wash.)*, 1958, *44:*46–49.
14. GRANIT, R. *J. Neurophysiol.*, 1945, *8:*195–210; also *Nature (Lond.)*, 1943, *151:*11–14.
15. GRANIT, R. *Receptors and sensory reception.* New Haven, Yale University Press, 1955.
16. HARTLINE, H. K. and RATLIFF, F. *J. gen. Physiol.*, 1958, *41:*1049–1066.
17. HECHT, S. Pp. 704–828 in *A handbook of general experimental psychology*, C. MURCHISON, ed. Worcester, Clark University Press, 1934.
18. HECHT, S. *Amer. Scientist*, 1944, *32:*159–177; also pp. 1–21 in *Visual mechanisms*, H. KLÜVER, ed. Lancaster, Pa., Jaques Cattell Press, 1942.
19. HECHT, S., HAIG, C. and CHASE, A. M. *J. gen. Physiol.*, 1937, *20:*831–850.
20. HSIA, Y. and GRAHAM, C. H. *Proc. nat. Acad. Sci. (Wash.)*, 1957, *43:*1011–1019.
20a. HUBEL, D. H. and WIESEL, T. N. *Physiologist*, 1964, *7:* 162.
21. KUFFLER, S. *J. Neurophysiol.*, 1953, *16:*37–68.
22. LUCKIESH, M. and MOSS, F. K. *The science of seeing.* New York, Van Nostrand Co., 1937.
23. McFARLAND, R. A. and EVANS, J. N. *Amer. J. Physiol.*, 1939, *127:*37–50.
23a. MARKS, W. B., DOBELLE, W. H. and MacNICHOL, E. F., *Science*, 1964, *143:*1181–1183.
24. MILES, W. R. *Fed. Proc.*, 1943, *2:*109–115.
25. POLYAK, S. L. *The retina.* Chicago, University of Chicago Press, 1941.
25a. PRITCHARD, R. M. Chap. 15 in *The oculomotor system*, M. B. Bender, ed. New York, Harper & Row, 1964.
26. RATLIFF, F. and RIGGS, L. A. *J. exp. Psychol.*, 1950, *40:*687–701.
27. RIGGS, L. A., RATLIFF, F., CORNSWEET, J. C. and CORNSWEET, T. N. *J. opt. Soc. Amer.*, 1953, *43:*495–501.
28. RUSHTON, W. A. H. *Nature (Lond.)*, 1957, *179:*571–573.
29. RUSHTON, W. A. H., *Nature (Lond.).*, 1958, *182:*690–692.
30. RUSHTON, W. A. H. *Ann. N. Y. Acad. Sci.*, 1958, *74:*291–304.
31. RUSHTON, W. A. H., CAMPBELL, F. W., HIGGINS, W. A. and BRINDLEY, G. S. *Optica acta*, 1955, *1:*183–190.
32. WALD, G. *J. gen. Physiol.*, 1935, *19:*351–371.
33. WALD, G. Pp. 1658–1667 in *Medical physics*, O. GLASSER, ed. Chicago, Year Book Medical Publishers, 1944.
34. WALD, G. Chap. 28 in *Handbook of physiology, Section 1: Neurophysiology*, vol. 1, J. Field, H. W. Magoun and V. E. Hall, eds. Washington, D.C., American Physiological Society, 1959.

34a. WALD, G. *Science,* 1964, *145:*1007–1016.

35. WALD, G. and CLARK, A. B. *J. gen. Physiol.,* 1937, *21:*93–105.

36. WALD, G., HARPER, P. V., JR., GOODMAN, H. C. and KRIEGER, H. P. *J. gen. Physiol.,* 1942, *25:*891–903.

37. WALLS, G. L. *The vertebrate eye and its adaptive radiation.* Bloomfield Hills, Mich., Cranbrook Institute of Science, 1942.

38. WEYMOUTH, F. W. *Amer. J. Ophthal.,* 1958, *46:*102–113.

39. YOUNG, T. *Phil. Trans.,* 1801, *92:*12–48.

CHAPTER 21

Binocular Vision and Central Visual Pathways

By THEODORE C. RUCH

VISUAL FIELDS AND BINOCULAR VISION

Visual Fields—Perimetry. By the visual field of an eye is meant the entire extent of the external world which can be seen without a change in the fixation of the eye. Because of the lens, the visual field is inverted upon the retina, so that objects in the upper visual field fall upon the lower half of the retina and objects in the right half of the visual field fall upon the left half of the retina. The retina is sensitive out to the ora serrata and, if the eye protruded sufficiently from its orbit, its visual field projected upon a flat surface would be a circle, the center of which would correspond to the fovea centralis. However, the nose, eyebrows and cheek bones cut off a considerable part of this field, giving it an irregular outline. The normal field of vision (Fig. 1) is therefore of little interest, but testing of the visual fields is an important clinical maneuver, especially in cases of suspected brain tumor.

To outline the visual field it is only necessary to keep the eye fixed and then to move a small object inward along a meridian until it is seen, keeping it at the same distance from the eye. This is repeated for each meridian and the results are combined upon an appropriate chart. An instrument, the perimeter, facilitates this process and is also useful for charting the peripheral fields. For plotting the central region of the visual field in detail, use is made of a large piece of black velvet marked off in degrees of visual angle and viewed from a distance of 1 meter (Bjerrum screen).

The outer zone of the retina has no color sensitivity. In this region, as ordinarily tested with light at moderate levels of illumination, a colored object gives rise only to an achromatic sensation. In passing toward the fovea color sensitivity develops gradually, the blue colors being perceived first and the greens last. The color zones of the retina may be plotted by means of a perimeter. Ferree and Rand[8] state that the color blindness of the periphery of the retina is relative and not absolute. An important innovation in perimetry is the use of the blind spot to control fixation and to detect formation of a pseudofovea (see below). For use of color and flicker fusion frequency in plotting visual fields, see Teuber et al.[31]

Binocular Vision. When the two eyes are fixed upon a point straight ahead, each eye has its own visual field that may be charted by

441

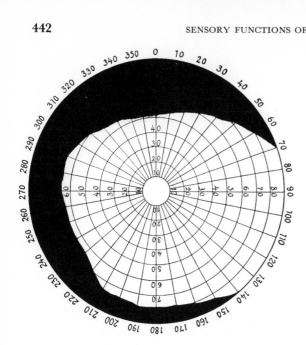

Fig. 1. Perimetric chart to show field of vision for *right* eye when eye looks straight ahead and does not move. Temporal field is to right, nasal to left of chart. Numbers along vertical and horizontal meridians are degrees of visual angle from center of fovea.

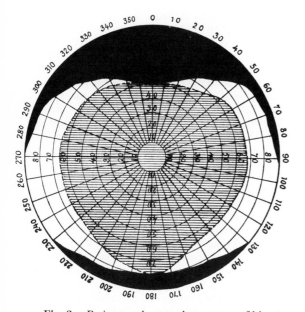

Fig. 2. Perimeter chart to show extent of binocular visual field. Shaded area is portion of visual field seen by both eyes; white areas at both sides are the monocular crescents seen only by extreme nasal portion of each retina.

means of the perimeter. But the two fields overlap for a considerable portion of their extent. This area of overlap constitutes the field of binocular vision (see Fig. 2). At both sides of this field is a region which can be seen by only one eye. It is known as the *monocular crescent,* or the *temporal half-moon.* Every point in the binocular field forms an image upon both retinas. Whether a given object is seen single or double depends upon whether its image does or does not fall upon corresponding points in the two retinas.

Corresponding points. Physiologically defined, corresponding points in the two retinas are those which, when simultaneously stimulated by the same luminous object, give a single sensation. Noncorresponding points are, of course, those which when so stimulated give two visual sensations. It is evident that the foveae form corresponding points or areas. When we look at any object, the visual axes of the two eyes converge upon and meet at the point looked at. If, while observing an object, one eyeball is gently pressed upon from the side, two images are seen, and they diverge farther and farther from each other as the pressure is increased. Experiment shows that portions of the retina symmetrically placed to the right side of the foveae correspond, and the same is true for the two left halves. The right half of the retina in one eye is noncorresponding to the left half of the other retina. Doubling of objects that do not fall on corresponding points is readily demonstrated for objects that lie either closer or farther away than the object looked at (physiologic diplopia). If one holds the two forefingers in the median plane, one close to the face and the other as far away as possible, the nearer finger is seen double when the eyes are fixed on the far one and vice versa. The reason for this is seen in Figure 3. In this same experiment, most people will find that closing one eye makes a finger appear out of line to one side, the right-hand finger being seen by the left eye and vice versa. If, when one eye is closed, the fingers stay lined up, the open eye is the dominant one. When both eyes are open this finger (image) out of line does not seem as clear as when only the heteronymous (opposite) is open. The image in this eye is partially suppressed.

Suppression of visual images. One of the images of an object falling upon noncorresponding points is usually ignored or suppressed. When failure to fix comes on suddenly, as in pressing

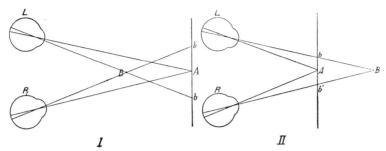

Fig. 3. Diagrams to show homonymous and heteronymous diplopia: In *I*, eyes are focused on *A*; images of *B* fall on noncorresponding points—that is, to different sides of foveae—and are seen double, being projected to plane of *A*, giving heteronymous diplopia. In *II*, eyes are focused on nearer point, *A*, and farther point, *B*, forms images on noncorresponding points and is seen double—homonymous diplopia—images being projected to focal plane *A*.

on one eyeball, double vision results. But in cases of long standing, the image from the abnormal eye is usually suppressed. The "suppressed" eye eventually shows a reduction or loss of visual ability, even blindness, when tested separately; this condition is called *amblyopia*.

Binocular rivalry. When the images of two dissimilar objects are thrown on corresponding parts of each retina, binocular rivalry ensues. If the image consists of vertical lines on one eye and horizontal lines on the other, only one field is seen at a time, first one, then the other; or the field is broken, vertical lines in part and horizontal lines in part. There is no genuine fusion in a continuous constant picture.

Judgments of solidity and depth.* Vision gives us knowledge not only of the surface area of objects, but also of their depth or solidity. The visual sensations upon which this conception is built are of several different kinds, partly monocular and partly binocular. If we close one eye and look at a bit of landscape or a solid object, we are conscious of the perspective, of the right relations of foreground and background. Nevertheless, it is true that with binocular vision the perception of depth and solidity are far more perfect. This is mainly because the slightly different views of an object given by the two eyes are subjectively combined to give the third dimension. This principle is illustrated by the stereoscope.

*Depth perception is measured with the Howard-Dolman apparatus. A short, upright rod is mounted 20 feet from the subject on a wire passing around a pulley. The two ends of the wire are manipulated by the subject until this rod and a stationary rod appear to be equidistant. The error is then measured and the average of repeated tests is made.

CENTRAL VISUAL PATHWAYS[24, 31]

Retina, Optic Nerve and Chiasm. The fibers composing the optic nerve originate in the ganglion cells of the inner layer of the retina. They converge to form the optic nerve and pierce the chorioid and scleral coats of the eyeball. Morphologically the point of convergence forms the optic nerve head, disc or papilla; physiologically it produces a *blind spot* in the visual field because only nerve fibers are present at that point. The nerve head lies 15° to the nasal side of the fovea centralis; because the lens reverses spatial relationships, the blind spot is 15° to the temporal side in the visual field.

Fibers from the macula lutea are numerous and form a distinct bundle running horizontally to the nerve head, the *maculopapillary bundle*. Fibers to the nasal side of the nerve head pursue a direct course like the spokes of a wheel. Since no fibers pass through the fovea, fibers from the temporal portion of the retina arch above or loop below the fovea centralis, forming a geometrically sharp "watershed" along a horizontal line drawn through the fovea to the temporal margin of the retina. In this fashion, the temporal retinal fibers (and some of the fibers of the nasal half) become separated into an upper and a lower quadrant by the interposition of the macular fibers,† an arrangement continued throughout the central visual pathways.

A vertical line drawn through the macula divides the retina into two hemimaculas and

† In discussion of the central visual pathways, the terms "macula" and "macular" do not always mean the region of the macula lutea. In clinical literature, these are almost synonyms for "central," and denote any central zone less than about 10° of visual angle.

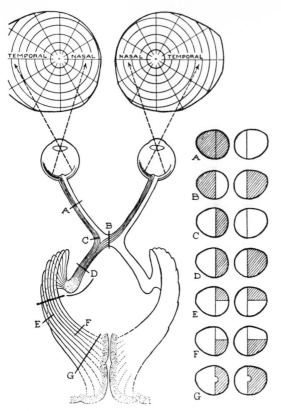

Fig. 4. Diagram of central visual pathways passing to left hemisphere. Shaded areas in inserts indicate visual field defects resulting from lesions at point indicated by corresponding letter on left-hand figure. For convenience, visual fields for two eyes are shown separated, but actually they superimpose so that vertical meridians coincide: *A,* complete blindness of left eye; *B,* bitemporal hemianopsia; *C,* unilateral nasal hemianopsia; *D,* right homonymous hemianopsia—interruption of either optic tract or geniculocalcarine projection; *E* and *F,* right upper and lower quadrant hemianopsias; *G,* right homonymous hemianopsia from a large lesion of occipital lobe. (From Homans, *A text-book of surgery,* 5th ed., Springfield, Ill., Charles C Thomas, 1941.)

hemiretinas. Fibers from the temporal hemiretina of the left eye continue through the *optic chiasm* and, without crossing, pass in the optic tract to the *lateral geniculate body* of the left side; those from the temporal side of the right eye enter the right optic tract (Fig. 4). Fibers from the nasal half of each retina decussate in the optic chiasm and enter the optic tract of the opposite cerebral hemisphere, where they join the uncrossed fibers from the temporal half of the other eye, thence to the lateral geniculate body. Thus, the termination for fibers from the nasal half of the retina is contralateral. Because of

this regrouping of fibers, lesions of the optic chiasm, or central to it, cause visual defects different from those induced by lesions of the retina or optic nerve.

The effects of lesions at various points in the visual system upon the visual fields of the two eyes are shown in Figure 4. It is also profitable to consider their effect on the field of vision when both eyes are open. From complete interruption of one optic nerve there is, on the same side as the lesion, a slight lateral narrowing of the field of vision when both eyes are open. This is due to loss of vision in one temporal half-moon (seen only by the extreme nasal portion of the ipsilateral retina). However, interruption of the visual pathway central to the chiasm on one side blocks impulses from *both* eyes, conveying impressions from one-half the binocular visual field plus one temporal half-moon. The result of such a lesion in, for example, the left hemisphere is a visual field defect known as *right lateral homonymous hemianopsia*—"half-blindness" because the blindness extends over a geometric half of the visual field; "homonymous" because the corresponding halves of the two retinas are blinded; "lateral" because nothing to one side is seen; and "right" because the disturbance is named for the side of the visual field defect, not for the side of the "retinal blindness." The lesion is always on the side opposite the visual field defect.

Occurring less commonly, an expanding tumor of the pituitary body, the stalk of which is located in the bay formed by the two optic tracts, may split the decussating fibers from the nasal half of each retina, producing a *bitemporal hemianopsia;* then only the nasal half of each visual field is seen. Similarly, a pathologic expansion of both internal carotid arteries lying in the angle formed by the optic nerve and tract of each side may interrupt the fibers from the two temporal hemiretinas, yielding a *binasal hemianopsia.* These are *heteronymous* because noncorresponding retinal fields of the two eyes are affected and little restriction is noticeable when both eyes are open.

Between the optic chiasm and the lateral geniculate bodies optic tract fibers, or collaterals from them, representing every portion of the hemiretinas, pass to the pretectal region lying just rostral to the superior colliculus. This group of fibers constitutes the afferent limb of the pupillary reflexes to light. These fibers were once believed to end in the superior colliculus, but now are known to end in the pretectal region.[19, 26] Hemianopsia *with* retention of the light reflex therefore characterizes lesions central to this regrouping. The "visual fibers" continue to the lateral geniculate body of the diencephalon, where they enter synaptic relations with the fourth order neurons, which continue on to the occipital lobe.

Lateral Geniculate Bodies and Geniculostriate Bundle. This nucleus is made up of six layers of cells separated by layers of fibers, giving the structure its conspicuous laminated appearance. Alternate layers of fibers are contributed by the hemiretinas of the two eyes.[4] Impulses from corresponding retinal points presumably first converge in the occipital cortex, which makes fusion a cortical function. In the monkey each optic nerve fiber breaks up into a spray of five or six branches, each branch ending by means of a *single* bouton related to the cell body (never the dendrites) of a neuron of the lateral geniculate body.[11] This is a remarkable instance of *divergence* and is the only known instance in which a cell is excited by single synapse stimulation.

By transneuronal[5] and Marchi[1] degeneration studies, the projection of the retina upon the lateral geniculate body has been established. Note in Figure 5 that the macular sector is interposed between sectors containing fibers from the upper and lower extramacular quadrants and that the lower retinal quadrant is lateral. Note also that, relative to its small retinal area, the macula is represented by a disproportionate amount of the nucleus. The oral-caudal relationship is the same as in the retina, i.e., the macular region is posterior to the periphery in both.

Fourth order neurons constituting the geniculostriate bundle, especially the inferior part, swing forward and around the ventricle of the temporal lobe before running posteriorly to the striate area of the occipital lobe. *Meyer's loop* or *detour,* so formed, accounts for the occurrence of visual field defects from lesions well forward in the temporal lobe (Cushing).

As the geniculostriate bundle enters the occipital pole, the macular fibers separate those from the upper and lower quadrants. Those representing the upper quadrant of the retina pass above the tip of the posterior horn and end in the superior lip of the calcarine fissure; those representing the lower retinal quadrant pass below the horn and end on the lower lip of the calcarine fissure. The macular fibers swing around the end of the ventricle and can be traced mainly to the posterior part of the calcarine fissure. The interposition of macular fibers between peripheral ones explains how a quadrant visual field defect having a sharp horizontal border can occur. An irregularly shaped pathologic process could produce a quadrant defect with a geometrically shaped horizontal boundary only if the fibers from the two quadrants were to some degree topographically separated as they are by intervening macular fibers.

Careful perimetry in cases of gunshot wounds has disclosed fields incompatible with the above arrangement of the visual radiation, e.g., sector-shaped field defects sometimes lying along the horizontal meridian.[29, 31] Also, quadrant defects having a sharp, straight, vertical border may fall short of or pass across the horizontal meridian. To explain these cases Spalding[29] has proposed that in the anterior portion of the geniculostriate bundle "the fibers subserving central vision are spread over the lateral aspect of the radiation, tending to congregate towards the intermediate point, whereas fibers subserving peripheral vision are spread out on the medial aspect, tending to congregate at the upper and lower margins." This is illustrated in Figure 6. Because of the exposed lateral posi-

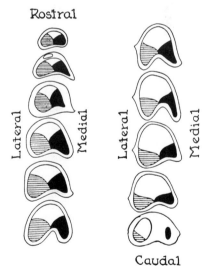

Rostral

Lateral Medial Lateral Medial

Caudal

Fig. 5. Sections through left lateral geniculate body of monkey. Terminations of fibers from retina are indicated as follows: *hatched area,* lower peripheral quadrant; *white,* macula, upper and lower quadrants; *black,* upper peripheral quadrant. According to the work of Le Gros Clark and Penman, this diagram shows too much macula at rostral end and too much peripheral representation at caudal end. (After Brouwer and Zeeman, *Brain,* 1926, *49*:1–35.)

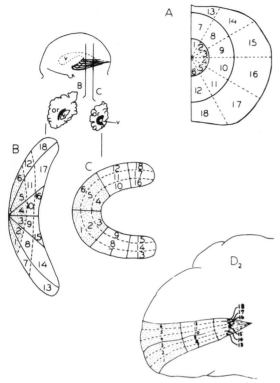

Fig. 6. Diagram of a hypothetical representation of the right homonymous visual field (*A*) and the corresponding fibers that serve this field in the anterior (*B*) and posterior (*C*) parts of the left optic radiation and along the lip (*D*) of the calcarine fissure. (After J. M. K. Spalding, from Teuber *et al.*, *Visual field defects after penetrating missile wounds of the brain.* Cambridge, Mass., Harvard University Press, 1960.)

tions of the fibers representing the horizontal meridian, this sector of the retinal field would be, as is the case, most often affected.

Macular Sparing.[25] A hemianopsia which includes macular vision is rarely caused by lesions of the occipital lobe. More often, the vertical or median border of the blind area is not a straight line ("macular splitting") but is indented so that 3° to 5° of central vision are "spared." Noted by Forster,[9] who in 1867 introduced the perimeter for the study of neurologic patients, macular sparing has been an intriguing neurologic puzzle for nearly a century.

The macula may escape when ischemia damages the cortical receiving area, because the macular projection area receives a double blood supply; its fibers may therefore be relatively less affected. In patients with bilateral thrombosis of the posterior calcarine artery, macular vision is spared. Other times the macula may escape although peripheral vision is affected because the latter is represented by so few fibers that

functional loss caused by pressure or ischemia has a greater effect on it. Some patients deviate their eyes slightly and form a pseudofovea (Fig. 7). However, Teuber *et al.*[31] have demonstrated that the "blind spot" is found in its normal position in some cases so that true macular sparing must exist.

Macular sparing after extensive surgical resections of the occipital lobe cannot be accounted for by either of the first two factors mentioned above. Two explanations have been advanced: (i) that the macular region is bilaterally represented in the cerebral cortex, and (ii) that the macula is extensively localized throughout the striate area so that only rarely is the whole representation destroyed. This might be accomplished without intermixing of macular and peripheral representations if the macular field extends forward, as shown in Figure 9. This would make an absolute central scotoma difficult to explain. To the first there are serious objections.[10, 30] For example, electrical activity is detectable in the macular representation of the left occipital lobe only when light is flashed upon the left hemimaculas of the eyes. Electrical responses of both striate areas suggestive of bilateral representation have never been observed. However, interest in this possibility has revived because some degree of macular sparing occurs in lesions of the tract and geniculate bodies, suggesting that crossing might occur lower in the system. In this case how an occipital lesion could ever cause splitting becomes the puzzle. Studies by Glickstein *et al.*[11a] with the Nauta technique for staining small degenerating axons rather than myelin sheaths of large axons are revealing visual fibers crossing in the corpus callosum to Area 18. If they serve visual sensation, they would explain macular sparing from posterior lesions and splitting from more anterior ones.

There is some presumptive evidence for diffuse localization of the macula, since macular sparing occurs in some lesions of the optic radiations, but electrical studies do not bear out this theory. However, the macular region may be more extensively localized anteriorly than was suggested in the previous section. That the macula is heavily represented at the posterior end of the calcarine fissure has been firmly grounded anatomically by mapping the visual cortex in monkeys.[30] Yet lobectomies which fall short of destroying the whole extent of the calcarine fissure tend to spare the macula; whereas, if resection is carried out farther for-

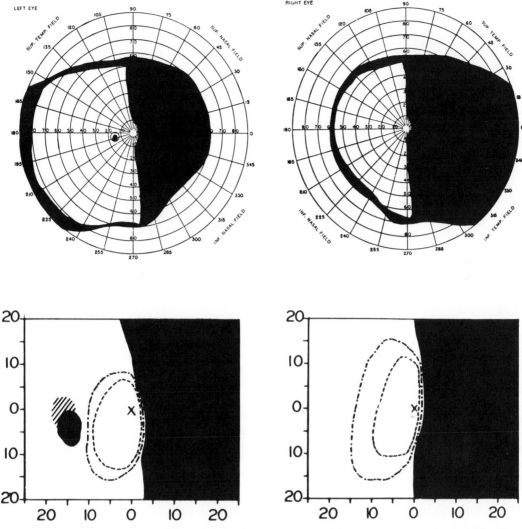

Fig. 7. Right homonymous "macular sparing" visual field defect presumably due to a shifting of fixation (pseudo-fovea). Note the indentation on the vertical boundary of the unseen portion of the visual field. In the lower half of the figure are plots of the central visual fields. The blind spot is displaced 4° to 5° downward and 2° to 3° to the right from the normal position (cross hatching). Dotted circles are color fields for green (inner) and red (outer) and are normally more nearly coincident. The ordinates and abscissae are in degrees from the center of the campimeter. (From Teuber *et al., Visual field defects after penetrating missile wounds of the brain.* Cambridge, Mass., Harvard University Press, 1960.)

ward to include the extreme anterior tip of the striate area, macular vision is not spared. It is almost necessary to suppose that the macular area extends farther forward than the representation of the peripheral retinal zones.

CORTICAL VISUAL AREAS

The cortical visual area in man is almost completely concealed from view in a longitudinal infolding on the mesial and cerebellar surfaces of the occipital lobe, the *calcarine* fissure. Cytoarchitecturally the region is characterized by a conspicuous line of Gennari visible to the naked eye without staining and often called the *striate area.* The cellular structure (Fig. 8) is the highly granular type associated elsewhere in the cerebral cortex with sensory function because of the great development of the outer and inner granular layers. The striate area, which is Area 17 in Brodmann's numeration, is surrounded by a concentric band, Area 18 or the *parastriate*

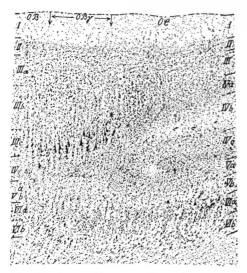

Fig. 8. Cytoarchitecture of transition zone (*asterisk*) between Area 17 (*right*) and Area 18 (*left*) of upper lip of calcarine fissure. On right (*striate area*) note that inner and outer layers of pyramidal cells are virtually absent. The almost clear area, *IVb*, corresponds to line of Gennari. Observe band of large pyramidal cells in layer *IIIc* of Area 18. Cell stain and 44× magnification. (From von Economo, *Zellaufbau der Grosshirnrinde des Menschen*, Berlin, J. Springer, 1927.)

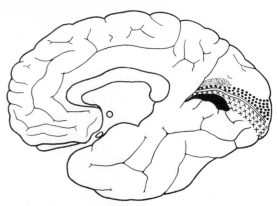

Fig. 9. Projection of retina upon calcarine fissure of man. Fine dots and black are, respectively, representation of upper and lower *peripheral* quadrants of retina; heavy dots and crosses are, respectively, representation of upper and lower quadrants of *macula*. Rostral extension of macular representation is hypothetical. (Modified from Brouwer, *Res. Publ. Ass. nerv. ment. Dis.*, 1934, *13*:529–534.)

cortex, and between them is an exceedingly abrupt transition in cytoarchitecture. A second more anterior concentric zone is the *peristriate* area, Brodmann's Area 19. The optic radiations terminate mainly in Area 17; some including crossing axons pass to Area 18.

Topographic Organization. Knowledge of the way fibers of the optic radiations terminate in the cerebral cortex aids in the diagnosis of damage to the occipital pole and permits deductions about function; clinical and anatomical studies have been followed by macro- and microelectrode recordings yielding greater detail and a greater wealth of functional interpretations.

As shown in Figure 9, the representation of the upper quadrant of the *retina* is on the upper lip of the calcarine fissure; that of the lower retinal quadrant is on the lower lip of the fissure. Thus lesions of the lower lip, for example, produce a defect in the upper quadrant of the visual field. Much evidence[13, 23] indicates that the anteroposterior dimension of the striate area corresponds to the periphery-macula (meridional) dimension of the retina. The rule is that the macula is posterior in the eye, and its representation is posterior in the lateral geniculate body and posterior in the occipital lobe. The

periphery is most anterior at these three levels. As in the geniculate body, the area of cortex devoted to the macula is very large compared to the area for the periphery.

How this arrangement came about may be easily visualized as follows: Imagine the left hemiretinas of the two eyes superimposed with their foveae coinciding. They are then folded forward from top to bottom along the horizontal meridian and inserted into the calcarine fissure with the fold coming at the bottom of the fissure and the point (fovea) posterior. If the meridians are imagined as closing like the blades of a Japanese fan, it becomes clear that the periphery will be located anteriorly. But this fails to suggest that a larger cortical area is devoted to the fovea than to the periphery. The ribs at the handle end of the fan would have to be farther apart to have the relations that exist in the cortex. Note that the free edges of the infolded retinas are the two halves of the vertical meridian which are *vis à vis* to the vertical meridian of the right hemiretinas located in the opposite hemisphere. This explains why midline lesions affecting both occipital lobes may produce a confluent midline scotoma of the right and left visual fields.

If this arrangement is correct, it means that at the occipital lobe the macular fibers for the first time cease to lie interposed between the upper and lower peripheral quadrant fibers. Such a rearrangement is somewhat unlikely. It is possible that the macular fibers do not all pass to the posterior end of the calcarine fissure, but form a wedge, the point of which is directed forward, separating the upper and lower quadrants as shown in Figure 9. Some evidence demands that a portion of the macular fibers extend even farther forward than the peripheral fibers.

Congruence of Field Defects.[31] The more carefully visual fields are plotted, the clearer it becomes that homonymous visual fields have the same general shape but are not strictly identical or congruent. Such incongruence is manifest along the vertical border of an hemianopsia and along the margins of a scotoma. Minor incongruence from lesions in or near the geniculate bodies presents no problem, since the contributions from the two eyes do not fuse in the geniculate body; further, macular fibers may spread diffusely in the radiation and then reunite. However, visual fusion is supposed to involve convergence at the striate cortex level so that a scotoma should show a mathematical congruence, although it never does. Electrophysiologic evidence throws some light on this problem.

Functional Significance of Topographic Organization. What is the significance of the topographic organization of the occipital lobe? Is it simply an engineering convenience, or is it the neural basis for detail vision, vision of forms and patterns and visual localization? Is it possible to think that the pattern of light on the retina is translated into a pattern of impulses on the occipital cortex with each unit holding its topographic position relative to other units? That this is the case is suggested by the fact that minute injuries of the cortex produce contiguous areas of blindness of the visual field. That the retina is projected point-to-point on the cortex is confirmed anatomically within the limits of our techniques. Thus, Polyak[23] finds that a lesion of the occipital cortex 1 sq. mm. in extent causes a degeneration confined to a single band of cells in the geniculate body only four to five cells wide. Moreover, the extent of the striate cortex devoted to the fovea justifies belief that the fineness of grain in the occipital cortex is the basis for the high degree of visual acuity exhibited by the fovea.

Talbot and Marshall[22, 30] recorded the points of maximal electrical activity in the striate area of the monkey while systematically exploring the retina with a point of light. The foveal representation is situated at the anterior border of the striate area on the lateral surface of the occipital lobe not far from the ear (Fig. 10). This region becomes posterior when the striate area largely disappears from the free surface of the cortex in the chimpanzee and man as a result of an expansion of the parietal association area. Even in the monkey, only 8° of the periphery (little more than the macular area) is on the wide expanse of the free surface of the occipital cortex. The first 8° are arranged in concentric bands medial to the fovea. The portion of the striate area devoted to the hemifovea is 6 mm. in radius. Retinal distance and cortical distance compare

as follows: within the foveal representation, 1 mm. of cortex is devoted to only 2′ of visual angle; whereas at the representation for 5° from the fovea, 18′ of visual angle are crowded into 1 mm. Much greater ratios must obtain for the extreme peripheral regions of the retina. This is borne out when the buried as well as the exposed visual cortex of the baboon is mapped out from reconstructed results of many recordings from penetrating electrodes.[7] In moving from the foveal to the peripheral representation in the cortex (Fig. 11), it can be seen that cortex available for visual discrimination decreases rapidly, little being available to serve the periphery of the retina. The falling off is equal in all

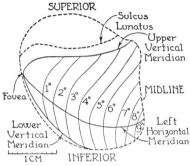

Fig. 10. Map showing projection of retina upon occipital lobe of monkey as charted by electrical methods. Left occipital lobe is shown as viewed from behind; foreshortening decreases apparent size of central representation. (Redrawn from Talbot and Marshall, *Amer. J. Ophthal.,* 1941, *24*:1255–1264.)

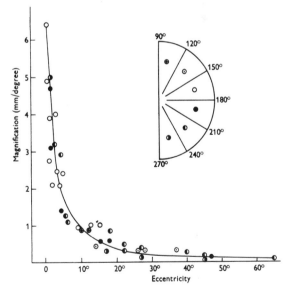

Fig. 11. A plot of the millimeters of cortical distance devoted to each degree of the visual field for central and peripheral areas (eccentricity), showing the rapidity of fall-off in magnification and that it is equal in all directions. The data for six radii have been grouped. (From Daniel and Whitteridge, *J. Physiol.,* 1961, *159*:203–221.)

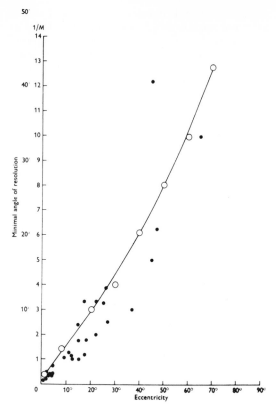

Fig. 12. The minimal angle of resolution in minutes for man (open circles) (from Weymouth's data) and the reciprocal of the degrees of visual field served by one millimeter of cortex (monkey) are both plotted against degrees of arc from the fovea. (Daniel and Whitteridge, *J. Physiol.*, 1961, *159:*203–221.)

meridians. The degrees of visual field served by a millimeter of cortex is called by Daniel and Whitteridge[7] the "magnification factor." At the fovea this magnification is more than 6, which, analogous to light magnification, is consistent with the fact that one sees finer detail in this region.

Figure 12 shows that the minimal angle of resolution (MAR) and the reciprocal of the amount of cortex devoted to each degree of visual field agree quite well throughout the retina. It appears to take an equal amount of cortex to do an equally fine discrimination whether in the periphery or in the fovea. For the monkey 67 μ of cortical distance, the width of about 5 cells in the densest part of layer IV, corresponds to the minimal angle of resolution measured at the fovea.[7]

Magnification of the retina on the striate cortex can be determined in yet another way. In the monkey the number of cells in the lateral geniculate body is approximately the same as the number of fibers in the optic nerve, on the order of 1,000,000. In the striate cortex the number of cells increases to more than 145,000,000. Talbot and Marshall calculate that a circular foveal area 1' in diameter (5 μ, or the width of 2 foveal cones) is represented by a cortical region 100 times as wide (0.5 mm.) with an area 10,000 times as great.

With nerve cells spaced at 20 μ, the ratio between cone and cortical cell is 1:100.

In the physical transmission of light to the retina, the energy tends to spread over a wide region, and in neural transmission there is a further tendency for lateral spread of excitation; yet the cortical grain is finer than the retinal grain. As seen in Chapter 19, acuity is a question of discrimination of intensity differences between peaks and valleys of excitation, discriminations much less than cone width are theoretically possible because of the fine cortical grain. An offset in a line of only 2.5" of visual angle (vernier acuity of "aligning power") is discriminable. Perhaps the fine cortical mosaic is used for such discriminations or for registering the slight differences in the images seen by the two eyes which form the basis of stereoscopic vision. On the other hand, the multiplicity of units may be significant for intensity discrimination, the number of active units being one way of reflecting intensity.

FUNCTIONAL ABILITIES OF SINGLE NEURONS

Cortical destruction, experimentally or pathologically produced, gives insight into the kinds of visual function in which given areas participate. The recordings of evoked potentials from a small area, but with many hundreds of cortical cells, reveals much information about the organization of the visual projection system. The recording by Hubel and Wiesel[13, 14, 15] from single cortical units, especially with respect to the organization of their receptive fields, has in recent years given insight into how the cerebral cortex analyzes the spatial aspects of a stimulus object.

Receptive Fields of Geniculate Neurons. The frog, which is adept at detecting and catching small insects, can apparently accomplish at the ganglion cell level some of the detection and rejection[22a] which in mammals requires the geniculate bodies and cerebral cortex.

Even in the monkey the geniculate bodies seem to accomplish little more than the retina.[14] Like the rods of the retina, some geniculate cells (Type III) have no color sensitivity.[17] Other cells (Type I) respond to white light and to monochromatic stimulation of the retina.[17] In both cases their receptive fields are round and, like the receptive field of ganglion cells, divided into a central field and a surrounding concentric ring, with mutual antagonism between the field and the ring.[14] (For some geniculate cells specific color cones acting antagonistically to one another are spread evenly throughout the receptive field.) Light falling on the periphery of a receptive field for a typical geniculate cell inhibits responses to the stimulation of the central zone and vice versa. The notable difference between geniculate and ganglion cells is the greater ability of the inhibitory surrounds of the geniculate cells to inhibit responses to stimulation of an excitatory center. This accounts for the initially puzzling fact that diffuse illumination of the retina produces very little activity or even none in many geniculate cells.

Simple Cortical Neurons.[13, 15] Although the receptive fields of many visual cortical neurons have the mutually antagonistic center and peripheral zone, the field is never round. The receptive field of a *simple* cortical neuron is often a long and narrow ellipse or oval, the division between center and periphery being a straight line; often the fields are not bilaterally symmetrical, the peripheral cells being massed on one side and few on the other side of the elongated slender center. This may be carried to the degree that the annular structure is replaced by an excitatory and inhibitory field lying side by

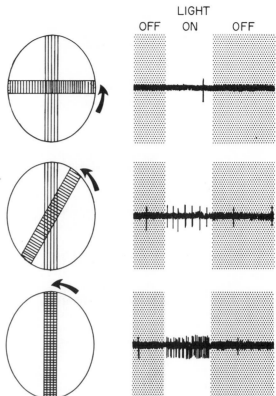

Fig. 14. Behavior of a line detector neuron of the striate area. At the left is shown the orientation of the horizontal illuminated slit in relation to the vertical elongated excitatory center of the receptive field and at the right the action potentials of the cortical neuron. The amount of cortical discharge depends on the mixture of excitation (center) and inhibition (periphery) discharge onto the cortical cell. (After Hubel, *Scientific American*, 1963, *209*:54–62.)

side (as *g* in Fig. 13). The division between center and periphery or between halves of an unsymmetrical field is always a straight line. The orientation of this axis varies from cell to cell and may be up, down, or in all intervening degrees of obliqueness (compare *a* with *c*, Fig. 13).

Even the symmetrical simple cell has potentialities for spatial discrimination, because the shape and spatial orientation of the stimulus are critical to the neuron's responsiveness. As in Figure 14, an elongated light patch may produce no discharge if it is at right angles to the axes of the receptive field, because it includes the inhibitory fringe. A thin slit of light or the edge of an object properly oriented may produce a massive discharge. This means that the retina is concerned with lines (and with the con-

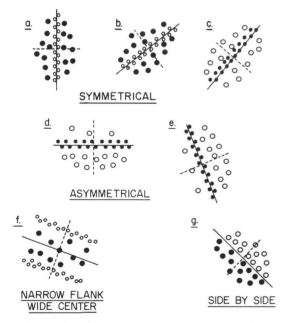

Fig. 13. Receptive field of single cortical neuron of the "simple" variety (filled circles are inhibitory and open circles excitatory). Continuous line represents the axis of the field and may be vertical, horizontal or oblique. Inhibitory and excitatory units may or may not be evenly distributed on each side of the axis, but the over-all contour of the receptive field is never round. (After Hubel and Wiesel, *J. Physiol.*, 1959, *148*:574–591.)

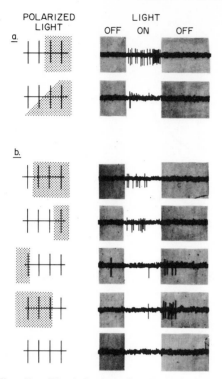

Fig. 15. The behavior of a "complex" cortical cell in the visual area to various illuminations of its large receptive field ($8 \times 16°$). The vertical and horizontal lines are used to suggest that simple cells with similarly oriented receptive fields are connected with the complex cell, the response of which is shown by the record at the right. The contour of the light patch is critical, since the cell is a detector of vertical lines. Note that in *a* there is a train of responses to the vertical contour but only one response to the sloping one. The first two records of *b* show the discharge of the same complex visual cell (shown in *a*) to a light patch occupying the left portion of the receptive field. Note that the cortical cell discharges wherever the edge falls in the receptive fields in contrast with simple cells which discharge only as the edge passes the line separating the inhibitory from the excitatory parts of the receptive field. When light occupies the right side of the field, the discharge occurs when the light is off, but again is about the same wherever the edge falls. When the whole field is illuminated, there is no response. (From Hubel and Wiesel, *J. Physiol.*, 1962, *160:*106–154.)

tours of objects*) and that the orientation of a stationary contour can be detected. Since cells having receptive fields with widely varying axial orientations are intermingled in a given cortical area, some cells will be maximally responding even though the orientation of the contour is shifting. While this could be interpreted by the

* Internal details of an object can be resolved into lines and contours. See Chapter 20.

brain as movement, bilateral asymmetry of single receptive fields seems to provide certain single cortical neurons with the ability to detect the direction of movement.

Cells having a thin inhibitory fringe on one side and a fat one on the other respond differently to a contour oriented to its axis, depending on the direction from which it approaches. When the edge of a light patch approaches from the side of the thin fringe, a strong discharge occurs; on approach from the other side, the inhibitory fringe suppresses the center and, in extreme cases, no discharge occurs. A *single* cortical cell with properly organized field and a properly oriented axis could provide the information for knowing the direction of an object's movement. The cerebral cortex probably never behaves in quite such a simple fashion. Nevertheless, the basic device—the structuring of the receptive field—is a simple way of analyzing the lines and contours of the external world into modal points of heightened neuronal activity.

Complex Cortical Neurons. The receptive fields of "complex cells" are homogeneous rather than separated into excitatory and inhibitory zones but are even more sensitive to the orientation of a straight line or contour than are simple cells.[15] In fact, a straight contour can be detected anywhere in the field. The response of a typical complex neuron might be excitatory if the stimulus occupies the left portion and inhibitory if it occupies the right (Fig. 15). However, complex neuron behavior differs from single cell behavior (such as *g* in Fig. 13) in that the complex cell fires in some degree wherever the contour of the object impinges on the field rather than just at the border between inhibitory and excitatory fields.

Hubel and Wiesel[15] explain this behavior with a scheme involving a direct connection of the complex cell with simple striate area cells. They suggest that a complex cell is connected with several simple cells having the same excitatory and inhibitory field organization and axes with the same spatial orientation and distribution throughout the entire extent of the complex neuron's receptive field. This hypothesis is strengthened by the fact that simple cells having receptive fields in roughly the same retinal area and having the same inhibitory-excitatory field organization are arranged in surface-to-depth columns in the striate cortex. The arrangement greatly reduces the number of fibers needed to connect many simple cells with the complex cell and enable it to abstract a common property of contour orientation.

Because the retinal position of simple cells is

distributed over a certain small area, the complex cell could record the orientation, to some degree independently of position and hence of fine random eye movements.

Hypercomplex Cortical Neurons. About 5 to 10 per cent of the cells in Brodmann Area 18 and more than half of those in Area 19 are termed "hypercomplex."[16] As with complex cells, they respond especially well to borders of a stimulus object and, to stimulate effectively, the border must coincide with the axis of the receptive field of the unit. However, if this coincidence is too elongated, the unit's response may be inhibited. The receptive field of a hypercomplex cell seems to be broken up into activating and antagonistic fields, arranged end to end along an axis. The antagonistic field thus "stoppers" the response at one or both ends. Some hypercomplex cells appear to have two axes at right angles to each other so that a cross is an effective stimulus pattern. As in Area 17, cortical neurons with the same general receptive field orientation are found in the same cellular column. Hypercomplex cells are thought to receive axons from two complex cells (or groups of cells) whose fields lie end to end, one being inhibitory and one excitatory to the hypercomplex neuron. An inhibitory-excitatory-inhibitory arrangement of a field ("stoppered at both ends") would require three complex cells or groups of cells. An occasional hypercomplex cell with two axes of orientation could result from convergence on it of two hypercomplex cells, each with single axes and oriented 90° from one another. Hubel and Wiesel[16] point out the implications of these studies to perception somewhat as follows. In the striate area the complex cells respond well to the contours of forms. The border will activate those complex cells whose fields are (i) crossed by the boundary and (ii) oriented in the direction of the boundary. Hypercomplex cells with an antagonistic zone would be especially sensitive to curved contours, since the curvature would avoid the end antagonistic zone. Such studies hold promise for the eventual understanding of the neural basis of perception.

VISUAL FUNCTIONS OF STRIATE AREA

The role of the cerebral cortex in vision increases steadily throughout the phylogenetic series. The great visual acuity of birds and fish, which is legendary, is subserved entirely by subcortical structures. In the mammalian series, visual function becomes progressively corticalized or encephalized until, in primates, the superior colliculi serve largely reflex functions. A corollary of the increasing importance of the cortex is therefore that the cerebral cortex is essential for certain types of visual function, whereas other types can be carried on by subcortical structures.

In man, occipital lobectomy abolishes all types of visual discrimination—light from dark, lights of different intensities, colors and patterns (form), but in animals some visual ability is sustained by subcortical levels. Visual discrimination in animals is tested by establishing the habit of choosing between two differently illuminated alleys or stimulus objects in order to receive food. In rats, cats and dogs[21, 28] discrimination of light from dark, a rod function, survives complete removal of the striate areas. The ability to discriminate may be temporarily lost, but it seems to be merely the discriminatory habit which is upset because the discrimination itself is readily relearned. The fineness of discrimination is decreased, but not greatly so. In monkeys, the disturbance is more severe, but even these animals can relearn.

When discrimination between two bright lights or between patterns (form) is tested, functions involving cone vision, the opposite result is obtained. Such discriminations are not possible after destruction of the striate areas. Even in the rat, pattern vision is impossible and no amount of retraining restores the ability.

Much evidence indicates that the two categories of results reflect the duality of vision so obvious at the retina. The clinching evidence is based on the fact that monkeys exhibit rod and cone visibility curves similar to man's. After ablation of the occipital lobes, the monkey's visibility curve even at high illumination is that characteristic of rods.[19] The conclusion therefore is that rod vision is not corticalized to the same extent as cone vision, and that even in the monkey rod vision can be carried out at subcortical levels of the brain. However, pattern vision demands a topographically organized system of fibers consisting of multiple discrete units such as the foveal cones and their central connections provide.

Levels of Visual Function. Whether scotomata involve an all-or-nothing impairment of vision throws light on the function of the visual area. Teuber and his co-workers[31] have shown that in man scotomata should be interpreted in terms of levels of function. In the recovery from damage as opposed to destruction (and in passing from a stable scotoma to a normal part of the field) the defect is not equal for all visual functions. First to recover is a sensation of light without color, shape or direction. Awareness of movement returns early, but its direction or rate cannot be appreciated. When object vision returns the contours are fuzzy; and color is last to return. Appreciation of flicker is a sensitive test of cortical damage; areas bordering on a scotoma apparently normal in ordinary perimetry show a lowered cortical fusion frequency. In view of the supposed chemical nature of dark adaptation, it is surprising that the curve of dark adaptation falls slowly and never reaches normal low levels, nor does it show the cone-rod inflection (Chap. 20).

Areas 18 and 19.[3] These areas surrounding the striate area are strongly developed in the primates and are concerned with vision. Evidence indicates they are efferent as well as sensory. Stimulation of them induces eye movements (Chap. 12).

As is true of the somesthetic and auditory areas, there are a visual area II and a visual area III, each having some topographic organization.[16, 30] These areas coincide with cytoarchitectural Areas 18 and 19 respectively. The latency of the evoked responses in them, and their failure to survive ablation of Area 17, together with electrical and histologic evidence of connections of Area 17 with 18 and 19, qualify these areas as "association areas."[6, 16] However, the receipt of a thalamic projection system, as supported by anatomic[11a] and electrophysiologic evidence, makes them, like other so-called association areas (Chap. 23), difficult to identify electrophysiologically. The receptive fields of many single cells in Areas 18 and 19, like those in 17, respond to edges and lines, critically oriented in respect to the axis of the receptive field.[16] No simple cells are found outside visual area I. In Area 18, as noted previously, 5 to 10 per cent of the cells are hypercomplex, (the remainder are complex), while in Area 19 this increases to 58 per cent, indicating a higher level of sensory function. As brought out above, hypercomplex cells are superimposed on complex cells, giving meaning to the phrase "elaboration of input to visual area I" by the surrounding visual areas.

Several skilled investigators have sought by a wide variety of objective behavior techniques to discover disturbances of higher visual ability after destruction of this region. As we have seen, a great deal of higher visual function seems to be carried out by the primary receptive areas rather than by the intervention of association areas. Nevertheless, some brain activity of the highest levels involving visual function is performed by and carried out by association areas

sometimes at a considerable distance from the visual area. The subject, therefore, merges into the general problem of association area functions and will be discussed later (Chap. 23).

REFERENCES

1. BROUWER, B. and ZEEMAN, W. P. C. Brain, 1926, 49:1–35.
2. CHOW, K.-L., BLUM, J. S., and BLUM, R. A. J. comp. Neurol., 1950, 92:227–239.
3. CHOW, K.-L. and HUTT, P. J. Brain, 1953, 76:625–677.
4. CLARK, W. E. LE GROS. Brit. J. Ophthal., 1932, 16:264–284.
5. CLARK, W. E. LE GROS and PENMAN, G. G. Proc. roy. Soc., 1934, B114:291–313.
6. COWEY, A. J. Neurophysiol., 1964, 27:366–393.
7. DANIEL, P. M. and WHITTERIDGE, D. J. Physiol., 1961, 159:203–221.
8. FERREE, C. E. and RAND, G. Psychol. Rev., 1919, 26:16–41, 150–163.
9. FORSTER, R. Klin. Mbl. Augenheilk., 1867, 5:293–294.
10. FOX, J. C., JR. and GERMAN, W. J. Arch. Neurol. Psychiat. (Chic.), 1936, 35:808–826.
11. GLEES, P. and CLARK, W. E. LE GROS. J. Anat. (Lond.), 1941, 75:295–308.
11a. GLICKSTEIN, M., MILLER, J. and RUCH, T. C. Fed. Proc., 1964, 23:209.
12. HOLMES, G. and LISTER, W. T. Brain, 1916, 39:34–73.
13. HUBEL, D. H. and WIESEL, T. N. J. Physiol., 1959, 148: 574–591.
14. HUBEL, D. H. and WIESEL, T. N. J. Physiol., 1961, 155: 385–398.
15. HUBEL, D. H. and WIESEL, T. N. J. Physiol. 1962, 160: 106–154.
16. HUBEL, D. H. and WIESEL, T. N. J. Neurophysiol., 1965, 28:229–289.
17. HUBEL, D. H. and WIESEL, T. N. Physiologist, 1964, 7: Fall meetings.
18. KLÜVER, H. J. Psychol., 1941, 11:23–45.
19. MAGOUN, H. W. and RANSON, S. W. Arch. Ophthal. (Chic.), 1935, 13:791–811, 862–874.
20. MALMO, R. B. Psychol. Bull., 1940, 37:497–498.
21. MARQUIS, D. G. Res. Publ. Ass. nerv. ment. Dis., 1934, 13: 558–592. See also: Arch. Neurol. Psychiat. (Chic.), 1935, 33:807–815.
22. MARSHALL, W. H. and TALBOT, S. A. Pp. 117–164 in KLÜVER, H., ed. Visual mechanisms. Lancaster, Pa., Jaques Cattell Press, 1942.
22a. MATURNA, H. R., LETTVIN, J. Y., McCULLOCH, W. S. and PITTS, W. H. J. gen. Physiol., 1960, 43:Supplement 129.
23. POLYAK, S. Res. Publ. Ass. nerv. ment. Dis., 1934, 13:535–557.
24. POLYAK, S. The vertebrate visual system, H. KLÜVER, ed. Chicago, University of Chicago Press, 1957.
25. PUTNAM, T. J. and LIEBMAN, S. Arch. Ophthal. (Chic.), 1942, 28:415–443.
26. RANSON, S. W. and MAGOUN, H. W. Arch. Neurol. Psychiat. (Chic.), 1933, 30:1193–1202.
27. RIDDOCH, G. Brain, 1935, 58:376–382.
28. SMITH, K. U. J. genet. Psychol., 1937, 51:329–369.
29. SPALDING, J. M. K. J. Neurol. Neurosurg. Psychiat., 1952, 15:99–109; 169–183.
30. TALBOT, S. A. and MARSHALL, W. H. Amer. J. Ophthal., 1941, 24:1255–1264.
31. TEUBER, H. L., BATTERSBY, W. S., and BENDER, M. B. Visual field defects after penetrating missile wounds of the brain. Cambridge, Mass., Harvard University Press, 1960.

CEREBRAL CORTEX IN GENERAL: NEURO-PHYSIOLOGY OF BEHAVIOR

CHAPTER 22

Electrophysiology of the Cerebral Cortex: Consciousness

By ARNOLD L. TOWE

THE cellular elements of the cerebral cortex, like all other cells, have distinctive electrical properties. The cortical tissue, which is a collection of innumerable neuronal and glial elements, shows both a continuous, rhythmic alternation of electrical potential and a variety of localized, larger voltage responses consequent to receptor activity. The former rhythm is called "spontaneous" because its origin is not known; the latter responses are called "evoked" because they are closely associated with sensory input. Knowledge of the mechanism whereby the evoked potentials occur should lead to an understanding of the origin and meaning of spontaneous activity in the brain.

CONTINUOUS ACTIVITY[13, 14, 18, 19]

Although the continuous waxing and waning of electrical potential in the brain was known

some 50 years earlier, it remained for Hans Berger, in 1929, to announce that it could be recorded from the intact skull of man and to use it as an index of health and disease in the brain of man. Via leads placed on the human head, exceedingly small (up to 50 μV. peak-to-peak in normal adults), irregular potentials can be recorded from frontal, parietal, occipital and temporal regions. The record thus obtained (Fig. 1) is called an *electroencephalogram,* abbreviated EEG. Typical differences exist between any two regions, the pattern depending upon the "state of the system" and the manner of recording.*

* A *bipolar* recording shows the difference in potential between two active leads, and a *monopolar* recording shows the variation of potential at a single lead compared with a stable reference point. A good reference or indifferent lead is difficult to establish, so that "monopolar" recording is in some disrepute.

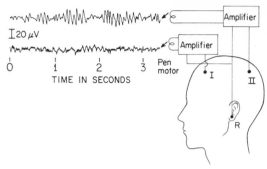

Fig. 1. Arrangement for recording EEG. The potential difference between frontal lead (*I*) and reference lead (*R*) shows low amplitude, fast activity of waking, relaxed human. Simultaneously, occipital lead (*II*) shows higher amplitude, slower activity.

Although the normal EEG consists of many different frequencies, one frequency predominates. This characteristic has proved more important than has amplitude of the wave and is used in naming the EEG pattern. If the dominant rhythm is between 8 and 14 per second, it is called an *alpha* rhythm; *beta* rhythms are those with frequencies of 14 to 60 per second; *theta* rhythms, 4 to 8 per second; and *delta* rhythms slower than 4 per second. Several other minor rhythms and "complexes" (e.g., spike and dome complex) are also recognized. In all these rhythms, the amplitude of the waves is inversely proportional to the typical frequency. By convention, high-frequency (short duration) waves are called "fast activity" and low-frequency (long duration) waves are called "slow activity."

State of the System. A whole constellation of factors affects the pattern of the EEG. At birth, the predominant rhythms are 0.5 to 2 per second and 20 to 50 per second; by 14 to 19 years, the adult pattern is fully developed. During childhood, the *theta* rhythms predominate; both the *delta* rhythms of infancy and the *theta* rhythms of childhood appear most clearly over the temporo-occipital regions of the brain. The precise EEG pattern that develops during maturation is typical of the individual and is stable, provided no disease or injury to the brain supervenes. Records from the frontal and parietal regions tend to show higher frequencies than records from the occipital region. However, during visual, attention-provoking stimulation, a fast rhythm of greatly reduced amplitude supersedes the normally preponderant *alpha* rhythm of the waking state; this phenomenon is called "alpha blocking" or "desynchronization."

When the sensory stimulus ceases to hold the individual's attention, the slower *alpha* rhythm reappears. The pattern of the EEG is also markedly altered when the blood or oxygen supply to the brain is altered. For example, slowing of the basic rhythm results when, in cerebral venous blood, O_2 saturation falls below 30 per cent, when blood sugar decreases to 35 mg. per ml., or when CO_2 level increases above 52 volumes per cent. On the other hand, fast activity predominates when CO_2 level decreases; forced overbreathing is used clinically to reveal certain latent abnormalities of the EEG.

A striking correspondence exists between the dominant frequency of the EEG and the apparent state of arousal of the individual (Fig. 2). In deep sleep, waves of 3 per second or less are seen; Bremer[5, 6] found a similar situation in the unanesthetized, isolated cerebrum produced by mesencephalic transection and concluded that sleep results from a functional deafferentation of the cerebral cortex. In moderately deep sleep, so-called "sleep spindles"—bursts of 10 to 12 per second activity—begin to appear. As sleep lightens, such bursts of activity appear at progressively shorter intervals, until the EEG is

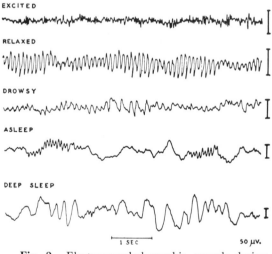

Fig. 2. Electroencephalographic records during excitement, relaxation and varying degrees of sleep. In fourth strip runs of 14/sec. rhythm, superimposed on slow waves, are termed "sleep spindles." Note that excitement is characterized by a rapid frequency and small amplitude and that varying degrees of sleep are marked by increasing irregularity and by appearance of "slow waves." (From Jasper, in Penfield and Erickson, *Epilepsy and cerebral localization*, Springfield, Ill., Charles C Thomas, 1941.)

gradually transformed into that typical of the waking state. Similar spindle activity is seen in an animal anesthetized with a barbiturate, the period between bursts being inversely related to the depth of anesthesia. As an individual goes from a drowsy to a relaxed to an excited state, the EEG progressively increases in frequency and decreases in amplitude. The behavioral change is called "arousal" and the electrical change is called "activation." These changes can be mimicked in an experimental animal by appropriate stimulation of the midbrain reticular formation.[26] Although activation of the EEG and behavioral arousal have been thought of as coeval, Feldman and Waller[11] have shown that this may not always be so. They produced EEG activation in cats made permanently somnolent by destruction of the posterior hypothalamus, and observed behavioral arousal in other cats with midbrain reticular lesions, lesions which rendered the EEG pattern of the cats "immobile" in slow activity or independent of the state of behavioral arousal. Nonetheless, EEG's do correlate with behavioral states in intact animals. *Theta* rhythms, 4 to 8 per second, develop during emotional stress and following withdrawal of pleasurable stimulation; they often appear in brain disease, especially in disease of thalamic structures. The slow *delta* rhythms not only dominate in deep sleep, but are often present in brain damage or disease, especially involving midline structures.

Focal damage to the cerebral cortex is localized electroencephalographically by the occurrence of irregular and abnormal activity (usually the slow activity mentioned above) in the neighborhood of the lesion or by the *reversal of phase* in records taken from opposite sides of the lesion with the reference lead over the lesion or acting as an indifferent lead. Asymmetry of the records from corresponding positions over the two hemispheres is very suggestive of focal damage. Epileptogenic lesions produce briefer waves, or "focal spike activity."

Epilepsy. The principal types of epilepsy cause distinctive electroencephalograms during the attack and brief, less pronounced, less characteristic abnormalities between attacks.[15] However, the latter are of major importance in diagnosis. Figure 3 shows the sequence of electrical events during an electroshock convulsion, which mimics the *grand mal* seizure of man. Fast activity is seen in the tonic period, and the clonic phase is marked by spike—slow-wave complexes, synchronous with the clonic jerks. The postseizure stupor is accompanied by high-voltage, slow, rolling waves which become very pronounced after repeated convulsions. *Petit mal* attacks consist of momentary lapses of responsiveness and consciousness without falling, often manifested to the observer only by a fixed stare. The EEG shows a doublet of a fast and a slow wave (spike and dome complex) repeated at the rate of about 3 per second. *Psychomotor epilepsy,* perhaps better called *epileptic automatisms,* usually originates in a focus in the temporal lobe. The attack takes the form of a stereotyped behavior pattern, sometimes an emotional outburst, of which the patient has no subsequent memory. In this, as in other instances of epilepsy arising from foci outside the sensory and motor areas, there is a strong element of "paralysis" rather than stimulation of function.

Physiologic Basis of the EEG. Several lines of evidence show that the EEG depends upon the electrical properties of cortical cells. Certain characteristics of the essential process can be surmised from the basic properties of individual cells. As shown in Chapter 2, the electrical space-constant of the cell body is so large that the cell body must behave nearly as a unit, i.e., shows no dipolar properties. On the other hand, the more distant and minute dendritic extensions of the soma, because of their high internal resistance, have space constants less than their own length and thus should be seen as dipoles by a distant electrode immersed in the same volume conductor. It is for this reason that many believe the EEG to result from the summation of dendritic activity, and especially of activity in any vertically oriented projections, which should be, on the average, closer to the surface electrode and show a greater solid angle. Recent evidence shows that the major part of the primary evoked response (see below) results from activity in neurons whose cell bodies occupy the upper third of the cortex.

Waves as seen in the EEG imply a nonrandom distribution of cellular activity. Synchrony and regular recurrence of cellular activity might be explained by reverberating activity in closed neuronal circuits or as a consequence of "spontaneous" rhythmic excitability changes in various neurons. A consideration of the environment in which a cortical cell is immersed leads to a qualitative understanding of the latter kind of explanation. If the extensive dendritic ramifications of a cortical neuron are influenced by the activity of adjacent neurons, whether ephaptically or by some more active process, then the entire cell membrane will be affected by the electrotonic spread of such changes. Consequently, in the absence of any disrupting input,

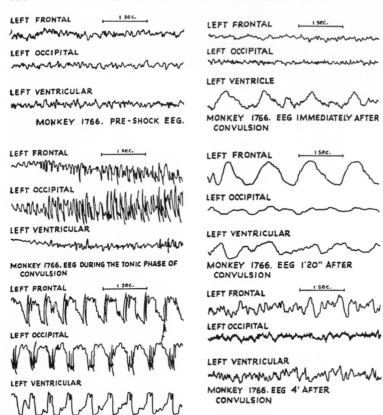

Fig. 3. Electroencephalographic records of successive stages of an electroshock convulsion in a monkey. One lead was taken from the lateral ventricles. Note especially the "slow waves" 1′ 20″ after the convulsion. These were associated with stupor which became more prolonged after repeated convulsions. (After Lennox *et al.*, *Electroenceph. clin. Neurophysiol.*, 1951, *3*:63–69.)

the excitability of cells in a local cluster would tend to vary as a unit. Likewise, the local cluster would synaptically activate other neurons in near synchrony with itself. This becomes a statistical process in which, eventually, the entire system might tend to fluctuate in excitability as a unit at some unique frequency. The process could be disrupted by an afferent input, but at the termination of such afferent domination, the system would again slowly establish its resting or "idling" condition. Andersen and Eccles[3] have proposed a different sort of mechanism dependent upon a prolonged, apparently recurrent, postsynaptic inhibition in primary thalamocortical projection fibers. This inhibition stops cell discharge for 100 msec.; no driving mechanism to discharge these neurons upon recovery to normal excitability has been proposed.

EVOKED CORTICAL POTENTIALS[7, 33]

In addition to the continuous electrical activity of the cerebral cortex, various discrete electrical changes can be produced by stimula-

tion of sense organs or of some point along the ascending pathways to the cerebral cortex. Study of such potentials reveals that two systems of fibers connect the sense organs with the cerebral cortex, one proceeding directly through three or four neurons with a high degree of topographic organization and the other branching from the direct route at the medullary and midbrain level, passing via the reticular substance of the brain stem and diencephalon, and eventually terminating diffusely in the cerebral cortex. A separate component of the latter pathway diffuses at the thalamic level. The properties of these two systems are largely known from the potentials they induce in the cortex and the manner in which they initiate or modify rhythmic potential phenomena. These evoked potentials will be described before the pathways leading to their production are discussed.

Single Neuron Response. Two classes of potential change occur in the cerebral cortex following sense organ stimulation: (i) a very abrupt alteration lasting one or two milliseconds and (ii) a more slowly developing, much longer lasting voltage variation. The former change is associated with the electrical field in the immediate vicinity of an active cortical cell, and is usually called the "unit spike." Not until recently did techniques for prolonged, systematic observation of such unit activity in the cerebral cortex become available[4]; these extracellular unit spike recordings are now readily obtained and sample a much wider range of neurons than intracellular recordings in the same tissue. Microelectrodes less than 2 microns in tip diameter are usually used to avoid damaging the cell whose activity is being recorded. The patterns of activity of cortical neurons have been found to be highly complex, but one generalization is possible: *No facet of neuron response is invariant* (Fig. 4). Although their behavior is probabilistic, statistical studies show that real and systematic differences in discharge patterns do exist between neurons[4, 34]; differences in temporal patterns are believed to convey sensory information.

Cortical neurons are "discriminatory" in their behavior. In the somatosensory cortex, as we have seen, it is not uncommon for a neuron to respond to deflection of the hairs in an area of 1 square centimeter but to no other input—or to cutaneous touch in a larger area. The area of skin effective in discharging the neuron (the *receptive field*) is often ringed by a band of skin which, when stimulated, prevents the neuron from responding to any excitatory input for periods of 100 to 200 milliseconds (the "inhibitory surround"). The boundary between the excitatory field and the inhibitory surround is not sharp; it is a tenuous region where the excitatory process provoked by the stimulus and impinging on the neuron becomes too feeble to be detectable. Neurons responsive to stimulation distally (e.g., hand or foot) have smaller receptive fields than neurons responsive to more axial sites of stimulation; however, a few large receptive fields can be found distally on the limbs. One class of cortical neuron consistently shows very large receptive fields—even to the extent of crossing the midline into ipsilateral regions.[35] By contrast with those in primary sensory cortex, neurons in motor cortex and in association areas characteristically respond to a wide range of stimuli of various modalities.

Primary Evoked Response.[2] When a large electrode is placed on the cortical surface, it is possible to record the second sort of potential change mentioned above. Stimulation of a sensory organ, a sensory nerve or a thalamic relay nucleus results in a very large (about 1 mV.),

diphasic potential (Fig. 5*A, B*) restricted to the sensory receiving areas of the cortex. As pointed out previously, such responses are used to map the projection of the body surface, retina or cochlea on the cortical sensory areas. This mapping is possible because the primary response results from synchronous activity in the direct, fast-conducting sensory pathways, which show a high degree of topographic organization. Since the primary response resulting from stimulation of a local site on the skin appears over a large extent of cortex, the mapping is accomplished by associating the site on the cortex yielding the *largest amplitude* primary response with the skin site stimulated.

The configuration of the primary response changes with the recording position; on the surface of the cortex it usually has an initial positive phase followed by a long-duration negative, phase, whereas deep in the cortex it is inverted (Fig. 5*D*). The level of "reversal" of the primary response is 0.2 to 0.3 mm. below the pial surface.

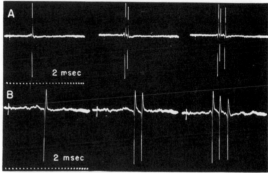

Fig. 4. Extracellular spikes of two neurons (A, B) recorded from monkey postcentral gyrus, showing variation in initial spike latency and number of spikes per discharge when sampled at three different times. Positivity downward. (Towe and Amassian, *J. Neurophysiol.,* 1958, *21*:292–311.)

Although no single cortical structure can yet be designated as *the* source of the gross cortical potentials, it is evident that the external granular layers are intimately involved.[35] The major vertical component of current flow during the primary response occurs in these layers (0.2 to 0.8 mm. below the pial surface). The evoked primary response begins as activity ascends into the fine terminal ramifications of the thalamocortical afferent fibers and continues for 20 to 30 milliseconds. Single cortical neurons are active throughout the duration of the primary response, discharging either once or firing repetitively. Maximum spike discharge occurs

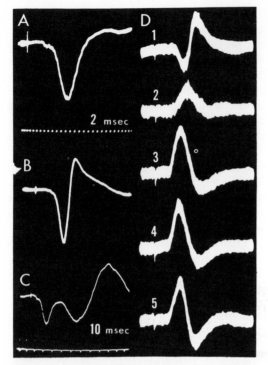

Fig. 5. Primary evoked discharge recorded from cat. *A,* Primary response recorded from cortical surface of somatosensory area I. *B,* Primary from somatosensory area II. *C,* Primary response and secondary discharge from area I. *D,* Superimposed microelectrode traces from surface (1) in 480 μ steps to 1920 μ (5), showing reversal of primary discharge and change in initial response latency with depth.

halfway through the primary response at the level of termination of thalamocortical afferent fibers (Fig. 6). The precise mode of spread of activity above and below the level of termination of the afferent fibers is unknown, but activity spreads upward from this level at 0.1 to 0.2 meters per second (apparently too slowly for conduction along apical dendrites or fine afferent fibers).

Repetitive Waves.   In the lightly anesthetized animal, a short train of 8 to 12 per second positive waves sometimes follows the primary evoked response. These waves, initiated by the primary response volley in the thalamus, have been described as a thalamic afterdischarge (Adrian) and as a result of reverberating activity between thalamus and cortex (Chang). The findings of Andersen and Eccles mentioned above support Adrian's afterdischarge hypothesis. The repetitive waves are restricted to the same area of cortex as the primary evoked response.

Secondary Discharge.[12]   In deep anesthesia, the primary evoked response is often followed by a second positive-negative potential (Fig. 5C) that appears throughout both hemispheres after a fairly uniform latency (30 to 80 milliseconds). This phenomenon does not depend upon spread of activity from the primary focus but appears to be mediated via the diffuse projection system described above. In the primary sensory receiving areas, the neurons that discharge during the primary evoked response do not respond during the secondary discharge; a different set of cortical neurons is involved.[33] Furthermore, the secondary discharge is not everywhere the same; the secondary associated with the visual primary response appears to be a different phenomenon from that found simultaneously in association cortex.[32] The secondary discharge is very closely related to the following two phenomena.

Spontaneous Cortical Bursts.   Under moderate to deep anesthesia and in the absence of known sensory stimulation, a succession of waves with a frequency of 8 to 12 per second waxes and wanes over wide areas of both hemispheres in near synchrony. These surface-negative waves are strikingly like "sleep spindles" and the *alpha* rhythm (Fig. 7). This phenomenon is not truly an evoked potential, although similar burst activity can be produced by stimulation of the thalamic reticular system.[10] The presence of spontaneous cortical bursts precludes the appearance of the generalized sec-

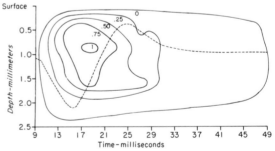

Fig. 6.   Distribution of neuron response in time after contralateral forepaw stimulation and depth below the cortical surface in the "sensory-motor" cortex of the cat. The graph should be read like a contour map; it shows the density of neuron spike activity. Most spike discharge occurs 0.7 to 1.0 mm. deep in the cortex, 17 to 20 milliseconds after the forepaw stimulus. Dashed line shows the associated primary evoked response recorded from the surface. (After Towe, Patton and Kennedy, *Exp. Neurol.,* 1964, *10:*325–344.)

ondary discharge—apparently an "occlusive" process—without altering a primary evoked response. Such burst activity can be regarded as a manifestation, not a cause, of the periodic waxing and waning of excitability in the "idling" system, because most evoked responses are potentiated during burst activity and depressed during the interburst periods. Because burst activity can be recorded from the thalamus and can be produced in the cortex by stimulation of the thalamic reticular system, it has been thought that it originates in and is regulated by the thalamus, or that it reflects a thalamocortical reverberating system. However, Jasper[20] has demonstrated burst activity from isolated cortex and has found that spindle bursts may occur independently in the thalamus and cortex of intact animals. Despite their similarity, spontaneous cortical bursts and repetitive waves do not share the same neuronal elements; the former are produced via a diffuse thalamic projection system whereas the latter depend upon the "specific thalamic nuclei" for their production.

Recruiting Response. Repetitive shocks delivered to the intralaminar thalamic nuclei produce a series of diphasic (negative-positive) potentials in both hemispheres after a 15 to 60 millisecond delay. If 5 to 15 stimuli are delivered each second, the amplitude of the potentials builds up during the first few shocks (Fig. 7) and then proceeds to wax and wane at a frequency of 8 to 12 per second.[25] Not only are the shape and frequency of this response similar to those of spontaneous cortical bursts, but its distribution in the cortex is identical to that of burst activity. Discovery of this phenomenon[25] and an observation by Bremer, described later, initiated the physiologic analysis of the electroencephalogram.

Neural Basis of Recruiting Response and Spontaneous Cortical Bursts. Study of the cortical potentials resulting from stimulation of the thalamus has led to a new, functional classification of the thalamic nuclei. Because focal stimulation of the relay and association nuclei results in short-latency (1 to 5 milliseconds) localized activity in the cortex, these structures are considered "specific thalamic nuclei."

The name derives from the writings of Lorente de Nó, who described two types of thalamocortical afferents in Golgi preparations. The "specific" afferents come from relay nuclei and end with many synaptic terminals in layer IV, but have little lateral spread throughout the cortex. They thus form a point-to-point projection. The "nonspecific" thalamocortical afferents terminate less profusely but more widely, giving branches to more than one and perhaps many cytoarchitectural areas. Their origin in the thalamus is not known anatomically, and whether such afferents form the diffuse thalamocortical projection system is problematic.

Stimulation of other thalamic nuclei results in widespread, bilateral cortical activation of the recruiting type. Such nuclei are considered "nonspecific thalamic nuclei." They include the midline and intralaminar nuclei, including n. ventralis anterior and n. centrum medianum, and the more lateral reticular nucleus.[31] The reticular nucleus is continuous with the midbrain reticular substance through the zona incerta. Although stimulation of these thalamic nuclei sometimes has an effect on cortical electrical activity different from that of stimulation of the brainstem reticular system, the nuclei are collectively considered to be a continuation of the midbrain reticular substance.

Because the nonspecific thalamic nuclei did not appear to be sufficiently endowed with pro-

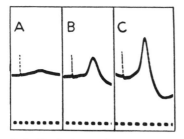 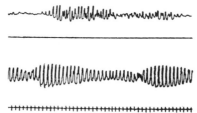

Fig. 7. *Left,* Cortical recruiting response to three successive shocks to intralaminar thalamic region. Initial vertical line is shock artefact. Negativity is upward. *Right,* A "spontaneous" 1–12/sec. burst (*upper record*) and a waxing and waning response (*lower record*) to continuously repeated shocks to intralaminar thalamic region. Bottom line is stimulus signal. (From Morison and Dempsey, *Amer. J. Physiol.,* 1942, *135*:281–292.)

jection fibers to the cortex, McLardy[24] proposed that their effect on cortical activity depends upon an intrathalamic diffusion system which activates specific thalamic relay and association nuclei. Starzl and Magoun[29] later concurred in this proposal. However, when Hanbery and Jasper[17] selectively destroyed the relay and association nuclei and then stimulated the centrum medianum or the n. ventralis anterior, recruiting potentials appeared in the cortex to which the relay nuclei project. Evidently these two nuclei, neither of which is known to project directly to the cerebral cortex, have their effect via the reticular nucleus. Rose[28] and Chow[9] have shown that the n. reticularis of the thalamus projects to the cortex in a systematic manner. The anteroposterior axis of the nucleus is represented mediolaterally on the cortex; the dorsoventral axis appears in a caudorostral arrangement. Hanbery and coworkers[16] have proposed that the thalamic reticular nucleus is the final outflow to the cortex of the reticular system.

The cortical neurons activated via the diffuse projection system are scattered widely throughout the cerebral mantle; in the primary sensory receiving areas they are not the same neurons activated during the primary evoked response. Specific thalamocortical afferent fibers break into dense terminal arborizations in layer IV, while the nonspecific afferents seem to be more widely distributed and to terminate more densely in the superficial layers. It is the cortical neurons discharged via the diffuse system that produce the continuous electrical activity of the brain known as the EEG.

ACTIVATION OF THE EEG; ALERTNESS AND SLEEP[23]

It is now evident that the EEG's of the waking and the sleeping animal are strikingly different and that afferent stimulation can transform the EEG into the "alerted" pattern. The latter phenomenon is termed *activation* or "desynchronization." Moruzzi and Magoun[26] discovered that stimulation of the reticular substance of the brain resulted in a phenomenon resembling activation (Fig. 8), and interpreted the effect as a desynchronization of cortical cellular activity. Bremer[5] had shown earlier that a waking pattern prevailed in the unanesthetized cat following a bulbospinal transection (*encéphale isolé*), but that the cortex falls into a kind of sleep after a mesencephalic transection that leaves the blood supply intact (*cerveau isolé*). The latter transection deprives the rostral part of the nervous system of the trigeminal and vestibular inputs that maintain the waking pattern in the *encéphale isolé* preparation.[27] Although it previously had been thought that the arrival of impulses over the direct sensory pathways (specific projection system) was responsible for the alerting of the cerebral cortex by a sensory stimulus, the analysis by Magoun and his coworkers[22, 30] showed otherwise. As illustrated in Figure 9, impulses carried in a system of fibers branching from the main sensory systems and traversing a slower, multisynaptic route through the reticular substance of the brain are actually responsible. This explains why a sensory stimulus evokes a potential in the somatosensory areas within 10 milliseconds,

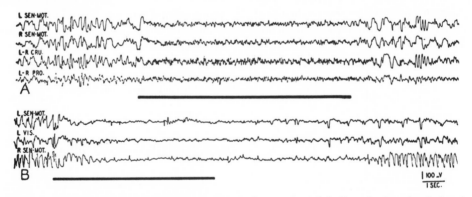

Fig. 8.   Desynchronization of electrical activity of cortex by left bulboreticular stimulation during period marked by horizontal black line. *A* is from an "encéphale isolé" cat lightly anesthetized; *B* is from intact cat heavily anesthetized with chloralosane. Abbreviations at left give origin of activity: sensorimotor areas, gyrus cruciatus or proreus and visual area. (From Moruzzi and Magoun, *Electroenceph. clin. Neurophysiol.*, 1949, *1*:455–473.)

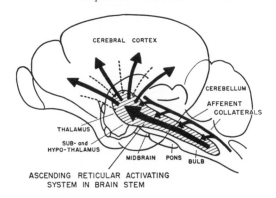

Fig. 9. Sagittal section of cat brain showing neural basis of arousal response. (From Starzl *et al.*, *J. Neurophysiol.*, 1951, *14*:479–496.)

whereas the changes in the *alpha* rhythm associated with sensory stimulation appear only after 40 to 60 milliseconds.

Experimental sensory stimuli cause replacement of the highly synchronized, large-amplitude, long-lasting potentials of barbiturate-induced sleep by low-amplitude, fast activity, an event termed activation. It is clear that the arrival of nerve impulses at the cortex over the familiar sensory pathways does not "wake up" the cerebral cortex since a sensory stimulus will still cause the cortical activation response when these pathways are interrupted by a lesion placed laterally in the midbrain. The specific relay nuclei of the thalamus have been by-passed, and impulses are still reaching the cortex. Consistently, evoked potentials can be recorded in the reticular substance after sensory stimulation. Throughout the brain stem, collaterals given off by the somatosensory and au-

ditory systems enter the central reticular substance (ventromedial reticular substance and tegmentum bordering the periaqueductal gray). Impulses ascend slowly and enter the dorsal hypothalamus, the subthalamus and the reticular and ventromedial part of the thalamus. They then pass on into the internal capsule and finally reach the cerebral cortex. On the other hand, the specific relay and association nuclei are not activated by midbrain reticular substance. Thus, cortical activation occurs after destruction of all but the basal part of the thalamus and the hypothalamus.

The similarity of cortical activation resulting from stimulation of the ascending reticular system and that accompanying "normal" waking can be seen by comparing Figures 2 and 8. The sleeplike state of the cortex in Bremer's *cerveau isolé* preparation was analyzed in the experiment shown in Figure 10. When the ascending afferent systems were interrupted in the midbrain, the animal was awake and the EEG corresponded. However, if the reticular activating system was interrupted by medially placed lesions, the animal was continuously somnolent and the EEG showed slow waves and spindles typical of sleep. Thus, despite the integrity of the long sensory and motor pathways, the animal was not "conscious" and did not move. A chronic state of somnolence can be produced without the accompanying EEG changes by bilateral destruction of the posterior hypothalamus without involvement of the midbrain reticular formation.[11] Thus, the diffuse "reticular activating system" is yet more diffuse, involving a separate system for behavioral arousal.

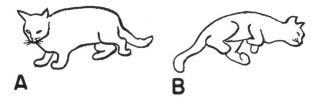

Fig. 10. Typical behavior and EEG records of cats with midbrain lesion sparing tegmentum (*A* and *A'*) and with lesion of tegmentum (*B* and *B'*). Cat *B* appeared continuously asleep or comatose during postoperative survival. (After Lindsley *et al.*, *Electroenceph. clin. Neurophysiol.*, 1950, *2*:483–498.)

AWAKE : MIDBRAIN LESION AFFERENT PATHS

A'

CC-17 21ST PO. DAY

ASLEEP : LESION MIDBRAIN TEGMENTUM   100 μV

B'

CC-12 12TH PO DAY   1 SEC.

Such observations explain the akinetic states which occur clinically[8] and which can be produced experimentally by lesions in the region of the periaqueductal gray matter and posterior hypothalamus. If the EEG records shown in this chapter are studied, it will be seen that the EEG varies from the high-frequency response of the excited state through the slower activity of the relaxed state to the slow activity of sleep and the long, rolling waves of stupor following multiple electroshock convulsions.[21] Feldman and Waller[11] have demonstrated that this association between state of arousal and activation may not be causal. Adametz[1] has further shown that the severity of the behavioral deficit following bilateral lesions in the midbrain tegmentum depends not only on the size of the lesions but also on whether they are produced in one stage or successively in two or more stages. This shock factor, or *diaschisis*, is illustrated clinically by the paucity and late appearance of neurologic deficits in slowly developing lesions of the central nervous system as compared with the dramatic and debilitating deficits in acute injury or rapidly developing lesions.

REFERENCES

1. ADAMETZ, J. H. *J. Neurosurg.*, 1959, *16*:85–97.
2. ADRIAN, E. D. *J. Physiol. (Lond.)*, 1941, *100*:159–191.
3. ANDERSEN, P. and ECCLES, J. C. *Nature*, 1962, *196*:645–647.
4. AMASSIAN, V. E. *Electroenceph. clin. Neurophysiol.*, 1953, *5*:415–438.
5. BREMER, F. *C. R. Soc. Biol. (Paris)*, 1935, *118*:1235–1242.
6. BREMER, F. *Boll. Soc. ital. Biol. sper.*, 1938, *13*:271–290.
7. BREMER, F. *Some problems in neurophysiology.* London, Athlone Press, 1953.
8. CAIRNS, H. W. B. *Brain*, 1952, *75*:109–146.
9. CHOW, K. L. *J. comp. Neurol.*, 1952, *97*:37–59.
10. DEMPSEY, E. W. and MORISON, R. S. *Amer. J. Physiol.*, 1942, *135*:293–300.
11. FELDMAN, S. M. and WALLER, H. J. *Nature*, 1962, *196*:1320–1322.
12. FORBES, A. and MORISON, B. R. *J. Neurophysiol.*, 1939, *2*:112–128.
13. GIBBS, F. A. Pp. 361–370 in Glasser, O., ed., *Medical physics.* Chicago, Year Book Publishers, Inc., 1944.
14. GIBBS, F. A. and GIBBS, E. L. *Atlas of electroencephalography*, 2nd ed. Cambridge, Mass., privately printed, 1950 and 1952, 2 vols.
15. GIBBS, F. A., GIBBS, E. L. and LENNOX, W. G. *Arch. Neurol. Psychiat. (Chic.)*, 1938, *39*:298–314.
16. HANBERY, J., AJMONE-MARSAN, C. and DILWORTH, M. *Electroenceph. clin. Neurophysiol.*, 1954, *6*:103–118.
17. HANBERY, J. and JASPER, H. *J. Neurophysiol.*, 1953, *16*:252–271.
18. HILL, D. and PARR, G., eds. *Electroencephalography, a symposium on its various aspects.* London, Macdonald, 1950.
19. JASPER, H. H. Chap. 14 in Penfield, W. and Erickson, T. C. *Epilepsy and cerebral localization.* Springfield, Ill., Charles C Thomas, 1941.
20. JASPER, H. H. *Electroenceph. clin. Neurophysiol.*, 1949, *1*:405–420.
21. LENNOX, M. A., RUCH, T. C. and BUTERMAN, B. *Electroenceph. clin. Neurophysiol.*, 1951, *3*:63–69.
22. MAGOUN, H. W. *Res. Publ. Ass. nerv. ment. Dis.*, 1952, *30*:480–492.
23. MAGOUN, H. W. *The waking brain.* Springfield, Ill., Charles C Thomas, 1958.
24. McLARDY, T. *Electroenceph. clin. Neurophysiol.*, 1951, *3*:183–188.
25. MORISON, R. S. and DEMPSEY, E. W. *Amer. J. Physiol.*, 1942, *135*:281–292.
26. MORUZZI, G. and MAGOUN, H. W. *Electroenceph. clin. Neurophysiol.*, 1949, *1*:455–473.
27. ROGER, A., ROSSI, G. F. and ZIRONDOI, A. *Electroenceph. clin. Neurophysiol.*, 1956, *8*:1–13.
28. ROSE, J. E. *Res. Publ. Ass. nerv. ment. Dis.*, 1952, *30*:454–479.
29. STARZL, T. E. and MAGOUN, H. W. *J. Neurophysiol.*, 1951, *14*:133–146.
30. STARZL, T. E., TAYLOR, C. W. and MAGOUN, H. W. *J. Neurophysiol.*, 1951, *14*:461–477.
31. STARZL, T. E. and WHITLOCK, D. G. *J. Neurophysiol.*, 1952, *15*:449–468.
32. TORRES, F. and WARNER, J. S. *Electroenceph. clin. Neurophysiol.*, 1962, *14*:654–663.
33. TOWE, A. L. *Confin. neurol. (Basel)*, 1956, *16*:333–360.
34. TOWE, A. L. and AMASSIAN, V. E. *J. Neurophysiol.*, 1958, *21*:292–311.
35. TOWE, A. L., PATTON, H. D. and KENNEDY, T. T. *Exper. Neurol.*, 1964, *10*:325–344.

CHAPTER 23

The Homotypical Cortex—
The "Association Areas"

By THEODORE C. RUCH

THE classic primary sensory areas with their highly granular cortex and the classic motor areas with their agranular cortex constitute only a fraction of the cerebral mantle. Both are specializations of the basic cellular pattern. The intervening area, increasingly extensive in the mammalian and primate series, has all of the six cellular layers and therefore is called homotypical cortex. This term can be considered a synonym for, and preferable to, the conventional designation, "association areas." In the light of laboratory experimentation, it is not clear what the "association areas" associate. For example, the classic idea that they associate (connect) the primary sensory areas with the motor area in an immediate fashion is not established. The view of the homotypical cortex in which the primary motor and sensory areas are islands is more elusive and nebulous than the idea of "linkage" conveyed by the term "association area." The breakdown of the association concept resulted from several developments in the 1930's, namely (i) that the function of the prefrontal area is concerned with recent memory (Jacobsen[19]) and that ablation of it causes hyperactivity (Richter and Hines[43]), (ii) the motor and somatosensory areas are self-sufficient, each having both an afferent input and an efferent output; (iii) areas of homotypical cortex proved to have a sensory function independent of the neighboring sensory cortex, e.g., the posterior parietal lobes (Areas 5 and 7) perform somatosensory discrimination independent of the input to the primary somatosensory area (Ruch[48]), a phenomenon especially well documented for the association areas surrounding the primary auditory areas (Chap. 18); (iv) all classic association areas, with the possible exception of the temporal lobe and a portion of the prefrontal lobe, receive a projection from the thalamus and, hence, are not dependent only upon impulses relayed from the primary sensory areas (Walker[55]), and (v) some association areas have direct descending projections to subcortical structures, e.g., to the hypothalamus and caudate nucleus.

Where the homotypical cortex borders on sensory and motor areas the cortex is transitional in structure. Three general association areas are recognized: (i) frontal (or prefrontal), (ii) anterior temporal, and (iii) parietotemporo-preoccipital area. These cortical regions are phylogenetically more recent and become myelinated later in development than the primary sensory and motor areas.

Far from being a mere link between sensory and motor areas or an appendage to sensory areas where association occurs, the homotypical cortex has a rich and varied input, the full extent of which will not be known until the Nauta stain is fully exploited.

The whole prefrontal lobule systematically receives fibers from the large lateral (neothalamic) portion of nucleus medialis dorsalis of the thalamus.[56] The anterior cingulate gyrus (mesopallium) receives fibers from the hypothalamus by way of the mammillothalamic tract and the anterior thalamic nuclei. As pointed out in Chapter 15, the pulvinar, a large and recently developed thalamic nucleus, projects to the entire parietotemporo-preoccipital sector (except the insula and superior temporal gyrus) and the lateral surface of the temporal lobe. Nucleus lateralis posterior and n. lateralis dorsalis project to the parietal association cortex. In addition to these connections, the entire cerebral cortex, as mentioned in the previous chapter, receives fibers from n. reticularis of the thalamus.

PREFRONTAL AREAS[5, 57]

Connections. The "frontal association area," also known as the prefrontal area or lobule, occupies the anterior pole of the frontal lobe. It extends fully upon the orbital surface of the frontal lobe and merges posteriorly with olfactory structures. On the dorsolateral surface of the hemisphere its posterior border is Area 8, which is transitional, both cytoarchitecturally and functionally. Because the "free" and orbital surfaces of the frontal lobe are projection areas of a single nucleus (n. medialis dorsalis, pars lateralis), this region is sometimes called the "orbitofrontal" cortex.[44] The orbital and lateral surfaces receive projections from cytoarchitecturally different parts of the dorsomedial nucleus (Fig. 1) and one area on the medial and most dorsal portions of the frontal lobule appears now to have no projection and may be truly "association" cortex.[2] The afferent input to the orbital surface from the amygdala, septal and tegmental regions via the magnocellularis zone of the dorsomedial nucleus has been identified. The input to the parvicellular portion of this nucleus and, hence, to the free surface of the frontal lobe remains in doubt.

Studies by Nauta[36] indicate three main streams of

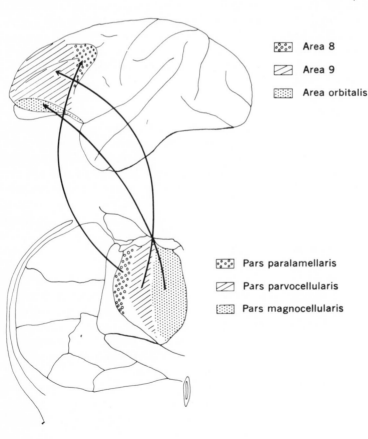

Area 8
Area 9
Area orbitalis

Pars paralamellaris
Pars parvocellularis
Pars magnocellularis

Fig. 1. Projections from zones of the nucleus medialis dorsalis to subregions within the frontal granular cortex. (From Akert, K, Chap. 18 in *The frontal granular cortex and behavior.* New York, McGraw-Hill Book Co., 1964.)

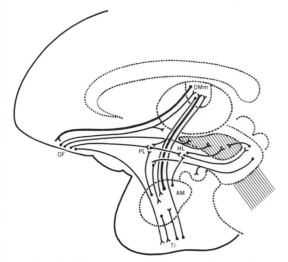

The frontal pole appears to be the way the neocortex funnels impulses into the limbic system. Such connections arise from the lateral convexity of the frontal region as well as from the medial and orbital surface. Also efferent projections of the prefrontal cortex converge with those of the limbic forebrain (septum, an-

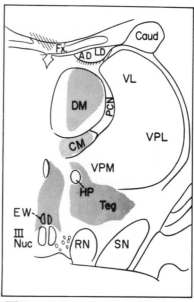

Fig. 2. Connections of the caudal part of the orbital surface of the frontal lobe (OF) with the dorsomedial nucleus (DMm) and with the amygdalar complex (AM) indirectly through the inferior surface of the temporal lobe (TI). The small round dot indicates the cell body, and the bifurcation at the other end symbolizes terminal arborization. Note that connections with the lateral preoptic and hypothalamic regions (PL, HL) link the system to the mesencephalic reticular formation. (From Nauta, *Brain*, 1962, *85*:505–520.)

efferent projection fibers from the prefrontal lobe, all of which connect with structures involved in emotional behavior or visceral control.

(i) From the lateral as well as the mesial surface, fibers join the cingulum and distribute terminals to the gyrus cinguli, gyrus fornicatus and, streaming ventrally, terminate as far forward as the presubicular region.

(ii) Fibers from the orbital surface and from the lateral surface inferior to the sulcus principalis pass through the large uncinate bundle to the temporal lobe, which is known to project to the amygdalar complex. Nauta[36] sees a three-way system of reciprocal connections between the orbital surface, the amygdala complex and the medial or magnocellularis part of the dorsomedial nucleus. For further details, especially, on the multiple efferent connections of this system with the hypothalamus, see Figure 2.

(iii) A subcortical stream originating widely in the frontal cortex mainly enters the internal capsule and connects, both directly and via collaterals, with the head of the caudate nucleus and the putamen. There are also direct connections with the hypothalamus, especially its lateral part, and with the intralaminar nuclei and reciprocal connections with the dorsomedial nucleus. Other important connections are with the subthalamic region and the rostral mesencephalic gray substance. When the orbitofrontal region is removed en masse, further details of its projection can be made out,[8] as shown in Figure 3.

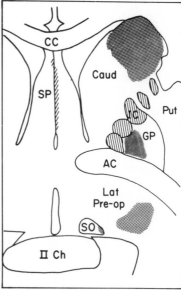

Fig. 3. Connections based on prefrontal lobectomy (sparing Area 8) showing more extensive subcortical areas with degenerating fibers and terminals than text description based on smaller lesions. Crosshatching, terminal fibers; oblique lines, fibers of passage; shading, both types of degeneration. The abbreviations are mnemonic. (From DeVito and Smith, *J. comp. Neurol.*, in press.)

terior cingulate gyrus) to end in the hypothalamus and rostral mesencephalon.

Ablation — Hyperactivity.[22, 27, 38, 49] Reflexes, posture and discrete movement are not affected by ablation of the orbitofrontal cortex; nor can any definite impairment of general intelligence be measured. However, definite disturbances of *behavior* are produced. Unlike those of the language functions, the behavior disturbances are marked only when the frontal areas are damaged *bilaterally*. As recently as 1922, Bianchi described in purely mentalistic terms from "naked eye" observations the results of extirpating the orbitofrontal areas in animals. Since that time, definite, objectively demonstrable disturbances of behavior have been discovered, and methods have been devised for quantifying them.

In monkeys ablation of the entire orbitofrontal lobule or its subareas induces a state of hyperactivity manifested by incessant, stereotyped walking or pacing, much like that of certain zoo inhabitants (notably the carnivores). The pacing appears aimless. It is continued for hours, almost without pause, but ceases in darkness. In its extreme form it is almost maniacal. This hyperactivity, like that of certain problem children, is stopped by amphetamine and certain other cerebral excitants. It has been observed in cats, rats and monkeys, but not as yet in chimpanzees or man. The squirrel monkey appears not to develop hyperactivity after prefrontal lesions.[33] In *Macaca mulatta* monkeys it seems to appear sometime between one and two years of age. To some degree, the whole orbitofrontal cortex is concerned with the regulation of activity,[22] but bilateral lesions of posterior portions of the orbital surface (Area 13 of Brodmann) produce nearly maximal hyperactivity.[49] Livingston *et al.*[27] studied quantitatively the activity before and after lesions of Area 13 and estimated that activity increased eight to sixteen times following the lesion. The onset of hyperactivity is more rapid after lesions of Area 13; some prefrontal ablations sparing this region do not result in marked hyperactivity.

The enduring hyperactivity is usually preceded by a period of hypoactivity: apparent apathy, drooping of the head, sluggishness of movement, blankness of expression, and a tendency to sit staring into space and to ignore human presence. (This sequence of underactivity followed by overactivity—cf. flaccidity–spasticity—usually means that the ablated structures contain neurons of opposite influence on the function observed. This would lead to the prediction of a system originating in the prefrontal lobes which *facilitates* locomotor activity.) This state of hypoactivity, which may also be ascribed to diaschisis, lasts from several days to two or three weeks after operation. It gradually gives way to bouts of stereotyped pacing, which punctuate the periods of inactivity; these bouts of activity become progressively longer. Once established, the pacing persists indefinitely (Fig. 4). When hyperactivity is severe, random activities—the varied patterns of manipulations and posturings, the quick play of grimacing, and head and eye movements—give way to stereotyped walking.

Recent evidence suggests that the hyperactivity may result from an interruption of fibers passing to the hypothalamus, since, in rats, lesions in septal–preoptic regions[29] produce incessant running behavior reminiscent of that following stimulation of certain hypothalamic areas by implanted electrodes.[28] As will be discussed later, lesions in the head of the caudate nucleus of the monkey also produce a hyperactivity that is diminished by darkness; interestingly, these lesions need not be bilateral to produce their effect.[7]

Ablation — Delayed Response.[5, 19, 57] Responses to the temporally and spatially immediate environment constitute much of an animal's behavior. However, many responses, although called forth by the immediate situation, owe their direction to sensory information gained previously. Experimentally, this capacity is assessed by the delayed response test, which may take a variety of forms. In one form, a monkey or chimpanzee is allowed to view through bars a piece of food being deposited beneath one of two or more cups on a sliding tray. An opaque door is then lowered in front of the animal for a chosen interval. The tray is then pushed forward to the cage and the door is raised, permitting the animal to reach the cups. The animal is allowed to select one cup, the reward being obtained if the proper cup is selected. With training, a normal monkey makes successful choices after delays as long as 90 seconds between seeing the food and choosing among the cups. After bilateral orbitofrontal ablation, even delays as short as 5 seconds make successful response a matter of chance; the animal is at a complete loss in selecting the cup concealing the food. (In fact, only that fraction

making up the banks and depths of *sulcus principalis* within the wings of the arcuate fissure, e.g., Figure 2, Chapter 12, need be ablated to produce nearly maximal deficit in delayed response.[35]) Neither unilateral frontal lobule ablation nor extirpation of other cortical areas has this effect. However, lesions in the caudate nucleus produce a similar deficit in delayed alternations (see below). No other part of the cerebral cortex can substitute for the orbitofrontal areas in this capacity, since the problem cannot be relearned. Nor is complete failure in the delayed response test due to a general impairment of intelligence or ability to learn. After frontal lobectomy, monkeys can retain or learn a visual discrimination quite as well as normal monkeys. A chimpanzee with a prefrontal lobectomy can successfully perform the "stick and platform" problem, which assesses the animal's ability to solve complex problems.[20]

A chimpanzee in a barred cage is confronted with a platform on which a piece of food and a stick or rake have been placed. The food is out of arm's reach but can be reached if the rake is used. After this task is mastered, a series of sticks is introduced, a short stick being used to secure a longer stick, etc., until one long enough to reach the food is obtained. An orbitofrontal lobectomized chimpanzee is able to grasp these relations and organize a serial response involving four sticks, but only if the whole problem is within its view

at one moment. If two platforms are used, the lobectomized animal fails totally when a stick from one platform must be carried to the other in order to secure the next longer stick, and it experiences great difficulty when only one stick is involved but the food is on the other platform.

A test similar to delayed response is that of *delayed alternation,* in which the animal learns to make alternate right and left turns and to remember which turn comes next, despite an enforced delay after each turn is completed. Even rats show definite deficiencies in this problem after bilateral injury to the frontal poles. Monkeys with similar lesions are deficient in *double alternation* problems in which the correct choices are RRLLRRLL.[25]

The inability to perform delayed response and delayed alternation may be operationally termed incapacity for "immediate memory," for, in fact, this is what the monkey fails to do—remember under which cup the reward lies. "Memory," when the right and wrong places change from trial to trial, differs from remembering a visual discrimination when a given intensity is always right or wrong, or remembering a motor skill like ice skating in which standing up or sitting down is right or wrong. The latter two types of remembering are not affected by prefrontal lesions. Several causes for failure

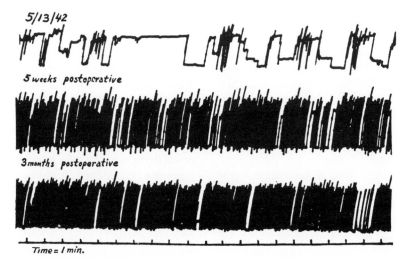

Fig. 4. Activity records of monkeys before and after posterior orbital lesions. Freely movable bottom of oblong activity cage rests on pneumatic pad connected to tambour which records upon kymograph. Any movement toward or away from end resting on pad causes a pen excursion, height roughly reflecting extent of animal's movement. In top record, notice varied pattern of activity and frequency of small movements of a normal monkey indicated by small pen excursions. Second and third strips show hyperactivity induced by bilateral ablation of Area 13. Observe absence of pauses longer than a few seconds and that hyperactivity was undiminished three months after operation. (From Ruch and Shenkin, *J. Neurophysiol.,* 1943, 6:349–360.)

CONDITIONED EMOTIONAL RESPONSE
Monkey #471 (Roxanne)

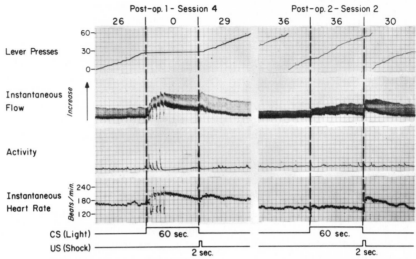

Fig. 5. The three panels of records on the left are (i) controls showing the resting state (ii) the effect of conditioned (light) and (iii) the unconditioned (shock) stimuli on lever pressing to receive food pellets and on instantaneous aortic blood flow, heart rate and general body activity, which is also reflected as an artifact in flow and rate records. The same records on the right were obtained after bilateral ablation of the frontal lobes anterior to Area 8 and a small lesion in the hypothalamus. (Unpublished records furnished by O. A. Smith, Jr. See also Stebbins and Smith, *Science,* 1964, *144*:881–883.)

of immediate memory have been suggested and tested. Also, factors mitigating the absolute nature of the loss may afford a clue to its mechanism. For example, emphasizing the correct cup or increasing motivation has been found to decrease the severity of the effect of prefrontal lesions on delayed response. They may simply make the task easier, and the impaired animals have more room for improvement than the normal, control animals. Many of these are general, i.e., effective on many of the deficits following neural lesions. It is the factors specific to delayed response which are analytical and will be mentioned.

The defect basic to "loss of immediate memory" may be one or several of the following: (i) failure to attend (as might be caused by hyperactivity), (ii) passive but rapid decay of the "stimulus set," (iii) active interference with the set, i.e., distractability, and (iv) preservation of sets from one trial to another. Indeed, reduction of external stimuli (and of activity) through elimination of light during the delay period, administration of sedative drugs, exposure of the correct object of two which are presented later, or "heightening attention to the stimulus" results in improved performance by lobecto-

mized monkeys. Clearly, the loss of this capacity to respond correctly after a delay is not absolute.

Ablation—Emotion. Clinical observations, visceral changes resulting from stimulation in animals (Chap. 26), and the anatomic connections of the prefrontal homotypical cortex to the hypothalamus and limbic system suggest that the frontal areas are concerned with emotion. This has been recently established[52] with the conditioned emotional response (CER) as documented by the heart rate and the instantaneous rate of blood flow in the aorta, on the one hand, and the rate of lever pressing to obtain small rewards on the other. As seen in Figure 5, at the onset of a conditioned stimulus, a light which has previously been associated with electric shock, lever-pressing ceases and flow and heart rate increase sharply—as much as or even more than changes elicited by the unconditioned stimulus, an electric shock. After combined lesion of the frontal lobes and of a critical area in the hypothalamus (neither lesion alone is effective), lever-pressing continues unaltered after the conditioned signal, and the circulatory responses are reduced to a small delayed rise in blood flow. That the brain mechanism of induced autonomic response is intact is shown by the persisting response to the electric shock (extreme right). The most likely interpretation is that the frontal areas in this case form a learned link between a light stimulus and the lower centers controlling vascular responses, a function shared by the hypothalamus.

Ablation—Neurosis.[20, 26, 31, 38] Certain experimental situations produce behavior in animals which strongly resembles neurotic behavior in man, although the identity of the two states is not yet proved. The classic experiment was conducted in Pavlov's laboratory in 1914 and involved the discrimination of a circle from an ellipse. A dog was "conditioned" to salivate when confronted with a circle, but not when an ellipse appeared. The ellipse was then made progressively more circular until the difference was no longer discriminable. Continued training failed to improve discrimination and, in fact, the habit deteriorated. The animal displayed neurotic behavior which Pavlov[38] described as follows:

"At the same time the whole behaviour of the animal underwent an abrupt change. The hitherto quiet dog began to squeal in its stand, kept wriggling about, tore off with its teeth the apparatus for mechanical stimulation of the skin, and bit through the tubes connecting the animal's room with the observer, a behaviour which never happened before. On being taken into the experimental room the dog now barked violently, which was also contrary to its usual custom; in short, it presented all the symptoms of a condition of acute neurosis."

Experimental neurosis is not merely a momentary emotional response. In sheep, the neurosis continues to affect behavior outside the experimental situation.[26] Twenty-four hour records of spontaneous activity or respiratory rhythm and of heartbeat yield evidence of an excited state that persists outside the experimental room. Paradoxically, birds seem susceptible to something like experimental neurosis despite their primordial cerebral cortex. Pigeons have been reported to display excessively agitated behavior or to become cataleptic for 5 to 30 minutes when confronted with "indiscriminable" visual figures in place of the readily discriminated training figures.[54]

Monkeys and chimpanzees working on difficult discrimination problems or problems near threshold tend to exhibit neurotic behavior like that of Pavlov's dogs. In a highly emotional chimpanzee unable to perform delayed reactions successfully in preoperative tests, Jacobsen[20] observed the following behavior:

"This animal was extremely eager to work and apparently well motivated; but the subject was highly emotional and profoundly upset whenever she made an error. Violent temper tantrums after a mistake were not infrequent occurrences. She observed closely loading of the cup with food, and often whimpered softly as the cup was placed over the food. If the experimenter lowered or started to lower the *opaque door* to exclude the animal's view of the cups, she immediately flew into a temper tantrum, rolled on the floor, defecated and urinated. After a few such reactions during the training period, the animal would make no further responses to this test, although she responded eagerly if examined on different problems. Training on this situation was continued daily for three weeks. At the beginning, the animal had been eager to come to the experimental room, and when released from the living quarters ran to the transfer cage, opened the door and entered. But by the end of this period it was necessary to drag the animal from the living cage to the transfer cage, and in turn force her into the experimental cage. It was as complete an 'experimental neurosis' as those obtained by Pavlov's conditioned reflex procedures."

After bilateral lobectomy the animal's behavior changed profoundly. She now entered the experimental room and worked with alacrity. Mistakes and failures to obtain food caused no emotional manifestation although many more errors were made than before operation. "It was," in Jacobsen's words, "as if the animal had . . . placed its burdens on the Lord."

These observations by Jacobsen provided a rationale for "psychosurgical" operations upon the frontal areas. In 1935, Egas Moniz, a Portuguese neurologist, introduced an operation—frontal lobotomy—designed to interrupt most of the connections between the orbitofrontal area and the deeper portions of the brain without completely isolating it from the remainder of the cerebral cortex.* Certain neurotic symptoms of man, like those experimentally engendered in the chimpanzee, are altered by lobotomy. The effects of this procedure are most favorable in disorders characterized by emotional tension, e.g., anxiety neuroses, involutional depression and manic-depressive psychosis. This does not mean that the patient becomes incapable of displaying emotion; he may even be emotionally over-reactive. But, the force of the emotion or its connection with imagination and thought processes is reduced. Anxieties, thoughts or delusions which have distressed and incapacitated the patient may persist, but are remote and of no concern. Unfortunately, other matters, such as household

* For this work he shared the Nobel Prize with Hess in 1949.

duties, sexual proprieties or regard for the feelings of others, may also become of no concern to the patient.

Frontocaudate Relations.   The caudate nucleus has long been associated with the control of voluntary movement (Chap. 13). Its anatomic position in the core of the frontal lobes, the newly established corticocaudate connections and some behavioral evidence suggest that the caudate nucleus (and perhaps other basal ganglia) are concerned with behavior functions as well as motor skills. On the anatomic level, Nauta[36] and DeVito and Smith[8] agree that terminal degeneration from prefrontal lesions occurs in the caudate nucleus as direct connections or by collateralization from fibers in the surrounding white matter. There is a strong possibility that fibers from the prefrontal cortex pass through the caudate nucleus since it shrinks greatly in size after prefrontal lesions and has a minutely punched-out appearance.[4] Obviously, prefrontal lesions, if deep posteriorly, may injure the caudate nucleus or its projection fibers, and, vice versa, a caudate lesion might affect the cortical projections passing beside and certainly any passing through the caudate nucleus.

Davis[7] has found that bilateral lesions of the caudate nucleus produce hyperactivity measured objectively; this hyperactivity ceases during darkness. The fact that *unilateral* lesions of the head of the caudate produce increased activity (circling) suggests that the increased walking may differ from that produced by prefrontal lesions and may be like that from lesions of Area 8.[21] Moreover, large, bilateral caudate lesions may not produce hyperactivity[9] and, in view of the anatomic relationships, negative evidence may outweigh positive evidence. Finally, the inhibitory influence of "caudate stimulation," consistent with a release of motor activity following ablation, may be caused by spread of current to fibers in the adjacent white matter, presumably coming from the prefrontal lobe (Chap. 13).

That the caudate nucleus is concerned with cognitive behavior is clearer. Bilateral lesions of the head of the caudate nucleus produce defects in delayed alternation[45] proportional to the size of the lesion;[47] similar deficits in delayed response are found.[3]

The caudate nucleus and other basal ganglia (globus pallidus) may also be involved in the third behavioral category, emotion, in which the prefrontal cortex has been implicated. The rate of extinction of a conditioned avoidance response in which a neutral stimulus is given significance by combining it with an "affective stimulus" and then withholding the affective stimulus is often considered to be indicative of neurosis and emotionality. A *decreased* rate of extinction indicates anxiety and fear. Lesions of the caudate nucleus, alone or in combination with frontal lesions, and lesions of the globus pallidus[24]—like lesions in areas more usually associated with emotion—increase the rate of extinction for some time after the operation. Thus, the basal ganglia may be concerned with the behavioral as well as the motor aspects of frontal lobe function, either as a relay station or as a detour in the pathways from the anterior and the more posterior motor areas of the frontal lobe.

FRONTAL LOBE FUNCTION IN MAN[10, 11, 32, 34, 53]

Damage of the orbitofrontal area in man produces a bewildering diversity of symptoms difficult to describe. These vary from patient to patient even though the lesions are closely similar. The manner of damage may be natural (trauma or tumor) or intentional (lobotomy, lobectomy, topectomy or gyrectomy).*

Whether the damage is bilateral is certainly important. Surgical cases provide the best evidence of the physiology of the orbitofrontal lobule in man, although the recent work of Weinstein and Teuber[58] on patients with penetrating wounds of the brain affords better information on the pre-injury status than is usually available. In both cases, evaluation of brain injury must take account of the possibility that the scar rather than the loss of frontal tissue is the source of abnormal neural discharge,[16] which in turn causes behavioral deficits and abnormalities. Postmortem study of the lesion is rare. In one extensively reported case, tumors were found at necropsy in many regions besides the original frontal one removed surgically. In fact, the prefrontal area's reputation for producing varied and inconsistent results may be based on the paradoxical reason that tumors may grow there with relatively few symptoms

* In lobotomy (or leukotomy) the fibers of the white matter of the prefrontal lobe are incised; in the other three operations, a lobule, cytoarchitectural area or gyrus, respectively, is removed.

to call attention to them, in contrast with more posterior tumors which quickly cause motor, somatosensory and visual disturbances.

Four factors contribute to the diversity of symptoms: (i) The symptoms have not been adequately reduced to objective description; (ii) different investigators studying single cases emphasize different symptoms prominent in their individual cases; (iii) except with penetrating wounds, the patients are usually psychiatrically abnormal before lobotomy and no control group with surgical damage elsewhere in the brain is available; and (iv) a control group having tumors or trauma in other regions was not studied. Teuber's[53] analysis of the pitfalls in frontal lobe studies is widely applicable to the clinical study of the brain. The following are some of the more frequently encountered disturbances.

Intelligence and Intellectual Functions.[34, 53] The prefrontal lobes, because of their prominence in man (and for very little other reason), were once considered the seat of the "intellectual" functions. However, loss of intelligence as tested by familiar mental tests is not conspicuous after orbitofrontal lobotomy;[16, 46] indeed, the most careful work comparing pre-injury scores on the Army General Classification Test with similar scores obtained ten years after destruction of the frontal lobes through penetrating wound injury has failed to show any intelligence deficit.[58, 59] In studies of lobotomy cases the greatest reliance should be placed on a comparison of test scores prior to the psychiatric disorder leading to the lobotomy. Rosvold and Mishkin[46] found both the immediate pre- and postlobotomy scores to be lower. Lobotomy has been observed to improve rather than hinder performance on intelligence tests,[10] probably by relieving the patients of anxiety. Thus, the frontal lobes are clearly not the traditional "seat of intelligence"—but they do contribute to intelligence, as do other parts of the cerebral cortex.

Recent attempts to find and to characterize cognitive defects due to frontal pole lesions have met with surprising difficulty. The more carefully sources of error in experimental design are eliminated and the more sophisticated the tests, the more elusive become the defects. Thus, if patients with posterior "association" area injury are included as a control for brain damage *per se,* they sometimes have more difficulty than the experimental group not only with verbal tests, as would be expected, but with nonverbal tests as well.

Many tests expected to present difficulty do not do so. Milner,[34] like many others, has found that one of the tasks most sensitive to prefrontal damage is a "sorting test." As shown in Figure

  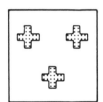 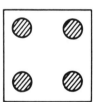

  Red
Green
Yellow
Blue

Fig. 6.   Wisconsin Card Sorting Test. The response cards in the pack are placed by the patient in front of the appropriate cue cards according to whether the instruction for matching is color, number or form. The exposed card matches three of the four response cards. (Milner, Chap. 15 in *The frontal granular cortex and behavior,* Warren and Akert, eds., New York, McGraw-Hill Book Co., 1964.)

Fig. 7. A sample test field, used to test visual searching, contains 40 patterns (some repeated, so that there are 48 in all) distinguished by either shape or color or both. In each trial a duplicate of one of the patterns appears in the center of the screen (here a filled circle); the subject's task is to find the matching pattern in the periphery. (From Teuber, in *The frontal granular cortex and behavior.* Warren and Akert, eds. New York, McGraw-Hill Book Co., 1964.)

6, the patient sees four stimulus cards differing in color, form and number of geometric designs. The patient matches each card in his pack to one of the stimulus cards according to one cue, e.g., color, until ten consecutive responses are made and then that cue becomes wrong and another becomes right, etc., until all cues have been used.

Analysis shows that the errors of patients with dorsolateral frontal lesions, as opposed to those with lesions of posterior cortical areas, are perseverative, i.e., the patients tend to continue using a cue after it has ceased to be correct. A similar tendency has been detected in animal experiments and is a possible explanation of hyperactivity.

As with delayed response, the inability to shift response to meet changing environmental response is subject to more than one explanation, possibly to an inability to suppress an acquired response tendency or to a perseverative interference from previous sensory cues.

Teuber[53] found that posterior cortical lesions (traumatic) can produce as great or greater deficits than frontal lesions in tests of intelligence: sorting tests, problem-solving, and standard and specially designed tests of recent memory. Paradoxically, he found that patients with frontal lesions were relatively more affected by

tests involving perception, as in the "visual searching" test shown in Figure 7. Tests involving shifting of perceptions (or stabilization of perception when the body's position is shifted) were relatively more affected when the injury was frontal than when more posterior in the brain.

The challenge presented by the frontal (and the posterior) homotypical cortex is not only to discern a unitary defect and to characterize it verbally, e.g., in such terms as "inflexibility of behavior" and "perseveration," but also to analyze it in terms of its neural mechanisms.

Personality Changes. Since 1848, the date of the famous "crowbar" case of Phineas P. Gage, the relation of the frontal areas* to personality has been recognized. The nature of such changes is not the same in all cases of frontal lobe damage, but some form of personality alteration is usually reported.

Phineas P. Gage, an "efficient and capable" foreman, was injured on September 13, 1848, when a tamping iron was blown through the frontal region of his brain. He suffered the following change in personality, according to the physician, J. M. Harlow, who attended him. "He is fitful, irreverent, indulging at times in the grossest profanity (which was not previously his custom), manifesting but little deference to his fellows, impatient of restraint or advice when it conflicts with his desires, at times pertinaciously obstinate yet capricious and vacillating, devising many plans for future operation which are no sooner arranged than they are abandoned in turn for others appearing more feasible. . . . His mind was radically changed, so that his friends and acquaintances said he was no longer Gage."†

The absence of consistency of purpose and behavior reported in this classic description is noted in many cases of damage to the orbitofrontal areas. The patients are highly distractable, turning from one activity to another according to the novelty of a fresh stimulation rather than to any plan. A lack of foresight, an inability to plan activity, and a failure to anticipate future events on the basis of past experience —all intellectual functions—contribute to a lack of continuity in behavior. The patient may not feel the ambitions, responsibilities and proprieties of his life circumstances and may be so

* In respect to localization, a crowbar leaves something to be desired; the lesions were probably frontal and if they were also hypothalamic, the fact that personality and emotionality is changed by brain damage has been before the laboratory scientist for more than a century.

†Harlow, *Boston med. surg. J.,* 1848, *39:*389.

altered that he seems a different and sometimes unacceptable person to his relatives and friends. A classic character change is *Witzelsucht,* a tendency toward frivolous and sometimes stupid and tedious joking, often at the expense of others. Some patients react with a light remark to situations of considerable gravity, and their ebullient spirits may conceal an emotional dulling. In other cases, unresponsiveness, inertia, apathy and masking of facies are characteristic, especially in the early postoperative period, and may alternate with restlessness. This calls to mind the sequence of events observed in the monkey after frontal lobectomy and after lesions of Area 13—apathy followed by an excess of activity—which in both instances is likely to be perseverative and stereotyped.

It is equally certain that the personality changes following extensive bilateral lobectomies may be slight and transitory, as in the case thoroughly studied by Hebb and Penfield.[16] More than 50 investigators from several disciplines applied a highly diversified battery of objective personality tests to a series of topectomy patients.[32] Although striking initial defects and some persisting ones were observed, no stable, characteristic pattern could be demonstrated. The results varied from individual to individual with similar lesions. It is as though the orbitofrontal lobes embody the emotional development and experience of each individual and their loss effects a change according to the original personality structure.

Lobectomy is becoming unpopular because the operation may deprive the patient of further psychiatric treatment, may alter the patient–family relationship, and produces an unfavorable admixture of desirable and undesirable effects. On the other hand, many patients have been relieved of intense suffering, saved from suicide or drug addiction and restored to something approaching a normal existence. In recent years, medication has tended to replace "psychosurgery."

TEMPORAL LOBES

Animal Experiments. Apart from the small area on the superior surface devoted to audition (Heschl's gyrus), the temporal lobe consists of a wide expanse of cerebral cortex receiving few thalamocortical projection fibers and having abundant reciprocal connections with other ho-

motypical areas. The temporal lobe intimately interconnects with auditory and visual association cortex, with the prefrontal cortex—especially the orbital gyrus—and with the limbic system. As a part of a band extending across the orbital, uncinate and cingulate gyri, the tip of the temporal lobe is involved in respiratory and vasomotor phenomena and perhaps emotion (Chap. 26).

The search for an association function in the homotypical cortex (Areas 18 and 19) immediately adjacent to the striate area has been unsuccessful.[1, 23] A search of the parietotemporo-preoccipital area was also substantially negative in respect to visual discrimination learning, though some difficulties with more elaborated somatosensory and visual learning were found. Quite suprisingly, the temporal lobe has proved to be concerned with the learning and memory of visual discriminations.[4]

A monkey, after bilateral lesions of the inferotemporal cortex (Area 21 of Brodmann), learns a visual discrimination habit more slowly than monkeys with lesions in any other part of the homotypical cortex. Moreover, if animals are first trained to criterion on a visual problem and then subjected to inferotemporal lesions, memory of the correct response is lost. The deficit caused by such temporal lesions is specific to that region and to visual problems, though the visual pathway (Meyer's loop) is not damaged. No other cortical lesions produce a comparable effect, and discriminations involving other sensory modalities are not affected by inferotemporal lesions. However, it has been learned more recently that the memory defect is not absolute. If the monkeys are trained sufficiently beyond a conventional criterion performance (90 per cent correct in a day's trials), the habit will survive the ablation.[6, 37] This raises an interesting problem as to what is the neural difference between a "just learned" and a "well learned" problem. Other examples of cortical areas which participate in learning but are widely removed from the receptive area involved in the test will be discussed in the next chapter.

Observations on Man. In the late nineteenth century, Hughlings Jackson recognized the relationship of the visual and auditory hallucinations of epileptic patients to irritating lesions in the temporal lobes—which also involved the sense of smell when a tumor encroached on nearby rhinencephalic structures.[18] Penfield[39] found that complex, well formed visual and auditory images corresponding to the past events in the individual's life are aroused by electrical stimulation of the temporal lobe surface during a brain operation. If, in Penfield's example, the patient hears music, it seems to be a specific rendition he had heard years before. He may see the orchestra or the singer, and he may re-experience the emotion aroused in him by the music long ago.

Such hallucinatory re-enactments or "flashbacks" occur at the normal tempo of life. They are elicited from the temporal lobe between the auditory and the visual sensory areas, and there is no overlap with the zone of cortex devoted to the ideational processes of speech.[39] Whereas these "evoked memories" have a clarity and tempo akin to normal memories, electrical stimulation of the temporal lobe in conscious patients paradoxically may alter the character of immediate conscious experience of what is going on at the time. As during temporal lobe epileptic discharge, the patient may feel "distant" or removed from the immediate situation. Events unfold at a slower tempo and seem absurd or fearful; they may seem strange or they may seem to have occurred before (*déjà vu* phenomenon). Occasionally the patient feels that he is far away in space and observing himself.

A syndrome of temporal lobe disease is widely recognized, the presenting symptoms varying with the locus of the lesion. With medially located tumors, "uncinate fits,'' attacks of unpleasant olfactory sensations, are frequent. Tinnitus, a slight decrease in auditory acuity and, occasionally, narrowing of the peripheral visual field opposite the lesion (involvement of adjacent visual radiation fibers) are evident. However, "dreamy states" characterize temporal lobe disease—brief or prolonged bouts of arrested consciousness, unaccompanied by convulsions, in which the individual passes off into a dream world of vivid visual and auditory hallucinations. He frequently shows some speech deficit and a poor sense of time and space. The clinical syndrome from irritative lesions obviously resembles the subjective responses to electrical stimulation of the temporal lobes.

AGNOSIA, APRAXIA, APHASIA

The loss of the memory of learned reactions,

sometimes referred to as intellectual functions, which results from cortical damage takes three principal forms—agnosia, apraxia and aphasia.

Agnosia. By this is meant loss of the ability to recognize common objects, i.e., to perceive the significance of sensory stimuli. Four forms of agnosia are distinguished: (i) *astereognosis* or tactual agnosia, the failure to recognize common objects by palpating them (see Chap. 14); (ii) *auditory agnosia* or *psychic deafness,* which merges into aphasia; (iii) *visual agnosia* or *psychic blindness,* the inability to appreciate the meaning of objects seen, of colors or of visual space in the absence of a primary visual defect; and (iv) *autotopognosis* (e.g., *finger agnosia*), failure to recognize the parts of the body, to differentiate right and left or, in general, to recognize the relationship of objects to the body.

Apraxia. In 1886, Hughlings Jackson described a selective disturbance of the higher levels of motor function known as apraxia. His patient could not stick out his tongue when asked to do so, but used it well in semiautomatic acts such as chewing and swallowing. There was no true paresis or paralysis. Thus, motor apraxia is characterized by an inability to perform voluntary movements in the absence of motor paralysis.

Both agnosia and apraxia are usually accompanied by some primary sensory or motor deficit, respectively, but not sufficient to explain the difficulties exhibited.

Aphasia.[15, 42, 60] The word "aphasia" means literally a loss of the power of speech, but the term as now used includes any marked interference with the ability either to use or to comprehend symbolic expressions of ideas by spoken or written words or by gestures, and any interference with the use of language in thinking. Formerly a sharp distinction was made between sensory and motor aphasia. By "motor aphasia" was meant the inability to speak in the absence of paralysis of the muscles of articulation; "sensory aphasia" was an inability to understand written, printed or spoken symbols of language in patients without defective vision or hearing. The aphasias are still so described, but later work indicates that the clean-cut separation formerly claimed rarely, if ever, exists in clinical cases; intermediate forms are far more numerous.

Motor or expressive aphasia. The first definite identification of the portion of the brain involved in motor aphasia seems to have been made in 1825 by Bouillaud, who attributed the defect to lesions of the frontal lobe. Then, in 1886, Marc Dax drew attention to the relationship between aphasia and lesions in the left cerebral hemisphere.

Broca made a more restricted localization—the posterior part of the third or inferior frontal convolution. This region is anterior to the lateral end of the precentral gyrus (region S in Fig. 8) and is known as Broca's area. It is now recognized that this localization is too limited and that defects in the power of speech also result from lesions of contiguous areas. Broca's region is not the cortical representation of the muscles of speech in the precentral gyrus but lies just anterior to it. (Broca's area has a characteristic cytoarchitecture, even in monkeys [Area 44 of Brodmann], and is possibly a development of the portion of Area 6 from which vocalization can be produced in monkeys by direct electrical stimulation.) As a result, aphasia occasionally occurs without voluntary paralysis of these muscles; also, the motor act of speech may sometimes be disturbed with relatively little influence on the symbolic aspect of speech.

Broca's area and adjacent regions apparently are necessary in forming the organized complex of appropriate sounds and words with which to name objects and to express concepts. Lesions affecting this area destroy more or less the ability to use spoken words appropriately. Motor aphasia may be exhibited in all degrees of completeness and in many curious varieties.

The individual may retain a limited number of words with which to express his whole range of ideas, as, for instance, in the case described by Broca in which the word "three" was made to serve for all numerical concepts. Or, only the last words spoken before a bursting cerebral vessel may survive. Thus, an English woman stricken while ordering boiled beef for luncheon had for expressing her whole range of ideas but one word—"horseradish." Automatic word series—e.g., the days of the week or counting—tend to survive, as does reactive speech demanded by a particular situation—for example, "hello" and "good-bye." When no words can be commanded for the expression of ideas (propositional speech), speech expressive of emotion—ejaculations or swearing—may persist. Usually associated with disturbance of speech is a loss of ability to write (agraphia), whether spontaneously, to dictation or from copy. Since writing involves a different set of muscles, it was natural to assume that a different cortical area is responsible for this form of expression, as in Figure 8. Although pure agraphia is rare, in some aphasics the expression of thoughts by writing is more definitely affected than is speech. When the difficulty is

in finding the word and writing it correctly, agraphia is considered comparable to aphasia; when the errors are in forming the letters, the disturbance is related to apraxia.

Sensory or receptive aphasia. In this form of aphasia, the individual suffers from an inability to *understand* spoken or written language. Classically, inability to understand spoken language (word deafness) has been attributed to lesions involving the superior and middle temporal convolutions contiguous to the cortical center for hearing (H, Fig. 8); loss of power to understand written or printed language (word blindness, alexia) is traced to lesions centered on the inferior portion of the posterior parietal lobule, the gyrus angularis, contiguous to the occipital visual area (V, Fig. 8). This separation is much too schematic. Weisenberg and McBride[60] found that some patients have greatest difficulty in comprehending spoken words; for others, the greatest difficulty is with written language; but many patients have equal trouble in both spheres. It is possible that cases of reputed word blindness or word deafness are in reality special manifestations of visual and auditory agnosia. Furthermore, Weisenberg and McBride found little evidence of pure sensory aphasia. Because of the associated expressive difficulties, they refer to this group as "predominantly receptive aphasia."

The foregoing descriptions of aphasia are strongly influenced by the "pure case" and are couched in abstract and nonquantitative termi-

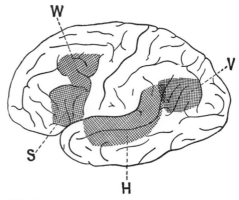

Fig. 8. Lateral aspect of human hemisphere indicating one view of localization of language areas; cortical area *V,* damage to which produces mainly word blindness; cortical area *H,* damage to which produces mainly word deafness; cortical area *S,* damage to which causes loss of articulate speech; cortical area *W,* damage to which particularly affects ability to write. (After Donaldson.)

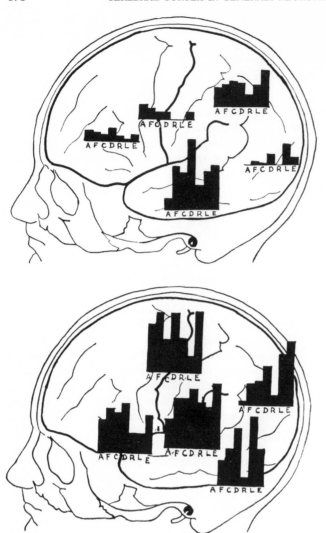

Fig. 9. A quantitative representation (average from a series of patients) of the disturbance of various aspects of language (abscissae of the histograms). The upper half of the figure represents lesions confined to one lobe, except for the cases represented by the histogram straddling the central fissure, i.e., lesions of the pre- and postcentral gyrus. In the lower half of the figure two lobes or lobules were damaged. The histogram beginning at the top represents lesions in the fronto-parietal, fronto-temporal, parieto-temporal, parieto-occipital and temporo-occipital. A, Articulatory disturbances. F, Difficulties in the fluency of speech. C, Disturbances of verbal comprehension. D, Disturbances of naming. R, Disturbances of repetition. L, Disturbances in reading. E, Disturbances of writing.

nology of faculty psychology; current attempts to classify speech difficulties have become more operational and quantitative even to the point of employing the techniques of the philologists, who can characterize Americanese, U-Talk or Swahili with the same notation.[42] Figure 9 represents a less ambitious attempt to describe quantitatively the disturbances of the various aspects of speech characteristic of lesions in the various lobes of the brain. In each case, seven aspects of speech are shown by a histogram mnemonically labeled (in French); each bar represents the degree of disturbance on the conventional, clinical, five-point scale, in which scaling units were carefully defined. Note that the temporal and, in lesser degree, the parietal lobe lesions cause a significantly greater disturbance than lesions in other lobes. When two or three lobes are damaged, the disturbance of

speech is greatly increased. The profile of the histogram indicating kind of disturbances varies when the lesion is in different lobes, the motor difficulties being *relatively* more prominent in anterior lesions and defects in the more sensory aspects of language being more prominent after the posterior lesions—so-called "sensory aphasia." These more quantitative studies bear out those of Weisenberg and McBride.[60]

Aphasia as an intellectual defect. Aphasics once labeled "expressive" or "receptive" are found, on close examination, to have disturbances of language as a symbolic function and disturbances of intellectual function in general.

Disturbance of the language mechanism at a high level is *amnesic aphasia*, which may exist in a relatively pure form. In this form of aphasia, which may appear with lesions anywhere in the dominant speech cortex, the articulation of words is normal and the understanding of language is not gravely affected. Nevertheless, the patient finds the naming of objects difficult and often searches for words while speaking. According to Schiller,[50] some difficulty in word finding is evident in all true aphasias. Temporal lobe aphasia presents, above the impairment of hearing, both difficulty of understanding and of memory for spoken language. According to Goldstein,[12] there are disturbances of an intellectual character—e.g., the inability to categorize, to sort miscellaneous collections of objects according to classes. These defects are supposed to result not from lesions affecting the speech areas, but from widespread although not severe cortical damage.

REFERENCES

1. ADES, H. W. and RAAB, D. H. *J. Neurophysiol.,* 1949, *12:* 101–108.
2. AKERT, K. Chap. 18 in WARREN and AKERT.[57]
3. BATTIG, K., ROSVOLD, H. E. and MISHKIN, M. *J. comp. physiol. Psychol.,* 1960, *53:*400–404.
4. BURANDT, D. C., FRENCH, G. M. and AKERT, K. *Confin. neurol. (Basel),* 1961, *21:*289–306.
5. CHOW, K. L. and HUTT, P. J. *Brain,* 1953, *76:*625–677.
6. CHOW, K. L. and SURVIS, J. *Arch Neurol. Psychiat. (Chic.),* 1958, *79:*640–646.
7. DAVIS, G. D. *Neurology,* 1958, *8:*135–139.
8. DEVITO, J. L. and SMITH, O. A., JR. *J. comp. Neurol.,* in press.
9. DEVITO, J. L. and RUCH, T. C. Unpublished observations.
10. FREEMAN, W. and WATTS, J. W. *Psychosurgery in the treatment of mental disorders and intractable pain,* 2nd ed. Springfield, Ill., Charles C Thomas, 1950.
11. FULTON, J. F. *Functional localization in the frontal lobes and cerebellum.* Oxford, Clarendon Press, 1949.
12. GOLDSTEIN, K. *Language and language disturbances.* New York, Grune & Stratton, 1948.
13. GROSS, C. G. and WEISKRANTZ, L. *Exp. Neurol.,* 1962, *5:* 453–476.
14. GROSS, C. G. and WEISKRANTZ, L. Chap. 5 in WARREN and AKERT.[57]
15. HEAD, H. *Aphasia and kindred disorders of speech.* New York, Macmillan Company, 1926.
16. HEBB, D. O. and PENFIELD, W. *Arch. Neurol. Psychiat. (Chic.),* 1940, *44:*421–438.
17. HÈCAEN, H. and ANGELERGUES, R. In: de Reuck and O'Connor.[42]
18. JACKSON, J. H. and BEEVOR, C. E. *Brain,* 1889, *12:*346–357.
19. JACOBSEN, C. F.. *Comp. Psychol. Monogr.,* 1936, *13,* no. 63:3–60.
20. JACOBSEN, C. F., WOLFE, J. B. and JACKSON, T. A. *J. nerv. ment. Dis.,* 1935, *82:*1–14.
21. KENNARD, M. A. and ECTORS, L. *J. Neurophysiol.,* 1938, *1:* 45–54.
22. KENNARD, M. A., SPENCER, S. and FOUNTAIN, G., JR. *J. Neurophysiol.,* 1941, *4:*512–524.
23. LASHLEY, K. S. *Genet. Psychol. Monogr.,* 1948, *37:*107–166.
24. LAURSEN, A. M. *Acta physiol. scand.,* 1963, *57:*81–89.
25. LEARY, R. W., HARLOW, H. F., SETTLAGE, P. H. and

GREENWOOD, D. D. *J. comp. physiol. Psychol.,* 1952, *45:* 576–584.
26. LIDDELL, H. S. Chap. 26 in *Physiology of the nervous system,* 3rd ed., J. F. Fulton, ed. New York, Oxford University Press, 1949.
27. LIVINGSTON, R. B., FULTON, J. F., DELGADO, J. M. R., SACHS, E., JR., BRENDLER, S. J. and DAVIS, G. *Res. Publ. Ass. nerv. ment. Dis.,* 1948, *27:*405–420.
28. MAIRE, F. W. Unpublished observations.
29. MAIRE, F. W. and PATTON, H. D. *Amer. J. Physiol.,* 1954, *178:*315–320.
30. MALMO, R. B. *J. Neurophysiol.,* 1942, *5:*295–308.
31. MASSERMAN, J. H. *Behavior and neurosis; an experimental psychoanalytic approach to psychobiologic principles.* Chicago, University of Chicago Press, 1943.
32. METTLER, F. A., ed. *Selective partial ablation of the frontal cortex; a correlative study of its effects on human psychotic subjects.* New York, Paul B. Hoeber, Inc., 1949.
33. MILES, R. C. and BLOMQUIST, A. J. *J. Neurophysiol.,* 23: 471–484, 1960.
34. MILNER, B. Chap. 15 in WARREN and AKERT.[57]
35. MISHKIN, M. *J. Neurophysiol.,* *20:*615–622, 1957.
36. NAUTA, W. J. H. Chap. 19 in WARREN and AKERT.[57]
37. ORBACH, J. and FANTZ, R. T. *J. comp. physiol. Psychol.,* 1958, *51:*126–129.
38. PAVLOV, I. P. *Conditioned reflexes: an investigation of the physiological activity of the cerebral cortex.* London, Oxford University Press, 1927.
39. PENFIELD, W. and KRISTIANSEN, K. *Epileptic seizure patterns.* Springfield, Ill., Charles C Thomas, 1951.
40. PENFIELD, W. and PEROT, P. *Brain,* 1963, *86:*595–696.
41. PRIBRAM, H. B. and BARRY, J. *J. Neurophysiol.,* 1956, *19:* 99–106.
42. de REUCK, A. V. S. and O'CONNOR, M., eds. *Disorders of language.* Ciba Foundation Symposium. Boston, Little, Brown and Co., 1964.
43. RICHTER, C. P. and HINES, M. *Brain,* 1938, *61:*1–16.
44. ROSE, J. E. and WOOLSEY, C. N. *Res. Publ. Ass. nerv. ment. Dis.,* 1948, *27:*210–232.
45. ROSVOLD, H. E. and DELGADO, J. M. R. *J. comp. physiol. Psychol.,* 1956, *49:*365–372.
46. ROSVOLD, H. E. and MISHKIN, M. *Canad. J. Psychol.,* 1950, *4:*122–126.
47. ROSVOLD, H. E., MISHKIN, M. and SZWARCBART, M. K. *J. comp. physiol. Psychol.,* 1958, *51:*437–444.
48. RUCH, T. C. *Res. Publ. Ass. nerv. ment. Dis.,* 1934, *15:* 289–330.
49. RUCH, T. C. and SHENKIN, H. A. *J. Neurophysiol.,* 1943, *6:*349–360.
50. SCHILLER, F. *J. Neurol. Psychiat. (Chic.),* 1947, *10:*183–197.
51. SERAFETINIDES, E. A. and FALCONER, M. A. *Brain,* 1963, *86:*333–346.
52. STEBBINS, W. C. and SMITH, O. A., JR., *Science,* 1964, *144:* 881–883.
53. TEUBER, H.-L. Chap. 20 in WARREN and AKERT.[57]
54. TOWE, A. L. *J. comp. physiol. Psychol.,* 1954, *47:*283–287.
55. WALKER, A. E. *The primate thalamus.* Chicago, University of Chicago Press, 1938.
56. WALKER, A. E. *J. comp. Neurol.,* 1940, *73:*59–86.
57. WARREN, J. M. and AKERT, K., eds. *The frontal granular cortex and behavior.* New York, McGraw-Hill Book Co., 1964.
58. WEINSTEIN, S. and TEUBER, H.-L. *J. comp. physiol. Psychol.,* 1957, *50:*535–539.
59. WEINSTEIN, S. and TEUBER, H.-L. *Science,* 1957, *125:*1036–1037.
60. WEISENBERG, T. and McBRIDE, K. E. *Aphasia, a clinical and psychological study.* New York, Commonwealth Fund, 1935.

CHAPTER 24

Neurophysiology of Learning and Memory

By MITCHELL GLICKSTEIN

ONE of the most characteristic attributes of man and of higher animals is the ability to learn, to modify behavior as a result of experience. It is now a basic postulate, although it did not appear self-evident to the ancients, that all of the remarkable functions of learning and memory are mediated by the nervous system.

In broadest terms, learning is a kind of plasticity of the nervous system. The nervous system, especially in mammals, can store information, can modify response to stimuli, and can even recover functionally from irreversible structural damage. It is a common clinical observation that the initial severe impairment following trauma or vascular damage to the nervous system may improve with time, even to the point that initial deficits disappear entirely. Since residual brain damage is still present at the end of improvement, the mechanism of recovery is a central question allied to learning. How is the brain reorganized when an aphasic patient regains the power of speech? Our understanding of the mechanism of plasticity is very limited. There is, however, a body of knowledge gained from laboratory experiments that establishes something of the nature of the problem and provides suggestions about its ultimate solution.

It is useful to distinguish at the outset between two related aspects of the problem of neural mechanisms in learning and memory. One is the detailed molecular changes associated with these phenomena; the other is the neural organization as it relates to learning and memory. There must be some morphologic change in the nervous system which is identifiable with the process of learning. Several theories relating learning to structural changes at the synapse or chemical alterations within nerve cells have been proposed. At present, however, all such explanations are largely speculative; even if one or more of them should prove correct, an important problem would remain unsolved—the problem of total organization of the nervous system for learning and memory. How does an organism store and retrieve information? Are memory traces stored in single cells or groups of cells, or are they a property of the entire nervous system? Are memory traces singly or multiply represented?

The two problems—molecular basis of memory and brain organization for learning—are not identical, although they are closely interrelated. The interrelationship may be exemplified by an analogy to a computer. In most complex digital computing machines some part of the structure is devoted to a form of "memory store." Relays, magnetic cores, tapes, etc., are among the storage devices. But an understanding of the specific "memory" mechanism would not give complete insight into the role of memory elements in the function of the machine. In order to understand this role, much more knowledge of the coding of input to the memory store and the way the information is retrieved and used is needed. In the problem of brain function, an analogous distinction exists between detailed molecular or physical changes identifiable with learning and the total neural organization for processing, coding and storing sensory input.

The most puzzling feature of learning is the time scale. Neurophysiologists are accustomed to neural events which occur in milliseconds or, at most, seconds. In contrast, learned material and motor skills may be retained over many years. Hence, it seems likely that learning mechanisms differ qualitatively and quantitatively from simple reflexes.

Of the many experimental studies dealing with learning, most concern behavioral changes brought about by varying environmental conditions rather than underlying physiologic mechanisms. For example, studies have dealt with the effects of varying the time between learning trials on the speed of learning. In other experiments the effect of varying the amount and timing of rewards has been studied. Since such studies provide a basis of facts and techniques for physiologic analysis, some of them will be reviewed.

TYPES OF LEARNING

Behavioral studies of learning fall into two broad classes. The first is a type of learning situation in which the subject plays a relatively *passive* role in the training, as exemplified by Pavlovian conditioning and by habituation. In the second type of learning situation, the subject plays a relatively more active role, as in the experiments on the acquisition and retention of such behavior as bar pressing, maze learning and avoidance of painful stimuli.

Often some one type of learning situation is assumed to be the "simplest" or the "most general" type of learning. For example, Pavlovian conditioning, to be described below, has often been considered as *the* model for all learning. However, no model theory or experimental approach seems clearly to be the simplest or the most logical candidate for physiologic study.

Pavlovian Conditioning. Many of the early studies of learning in animals were conducted in the laboratory of I. P. Pavlov.[42] Accordingly, the technique he employed for study of the learning mechanism has been called *Pavlovian* or classical conditioning. In a typical experiment, a dog in a restraining harness was presented with a variety of stimuli and its responses, usually the secretion of saliva, were measured. Figure 1 shows the apparatus. Pavlov found that repeated presentation of a stimulus, which in itself elicited no salivation, e.g., a bell, called

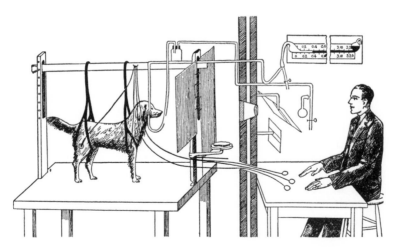

Fig. 1. Dog in apparatus used by Pavlov for establishing or experimenting upon conditioned responses. Observer is in separate room with three keys to manipulate. With one of the keys he controls injection of acid into mouth, resulting flow of saliva being indicated by scale (greatly enlarged) above his head. With other two keys he can stimulate mechanically skin of dog at two points, one on foreleg and one on hindleg. (After Pavlov, *Lectures on conditioned reflexes,* 1927.)

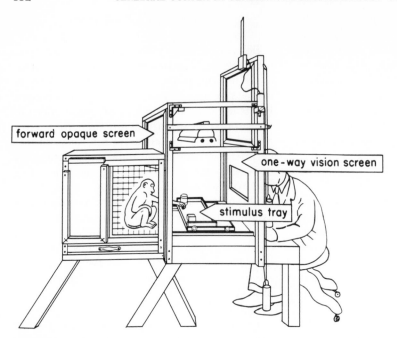

forward opaque screen

one-way vision screen

stimulus tray

Fig. 2. Sketch showing Wisconsin General Test Apparatus suited to primates. The experimenter can present the monkey with a variety of discrimination tasks and remain unobserved during the training. (From Harlow and Bromer, *Psychol. Rec.*, 1938, 2:434–436.)

the *conditioned stimulus* (CS), when quickly followed by the presentation of a salivation-eliciting stimulus such as food or a weak acid, the *unconditioned stimulus,* brought about a striking behavioral change. Initially, the dog salivated only to the presentation of the unconditioned stimulus, e.g., food. In time, after a number of pairings of bell with food, a salivary response to the bell alone gradually developed. Pavlov termed this response to the bell a *conditioned reflex.*

Studies of conditioned reflexes have led to many important observations about the nature of the learning process. Pavlov found, for example, that conditioning would occur only if the conditioned stimulus preceded the unconditioned stimulus. If the bell was presented after the food, despite repeated trials, "backward conditioning" was never clearly established.

Pavlov also found that after a conditioned response was well established, repeated presentation of the conditioned stimulus (bell) alone elicited less and less salivation on successive presentations until finally the bell alone elicited no salivary response at all. This progressive decrease in the conditioned response to the conditioned stimulus presented alone Pavlov termed *extinction.* He suggested that extinction was not simply due to a passive "forgetting" of the conditioned response, but was an active process brought about by some "inhibitory" mechanism. Evidence for an inhibitory process

in extinction is that if the same animal is tested with the bell alone after a rest period, the conditioned response typically reappears. That is, there is spontaneous recovery of the conditioned reflex. After conditioning is established, a stimulus similar in some respect to the conditioned stimulus will also elicit a conditioned reflex. For example, if a bell with a different tone is now presented, it too will elicit salivation. This phenomenon Pavlov called *generalization.* He further found that with further training he could teach the animal to *discriminate* between reinforced (paired with food) and unreinforced (unpaired with food) stimuli.

In the original classical conditioning experiments, the interval between the onset of the conditioned stimulus and the unconditioned stimulus was brief: on the order of 1 to 5 seconds. In such cases, the conditioned response of a trained animal typically occurs almost immediately after the onset of the conditioned stimulus. If in such an animal the interval between presentation of conditioned and unconditioned stimuli is increased, the latency of the conditioned response gradually increases. Pavlov termed such responses *delayed reflexes.*

Habituation. If an animal is subjected to an unfamiliar stimulus, it actively "attends" to the stimulus; e.g., the dog turns its head in the direction of a novel sound. Pavlov considered such a response to be general and innate in all men and animals and termed it the "investigatory" or

"What is it?" reflex. It is now more usually termed the "orienting reflex." If the stimulus is presented repeatedly, such orienting behavior gradually decreases until finally no detectable behavioral response is elicited. The decrement in behavioral response produced by repeated presentation of an unreinforced stimulus is called *habituation*. Since habituation typically occurs within a few trials and is observed in many species,[56] it has been used as an experimental model of neural plasticity.

Instrumental Conditioning.   In Pavlovian conditioning, the animal is a passive participant in the experimental procedure, stimuli and food being presented to him in fixed order irrespective of his behavior. In *instrumental conditioning*, by contrast, the animal must make some response, which determines whether the conditioning is or is not *reinforced*. The apparatus is thus used as an instrument upon which the animal performs and the behavior is termed an *instrumental response*. One of the earliest studies of instrumental conditioning utilized the problem box of Thorndike.[55] A cat was placed inside a box with food outside. To reach the food the animal had to manipulate one or more catches on the door of the box. In successive trials the time necessary for the animal to emerge from the box and gain its reward became less and less. Thus, the animal was required to respond actively to be reinforced.

Since then a large number of problem boxes, mazes, and discrimination apparatuses have been developed and are classified as instrumental learning devices. One of these which has become widely used is the *Wisconsin General Test Apparatus* (WGTA) (Fig. 2). A monkey is placed in a testing cage in which is a tray containing one or more hollowed-out wells. These wells may be covered by blocks on which are painted or mounted distinctive patterns, colors, or objects. Animals learn to displace distinctive blocks to obtain a raisin or other reward. Such *discrimination learning* is useful in studies on cortical localization in learning and sensory function.

Another technique involves a specific instrumental response to escape from or avoid entirely a noxious stimulus. As an example of such *escape and avoidance conditioning*, an animal is placed in one part of a two-compartment box with a grid floor. At a specified time or after the onset of a distinctive stimulus, the grid floor of the starting compartment is electrified, delivering a mild shock to the animal's feet so that it must *escape* to the non-shock side of the box, which it does more and more promptly with successive trials. If this procedure is repeated often enough, the animal learns to leave the starting compartment immediately, *before* the onset of voltage in the grid floor. That is, he learns to *avoid* the noxious stimulus entirely.

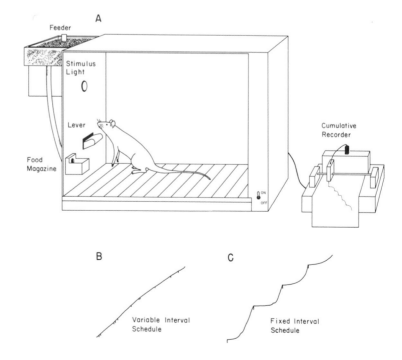

Fig. 3. *A,* Diagram of a typical "Skinner Box." Pressing the lever will lead to the delivery of a pellet in the food magazine below. Each lever press is registered by advancing the recorder pen upward on a slowly moving paper. *B* and *C,* Typical cumulative records of behavior during variable and fixed interval reinforcement. Downward deflections are reinforced responses.

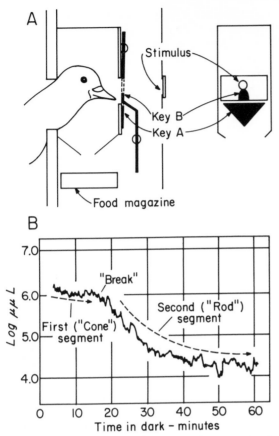

Fig. 4. *A,* Apparatus for determining visual thresholds in the pigeon. Side view left; pigeon's view at right. Use of two keys is explained in the text. *B,* Curve of dark adaptation in the pigeon, obtained by continuous recording of brightness threshold in a darkened chamber. (After Blough, *J. comp. physiol. Psychol.,* 1956, *49:*425–430.)

Skinner[47] has developed a sensitive, flexible and widely used apparatus for the study of instrumental responses (called *operant* responses by him) which automatically records the responses. An animal is put into a chamber containing a lever, which if depressed delivers a small pellet of food. The apparatus is arranged to permit cumulative recording of such lever-pressing responses. Once the lever-pressing response is well established, any desired modifications in the delivery of reinforcement may be instituted. For example, the animal may receive food for only every fifth lever press. Alternatively, it might be reinforced for a lever press only after a fixed or variable interval of time has elapsed. Each of these so-called *schedules of reinforcement* produces characteristic temporal distributions of behavioral response.[15] Figure 3

shows a typical Skinner Box and some characteristic cumulative records of lever pressing under varying schedules of reinforcement.

The Skinner Box can also be used for discrimination training. One way is by reinforcing the animal only in the presence of a specific stimulus. For example, pressing the lever might activate the feeder only when a lighted window over the lever is illuminated.

The Skinner Box is a versatile instrument. It may be modified to study a variety of species; the behavior required is not necessarily restricted to lever pressing, nor is food the only effective reinforcer. Pigeons, for example, are usually trained to peck a key in the Skinner Box. The apparatus may even be modified so that the response is instrumental for the avoidance of a mild shock. It is initially highly improbable that behavior such as lever pressing in the Skinner Box or cup displacement in the WGTA will occur on the part of an untrained animal. Therefore, attainment of the desired behavior is not usually left to chance. Rather, the behavior is gradually *shaped* by reinforcing successive approximations to the desired response. For example, a rat might first be reinforced whenever it was *near* the lever, then whenever it *touched* the lever, and finally only after it had *pressed* the lever. By skillful use of shaping, many behavioral responses can be rapidly trained.

Some of the experimental techniques employed in the study of learning have proved widely useful for other problems. By skillful use of reinforcement one may measure physiologic variables in experimental animals which in man are mediated by verbal report, e.g., sensory threshold. For example, Blough[1] trained pigeons in a box containing two keys so that they pecked at key A when a standard light was on and key B when the light was off. He then arranged a circuit, such that pecking on key A not only recorded the fact of pecking, but also lowered the illumination of the standard. Thus, the pigeon would now peck until the illumination had been reduced below its visible threshold. Then the pigeon pecked at key B. Key B recorded the fact of pecking and also *increased* the illumination. In this way, it was possible to establish a precise visual intensity threshold for the pigeon. The apparatus and one application are shown in Figure 4. Such behavioral data can be as precise as any obtainable from a human subject. By appropriate use of conditioning techniques, it has been possible to determine thresholds for several modalities of sensation and to measure in experimental animals such phenomena as reaction time[54] and to plot perimetric visual fields.[9]

In the preceding discussion of behavioral studies, the important concept of reinforcement has not been defined. The word is used in a rather different way in Pavlovian and instrumental learning. In Pavlovian conditioning reinforcement refers simply to the temporal pairing of conditioned and unconditioned stimuli. In instrumental learning, it is the prompt pairing of a *response* and some relevant stimulus consequence such as food. The stimulus consequence often is thought to produce satisfaction of a drive or need.

CENTRAL "CIRCUITS" IN LEARNING

Ablation and Stimulation. Many of the early investigators of the neural basis of learning attempted to determine the central point at which the learning process occurs, and in search of this point they followed the route which is taken by neural activity from the sensory input to the motor output in learned behavior. Like Pavlov's experiments, such a view of the learning process is obviously modeled after the concept of a reflex. It is not surprising, therefore, that many early investigators used Pavlovian conditioning as a basic tool in an attempt to learn at what point in the nervous system the learned connection between the conditioned stimulus and the unconditioned response takes place. Many studies have shown that Pavlov's own view of a reflex-like pathway within the cortex is far oversimplified. Lashley[31] found that retention of learned responses in rats is unaffected by deep cuts that section transcortical association fibers connecting visual and motor cortex. Moreover, Sperry has reported that extensive subpial crosshatching,[49] and transverse implantation of tantalum metal[51] or mica[50] within the cortex are without effect on learning or memory, skilled visual discrimination, or precisely patterned movements.

Loucks was one of the first to analyze classical conditioning neurophysiologically. He originated a technique for stimulation of neural centers and pathways with buried electrodes in un-anesthetized animals.[35] * He used such stimulation in an effort to determine the neural structures essential for learning. He found that central stimulation could serve as the conditioned stimulus.[37] Thus, instead of using a peripheral sensory stimulus such as light or tone, he established that direct stimulation of a spinal afferent pathway or the cerebral sensory cortex may serve as a conditioned stimulus for salivation or leg flexion when appropriately paired with food or shock. In contrast, Loucks was unable to establish a conditioned response when central stimulation was applied to the motor side.[36] An electrode was placed in a cortical region which reliably elicited leg flexion in experimental animals. Despite hundreds of pairings of other (conditioned) stimuli with stimulation of such a cortical point, a response to the conditioned stimulus alone was never observed. The point of stimulation was below the point of connection of the conditioned stimulus and the unconditioned response. These studies seemed to indicate that the connection between a conditioned and unconditioned response occurs somewhere between the sensory and motor areas of the cortex. Several experiments, early and recent, suggest that this is not so.[31, 49]

Recently, many of these pioneering observations of Loucks have been repeated and extended. Doty *et al.*[11] were able to employ cortical stimulation as a CS (thus confirming Loucks), and have also reported conditioning established by using brain stimulation as the unconditioned stimulus. Resolution of these discrepant observations awaits further experimentation.

Electrical Recording. A number of recent studies have employed electrical recording of neural activity in chronic experimental animals in an attempt to gain further information on possible neural circuits involved in learning. One of the first such studies was reported by John and Killam.[28] They suggested that low frequency stimuli might serve as "tracers" for detecting those neural structures "processing" the conditioned stimulus. They reasoned that if electrical activity at the frequency of the "tracer" stimulus could be recorded from a given nucleus or tract at one phase of the learn-

---

*He buried the secondary of an induction coil and led wires from it to the brain. A primary coil was placed just over the secondary to induce a current in it. No electrodes are passed through and cemented to the skull.

ing process, this would constitute evidence that the structure was involved in the learning process at that time. They used a 10 per second flickering light as CS and recorded evoked 10 per second activity in many brain sites. If the CS were presented repeatedly without reinforcement (habituation) such activity was seen to drop out and in fact was recorded with difficulty even in the primary visual pathways themselves. When the 10 per second stimulus was now paired with painful foot shock in a double grill box (avoidance conditioning), activity recurred at the flash frequency in many (but not all) of the recording sites.

These studies give us a valuable introduction to the problem of the neural pathways of conditioning. Many of the techniques and principles described are new and there is still a good deal of contradiction and confusion in the literature. Thus, they have not as yet provided conclusive evidence as to a route from the conditioned stimulus to the unconditioned stimulus. The question of the locus or loci at which the conditioned and unconditioned stimuli interact is still an unsettled one.

Spinal and Subcortical Conditioning. Closely related to the problem of the neural circuits involved in conditioning is the question of the neural structures which might be capable of being conditioned. For example, studies have been directed at determining whether conditioning may occur in the spinal cord alone. If spinal conditioning were possible, one might hope to have a simpler preparation for the study of learning. Moreover, a demonstration of spinal conditioning bears upon the problem of neural plasticity: Is it a property of all groups of neurons? The weight of the evidence[16] suggests that spinal conditioning of adult mammals either does not occur or that it is, at best, a very crude type of response. On the other hand, experiments[10] have shown that the cerebral cortex is not necessary for establishment of learned responses. However, conditioning in a decorticate animal is slowly established and is crude in the sense that only a gross, widespread conditioned response is obtained after the cortex is ablated. We might infer from these studies that the cortex is a basic and important site of at least some learning processes. However, to conclude that the cortex is the only organ of learning would be wrong. Learning *may* occur in the absence of a cerebral cortex in the mammal, and is certainly exhibited by many nonmammalian forms with little true cerebral cortex. The pigeon, for example, is capable of rapidly learning extremely refined and difficult visual discriminations. Indeed, excellent discrimination learning has been clearly demonstrated in the octopus.

Evoked Potentials During Habituation. We have already given an example of chronic electrical recording from experimental animals used to study possible pathways in establishment of a conditioned response. A number of studies have been reported attempting to determine whether changes in such potentials might be associated with changes in the "significance" of the stimulus evoking them. Habituation has been described as a decrement in behavioral response associated with repeated presentation of an unreinforced stimulus. It is natural to wonder whether habituation is correlated with any observable changes of the evoked potential elicited by the habituated stimulus. Parallel with the development of behaviorally observed habituation there is a corresponding decrease in the amplitude or distribution of evoked potential recorded from the cortex.[17, 25, 39] Such changes have been seen in subcortical sensory relays as well. A decrement may even be seen in the "arousal" effects elicited by repeated stimulation of the brain stem reticular formation.[20]

If a habituated stimulus is paired with an unconditioned stimulus such as shock to the paw, a gradual increase in the amplitude of the potential evoked by the conditioned stimulus and a more widespread distribution are recorded. Obviously, then, neurophysiologic changes in evoked potentials may be associated with behavioral changes. However, although such observations may point the way to studies of neural events associated with learning, there are some cautions in interpreting such data at present. One problem of these studies is a lack of clarity in the meaning of the term *response*. The word is borrowed from behavioral experiments, in which it has a direct meaning: that which the animal *does*. In evoked potential studies the concept of response is often carried over and applied to an electrical event such as the amplitude of an evoked potential. Some authors tend to cloud the important distinction between such electrical "responses" and a behaviorally observed event. Since the precise mechanism of evoked potentials is itself still unclear, such research at present can serve only as a rather crude index of possible brain mechanisms in habituation and arousal.

THE LOCUS OF MEMORY STORAGE

The studies already presented concern neural circuits, minimal necessary amount of neural tissue, and electrical correlates of learning. The studies in the present section are largely concerned with the *locus* of memory storage. Typically, these studies have sought to establish whether memory is stored in any single brain locus or whether it is stored more diffusely. The questions have been asked: Are storage patterns different for motor as opposed to sensory learning? Is learning associated with one or another sensory input stored in any characteristic locus relative to the anatomic projections of that sense? Typically, these studies have used some form of instrumental learning as a basic tool. Animals have been trained to perform a response and the effects on that response of brain lesions has been tested.

Cortical Ablations. Many of these studies have their origin in the work of Lashley, a psychologist, whose life work spanned more than thirty years, during which he originated many of the ideas and experimental approaches currently employed in the study of the neural basis of learning and memory.[31, 33] Two major sequences of Lashley's experiments form the basis for many subsequent experiments. Their objective is not to study instrumental conditioning as such, but rather the perceptual or sensory reorganization involved in learning and memory. Instrumental conditioning has been employed to provide an *index* of such reorganization. Although Lashley's studies did not answer the problem of brain mechanisms in learning, they swept away oversimplified and speculative explanations; any final understanding will have to take account of his many observations on the nature of the "engram"—the name he used for the neural substrate of learning. In one of Lashley's first experiments rats were trained to select one of two passageways in a discrimination apparatus, the one leading to food being signaled by the presence or absence of a light. Lashley found that rats mastered this discrimination after complete destruction of striate cortex and, in fact, equaled the performance of their normal cage mates. However, if the brightness discrimination was learned prior to the lesion, the response was lost but could be reacquired in the same number of trials. Lashley found that if the optic tectum and pretectal regions were destroyed as well, the brightness discrimination was permanently abolished. He concluded that in the absence of visual cortex, brightness learning was mediated by the tectum, but that the tectum did not participate in visual learning so long as the cortex was intact.

For his second series of experiments, Lashley devised a simple maze. He studied acquisition of maze running ability in rats which had been subjected to prior cortical lesions, and retention in rats which were trained as normals and *then* were operated upon. Cortical lesions made it relatively difficult for a naive animal to acquire the maze response or for a trained animal to reacquire it after lesion. Also, cortical lesions interfered with retention of a preoperatively learned maze response. Lashley looked carefully for the localization of this learning in one or another region of the cerebral cortex. He found that in no case was loss of the maze response associated specifically with damage to any single cortical structure, but was in every case a function simply of the *amount* of cortical tissue removed. Lashley's theoretical explanation of these experimental results was that the cortex has a nonspecific, "mass action" effect and that cortical lesions interfere with the acquisition and/or retention of the solution to a difficult problem independent of locus.

Lashley's conclusions were quickly criticized[26] because the learning of the maze habit is contingent on many sensory cues. Hence, it might be expected that no specific localization would be found for it. If the maze habit were partly learned on a visual and partly on a proprioceptive basis, learning would not be completely impaired by a lesion which affected only visual or proprioceptive function. Moreover, it is very difficult to disentangle the two effects of a lesion, namely, sensory loss and learning ability *per se*, and hence to evaluate whether the phenomenon of "mass action" truly exists.

Man and animals learn an amazing variety of motor skills. Lashley[30] asked whether the learned element of these skills is "localized" in the classical motor cortex. He trained monkeys to manipulate locks and hasps to obtain food, and then ablated large areas of cortex anterior to the central sulcus. While there was a great deal of postoperative paralysis, when the animals were somewhat recovered and presented with the problem boxes, they successfully and errorlessly performed the task that had been

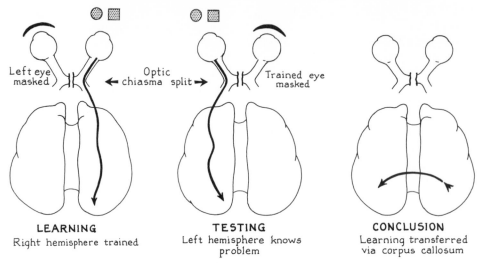

Fig. 5. Diagram of training and testing procedures for studying interocular transfer in a cat after section of the optic chiasma. (After Myers, *J. comp. physiol. Psychol.*, 1955, *48:*470–473.)

learned preoperatively. Thus, the mechanisms of execution were affected but the "know-how" of the habit was not.

Many other studies have shown that learned motor responses are not *simply* localized within the brain. Lashley[31] found that rats with cerebellar lesions were so disturbed that they rolled instead of running a previously learned maze but with no decrease in accuracy of performance.

Chimpanzees with massive bilateral lesions of parietal cortex which caused severe initial inability to discriminate between weights showed not the slightest defect in the habit of alternately "hefting" the weights before selecting one—except that due to paralysis.[43]

In classical neurology, learning has been ascribed to the association cortex. For example, the visual impulses which project to striate cortex classically are thought to be stored in the immediately surrounding prestriate cortex Areas 18 and 19 of Brodmann). To test this, Lashley[32] made massive lesions of prestriate cortex in experimental animals, and found little or no decrement in learning or retention of visual patterns.

So far most of the evidence for engram localization has been negative. However, two phenomena reliably associated with damage to association cortex in primates were discussed in the previous chapter. One is Jacobsen's discovery[27] that lesions to the frontal lobes anterior to the arcuate sulcus resulted in an inability of a monkey or chimpanzee to perform a task re-

quiring memory of the position of an object during a period of forced delay (the so-called delayed response). While such frontal lesions appear to affect immediate memory in the monkey, paradoxically, they seem to be without a major effect on long-term memory (or the initial acquisition) of a discrimination habit. In contrast, as pointed out previously, such visual discrimination habits are lost after lesions of the inferior temporal Area 21 (Brodmann) of the monkey,[6] an association area. The effects of these lesions far removed from the visual areas are not attributable to mere sensory loss; no effect on the visual acuity of monkeys is found.[57] Recently studies of the mechanisms involved in these association cortex functions have suggested that they are mediated by cortico-cortical pathways. Chow[7] has shown that the inferotemporal cortex is functionally connected to striate cortex via cortico-cortical association fibers presumably relaying in prestriate cortex. An analysis of the pathways involved in delayed response performance suggests that the occipital cortex is probably in functional connection with frontal cortex via a cortico-cortical route.[22]

Interhemispheric Transfer of Learning. The localization of learned response can be studied free of possible damage to sensory areas or pathways in experiments involving section of the corpus callosum. This operation is not associated with any obvious changes in an animal's behavior or its sensory or motor capacity.[29] Similarly, intensive neurologic study of patients with surgical section of part or all of the corpus

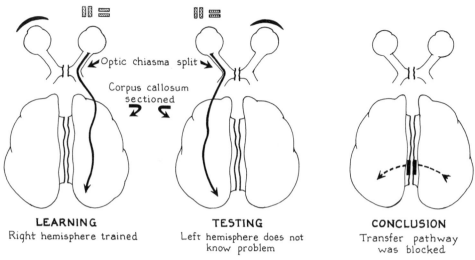

LEARNING
Right hemisphere trained

TESTING
Left hemisphere does not
know problem

CONCLUSION
Transfer pathway
was blocked

Fig. 6. Diagram of training and testing procedures for studying interocular transfer in a cat after section of the optic chiasma and corpus callosum. (After Myers, *Brain,* 1956, *79:*358–363.)

callosum revealed little effect on motor, sensory or intellectual functions.[2] The function of the corpus callosum was mysterious, although, retrospectively, there was a clue to this puzzle. Bykov,[5] in Pavlov's laboratory, found that if a normal dog is conditioned to salivate to tactile stimulation of a specific point on the body surface, stimulation of a contralateral point elicits the conditioned response. He then showed that section of the corpus callosum abolished such generalization. Moreover, he found that it was possible to establish independent conditioned responses in the two hemispheres after section of the corpus callosum. Bykov's experiments were largely ignored until recently when a series of experiments on the corpus callosum were inaugurated in Sperry's laboratory. In the first of these studies, Myers[40] sectioned the optic chiasm of cats in the midline so that impulses from the eyes would go only to the optic cortex of the same side. He then trained the cats to discriminate between two visual forms with one eye covered. He found that animals would reliably perform the problem when tested with the second eye (previously covered). Cats showed excellent interhemispheric transfer. Since the left eye projected only to the left hemisphere and the right eye only to the right hemisphere, something must have been transferred from the left to the right hemisphere. However, if the corpus callosum was sectioned as well as the optic chiasm, the two hemispheres appeared to function independently for learning and memory. Animals could be trained using one or the other eye, but

a problem learned with one eye and hemisphere while the other eye was masked would not transfer to the second eye and hemisphere. The animal gave no evidence of any benefit from the prior training. Figures 5 and 6 illustrate these experiments diagrammatically. Figure 7 shows learning curves for a learned visual discrimination from each eye in succession. As a matter of fact, Sperry *et al.*[52] have shown that opposite habits can be established easily in the two hemispheres of animals with chiasm and callosum sectioned. More recent studies have elaborated these findings.

The majority of somesthetic input is contra-

Fig. 7. Learning curves, left and right eye for cat, Gbb, which had been previously subjected to splitting of optic chiasma and corpus callosum. In this animal, learning proceeded at the same rate in each hemisphere. There was no evidence of the animal's having benefited from prior uniocular training when tested for transfer to the untrained eye. (After Sperry *et al., J. comp. physiol. Psychol.,* 1956, *49:*529–533.)

lateral; it would appear likely that section of corpus callosum alone would block interhemispheric transfer of responses to somesthetic stimuli. Callosum-sectioned cats trained to respond differentially to one of two tactile cues with one paw showed no transfer of this habit when tested with the second paw.[53] More recently, this absence of interhemispheric transfer in "split brain" animals has been shown for visual and tactile discrimination in the monkey.[12, 21]

However, some limitations on the role of the corpus callosum are indicated by the experiments of Meikle and Sechzer,[38] who trained cats which had undergone prior sections of the optic chiasm and corpus callosum to make a brightness discrimination with one eye. Such responses transferred to the second eye. Their results suggest that still other midline connections were able to function for the interhemispheric elaboration of learned response.

The role of the corpus callosum in interhemispheric transfer can be explained in two ways. The corpus callosum may either be used to establish an engram in the contralateral hemisphere as well as the originally trained hemisphere, or it simply might allow the second hemisphere to "read" the engrams of the first. To study this problem, Myers[41] first sectioned the optic chiasm of cats, trained them monocularly to discriminate a visual form and then ablated the visual cortex ipsilateral to the eye that had been trained. For simple visual problems, the second hemisphere exhibited good knowledge of the learned problem despite the cortical ablations, suggesting that for these simpler problems a dual trace or engram system had been established.

Such demonstrations of multiple engrams allows a re-evaluation of the results of some of Lashley's experiments. It is clear that the same engrams may be stored in more than one locus in the brain. Thus, the results obtained by Lashley might have been brought about by this very multiplicity of cortical representation. Multiple storage of memory might tend to give the appearance of a "mass action" or nonspecific nonlocalizable function of memory.

Cortical ablations are irreversible, making it difficult to describe the function of a cortical region by inference from the loss caused by ablation. To circumvent this difficulty, some have used spreading depression to produce a *reversible* functional decortication. Bures[3] observed that if spreading depression were initiated by appli-

cation of 25 per cent KCl and confined to one hemisphere of the rat, memory for responses formed during the depression tended to be localized in the hemisphere which was active during the training. In effect, he showed that the formation of memory can be channeled by functionally ablating one of the two hemispheres during training.

MECHANISMS OF MEMORY

Temporary Memory Storage (Consolidation Hypothesis). Many of the foregoing studies have been concerned with how much an animal can learn and others with the process of acquisition of learning *per se*. Similarly, it is becoming clear that "engram formation" should be distinguished from "engram storage." It seems probable that there is a major difference in the way information is temporarily stored as it is being acquired and the way it is permanently stored in the brain. Such a "two-process" theory of memory acquisition and storage has been proposed by Hebb,[23] and his theoretical arguments have stimulated much of the research on a two-process theory of memory. In briefest terms, he suggested that initially (during a learning "trial" for example) an immediate "trace" is established which is evanescent and unstable. Moreover, this temporary trace "might cooperate with the structural change, and carry the memory until the growth change is made."[23]

The evidence for some such two-process mechanism comes from experimental studies with animals as well as clinical observation on *retrograde amnesia*. Following a severe blow to the head, electroconvulsive shock or some other such massive trauma,[44] memory for events just preceding the event is lost, hence "retrograde amnesia." Temporary memory traces seem more evanescent and more easily interfered with by severe cortical insults. Evidence of a "consolidation process" is exemplified by the work of Duncan,[13] who trained animals with one trial per day to leave the starting chamber of a two-compartment box immediately in order to avoid a mild shock. Seizures were induced electrically at varying times after each training trial, at intervals varying from a few seconds to several hours. The acquisition of the habit was disrupted regularly only in the animals experiencing seizures shortly after each training trial.

If the seizures were induced one or more hours later, acquisition of the learned response was not disturbed (Fig. 8). These data suggest that the temporary traces aroused in the situation were slowly being stored in permanent memory and that if a major brain insult, such as electroconvulsive shock (ECS), was inducd during the storage period, acquisition of the habit was retarded.

In Duncan's experiment,[13] disruption of consolidation was inferred from retardation of learning. However, if the ECS were painful and the animals were made afraid of the compartment into which they ran, this too might retard learning. Duncan attempted to rule out this possibility by comparing the effects of ECS with the effects of (painful) foot shock to animals in a control group. These animals showed some retardation of avoidance learning but not nearly so much as those given ECS.

Coons and Miller[8] suggested that fear may be a very important confounding variable in such experiments. They showed that, under suitable conditions with many (24) ECS administrations, the fear effect may completely mask any presumed disruption of consolidation. Thus, if disruption of consolidation with ECS was to be shown unequivocally, a better technique was needed. One-trial avoidance learning seems to be such a technique. In one-trial avoidance learning the subject first learns to respond (for

example, running down an alley toward a drinking spout) until a stable level of performance is reached. Next, a *single* intense foot shock is administered for making the response. The effect of this foot shock is to suppress the response completely. At predetermined times after the foot shock, ECS is given. The test is whether the animals given ECS will "forget" the foot shock and respond when tested the next day. There are several advantages of one-trial avoidance. First, the fear and disruption of consolidation effects are pitted against each other. If ECS is simply fear-producing, it is to be expected that this fear would simply add to that produced by the foot shock, to produce more pronounced avoidance learning. Another advantage is that disruption of consolidation can be shown after only one administration of ECS.

A one-trial avoidance experiment by Heriot and Coleman[24] produced a pronounced consolidation effect. King,[28a] also using one-trial avoidance, showed a consolidation effect that fully confirmed Duncan's interpretation.

Physical Basis of Memory. The most easily conceived theories of memory involve a physical change as the memory trace. Such theories have been of two sorts; one predicates some form of active electrical process, the other, a more permanent alteration in brain chemistry or synaptic structure.

Short-term memory. One of the suggestions that have been made for the memory trace is a reverberatory circuit in the brain: that memory is stored by closed chains of neurons reactivating one another.[4] Long-term memory traces are strongly resistant to deep anesthesia and disruptive effects such as electrically induced seizures. These data tend to discount such a reverberation process as the basis for all learning. However, the experiments supporting a consolidation hypothesis suggest that a reverberatory mechanism might account for some of the temporary retention prior to permanent storage.

Neural plasticity as learning models. Any time the nervous system behaves differently as a result of previous activity a kind of learning in the broadest sense has occurred. For example, the recovery from brain damage or transection of the spinal cord (Chap. 8) beyond that due to subsidence of edema, pressure or vascular deprivation is reminiscent of learning.

Many investigators have examined simple neural phenomena which might give some clue to the nature of learning mechanisms. One such

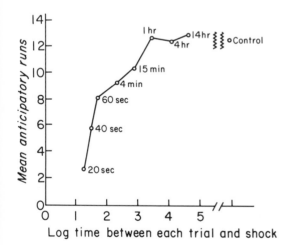

Fig. 8. Efficiency of learning in rats subjected to post-trial electroconvulsive seizures. The data suggest that some process ("consolidation") may be required for an event to be stored in permanent memory. These data also suggest that the consolidation mechanism is essentially complete after one hour. (From Duncan, *J. comp. physiol. Psychol.*, 1949, *42*:32–44.)

phenomenon is so-called "mirror-focus epilepsy." Alumina cream applied to the surface of an animal's cortex may lead to abnormal electrical activity at that point and periodic epileptic convulsions. If the animal is examined several days later, a similar focus of disordered electrical activity may be identified in the contralateral hemisphere. This "mirror-focus" epilepsy takes several days to become established and is prevented by prior section of the corpus callosum. It has been suggested that the elaboration of such "mirror foci" might serve as a simple model for the plastic changes one observes in the nervous system.[39]

Another proposed model of neural plasticity is post-tetanic potentiation. As was stated in Chapter 6, rapid and prolonged stimulation of the presynaptic limb of a monosynaptic reflex arc causes a long-term hyperexcitability of that reflex (post-tetanic potentiation). Eccles and McIntyre[14] found that this post-tetanic potentiation may last as long as several hours in a chronically de-afferented preparation, and suggested that this phenomenon might serve as a model for synaptic plasticity in general and might be studied to gain insight into the structural basis of learning.

Another model of synaptic plasticity is Bechterew's nystagmus. If one vestibule of an animal is damaged a characteristic nystagmus is produced that disappears in time. Damage to the second vestibule produces a nystagmus opposite in direction from that of the first. Since a single stage *bilateral* operation produces no such effect, there must have been some dynamic recovery of functional equilibrium which was upset by the second operation. Such a recovery process is another example of neural plasticity.

Permanent Memory Storage. Several explanations of the permanent memory trace based on structural changes have also been proposed. For example, it has been suggested[23] that activation of a synapse might induce a dendritic growth or new formation of the axonic *boutons terminaux*, which would strengthen the connection between two neurons. Growth of posterior root axons has been established in the segments below a spinal transection (Chap. 8).

A more recent theory of learning is that it is somehow stored in large molecules within the central nervous system. The recent advances in genetics demonstrate that enormous amounts of information can be precisely coded by large molecules such as deoxyribonucleic acid (DNA) and ribonucleic acid (RNA). Thus, a molecular coding might also account for the large capacity of the nervous system for memory storage, as well as for its multiplicity of localization, though no plausible schema for translation of nerve impulses into molecular structure and vice versa has been forthcoming. Some authors[18] have argued that the glial cells are involved in such microcoding.

SUMMARY

In summing up the state of our knowledge of the all-important problem of learning, no general theory of learning or its mechanism can be advanced. Nevertheless, much progress has been made over the past 50 years in *techniques* for the study of learning. Techniques for the objective and quantitative study of behavior have been developed. Animals have been taught to perform well at tasks which were thought impossible in an earlier generation. Moreover, the need to distinguish between short-term and permanent memory in analysis of the learning process has been demonstrated. It is clear that permanent memory storage is not localized in any restricted region of the brain. However, the recent studies of interhemispheric transfer and of pathways mediating immediate memory and visual discrimination learning show the importance of cortico-cortical circuits for learning and memory. Moreover, the demonstration of multiple storage of memory traces explains some of the more perplexing aspects of Lashley's discoveries. Progress in our understanding of such storage may come from detailed study of a restricted neural pathway, which induces memory traces such as interhemispheric connections. It may be expected that a combining of experimental behavioral techniques with a careful regard for known anatomic and physiologic mechanisms will yield increasing information on the general problem of brain mechanisms in learning. Although the understanding of the mechanism of learning and neural plasticity is elusive, the prediction of Sherrington[46] in 1906 is still valid:

"New methods of promise seem to me those lately followed by Franz, Thorndyke [sic], Yerkes, and others. For instance, the influence of experimental lesions in skilled actions recently and individually, i.e., experimentally acquired. . . . by combining the methods of comparative psychology (e.g., the labyrinth test*) with the methods of experimental physiology, investigation may be expected ere long to furnish new data of importance toward the knowledge of movement as an outcome of the working of the brain."

* "Maze test."

REFERENCES

1. BLOUGH, D. S. *J. comp. physiol. Psychol.,* 1956, *49:*425–430.
2. BREMER, F., BRIHAYE, J. and ANDRE-BALISAUX, G. *Schweiz. Arch. Neurol. Psychiat.,* 1956, *78:*31–87.
3. BURES, J. In: *The central nervous system and behavior,* M. Brazier, ed. New York, Josiah Macy, Jr., Foundation, 1959.
4. BURNS, B. *The mammalian cerebral cortex.* London, Edward Arnold, 1958.
5. BYKOV, K. *Zbl. ges. Neurol. Psychiat.,* 1925, *39:*199.
6. CHOW, K. L. *J. comp. physiol. Psychol.,* 1952, *45:*109–118.
7. CHOW, K. L. In: *Brain mechanisms and learning,* J. Delafresnaye, ed., Springfield, Ill., Charles C Thomas, 1961.
8. COONS, E. E. and MILLER, N. E. *J. comp. physiol. Psychol.,* 1960, *53:*524–531.
9. COWEY, A. *Nature (Lond.),* 1962, *193:*302.
10. CULLER, E. A. and METTLER, F. A. *J. comp. Psychol.,* 1934, *18:*291–303.
11. DOTY, R. W., RUTLEDGE, L. T., JR. and LARSEN, R. M. *J. Neurophysiol.,* 1956, *19:*401–415.
12. DOWNER, J. L. DE C. *Fed. Proc.,* 1958, *17:*37.
13. DUNCAN, C. P. *J. comp. physiol. Psychol.,* 1949, *42:*32–44.
14. ECCLES, J. C. and McINTYRE, A. K. *J. Physiol.,* 1953, *121:*492–516.
15. FERSTER, C. B. and SKINNER, B. F. *Schedules of reinforcement.* New York, Appleton-Century-Crofts, Inc., 1957.
16. FORBES, A. and MAHAN, C. *J. comp. physiol. Psychol.,* 1963, *56:*36–40.
17. GALAMBOS, R. In: *The central nervous system and behavior.* M. Brazier, ed. New York, Josiah Macy, Jr., Foundation, 1958.
18. GALAMBOS, R. *Proc. nat. Acad. Sci., (Wash.),* 1961, *47:*129–136.
19. GLICKMAN, S. E. *Psychol. Bull.,* 1961, *58:*218–233.
20. GLICKMAN, S. E. and FELDMAN, S. M. *Electroenceph. clin. Neurophysiol.,* 1961, *13:*703–709.
21. GLICKSTEIN, M. and SPERRY, R. W. *J. comp. physiol. Psychol.,* 1960, *53:*322–327.
22. GLICKSTEIN, M., ARORA, H. A. and SPERRY, R. W. *J. comp. physiol. Psychol.,* 1963, *56:*11–18.
23. HEBB, D. O. *The organization of behavior.* New York, John Wiley & Sons, 1949.
24. HERIOT, J. T. and COLEMAN, P. D. *J. comp. physiol. Psychol.,* 1962, *55:*1082–1084.
25. HERNANDEZ-PEON, R. *Electroenceph. clin. Neurophysiol.,* 1960, Suppl. *13:*101–114.
26. HUNTER, W. S. *J. gen. Psychol.,* 1930, *3:*455–468.
27. JACOBSEN, C. F. *Comp. Psychol. Monogr.,* 1936, *13,* no. 63: 3–60.
28. JOHN, E. R. and KILLAM, K. F. *J. Pharmacol. exp. Ther.,* 1959, *125:*252–274.
28a. KING, R. A. *J. comp. physiol. Psychol.,* 1964 (in press).
29. KORANYI, A. V. *Pflüg. Arch. ges. Physiol.,* 1890, *47:*35–42.
30. LASHLEY, K. S. *Arch. Neurol. Psychiat. (Chic.),* 1924, *12:*249–276.
31. LASHLEY, K. S. In: *Physiological mechanisms in animal behavior.* Symposium of the Society for Experimental Biology. New York, Academic Press, 1950.
32. LASHLEY, K. S. *Genet. Psychol. Monogr.,* 1948, *37:*107–166.
33. LASHLEY, K. S. *Brain mechanisms and intelligence.* Chicago, University of Chicago Press, 1929 (Reprinted, New York, Dover Publications, 1963.)
34. LEUKEL, F. A. *J. comp. physiol. Psychol.,* 1957, *50:*300–306.
35. LOUCKS, R. B. *J. comp. Psychol.,* 1934, *18:*305–313.
36. LOUCKS, R. B. *J. Psychol.,* 1935, *1:*5–44.
37. LOUCKS, R. B. *J. comp. Psychol.,* 1938, *25:*315–332.
38. MEIKLE, T. H. and SECHZER, J. A. *Science,* 1960, *132:*734–735.
39. MORRELL, F. *Physiol. Rev.,* 1961, *41:*443–494.
40. MYERS, R. E. *Brain,* 1956, *79:*358–363.
41. MYERS, R. E. In: *Brain mechanisms and learning.* Springfield, Ill., Charles C Thomas, 1961.
42. PAVLOV, I. P. *Conditioned reflexes,* G. V. Anrep, tr. and ed. Oxford, Oxford University Press, 1927 (Reprinted, New York, Dover Publications, 1960.)
43. RUCH, T. C. *Res. Publ. Ass. nerv. ment. Dis.,* 1934, *15:*289–330.
44. RUSSELL, W. R. and NATHAN, P. W. *Brain,* 1946, *69:*280–300.
45. SHARPLESS, S. and JASPER, H. H. *Brain,* 1956, *79:*655–680.
46. SHERRINGTON, C. S. *The integrative action of the nervous system.* New Haven, Conn., Yale University Press, 1947.
47. SKINNER, B. F. *The behavior of organisms.* New York, Appleton-Century-Crofts, 1938.
48. SKINNER, B. F. *Amer. Scient.,* 1957, *45:*343–371.
49. SPERRY, R. W. *J. Neurophysiol.,* 1947, *10:*275–294.
50. SPERRY, R. W. and MINER, N. *J. comp. physiol. Psychol.,* 1955, *48:*463–469.
51. SPERRY, R. W., MINER, N. and MYERS, R. E. *J. comp. physiol. Psychol.,* 1955, *48:*50–58.
52. SPERRY, R. W., STAMM, J. S. and MINER, N. *J. comp. physiol. Psychol.,* 1956, *49:*529–533.
53. STAMM, J. S. and SPERRY, R. W. *J. comp. physiol. Psychol.,* 1957, *50:*138–143.
54. STEBBINS, W. C. and LANSON, R. N. *J. exp. Anal. Behav.,* 1961, *4:*149–155.
55. THORNDIKE, E. L. *Psychol. Monogr.,* 1898, *2:*No. 8.
56. THORPE, W. H. *Learning and instinct in animals.* London, Methuen, 1963.
57. WEISKRANTZ, L., MIHAILOVIC, L. and GROSS, C. G. *Science,* 1960, *131:*1443–1444.

CHAPTER 25

Physiologic Basis of Motivation

By ORVILLE A. SMITH, JR.

INTRODUCTION

BEHAVIOR is characterized by two phenomena —*plasticity*, or the ability to acquire new modes of responding, and *energetics,* or variability in the intensity of responding. The learning process accounts for the first and the process of motivation for the second. At one moment, an organism may act very rapidly and forcefully, while at another time it may act slowly and with little vigor or enthusiasm, or it may not act at all. The kinds of environmental variations which bring about the changes in the intensity of behavior may be quite diverse (e.g., water deprivation, intense illumination, pain, fatigue, etc.), but the commonality of their effects on behavior allows one to infer that a common physiologic process is being evoked. This process is called *motivation.*

The same variations which affect the intensity of behavior may also guide the organism's behavior so that one part of the environment is responded to in preference to other parts; e.g., the hungry rat eats avidly from a dish of food, ignoring a water cup; the same rat when thirsty drinks from the cup and ignores the food.

Motivation, then, has two major aspects, one concerned with the intensity or vigor of the behavior, which may be labeled the *drive* aspect, the other concerned with the guidance of the behavior, which may be labeled the *directional* aspect. The latter is so intimately related to the topics of learning and perception that for the purposes of this chapter it will be referred to but briefly.

Measurement of Drive. One method of measuring the drive aspect of motivation has been to observe the effect produced on a measurable facet of behavior by varying the intensity of a stimulus. The stimuli to be varied may be internal to the organism (e.g., the amount of food or water deprivation) or external (e.g., the strength of an electric current applied to the skin or the degree of illumination). The biologic effects of such stimuli have traditionally been assessed by measuring (i) gross motor activity, (ii) latency of a learned response, (iii) how much obstruction will prevent an animal from achieving a goal, (iv) allowing the animal a choice of two or more stimuli (preference method), (v) the force (or amplitude) of a response, and (vi) autonomic measures.

Figure 1 illustrates the simultaneous measurement of three variables as a function of the number of hours of food deprivation.

Relation between Motivation and Learning. The relationships between these variables are not simple. For one thing, measuring drive which is unaffected by learning is by itself difficult. In his *Principles of Behavior*, Clark L. Hull[36] attempted to formalize the determinants of behavior with the equation $S^ER = S^HRX\ D$; S^ER is the symbol for the reaction potential or what the organism actually does, S^HR the symbol for habit strength or the degree of learning in a specific stimulus situation, and D the symbol for drive or the organism's motivational status. The equation, of course, indicates that if either S^HR or D equals zero the organism does nothing; therefore the drive aspect uninfluenced by learning cannot be measured.* As a further complication, in a later revision, Hull[37] indicated his belief that other variables such as "stimulus intensity dynamism," reward magnitude and delay of reinforcement were also primary factors in the equation and also acted multiplicatively with S^HR and D. Also, a commonly used defining characteristic of a motivating stimulus is that it mediate new learning.

* Several autonomic measures show promise of reflecting motivational level independent of learned responses, especially skin conductance.

Learning and motivation are further interrelated by the factor of "acquired or secondary drive." Originally innocuous stimuli which have been associated with a situation inducing considerable motivation in an organism may themselves acquire an ability to increase motivation in that organism. These acquired drives are responsible for the major portion of human behavior, such as the drive for social position or money for its own sake.

Problems in Dealing with Motivation. A motivational state is usually inferred from a particular kind of behavior and is given a name. The name is generally chosen from the vocabulary developed from our own introspections. For example, when an organism drinks water the inference is that a state of "thirst" has energized it to drink. Having once applied this term, a person tends to assume that only one biologic mechanism is responsible for this state and the resultant behavior. Using drinking behavior and the motivational state of "thirst" implied from that behavior, let us examine possible reasons for the drinking behavior:

(i) Water deprivation. This is the usual physiologic situation that elicits drinking behavior. The neural mechanisms responsible for this behavior involve the hypothalamic osomoreceptors, which sense the high tonicity of the plasma (Chap. 11), and

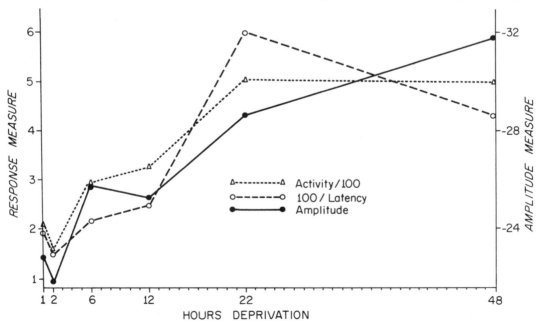

Fig. 1. Gross bodily activity, latency of response between a signal and pushing a panel to receive a food reward (left ordinate), and the amplitude of the panel pushing (right ordinate) as a function of number of hours of food deprivation.

the cells of the lateral hypothalamus, which are somehow necessary for drinking.[50]

(ii) Dry mouth drinking. Epstein[19] has shown that if the salivary glands are removed from rats that are fed only a dry food, they exhibit a peculiar behavior which involves taking a piece of food and immediately following this with a small drink of water. This occurs even if the rat is completely hydrated, probably because there must be some moisture in the mouth and throat for the animal to swallow the food.

(iii) Emotional drinking. If rats are placed in a cage in which they have previously been given a painful shock, they will drink more water than control animals never shocked in the cage.

(iv) Avoidance drinking. Animals can be trained readily to drink water to avoid receiving a painful stimulus. Very large quantities of water may be ingested through this procedure.

(v) Reinforcement schedule drinking. Falk[23] showed that putting rats on a variable interval reinforcement schedule* increased water intake threefold over normal.

In the last four examples, dehydration due to water deprivation clearly is not the stimulus for drinking behavior. Yet, if the drinking behavior is used as the defining characteristic of "thirst," all these situations are immediately assumed to have a common origin in the motivational state "thirst" and, therefore, a common physiologic mechanism. It is much more meaningful to speak of dehydration drinking, emotional drinking, dry mouth drinking, etc., because the relevant mechanism is specified.

Similarly, the biologic reasons for eating may be as varied as for drinking. Sexual activity is often a result of stressful situations or a means of asserting dominance as well as a function of deprivation of sexual activity or of the time of the estrous cycle.

Other problems in using motivation as a meaningful scientific concept have arisen because of (i) the large number of factors which can influence the intensity of behavior, (ii) the wide range of organisms (ameba to man) which are under consideration, and (iii) the great

* A procedure used in learning studies in which a reward is given to an animal on the basis of his responding after a variable time interval has elapsed (Chap. 24).

variety of related terms available, each of which generally involves a failure of precise definition. Thus, the scientific utility of the motivation concept has been hampered by the use of terms such as *desire, wish, want, need,* etc., all of which may acquire slightly differing connotations.

MECHANISMS ALTERING INTENSITY AND DIRECTION OF BEHAVIOR

A usually unstated and unproved but rather obvious assumption is that, when the behavior output of a normal animal changes in magnitude, the change must result from alterations of central nervous system activity. Such activity can be influenced in several ways: (i) by afferent input, (ii) by humoral mechanisms, or (iii) by intrinsic activity.

Afferent Input. This is broken down into two familiar categories (Chap. 14), exteroceptive and interoceptive stimuli.

Exteroceptive stimuli. It may be stated, in general, that any sensory input has drive properties if it is intense enough. Loud auditory stimuli, intense illumination and temperature extremes have all been used to motivate avoidance behavior in animals. Other sensory inputs may be motivating in a positive fashion. Prime examples of this may be seen in the work of Young[69] and, more recently, of Pfaffman[54] dealing with taste; the former author made clear the presence of strongly motivating taste preferences; the latter has demonstrated especially well the effects of various taste stimuli on activity of nerve cells in the classic taste pathway which correlate with the preferences.

There is some evidence that a certain degree of any afferent input is optimal for a particular organism at a particular time and that the organism will seek to avoid the extremes of that input; however, it is also true that some inputs are much more motivating than others and, judged from human experience, these have a strong affective (subjective pleasure or pain) component. Generally, these are the stimuli of major concern in the study of motivated behavior.

Studies of sensory deprivation[34] in man show that the lack of sensory input may be as disturbing as excessive input and that the human organism, at least, develops hallucinations or false sensory effects when sensory deprivation is protracted. Some believe that certain hospital situations involve sufficient sensory deprivation to produce psychiatric symptoms in patients. The fact that the central nervous system is not merely a passive receiver and transmitter of afferent information because sensory input may be altered by central neural mechanisms has been mentioned previously (Chap. 12). Stimulation of reticular formation,[27] the cerebral cortex,[38] and the medullary pyramids[1] has been shown to exert such an effect.

Hernandez-Peon[33] has demonstrated in the unanesthetized animal that changing the motivational status of an animal can alter the amplitude of an auditory evoked potential. The suggested utility of this phenomenon is the reduction of distracting sensory influences when a high degree of concentration or attention is required.

Interoceptive stimuli. Stimuli coming from within the body, especially the viscera, are a major source of motivational afferents. Visceral movement or stretching or changes in the diameter of blood vessels may provide afferent input signaling bodily conditions which require, among other adjustments, the initiation of complex behavior to relieve the conditions. However, because other than free nerve endings are few in viscera and because most of the afferent fibers are small and either thinly myelinated or unmyelinated and therefore difficult to study, little is known about the kind or quantity of information conveyed by them (Chap. 17). There is a definite indication that sensory information is carried by larger myelinated fibers from the viscera to cortical levels.[2]

Humoral Mechanisms. Another major route of influence on central nervous system activity is the penetration of blood-borne hormones, nutrients or metabolites through the blood–brain barrier to act directly upon particular nerve cells. The blood–brain barrier is effective largely on the basis of mechanical resistance to passage of relatively large molecules through the capillary wall or through the membranous end feet of the neuroglia which surround the capillaries. The site of the blood–brain barrier is discussed in Chapter 47.

Endocrine secretions. Certain endocrine secretions have been shown to influence directly the activity of specific areas of the central nervous system. For example, Dell[17] has shown the facilitatory effects of epinephrine upon the ascending reticular activating system (ARAS), and Sawyer[59] has shown that the sexual hormones may lower the threshold of a response to electrical stimulation of the reticular formation.

Tonicity changes. Inasmuch as there is some exchange between blood plasma and the fluid surrounding the nerve cells, it is reasonable to expect that changes in the tonicity of the plasma may influence the excitability of certain nerve cells. Such an effect may be illustrated by infusing hypertonic saline into the carotid arteries or directly into the ventricles themselves. A strongly motivated drinking behavior will immediately appear.

Nutritive substances and products of metabolism. During normal metabolism certain constituents of the blood increase in concentration and others decrease; these changes are reflected across the blood–brain barrier and may result in altered neural activity. The glucose–insulin balance is an obvious example of this: A deficiency of glucose, due to an overabundance of insulin, may bring about severe behavioral changes or even violent seizures.

Although metabolites such as lactic acid have been suspected of having motivational effects as concomitants of fatigue, such a relationship has not been definitely established.

Blood temperature. Another potentially powerful blood-borne factor is the temperature of the blood itself. Obviously, this factor, along with skin temperature, should play a major role in elicitation of motivated behavior concerned with regulation of body temperature, such as seeking shelter, curling up, etc. In addition, blood temperature may well influence all neural activity in general, purely because of the dependence upon temperature of all chemical reactions, including those of neural metabolism. Essman *et al.*[22] have shown that hypothermia can prevent the learning of an escape response.

Intrinsic Neural Activity. Although afferent input and humoral effects are the most obvious means of altering central nervous activity and, consequently, the intensity of behavior, certain behavior changes are not immediately referable to these sources. When the source of the effect is obscure, the appeal is made to "intrinsic" factors, and if the behavior under consideration has a temporally linked rhythm, it is suggested that a "biologic clock" is operative. Many types of behavior and physiologic processes may show a temporally determined repetitiveness such as sleep, eating, sexual behavior in the female, activity, etc. Most of these can be linked to a rhythmic process going on either outside the organism or at least outside the central nervous system. These processes can then act upon the central nervous system via a humoral or afferent route. However, some changes can be shown to be independent, or partially so, from other cyclic events; the natural conclusion from this is that the central nervous system has "clock" propensities of its own which may determine changes in the absence of an external stimulus.[29]

In animals, synchronous cortical discharges which are "spontaneous" when all afferent inputs have been successfully removed[9] suggest the existence of intrinsic neural activity with which, in the normal animal, incoming sensory effects may interact.

In lower animals, it can be shown that the central nervous system has pre-existing connections which may be activated to bring about inflexible but intricate patterns of behavior called *instincts*. Tinbergen[68] has shown that these behavior patterns are specific to a particular species and are triggered or released only by a particular external stimulus sometimes acting effectively only when a particular physiologic state has been induced in the animal, e.g., during mating or nesting seasons. Observation gives the impression that this is strongly motivated behavior. This particular combination of intrinsic neural processes and connections elicited only by a specific stimulus is most easily observed in insects, fish and birds. In the mammal the same situation may hold but, if so, its effectiveness is soon suppressed by a more flexible nervous system and the resultant greater learning abilities.

INITIATION AND METERING OF MOTIVATED BEHAVIOR

Traditionally, investigators have tried to determine which *one* input is responsible for establishing the motivational state in the organism; often this input has been extended to include the mechanism for termination of the state as well. A classic example of this is the dry throat theory of thirst postulated by Cannon.[11] He assumed that sensory receptors in the throat were sensitive to dryness and that, when the organism became dehydrated, the amount of saliva produced in the mouth decreased, thus causing a dry throat. The animal then supposedly was

motivated to ingest water, which consequently moistened the receptors in the throat and brought about the cessation of drinking. Thus, the initiation and termination of the behavior were held to be controlled by a single mechanism. The inadequacy of this theory is clear from the observation that once an animal takes a single swallow of water, the receptors in the throat are as wet as they will ever be and yet drinking continues for a long period.

Research in motivation over the last 25 years has shown that, although there may be in general a major factor responsible for the initiation of a specific behavior, the behavior may be influenced by multiple factors affecting the central nervous system through many of the routes listed above. Also, it seems that if the dominant source of information is removed, another may be substituted which, after a short time, initiates and regulates the behavior appropriately. In the case of water intake, it can be shown that either gastric or oral factors may serve to "meter" water intake of a water-deprived animal. Several of the most common sources of physiologically based motivation will be reviewed with special reference to the stimuli which *initiate* the behavior and those which *meter* the behavior and eventually result in *satiation*.

Initiation of Food Intake.   Since the time of Cannon and Washburn,[12] contractions of the stomach and duodenum have been considered critical to eliciting the sensation called "hunger" and subsequent eating behavior. These contractions are probably related to the well known hunger pangs but are not solely responsible for the initiation (much less the metering) of food intake inasmuch as this is adequate when sensory connections from the stomach have been removed. There is greater gastric motility when food is present in the stomach than when it is completely empty. Gastrectomized human patients still report feelings of hunger.

Mayer[47] has suggested a "glucostatic" theory, according to which blood glucose utilization by certain cells of the nervous system is the critical factor in initiating and controlling food intake (Chaps. 11 and 55). According to this theory, low glucose levels—hence, low glucose utilization—excite certain neural elements in the hypothalamus and bring about the sensation of hunger. This theory will not encompass all the experimental facts[26] and must be considered as one of a whole complex of factors.

"Metering" Food Intake (Satiation). The problem of "metering" food intake, or satiation, is a related, though different, problem. Taken in the temporal order of events, metering might occur in the mouth and throat as a function of the quantity and taste of materials passing through these areas. By means of esophogeal fistulas so that food is chewed and swallowed but never reaches the stomach (sham feeding), it has been shown that animals eventually do stop eating, but that the total food intake is much larger than it would have been if food had actually reached the stomach.[39] So, metering via oral–pharyngeal feedback does occur but is somewhat gross.

In contrast, Epstein and Teitelbaum,[21] using an ingenious oral–esophageal bypass, have demonstrated that the rat can regulate food and water intake perfectly without the modalities of taste, smell and tactile or proprioceptive information from the mouth, pharynx or esophagus. They conclude that postingestion factors are sufficient ". . . to control the onset of feeding, the size of individual meals and the total amount of food eaten during a single day and for longer periods of time up to more than a month."

In attempting to determine the exact postingestion factors responsible, Janowitz and Grossman[39] have emphasized the role of stomach distension. One of the appealing aspects of the distension hypothesis is the immediacy of the effect. Any hypothesis of satiation based on metabolic factors is faced with explaining why the cessation of eating occurs long before digestion or absorption can occur. For example, the "glucostatic" theory asserts that for satiety to occur the critical neural cells must have available a high blood glucose level and sufficient insulin to allow a high rate of glucose utilization by these cells. However, in most animals, eating is so rapid that there is no time for digestion and the production of glucose before eating stops. In animals that eat rapidly there is an accompanying sympathetic reaction (as shown by increased heart rate and blood pressure, Fig. 3, Chap. 35) which could lead to the immediate production of glucose by glycolysis in the liver. This would lead to immediate increases in insulin release by the pancreas, and the necessary humoral situation at the critical neurons would be established. This could also be the reason for the abolition of hunger by acute psychologic stress, which has a sympathetic component.

The fat depots of the body may also be involved in this regulation. Kennedy[40] has suggested that a metabolite in equilibrium with fat depots acts upon the hypothalamic centers to control their activity. Studies with parabiotic rats[35] in which one member is made hyperphagic and the other subsequently becomes very thin support this idea.

Mook[51] has assessed the relation between oral and postingestional determinants of intake by producing both esophageal and gastric fistulas in the same animals so that the same or different substances could be presented orally and intragastrically, simultaneously. He concluded that the postingestional effect is not substance-specific and that the critical factor may be a gastric osmoreceptor. If different substances of equal osmolarity are presented to the mouth and stomach, the animal proceeds to consume the substance presented to the mouth at the normal rate for that substance. However, if different substances of differing osmolarity are presented to the mouth and stomach, respectively, consumption of the substance presented to the mouth is determined by the osmolarity of the substance introduced into the stomach. He concludes that food intake is determined by positive and negative oral factors (largely taste) and by a postingestional osmotic mechanism, thereby substantiating earlier work.[55, 61, 64]

The relationships between body temperature and food intake have led Strominger and Brobeck[65] to propose that the "specific dynamic action" (SDA) of foodstuffs is also a factor in the regulation of food intake. This hypothesis suggests that the heat produced by SDA (Chap. 11) of various foods is sensed by the critical neurons in the hypothalamus and that this results in satiety and the cessation of eating.

Control of food intake is therefore highly complex and involves many regulating mechanisms. The interactions between these factors and motivated behavior are highlighted by the work of Miller and Kessen,[49] who showed that animals learn to perform a new response when food is injected directly into the stomach, thus satisfying metabolic needs, but that they learn much more rapidly when allowed to take the same food orally, thus involving both oral and postingestional factors.

The cells of the lateral hypothalamic nucleus and the ventromedial hypothalamic nucleus are assumed to be the excitatory and inhibitory neurons, respectively, for the initiation and metering of food intake (Chap. 11). Other neu-

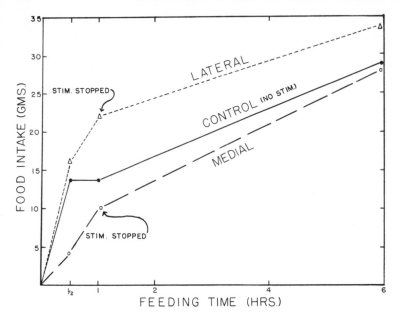

Fig. 2. Regulation of food intake by electrical stimulation of the lateral and medial hypothalamus in the same rat. The control record is the intake during a six-hour period averaged over three days. Stimulation of either the medial or lateral hypothalamus was carried out during the first hour of eating. At time 0 the rat had been deprived of food for 18 hours. (From Smith, in *Electrical stimulation of the brain.* D. E. Sheer, ed. Austin, University of Texas Press, 1961.)

ral areas have also been shown to influence food intake. Maire[57] has found that stimulation of the premammillary area and the anterior thalamic nucleus results in a precisely controlled food intake. The relation of these areas to the action of the hypothalamic control areas is obscure, but they may be linked together.

Eating as an index of motivation. It is tempting to infer the existence of a motivational state by observing consummatory behavior; e.g., an animal that is eating is therefore hungry and motivated to obtain and ingest food. The effects produced on food intake by appropriate ablation or stimulation (Fig. 2) of the hypothalamic control areas are so dramatic that they have been assumed to reflect changes in the organism's motivational state. However, Miller[48] and Teitelbaum[66] demonstrated that animals made hyperphagic by lesions of the ventromedial hypothalamus showed a *decreased* effort to obtain food despite the fact they consumed large quantities of food if given free access to it. While stimulation of this part of the hypothalamus reduces food intake,[62] as predicted from the effects of ablation, it also leads rats actively to avoid receiving such stimulation; therefore, the decreased food intake may be secondary to the noxiousness or upsetting effects of the stimulus.[42] On the contrary, however, lateral hypothalamic stimulation has qualified in all respects as increasing motivational state as well as food intake.[53] Maire has shown dramatically, if not quantitatively, that stimulus of the pre-

mammillary area induces truly motivated eating behavior (Fig. 3).

Recently, Baillie and Morrison[4] have questioned the assumption that the aphagia produced by lateral lesions has primarily a motivational basis. They suggest the effect to be primarily an inability to consume the food because their animals with lesions continued to press a lever for direct intragastric delivery of food while refusing both food and water orally.

Water Intake. Possible reasons for an animal's ingestion of water have already been mentioned. If we focus our attention on drinking elicited by water deprivation and ask the same questions that were asked about food intake, i.e., which stimuli initiate the behavior and which are responsible for the metering and eventual satiety effect, the following facts emerge:

The initiation of drinking results either from increased osmotic pressure of the plasma or from decreased extracellular volume.[23] The relationship between excretion and intake is important here, for both mechanisms act to keep the body in optimal water balance. There is little doubt that the supraoptic nuclei of the hypothalamus respond to changes in osmotic pressure by releasing antidiuretic hormone or a precursor to it, so that water excretion from the kidneys is retarded (Chap. 11). The effect of electrically activating these cells and the subsequent effect on drinking is shown in Figure 4. However, there seem to be other neural mechanisms which lead to the active and immediate intake of water. Andersson and McCann,[3] using goats, have shown that saline injection into, or electrical stimulation of, an area between the fornix and mammillothalamic tract leads to drinking. Figure 5 illustrates this effect from stimulating a similar locus in the rat. The lateral hypothalamic nucleus also plays a role in water intake.[50] Bilateral lesions of this region lead to a combined aphagia and adipsia,[68] providing a neurologic basis for the often observed positive relation between food and water intake.

A premammillary area close to that concerned with eating also causes drinking when stimulated (Maire[57]).

"Metering" is also carried out by an oral factor (Epstein[20]). Again, this type of metering with the consequent satiation occurs before any change in either tonicity or volume of the blood.

Sexual Behavior. Mating provides the prime example of behavior regulated by the production and subsequent action of an intrinsic biologic substance. The chemical substances concerned are testicular hormones in the male and ovarian hormones in the female. In lower mammals, if the sex glands are removed, sexual behavior ceases after a time, but the replacement of testosterone in the male and both estrogen and progesterone in the female reinstates appropriate sexual activity for these animals. Prepubertal male cats show male sexual behavior when given testosterone and female sex behavior patterns when stilbestrol is administered.[25] This reversibility does not hold in adult cats, however.

In rats, the initiation of mating behavior is due entirely to the availability of a sexually receptive female to a sexually mature male. Previous experience seems to play no role[7] and copulation is perfect without such experience. This example of innate behavior (an excellent example of "instinct") does not hold as specifically for other species.

The relation between the presence of one kind of hormone and the elicitation of a particular kind of sexual behavior does not apply rigidly. Young[70] prefers to emphasize the action of the hormone on the existing soma or substrate of all the tissues mediating sexual behavior, which implies that whatever behavior patterns are laid down by genetics or experience may be merely activated or brought into play by the presence of the hormone. Prenatally, the

hormones have an organizing function on subsequent mating behavior, particularly in the fe-

A. Before stimulus

B. Stimulus starts

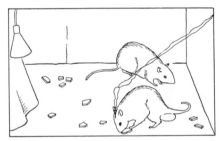

C. Stimulus continues

D. Stimulus ends

Fig. 3. Male rat with electrodes implanted in the premammillary area placed in a cage containing a female rat in heat and food pellets scattered on the floor. *A,* The male begins sexual activity with female. *B,* Electric stimulation through implanted electrodes begins and the male promptly leaves the female and approaches food pellet. *C,* Stimulation continues, male rat eats food pellet. *D,* Stimulation ceases, male rat drops food and returns to female, sexual behavior is reinstated. (Furnished by F. W. Maire.)

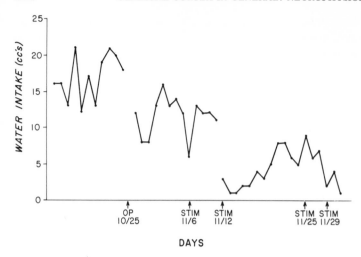

Fig. 4. Water intake following electrical stimulation of the supraoptic nuclei of a rat is decreased considerably. The effect is of long duration after the second (11/12) stimulation day. Control water intake is shown at the left before implantation of electrodes (OP 10/25). Effect is presumably secondary to increased water reabsorption in the kidneys due to extra output of antidiuretic hormone subsequent to stimulation.

male.[56] The experimental literature varies widely in affirming or denying the specificity of hormone to kind of behavior in the adult.

The initiation of sexual behavior is dependent not only upon the presence of the androgen in the male but also upon the action of the female hormones on the tissues of the female to produce the secondary sexual characteristics. In many cases it is the presence of these changes during estrus, such as the vivid red, swollen perineal region of monkeys, which acts as a trigger or releaser of sexual behavior in the male. This relationship is very important for species survival, for these changes occur concomitantly with ovulation and hence with fertility.*

There is a distinct change in phylogeny in the dependence of sexual behavior upon the hormones for its initiation. In birds and fish sex behavior is locked to seasonal variations and hormonal production, whereas in subhuman primates sexual behavior may occur at any time during the female cycle, but the greatest frequency is coincident with estrus and ovulation. Also, incompatibility can play a role at this level, certain individuals of both sexes showing preferences for certain sexual partners. In these animals the variety of sexual behavior also increases. In chimpanzees there have been reports of masturbation, homosexuality, rape, frigidity and prostitution.[6] In humans the increased role of psychological factors over hormonal action in determining sexual behavior can easily be documented. Many women past the menopause continue to have sexual desires, and castrated men sometimes continue to lead a normal sex life. In contrast, the castrated rat will not be aroused by a female in estrus until the appropriate sex hormone is injected. Kinsey et al.[41] have reported that the American female shows peaks of sexual desire just pre- and postmenstrually and actually an ebb in desire just at midcycle, when ovulation occurs. It has been suggested that this phylogenetic change in behavior, which is contrary to the biologic princi-

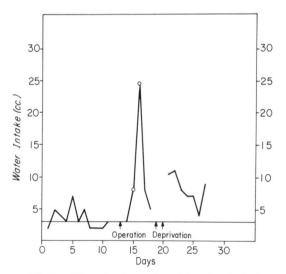

Fig. 5. Water intake produced by electrical stimulation of rostrodorsal hypothalamus of a rat. Open circles indicate days when short-term stimulation was carried out. The effect of two days' water deprivation is shown at right. This amount of deprivation does not produce water intake equivalent to stimulation of hypothalamus during the second period.

*In our primate quarters an exceptionally intelligent male monkey succeeded in picking the lock on his cage and the lock on the cage of a female in full estrus. The two animals were found free in the room the next morning, proving that "love laughs at locksmiths." Exactly 170 days later the female gave birth to an infant.

ple of species survival, is due to the effect of social factors, that is, the avoidance of excessive pregnancies, which seems to be able to overcome the basic biologic mechanisms.

In general, the initiation of sexual behavior shifts in phylogeny from a dependence on hormones to a greater dependence upon sensory factors, learning and the involvement of a more complex neural organization.

Satiation of sexual behavior is easily identifiable in the climax or orgasm. The sensory input from repeated mechanical stimulation of the glans penis in the male and the clitoris in the female acts on the central nervous system until an as yet undefinable neural process leads to ejaculation in the male and uterine and vaginal contractions in the female. In the young male particularly, psychological sexual stimuli may substitute for mechanical stimulation and ejaculation may occur in company with erotic dreams. One last facet that again illustrates the increasingly greater dependence of human sexual behavior upon psychological and experiential factors comes from medical reports of somatically male hermaphrodites who have been mistakenly raised as girls. These individuals acquire the mannerisms and characteristics of the female and prefer to be raised and considered as female.[70]

All levels of the nervous system contribute to the integration of sexual behavior. The spinal cord can integrate enough sexual mechanisms to produce penile erection and ejaculation. No complete pattern of sexual behavior is possible in animals with cord section, and paraplegics report a complete dissociation between their sexual feelings and the random priapisms which occur. With an intact brainstem, including most of the midbrain, some posturing involved in mating can be induced by stimulating the vagina. Again, no complete sexual behavior can be elicited.

Through its connections with the pituitary gland, the hypothalamus is critical for both the biologic fact of ovulation and the mechanism of estrus with its consequent mating behavior. These two facets of reproduction may be separated by differential lesions of the hypothalamus. Lesions of the anterior hypothalamic nucleus lead to anestrus (failure to come into estrus and mate) but do not interfere with ovulation. The fact that administration of additional female hormones to these animals does not reinstate estrus provides strong evidence that the hormones normally producing estrus are acting

on this region of the hypothalamus and that this is a critical region in the organization of the somatic behavior involved in mating. Lesions placed between the ventromedial nucleus and the mammillary body result in atrophy of the ovaries and a failure of estrus, an effect probably upon the pituitary gonadotrophin. In contrast to the animals with anterior hypothalamic lesions, however, if estrogen replacement therapy is established, these animals demonstrate appropriate mating behavior.[60]

Other studies have shown that stimulation of the ventromedial nucleus produces ovulation.[32, 46] Male sexual behavior is also influenced by the action of the hypothalamus; stimulation of the tuberal region in the rat results in ejaculation, and stimulation of several areas of the septum and hypothalamus produces erections in squirrel monkeys.[45]

The cerebral cortex is relatively unimportant for mating behavior in most female mammals. In rats, removal of all the neocortex does not interfere with the estrus cycle, mating, pregnancy or delivery.[16] In the male rat however, the same lesions drastically impair sexual behavior.[5]

In contrast to neocortical removal, removal of rhinencephalic structures such as pyriform cortex and underlying amygdala may result in such extreme forms of hypersexuality that the appropriate sex object is not recognized and mating will be attempted with almost anything that moves (Chap. 26).

Temperature. The maintenance of body temperature is of such critical importance to survival of the organism that a very elaborate and accurate control system has evolved. This system involves changes at the autonomic level, not affecting the animal's gross behavior, and also at the somatic level, such as shivering, increased locomotion and the mediation of new learning. Hardy[28] has analyzed the system as having two sources of control: (i) *Automatic control* involves the two thermal capacities, core and peripheral tissues; three mechanisms, heat production (shivering and nonshivering thermogenesis), sweating and vasomotor activity; two detection systems, hypothalamic and cutaneous receptors; and an integrating system via autonomic central areas of the brain. (ii) *Servocontrol* involves behavioral adjustments such as altering amounts of clothing or shelter or in some other fashion using an external source to balance heat load or loss discrepancies.

Low ambient temperatures motivate rats to

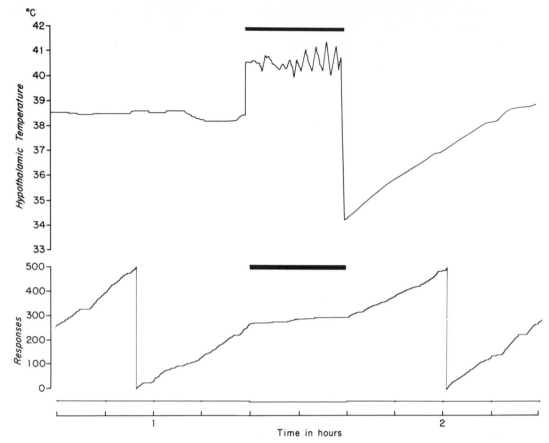

Fig. 6.   Relation between hypothalamic temperature and bar-pressing to activate a heat lamp. Rats placed in a 0° C. environment learn to press a lever (cumulative record, lower line) to receive a 2-second exposure to a heat lamp. Hypothalamic temperature (upper line) shows that rat is receiving enough heat lamp warming to maintain a constant body temperature. When hypothalamus is heated (black bars on both records) the bar-pressing nearly stops and the failure to receive warmth from the heat lamp drops body temperature to 34.5° C. At the cessation of hypothalamic warming, the bar-pressing and consequent warming by the lamp are resumed and normal body temperature is again re-established. (Courtesy of H. J. Carlisle.)

press a bar which activates a mechanism to supply warm air[15] or turn on infrared heat lamps.[13] These observations provide the rationale for classifying the behavior involved in temperature maintenance as motivated behavior.

This behavior is initiated either by activation of temperature receptors in the skin or by change in the temperature of the blood. Normally, these two effects occur together, but it is not clear that these two sources of input work together to induce heat loss mechanisms in cases of overheating and heat conservation responses in cases of cooling. It has been suggested that the heat loss mechanisms are more directly controlled by blood temperature and heat conservation by peripheral receptor action.[8]

The critical role of the anterior hypothalamus in regulating heat loss mechanisms has been definitely established (Chap. 11) by ablation, stimulation and recording studies. These demonstrations have all been concerned with the automatic control source. Recently, two complementary studies demonstrated its role in the servocontrol source. Satinoff[58] succeeded in training rats to press a bar to turn on an infrared heat source when the hypothalamus was cooled, even when room temperature was normal. Carlisle[14] has achieved the complementary result of training animals in a cold chamber to press a bar for infrared exposure; when the anterior hypothalamus is heated, bar-pressing for the heat source ceases even though blood temperature has dropped precipitously (Fig.

6). These studies indicate that the anterior hypothalamus can override the effect of information coming in from the peripheral temperature receptors. The results also are tantamount to asking the animal whether he feels cold and receiving a "yes" or "no" answer.

BASIC HEDONIC DRIVES

Some behavior appears to be energized by stimuli which have no immediately identifiable strong survival value. Reference has already been made to the motivating properties of taste, and although taste preferences may be greatly affected by the learning process, the presence of inborn highly selective taste preferences in young infants is readily demonstrable.

In this same category falls the work of Harlow,[30] who has demonstrated a drive originating in the cutaneous modalities underlying the perception of texture. In studying the behavior of newborn monkeys, Harlow has shown that they prefer a terry cloth surrogate mother to one constructed of wire mesh. This preference continues in the face of feeding the infant only when it is on the wire mother and never feeding it in association with the terry cloth mother. The fact that the terry cloth is very similar to the natural mother's ventral surface, to which a baby monkey usually clings, may be irrelevant but probably is not.

Harlow[31] has also shown a strong "manipulation" or "curiosity" drive in which monkeys learn to operate complex puzzle boxes for no apparent reward. They will also learn complex tasks merely for the sake of viewing other monkeys.[10]

These behaviors may, in the long run, be extremely important in a teleologic sense, but the neural mechanisms underlying these actions, with the exception of the investigations of taste, have not been examined with neurophysiologic techniques.

Evidence which can be interpreted as delineating a neural apparatus for a hedonistic aspect of consummatory response will be discussed in the next chapter.

NEURAL SYSTEMS INVOLVED IN MOTIVATED BEHAVIOR

Manipulating different environmental and physiologic variables results in changes in behavior which have a common form. That is, food deprivation, water deprivation, sexual deprivation, temperature extremes, painful stimuli, particular tastes, visual stimulation, etc., will all mediate new learning, decrease the latency of response, increase activity and increase the amplitude of a response. It is reasonable to expect that, if all these varying stimulus situations have identical effects on behavior, there should be a common underlying neural system responsible for these effects.

One attempt to systematize the topic of motivation by postulating a common neurologic basis was that of Morgan,[52] who developed the concept of a "central motive state." He conceived of this "central motive state" as being the neural integrative activity "into which motivating factors pour and from which patterns of motivated behavior emerge." Although he stated that the central motive state is not specifically located in any particular part of the nervous system, he implicated the hypothalamus and other subcortical structures as being more important than other neural regions. Stellar,[63] in a direct development of this viewpoint, made the structures and the interrelationships much more specific by asserting that "the amount of motivated behavior is a direct function of the activity in certain excitatory centers of the hypothalamus," and that the amount of activity is determined by inputs from inhibitory hypothalamic centers, sensory stimuli, the internal environment and cortical and thalamic centers.

In a parallel development, Duffy[18] for many years has expounded the notion that it is profitable to arrange behavior on a continuum of intensity. This concept has received neurophysiologic support in the studies of the ascending reticular activating system (Chap. 20) and the integrative writings of Lindsley,[43] who believes that the "brain rhythm . . . changes constitute a kind of continuum, paralleled by behavioral changes, and both appear to be regulated by the ARAS . . . of the brain stem."

Although Lindsley presents evidence for a specific as well as this generalized functioning of the reticular system, depending on the kind of input, the very compelling experimental literature showing the complete patterns of highly specific motivated behavior which may be elicited from stimulating a restricted portion of the hypothalamus demands that the hypothalamus play an important role in the regulation of hunger, thirst and body temperature (and very probably sex and maternal behavior). These two systems probably work in conjunction to provide the major facets of motivated behavior, intensity and direction. Indeed, the experimental result demonstrating the importance of an "extrathalamic" cortical activation route passing through the "basal diencephalon"[44] (another term for the hypothalamus and subthalamus) may be very pertinent in this regard.

The problems of motivation merge into those of emotion, and in fact the two are difficult to distinguish. The discussion of sexual behavior could well appear in the chapter on emotion and the discussion there on intracranial self-stimulation is pertinent to the problem of the neural basis of motivation as well as emotion.

REFERENCES

1. ADKINS, R. J. Corticofugal modulation of peripheral receptive fields of cells in the somotosensory cortex of cat. Ph.D. dissertation, University of Washington, 1965.
2. AMASSIAN, V. E. J. Neurophysiol., 1951, 14:433–444.
3. ANDERSSON, B. and McCANN, S. M. Acta. physiol. scand., 1955, 33:333–346.
4. BAILLIE, P. and MORRISON, S. D. J. Physiol., 1963, 165: 227–245.
5. BEACH, F. A. J. comp. Psychol., 1940, 29:193–246.
6. BEACH, F. A. Hormones and behavior. New York, Paul B. Hoeber, Inc., 1948.
7. BEACH, F. A. J. comp. physiol. Psychol., 1958, 51:37–38.
8. BENZINGER, T. H., PRATT, A. W. and KITZINGER, C. Proc. nat. Acad. Sci. (Wash.), 1961, 47:730–739.
9. BREMER, F. Electroenceph. clin. Neurophysiol., 1949, 1:177–193.
10. BUTLER, R. A. J. comp. physiol. Psychol., 1953, 46:95–98.
11. CANNON, W. B. The wisdom of the body. London, Kegan Paul, Trench, Trubner & Co., Ltd., 1932.
12. CANNON, W. B. and WASHBURN, A. L. Amer. J. Physiol., 1912, 29:441–454.
13. CARLISLE, H. J. Behavioral temperature regulation in the rat and monkey. Ph.D. dissertation, University of Washington, 1964.
14. CARLISLE, H. J. Personal communication.
15. CARLTON, P. L. and MARKS, R. A. Science, 1958, 128:1344.
16. DAVIS, C. D. Amer. J. Physiol., 1939, 127:374–380.
17. DELL, P. Chap. 18 in The reticular formation of the brain, H. H. JASPER, ed. Boston, Little, Brown & Co., 1958.
18. DUFFY, E. Activation and behavior. New York, John Wiley & Sons, 1962.
19. EPSTEIN, A. N. Personal communication.
20. EPSTEIN, A. N. Science, 1960, 131:497–498.
21. EPSTEIN, A. N. and TEITELBAUM, P. J. comp. physiol. Psychol., 1962, 55:753–759.
22. ESSMAN, W. B. and SUDAK, F. N. J. appl. Physiol., 1942, 17:113–116.
23. FALK, J. L. In: Nebraska symposium on motivation, M. R. JONES, ed. Lincoln, Neb., University of Nebraska Press, 1961.
24. GLICKMAN, S. E. Canadian J. Psychol., 1958, 12:45–51.

25. GREEN, J. D., CLEMENTE, C. D. and DE GROOT, J. J. comp. Neurol., 1957, 108:505–545.
26. GROSSMAN, M. I. Ann. N.Y. Acad. Sci., 1955, 63:76–91.
27. HAGBARTH, K. E. and KERR, D. I. B. J. Neurophysiol., 1954, 17:295–307.
28. HARDY, J. D. In: The Harvey lectures, Ser. XLIX. New York, Academic Press, 1955.
29. HARKER, J. E. The physiology of diurnal rhythms. Cambridge, Cambridge University Press, 1964.
30. HARLOW, H. F. Sci. Amer., 1959, 200:68–74.
31. HARLOW, H. F., HARLOW, M. K. and MEYER, D. R. J. exp. Psychol., 1950, 40:228–234.
32. HARRIS, G. W. J. Physiol., 1948, 107:418–429.
33. HERNANDEZ-PEON, R., SCHERRER, H. and JOUVET, M. Science, 1956, 123:331–332.
34. HERON, W. In: Sensory deprivation, P. SOLOMON, ed. Cambridge, Harvard University Press, 1961.
35. HERVEY, G. R. J. Physiol., 1959, 145:336–352.
36. HULL, C. L. Principles of behavior. An introduction to behavior theory. New York, Appleton-Century, 1943.
37. HULL, C. L. Essentials of behavior. New Haven, Conn., Yale University Press, 1951.
38. JABBUR, S. J. and TOWE, A. L. In: Nervous inhibition, E. FLOREY, ed. New York, Pergamon Press, 1961.
39. JANOWITZ, H. D. and GROSSMAN, M. I. Amer. J. Physiol., 1949, 159:143–148.
40. KENNEDY, G. C. Proc. Roy. Soc., 1953, 140B:578–596.
41. KINSEY, A. C., POMEROY, W. B., MARTIN C. E. and GEBHARD, P. H. Sexual behavior in the human female. Philadelphia, W. B. Saunders Co., 1953.
42. KRASNE, F. B. Science, 1962, 138:822–823.
43. LINDSLEY, D. B. In: Nebraska symposium on motivation. Lincoln, Neb. University of Nebraska Press, 1957.
44. LINDSLEY, D. B., BOWDEN, J. W. and MAGOUN, H. W. Electroenceph. clin. Neurophysiol., 1949, 1:475–486.
45. MacLEAN, P. D., PLOOG, P. W. and ROBINSON, B. W. Physiol. Rev., 1960, 40(suppl. 4):105–112.
46. MARKEE, J. E., SAYER, C. H. and HOLLINSHEAD, W. H. Endocrinology, 1946, 38:345–357.
47. MAYER, J. Ann. N. Y. Acad. Sci., 1955, 63:15–43.
48. MILLER, N. E., Ann. N. Y. Acad. Sci., 1955, 63:141–143.
49. MILLER, N. E. and KESSEN, M. I. J. comp. physiol Psychol., 1952, 45:555–564.
50. MONTEMURRO, D. G. and STEVENSON, J. A. F. Canad. J. Biochem., 1957, 191:248–254.
51. MOOK, D. G. J. comp. physiol. Psychol., 1963, 56:645–659.
52. MORGAN, C. T. Physiological psychology. New York, McGraw-Hill Book Co., 1943.
53. MORGANE, P. J. Amer. J. Physiol., 1961, 201:838–844.
54. PFAFFMAN, C. Psychol. Rev., 1960, 67:253–268.
55. PFAFFMAN, C. In: Nebraska symposium on motivation. Lincoln, Neb., University of Nebraska Press, 1961.
56. PHOENIX, C. H., GOY, R. W., GERALD, A. A. and YOUNG, W. C. Endocrinology, 1959, 65:369–382.
57. RUCH, T. C., MAIRE, F. W. and PATTON, H. D. Abst. Comm., Congr. int. Physiol., 1956, 20:788–789.
58. SATINOFF, E. Amer. J. Physiol., 1964, 206:1389–1394.
59. SAWYER, C. H. In: Reticular formation of the brain. H. H. JASPER, ed. Boston, Little, Brown & Co., 1958.
60. SAWYER, C. H. and ROBISON, B. J. clin. Endocrinol., 1956, 16:914–915.
61. SMITH, M. and DUFFY, M. J. comp. physiol. Psychol., 1957, 50:601–608.
62. SMITH, O. A. Chap. 25 in Electrical stimulation of the brain. D. E. Sheer, ed. Austin, University of Texas Press, 1961.
63. STELLAR, E. Psychol. Rev., 1954, 61:5–22.
64. STELLAR, E., HYMAN, R. and SAMET, S. J. comp. physiol. Psychol., 1954, 47:220–226.

65. STROMINGER, J. L. and BROBECK, J. R. *Yale J. Biol. Med.,* 1953, *25:*383–390.

66. TEITELBAUM, P. *J. comp. physiol. Psychol.,* 1957, *50:*486–490.

67. TEITELBAUM, P. In: *Nebraska symposium on motivation.* M. R. JONES, ed. Lincoln, Neb., University of Nebraska Press, 1961.

68. TINBERGEN, N. *The study of instinct.* Oxford, Clarendon Press, 1951.

69. YOUNG, P. T. *Motivation of behavior.* New York. John Wiley & Sons, Inc., 1936.

70. YOUNG, W. C. Chap. 19 in *Sex and internal secretions,* vol. II. Baltimore, Williams & Wilkins Co., 1961.

CHAPTER 26

Neurophysiology of Emotion

By THEODORE C. RUCH

MOTIVATION or drive is a neural process which impels the organism to some action or goal, the attainment of which results in drive reduction. Less specifically, it is a state of alertness which increases the readiness to action. Emotion is often the end point of motivated behavior whether culminated or frustrated; bodily activity is then heightened, as primitively illustrated by fight, flight and sex behavior. Emotion may also be less manifest in action than in feeling; e.g., homesickness, in fact, may be expressed by retardation of activity, a slumping posture and a facial expression of sadness. Although emotion is a protean, multifaceted form of behavior which is difficult to define, an interesting definition has been provided by a neuropathologist, Vonderahe:[62]

"Emotion is a way of feeling and a way of acting. It may be defined as a tendency of an organism toward or away from an object, accompanied by notable bodily alteration. There is an element of motivation—an impulsion to action and an element of alertness, a hyperawareness or vividness of mental processes. There is of course the opposite, a depression of movement."

We can see from this definition that emotion has four aspects:

(i) *Cognition.* A situation must be perceived, related to past experiences and evaluated before emotion occurs. This evaluation mainly reflects past experience and the cultural influences of the family, society, etc., and often occurs not in a conscious, deliberate way but sometimes occurs with great suddenness and, according to many, on a "subconscious" level. Cognitive factors determine to what "fighting words," to what flag, to what development of the gluteal region man responds. They also determine what emotion in kind and degree is appropriate to a given situation. These complex evaluations are ascribed to the neocortex of the brain. However, there is evidence (see Chap. 23) that the prefrontal lobe is necessary for conditioned emotional responses of the cardiovascular system in simple conditioned avoidance situations.[55] Finally, not all emotion flows along a motivation→ stimulus→consummatory reaction. Much emotion or "frustration" occurs from blocking this flow. The cognitive aspect of emotion is mainly in the provenance of psychology, but some ways of evoking emotion in animals are simple enough to permit physiologic analysis.

(ii) *Expression.* Emotion is expressed outwardly in the form of somatic and autonomic activities—facial expression, lacrimation, vocalization, hair standing erect, flushing or paling, laughter, fighting or flight. Emotions are also "expressed" internally in the form of visceral and vascular changes executed by the sympathetic and parasympathetic nervous systems (Chaps. 10 and 11). Another kind of emo-

508

tional expression is muscle tension, which, as we have seen (Chap. 16), causes discomfort and pain. Even if the obvious expression of emotion is suppressed as "inappropriate" in our society, the internal expressions may well occur or possibly be intensified. These especially are considered by some to be the cause of psychosomatic illness.

(iii) *Experience* is the subjective aspect of emotion that one feels when "emotional." On an introspective basis, psychologists once divided emotions into two categories by *affect:* those which are *pleasant* and those which are *unpleasant.* These feelings are conscious experiences and, therefore, are difficult to study quantitatively and objectively. Moreover, as was seen earlier in the discussion of sensation, there is evidence that the expressive and experiential aspects of emotion are dissociable by various lesions of the nervous system; this dissociation can be demonstrated in both animals and human patients. Despite these difficulties, some insight can be gained into what is presumptively the affective aspect of emotion even in animals.

(iv) *Excitement.* It is a matter of common knowledge that when we experience certain emotions we look and feel excited and our friends say, "Now, don't get excited" (which makes us more excited). As the above definition suggests, our mental processes may be excessively vivid. Conversely, sluggish and dull mental processes are commonly experienced during some emotions. The subjective side of excitement, like its affect, would seem impossible to study. However, as seen in the discussion of the ascending reticular systems, there seem to be reliable objective signs of alertness and excitement (electroencephalographic patterns) which can be used in animal experiments.

Emotion will be discussed in terms of the preceding categories, the first section dealing with what can be studied objectively and the second with what can be inferred about subjective events from objective study. The excitement parameter is discussed last. Although the hypothalamus and rhinencephalon are discussed separately here, they do not function separately. The chapter is centered on neural mechanisms to the neglect of a large and important body of psychophysiologic studies relating autonomic and somatic responses to stimulus situations calculated to arouse emotion. The patterning of emotional response will be discussed briefly.

EXPRESSION OF EMOTION[30]

Studies in which refined instrumentation, standardization of stimuli and quantitation are used indicate that, in man, emotional reactions to given situations certainly do not involve exclusively either sympathetic or parasympathetic discharge, an idea going back to Cannon (Lacey *et al.*; see Knapp[30]). In fact, correlation coefficients between specific autonomic reactions in individuals responding to the same situation tend to be low. The responses during psychiatric interview and therapy become complicated when more than one response is recorded.[31] Another finding in recent laboratory work is the suprisingly great autonomic response to cognitive functions; e.g., cardiac acceleration while the subject is doing mental arithmetic is as great as during a "cold pressor test" (immersion of the foot in ice water at 4° C.).[30]

In considering the neural basis of emotion we must keep in mind all of the factors just discussed. The expression and the experience of emotion are the main concern of this chapter, and their interrelations are far from obvious. While we would say that we run away because we are afraid, whether this or the reverse is the actual sequence has been debated since 1890, when William James and Lange independently suggested that emotional states (e.g., fear) result from rather than cause overt manifestations of emotion. Emotional experience and expression are not inseparably linked. Certain neurologic patients (pseudobulbar palsy) exhibit involuntary bouts of laughing and crying without experiencing emotion; conversely, patients with other lesions (parkinsonism) may experience emotion while remaining completely impassive and expressionless.[22]

Hypothalamus and Emotion. The visceral, vascular and glandular changes resulting from activity of the autonomic nervous system are elicited by stimulation at many levels of the central nervous system. These changes have already been discussed in their relation to the control of bodily processes.

They can also be profitably examined as contributors to the bodily manifestation of emotion. In 1890, Goltz described a dog whose cerebral cortex he had removed. Were externally expressed emotion executed by the cortical motor areas, none would have been seen in this decorticate dog. However, not only did it manifest reactions recognized as rage, but these were aroused by inconsequential stimuli. Thus, the apparatus for this kind of emotion was released from inhibitory control exerted by the cerebral cortex. On the other hand, Sherrington noted that the acute decerebrate animal is nearly, if not entirely, without emotional expression.* This finding narrowed the locus for the execution of a full angry display to the basal ganglia, diencephalon and anterior midbrain. Karplus and Kreidl in 1914 discovered that stimulating the hypothalamic portion of the diencephalon resulted in a variety of visceral responses.

In 1928, Bard made transections which localized the neural mechanism of rage chiefly to the diencephalon. By longitudinal sections removing the thalamus he narrowed the localization to the hypothalamus. The excitement or dynamic aspect of emotion is pointed up by the fact that the retention of a relatively few cubic millimeters of hypothalamic tissue makes the difference between a preparation which is an emotional vegetable and one which at a slight touch, or even "spontaneously," will go into a paroxysm of activity—struggling, baring of the claws, spitting, pupillary dilation, erection of hair and a variety of internal visceral responses. Whether this response is, in fact, "sham rage" (Bard) and a "pseudoaffective state" (Sherrington) will be discussed later.

It is important that these experiments should not be generalized to encompass emotional displays other than rage; it is still not known where all emotional activities are managed. However, basic sexual behavior appears to be integrated in the diencephalon. When given estrogens, a decorticate female cat displays normal feline estrous behavior, which Bard divides into (i) courtship activity (playful rubbing and rolling, vocalizing, estrous crouching, and treading with hind legs) and (ii) the after-reaction (frantic rubbing, licking, squirming, and rolling following vaginal stimulation). As with rage, the chronic high mesencephalic decerebrate cat shows only fragments of this behavior, the induced activity falling short of the full pattern of estrous behavior exhibited by normal and decorticate cats.

The neural mechanisms for the basic elements of sexual behavior and rage are localized

in the hypothalamus. It must be remembered that the principle of "levels of function" applies in this field, and many other neural structures are also involved.

DETAILED LOCALIZATION OF EMOTIONAL ACTIVITY IN HYPOTHALAMUS. Although the hypothalamus is a small structure, it contains the apparatus for several kinds of emotional behavior as well as a variety of feeding, drinking and satiety centers.

Focal stimulation and localized lesions have demarcated a restricted hypothalamic region concerned with emotional display. Lesions of the ventromedial nuclei of the hypothalamus induce rage and savageness in animals, which make well-directed attacks toward the experimenter.[60] Focal stimulation of unanesthetized, unrestrained animals through implanted electrodes with their tips in the hypothalamus† is highly valuable in more precise localization of the hypothalamic subcortical areas concerned with emotion.[19] The same point can be stimulated in successive animals with different strengths and durations of stimulation, and the exact point of stimulation can be determined histologically. Two types of behavioral (defensive) responses are obtained: (i) a fight or rage-like pattern (growling and hissing, flattening of the ears, piloerection and other sympathetic responses) and (ii) a flight or fearlike pattern (pupillary dilation, darting of eyes to and fro, turning of head from side to side as though searching for a pathway of escape, and finally flight). These are patterns, not fragments, of behavior involving somatic and visceral responses of the body as a whole. They are directed toward the experimenter or a weak point in a cage, respectively. They look like the way a cat responds to natural stimulus objects, e.g., a barking dog. In addition, visceral and other acts, such as micturition, defecation, salivation, retching and sniffing, can be elicited by stimulation of regions rather widely distributed through the hypothalamus.

According to the Zurich physiologists,[19, 21] the defense reaction is focused in the dorsal part of the midthalamus surrounding the descending column of the fornix; it extends forward into the preoptic and ventral septal area and caudally into the posterior hypothalamus and expands in the central gray matter of the mid-

---

* In a cat with a *chronic* section at the level of the midbrain, high threshold fragmentary expressions of anger can be elicited.[4] These responses indicate some participation of midbrain centers in emotional expression, but fall short of the integrated rage behavior seen in cats with transections above the hypothalamus.

†W. R. Hess of Zurich, Switzerland shared the Nobel Prize for introducing (1927) and prosecuting such studies of emotion.

brain. It is thus a narrow lamina 1 to 1.5 mm. in thickness running the whole length and slightly beyond the hypothalamus. Hunsperger[21] places flight reactions externally and fright reactions centrally in this lamina. According to Nakao,[40] loci for the two types of responses are found in the same concentric lamina, but flight mechanisms are manifest after stimulation of regions more rostral than those serving aggressive reactions. Similar reactions are obtained by stimulating the amygdalar region of the rhinencephalon.

Regardless of the details of localization, there are indications that an area beginning in the telencephalon, extending entirely through the hypothalamus and into the midbrain, instigates flight and aggressive motor behavior with accompanying autonomic manifestations; many other points in the hypothalamus, the hippo-

campus and the cerebral cortex that have been explored do not give rise to these emotional responses. Further, a system of fibers involving the ventromedial nucleus appears to restrain emotional behavior, since rage and savageness occur in exaggerated form when these nuclei alone are destroyed.[55]

Limbic System; Rhinencephalon.[6, 7, 24, 49] A medial complex of cortex, subcortical nuclei and the tracts which connect them with the hypothalamus and other structures is known anatomically as the "rhinencephalon," literally "nose brain" (Fig. 1). It received this name because the olfactory tract enters it. However, the "nose brain" is well developed in animals having few or no olfactory receptors. According to electrophysiologic studies, only a fraction of the rhinencephalon is activated by olfactory stimuli. Ablation and stimulation studies indicate that

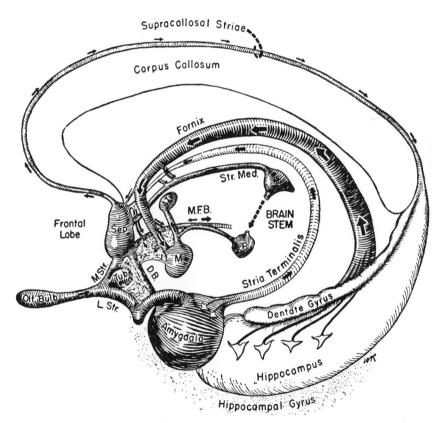

Fig. 1. Schematic representation of relationship of main subcortical structures and connections of rhinencephalon, drawn as though all of them could be seen from medial aspect of right hemisphere. For diagrammatic purposes some connections have been given an arbitrary course. Abbreviations: *A.T.,* anterior thalamic nucleus; *D.B.,* diagonal band of Broca; *H.,* habenula (part of epithalamus); *I.P.,* interpeduncular nucleus; *L.Str.,* lateral olfactory stria; *M.,* mammillary body (part of posterior hypothalamus); *M.F.B.,* medial forebrain bundle; *M.Str.,* medial olfactory stria; *Olf. Bulb,* olfactory bulb; *Sep.,* region of septal nuclei; *Str. Med.,* stria medullaris; *Tub.,* olfactory tubercle (head of caudate immediately underneath). (After Krieg; from MacLean, *Psychosom. Med.,* 1949, *11:*338–353.)

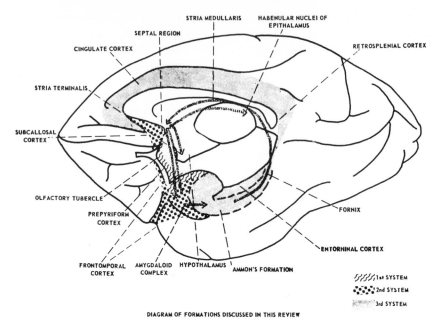

STRIA MEDULLARIS   HABENULAR NUCLEI OF
                                            EPITHALAMUS
              SEPTAL REGION

       CINGULATE CORTEX   RETROSPLENIAL CORTEX

STRIA TERMINALIS

SUBCALLOSAL
   CORTEX

OLFACTORY TUBERCLE

     PREPYRIFORM   FORNIX
        CORTEX

                                                         ENTORHINAL CORTEX

FRONTOMPORAL   AMYGDALOID   HYPOTHALAMUS   1st SYSTEM
   CORTEX   COMPLEX   AMMON'S FORMATION   2nd SYSTEM
                                                                   3rd SYSTEM

DIAGRAM OF FORMATIONS DISCUSSED IN THIS REVIEW

Fig. 2. Drawing of medial and basal surfaces of brain showing divisions of the rhinencephalon. Note smallness of first system, which has direct connections with olfactory bulb. Second system is defined as structures connected with the first system but not the bulb. Third system includes hippocampus and other structures of Ammon's cortex and juxtallocortex in entorhinal (inferior), retrosplenial (posterior) and cingulate (superior and anterior) regions. Most of discussion in text pertains to the second system. (From Pribram and Kruger, *Ann. N. Y. Acad. Sci.*, 1954, *58:*109–138.)

the nonolfactory portions of the rhinencephalon are concerned with emotional life. MacLean,[36] to avoid the olfactory implications of "rhinencephalon," has popularized the terms "limbic lobe" and "limbic system." First used by Broca to describe this area, "limbic" means border. The cerebral hemispheres arise as a tremendous outgrowth from the diencephalon. The hilus or neck of this growth forms a concentric ring of cerebral cortex which, in a sense, is a *border* of the great neocortical vesicle.

The major part of the limbic system is composed of two rings of limbic cortex and associated subcortical nuclei. The inner ring of three-layered cortex includes part of the hippocampal formation and is phylogenetically the most primitive, being generally referred to as the "archipallium" or "allocortex." This area includes structures with olfactory connections (the olfactory tubercle, the prepyriform cortex, the periamygdaloid cortex, the corticomedial nuclei of the amygdala) and certain structures and areas which are connected with the thalamus and hypothalamus, mainly the entorhinal area and the hippocampus. The next ring is designated "juxtallocortex," "mesopallium" or "transitional" cortex; it is homotypical six-

layered cortex. In its structure and phylogenetic history it is intermediate between the archipallium and the surrounding "neopallium" or "neocortex," from which it is separated by the cingulate sulcus. This outer ring consists of the cingulate gyrus and, anteriorly, the orbitoinsulotemporal cortex and, posteriorly, the presubiculum. Two important subcortical masses, the septal nuclei and the basolateral amygdalar nuclei, are associated with mesopallium. (Note in Figure 2 that Pribram and Kruger classify some of the mesopallium with their second system and some with the third.) The efferent projections from the mesopallium pass to subcortical centers, largely by way of the striatum. The fornix is the main efferent projection for the archipallium, which sends fibers to the septal region, the hypothalamus and the midbrain. The neuroanatomy of the rhinencephalon or limbic system is too complex to permit detailed description. Figures 1 and 2 represent it and some of its connections in a highly simplified fashion.

MESOPALLIUM. As pointed out in Chapter 12, the neopallium subserves some visceral functions, the responsible foci appearing to be discrete, specialized and generally associated with motor or sensory areas. Thus salivation is initiated from points ventral to the face area, pupillary dilation and lacrimation from the frontal eye fields, and limb vasoconstrictor responses by points in the arm and leg areas. We have also seen that stimulation of mesopallium results in autonomic responses. That stimulation of its orbital portion causes changes in respiration and visceral function was discovered in 1894 and again noted in 1940,[3] but not until 1949 was it learned that much of the mesopallium gives rise to respiratory, vascular and visceral changes when electrically excited. Kaada and his associates[25] have shown (Fig. 3) that such results are obtained by stimulating the whole stretch of cortex running from the anterior cingulate

gyrus across the posterior orbital surface to the insula, the temporal pole, the pyriform cortex, the periamygdaloid and the posterior hippocampal cortex. As with hypothalamic stimulation, a wide variety of visceral responses to limbic stimulation have been obtained in both animals and man, but in general these responses are of lesser magnitude than are those induced by hypothalamic stimulation.

Many limbic areas affect the same visceral structure, and stimulation of the same point in the limbic lobe will cause several kinds of visceral or vascular responses. In fact, the various segments of the limbic cortex appear to be closely interrelated but only poorly connected with the neopallium. By applying strychnine to

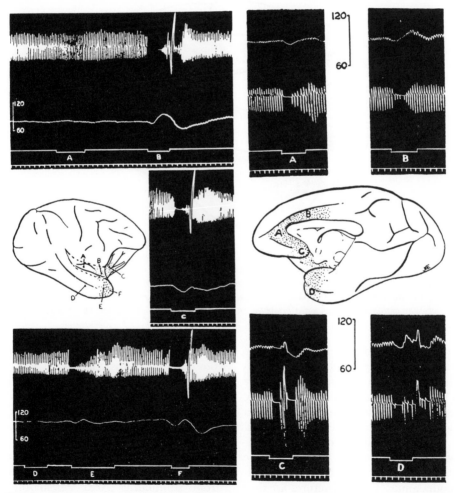

Fig. 3. Responses to stimulation of limbic cortex. *Left,* Respiratory (*upper record*) and blood pressure response (*lower record*) resulting from electrical stimulation of points designated on brain map. Insula, containing points *A* and *B,* is visualized by separation of temporal and frontoparietal operculum. Respiratory movements recorded through tracheal cannula. Stroke upward indicates expiration. *Right,* Same for mesial surface except that blood pressure is now the upper record. (From Kaada et al., *J. Neurophysiol.,* 1949, *12*:347–356.)

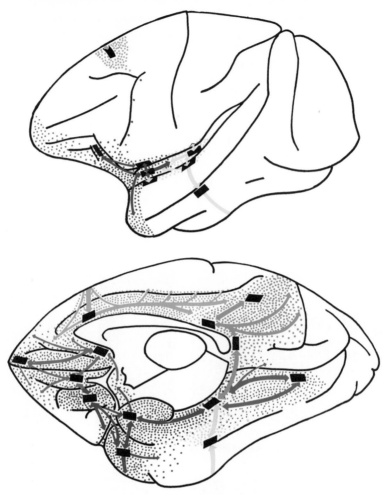

Fig. 4. Schematic representation of lateral (*top*) and mediobasal (*bottom*) surfaces of macaque brain showing segments of phylogenetically old and new cortex which appear related on basis of strychninization studies. Black rectangles indicate areas to which strychnine was applied. Respective colors indicate reciprocally connected areas. Note overlapping of shading at fringes. Extent of firing into neopallium is not shown. (Based on experiments by MacLean and Pribram; from Fulton, *Frontal lobotomy and affective behavior; a neurophysiological analysis.* New York, W. W. Norton and Company, 1951.)

various limbic areas and searching the limbic lobe for strychnine spikes, the interconnections between limbic areas shown in Figure 4 were identified. The interconnectedness of the limbic system is shown by the fact that stimulation in it produces prolonged repetitive afterdis-charges, detectable electroencephalographi-cally,[17] which spread readily throughout the limbic system and only to related structures such as the hypothalamus. These structures are thus identified as closely associated with the limbic system. However, the boundaries between mesopallium and neocortex should not be drawn too sharply because the supplementary motor area (Chap. 12) is half in each.

The responses of limbic structures to stimula-tion may mean that they serve as a regulatory system for visceral and vascular function super-imposed upon the hypothalamus. On the other hand, the responses may mean that the limbic lobe is concerned with emotion. An involvement in emotional expression is suggested by the kind of somatic muscular response resulting from stimulation of these areas, e.g., vocalization from stimulating Area 24 in the anterior cingulate gyrus.

SUBCORTICAL LIMBIC STRUCTURES. The par-ticipation of the limbic system in emotion is especially clear when the subcortical limbic structures, e.g., the septal and amygdalar nuclei, are stimulated or ablated. The amygdalar nuclei lying beneath the pyriform cortex seem to be peculiarly important. The amygdala is a complex of nuclei with connections with the olfactory bulb and the temporal neocortex. The amygdala also projects to the septal region and the hypothalamus via the stria terminalis. The septal nuclei, rhinencephalic structures lying along the midline just beneath the anterior genu of the corpus callosum, are widely connected with structures known to be concerned with emotion and motivation—the preoptic region, the hypothalamus, the hippocampus, the brain stem tegmentum and the habenulae.

Stimulation experiments. Stimulation experiments by Gastaut[14] in France and Mac-Lean[34, 37] in America focused attention on the amygdalar and periamygdalar region. Stimulation of these structures through implanted electrodes in unanesthetized cats and monkeys elicited responses clearly related to "eating" and the upper end of the gastrointestinal tract—sniffing, licking, biting, chewing, chop-licking,

gagging and retching (Fig. 5). (Somewhat inconsistently, hyperphagia following amygdalar lesions has been reported.[16]) A second category of responses were respiratory and autonomic responses elicited from the mesopallium directly. A third group of responses were classified as components of defense—attack, retraction of ears, growling and hissing, and protrusion of claws.

The defense responses elicited from the amygdala are similar to those from the hypothalamus and midbrain, but aggressive responses may be more easily obtained from the amygdala. All agree that the amygdala exerts its effects by way of the hypothalamus and midbrain, but the pathway is in question. Fernandez de Molina and Hunsperger[13] picture a hierarchy of centers, i.e., the amygdala, connecting by the circuitous stria terminalis with the hypothalamus, which in turn connects with the midbrain central gray matter. Hilton and Zbrozyna[20] contend that interruption of the stria terminalis does not block the effect of

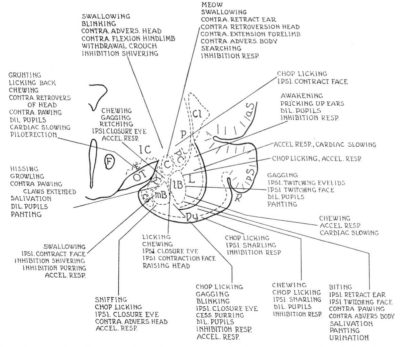

Fig. 5. Cross section through midregion of amygdala showing types of oral, facial and other behavior resulting from stimulation. Note the divisions of the amygdala and its relationship to other brain structures. Abbreviations: *LB* and *mB*, lateral and medial parts of basal nucleus of amygdala; *L*, lateral nucleus; *C*, central nucleus of amygdala; *F*, fornix; *OT*, optic tract; *Py*, pyriform cortex; *R*, rhinal fissure; *Cl*, claustrum; *P*, pulvinar; *IC*, internal capsule; *Co*, cortical nucleus of amygdala; *E*, entopeduncular nucleus; *M*, medial nucleus of amygdala; *PC*, putamen-central amygdaloid complex; *aS*, anterior sylvian gyrus; *pS*, posterior sylvian gyrus. (From MacLean and Delgado, *Electroenceph. clin. Neurophysiol.,* 1953, 5:91–100.)

amygdala stimulation permanently; they provide evidence for a narrow band of fibers connecting the amygdala more directly to the hypothalamus along its entire length. Nauta[41-43] has described a ventral amygdalo-fugal pathway in the same location as the narrow band of points yielding the defense reaction.

When amygdala stimulation was played against stimulation of a hypothalamic point proved to elicit aggressive behavior, the effect was sometimes facilitative, but more often it suppressed attack.[11] The two effects were obtained from different amygdalar loci. The suppressive effect especially supports the thesis that the amygdala is "upstream" to the hypothalamus in organizing emotional behavior.

Ablation of septal region.   Lesions of this anterior, medial limbic region reduce responses in a "fear" or "anxiety" situation.[8] To establish an anxiety-producing stimulus, a clicking noise lasting three minutes was followed immediately by a painful shock to the feet. After a few such presentations the clicking noise alone caused an anxiety response—crouching, micturition and defecation. To obtain an objective measure of this conditioned fear or anxiety, rats were trained to depress a lever in order to secure a drop of water. The animals were rewarded only once in 60 seconds so that the rate of lever-pressing would remain high. The degree to which the clicking noise interfered with the lever pressing was taken as a measure of anxiety. In unoperated control rats, conditioned anxiety completely inhibited bar-pressing for water. After lesions of the septal region, the effect of the clicking noise on lever-pressing was much less pronounced.

Other methods supplied evidence of increases in other emotional behavior after such lesions. Following the operation, the rats were placed in a group cage. On emerging from anesthesia they were soon engaged in a free-for-all. Tame rats which had been petted freely with bare hands could now be handled only with gloves; they repeatedly attacked a bar of steel placed in front of them. Such attacks are not like sham rage but are extremely skillful and well directed. It can be concluded that the animals have become more excited and more savage, that they are less fearful and anxious.

Amygdalar ablations.   In 1937, Klüver and Bucy[28, 29] produced bizarre behavioral disturbances (visual agnosia, exploration by smelling, compulsive exploratory behavior) in monkeys

following bilateral temporal lobectomy which destroyed important limbic structures. Some of these behavior changes have already been described. Noted, too, were profound changes in emotional behavior in the direction of passivity or unresponsiveness. Objects which normally excite fear or wariness—a snake, a stranger, a cat or a dog—were approached without hesitation and without the vocalization and facial behavior which denote fear in the monkey. By contrast, other types of emotional behavior, especially sexual activity, were intensified and were aroused by an unusual diversity of objects. The monkeys manifested sexual behavior toward the opposite sex, the same sex, and themselves in a degree far beyond that seen in normal male monkeys. Also manifest was excessive oral behavior—biting and sucking of various parts of the body or inanimate objects.

In 1937 Papez[48] reached the conclusion from neuroanatomic considerations that the rhinencephalic structures were linked to the hypothalamic, thalamic and limbic cortical structures to form a neural mechanism of emotion. The impact of these two papers was postponed by World War II, but these pioneering studies probing the neural basis of emotion have since been widely extended in a number of laboratories throughout the world.

Of the limbic structures destroyed in Klüver and Bucy's operation, it is the amygdalar nuclei and overlying pyriform cortex whose loss produces the emotional changes. Ablation restricted to the limbic areas involved in Klüver and Bucy's experiments produces the emotional but not the cognitive part (e.g., psychic blindness) of the syndrome exhibited by their monkeys (but see below). Many investigators have reported fragments of the Klüver–Bucy syndrome resulting from lobectomy in animals[58] and even in man;[57] the most dramatic demonstration has been that by Schreiner and Kling.[52-54] After removal of the amygdalar nuclei and the overlying rhinencephalic cortex, cats and monkeys became exceedingly docile. The agouti and lynx, two animals selected for their savage natures, similarly became docile for a period of weeks following amygdalectomy. In recent confirmatory experiments indifference to a live mouse and absence of agressive behavior was demonstrated in nine cats with complete amygdalar lesions.[56]

Operated cats and monkeys clearly demonstrated hypersexuality, which they exhibited toward either sex without discrimination or toward animals of a different species, such as the hen. The sexual activity diminished after castration but was not caused by an increased production of testosterone. These results were confirmed, and the area concerned with sexual behavior has been delimited.[16] Hypersexuality follows lesions restricted to the pyriform cortex (Fig. 6) overlying the basal amygdalar nucleus but not lesions confined to the nucleus.

While a certain amount of placidity or calmness may follow many brain operations, that following amygdalectomy is specific. It is interesting that a placid amygdalectomized animal is made savage and rageful by lesions of the ventromedial nucleus of the hypothalamus.[52]

Conversely, rats made savage by septal lesions have been made placid by amygdalectomy.[26]

Some investigators have been unable to confirm these findings; others not only have observed the same disorders but have obtained them by producing fractional lesions of the amygdalar nuclei or the overlying cortex. This variation is perhaps not surprising when dealing with a behavior which is complex and difficult to quantify and study objectively, on the one hand,* and with an exceedingly complex neural structure on the other. Somewhat the

* For example, Rosvold *et al.*[51] have shown that an amygdalectomized baboon which was aggressive in a cage situation was submissive in a group hierarchy situation.

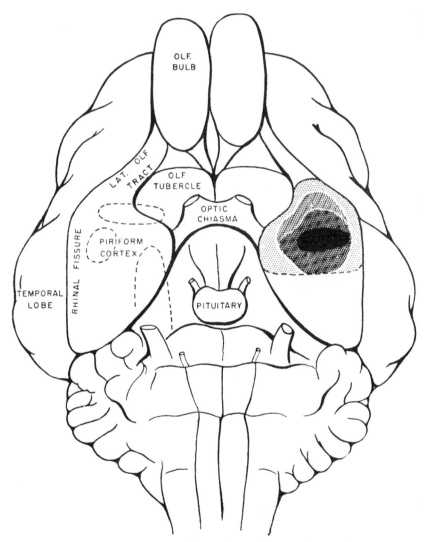

Fig. 6. Ventral aspect of cat brain showing surface projection of areas where destruction caused specific behavior problem. On right is concentric stipple circle showing quartile incidence of involvement in animals exhibiting hypersexuality. (From Green *et al.*, *J. comp. Neurol.*, 1957, *108*:505–545.)

same difficulties were encountered in early studies of the hypothalamus, and these were resolved by the discovery that the hypothalamus contains pairs of oppositely acting centers. The same may be true of the limbic lobe.

The sorting out of symptoms in the Klüver–Bucy syndrome into limbic and neocortical has been unduly influenced by the demonstration of cognitive learning functions in the nearby inferotemporal region. The unconscious assumption that the behavioral changes of emotional significance are ascribable solely to the limbic structures is not sustained. Akert et al.[2] removed the neocortex of the temporal lobe contiguous across the rhinal fissure with the limbic cortex (see Fig. 6) with slight damage to it or the underlying nuclei. Some oral tendencies were exhibited transiently; fear of snakes, brooms, nets and hoses was absent for a month after operation, when reaction to these objects progressively returned. Akert et al. point out that a less severe and permanent effect on fearfulness is consistent with anatomic connection of the temporal cortex with the amygdala and other rhinencephalic structures. Such projections provide one means by which the amygdala is connected with the receptive and cognitive apparatus of the cerebral cortex.

ARCHIPALLIUM. Despite the anatomically well established connections of the hippocampal formation with the hypothalamus via the fornix and with the anterior cingulate gyrus (Area 24) via the mammillary bodies and the anterior thalamic nuclei, the emotional significance of these connections, hypothesized by Papez[48] and others[33] has not been clearly established experimentally. Although rather intangible changes in emotionality have been described as following lesions of Area 24 and other areas of the mesopallium, interference with this system is not accompanied by gross changes in emotional behavior like those following interference with the subcortical limbic nuclei. In one of the few studies[15] in which the hippocampal formations have been selectively but nearly completely ablated, changes in emotional behavior were confined to one element of the Klüver–Bucy syndrome—tameness and fearlessness. Monkeys and cats were nonreactive to the snake and dog test, respectively. The decrease in aggressiveness was only partial. Hypersexuality was not observed and the animals were possibly hyposexual. Oral tendencies were not observed. It is now clear that the hippocampal formation

does not execute any gross form of emotional behavior.

Quite possibly Papez's system serves the cognitive and other subjective aspects of emotion. There is, in fact, some evidence that the hippocampal formation is concerned with the subjective or inner aspect of emotion. We are left with the original deduction from anatomy that it is part of a system by which the limbic and neocortical functions are related to one another in a manner too subtle for present methods of analysis.

AFFECTIVE ASPECTS OF EMOTION

Sherrington, recognizing the dangers of inferring subjective experiences from motor behavior, spoke of "pseudoaffective" reflexes in the decerebrate cat. Cannon, in turn, cautiously spoke of "sham rage" in the decorticate or high decerebrate animal, implying that only the external and not the subjective manifestations of rage occurred. The groundwork for what may seem paradoxical—an objective attack on a subjective phenomenon—was laid by Loucks from 1934 to 1938, when he applied the buried-electrode technique to the analysis of the neural basis of conditioned reflexes.

Since Pavlov, it has been known that if a "neutral" stimulus (the conditioned stimulus) producing no visible reaction, or a reaction unrelated to the conditioned response, is presented at the proper time interval with or before a stimulus which causes a given reaction (the unconditioned stimulus and response, respectively), the conditioned stimulus subsequently presented alone will produce the same reaction (conditioned response). By stimulating at various points along the pathway of the *unconditioned* reflex (foot withdrawal from electric grid) from sense organ to muscle, Loucks and others found that stimulation of sense organs, posterior root or columns of the spinal cord, and thalamus can serve as an unconditioned stimulus; stimulation of the motor cortex, the anterior root, or the muscle, though producing a response, cannot serve as an unconditioned stimulus. In other words, a stimulus on the afferent side of the reflex is effective as an unconditioned stimulus; a stimulus on the efferent side is ineffective. It is also known that conditioning is exceedingly difficult and may be impossible if a neutral stimulus produces the unconditioned response, e.g., light→pupillary constriction or tendon tap →knee jerk. Going one step farther, one can restate this issue in terms of affect. The reflexes which serve well are those produced by unconditioned stimuli which a man would call pleasant or unpleasant—for example, an electric shock, or food or acid placed in the mouth.

Role of Hypothalamus in Affect. Masserman[39] applied the same type of analysis to the emotional display elicited by hypothalamic stimulation. He asked: Is the hypothalamus simply a motor structure organizing the external expression of emotion, or is it "upstream" on the afferent side? If hypothalamic stimulation can serve as an *un*conditioned reflex stimulus, then, following Loucks' analysis, the hypothalamus is upstream. Masserman established a series of criteria which have proved very useful in determining whether an emotional manifestation resulting from a central lesion or stimulus is a pseudoaffective or sham emotion. These criteria are: (i) Is the aggressive activity directed toward any specific object? (ii) Does the display inhibit and replace other activity? (iii) Does the display outlast the stimulus as does emotional excitement in intact animals? (iv) Does the animal become conditioned against the environment (the experimental box)? (v) Will brain stimulation serve as an unconditioned reflex in formal conditioning experiments? He answered these questions negatively for hypothalamic stimulation. Subsequent investigators have uniformly answered the same questions positively, and the reason for the discrepancy is not known.

Masserman's criteria have been widely used by others in working out the neurophysiology of emotion and motivation. Nakao,[40] like others, observed that the emotional display is not blind and undirected. When it is ragelike, it can be directed toward the experimenter or toward an innocent feline bystander; if the display is fearlike, attempts to escape are directed toward a weak point in the cage. Both Nakao and Delgado *et al.*[9] have found that hypothalamic stimulation giving rise to hissing, baring of teeth, biting, scratching, attempts to escape, etc., serve very well as unconditioned stimuli. Moreover, it is possible to show how the animal "interprets" the hypothalamic stimulation. Nakao placed an animal with electrodes implanted in its hypothalamus in a box with an electrified grid floor. He then taught the animal to turn off a shock to the feet by manipulating a paddle. The first time a hypothalamic shock is delivered, some

animals immediately turn off the shock. Delgado *et al.*[9] have shown further that the hypothalamic shock can motivate learning *de novo* and can act as a punishment strong enough to inhibit an animal's approaching food.

How well a hypothalamic stimulation in cats will serve as an unconditioned stimulus for a conditioned avoidance response depends on whether a flight or a rage type of reaction is elicited. When a flight reaction resulted, paddle pushing motivated by food stimulation was transferred to the hypothalamic stimulation immediately, whereas transfer did not occur when the stimulus produced fight reactions.[40]

Other subcortical regions give rise to emotional reactions which can be used as unconditioned stimuli.[10] Many of these regions are on the classic pain pathways. Others, like the hypothalamus and the medial nucleus of the amygdala (see below), are not. Electrical stimulation of the amygdala in man yields subjective reports of fear and rage.[18]

It should not be thought that the hypothalamus working alone is capable of initiating directed emotional behavior. The cerebral cortex is necessary for this. The emotional behavior of Goltz's decorticate dog or that resulting from hypothalamic stimulation in decorticate cats is not directed. It is quite possible that the hypothalamus discharges upward to the cerebral cortex, which directs the attack. Nor can it be assumed that the hypothalamus is the site of the affective experience, or whatever cerebral process is necessary for a stimulus to serve as an unconditioned stimulus. The hypothalamus may discharge to a thalamic or other area essential to affect. Additional investigation is necessary to work out these relations, but it is clear that the hypothalamus is more than an efferent structure downstream in the apparatus for emotional behavior. Further evidence of this is obtained from self-stimulation experiments (see below).

Self-stimulation. As pointed out in Chapter 25, if electrodes are implanted in the brain and the switch* which closes a stimulating circuit is arranged so that it can be manipulated by the animal, the affects of stimulation can be deduced from the animal's behavior. With the electrode tip in certain places in the animal's brain and the bar where the animal can close it

---

*The switch is usually activated by a bar or lever inserted into the testing box, so the laboratory jargon has become "bar-pressing" or "lever-pressing."

accidentally, in a few trials he will have learned the connection between the bar and the shock and will thereafter shun the bar. Quite otherwise, when the electrodes are in some other parts of the brain, the animal will stimulate itself repeatedly, as often as 5000 times per hour—more than once a second.[47] If permitted, this behavior will be continued to the point of exhaustion. In hour-long tests continued for a month no sign of satiation developed.[46] Shocks in still other areas are indifferent, i.e., the animal neither seeks nor avoids stimulation. That forms of behavior other than bar pressing can be motivated by self-stimulation has been proved in a variety of ways. A rat can be trained to run a maze for a brain shock as a reward, or will cross an electrified grid in order to receive a brain shock. In a Skinner box, a rat may press a bar more rapidly for a brain shock than for food.[6]

The rate of bar-pressing is used to measure the efficacy of given electrode positions. Self-stimulation results when the tip of the electrode is at any point in a rather wide extent of the brain. The neocortex, however, is a quite indifferent locus. The most effective regions are in the hypothalamus and the limbic system. The posterior hypothalamus just anterior to the mammillary bodies yields very high rates, perhaps the highest; the anterior hypothalamus yields much lower rates. The active points extend caudally into the midbrain tegmentum and rostrally into the preoptic region, the septal region and the median forebrain bundle. Other parts of the limbic system produce bar-pressing, but at low rates.

If mentalistic interpretations are permitted, drives and emotions can be divided into pleasant and unpleasant ones. Self-stimulation may indicate some pleasurable affect or some satisfaction resulting from the brain stimulus, although this is a point of view contested by many. Another approach to analysis of the phenomenon of self-stimulation is to establish a state of anxiety and discover either its effect on self-stimulation or the effects of self-stimulation on the anxiety. As in his experiments on ablation of the septal region, Brady[7] established two operant conditioned responses in a Skinner box, pressing the lever for water and for a brain shock. A clicking noise had previously been given anxiety-producing qualities by linking it with a shock to the feet. The clicking sound alone was then sufficient to elicit an anxiety response and to inhibit

bar-pressing for water. If self-stimulation in the median forebrain bundle was substituted for the water reward, bar-pressing was not suppressed by the conditioned anxiety, i.e., the clicking noise. Analysis shows that this persistence of bar-pressing is not due simply to self-stimulation being a more powerful reward. It may be "peace" rather than "joy" that is obtained by self-stimulation.

The difficulties besetting interpretation of self-stimulation experiments are somewhat analogous to those encountered in considering ablation experiments. With certain electrode placements, Roberts[50] found that stimulation would motivate some kinds of learning but not others. He suggested that the stimulation was rewarding at the onset but quickly became punishing, supposedly by summation within an aversive system simultaneously stimulated.[4] The apparent preference for short bouts of stimulation seems to be due to movements resulting from the stimulation, which release the bar. In two-bar experiments, one closing the circuit through the brain and the other opening it, preferred durations of stimulation increased tenfold.[59] The latter seconds of the stimulation were clearly not aversive.

Such discrepancies and other considerations have led to the development of a preference technique in which the rat receives brain stimulation or avoids it by walking from one compartment of a box to the other. The compartment yielding brain stimulation is randomly changed every minute so that repeated choices are made. The time spent in each chamber and the stimulus condition are recorded. This apparatus has the great advantage of determining the amount of aversive response. In bar-pressing, certain negative loci of brain shock may simply cause the rat to shun the bar, an unquantitative "yes—no" response.

By the preference method the most strongly aversive tegmental area coincides with the modern description of the pain tracts, namely, the dorsal portion of the central gray area and the dorsomedial tegmentum, especially the deeper layers of the superior colliculus or the nucleus of the posterior commissure. In contrast with the slow development of positive behavior to posterior hypothalamic stimulation, behavioral aversive responses developed within the first two 20-minute periods.

In one experiment the rat in the active compartment received hypothalamic and tegmental shocks alternating every 0.1 second. The interpolation of tegmental shocks, though strongly aversive when delivered alone, had relatively slight effects on rate of acquisition and level of positive responses from hypothalamic stimulation.

One large unknown in all self-stimulation experiments is whether the positive and negative reactions are central or secondary to the sensory return from visceral and vascular effects of the stimulus. It is profitless to deduce "pleasant" or "unpleasant" experience from approach or escape behavior insofar as laboratory experiments are concerned. Nevertheless, from a clinical point of view there is no denying the value of discovering where unpleasant experience is elaborated, especially if this proves to be a circumscribed area subject to surgical destruction. The practical consequences of learning the neural localization of pleasant feelings have yet to be contemplated.

EXCITEMENT

The importance of the excitement or dynamic aspects of emotion is clear since we often categorize psychiatric patients as manic or depressed. Whether in animals the overt signs of overactivity reflect a conscious state of excitement is not certain, but a parallelism can be assumed. The external manifestations of excitement can be increased or reduced by neural lesions. Thus while acting unopposed by more cephalad levels, as after a high decerebration, the posterior hypothalamus causes sham rage. Destruction of the posterior hypothalamus in otherwise intact animals results in somnolence, drowsiness, cataplexy, general stolidity and inactivity. The posterior hypothalamus is therefore a way station in the *descending* system producing emotional display and in the *ascending* reticular systems producing alertness and wakefulness (Chap. 22). Somewhat more anteriorly, destruction of the ventromedial nucleus produces hyperactivity as well as savageness. Maire and Patton[38] have demarcated the levels at which lesions produce general bodily hyperactivity, namely, the preoptic and anterior hypothalamic areas. Some anterior lesions produce hyperactivity combined with fatal pulmonary edema. This combination is a familiar sequel to mania.

Lindsley[32] has proposed an activation theory of emotion, perhaps better considered as the activation aspect of emotion. According to this theory, a discharge of hypothalamic nuclei downward, which produces the external aspect of emotions, is accompanied by a discharge upward which produces the subjective alertness or excitement typical of emotion. As we have seen in Chapter 22, this theory is well substantiated.[33] It is perhaps not too much to hope that underactivity of such a system will eventually be identified as causing the flatness of emotion in the schizophrenic and the obtunding of mental processes and depression of postural and motor activities in the depressed patient.

REFERENCES

1. ABRAHAMS, V. C., HILTON, S. M. and MALCOLM, J. L. *J. Physiol.*, 1962, *164*:1–16.
2. AKERT, K., GRUESEN, R. A., WOOLSEY, C. N. and MEYER, D. R. *Brain*, 1961, *84*:480–498.
3. BAILEY, P. and SWEET, W. H. *J. Neurophysiol.*, 1940, *3*: 276–281.
4. BARD, P. and MACHT, M. D. In: *Ciba Foundation symposium on the neurological basis of behavior*, G. E. W. WOLSTENHOLME and C. M. O'CONNOR, eds. Boston, Little, Brown and Co., 1958.
5. BOWER, G. H. and MILLER, N. E. *J. comp. physiol. Psychol.*, 1958, *51*:669–674.
6. BRADY, J. V. In: *Biological and biochemical bases of behavior*, H. F. HARLOW and C. N. WOOLSEY, eds. Madison, University of Wisconsin Press, 1958.
7. BRADY, J. V. In: *Reticular formation of the brain, Henry Ford Hospital International Symposium*, H. H. JASPER, L. D. PROCTOR, R. S. KNIGHTON, W. C. NOSHAY and R. T. COSTELLO, eds. Boston, Little, Brown and Co., 1958.
8. BRADY, J. V. and NAUTA, W. J. H. *J. comp. physiol. Psychol.*, 1953, *46*:339–346.
9. DELGADO, J. M. R., ROBERTS, W. W. and MILLER, N. E. *Amer. J. Physiol.*, 1954, *179*:587–593.
10. DELGADO, J. M. R., ROSVOLD, H. E. and LOONEY, E. *J. comp. physiol. Psychol.*, 1956, *49*:373–380.
11. EGGER, M. D. and FLYNN, J. P. *J. Neurophysiol.*, 1963, *26*: 705–720.
12. FERNANDEZ DE MOLINA, A. and HUNSPERGER, R. W. *J. Physiol.*, 1959, *145*:251–265.
13. FERNANDEZ DE MOLINA, A. and HUNSPERGER, R. W. *J. Physiol.*, 1962, *160*:200–213.
14. GASTAUT, H., NAQUET, R., VIGOUROUX, R. and CORRIOL, J. *Rev. neurol.*, 1952, *86*:319–327.
15. GOL, A., KELLAWAY, P., SHAPIRO, M. and HURST, C. M. *Neurology (Minneap.)*, 1963, *13*:1031–1041.
16. GREEN, J. D., CLEMENTE, C. D. and DE GROOT, J. *J. comp. Neurol.*, 1957, *108*:505–545.
17. GREEN, J. D. and SHIMAMOTO, T. *Arch. Neurol. Psychiat. (Chic.)*, 1953, *70*:687–702.
18. HEATH, R. G., MONROE, R. R. and MICKLE, W. A. *Amer. J. Psychiat.*, 1955, *111*:862–863.
19. HESS, W. R. and BRUGGER, M. *Helv. physiol. Acta*, 1943, *1*:33–52.
20. HILTON, S. M. and ZBROZYNA, A. W. *J. Physiol.*, 1963, *165*:160–173.
21. HUNSPERGER, R. W. *Helv. physiol. Acta*, 1956, *14*:70–92.

22. IRONSIDE, R. *Brain,* 1956, *79:*589–609.
23. JASPER, H. H., PROCTOR, L. D., KNIGHTON, R. S., NOSHAY, W. C. and COSTELLO, R. T., eds. *Reticular formation of the brain, Henry Ford Hospital International Symposium.* Boston, Little, Brown and Co., 1958.
24. KAADA, B. R. *Acta physiol. scand.,* 1951, *24*(Suppl. 83):1–285.
25. KAADA, B. R., PRIBRAM, K. H. and EPSTEIN, J. A. *J. Neurophysiol.,* 1949, *12:*347–356.
26. KING, F. A. and MEYER P. M. *Science,* 1958, *128:*655–656.
27. KLÜVER, H. *J.-Lancet,* 1952, *72:*567–577.
28. KLÜVER, H. and BUCY, P. C. *J. Psychol.,* 1938, *5:*33–54.
29. KLÜVER, H. and BUCY, P. C. *Arch. Neurol. Psychiat. (Chic.),* 1939, *42:*979–1000.
30. KNAPP, P., ed. *Expression of the emotions in man.* New York, International Universities Press, 1963.
31. LACEY, J. I. In: *Research in psychotherapy.* Washington, D.C., American Psychological Assoc., 1959.
32. LINDSLEY, D. B. Chap. 14 in *Handbook of experimental psychology,* S. S. Stevens, ed. New York, John Wiley and Sons, 1951.
33. MACLEAN, P. D. *Psychosom. Med.,* 1949, *11:*338–353.
34. MACLEAN, P. D. *Electroenceph. clin. Neurophysiol.,* 1952, *4:* 407–418.
35. MACLEAN, P. D. *Psychosom. Med.,* 1955, *17:*355–366.
36. MACLEAN, P. D. *J. nerv. ment. Dis.,* 1958, *127:*1–11.
37. MACLEAN, P. D. and DELGADO, J. M. R. *Electroenceph. clin. Neurophysiol.,* 1953, *5:*91–100.
38. MAIRE, F. W. and PATTON, H. D. *Amer. J. Physiol.,* 1956, *184:*345–350.
39. MASSERMAN, J. H. *Psychosom. Med.,* 1941, *3:*3–25.
40. NAKAO, H. *Amer. J. Physiol.,* 1958, *194:*411–418.
41. NAUTA, W. J. H. *J. Anat. (Lond.),* 1961, *95:*515–531.
42. NAUTA, W. J. H. *Brain,* 1962, *85:*505–520.
43. NAUTA, W. J. H. Chap. 19 in *The frontal granular cortex and behavior.* J. M. WARREN and K. AKERT, eds. New York, McGraw-Hill Book Co., 1964.
44. OLDS, J. *J. comp. physiol. Psychol.,* 1956, *49:*281–285.
45. OLDS, J. *J. comp. physiol. Psychol.,* 1958, *51:*675–678.
46. OLDS, J. *Physiol. Rev.,* 1962, *42:*554–604.
47. OLDS, J. and MILNER, P. *J. comp. physiol. Psychol.,* 1954, *47:* 419–427.
48. PAPEZ, J. W. *Arch. Neurol. Psychiat. (Chic.),* 1937, *38:*725–743.
49. PRIBRAM, K. H. and KRUGER, L. *Ann. N. Y. Acad. Sci.,* 1954, *58:*109–138.
50. ROBERTS, W. W. *J. comp. physiol. Psychol.,* 1958, *51:*391–399; *idem,* 400–407.
51. ROSVOLD, H. E., MIRSKY, A. F. and PRIBRAM, K. H. *J. comp. physiol. Psychol.,* 1954, *47:*173–178.
52. SCHREINER, L. and KLING, A. *J. Neurophysiol.,* 1953, *16:* 643–659.
53. SCHREINER, L. and KLING, A. *Arch. Neurol. Psychiat. (Chic.),* 1954, *72:*180–186.
54. SCHREINER, L. and KLING, A. *Amer. J. Physiol.,* 1956, *184:* 486–490.
55. SMITH, O. A., JR. and NATHAN, M. A. *Physiologist,* 1964, *7:*259.
56. SUMMERS, T. B. and KAELBER, W. W. *Amer. J. Physiol.,* 1962, *203:*1117–1119.
57. TERZIAN, H. and ORE, G. D. *Neurology,* 1955, *5:*373–380.
58. THOMSON, A. F. and WALTER, E. A. *Folia psychiat. neurol. et neurochir. neerl.,* 1950, Brower Memorial Volume, 444–452.
59. VALENSTEIN, E. E. *Psychol. Rev.,* 1964, *71:*415–437.
60. VALENSTEIN, E. E. *J. comp. physiol. Psychol.,* In press.
61. VALENSTEIN, E. S. and VALENSTEIN, T. *Science,* 1964, *145:* 1456–1458.
62. VONDERAHE, A. R. *New Scholasticism,* 1944, *18:*76–95.
63. WHEATLEY, M. D. *Arch. Neurol. Psychiat. (Chic.),* 1944, *52:* 296–316.
64. WOOD, C. D., SCHOTTELIUS, B., FROST, L. L. and BALDWIN, M. *Neurology,* 1958, *8:*477–480.

INDEX

Page numbers in *italic* type refer to illustrations.